MULTI-SULFUR AND SULFUR AND OXYGEN FIVE- AND SIX-MEMBERED HETEROCYCLES

Part One

David S. Breslow

Herman Skolnik

Hercules Research Center, Hercules Incorporated, Wilmington, Delaware

1966

INTERSCIENCE PUBLISHERS

a division of John Wiley & Sons

New York - London - Sydney

First published 1966 by John Wiley & Sons, Ltd.

All Rights Reserved

Library of Congress Catalog Card Number 66-18380

PRODUCED BY Uneoprint
set on electric keyboards with Φotomath
photo-reproduced and printed offset

at The Gresham Press
UNWIN BROTHERS LIMITED
Old Woking   Surrey   England

THE CHEMISTRY OF HETEROCYCLIC COMPOUNDS

The chemistry of heterocyclic compounds is one of the most complex branches of organic chemistry. It is equally interesting for its theoretical implications, for the diversity of its synthetic procedures, and for the physiological and industrial significance of heterocyclic compounds.

A field of such importance and intrinsic difficulty should be made as readily accessible as possible, and the lack of a modern detailed and comprehensive presentation of heterocyclic chemistry is therefore keenly felt. It is the intention of the present series to fill this gap by expert presentations of the various branches of heterocyclic chemistry. The subdivisions have been designed to cover the field in its entirety by monographs which reflect the importance and the interrelations of the various compounds and accommodate the specific interests of the authors.

Research Laboratories
Eastman Kodak Company
Rochester, New York

Arnold Weissberger

PREFACE

On accepting the assignment to write a definitive chemistry of five-
and six-membered heterocycles containing more than one sulfur,
oxygen and sulfur, and their selenium and tellurium analogs, we went
through the Ring Index by A. M. Patterson and L. T. Capell (2nd edition,
1960, by A. M. Patterson, L. T. Capell, and D. F. Walker), page by page,
compound by compound. We found over 200 parent rings within the
defined scope of this volume. We assigned to them the RRI (Revised
Ring Index) number in the text and provided an index to them in the
second part of this volume. Many parent rings in the volume, however,
had not yet been assigned RRI numbers. Most of these entered the
literature since the coverage of the Ring Index and are undoubtedly in
the supplements, which issued after the manuscript went to press;
only a relatively small number are without RRI numbers because the
Ring Index missed them or chose to consider them uncertain.

An assignment that covers over 200 parent heterocyclics meant that
this number was the minimum number of subjects that we had to consult in the indexes of the standard reference works, such as Chemical
Abstracts, Chemisches Zentralblatt, and Beilstein. Our burden of
searching the literature was lightened considerably by the Index of
Ring Systems in Chemical Abstracts. There were two major difficul-
ties in finding the references in the standard reference works: the
plethora of names for a given compound and the unrelatedness of the
nomenclature in the many classes of a heterocyclic moiety. Because
nomenclature of the heterocyclics is a major problem, we devoted considerable attention to it throughout the volume and in the subject index.
Chemical Abstracts nomenclature was followed, particularly for the
heterocyclics. In the case of reactants used in the synthesis of a
heterocyclic moiety, we carefully avoided nomenclature which might
be confused with a heterocyclic name. For example, we preferred
dimercaptoethane over ethanedithiol when it was used in the synthesis
of the dithiole ring.

Although the assignment *per se* essentially dictated the scope for the
contents of this volume, the order of arrangement and method of treatment are the result of our own deliberations. There are a number of
variables which might influence the order of arrangement, such as
size of the heterocyclic ring, kinds of heteroatoms, number of heteroatoms, synthetic methods, reactions and reactivity, etc.

Fortunately, these and other variables are not mutually exclusive. Each
of us, having been heavy users of the chemical literature for the past
twenty-five years, tended to think in terms of the reader's viewpoint
and how he might want to consult this volume. These considerations
led us to the arrangement which is best known to users of the Ring
Index and of the Index of Ring Systems in Chemical Abstracts, viz.,
the size of the ring and the number of heteroatoms. Consequently, five-
membered rings are together in the first part and six-membered rings
in the second part of this volume. As in the Ring Index and Index of
Ring Systems in Chemical Abstracts, the heterocyclic systems are

Preface

classified in order of increasing carbon atoms. Our logic divided the heterocyclic systems into twelve major units. The selenium and tellurium heterocyclics, because of their relatively small literature, were treated similarly in one unit.

Our experience as readers of the chemical literature, particularly in heterocyclic chemistry, led us to adopt the heterocyclic moiety pattern within each of the major heterocyclic systems. For example, Chapter 4, on the C_3OS ring system, is in two parts: the 1, 2-oxathiole moiety and the 1, 3-oxathiole moiety. The arrangement within a moiety is in ascending order by number of rings and number of atoms in each ring. We did make an exception, however, in this order, viz., spiro compounds are treated as derivatives of the heterocyclic class. Thus, spiro derivatives of 1, 3-dithiolane are discussed under 1, 3-dithiolane (Chapter 5, Section II A-4) and spiro derivatives of 1, 3-benzodithiole under 1, 3-benzodithiole (Chapter 5, Section II D-3).

The treatment of subject matter for each heterocyclic class is in the order: preparation, structure, properties, reactions, and uses. Our method of treatment, however, was not to summarize the literature completely and thoroughly in the text, but to review the literature selectively and eclectically, to establish the soundness and validity of what is known, and to point out what needs to be confirmed and extended. To the best of our ability and within the confines of the sources available to us, the literature has been exhaustively covered through most of 1962. The details of this coverage, such as preparation, yields, and properties (melting point, boiling point, index of refraction, density, etc.) are thoroughly tabulated and referenced. Physiological properties are noted in the text. The emphasis of the text is on the chemistry of the many ring systems within the scope of the assignment. Particular attention has been directed to the updating of the chemistry and to the elucidation of reaction mechanisms in terms of modern concepts. Because of this emphasis and direction, the text includes discussions of crystallographic studies, conformational analyses, and spectroscopic studies.

Unfortunately, this type of arrangement separates similar compounds from each other. For example, any one interested in the chemistry of sulfite esters must consult many sections in at least two chapters. A similar problem arises in the chemistry of 1, 2-disulfides. Although this was unavoidable, we hope the Contents and Subject Index will ease the problem of finding the desired information.

Because the subject index to this volume is different from other book indexes, we think a brief description may be to the reader's advantage. Every heterocyclic covered in the text is indexed specifically and the heterocyclics cited in the tables are indexed generically. The page citation designates that the page pertains to synthesis (s), property (p), or reaction (r) of the chemical or to a listing in a table (t). The heterocyclics are indexed by the heterocyclic parent compound with the sub-

Preface

stituents inverted. Thus, 4-methyl-1, 3, 2-dioxathiolane 2-oxide is indexed as

1, 3, 2-Dioxathiolane 2-oxide, 4-methyl-

Reactants used in the syntheses of the heterocyclics are indexed, but not chemicals reacted with the heterocyclics. We think the indexing of the reactants is a real advantage as they are a common basis for relating the syntheses of heterocyclics. Uses and application of the heterocyclics and of their reaction products are indexed under the use or application, such as detergent, dye, pesticide, pharmaceutical, etc. A use or application is designated by the letter u following the page citation under the heterocyclic entry in the index. Spectroscopic properties, such as ultraviolet, infrared, nuclear magnetic resonance, and X-ray, are also subjects in the index.

From the perspective of the end of our assignment, we are acutely aware of the genius and labor of the hundreds of chemists whose contributions through time and space have constituted the facts and design of this volume. We are all the more impressed with the continuing and cumulative nature that the whole of chemistry imposes on any given area of chemistry, such as that encompassed by this volume, and how well the essence of this nature has been captured by our heritage, the chemical literature.

We gratefully acknowledge the encouragement of our friends and of the Research Department of Hercules Incorporated. We are grateful for the typing assistance the Hercules Research Center provided.

Most of all, we gratefully acknowledge the encouragement and support of our families. Their patience and understanding were completely essential for this undertaking.

Wilmington, Delaware
January, 1966

David S. Breslow

Herman Skolnik

CONTENTS

CONTENTS OF PART ONE

Contents of Part One

Contents of Part One

Contents of Part One

Contents of Part One

Contents of Part One

Contents of Part One

Contents of Part One

Contents of Part One

Contents of Part One

C₂O₂S RING SYSTEMS

Five-membered rings containing two oxygens and a sulfur are known with only one arrangement of the hetero atoms, 1, 3-dioxa-2-thia. The compounds with this arrangement are cyclic sulfite and sulfate esters of 1, 2-dihydroxy compounds, cyclic anhydrides of acid sulfite esters of 2-hydroxy acids, and glyoxal sulfate.

I. C₂O₂S 1, 3, 2-DIOXATHIOLANE (1) AND 1, 3, 2-DIOXATHIOLE (2)

1   **2**

(RRI 105)

Chemical Abstracts indexes this ring system under the above names. Alternative names are 1, 3-dioxa-2-thiacyclopentane and -pentene. However, the compounds are invariably found under the parent hydroxy compounds and these names are rarely used.

A. SULFITE ESTERS

1. Preparation

1, 3, 2-Dioxathiole 2-oxides, cyclic sulfites of enediols, have not been reported. 1, 3, 2-Dioxathiolane 2-oxides, cyclic sulfites of 1, 2-glycols, are prepared in excellent yields by treating a glycol with thionyl chloride.[7,9,24,41,52,57,58,74,78,88]

$$-\overset{|}{\underset{OH}{C}}-\overset{|}{\underset{OH}{C}}- \ + \ SOCl_2 \longrightarrow \ \text{(ring structure)} \ + \ 2\,HCl$$

The use of methylene chloride as a solvent has been reported to improve the yield.[41] Pyridine has been used frequently,[34,52,67,69] but it appears to have little if any effect, in contrast to its effect on the reaction of simple alcohols with thionyl chloride, where its use leads to the formation of alkyl halides. The synthesis has been applied to primary, secondary, and tertiary alcohols. Pritchard and Lauterbur[67a] raised the yield of 4, 4-dimethyl-1, 3, 2-dioxathiolane 2-oxide (**2a**) from 20% to 60% by carrying out the reaction in benzene and sweeping out hydrogen chloride with an inert gas.

[For references, see pp. 57-61.]

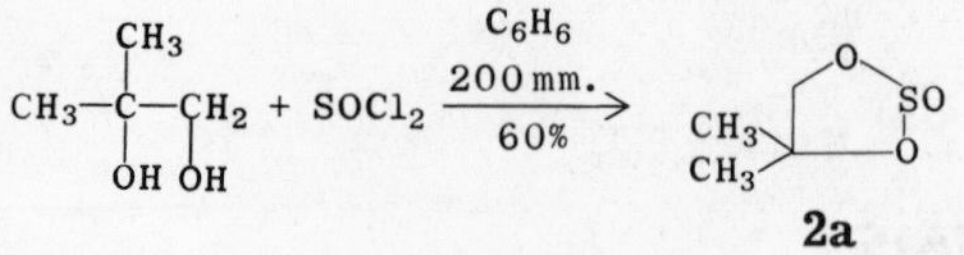

2a

It is interesting that even pinacol, which is prone to undergo acid-catalyzed rearrangement, was reported by Szmant and Emerson[80] to give a 55% yield of cyclic sulfite (**3**).

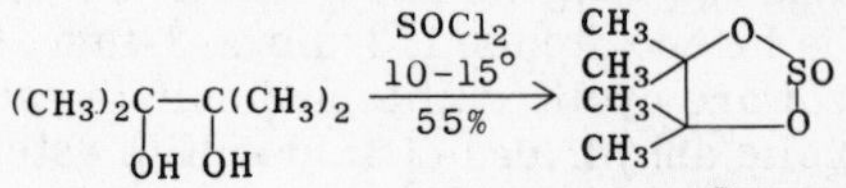

3

Majima and Simanuki[57] reported that glycerol yields 4-chloromethyl-1, 3, 2-dioxathiolane 2-oxide (**4**). De la Mare, Klyne, and co-workers, [32] obtained the same compound from 3-chloro-1, 2-propanediol; in this instance pyridine had a deleterious effect, a mixture of dichlorohydrin and trichloropropane being obtained.

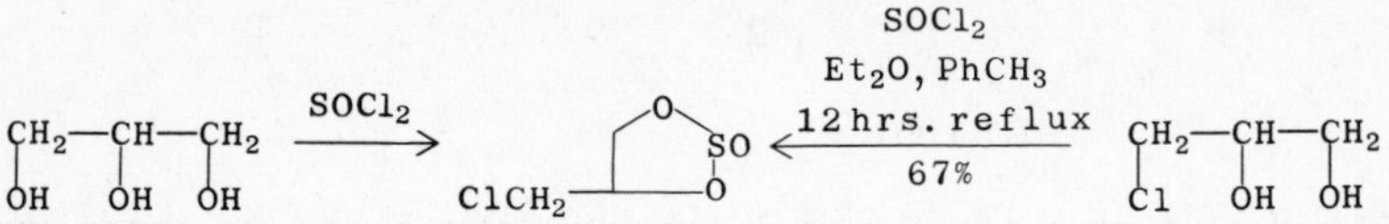

4

Majima and Simanuki[57] found that DL-erythritol gave a bis(cyclic sulfite) (**5**); according to Kitasato and Sone[52] a bis(cyclic sulfite) (**6**) was also formed from diethyl mucate.

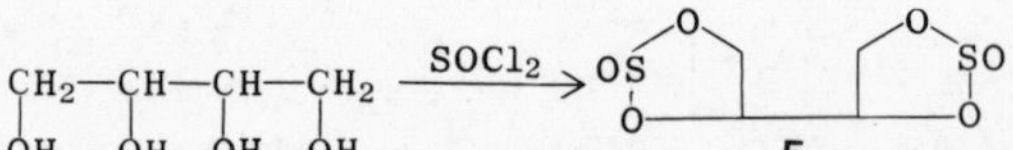

5

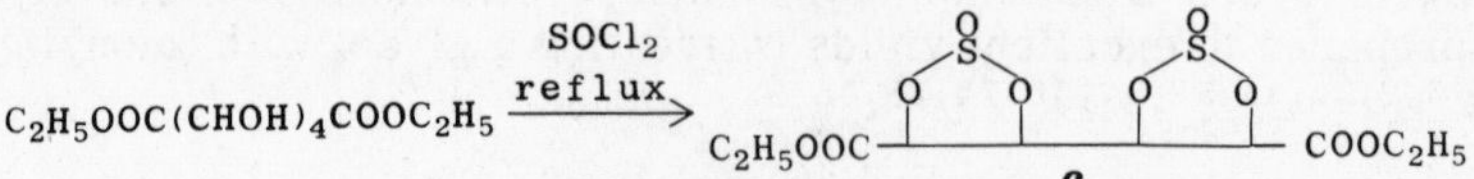

6

D-Mannitol[52,57] yielded a tris(cyclic sulfite) (**7**). According to Majima and Simanuki[57] treatment of the sulfite with thionyl chloride and pyridine, presumably at an elevated temperature, yields a tetrachlorohexylene glycol sulfite of undetermined structure, either (**8**) or (**9**), providing no rearrangement has taken place.

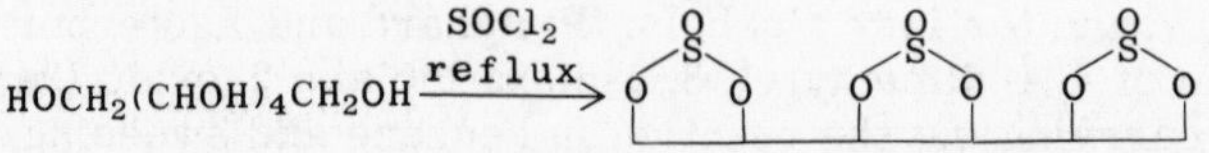

$$HOCH_2(CHOH)_4CH_2OH \xrightarrow[\text{reflux}]{SOCl_2}$$

7

$$\xrightarrow{\text{SOCl}_2,\ \text{C}_5\text{H}_5\text{N}}$$

$$\text{ClCH}_2(\text{CHCl})_3 \qquad \mathbf{8} \qquad \text{or} \qquad \begin{array}{c} \text{ClCH}_2\overset{\displaystyle\text{Cl}}{\underset{\displaystyle\text{Cl}}{\text{CH}}} \\ \text{ClCH}_2\text{CH} \end{array} \qquad \mathbf{9}$$

It should be pointed out that there is no direct evidence that these polyhydroxy compounds yield five-membered cyclic sulfites, and not six-membered. Thus, Zinner, Sych, and Schneider[89] suggested that the bis(cyclic sulfites) prepared from D-xylose mercaptals might be 1, 3, 2-dioxathianes (**9a**) rather than 1, 3, 2-dioxathiolanes (**9b**), by analogy with the reaction of these sugar derivative with acetone.

$$\text{HOCH}_2(\text{CHOH})_3\text{CH(SR)}_2 \xrightarrow[\underset{20-22\%}{}]{\text{SOCl}_2,\ \text{C}_5\text{H}_5\text{N} \atop -15^\circ} \qquad \mathbf{9a} \qquad \text{CH(SR)}_2 \qquad \text{or}$$

$$\mathbf{9b} \qquad \text{—CH(SR)}_2$$

However, the fact that glycerol yields a five-membered cyclic sulfite and that cyclic sulfites are prepared more readily from 1, 2-glycols than from 1, 3-glycols (see Chapter 8, section I A-1a) suggests that the 1, 3, 2-dioxathiolane structure is more reasonable for these compounds and they are therefore listed here. Nevertheless, there is some evidence that 1, 4-anhydroxylitol forms a six-membered cyclic sulfite rather than a five (see Chapter 8, section I B), and more definitive evidence as to the structure of these compounds is required.

Asselineau[10,11] prepared the cyclic sulfite esters of a number of esters and amides of mycolic acid. Inasmuch as the structure of mycolic acid is unknown, it is not known whether these compounds are derivatives of 1, 3, 2-dioxathiolane or 1, 3, 2-dioxathiane. Boehm[17] chlorinated cellulose with thionyl chloride and pyridine; he postulated the intermediate formation of a cyclic sulfite, which then reacted with pyridine hydrochloride to yield the chlorinated cellulose.

$$\begin{array}{c} -\text{C}-\text{O} \\ -\text{C}-\text{O} \end{array}\!\!\text{SO} + \text{C}_5\text{H}_5\text{N}\cdot\text{HCl} \longrightarrow \begin{array}{c} -\text{C}-\text{OH} \\ -\text{C}-\text{Cl} \end{array} + \text{C}_5\text{H}_5\text{N} + \text{SO}_2$$

Several novel syntheses of cyclic sulfites have been reported. Bissinger, Fredenburg, and co-workers,[14] prepared 4-vinyl-1, 3, 2-dioxathiolane 2-oxide (**10**) by the alcoholysis of dimethyl sulfite with erythrol.

[For references, see pp. 57-61.]

$$CH_2{=}CH{-}\underset{\underset{OH}{|}}{CH}{-}\underset{\underset{OH}{|}}{CH_2} + (CH_3)_2SO_3 \xrightarrow[86\%]{120°} CH_2{=}CH{-}\overset{O}{\underset{O}{\diagdown}}SO + 2\,CH_3OH$$

10

In a somewhat related synthesis, Hesse[50,50a] found that treatment of an alcohol with sulfur dioxide and diazomethane gave a mixed sulfite ester. Presumably the alcohol and sulfur dioxide are in equilibrium with the half-ester of sulfurous acid, which is methylated by diazomethane. When applied to ethylene glycol, methyl 2-hydroxyethyl sulfite (**11**) was formed, and this on heating was converted into ethylene sulfite.

$$HOCH_2CH_2OH + SO_2 \rightleftharpoons HOCH_2CH_2OSO_2H \xrightarrow{CH_2N_2} HOCH_2CH_2OSO_2CH_3$$

11

$$\xrightarrow{\Delta} \overset{O}{\underset{O}{\diagdown}}SO + CH_3OH$$

Several patents have appeared on the synthesis of ethylene sulfite from ethylene oxide and sulfur dioxide. Thus, according to Viard[76,85] the 1:1 complex of ethylene oxide and sulfur dioxide, formed from the two reagents at room temperature, is treated with a tertiary amine. A polymer is formed, and this on heating is converted into ethylene sulfite; both reactions are essentially quantitative.

$$\underset{CH_2}{\overset{CH_2}{>}}O{\cdot}SO_2 \xrightarrow[98\%]{\substack{PhNR_2 \\ 30\,hrs.\ 0{-}10°}} [-CH_2CH_2OSO_2-]_n$$

$$\xrightarrow[97\%]{30{-}60\,min.\ 140{-}150°} \overset{O}{\underset{O}{\diagdown}}SO$$

Gruschke[48] has reported the direct preparation of ethylene sulfite by passage of ethylene oxide and sulfur dioxide over silver oxide on charcoal catalyst at 220°. According to Dietrich and Höfermann,[36] however, the conversion is incomplete by this process, and better results are obtained by carrying out the reaction in the liquid phase under pressure.

$$\underset{O}{\overset{CH_2{-}CH_2}{\diagdown}} + SO_2 \xrightarrow[92\%]{\substack{140° \\ 25\,atm.}} \overset{O}{\underset{O}{\diagdown}}SO$$

Razuvaev, Étlis, and Grobov[68a] were unable to obtain ethylene sulfite by these procedures. According to these authors the reaction is catalyzed by quaternary ammonium salts. Heating equimolar quantities of ethylene oxide and sulfur dioxide for 3 hours at 110–120° in the presence of a catalytic quantity of tetraethylammonium bromide yielded a polymer which, on distillation with a free flame, gave a 57% yield of ethylene sulfite plus some dioxane and acetaldehyde. In this manner they prepared 4-methyl-, 4-chloromethyl-, and 4-hydroxymethyl-1,3,2-dioxathiolane 2-oxide from propylene oxide, epichlorohydrin, and glycidol, respectively.

England, Dietrich, and Lindsey[36b] reacted tetrafluoroethylene with undistilled sulfur trioxide, and found that three products were formed: 3, 3, 4, 4-tetrafluoro-1, 2-oxathietane 2, 2-dioxide (**11a**); 4, 4, 5, 5-tetrafluoro-1, 3, 2-dioxathiolane 2-oxide (**11b**); and 5, 5, 6, 6-tetrafluoro-1, 3, 2, 4-dioxadithiane 2, 2, 4, 4-tetroxide (**11c**).

11a **11b** **11c**

Although **11b** could not be separated from **11a** by distillation, both a neutral equivalent determination on the mixture and NMR indicated its presence. This was confirmed by treatment with amines, aniline yielding oxanilide and cyclohexylamine N, N'-dicyclohexyloxamide, neither product being formed from pure **11a**. With freshly distilled sulfur trioxide **11a** was formed in nearly quantitative yield.

The cyclic sulfites which are reported in the literature are listed in Table 1.

2. Structure and Physical Properties

1, 3, 2-Dioxathiolane 2-oxides very probably exist as slightly puckered five-membered rings, although the actual structure has not been determined. Ethylene sulfite has been reported by Arbuzov and co-workers[7,8,8a] to have a dipole moment of 3. 65 D, and a parachor of 194. 3. Using bond lengths and angles determined on open-chain sulfites, it was calculated that a planar ring structure had a dipole moment (3. 48 D) closest to the experimental value. They concluded, however, that the ring is puckered, with the sulfur atom about 40° out of the plane and with **11d** (4. 56 D) contributing more to the structure than **11e** (2. 04 D).

11d **11e**

Pritchard and Lauterbur[67a] found a dipole moment for ethylene sulfite of 3. 74 D, which they claimed is in agreement with a planar or a slightly puckered ring. Inasmuch as the three oxygens on the sulfur are not in a plane, the four hydrogens are not equivalent, and these authors found a very complicated proton magnetic resonance spectrum for ethylene sulfite attributable to this dissymmetry. 4, 4-Dimethyl-1, 3, 2-dioxathiolane 2-oxide (**2a**) gave a simpler spectrum, a quadruplet for the two ring protons and two singlets for the non-equivalent methyl groups.

[For references, see pp. 57-61.]

5

TABLE 1. 1,3,2-Dioxathiolane 2-Oxides

Substituent	Glycol	Yield (%)	M.p. (°C)	B.p. (°C)	B.p. (mm)	Other properties	Ref.
None	Ethylene glycol	57		55-57	4	$n_D^{25}1.4450, d_4^{25}1.4375$	68a
				64-65	12	$n_D^{20}1.4455, d_4^{20}1.4313$	7
				64.5-65	12	$n_D^{20}1.4455, d_4^{20}1.4340$	8
				64-66.5	12		57
				63	13	$n_D^{25}1.4446$	67a
		79		70	20	$n_D^{20}1.4461$	42a
		90-95		70-71	20		76, 85
				71.5-72	20		86
				73	27	$n_D^{25}1.4450$	81a, 81b
		75		86	35	$n_D^{25}1.4443$	80
		90		86-88	38		24
				84	43	$n_D^{25}1.4448$	31a
				90	42	$n_D^{25}1.4448$	32
				92	50	$n_D^{25}1.4451, d_4^{25}1.4320$	63
				88	52	$n_D^{25}1.4450$	21
				173.5	760		36
				173	760		48
4-CH₃-	Propylene glycol	48		50-52	4	$n_D^{25}1.4350, d_4^{25}1.2765$	68a
				58	9	$n_D^{25}1.4359$	21
		55		58	12	$n_D^{25}1.4353$	67a
				92	40	$n_D^{25}1.4354$	32
				174	760	$n_D^{25}1.4361, d_4^{25}1.2882$	63

6

Substituent	Name	Yield, %	m.p., °C	b.p., °C (mm)	Physical constants	Ref.
4-$ClCH_2$-	3-Chloro-1,2-propanediol			100 (16)		57
		72		81-84 (4)	$n_D^{25}1.4805,\ d_4^{20}1.5136$	63a
		67		95 (12), 210 (760)	$n_D^{25}1.4808$	32, 12b, 12c
4-$HOCH_2$-	Glycerol	29		112-114 (3)	$n_D^{20}1.4723,\ d_4^{20}1.4862$	68a
4-$C_6H_5OCH_2$-	Glycerol α-phenyl ether	8.3		85-91 (8)	$n_D^{25}1.5020$	12b
4-(o-$CH_3C_6H_4OCH_2$-)	Glycerol α-o-tolyl ether	9.6		106-107 (30)	$n_D^{25}1.5099$	12b
4-($CH_2{=}CH$-)	Erythrol	86		56-58 (3)	$n_D^{20}1.4588$	14
4-($C_6H_5CHNC_5H_{10}$)·HCl	1-Phenyl-1-piperidino-2,3-propanediol	66	84-86			30
4-(1,3,2-Dioxathiolan-4-yl 2-oxide)	DL-Erythritol		94-95			57
4-[($CH_3S)_2CH$-]-5-(1,3,2-dioxathiolan-4-yl 2-oxide)	D-Xylose dimethylmercaptal	22	94		$[\alpha]_D^{19}\ -27.1°$	89
4-[(iso-$C_3H_7S)_2CH$-]-5-(1,3,2-dioxathiolan-4-yl 2-oxide)	D-Xylose diisopropylmercaptal	20	121		$[\alpha]_D^{18}\ -145.2°$	89
4,4-(CH_3-)$_2$	Isobutylene glycol	60		53 (10)	$n_D^{25}1.4292$	67a
$trans$-4,5-(CH_3-)$_2$	D-(−)-2,3-Butanediol	91		60.5-60.7 (10)	$n_D^{25}1.4300,\ d_4^{25}1.1942$; $[\alpha]_D^{25}\ +20.32°$	41
		70		177-178	$n_D^{25}1.4296,\ d_4^{25}1.192$; $[\alpha]_D^{25}\ +19.92°$	74
cis-4,5-(CH_3-)$_2$	meso-2,3-Butanediol	78		188-189	$n_D^{25}1.4368,\ d_4^{25}1.211$	74
4,5-(CH_3-)$_2$	2,3-Butanediol			67 (14)	$n_D^{25}1.4380$	21
				74-76 (8)		55a
				70-71 (12)		34
				67-68 (9)	$n_D^{20}1.4349,\ d_4^{25}1.215$	63
cis-4,5-(C_6H_5-)$_2$	meso-Hydrobenzoin	100	131			69
			127-129			52
		83	126-128			67

TABLE 1. 1, 3, 2-Dioxathiolane 2-Oxides (contd)

Substituent	Glycol	Yield (%)	M.p. (°C)	B.p. (°C)	(mm)	Other properties	Ref.
trans-4,5-(C$_6$H$_5$-)$_2$	DL-Hydrobenzoin		84				69
		83	84-86				67
trans-4,5-(CH$_3$OOC-)$_2$	Dimethyl d-tartrate	90-95		157.5	12.3	$d_4^{19.5}$ 1.4445	78
				274	770		78
trans-4,5-(CH$_3$OOC-)$_2$	Dimethyl DL-tartrate	90-95		158.5	12.2		78
				276	770		78
trans-4,5-(C$_2$H$_5$OOC-)$_2$	Diethyl d-tartrate	84		167	11.5	$d_4^{19.5}$ 1.3257	78
				279	770		78
				160	12	$d_4^{19.5}$ 1.329, $[\alpha]_D^{19.5}$ −183.8°	58
						$d_4^{9.5}$ 1.342, $[\alpha]_D^{9.5}$ −185.4°	58
				159	11	$d_4^{20.3}$ 1.3221, $[\alpha]_D^{20.3}$ −182.56°	88
trans-4,5-(n-C$_3$H$_7$OOC-)$_2$	Di-n-propyl d-tartrate	90-95		176	12	$d_4^{19.5}$ 1.2378	78
				172.5	10.5		78
				295	770		78
4,5-(CH$_3$OOCCH$_2$-)$_2$	Dimethyl 3, 4-dihydroxy-adipate	60		139-140	0.3		53
4-[CH$_3$(CH$_2$)$_7$]-5-[-(CH$_2$)$_7$COOCH$_3$]	Methyl 9, 10-dihydroxy-stearate		~25				11
4,5-(1, 3, 2-Dioxathiolan-4-yl 2-oxide)$_2$	D-Mannitol			220-228	3.5		57
4,5-(5-Carboxyethyl-1, 3, 2-dioxa-thiolan-4-yl 2-oxide)$_2$	Diethyl mucate		~0				52
			119				52
4,4,5-(CH$_3$-)$_3$	Pinacol	55	44-45	170-180	4.5-6		21, 80
Tetrachlorohexylene glycol sulfite	D-Mannitol trisulfite		50.5				57

2a

Because of the non-coplanarity of the oxygen atoms, a 4-substituted derivative should exist in two forms, *cis* and *trans*. Pritchard and Lauterbur succeeded in separating propylene sulfite into two stable isomers by vapor phase chromatography; their refractive indices differed by 0.0012 at 25° (D line). By a detailed analysis of their complicated proton magnetic resonance spectra, the authors assigned a *cis* structure (**11f**) to the slow-moving isomer and a *trans* (**11g**) to the fast; the *cis-trans* ratio in a normal preparation was 1:2.

11f   **11g**

1,3,2-Dioxathiolane 2-oxides symmetrically substituted in the 4,5-positions should exist in three isomeric forms.

Here no isomerism attributable to the sulfoxide oxygen has been reported; *meso*- and DL-hydrobenzoin[67,69] and 2,3-butanediol[74] have each been reported to give only one cyclic sulfite.

The simple cyclic sulfites are generally colorless, distillable liquids, although some exist as crystalline solids. They are generally soluble in the common organic solvents, and the lower members of the series are also appreciably soluble in water. Thus, ethylene glycol sulfite has a water solubility of 16–18% at 25°,[31,63] and 3.8% water dissolves in it; the corresponding figures for propylene glycol sulfite are 8% and 2.1%.[63] According to Davies and Tillett[31] certain salts increase the solubility of ethylene glycol sulfite in water, while others decrease the solubility.

Szmant and Emerson[80] and de la Mare, Klyne, and co-workers,[32] have both investigated the infrared spectra of cyclic sulfites of 1,2-glycols. The results are in excellent agreement, the former finding absorption at 1220–1225 cm^{-1} and the latter at 1214–1215 cm^{-1}; this is considered to be the stretching frequency of the S → O bond.

[For references, see pp. 57-61.]

Chapter 1

3. Reactions

Cyclic sulfite esters of 1, 2-glycols are reasonably stable thermally. Denivelle[34] reported that calcium oxide at 275° converts the sulfite of 2, 3-butanediol (12) into a mixture of epoxide and 2-butanone, while passage over clay at 575° gives a low yield of butadiene.

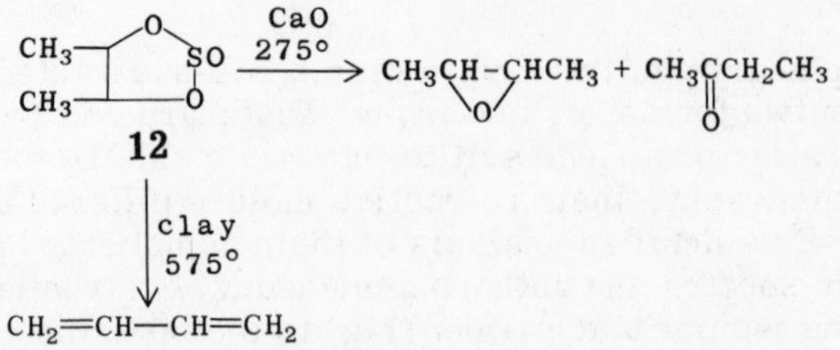

Price and Berti[67] investigated the pyrolysis of the cyclic sulfites of *meso-* and DL-hydrobenzoin at about 240°. The *cis* sulfite (13) from the *meso* isomer decomposes smoothly and in good yield to desoxybenzoin, while the *trans* sulfite (15) from the DL-isomer yields diphenylacetaldehyde almost quantitatively. These differences were explained by the formation of bridged phenonium ion intermediates, 14 and 16. In the phenonium ion 14 derived from the *cis* sulfite, the sulfinate ion is *trans* to the phenyl-activated β-hydrogen, and is therefore forced to stabilize itself by abstraction of the α-hydrogen.

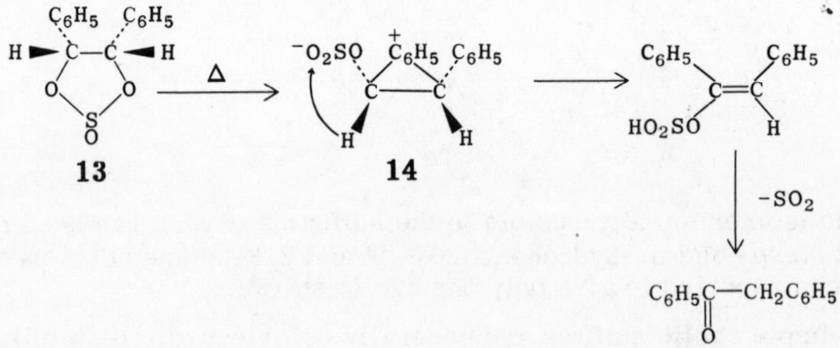

In the phenonium ion (16) derived from the *trans* sulfite, the sulfinate ion and the β-hydrogen are *cis*, and this proton migrates readily.

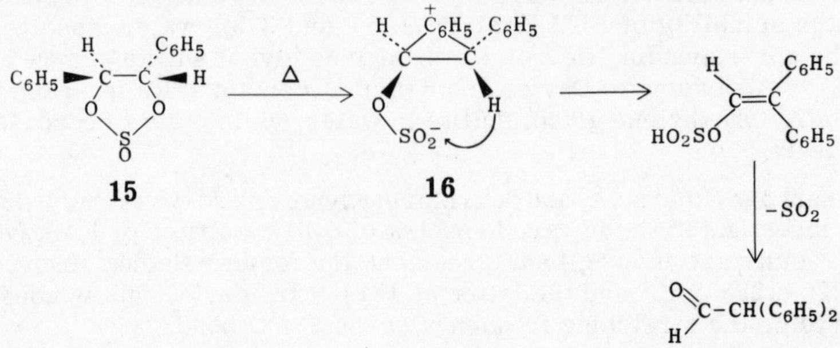

10

A similar explanation can be used to explain the results obtained by Gillis[42a] on heating ethylene sulfite with triethylamine at 180°. Bissinger, Kung, and Hamilton[14a] had found that under these conditions dimethyl sulfite yields methyl methanesulfonate. Gillis found that ethylene sulfite yields a variety of products, but only acetaldehyde and paraldehyde were identified.

Cyclic sulfites of 1, 2-glycols are hydrolyzed readily by dilute acid[20-23,23a,41,74,81b] or alkali.[20-23,41,52,58,74,78,81a] Robertson and Neish[74] were the first to investigate the hydrolysis. D-(−)-2, 3-Butanediol was converted into *trans*-4, 5-dimethyl-1, 3, 2-dioxathiolane 2-oxide; hydrolysis with dilute hydrochloric acid regenerated the glycol with complete retention of configuration. Garner and Lucas[41] confirmed these results, and showed that alkaline hydrolysis also regenerates the glycol with retention of configuration. Thus, reaction with thionyl chloride and hydrolysis of the cyclic sulfite both take place with inversion, or both reactions take place with retention. The latter view appears much more reasonable, indicating that both the formation and hydrolysis of the cyclic sulfites occur without affecting the carbon-oxygen bonds. Bunton, de la Mare, and co-workers[20,21] proved unequivocally that hydrolysis occurs by sulfur-oxygen bond fission by carrying out both acid- and base-catalyzed hydrolysis in the presence of H$_2$O^{18}; there was no isotopic enrichment in the glycol. They showed further that very little exchange takes place with the sulfoxide oxygen.

Davis[31a] investigated the alkaline hydrolysis of ethylene sulfite. The reaction was first order in hydroxide ion, and first order in cyclic sulfite. The rate of formation of one mole of sulfite ion equalled the rate of consumption of two moles of hydroxide, showing that there is no build-up of the open-chain monoester, in agreement with Bunton, de la Mare, and co-workers.[20-23] At 25° the rate of hydrolysis of ethylene sulfite was 360 times that of dimethyl sulfite. The reaction was formulated as follows:

Davis also found a very slow transesterification equilibrium with methanol; presumably, the mixed ester would cyclize rapidly.

Bunton, de la Mare, and co-workers[20,22,23] studied both the alkaline and acid hydrolysis of ethylene sulfite. The alkaline hydrolysis was too fast to be measured by their technique, but the much slower acid hydrolysis was investigated in detail. The mechanism was pictured as follows:

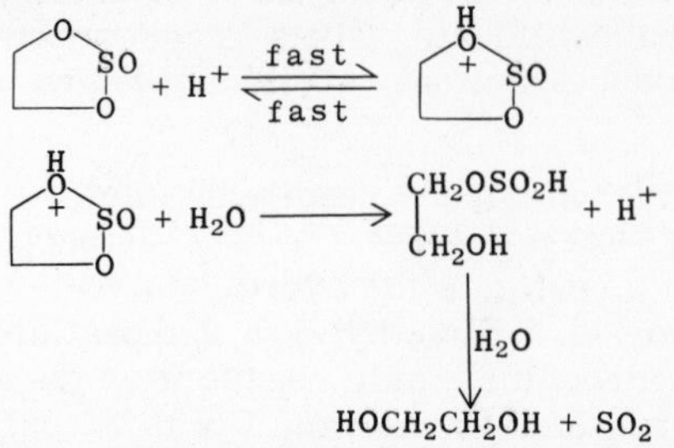

The evidence for their mechanism is discussed in Chapter 8, section I A-1a-(3). Suffice it to say here that Davis[31a] found the heats of hydrolysis of ethylene sulfite and dimethyl sulfite to be identical, as did Pagdin, Pine, and co-workers,[64a] for ethylene sulfite and trimethylene sulfite. Therefore, the rapid alkaline hydrolysis of ethylene sulfite cannot be attributed to strain in the five-membered ring.

Substitution on the ring has little effect on the rate of acid hydrolysis: 1, 3, 2-dioxathiolane 2-oxide, 1; 4-methyl derivative, 1; *trans*-4, 5-dimethyl, 0. 8; *cis*-4, 5-dimethyl, 1. 2; 4, 4, 5, 5-tetramethyl, 0. 7; 4-chloromethyl, 0. 3. This is in accord with the distance of the substituents from the point of attack, but is in marked contrast to the effect of alkyl substituents on the hydrolysis of γ-sultones (see Chapter 4, section I A-3a-(2)). The acid hydrolysis of cyclic sulfites is considerably slower than that of simple open-chain sulfites,[23a,81b] whereas the reverse is true for alkaline hydrolysis.[81a]

Reulos and LeTellier[69] reported that the cyclic sulfites of *meso*- and DL-hydrobenzoin, on heating with dry hydrogen chloride in dioxane, react to form the *erythro*- and *threo*-chlorohydrin, respectively. Since the sulfites are formed without configurational change, the reaction with hydrogen chloride must take place without inversion. This eliminates the possibility of the reaction proceeding *via* a carbonium ion or involving an S_N2 displacement. It is probably best explained by assuming the intermediate formation of a chlorosulfite; these are known to decompose to the corresponding chloride generally without inversion, presumably by an S_Ni process.[29]

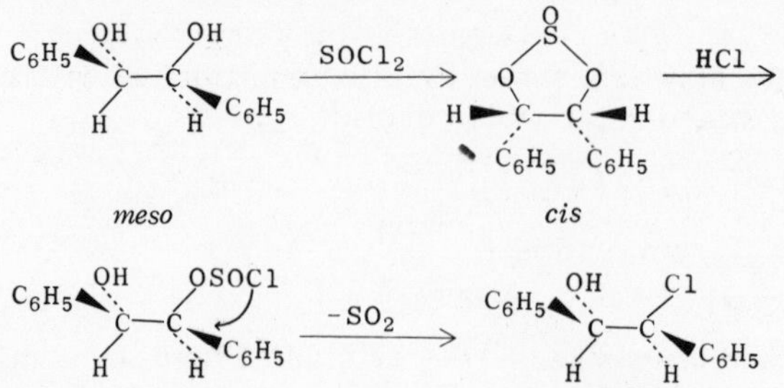

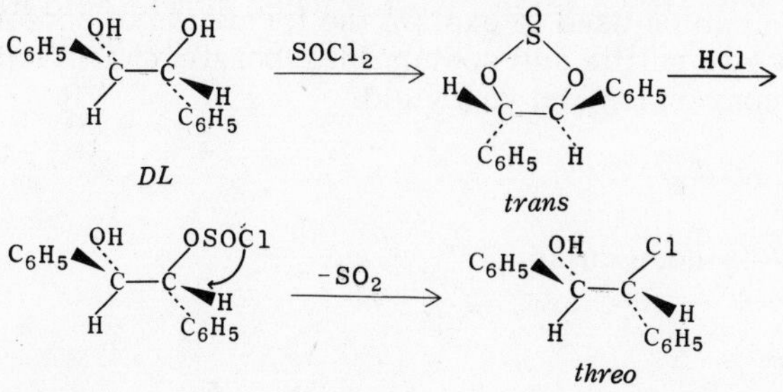

The alternative explanation advanced by Boozer and Lewis,[19] involving essentially an S_N2 displacement of chlorosulfite by dioxane, followed by displacement of the dioxane by chloride ion, would lead to the same results.

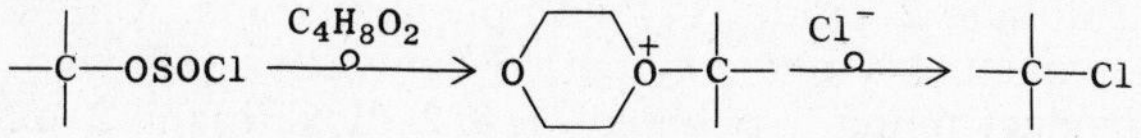

According to Hesse[50,50b] ethylene sulfite reacts with aldehydes in the presence of an acid catalyst to form 1, 3-dioxolanes; this too would presumably involve sulfur-oxygen cleavage,

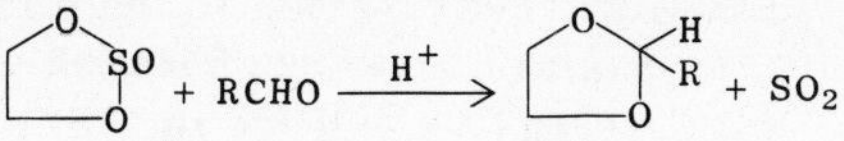

as would the formation of 2-hydroxyethylsulfuric acid from ethylene sulfite and sulfuric acid reported by Brunken and Poppe.[19e]

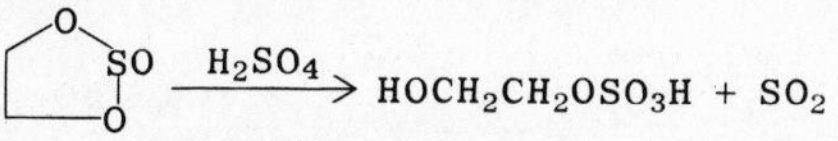

Several examples of carbon-oxygen cleavage in cyclic sulfites are known. Carlson and Cretcher[24,25] found that ethylene sulfite is an excellent hydroxyethylating agent for alcohols, phenols, carboxylic acids, and amines. The reaction may be carried out with acidic or basic catalysts or simply by heating. This reaction must undoubtedly involve carbon-oxygen cleavage, probably *via* an S_N2 displacement, as illustrated with phenol.

$$C_6H_5OH + B \longrightarrow C_6H_5O^- + BH^+$$

$$\xrightarrow{H^+} C_6H_5OCH_2CH_2OH + SO_2$$

[For references, see pp. 57-61.]

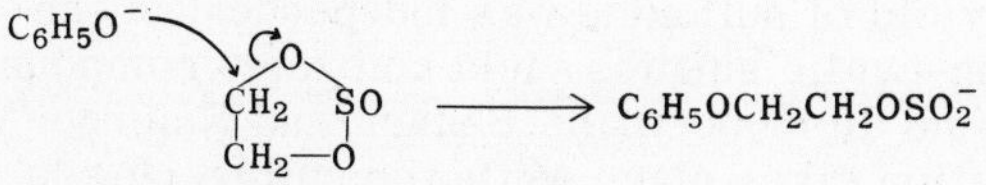

The same mechanism can be used to explain the formation of sodium isethionate from ethylene sulfite and sodium bicarbonate, which Smith[79a] has reported in 94% conversion and 85% yield.

$$\text{(ethylene sulfite)} \xrightarrow[\text{30 min. 169}^\circ]{\text{NaHCO}_3} \text{HOCH}_2\text{CH}_2\text{SO}_3\text{Na}$$

Presumably, the first step involves the formation of sodium sulfite or bisulfite, which then attacks the cyclic compound to yield isethionate and to regenerate the nucleophilic reagent.

Ben-Ishay[12b] obtained an unusual result when he reacted 4-chloro-methyl-1, 3, 2-dioxathiolane 2-oxide (17) with phenoxide ion. Only a small amount of the expected 4-phenoxymethyl derivative (18) was formed, the major product being 5-phenoxy-1, 3, 2-dioxathiane 2-oxide (19). o-Cresol and theophylline[12c] reacted similarly.

$$\text{ClCH}_2\text{—} \xrightarrow[\text{1 hr. reflux}]{\text{C}_6\text{H}_5\text{ONa, EtOH}} \text{C}_6\text{H}_5\text{OCH}_2\text{—} + \text{C}_6\text{H}_5\text{O—}$$

(8.3%)   (66%)

17   **18**   **19**

The formation of 19 can be explained by an initial nucleophilic attack by phenoxide ion at C-4 followed by displacement of Cl by sulfite ion.

$$\text{ClCH}_2\text{—CH—} \underset{\text{C}_6\text{H}_5\text{O}^-}{\uparrow} \longrightarrow \text{C}_6\text{H}_5\text{O—CH—CH}_2\text{—Cl} \longrightarrow \text{C}_6\text{H}_5\text{O—CH} + \text{Cl}^-$$

19

Szmant and Emerson[80] uncovered still another reaction which appears to involve carbon-oxygen cleavage. They investigated the action of Grignard reagents on cyclic sulfites in order to determine if ring size has any effect on the reaction. Ethylene sulfite yielded 42-60% diphenyl sulfoxide and 3.4-23% ethylene bromohydrin, depending on the conditions of the reaction; the yield of sulfoxide was independent of the ring size. Inasmuch as non-cyclic sulfites yield no bromo compounds and ethylene sulfite forms no dibromoethane, Szmant and Emerson concluded that bromide formation takes place while the sulfite ring is intact, presumably by a nucleophilic displacement by bromide ion.

14

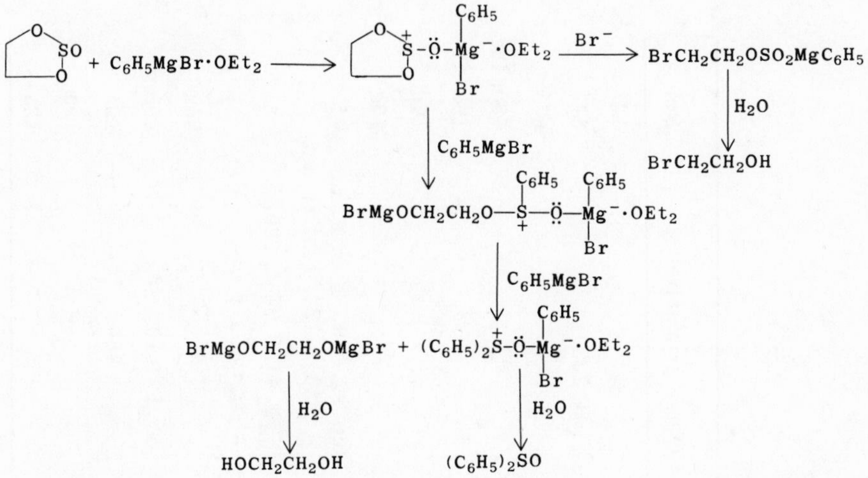

To account for the lack of bromide formation with non-cyclic sulfites, the authors reasoned that the cyclic sulfites have a more highly polarized carbon-oxygen bond, making them more prone to nucleophilic displacements; also, steric factors in the cyclic sulfites favor displacement.

Garner and Lucas[41] described the oxidation of the cyclic sulfite of 2, 3-butanediol to the corresponding sulfate with calcium permanganate.

Viard[84] has patented the photochemical chlorination of ethylene sulfite to form 2-chloroethyl chlorosulfate in excellent yield. If this is truly a photochemical reaction,

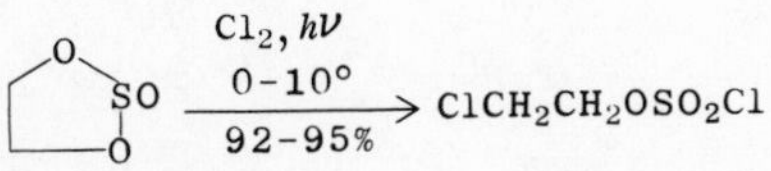

it is the only radical reaction reported for cyclic sulfites. Bissinger, Fredenburg, and co-workers,[14] attempted to polymerize 4-vinyl-1, 3, 2-dioxathiolane 2-oxide by heating with benzoyl peroxide at 70°, but sulfur dioxide was evolved and a black, gelatinous mass was formed.

4. Uses

Very few potential commercial applications have been reported for these compounds. Ham[27,48a] claimed that a polyester is formed from ethylene or propylene sulfite and a dicarboxylic acid under milder conditions than required with the glycol. The products, however, contained a considerable number of sulfite linkages and were lower melting than the corresponding unmodified polyester. No such disadvantage was reported by Farbwerke Hoechst,[37a] who claimed that ethylene sulfite is

TABLE 2. 1,3,2-Dioxathiolane 2,2-Dioxides

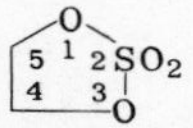

Substituent	Glycol	Yield (%)	M.p. (°C)	Other properties	Ref.
None	Ethylene glycol	23	99		12
			99	$d_4^{13}1.735$	54
			98		67a
		9.5	96-97		48b, 48c
		59-74	96-97		19e
		66	94-95		19d
		20-23	91-92		19c
4,5-(CH$_3$-)$_2$	D-(−)-2,3-Butanediol	45	6.1-6.4	b.p. 92.9-93.1° at 2 mm 123.8-124.0° at 10 mm $n_D^{25}1.4159, d_4^{25}1.2898$ $[\alpha]_D^{25} + 1.75°$	41
	meso-2,3-Butanediol	54	48-49.5		55a
4,5-(ClCH$_2$CHCl-)$_2$(?)	D-Mannitol	10	107	$[\alpha]_D^{15} + 105.1°$	49b
	Dulcitol	21	105	$[\alpha]_D + 88°$	19a
	Dulcitol	20	116		19a
4,4,5,5-(CH$_3$-)$_4$	Pinacol	52	dec. 131°		12a

superior to ethylene glycol because the reaction is irreversible and an excess of sulfite is therefore not required. Ethylene sulfite has been patented as a solvent for the purification of sulfur dioxide,[83] and as a spinning solvent for polyacrylonitrile,[74a] or in conjunction with dimethylacetamide, dimethylformamide, or nitromethane.[35] Cyclic sulfites have been patented as stabilizers for cellulose derivatives.[63]

B. SULFATE ESTERS

1. Preparation

Few cyclic sulfates of 1, 2-glycols have been reported, as indicated in Table 2. Baker and Field[12] prepared ethylene sulfate (20) by reacting ethylene dibromide with silver sulfate.

$$BrCH_2CH_2Br \xrightarrow[\substack{23\%}]{\substack{Ag_2SO_4 \\ xylene, reflux}}$$

20

According to Brimacombe, Foster, and co-workers,[19c] the reaction fails with 1, 2-dibromopropane. Garner and Lucas[41] prepared *trans*-4, 5-dimethyl-1, 3, 2-dioxathiolane 2, 2-dioxide (21) by oxidizing the cyclic sulfite ester of D-(—)-2, 3-butanediol with calcium permanganate.

21

Lichtenberger and Hincky[55a] prepared the *cis* isomer from *meso*-2, 3-butanediol in 54% yield. Baker and Burrows[12a] reported a 1% yield of ethylene sulfate by this procedure, but obtained a 52% yield of 4, 4, 5, 5-tetramethyl-1, 3, 2-dioxathiolane 2, 2-dioxide from pinacol sulfite. Attempts to use other oxidizing agents have been unsuccessful.[19c]

Although these two procedures are most frequently used, several others have been reported. Helferich and co-workers[49a-49c] and Bragg, Jones, and Turner[19a] prepared a number of cyclic sulfates of sugars and other polyhydroxy compounds by treatment with sulfuryl chloride and pyridine. Simultaneous replacement of hydroxyl by chlorine takes place. Thus, D-mannitol[19a,49b] and dulcitol[19a] yield tetrachloro cyclic sulfates. Bragg, Jones, and Turner proved that the mannitol derivative possesses a five-membered ring by cleaving the hydrolysis product with periodic acid, but they presented no evidence to substantiate their suggestion that the compound is 4, 5-bis(1, 2-dichloroethyl)-1, 3, 2-dioxathiolane 2, 2-dioxide (21a).

[For references, see pp. 57-61.]

$$\text{HOCH}_2(\text{CHOH})_4\text{CH}_2\text{OH} \xrightarrow[\substack{20-21\%}]{\substack{\text{SO}_2\text{Cl}_2,\ \text{C}_5\text{H}_5\text{N},\ \text{CHCl}_3 \\ 5°}} \quad \substack{\text{ClCH}_2\text{CH} \\ \\ \text{ClCH}_2\text{CH}} $$

21a

2, 5-O-Methylene-D-mannitol forms a trichloro derivative rather than a chlorinated sulfate. Sugar derivatives are discussed in section VII.

Ham[48b,48c] found that treatment of ethylene oxide with the dioxane-sulfur trioxide complex yields a heavy oil. Since it contained no free acid, it was presumably polymeric. Heating this oil *in vacuo* gave a low yield of ethylene sulfate.

$$\text{CH}_2\text{---CH}_2 \xrightarrow[]{\substack{\text{C}_4\text{H}_8\text{O}_2\cdot\text{SO}_3 \\ 10°}} [-\text{CH}_2\text{CH}_2\text{OSO}_3-]_n \xrightarrow[\substack{10\%}]{\substack{70-80°,\ 2\ \text{mm.}}} $$

Good yields have been reported[4,19e] from a related process in which a polymer is formed by treatment of 2-hydroxyethylsulfuric acid with thionyl chloride and then distilled at a higher temperature than used by Ham.

$$\xrightarrow[]{\text{H}_2\text{SO}_4} \text{HOCH}_2\text{CH}_2\text{OSO}_3\text{H} \xrightarrow[\substack{59\%}]{\substack{1.\ \text{SOCl}_2 \\ 15\ \text{hrs. reflux} \\ 2.\ \text{dist. }17\ \text{mm.}}} $$

Under similar conditions chlorosulfonic acid with ethylene sulfite gives a 65% yield of ethylene sulfate, while a mixture of thionyl chloride and sulfuric acid gives a 74% yield. The reaction fails with other 1, 2-glycols.

Another synthesis of ethylene sulfate involves treatment of glycol diacetate with dimethyl sulfate.[19d] The cyclic sulfate is obtained by distillation following the removal of methyl acetate, a reaction product, and excess dimethyl sulfate.

$$\text{CH}_3\text{COOCH}_2\text{CH}_2\text{OOCCH}_3 \xrightarrow[\substack{66\%}]{\substack{1.\text{Me}_2\text{SO}_4 \\ 2\ \text{hrs. }130°\ \text{and }360\ \text{mm.} \\ 2.\ 110-142°\ \text{at }3\ \text{mm.}}} $$

Apparently glycol monoacetate can also be used.[3]

2. Structure and Reactions

Pritchard and Lauterbur[67a] found that the proton magnetic resonance spectrum of ethylene sulfate consists of one sharp line, in marked contrast to the complicated spectrum of ethylene sulfite (section I A-2). If the ring is non-planar, there must be a rapid interconversion of the two forms (21b and 21c), since all the hydrogens are equivalent.

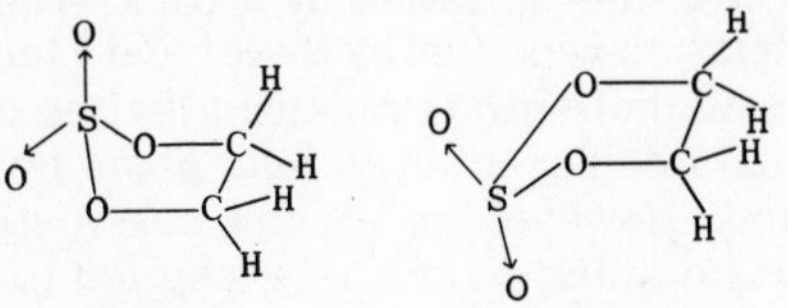

21b   **21c**

Baker and Field[12] found that ethylene sulfate hydrolyzes readily to 2-hydroxyethylsulfuric acid and alkylates catechol in the presence of base to 1, 4-benzodioxan (22).

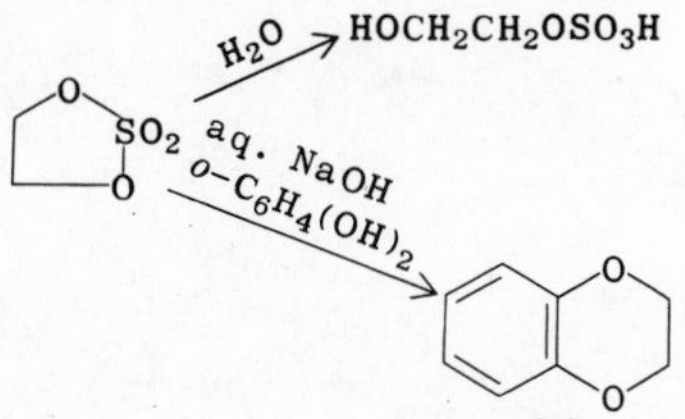

22

Garner and Lucas[41] investigated the hydrolysis more intensively. Acid hydrolysis of optically active *trans*-4, 5-dimethyl-1, 3, 2-dioxathiolane 2, 2-dioxide (21) gives the *meso* glycol (24), indicating inversion at one carbon atom and retention or an even number of inversions at the other. Although there is little evidence on the subject, it seems reasonable to assume that the ring is opened by nucleophilic attack by water leading to carbon-oxygen cleavage, in contrast to the hydrolysis of the cyclic sulfite esters. The intermediate (23) would then undergo sulfur-oxygen cleavage, in agreement with the results of Burwell[23b] on the acid hydrolysis of *sec*-butyl hydrogen sulfate.

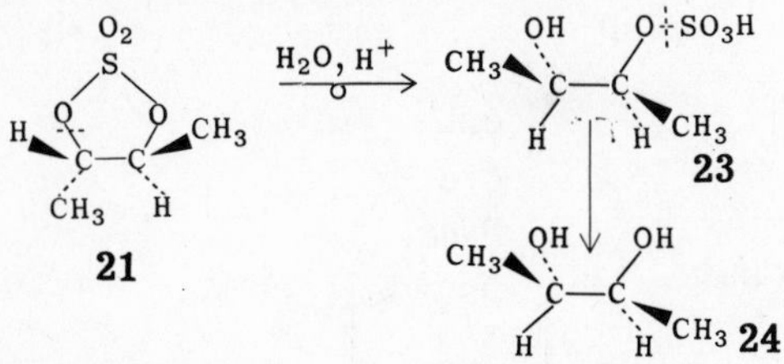

21   **23**   **24**

Basic hydrolysis gives mainly DL-glycol (25) with small amounts of *meso*- and D-glycols. This is more difficult to explain. Garner and Lucas suggested that the DL-glycol might result from the intermediate formation of the *cis* oxide; subsequent hydrolysis would give the DL-glycol. Two alternatives are possible to explain the formation of the *cis* oxide from the *trans* sulfate. Either the first step in the reaction

[For references, see pp. 57-61.]

involves a nucleophilic attack by hydroxide ion leading to inversion on one carbon atom followed by a front-side displacement of sulfate, or the first step involves sulfur-oxygen cleavage followed by a back-side displacement of sulfate. From the alkylation reported by Baker and Field[12] and the known alkylating power of dialkyl sulfates under alkaline conditions, the initial ring opening would be expected to take place by carbon-oxygen cleavage with inversion. However, in the few cases studied, it appears that five-membered cyclic sulfates are an exception to the rule and undergo alkaline hydrolysis by sulfur-oxygen cleavage (see section VIII B). The formation of the epoxide with inversion agrees with the inversion found by Burwell[23b] during the basic hydrolysis of *sec*-butyl hydrogen sulfate.

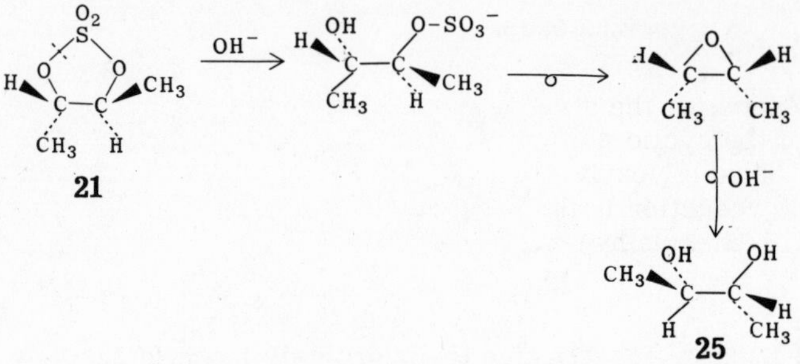

21

25

C. SULFATE ESTERS OF ENEDIOLS

In 1954 Rio[71] reported that 9, 10-bis(phenylethynyl)-9, 10-dihydroxy-9, 10-dihydroanthracene (**26**, R = H) or the corresponding methoxy derivative (**26**, R = CH$_3$) reacts with sulfuric acid in dioxane to give a crystalline compound, melting at 179-180°, which he formulated as 4-phenyl-5-(10-phenylethynyl-9-anthryl)-1, 3, 2-dioxathiole 2, 2-dioxide (**27**).

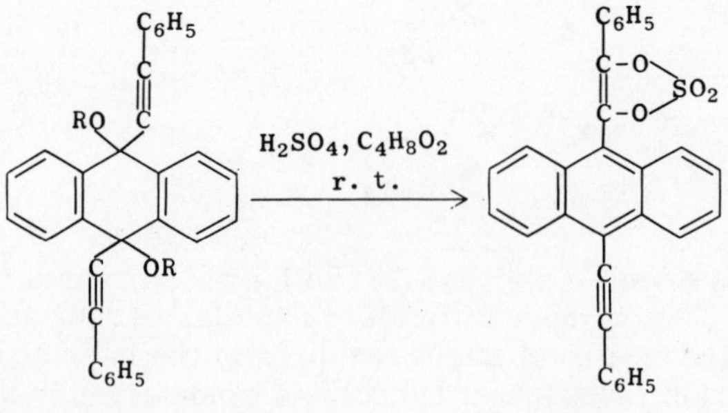

26   **27**

The structure was assigned initially on the similarity of the ultraviolet and visible spectra of **27** and the corresponding dihalogenated derivative (**28**).

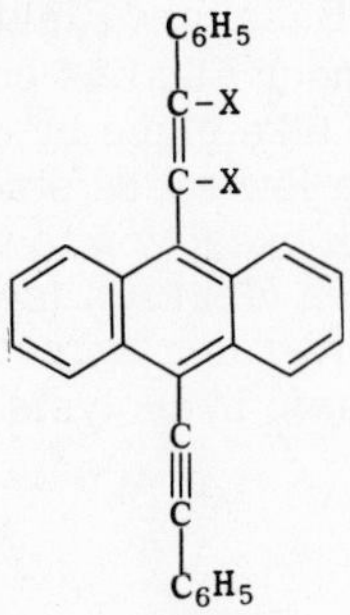

28

Further evidence for the structure was presented by Rio and Ranjon.[72] Treatment of the cyclic sulfate (**27**) with sodium bicarbonate in methanol yielded 9-phenylglyoxylyl-10-phenylethynylanthracene (**29**) and sulfur dioxide, while reduction in the presence of acid gave a good yield of 9-phenacyl-10-phenylethynylanthracene (**30**).

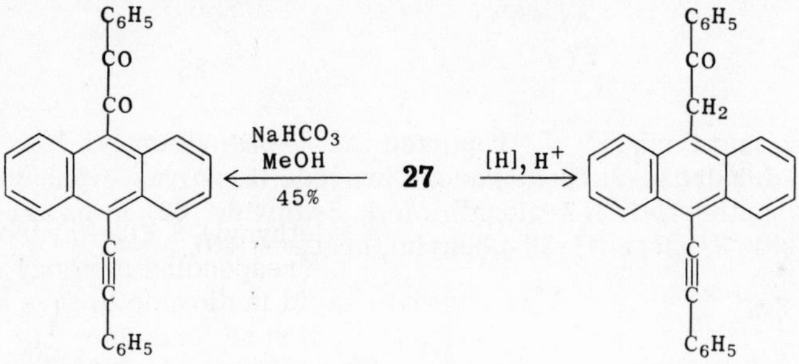

29 **30**

Rio[70] postulated the following mechanism to account for the formation of the enediol sulfate.

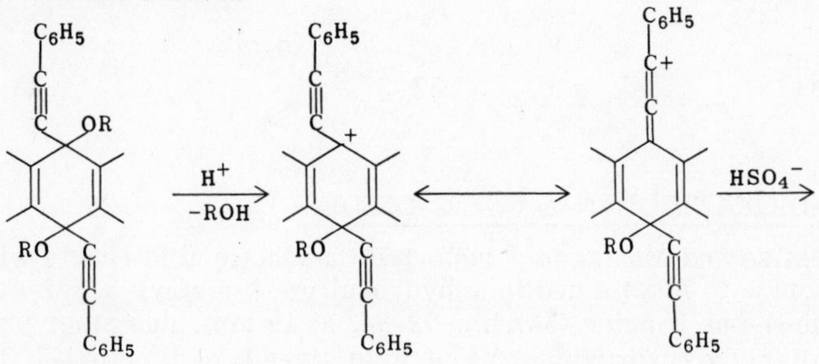

26

[For references, see pp. 57-61.]

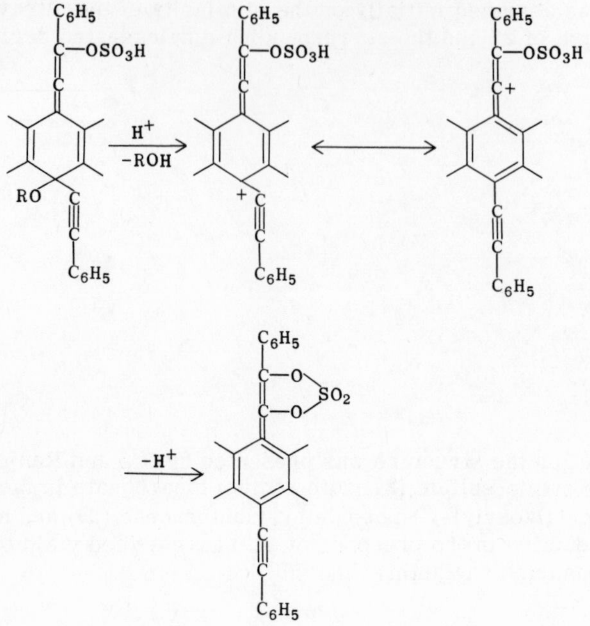

27

Similarly, Rio and Cornu[73, 73a] reported that 9-phenylethynyl-10-phenyl-9, 10-dihydroxy-9, 10-dihydroanthracene (**31**) gives 4-phenyl-5-(10-phenyl-9-anthryl)-1, 3, 2-dioxathiole 2, 2-dioxide (**32**), m.p. 211-212°; reduction yields 9-phenacyl-10-phenylanthracene (**33**).

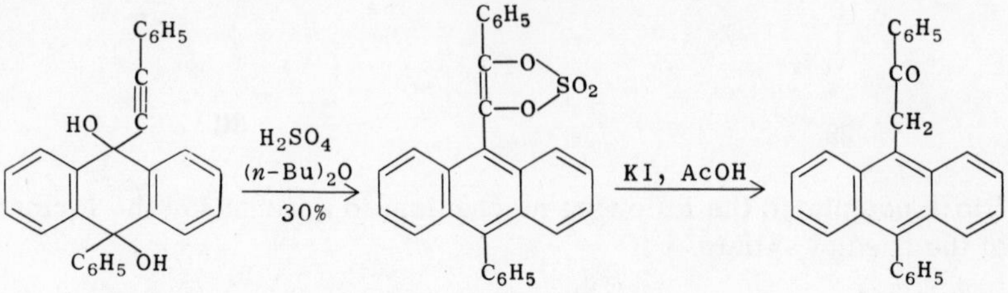

31   **32**   **33**

D.   1, 3, 2-DIOXATHIOLAN-4-ONE 2-OXIDES

In 1922 Blaise and Montagne[16] reported that lactic acid reacts with thionyl chloride to form a cyclic anhydrosulfite, 5-methyl-1, 3, 2-dioxathiolan-4-one 2-oxide (**34**), b.p. 72-74° at 19 mm, plus other products. Similarly, α-hydroxyisobutyric acid gives 5, 5-dimethyl-1, 3, 2-dioxathiolan-4-one 2-oxide (**35**), b.p. 63° at 21 mm.

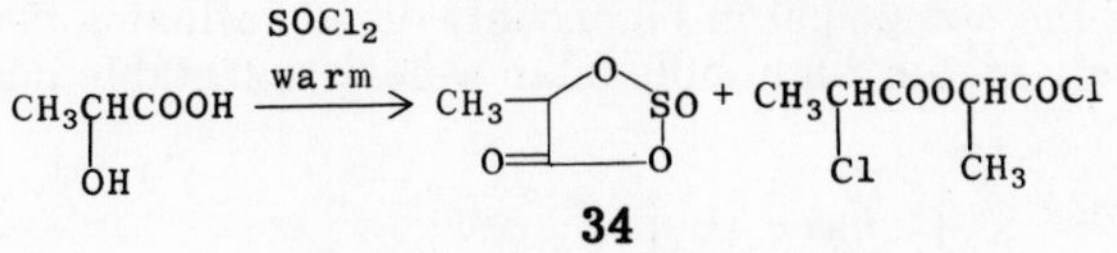

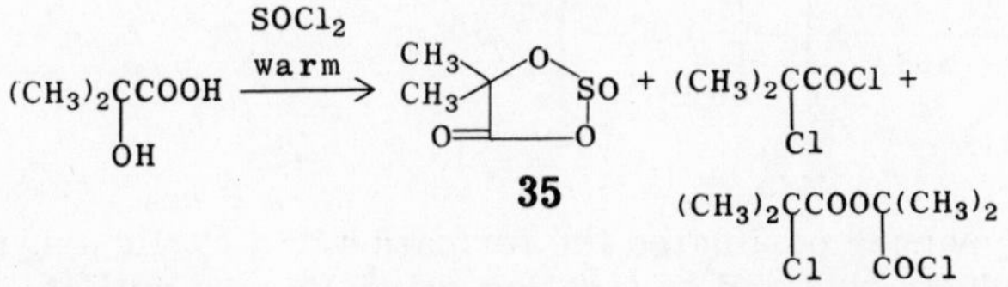

$$CH_3CHCOOH \xrightarrow[\text{warm}]{SOCl_2} \quad \textbf{34} \quad + \quad CH_3CHCOOCHCOCl$$

$$(CH_3)_2CCOOH \xrightarrow[\text{warm}]{SOCl_2} \quad \textbf{35} \quad + \quad (CH_3)_2CCOCl +$$

$$(CH_3)_2CCOOC(CH_3)_2$$

The compounds are unstable to heat, liberating sulfur dioxide and forming polylactides at 120-125°. They hydrolyze in moist air to liberate sulfur dioxide and regenerate the starting materials. The lactate, but not the isobutyrate, derivative yields an intermediate melting at about 90°, formulated by the authors as $CH_3CH(OSO_2H)COOH$ or $CH_3CH(OH)COOSO_2H$. Alcohols give esters and arylamines give amides, both with the liberation of sulfur dioxide, while phenylhydrazine liberates the acid.

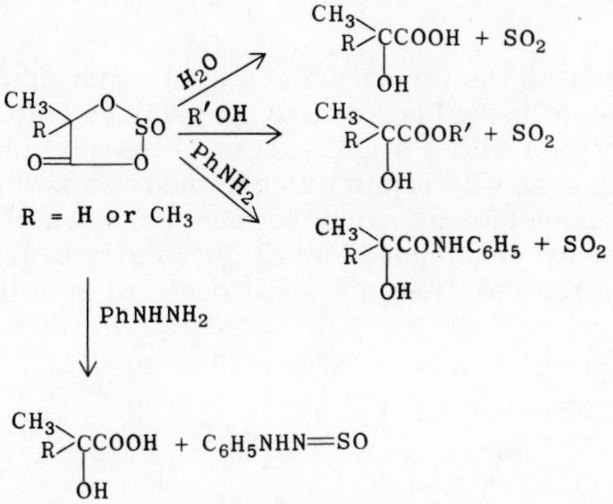

$$\begin{array}{c} CH_3 \\ R \end{array}\!\!>\!\!CCOOH + SO_2$$

$$\begin{array}{c} CH_3 \\ R \end{array}\!\!>\!\!CCOOR' + SO_2$$

$$\begin{array}{c} CH_3 \\ R \end{array}\!\!>\!\!CCONHC_6H_5 + SO_2$$

R = H or CH₃

$$\begin{array}{c} CH_3 \\ R \end{array}\!\!>\!\!CCOOH + C_6H_5NHN\!\!=\!\!SO$$

Glycolic acid was reported to give no cyclic anhydride.[15]

$$HOCH_2COOH \xrightarrow{SOCl_2} ClSO_2CH_2COCl + ClCH_2COOCH_2COCl$$

The chlorosulfite acid chloride is somewhat similar in properties to the cyclic anhydride and, since no analyses were reported for the anhydrides, their existence would appear to be in doubt. However, Alderson[5] has recently confirmed the formation of the anhydrosulfite (35) from α-hydroxyisobutyric acid in 69% yield, b.p. 53-55° at 16 mm, n_D^{25} 1.4294-1.4298. Whereas Blaise and Montagne[16] reported the formation of a readily hydrolyzable, presumably low molecular weight polylactide by heating the anhydrosulfite in bulk at 120-125°, Alderson claimed that heating the compound in rigorously dried refluxing benzene gives a relatively stable, high molecular weight, orientable polymer.

$$\underset{\textbf{35}}{\text{(structure)}} \xrightarrow[89\%]{\underset{52\,\text{hrs.}\,80^\circ}{C_6H_6}} \left[-\overset{CH_3}{\underset{CH_3}{\overset{|}{\underset{|}{C}}}}-COO- \right]_n + SO_2$$

Carré and Libermann[26] postulated the formation of a cyclic anhydride to explain the products obtained on treating mandelic acid with thionyl chloride. Meyer[59] refluxed mandelic acid with excess thionyl chloride and isolated benzaldehyde. McKenzie and Barrow[58] obtained benzylidene chloride in addition to the expected chloro-acid, and they believed the two products were formed by the breakdown of the expected intermediate in two different ways.

$$C_6H_5\underset{\overset{|}{OH}}{C}HCOOH \xrightarrow{SOCl_2} C_6H_5\underset{\overset{|}{O}SOCl}{C}HCOCl \nearrow \begin{array}{l} C_6H_5\underset{\overset{|}{Cl}}{C}HCOCl + SO_2 \\[2ex] C_6H_5CHCl_2 + SO_2 + CO \end{array}$$

Carré and Libermann postulated the formation of a cyclic anhydride (36) to explain the formation of benzaldehyde and benzylidene chloride. When mandelic acid was treated with a slight excess of thionyl chloride in ether at room temperature, an oily liquid was obtained. Treatment with ethanol yielded ethyl mandelate, as expected from the work of Blaise and Montagne.[16] The oil decomposed at 29-30° to give benzaldehyde and sulfur dioxide, and the reactions were rationalized as follows:

$$C_6H_5\underset{\overset{|}{OH}}{C}HCOOH \xrightarrow{SOCl_2} \underset{\textbf{36}}{\text{(structure)}} \longrightarrow C_6H_5CHO + SO_2 + CO$$

$$\downarrow SOCl_2$$

$$C_6H_5CHCl_2$$

The interaction of benzaldehyde and thionyl chloride is known to give benzylidene chloride.[56] Carré and Libermann advanced the same explanation for the formation of benzophenone from diphenylglycolic acid and thionyl chloride.[60]

II. C_4-C_2O_2S 2, 4-DIOXA-3-THIABICYCLO[3. 2. 0]HEPTANE (36a)

$$\begin{array}{c} H \\ | \\ H_2C\!\!\overset{7}{-}\!\!\overset{H}{\underset{6}{C}}\!\!\overset{1}{\underset{5}{<}}\!\!\overset{2\ 3}{\underset{4}{S}} \\ H_2C\!\!-\!\!\underset{\overset{|}{H}}{C}\!\!-\!\!O \end{array}$$

36a

Criegee and Noll[29a] prepared *cis*-1, 5, 6, 7-tetramethyl-2, 4-dioxa-3-thiabicyclo[3. 2. 0]heptane 3-oxide (**36b**), m.p. 100-101°, from 1, 2, 3, 4-tetramethyl-1, 2-cyclobutanediol. The glycol is undoubtedly *cis*, but the geometry of the other methyl groups is unknown.

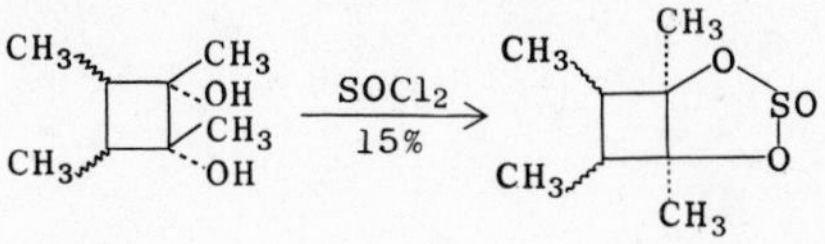

36b

III. C$_2$O$_2$S-C$_2$O$_2$S 1, 3, 2-DIOXATHIOLO[1, 3, 2]DIOXATHIOLE (37). GLYOXAL SULFATE

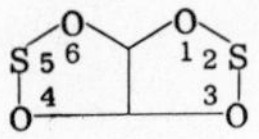

37

(RRI 870)

This ring system is indexed under the above name in Chemical Abstracts, but it is cross-indexed to "1, 1, 2, 2-ethanetetrol, cyclic sulfate", since the only representative is glyoxal sulfate (**38**).

Glyoxal sulfate was first prepared by Ott[64] from tetrachloroethane and fuming sulfuric acid in the presence of a mercuric sulfate catalyst in 32% yield.[75]

$$Cl_2CHCHCl_2 + 4\,SO_3 + 2\,H_2SO_4 \xrightarrow[\substack{50-60°}]{HgSO_4} (CHO_2SO_2)_2$$

38

The yield has since been improved by modifying the reaction conditions.[65,87] From the mode of preparation its structure was considered to be that of **39**.

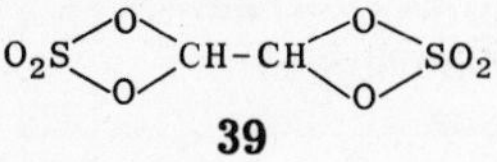

39

However, Baker and Field[12] suggested the much more reasonable structure with two five-membered rings (**38**) on the basis of its similarity (melting point and slight solubility in organic solvents) to methylene sulfate, which they showed to be dimeric (**40**).

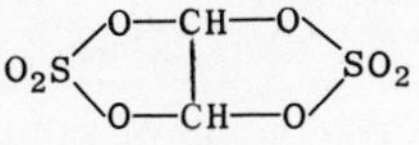

38 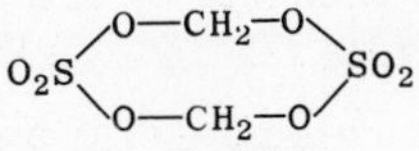   **40**

Baker and Field obtained what appeared to be more conclusive evidence by reacting glyoxal sulfate with ethylene glycol, the product (41) being identical with the reaction product of 2, 3-dichlorodioxane and ethylene glycol.[18]

$$\text{41}$$

However, it has since been shown[37,38] that two products are formed in the reaction of glyoxal sulfate with ethylene glycol, one melting at 136°, identical with the product isolated by Baker and Field, and a second melting at 111-112°. The two were considered to be *cis-trans* isomers. However, Faass and Hilgert[37] and Hassel and Rømming[49] have shown that the higher melting compound is the dioxane derivative (41), while the lower melting compound is the normal acetal (42).

$$\text{42}$$

Thus, the structure of glyoxal sulfate is not based on any chemical evidence, although it appears to be a reasonable one.

Glyoxal sulfate is a crystalline compound melting at 176-177° with decomposition.[64] When recrystallized from acetic acid it forms a solvate containing one molecule of acetic acid and melting at 121-122°.[39] Glyoxal sulfate reacts with water to form glyoxal[64] and is in general a convenient source of glyoxal for many reactions. Thus, it reacts with alcohols to form glyoxal tetraacetals.[12,38,39,68] Although Fischer and Taube[39] reported a 50% yield for the reaction with methanol and a 90% yield for the reaction with ethanol, it has been difficult, apparently, to reproduce their work. Purves[68] recommended the addition of a compound to tie up the sulfuric acid liberated. Fiesselmann and Hörndler[38] found that the reaction of glyoxal sulfate with excess ethanol gives only a 23% yield of glyoxal tetraethylacetal and 23.5% of tetraethoxy-1, 4-dioxane (43), the latter being formed by the reaction shown:

$$\text{43}$$

This was avoided with higher alcohols by using zinc oxide, *n*-propanol giving a 68% yield, and *n*-butanol a 64.5% yield of the desired acetals.

Fischer and Taube[39] investigated several other reactions of glyoxal sulfate. Heating with a mixture of acetic acid and anhydride gave a 70%

yield of glyoxal tetraacetate. Treatment with excess phenylmagnesium bromide gave a 44% yield of hydrobenzoin.

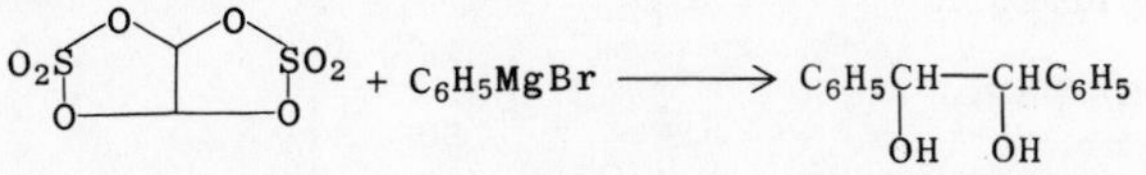

Acetone gave a product of unknown structure, while tertiary amines gave addition compounds which could not be purified. According to Reuter[69a] glyoxal sulfate reacts with aqueous sodium bisulfite to yield 1, 2-dihydroxyethane-1, 2-disulfonic acid.

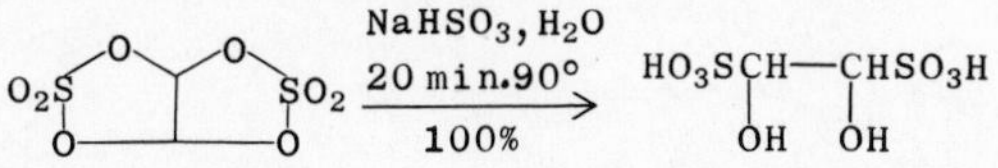

Anthrone (**44**) is reported to react with glyoxal sulfate to form a yellow dye.[13]

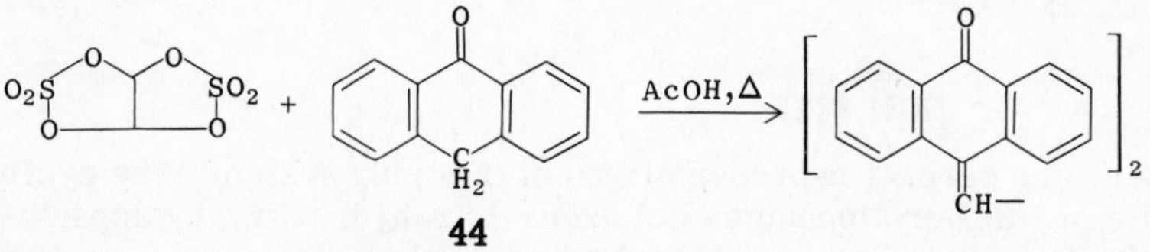

Glyoxal sulfate has been recommended as an acid catalyst for the partial hydration of myrcene.[61]

IV. C$_2$O$_2$S-C$_4$O FURO [3, 4-*d*]-1, 3, 2-DIOXATHIOLE (44a)

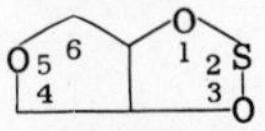

44a

Brimacombe, Foster, and co-workers,[19c] prepared the only member of this series, presumably *cis*-tetrahydrofuro [3, 4-*d*]-1, 3, 2-dioxathiole 2, 2-dioxide (**44b**), from 1, 4-anhydroerythritol and thionyl chloride. It melts at 106-108°.

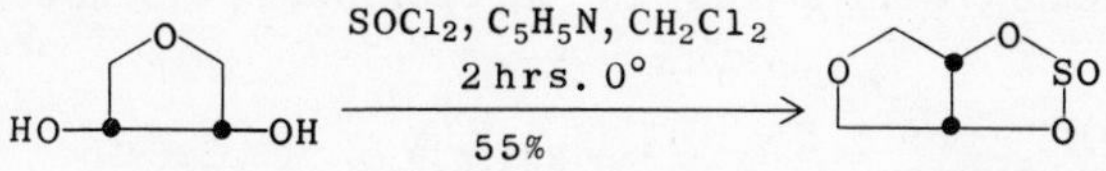

44b

V. C$_2$O$_2$S-C$_4$S THIENO [3, 4-*d*]-1, 3, 2-DIOXATHIOLE (45)

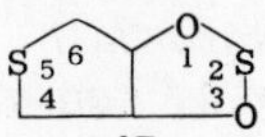

45

[For references, see pp. 57-61.]

27

Chapter 1

Procházka and Horák[67b] prepared *cis*-tetrahydrothieno [3, 4-*d*]-1, 3, 2-dioxathiolane 2, 5, 5-trioxide (**45a**) from *cis*-3, 4-dihydroxythiolane dioxide and thionyl chloride.

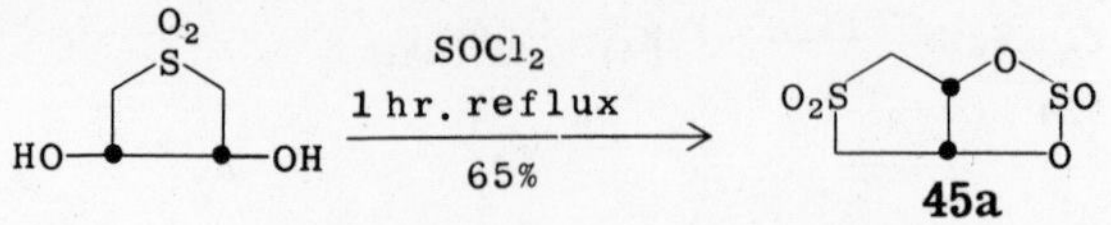

A lower yield was obtained in the presence of pyridine. The broad melting point of **45a**, 129-136°, would seem to indicate that some isomerization took place under these reaction conditions.

VI. C_2O_2S-C_5 3a*H*-CYCLOPENTA-1, 3, 2-DIOXATHIOLE (46)

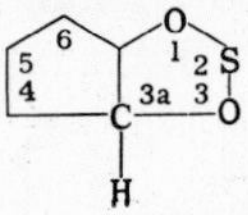

46
(RRI 871)

There are several representatives of this ring system. The cyclic sulfite of *trans*-cyclopentanediol, *trans*-tetrahydro-3a*H*-cyclopenta-1, 3, 2-dioxathiole 2-oxide (**47**), was prepared as a colorless oil, b.p. 115-118° at 15 mm, by Mousseron, Winternitz, and Mousseron-Canet[62] from the *trans*-glycol and thionyl chloride in the presence of pyridine; *trans*-2-chlorocyclopentanol was formed as a by-product.

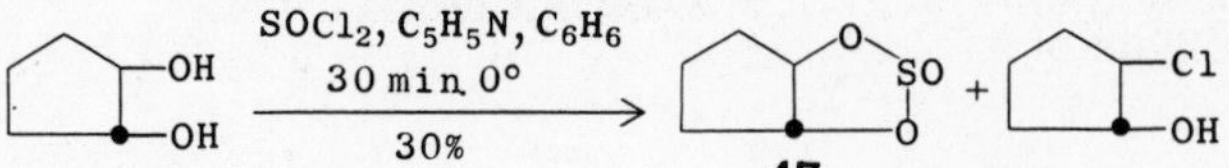

Reduction of the sulfite (**47**) with lithium aluminium hydride regenerates *trans*-cyclopentanediol quantitatively, proving that no rearrangement takes place during the formation of the sulfite. Treatment of the sulfite with hydrogen chloride in dioxane gives the chlorohydrin with retention of configuration, in agreement with the results of Tchoubar[81] on the corresponding cyclohexane derivatives; the mechanism is discussed in section VIII A.

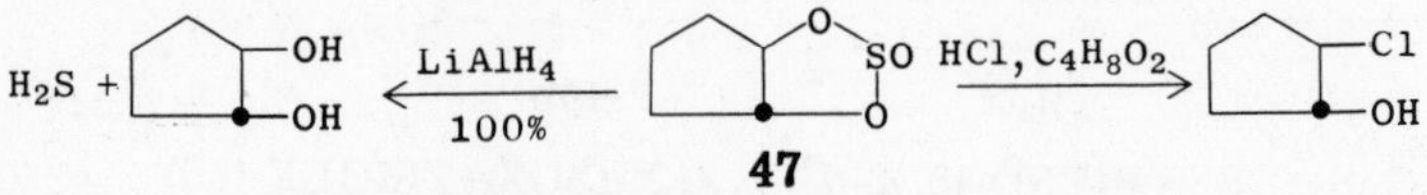

Lichtenberger and Hincky[55a] prepared 4-methyltetrahydro-3a*H*-cyclopenta-1, 3, 2-dioxathiole 2-oxide (**47a**), b.p. 97-98° at 13 mm, n_D^{21} 1. 4688, d_4^{21} 1. 239, from 1-methyl-2, 3-cyclopentanediol of unstated con-

28

figuration. Oxidation with calcium permanganate yielded the corresponding sulfone (47b), m.p. 25-26°.

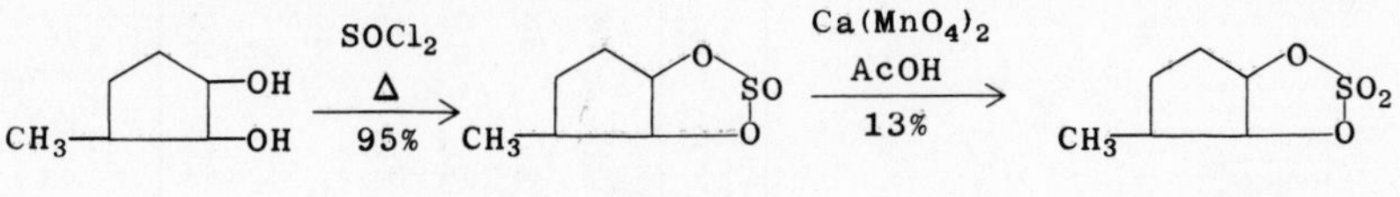

47a   **47b**

VII. C$_2$O$_2$S-C$_5$O 4H-PYRANO[3,4-d]-1,3,2-DIOXATHIOLE (47c)

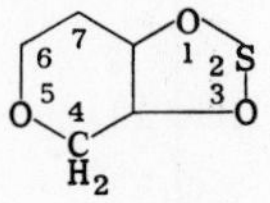

47c

This ring system is represented in its tetrahydro form by the cyclic sulfates of certain sugars; these are listed in Table 3. In 1921 Helferich[49a] reported that methyl α-D-glucopyranoside reacts with sulfuryl chloride and pyridine to form a cyclic sulfate ester, the free hydroxyls being simultaneously replaced by chlorines. Recently, Bragg, Jones, and Turner[19a] showed that Helferich's compound is methyl 4,6-dichloro-4,6-dideoxy-α-D-hexoside 2,3-sulfate (47d) by hydrolyzing it and treating the product with periodate. Two moles were used up and two moles of formic acid were formed; one mole was formed slowly, indicating the hydrolysis of a formyl ester, as expected from the assigned structure.

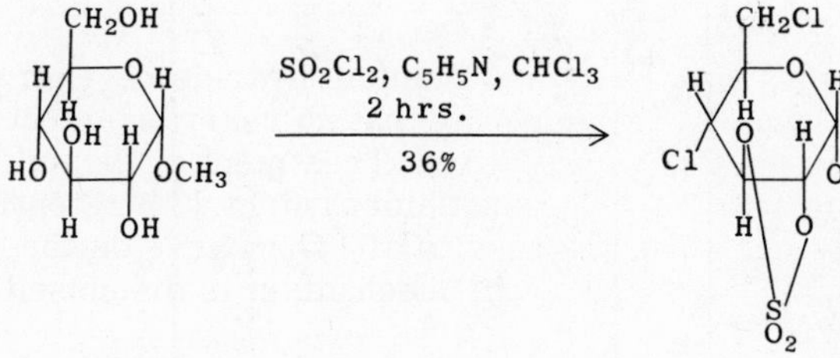

47d

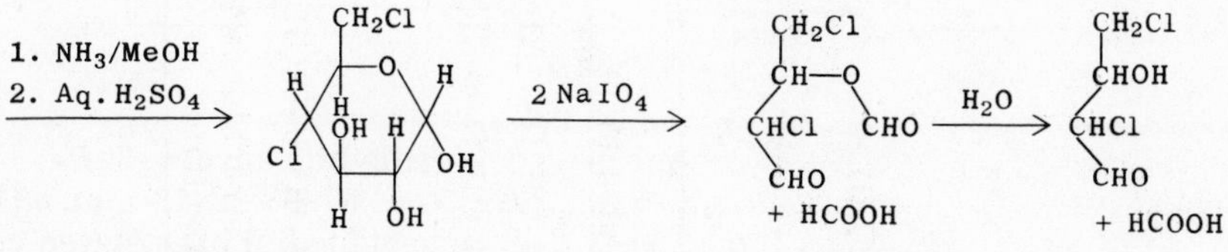

[For references, see pp. 57-61.]

TABLE 3. Cyclic Sulfates of Sugars

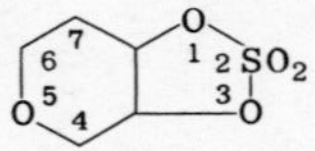

Substituent	Sugar	Yield (%)	M.p (°C)	$[\alpha]_D$	T (°C)	Ref.
4-CH$_3$O-7-Cl	Methyl β-D-arabinoside	27	108.5	−89°	20	19a
4-CH$_3$O-6-ClCH$_2$-7-Cl	Methyl α-D-glucopyranoside	36	106	+140°	17	49a, 49b
		30	104-105	+140°	20	19a
	Methyl β-D-glucopyranoside	5	137	−11.8°	19	49a
4-HO-6-ClCH$_2$-7-Cl·H$_2$O	Methyl α-D-glucopyranoside	63	104-106(dec.)			49c
Tetrachlorotetradeoxytrehalose disulfate	Trehalose	36		+152°	20	49b

Presumably, the methyl β-glucoside product[49a] has a corresponding structure. According to Helferich and co-workers[49c] hydrolysis of **47d** with concentrated hydrochloric acid at 25° removes the methoxyl group, whereas sulfuric acid at 70° hydrolyzes the sulfate ring; the latter appears unreasonable.

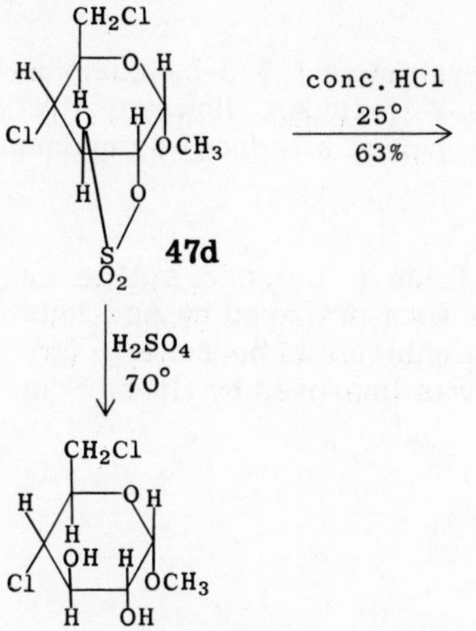

By the same reactions Bragg, Jones, and Turner[19a] showed that methyl β-D-arabinoside yields a 2,3-sulfate with a chlorine on C-4. Sucrose gives a mixture of di- and trichlorodeoxysucrose disulfates. The glucose portion was shown to be identical with that formed from methyl α-D-glucopyranoside; therefore, the fructose portion contains one chlorine and one cyclic sulfate ester, but the actual structure could not be determined because of decomposition during hydrolysis. Helferich and co-workers[49b] found that trehalose yields a tetrachloro disulfate. Considering the similarity between trehalose and a methylglucoside, **47e** would appear to be a reasonable structure for this derivative.

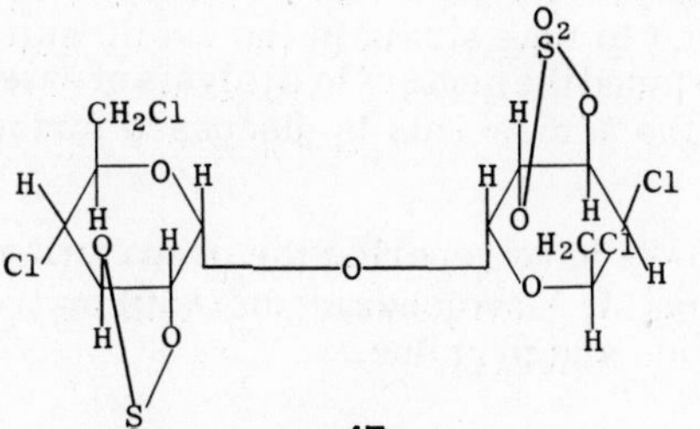

47e

It should be noted that the stereochemistry at C-4 is unknown in all these compounds.

[For references, see pp. 57-61.]   31

Chapter 1

VIII. $C_2O_2S-C_6$ 1, 3, 2-BENZODIOXATHIOLE (48)

48
(RRI 1101)

Chemical Abstracts indexes this ring system as 1, 3, 2-benzodioxa-thiole. An alternative name is 1, 3-dioxa-2-thiaindan. However, the compounds are generally found under the parent dihydroxy compound.

A. SULFITE ESTERS

The compounds reported are listed in Table 4. Catechol sulfite, or 1, 3, 2-benzodioxathiole 2-oxide (**49**), was first prepared by Anschütz and Posth[6] by refluxing catechol with thionyl chloride in benzene, in 66% yield according to Tillett.[81b] The yield was improved by Green[45] by using pyridine.

49

The cyclic sulfite is a colorless liquid, which hydrolyzes slowly in moist air, and reacts very slowly with acetic acid or anhydride even at 180°. In the presence of a trace of pyridine, hot acetic acid yields cate-chol monoacetate, while hot acetic anhydride forms the diacetate.

Tillett.[81b] and de la Mare, Tillett, and van Woerden[32a,32b] investi-gated the hydrolysis of catechol sulfite (**49**). The originally reported resistance to moisture is a result of its low solubility in water. Actu-ally, its hydrolysis is faster than that of ethylene sulfite by a factor of 10^4 in neutral solution and 10^5 in the presence of hydroxide ion. Both catechol sulfite and ethylene sulfite react with alkali 10^3 times faster than their open-chain analogs, diphenyl sulfite and dimethyl sulfite, respectively. Here, too, as with ethylene sulfite (see section I A-3), the increased rate cannot be attributed to ring strain in the cyclic sulfite; Pagdin, Pine, and co-workers,[64a] found the heats of hydrolysis of catechol sulfite and diphenyl sulfite to be the same. This is discussed further in Chapter 8, section I A-1a-(3).

Several authors[81,55,55a,62,67,19c] have reported the preparation of the cyclic sulfites of *cis*- and *trans*-1, 2-cyclohexanediol (**50**) by treat-ing the glycols with thionyl chloride and pyridine.

50

32

TABLE 4. 1,3,2-Benzodioxathiole 2-Oxides

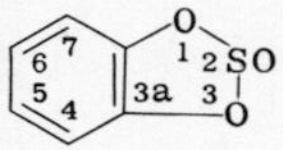

Substituent	Yield (%)	M.p. (°C)	B.p. (°C)	(mm)	Other properties	Ref.
None			210-211	760		6
			98.5-99	16	d^{15} 1.409	6
	96		137-138	105		45
cis-Hexahydro			126	20		81
	76	6-8	90	2	n_D^{20} 1.4832, d_4^{20} 1.2748	67
			121-122	17	n_D^{23} 1.4826, d_4^{23} 1.2699	55
			117-119	14		55a
trans-Hexahydro			122	20		81
	76	-15	94-96	2	n_D^{20} 1.4847, d_4^{20} 1.2654	67
			118-119	14	n_D^{22} 1.4837, d_4^{23} 1.2571	55
			116-117	14		55a
	72		72-75	0.1	n_D^{21} 1.4845	19c
cis-3a-CH$_3$-hexahydro	36		134-135	15		62
trans-3a-CH$_3$-hexahydro	31		108-110	5	n_D^{25} 1.4841, d_{25}^{25} 1.260	62
5-(ClOCCH=CH-)		88-97				37b

[For references, see pp. 57-61.]

According to Lichtenberger and Hincky[55] *cis*-1, 2-cyclohexanediol forms a sulfite much more readily than the *trans* isomer, and this can be used as a method for separating the two glycols. Mousseron, Winternitz, and Mousseron-Canet[62] prepared the cyclic sulfites of *cis*- and *trans*-1-methyl-1, 2-cyclohexanediol; the lower yields in this case may be attributed to the presence of a tertiary hydroxyl group. These authors proved that sulfite formation takes place without rearrangement, since reduction with lithium aluminum hydride regenerates the original glycol in every case.

Price and Berti[67] investigated the pyrolysis of the *cis* and *trans* sulfites. They found that they both decomposed smoothly and in excellent yields at 250-300°, the *cis* sulfite to cyclohexanone and the *trans* sulfite to cyclopentaldehyde, thus paralleling the pyrolysis of the hydrobenzoins (see section I A-3). In the *cis* sulfite (51) the axial oxygen should be more readily ionized. Simultaneous ionization, migration of the coplanar *trans* hydrogen, and loss of sulfur dioxide would give cyclohexanone.

51.

The *trans* sulfite (52) has both oxygens equatorial. These are coplanar with methylene groups, and thus the same mechanism leads to ring contraction.

52

Foster, Hancock, and Overend[40] studied the hydrolysis of 51 and 52. The *trans* sulfite 52 gave the *trans* diol under both acidic and basic conditions, apparently by sulfur-oxygen fission as postulated for the 1, 3, 2-dioxathiolane 2-oxides (see section I A-3). The *cis* sulfite (51), however, reacted differently. Acid hydrolysis gave the *cis* diol, presumably by sulfur-oxygen cleavage, but alkaline hydrolysis gave mainly the *trans* diol, indicating nucleophilic displacement by hydroxide with carbon-oxygen cleavage. There is no evidence as to whether inversion occurred in the first or second step of the hydrolysis, although the former seems more likely.

34

51

The difference between the two isomers might be attributed to their conformation. The *cis* sulfite has an axial oxygen, while the *trans* sulfite would be expected to have both oxygens equatorial. Axial substituents have been postulated to be more prone to nucleophilic displacement than equatorial.[36a]

Tchoubar[81] investigated the reaction of the two sulfites with dry hydrogen chloride in dioxane and found that only the *trans* sulfite (52) reacts at 80-90°. The product was the *trans* chlorohydrin, since treatment with base yielded the *cis* epoxide and the ring-closure is known to involve a Walden inversion. Tchoubar explained this by assuming the intermediate formation of the *cis* epoxide by loss of sulfur dioxide with inversion, followed by the known reaction of a *cis* epoxide with hydrogen chloride to form the *trans* chlorohydrin by inversion. Since the *cis* sulfite would yield the unknown *trans* epoxide, its lack of reactivity is understandable. However, the formation of epoxides under these conditions appears unlikely, and it is much more reasonable to assume that the reaction follows the same course as postulated for the hydrobenzoins (see section I A-3); formation of the *trans* hydroxychlorosulfite (53) as an intermediate followed by an S$_N$i reaction to the *trans* chlorohydrin.

52　　　　　　　　　　**53**

The formation of the hydroxychlorosulfite (53) should be a reversible reaction. The lack of reactivity of the *cis* sulfite could be attributed to the equilibrium being far on the side of the cyclic sulfite; the hydroxyl and chlorosulfite groups would be close together in the *cis* isomer.

Mousseron, Winternitz, and Mousseron-Canet[62] confirmed Tchoubar's results with the sulfites of both 1, 2-cyclohexanediol and 1, 2-cyclopentanediol. However, the results with 3a-methylhexahydro-1, 3, 2-benzodioxathiole 2-oxide were quite different. The *trans* isomer (54) gave a mixture of 2-methylcyclohexanone and *cis*-methyl-2-chlorocyclohexanol (55), the latter being formed by inversion. The authors explained these results by postulating two concurrent reactions, the ketone being formed by an S_N1 process and the chlorohydrin by an S_N2 process with inversion.

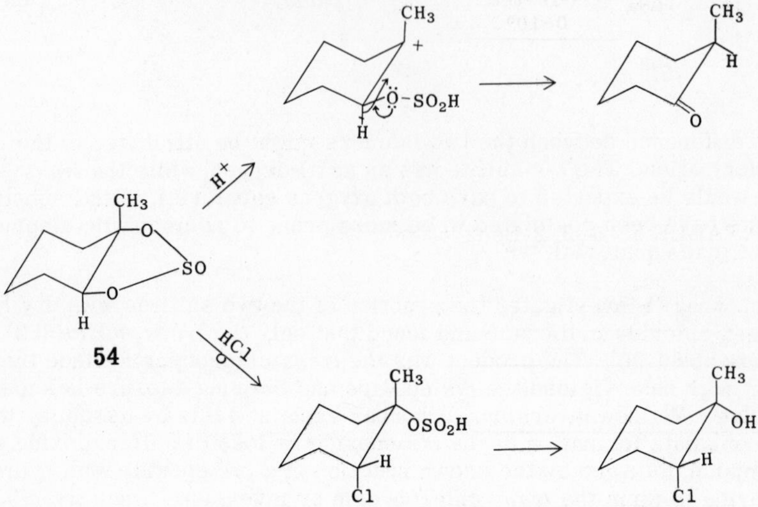

54

55

Although the formation of the ketone is understandable, it is difficult to see why the presence of a tertiary oxygen should affect the substitution at the secondary position. The *cis* sulfite, in agreement with Tchoubar, gave no chlorohydrin, the products being the ketone and recovered sulfite.

B. SULFATE ESTERS

The 1, 3, 2-benxodioxathiole 2, 2-dioxides which have been reported are listed in Table 5. Apparently the first synthesis of a cyclic sulfate of an aromatic dihydroxy compound was carried out by Pollak and Gebauer-Fülnegg.[66] Treatment of catechol with excess chlorosulfonic acid at an elevated temperature yielded a cyclic sulfate but also resulted in chlorosulfonation of the ring (56).

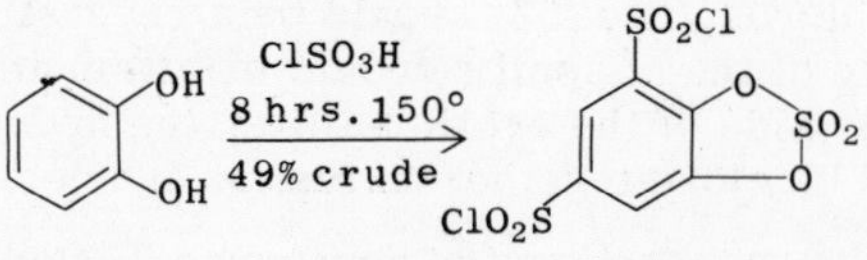

56

The stability of the ring was indicated by the reaction with aniline to form the bis(sulfonanilide) and with *N*-methylaniline to form the corresponding bis(methylanilide).

36

Denivelle[33] prepared the parent compound, 1, 3, 2-benzodioxathiole 2, 2-dioxide (57), in two steps.

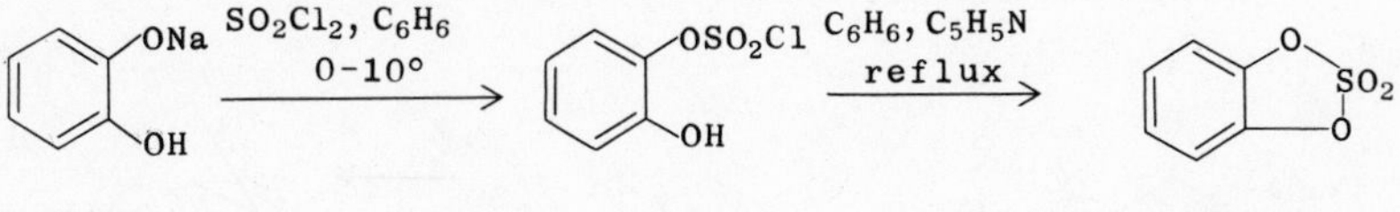

57

TABLE 5. 1, 3, 2-Benzodioxathiole 2, 2-Dioxides

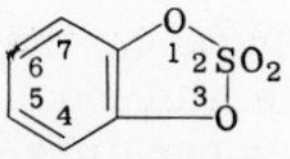

Substituent	Yield (%)	M.p. (°C)	B.p. (°C)	(mm)	Ref.
None		47	104	1	33
4, 6-(—SO$_2$Cl)$_2$	49	143			66
4, 6-(—SO$_2$NHC$_6$H$_5$)$_2$		304(dec.)			66
4, 6-[—SO$_2$N(CH$_3$)C$_6$H$_5$]$_2$		146			66
4, 5, 6, 7-Cl$_4$	57	125-126			77
trans-Hexahydro	14	60. 5-61. 5			55, 55a
	30	54-55			40, 19c
cis-Hexahydro	33	36-37			40, 19c
	27	41-43			55a

The intermediate compound is unstable and was not isolated pure. The cyclic sulfate was steam-distillable, gave no color with ferric chloride, and did not react with hot ethanol. Dilute hydrochloric acid hydrolyzed it quantitatively to catechol and sulfuric acid. The compound was reported to react with secondary amines under unstated conditions.

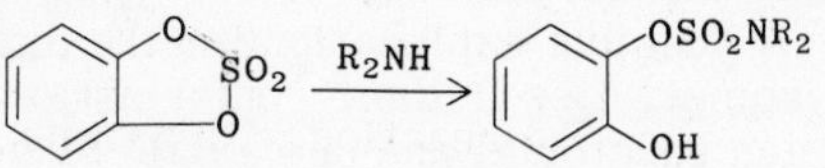

57

[For references, see pp. 57-61.]

Chapter 1

Schenck and Schmidt-Thomée[77] prepared the cyclic sulfate of tetrachlorocatechol (58) by irradiation of tetrachloro-o-benzoquinone and
sulfur dioxide. The reaction was presumed to take the following course:

The reaction was reversible, heating at 150-250° regenerating the original quinone and liberating sulfur dioxide. The sulfate was much less
stable than catechol sulfate, since methanol at room temperature converted it into tetrachlorocatechol. Surprisingly, tetrabromo-o-quinone
would not form a sulfate under these conditions, although a variety of
other o-quinones do (*vide infra*).

Foster and co-workers[40,19c] prepared the cyclic sulfates of *cis*- and
trans-1, 2-cyclohexanediol (59 and 60) by oxidizing the cyclic sulfites
with calcium permanganate. Attempts to carry out the oxidations with
ozone, potassium permanganate in acetone, or perbenzoic acid were unsuccessful. Lichtenberger and Hincky[55,55a] prepared the sulfates by
the same procedure and reported somewhat higher melting points. The
reaction fails with catechol sulfite.

Foster and co-workers[40,19b,19c] investigated the hydrolysis of the
cyclic sulfates under conditions similar to those used by Garner and
Lucas[41] with the 4, 5-dimethyl-1, 3, 2-dioxathiolane 2, 2-dioxides (see
section I B-2). They also carried out the same hydrolyses in the presence of H_2O^{18} in order to determine whether or not carbon-oxygen
cleavage occurred. It was shown that *cis*- and *trans*-1,2-cyclohexane-
diol monosulfates are hydrolyzed under acidic conditions by sulfur-
oxygen cleavage, since there was no isotopic enrichment in the glycols.
Although a monosulfate was isolated in only one case, it is reasonable
to assume it to be an intermediate in all these hydrolyses. Thus, any
isotopic enrichment encountered in acidic hydrolysis must be attributed
to carbon-oxygen cleavage during cleavage of the sulfate ring. The *cis*
sulfate (59) gave *trans* glycol with the expected amount of enrichment,
in agreement with the work of Garner and Lucas.[41] The *trans* sulfate
(60), however, yielded a mixture of isotopically enriched *cis* and *trans*
glycols, whereas from Garner and Lucas's results, the sole product
should have been the *cis* glycol. A possible explanation for the difference between the *cis* and *trans* isomers lies in their conformation.
The *cis* isomer (59) has one oxygen equatorial and one axial. Since an
axial group should be displaced more readily than an equatorial,[36a] it
is reasonable for the initial attack to take place by carbon-oxygen

38

cleavage of the axial bond with inversion. This would be followed by sulphur-oxygen cleavage of the monosulfate in agreement with the results obtained by Burwell[23a] with *sec*-butyl hydrogen sulfate. The *trans* isomer (60) would be expected to have both oxygens equatorial. Because of this less favorable conformation for an S_N2 reaction, carbon-oxygen cleavage might take place with carbonium ion formation. Solvolysis from the side opposite the hydrogen sulfate group would give the *trans* glycol, while attack on the same side would give *cis* glycol.

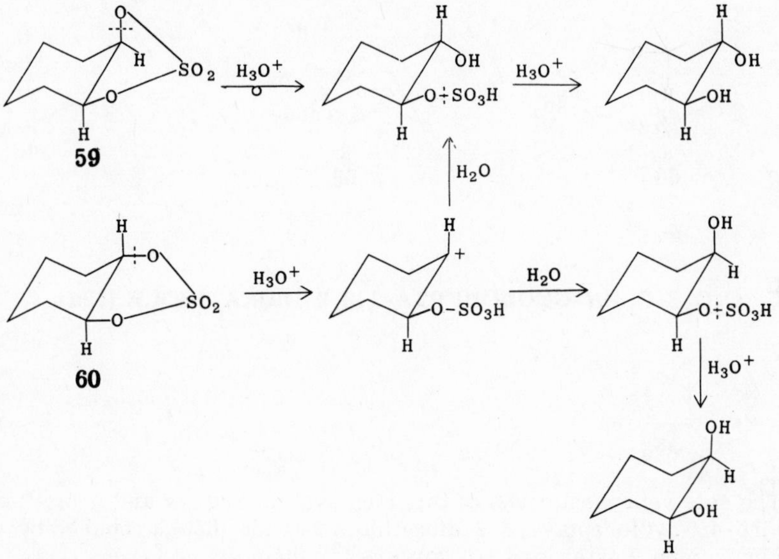

Under alkaline conditions the *cis* sulfate (59) yielded the *cis* diol monosulfate (61) as the major product and only a trace of *trans* diol. The lack of O^{18} in 61 indicates an initial sulfur-oxygen cleavage in 59, the *trans* glycol being formed by carbon-oxygen cleavage in 61 with inversion. The second step is in agreement with the results of Burwell,[23a] while the sulfur-oxygen cleavage in the first step appears to be the rule in these cyclic sulfates. The *trans* sulfate (60) yielded isotopically enriched *trans* glycol. Here, too, the first step must involve sulfur-oxygen cleavage to the *trans* diol monosulfate (62), since carbon-oxygen cleavage with inversion would result in the alkali-stable *cis* monosulfate (61), and the amount of O^{18} in the glycol indicated that two nucleophilic displacements by hydroxide ion could not have taken place. The further hydrolysis of the monosulfate (half-esters of sulfuric acid should be stable under these conditions) is readily explainable by epoxide formation because of the *trans* arrangement of the two groups in 62; ring opening with inversion would give *trans* glycol.

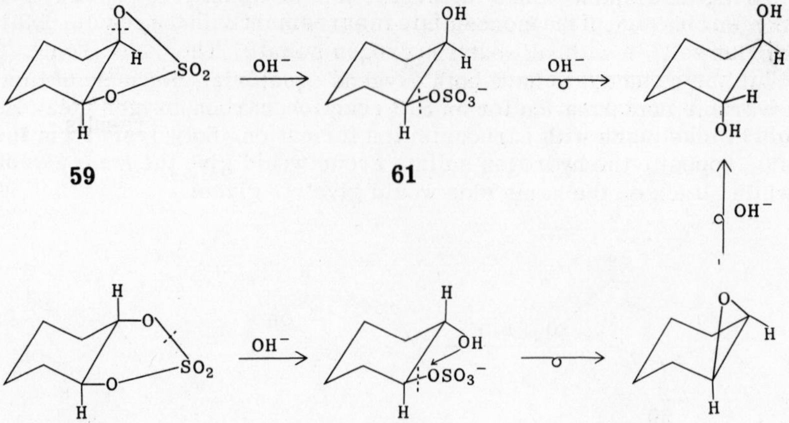

Chapter 1

59   **61**

60   **62**

IX. C_2O_2S-C_7 4*H*-CYCLOHEPTA-1,3,2-DIOXATHIOLE (62a)

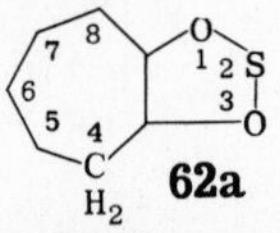

62a

The sole representatives of this ring system are *cis* and *trans*-hexa-
hydro-4*H*-cyclohepta-1,3,2-dioxathiole 2-oxide (**62b**), prepared by
Brimacombe, Foster, and co-workers,[19c] from *cis* and *trans*-1,2-
cycloheptanediol and thionyl chloride.

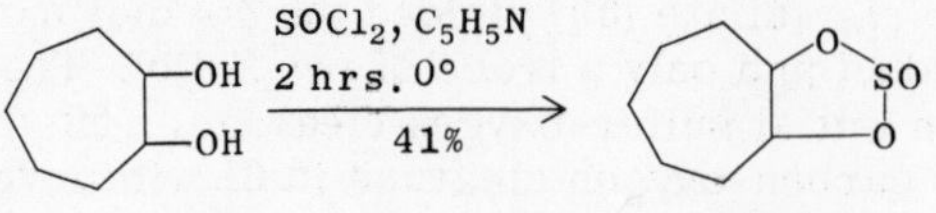

62b

The *cis* isomer boils at 90° at 0.5 mm, n_D^{24} 1.4860, and the *trans* isomer
at 92° at 0.5 mm, n_D^{24} 1.4865.

X. C_2O_2S-C_4O-C_4O 1,7,11,13-TETRAOXA-12-THIADISPIRO [4.0.4.3] TRIDECA-3,9-DIENE-2,8-DIONE (62c)

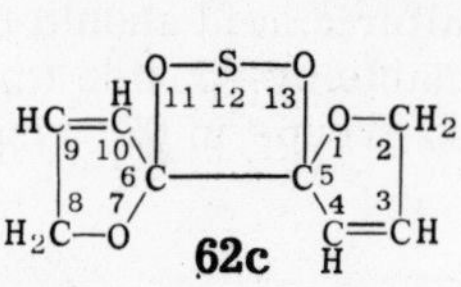

62c

40

trans-Bifurandione (**62d**), the intriguing compound prepared from carbon monoxide and acetylene, was oxidized by Holmquist, Sauer, and co-workers,[50c] to 2, 2'-dihydroxy-2, 2'-bifuran-5, 5'(2H, 2'H)-dione (**62e**). This yielded a cyclic sulfite, 1, 7, 11, 13-tetraoxa-12-thiadispiro-[4. 0. 4. 3]trideca-3, 9-diene-2, 8-dione 12-oxide (**62f**), m.p. 134-135°, plus a dichloride (**62g**).

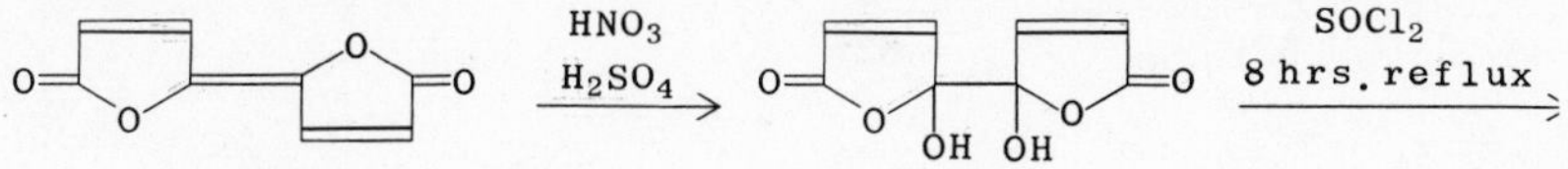

62d   **62e**

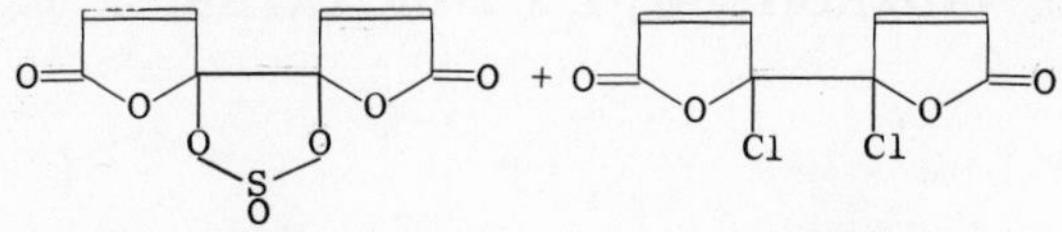

62f   **62g**

XI.   C$_2$O$_2$S-C$_4$N-C$_5$N 6H-CYCLOHEPTA-1, 3, 2-DIOXATHIOL-4, 8-IMINE (62h)

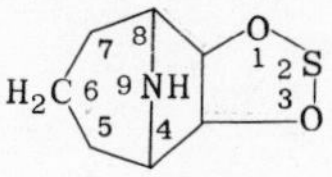

62h

TABLE 5a.   Derivatives of Hexahydro-6H-cyclohepta-1, 3, 2-dioxathiol-4, 8-imine

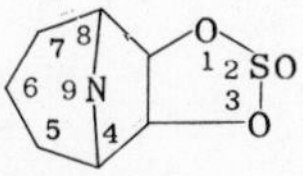

Substituents	Yield (%)	M.p. (°C)	Ref.
6-(O=)-9-CH$_3$- · HCl	90	330	88b
6-(O=)-9-CH$_3$-		186. 5-187 (dec.)	88b
6-(C$_6$H$_5$)$_2$CHCO$_2$-9-CH$_3$- · HCl	96	253 (dec.)	88b
6-(C$_6$H$_5$)$_2$CHCO$_2$-9-CH$_3$- · CH$_3$SO$_3$H		217-218	88b
6-(C$_6$H$_5$)$_2$CHCO$_2$-9-CH$_3$-		125-127	88b
[6-(C$_6$H$_5$)$_2$CHCO$_2$-9, 9-(CH$_3$-)$_2$]$^+$Br$^-$		205-207 (dec.)	88b

[For references, see pp. 57-61.]

Zeile and Heusner[88b] prepared several cyclic sulfites from teloidine (62i) and from teloidinone (62j) by standard procedures. These are listed in Table 5a.

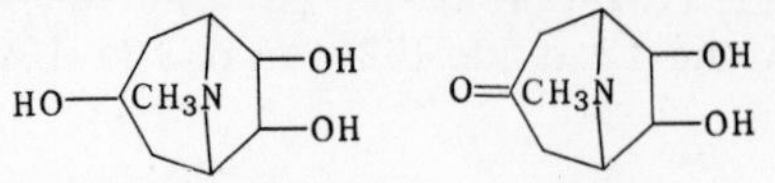

62i   **62j**

XII. C_2O_2S-C_5-C_6 $8H$-INDENO[1, 2-d]-1, 3, 2-DIOXATHIOLE (62k)

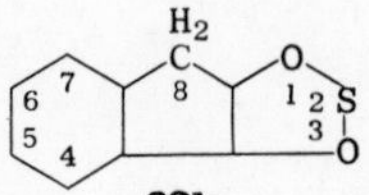

62k

Brimacombe, Foster, and co-workers,[19c] prepared *cis*-dihydro-$8H$-indeno[1, 2-d]-1, 3, 2-dioxathiole 2-oxide (**62–1**), m.p. 70°, from *cis*-1, 2-indanediol and thionyl chloride.

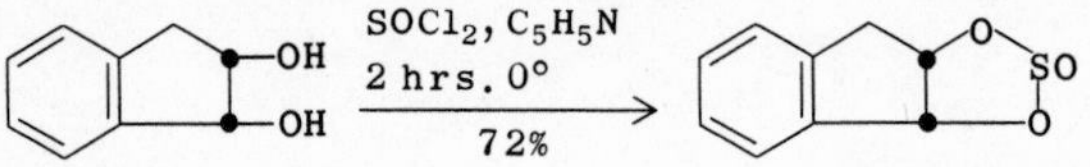

62-1

XIII. C_2O_2S-C_4O_2-C_5O $4H$, $6H$-1, 3, 2-DIOXATHIOLO[4, 5]PYRANO [3, 2-d]-m-DIOXIN (63)

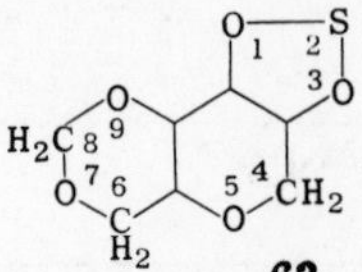

63
(RRI 2654)

The first representative of this ring system was 4-methoxy-8-phenyl-tetrahydro-$4H$, $6H$-1, 3, 2-dioxathiolo[4, 5]pyrano[3, 2-d]-m-dioxin 2-oxide (**64**), the 2, 3-sulfite of methyl 4, 6-O-benzylidene-α-D-glucopyranoside, prepared in the usual manner by Honeyman and Morgan,[51] m.p. 192-193°, $[\alpha]_D^{22}$ + 148. 4°. The compound is exceedingly sensitive to acid, being converted quantitatively into methyl α-D-glucopyranoside by a trace of acid in aqueous acetone; apparently the benzylidene group is labilized by the sulfite ring. Sodium methoxide in methanol removes the sulfite and regenerates the glucoside.

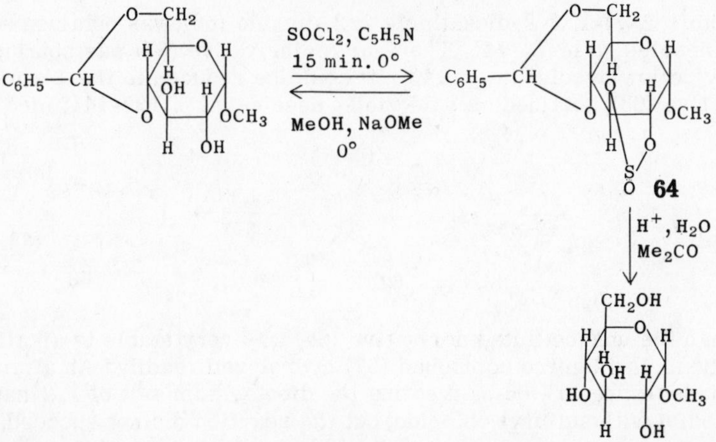

Brimacombe, Foster, and co-workers, [19c] attempted unsuccessfully to oxidize 64 to the cyclic sulfate with calcium permanganate in acetic acid; the sulfur was eliminated either before or after hydrolysis. Bragg, Jones, and Turner[19a] prepared the cyclic sulfate in 41% yield by treatment of methyl 4, 6-O-benzylidene-α-D-glucopyranoside with sulfuryl chloride and pyridine. The compound melts at 107° with decomposition and yields glucose on hydrolysis, first with methanolic ammonia and then with aqueous sulfuric acid. Thus, hydrolysis takes place with retention of configuration, if the reasonable assumption is made that no cleavage of carbon-oxygen bonds occurs during the synthesis of the cyclic sulfate.

XIV. C$_2$O$_2$S-C$_6$-C$_6$

A. NAPHTHO[1, 2-d]-1, 3, 2-DIOXATHIOLE (65)

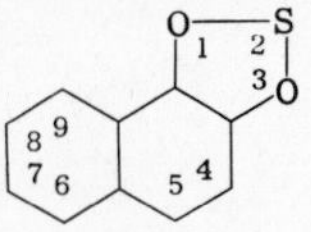

65
(RRI 2656)

Schenck and Schmidt-Thomée[77] prepared cyclic sulfates of 1, 2-dihydroxynaphthalenes by the photochemical condensation of quinones with sulfur dioxide described previously (see section VIII B).

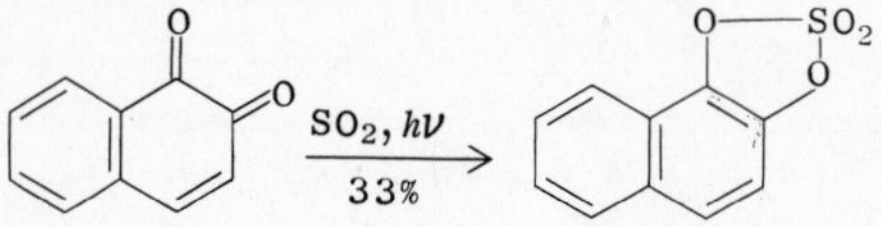

[For references, see pp. 57-61.]

Naphtho[1, 2-*d*]-1, 3, 2-dioxathiole 2, 2-dioxide (66), was obtained as white needles, m.p. 73-74°. The 4-nitro derivative (67) was obtained as canary yellow needles, m.p. 143°; it could be reduced to the 4-amino derivative (68), obtained as pale violet needles, m.p. 139-141° (dec.).

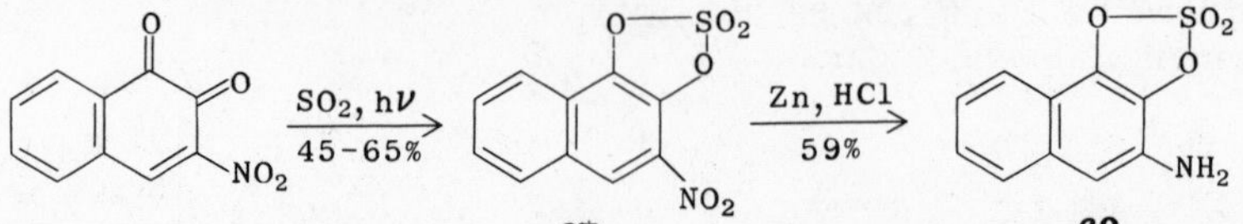

67   **68**

Although the unsubstituted derivative (66) was very stable to alkaline hydrolysis, the 4-nitro compound (67) hydrolyzed readily. An attempt was made to prepare 66 by treating the dipotassium salt of 1, 2-naphthalenediol with sulfuryl chloride, but the reaction did not succeed.

B.   NAPHTHO[2, 3-*d*]-1, 3, 2-DIOXATHIOLE (69)

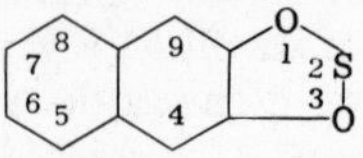

69

(RRI 2655)

Mousseron, Winternitz, and Mousseron-Canet[62] prepared *trans*-3a, 4, 9, 9a-tetrahydronaphtho[2, 3-*d*]-1, 3, 2-dioxathiole 2-oxide (70), m.p. 124-125°, from *trans*-2, 3-dihydroxytetralin and thionyl chloride. Reduction of the cyclic sulfite with lithium aluminum hydride regenerated the *trans* glycol, indicating that no rearrangement had taken place during ring formation.

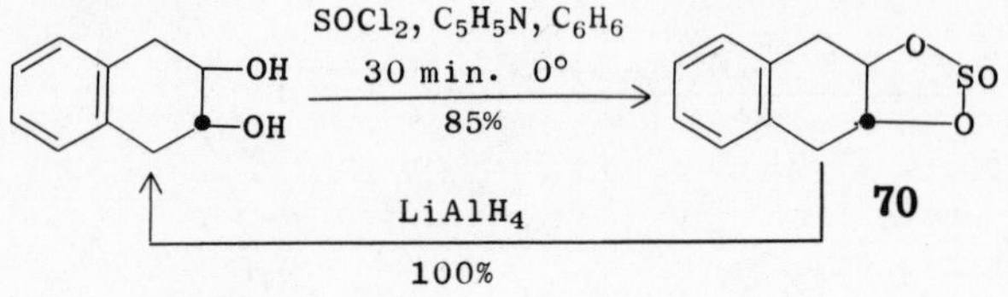

XV. C_2O_2S-C_6-C_6-C_6

A.   ANTHRA[1, 2-*d*]-1, 3, 2-DIOXATHIOLE (71)

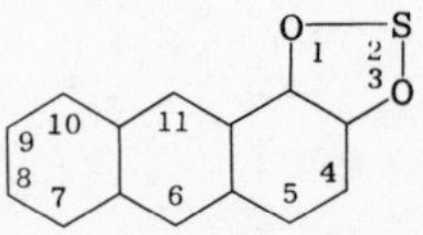

71

(RRI 4383)

1. Sulfite Esters

Green described the preparation of a series of cyclic sulfites of di-hydroxyanthracenes. 1, 2-Anthradiol (72) reacted with thionyl chloride, but no sulfite could be isolated. In the presence of two moles of pyridine, however, the cyclic sulfite (73) was isolated in good yield as brown crystals which darken

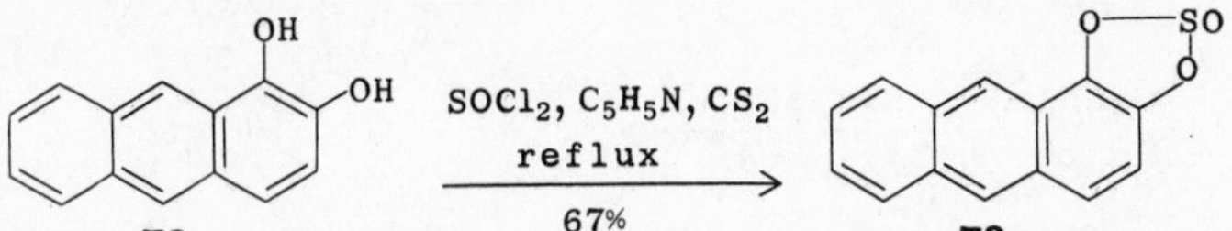

72   SOCl$_2$, C$_5$H$_5$N, CS$_2$ reflux   67%   73

at 125° and melt with decomposition at 138-139°.[46] The compound is stable to moist air. Treatment with concentrated sulfuric acid gives a dark orange solution changing to royal blue; dilution of the acid solution with water or treatment with cold dilute alkali regenerates the diol. Refluxing acetic acid gave no isolable product with the 1, 2-sulfite.

In contrast to 1, 2-anthradiol, dihydroxyanthraquinones react readily with thionyl chloride in the absence of pyridine. Thus, alizarin (74) yields the cyclic sulfite (75) almost quantitatively as primrose yellow crystals melting at 171-172°.[43]

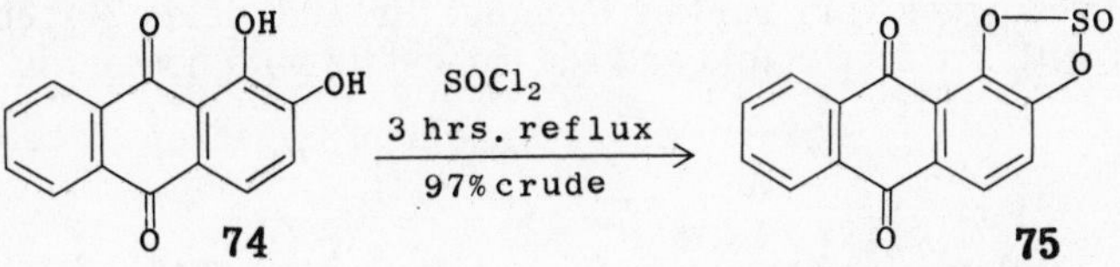

74   SOCl$_2$ 3 hrs. reflux   97% crude   75

The sulfite hydrolyzes readily on exposure to moist air, regenerating the diol. The products obtained on heating the sulfite with various acids appear to depend on the acid strength.[47] Thus, acetic, phenylacetic, phenoxyacetic, benzoic, cinnamic, o-toluic, and m- and p-bromobenzoic acids all yield 2-monoacylalizarins (76).

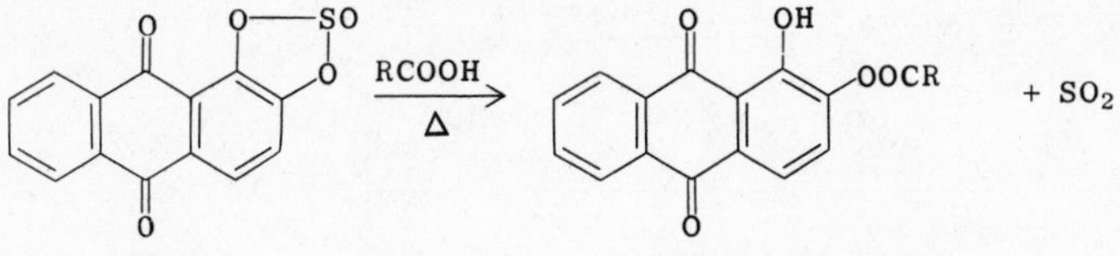

75   RCOOH   Δ   76   + SO$_2$

Monochloroacetic acid yields a mixture of alizarin and 2-acylalizarin, while dichloroacetic, dibromoacetic, and trichloroacetic acids yield only alizarin. The cyclic sulfite reacts with hot acetic anhydride, benzoic anhydride, acetyl chloride, or benzoyl chloride to form diacylalizarins, but succinic and phthalic anhydrides do not react. Heating the sulfite with ethanol, phenol, or arylamines liberates sulfur dioxide and regenerates alizarin, while alkyl halides and sulfates do not react.

Other polyhydroxyanthracenes react similarly. [44] Thus, purpurin (77) yields the cyclic sulfite (78) as yellow-brown crystals melting at 211-213°.

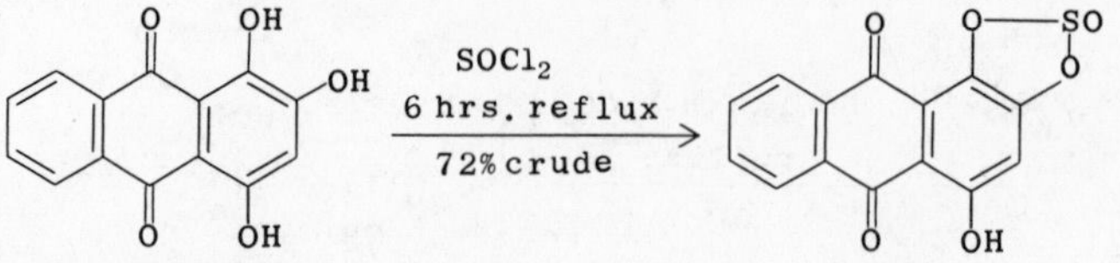

77   **78**

The sulfite hydrolyzes rapidly in moist air and yields 2-acetylpurpurin with hot acetic acid. Anthrapurpurin (79) yields the sulfite (80) as ochre crystals melting at 179° with decomposition.

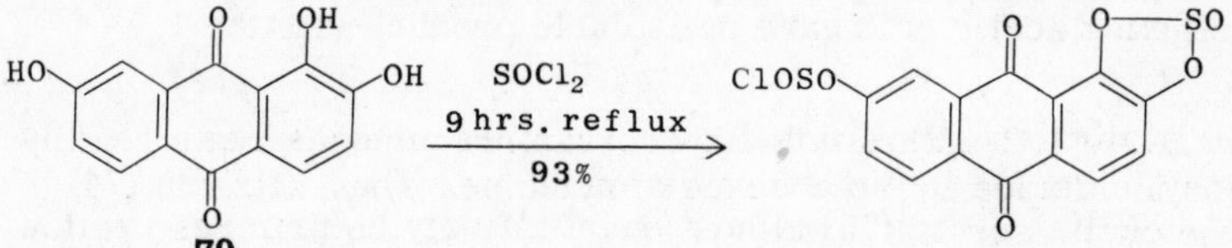

79   **80**

This sulfite hydrolyzes very rapidly in moist air, and yields 2-acetylan-thrapurpurin with hot acetic acid and the triacetate with hot acetic anhydride.

2. Sulfate Esters

Schmidt[79] postulated the formation of a cyclic sulfate (81) as an intermediate in the preparation of the dyestuff Alizarin Bordeaux or Quinalizarin (82). The ester, isolated as orange leaflets, yielded the dyestuff by solution in sodium hydroxide followed by refluxing with sulfuric acid or by heating at 170° with sulfuric acid.

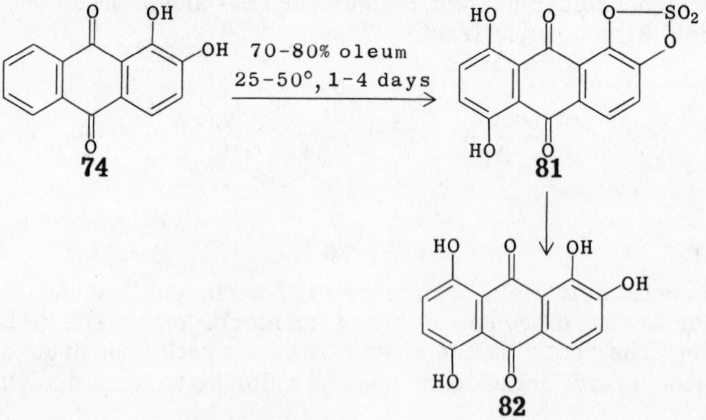

74   **81**

82

Gatterman[42] claimed that the same cyclic sulfate (81) is formed from quinizarin (1, 4-dihydroxyanthraquinone), indicating the correctness of the assigned structure.

More recently, Schenk and Schmidt-Thomée[77] reinvestigated this reaction in connection with their photochemical synthesis of cyclic sulfates. They obtained, following Schmidt's procedure, an 87% yield of cyclic sulfate as orange leaflets. This dissolved in hot caustic to give a red solution, presumably the salt of the half-ester. Acidification gave a yellow solution, the free half-ester, and heating the acid solution hydrolyzed this to Alizarin Bordeaux (82), a red precipitate. This sequence follows the reactions of certain of their cyclic sulfates (see section XV C). In an attempt to prove the structure of the cyclic sulfate, they heated 81 at 250-290° to liberate sulfur dioxide and Alizarin Bordeaux was indeed formed. However, if the sulfate reacted as did their other sulfates, the product should have been the corresponding quinone.

B. ANTHRA [2, 3-d] -1, 3, 2-DIOXATHIOLE (83)

83

Green[46] prepared the cyclic sulfite of 2, 3-anthradiol (84) by the same procedure as used with 1, 2-anthradiol (see section XV A-1); the

84

compound darkens at 180° and melts with decomposition at 188°. 84 is stable to moist air and gives a golden brown solution in sulfuric acid; dilution with water regenerates the cyclic sulfite. The cyclic sulfite does not react with refluxing acetic acid; in the presence of a trace of pyridine it slowly forms the diol with hot acetic acid and the corresponding diacetate with hot acetic anhydride.

Hystazarin (85), like the 1, 2-dihydroxyanthraquinones, reacts with thionyl chloride in the absence of pyridine to give the cyclic sulfite (86) as pale yellow-green plates melting at 200°.[44] In contrast to the 1, 2-dihydroxyanthraquinone sulfites, however, it hydrolyzes only slowly

[For references, see pp. 57-61.]

in moist air, regenerates hystazarin when heated with glacial acetic acid, and forms a diacetate only slowly with hot acetic anhydride.

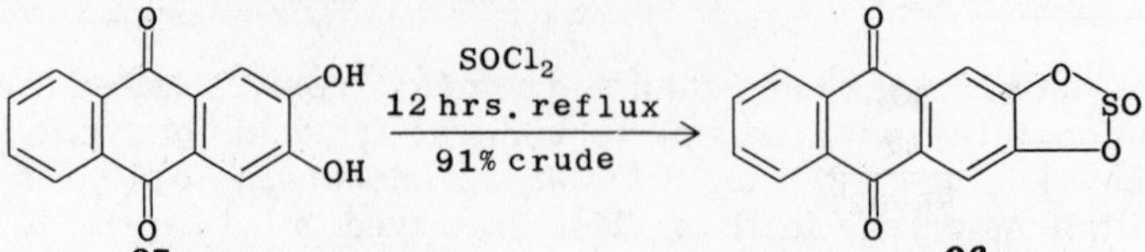

$$\underset{85}{} \xrightarrow[\substack{12\,\text{hrs. reflux}\\91\%\,\text{crude}}]{SOCl_2} \underset{86}{}$$

Anthragallol (**87**) could form a 1, 2-sulfite or a 2, 3-sulfite. It was isolated as greenish yellow rods, m.p. 218-220°, and was assigned the structure of a 2, 3-sulfite (**88**) on the basis of its reactions.

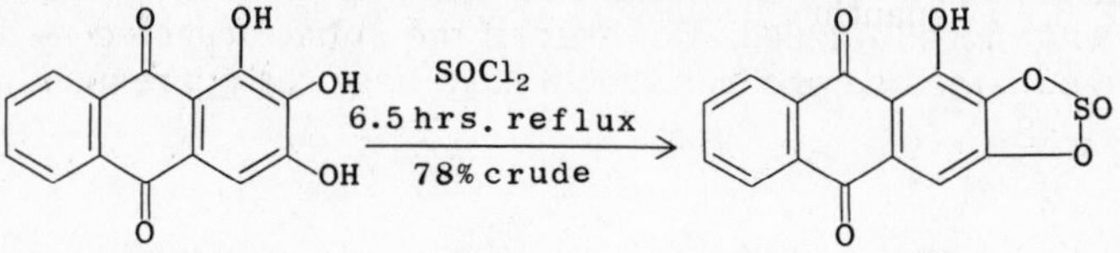

$$\underset{87}{} \xrightarrow[\substack{6.5\,\text{hrs. reflux}\\78\%\,\text{crude}}]{SOCl_2} \underset{88}{}$$

It hydrolyzes slowly with moist air, in contrast to the 1, 2-sulfites which hydrolyze rapidly. It gives a mixture of anthragallol and a mono-acetate (probably in the 3-position) with refluxing acetic acid, whereas the 1, 2-sulfites give exclusively the monoacetates. Conclusive proof was obtained by the reaction with hot acetic anhydride, which rapidly yielded 2, 3-diacetylanthragallol. Under the conditions of the reaction it was shown that a 1-hydroxyl is not esterified while a 3-hydroxyl is. Therefore, if the compound was a 1, 2-sulfite, a triacetate would have been obtained.

C. PHENANTHRO[9, 10-*d*]-1, 3, 2-DIOXATHIOLE (89)

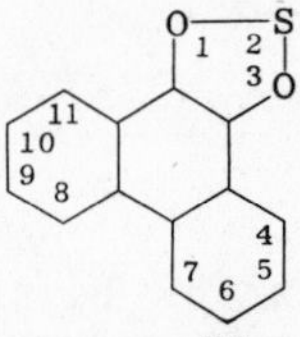

89
(RRI 4384)

This ring system is represented by cyclic sulfates of 9, 10-dihydroxy-phenanthrene prepared by Schenck and Schmidt-Thomée[77] from the corresponding quinone and sulfur dioxide as described previously (section VIII B). The compounds are listed in Table 6. The parent compound (**90**) decomposes quantitatively to the starting materials at 235°. It is very stable to alkaline hydrolysis and in this respect differs from the Alizarin Bordeaux intermediate (**81**) (section XV A-2). The nitro derivatives, however, are much less stable and their hydrolysis is similar to that of the Alizarin Bordeaux intermediate.

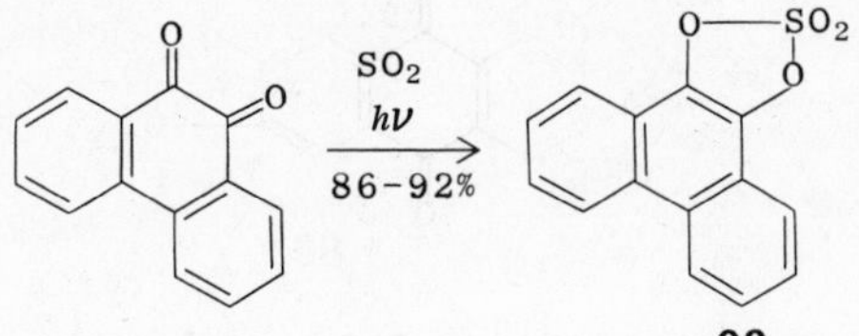

90

TABLE 6. Phenanthro[9, 10-*d*]-1, 3, 2-dioxathiole 2, 2-Dioxides

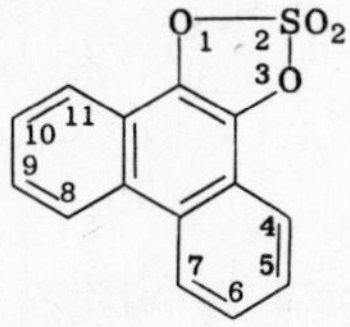

Substituent	Yield (%)	M.p. (°C)	Other properties	Ref.
None	86-92	202-203 (dec.)	white needles	77
5-NO$_2$	48	204-206 (dec.)	yellow needles	77
6-NO$_2$	17.5	190-191 (dec.)	pale yellow leaflets	77
	80			
7-NO$_2$	40	185-186 (dec.)	pale yellow needles	77
6, 9-(NO$_2$)$_2$	55-60	240-241 (dec.)	yellow needles	77

Nitration of **90** gives a mononitro derivative (**91**) or a dinitro derivative (**92**) depending on the conditions. Hydrolysis of the mononitro derivative (**91**) to the known 3-nitro-9, 10-dihydroxyphenanthrene, subsequently oxidized to the known 5-nitrodiphenic acid, served to identify the compound as 6-nitrophenanthro[9, 10-*d*]-1, 3, 2-dioxathiole 2, 2-dioxide. Similarly, the dinitro compound was shown to be the 6, 9-derivative (**92**) by heating to eliminate sulfur dioxide and to form the substituted phenanthraquinone (**93**), followed by oxidation to the known 5, 5′-dinitrodiphenic acid.

[For references, see pp. 57-61.]

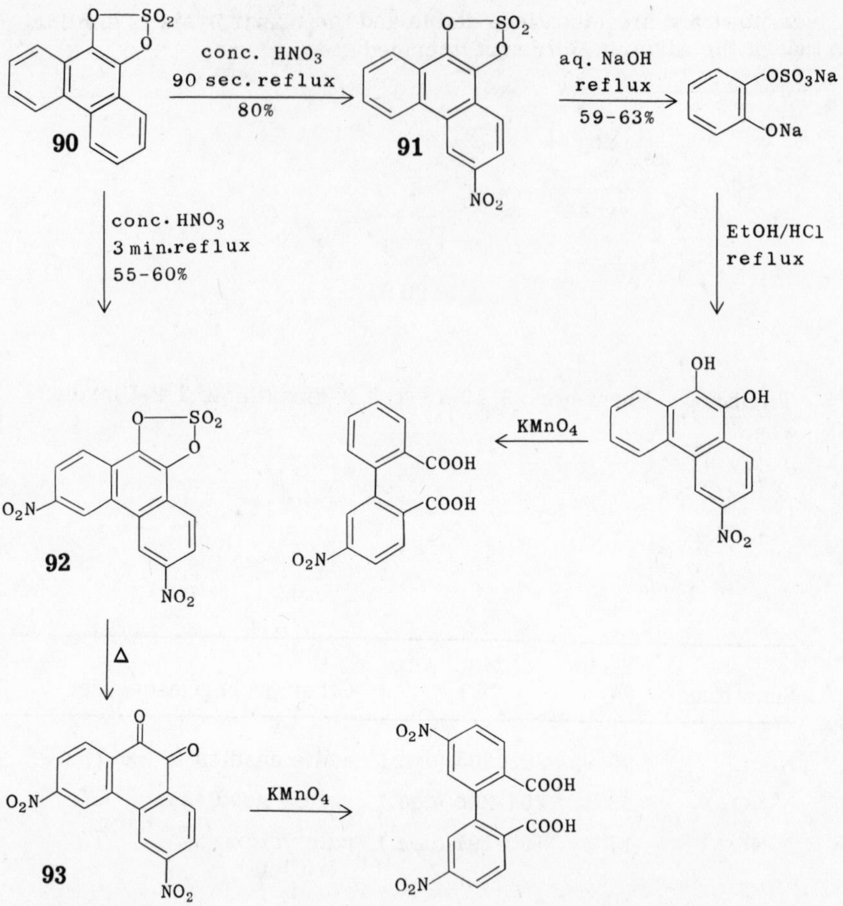

By irradiation of the corresponding 9, 10-phenanthrenequinones and sulfur dioxide, Schenck and Schmidt-Thomée prepared the cyclic sulfates of 2-nitro-9, 10-dihydroxyphenanthrene, 3-nitro-9, 10-dihydroxyphenanthrene, whose properties are identical with the compound (91) obtained by nitration of 90, and 4-nitro-9, 10-dihydroxyphenanthrene.

XVI. C_2O_2S-C_4N-C_4N-C_9O_2 [1, 3, 2]DIOXATHIOLO[4′, 5′: 8, 9][1, 6]-DIOXACYCLOUNDECA [2, 3, 4-gh]PYRROLIZINE (94)

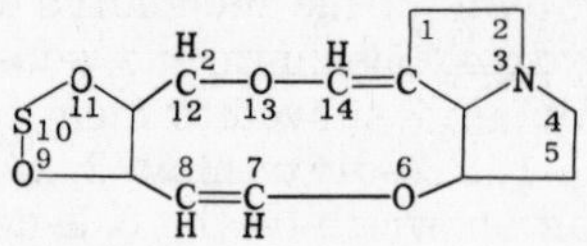

94

(RRI 4109)

The structure of monocrotaline (95), an alkaloid from *Crotalaria spectabilis,* was elucidated by Adams, Shafer, and Braun.[1] The alkaloid with thionyl chloride gave an almost quantitative yield of monocrotaline cyclic sulfite (96) as its hydrochloride, m.p. 226-226. 5° (dec.), $[\alpha]_D^{32}$ + 15. 26°; treatment with base gave the free sulfite (96), m.p. 155. 4-155. 8° (dec.), $[\alpha]_D^{35}$ + 37. 74°. It is interesting that such a high yield of cyclic sulfite was obtained from a glycol with two tertiary hydroxyl groups. The cyclic sulfite structure was indicated by the lack of hydroxyl absorption in the infrared and the presence in the infrared spectrum of lines which have been assigned to cyclic sulfites of 1, 2-diols (see section I A-2). Reduction of 96 opened one side of the lactone ring and yielded the cyclic sulfite of dihydromonocrotaline (97), m.p. 169. 5-170° (dec.). Similarly the reduction of the hydrochloride of 96 gave the hydrochloride of 97, m.p. 185. 8-186. 2° (dec.), $[\alpha]_D^{35}$ − 31. 74°. These and other reactions served to prove the structure of monocrotaline.

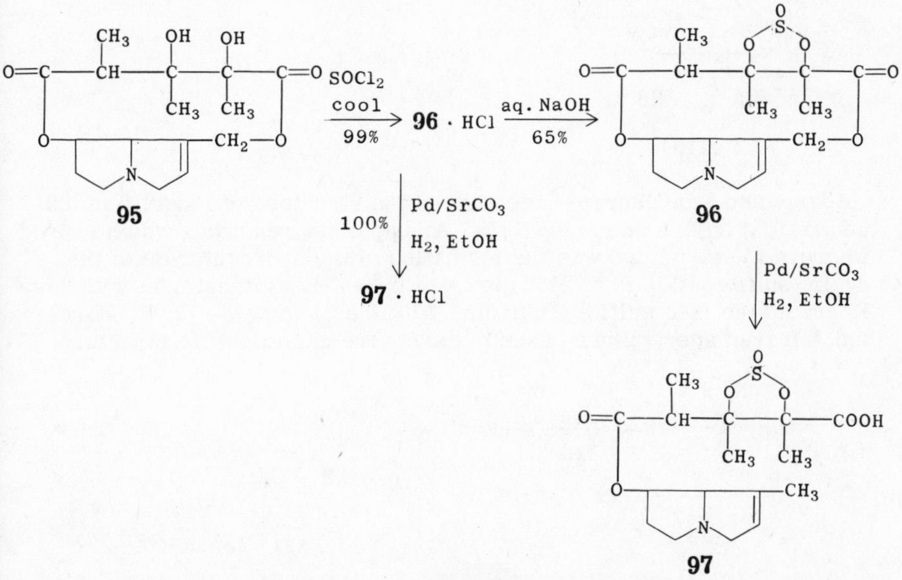

According to Yunusov and Plekhanova,[88a] the closely related alkaloid, trichodesmine (97a), also forms a cyclic sulfite hydrochloride, m.p. 170°, $[\alpha]_D$ + 11. 8°, which can be converted into the free cyclic sulfite, m.p. 151-152°. From this they concluded that trichodesmine, like monocrotaline, is a *cis* glycol. Adams and Gianturco[2a] had previously reacted the alkaloid with thionyl chloride, but had assigned an acid sulfite ester structure to the adduct, m.p. 172°, and concluded therefore that the alkaloid is a *trans* glycol. Although additional confirmation would be desirable, the *cis* structure appears more reasonable.

[For references, see pp. 57-61.]

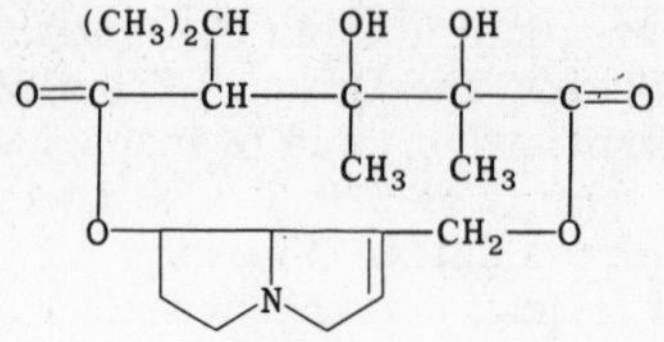

97a

XVII. C_2O_2S-C_4N-C_4N-$C_{10}O_2$ SPIRO[1, 6]DIOXACYCLODODECA
[2, 3, 4-gh]-PYRROLIZINE-9($8H$), 4'-[1, 3, 2]DIOXATHIOLANE
(98)

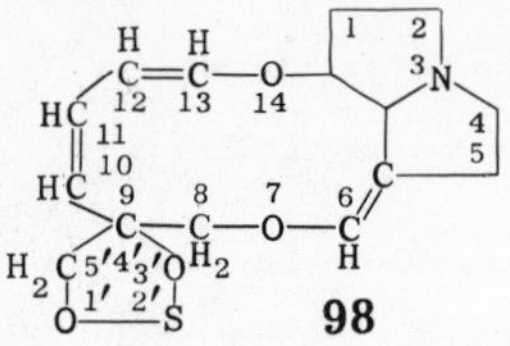

(RRI 4110)

Adams and Van Duuren[2] investigated the structure of riddelliine (**99**), an alkaloid from *Senecio riddellii*. Among other reactions which served to prove the structure was the formation of the hydrochloride of the cyclic sulfite (**100**), m.p. 215° (dec.), $[\alpha]_D^{28} - 41.5°$; treatment with base liberated the free sulfite (**100**), m.p. 170° (dec.), $[\alpha]_D^{28} - 17.4°$. Here, too, infrared spectra were used to assign the cyclic sulfite structure.

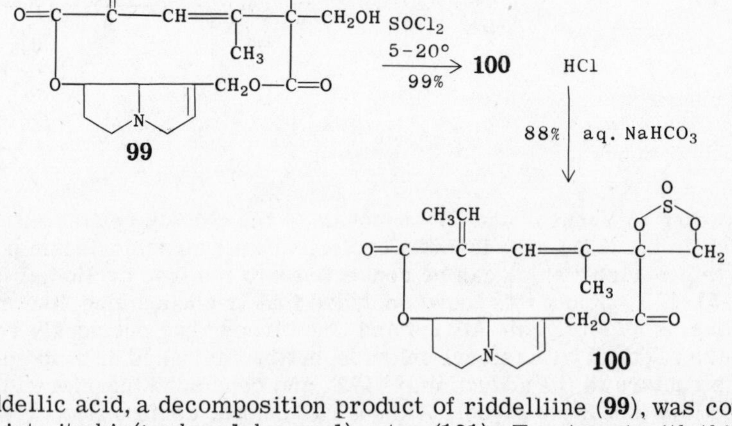

Riddellic acid, a decomposition product of riddelliine (**99**), was converted into its bis(p-phenylphenacyl) ester (**101**). Treatment with thionyl chloride yielded the bis(*p*-phenylphenacyl) ester of 4-(3-carboxy-1-methyl-1, 3-pentadienyl)-1, 3, 2-dioxathiolane-4-carboxylic acid 2-oxide (102), m.p. 78-80° (dec.), $[\alpha]_D^{28} - 11.3°$.

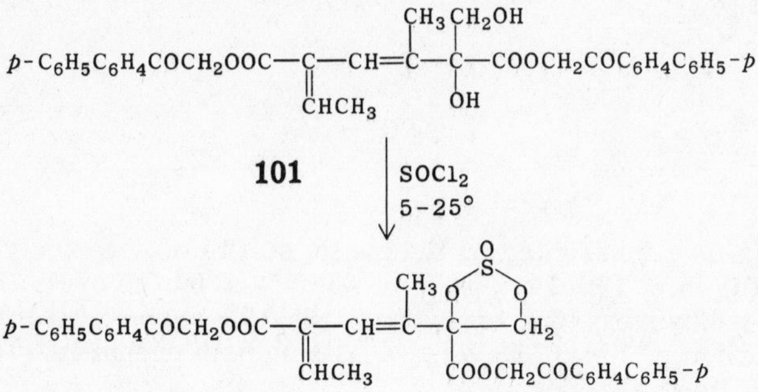

$$p\text{-}C_6H_5C_6H_4COCH_2OOC\text{---}\underset{\underset{CHCH_3}{|}}{C}\text{---}CH\text{=}\underset{\overset{CH_3\ CH_2OH}{|\quad\ |}}{C}\text{---}\underset{\underset{OH}{|}}{C}\text{---}COOCH_2COC_6H_4C_6H_5\text{-}p$$

101

SOCl$_2$
5-25°

$$p\text{-}C_6H_5C_6H_4COCH_2OOC\text{---}\underset{\underset{CHCH_3}{|}}{C}\text{---}CH\text{=}\underset{}{C}\text{---}\underset{\underset{COOCH_2COC_6H_4C_6H_5\text{-}p}{|}}{C}\text{---}CH_2$$

102

XVIII. C$_2$O$_2$S-C$_5$-C$_6$-C$_6$-C$_6$

A. CYCLOPENTA[1, 2]PHENANTHRO[4, 4a-*d*][1, 3, 2]DIOXATHIOLE (103)

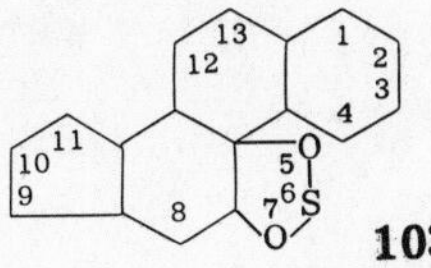

103

(RRI 5524)

This ring system is represented by the cyclic 9, 11-sulfite of 3β-acetoxy-5α-ergost-8(14)-ene-9, 11α-diol (104), m.p. 133-136°, prepared by Laubach, Schreiber, and co-workers.[52a]

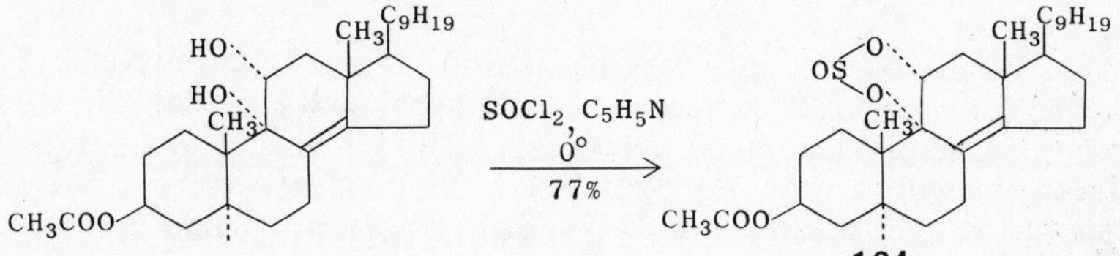

104

[For references, see pp. 57-61.]

B. CYCLOPENTA[1, 2]PHENANTHRO[1, 10a-*d*][1, 3, 2]DIOXATHIOLE (104a)

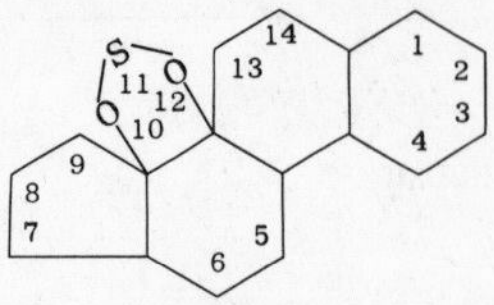

104a

This ring system is represented by the cyclic sulfite of 3-*O*-acetyl-scillirosidin (104b), m.p. 190-198°, $[\alpha]_D^{20}$ + 42. 2°, and by the cyclic 8, 14-sulfite of 8, 14-dihydroxy-5α, 14β-androstane-17β-carboxylic acid methyl ester (104c), m.p. 174-176°, $[\alpha]_D^{20}$ + 113. 0°, both prepared by von Wartburg and Renz.[85a,85b]

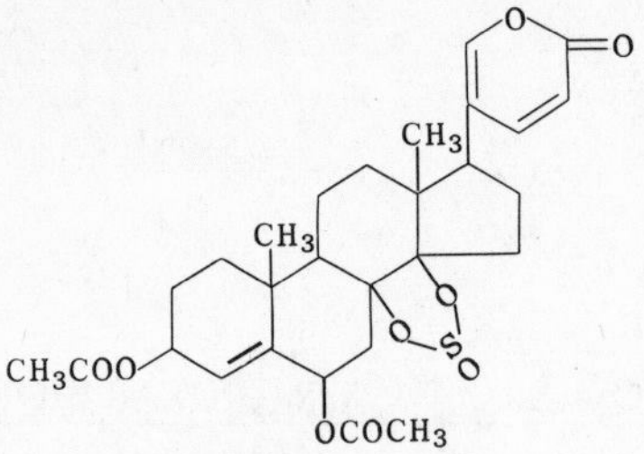

104b

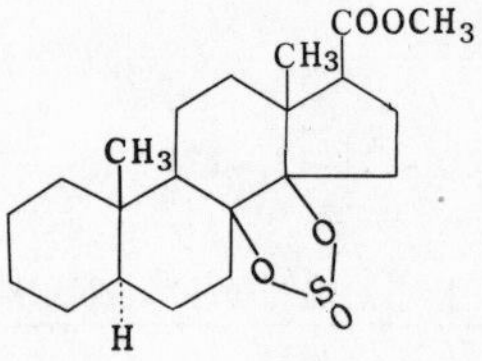

104c

XIX. $C_2O_2S-C_6-C_6-C_6-C_6$

A. CHRYSENO[5, 6-*d*]-1, 3, 2-DIOXATHIOLE (105)

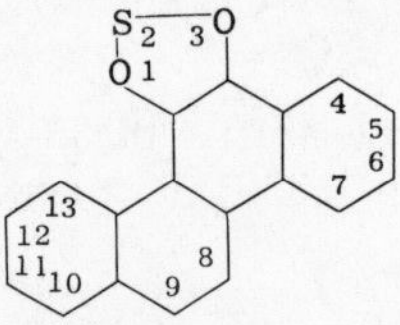

105
(RRI 5794)

The sole member of this ring system is the cyclic sulfate of 1, 2-dihydroxychrysene (106) prepared by Schenck and Schmidt-Thomée[77] by the procedure described previously. The compound was obtained as colorless needles, m.p. 221-222° (dec.). Its properties are similar to those of the cyclic sulfate of 9, 10-dihydroxyphenanthrene (see section XV C).

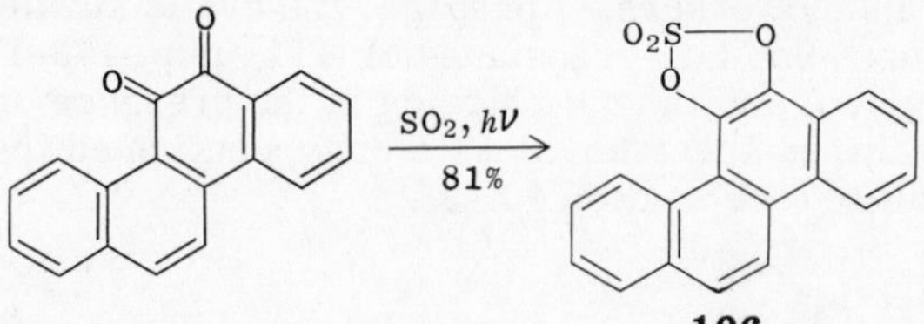

106

B. 4, 9-o-BENZENONAPHTHO[2, 3-d]-1, 3, 2-DIOXATHIOLE (107)

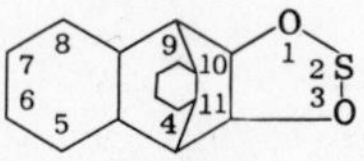

107

Vaughan and Yoshimine[82] prepared the cyclic sulfite of 9, 10-dihydro-9, 10-ethanoanthracene-11, 12-diol (108), m.p. 191. 2-192. 2°, from the *cis* glycol and thionyl chloride. Heating yielded a product which they formulated as 9, 10-dihydro-9, 10-methanoanthracene-11-carboxalde-hyde (109) by analogy with the work of Price and Berti[67] (see section VIII A).

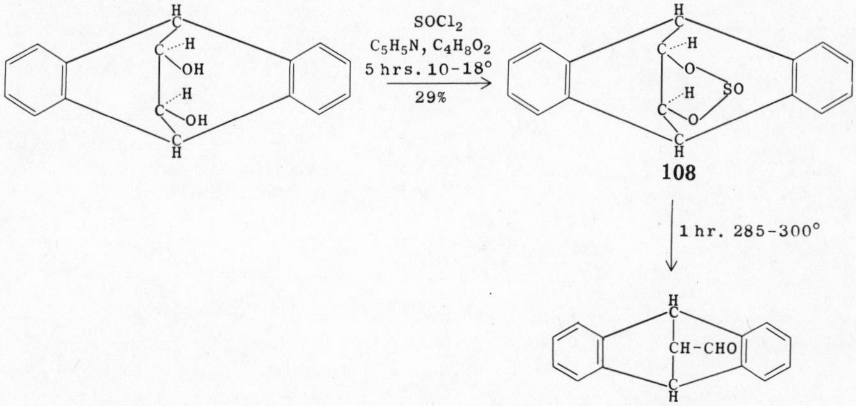

108

1 hr. 285-300°

109

XX. C_2O_2S-C_4O-C_4O-C_5-C_6-C_6 3H, 9H-11b, 13a-EPOXYCYCLO-PENTA[1, 2]PHENANTHRO[4, 4a-d][1, 3, 2]DIOXATHIOLE (110)

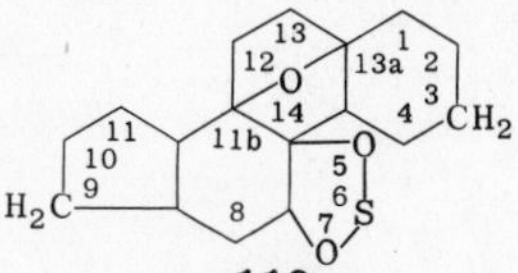

110
(RRI 6562)

[For references, see pp. 57-61.]

Clayton, Crawshaw, and coworkers,[28] prepared the cyclic sulfite of $5\alpha, 8\alpha$-epoxy-3β-acetoxy-$9\alpha, 11\alpha$-ergostanediol (**111**), m.p. 173-174°, $[\alpha]_D - 28°$, from the glycol and thionyl chloride in the presence of pyridine. A peak in the infrared spectrum at 1215 cm^{-1} confirmed the presence of the cyclic sulfite (see section I A-2).

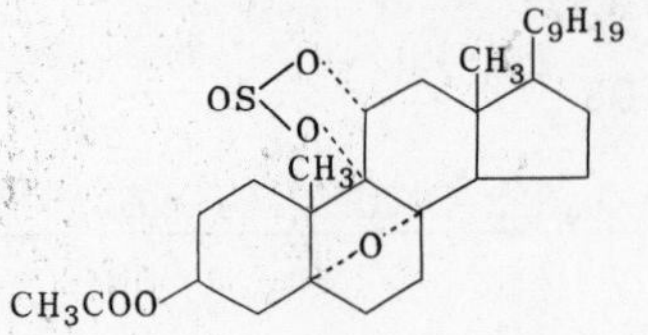

111

REFERENCES

1.   Adams, R., P. R. Shafer, and B. H. Braun, J. Am. Chem. Soc., **74**, 5612 (1952).

2.   Adams, R., and B. L. Van Duuren, J. Am. Chem. Soc., **75**, 4638 (1953).

2a. Adams, R., and M. Gianturco, J. Am. Chem. Soc., **78**, 1922 (1956).

3.   Agfa Wolfen Filmfabrik, Belg. Patent 552, 760 (1957).

4.   Agfa Wolfen Filmfabrik, Belg. Patent 558, 201 (1957).

5.   Alderson, T. (to Du Pont), U. S. Patent 2, 811, 511 (1957).

6.   Anschütz, R., and W. Posth, Ber., **27**, 2751 (1894).

7.   Arbuzov, B. A., and T. G. Shavsha, Doklady Akad. Nauk S. S. S. R., **69**, 41 (1949); Chem. Abstracts, **44**, 1297 (1950).

8.   Arbuzov, B. A., and V. S. Vinogradova, Izvest. Akad. Nauk S. S. S. R., Otdel. Khim. Nauk, **1950**, 297; Chem. Abstracts, **44**, 8718 (1950).

8a. Arbousow, B. A., Bull. soc. chim. France, **1960**, 1311.

9.   Asahina, Y., Ber., **45**, 2363 (1912).

10. Asselineau, J., and E. Lederer, Bull. soc. chim. France, **1955**, 1231.

11. Asselineau, J., and A. Ginsburg, Bull. soc. chim. France, **1955**, 1241.

12. Baker, W., and F. B. Field, J. Chem. Soc., **1932**, 86.

12a. Baker, W., and B. F. Burrows, J. Chem. Soc., **1961**. 2257.

12b. Ben-Ishay, D., J. Org. Chem., **23**, 2013 (1958).

12c. Ben-Ishay, D., Arch. Pharm., **292**, 98 (1959); Chem. Abstracts, **53**, 18047 (1959).

13. Berliner, R., B. Stein, and W. Trautner (to Grasselli Dyestuff Corp.), U. S. Patent 1, 646, 782 (1927); Chem. Abstracts, **22**, 323 (1928). I.G. Farbenind., Ger. Patent 453, 768 (1927).

14. Bissinger, W. E., R. H. Fredenburg, R. G. Kadesch, F. Kung, J. H. Langston, H. C. Stevens, and F. Strain, J. Am. Chem. Soc., **69**, 2955 (1947).

14a. Bissinger, W. E., F. E. Kung, and C. W. Hamilton, J. Am. Chem. Soc., **70**, 3940 (1948).

15. Blaise, E. E., and M. Montagne, Compt. rend., **174**, 1173 (1922).

16. Blaise, E. E., and M. Montagne, Compt. rend., **174**, 1553 (1922).

17. Boehm, R. L., J. Org. Chem., **23**, 1716 (1958).

18. Böeseken, J., F. Tellegen, and P. C. Henriquez, Rec. trav. chim., **50**, 909 (1931).

19. Boozer, C. E., and E. S. Lewis, J. Am. Chem. Soc., **75**, 3182 (1953).

19a. Bragg, P. D., J. K. N. Jones, and J. C. Turner, Can. J. Chem., **37**, 1412 (1959).

19b. Brimacombe, J. S., A. B. Foster, and M. Stacey, Chem. & Ind. (London), **1959**, 262.

19c. Brimacombe, J. S., A. B. Foster, E. B. Hancock, W. G. Overend, and M. Stacey, J. Chem. Soc., **1960**, 201.

19d. Brunken, J., and G. Glöckner (to VEB Filmfabrik Agfa Wolfen), Ger. Patent 1, 029, 382 (1958).

19e. Brunken, J., and E. J. Poppe (to VEB Filmfabrik Agfa Wolfen), Ger. Patent 1, 049, 870 (1959).

20. Bunton, C. A., P. B. D. de la Mare, D. R. Llewellyn, R. B. Pearson, and J. G. Pritchard, Chem. & Ind. (London), 1956, 490.

21. Bunton, C. A., P. B. D. de la Mare, P. M. Greaseley, D. R. Llewellyn, N. H. Pratt, and J. G. Tillett, J. Chem. Soc., 1958, 4751.

22. Bunton, C. A., P. B. D. de la Mare, and J. G. Tillett, J. Chem. Soc., 1958, 4754.

23. Bunton, C. A., P. B. D. de la Mare, A. Lennard, D. R. Llewellyn, R. B. Pearson, J. G. Pritchard, and J. G. Tillett, J. Chem. Soc., 1958, 4761.

23a. Bunton, C. A., P. B. D. de la Mare, and J. G. Tillett, J. Chem. Soc., 1959, 1766.

23b. Burwell, Jr., R. L., J. Am. Chem. Soc., 74, 1462 (1952).

24. Carlson, W. W., and L. H. Cretcher, J. Am. Chem. Soc., 69, 1952 (1947).

25. Carlson, W. W., (to Mellon Institute), U. S. Patent 2, 448, 767 (1948); Chem. Abstracts, 43, 673 (1949).

26. Carré, P., and D. Libermann, Compt. rend., 200, 1215 (1935).

27. Chemstrand Corp., Brit. Patent 769, 700 (1957); Chem. Abstracts, 51, 12552 (1957).

28. Clayton, R. B., A. Crawshaw, H. B. Henbest, E. R. H. Jones, B. J. Lovell, and G. W. Wood, J. Chem. Soc., 1953, 2009.

29. Cram, D. J., J. Am. Chem. Soc., 75, 332 (1953).

29a. Criegee, R., and K. Noll, Ann., 627, 1 (1959).

30. Cromwell, N. H., and A. Hassner, J. Am. Chem. Soc., 77, 1568 (1955).

31. Davies, E. D., and J. G. Tillett, J. Chem. Soc., 1958, 4766.

31a. Davis, R. E., J. Am. Chem. Soc., 84, 599 (1962).

32. De la Mare, P. B. D., W. Klyne, D. J. Millen, J. G. Pritchard, and D. Watson, J. Chem. Soc., 1956, 1813.

32a. De la Mare, P. B. D., J. G. Tillett, and H. F. van Woerden, Chem. & Ind. (London), 1961, 1533.

32b. De la Mare, P. B. D., J. G. Tillett, and H. F. van Woerden, J. Chem. Soc., 1962, 4888.

33. Denivelle, L., Compt. rend., 203, 194 (1936).

34. Denivelle, L., Compt. rend., 208, 1024 (1939).

35. De Witt, H. D. (to Chemstrand Corp.), U. S. Patent 2, 752, 318 (1956).

36. Dietrich, W., and H. Höfermann (to Chemische Werke Hüls), U. S. Patent 2, 833, 785 (1958). Ger. Patent 1, 019, 659 (1957). Brit. Patent 783, 561 (1957); Chem. Abstracts, 52, 5455 (1958).

36a. Eliel, E. L., in M. S. Newman, Steric Effects in Organic Chemistry, John Wiley & Sons, New York, 1956, p. 126.

36b. England, D. C., M. A. Dietrich, and R. V. Lindsey, Jr., J. Am. Chem. Soc., 82, 6181 (1960).

37. Faass, U., and H. Hilgert, Chem. Ber., **87**, 1343 (1954).

37a. Farbwerke Hoechst, Brit. Patent 781, 169 (1957); Chem. Abstracts, **52** 1682 (1958).

37b. Farmaceutici Italia Soc. anon., Brit. Patent 810, 376 (1959); Chem. Abstracts, **53**, 21819 (1959).

38. Fiesselmann, H., and F. Hörndler, Chem. Ber., **87**, 906 (1954).

39. Fischer, H. O. L., and C. Taube, Ber., **59B**, 851 (1926).

40. Foster. A. B., E. B. Hancock, and W. G. Overend, Chem. & Ind. (London), **1956**, 1144.

41. Garner, H. K., and H. J. Lucas, J. Am. Chem. Soc., **72**, 5497 (1950).

42. Gattermann, L., J. prakt. Chem., [2] **43**, 246 (1891).

42a. Gillis, R. G., J. Org. Chem., **25**, 651 (1960).

43. Green, A., J. Chem. Soc., **125**, 1450 (1924).

44. Green, A., J. Chem. Soc., **1926**, 2198.

45. Green, A., J. Chem. Soc., **1927**, 500.

46. Green, A., J. Chem. Soc., **1927**, 554.

47. Green, A., J. Chem. Soc., **1927**, 2930.

48. Gruschke, H. (to Farbwerke Hoechst), Ger. Patent 925, 473 (1955); Chem. Zentr., **1955**, 8028. Brit. Patent 753, 872 (1956); Chem. Abstracts, **51**, 5821 (1957).

48a. Ham, G. E. (to Chemstrand Corp.), U.S. Patent 2, 870, 127 (1959).

48b. Ham, G. E., J. Org. Chem., **25**, 864 (1960).

48c. Ham, G. E. (to Dow), U. S. Patent 3, 045, 027 (1962).

49. Hassel, O., and C. Rømming, Acta Chem. Scand., **10**, 136 (1956)

49a. Helferich, B., Ber., **54B**, 1082 (1921).

49b. Helferich, B., A. Löwa, W. Nippe, and H. Riedel, Ber., **56B**, 1083 (1923).

49c. Helferich, B., G. Sprock, and E. Besler, Ber., **58B**, 886 (1925).

50. Hesse, G., Angew. Chem., **70**, 134 (1958).

50a. Hesse, G., and S. Majmadur, Chem. Ber., **93**, 1129 (1960).

50b. Hesse, G., and M. Förderreuther, Chem. Ber., **93**, 1249 (1960).

50c. Holmquist, H. E., J. C. Sauer, V. A. Engelhardt, and B. W. Howk, J. Am. Chem. Soc., **81**, 3686 (1959).

51. Honeyman, J., and J. W. W. Morgan, J. Chem. Soc., **1955**, 3660.

52. Kitasato, Z., and C. Sone, Ber., **64B**, 1142 (1931).

52a. Laubach, G. D., E. C. Schreiber, E. J. Agnello, and K. H. Brunings, J. Am. Chem. Soc., **78**, 4746 (1956).

53. Legrand, M., Bull. soc. chim. France, **1953**, 540.

54. Lichtenberger, J., and R. Lichtenberger, Bull. soc. chim. France, **1948**, 1002.

55. Lichtenberger, J., and J. Hincky, Bull. soc. chim. France, **1951**, 796.

55a. Lichtenberger, J., and J. Hincky, Bull. soc. chim. France, **1961**, 1495.

56. Loth, F., and A. Michaelis, Ber., **27**, 2540 (1894).

57. Majima, R., and H. Simanuki, Proc. Imp. Acad. (Japan), **2**, 544 (1926); Chem. Abstracts, **21**, 1796 (1927).

58. McKenzie, A., and F Barrow, J. Chem. Soc., **99**, 1910 (1911).

59. Meyer, H., Monatsh., **22**, 415 (1902).

60. Meyer, H., Monatsh., **22**, 777 (1902).

61. Milas, N. A. (to Union Bay State Chem. Co.), U. S. Patent 2, 467, 330 (1949); Chem. Abstracts, **43**, 6219 (1949).

62. Mousseron, M., F. Winternitz, and M. Mousseron-Canet, Bull. soc. chim. France **1953**, 737.

63. Myles, W. J., and J. H. Prichard (to Celanese Corp. of America), U. S. Patent 2, 465, 915 (1949); Chem. Abstracts, **43**, 4853 (1949).

64. Ott, K. (to Chemische Fabriken vorm. Weiler-ter Meer), Ger. Patent 362, 743 (1922); Chem. Abstracts, **18**, 991 (1924).

64a. Pagdin, N., A. K. Pine, J. G. Tillett, and H. F. van Woerden, J. Chem. Soc., **1962**, 3835.

65. Perkins, M. A. (to Du Pont), U. S. Patent 1, 999, 995 (1935); Chem. Abstracts, **29**, 4026 (1935). Brit. Patent 447, 135 (1936); Chem. Abstracts, **30**, 6763 (1936).

66. Pollak, J., and E. Gebauer-Fülnegg, Monatsh., **47**, 109 (1926).

67. Price, C. C., and G. Berti, J. Am. Chem. Soc., **76**, 1211 (1954).

67a. Pritchard, J. G., and P. C. Lauterbur, J. Am. Chem. Soc., **83**, 2105 (1961).

67b. Procházka, M., and V. Horák, Collection Czechoslav. Chem. Communs., **24**, 609 (1959).

68. Purves, C. B. (to Research Corp.), U. S. Patent 2, 194, 405 (1940); Chem. Abstracts, **34**, 4742 (1940).

68a. Razuvaev, G. A., V. S. Étlis, and L. N. Grobov, J. Gen. Chem. U. S. S. R., **31**, 1230 (1961).

69. Reulos, D., and S. LeTellier, Compt. rend., **217**, 698 (1943).

69a. Reuter, J. (to Société de produits chimiques industriels), Fr. Patent 1, 143, 811 (1957); Chem. Abstracts, **54**, 1301 (1960).

70. Rio, G., Ann. Chim., **9**, 207 (1954).

71. Rio, G., Compt. rend., **239**, 982 (1954).

72. Rio, G., and A. Ranjon, Compt. rend., **240**, 98 (1955).

73. Rio, G., and P. J. Cornu, Compt. rend., **242**, 523 (1956).

73a. Rio, G., and P. J. Cornu, Bull. soc. chim. France, **1958**, 1540.

74. Robertson, F. M., and A. C. Neish, Can. J. Research, **25B**, 491 (1947).

74a. Rothrock, G. M. (to Du Pont), U. S. Patent 2, 706, 674 (1955).

75. Ruggli, P., and E. Henzi, Helv. Chim. Acta, **12**, 362 (1929).

76. Saint-Gobain, Brit. Patent 670, 159 (1952); Chem. Abstracts, **47**, 2767 (1953).

77. Schenck, G. O., and G. A. Schmidt-Thomée, Ann., **584**, 199 (1953).

78. Schiller, E., Ber., **42**, 2017 (1909).

79. Schmidt, R. E., J. prakt. Chem., [2] **43**, 237 (1891).

79a. Smith, R. M. (to Dow), U. S. Patent 2, 899, 461 (1959).

80. Szmant, H. H., and W. Emerson, J. Am. Chem. Soc., **78**, 454 (1956).

81. Tchoubar, B., Bull. soc. chim., [5] **11**, 207 (1944).

81a. Tillett, J. G., J. Chem. Soc., **1960**, 37.

81b. Tillett, J. G., J. Chem. Soc., **1960**, 5138.

82. Vaughan, W. R., and M. Yoshimine, J. Org. Chem., **22**, 528 (1957).

83. Viard, M. J. (to Saint-Gobain), U. S. Patent 2, 676, 872 (1954).

84. Viard, M. J. (to Saint-Gobain), U. S. Patent 2, 684, 977 (1954).

85. Viard, M. J. (to Saint-Gobain), U. S. Patent 2, 798, 877 (1957).

85a. von Wartburg, A., and J. Renz, Helv. Chim. Acta, **42**, 1620 (1959).

85b. von Wartburg, A., and J. Renz, Helv. Chim. Acta, **42**, 1643 (1959).

86. Wiest, G. (to I. G. Farbenindustrie), Ger. Patent 710, 350 (1941); Chem. Zentr., **1942**, I, 407.

87. Wolthius, E., and J. C. Lawler (to General Aniline and Film Corp.), U. S. Patent 2, 415, 397 (1947); Chem. Abstracts, **41**, 3118 (1947).

88. Wood, C. E., and S. D. Nicholas, J. Chem. Soc., **1928**, 1671.

88a. Yunusov, S. Yu., and N. V. Plekhanova, Doklady Akad. Nauk Uzbek. S. S. R., **1957**, No. 6, 19; Chem. Abstracts, **53**, 6276 (1959).

88b. Zeile, K., and A. Heusner, Arch. Pharm., **292**, 238 (1959); Chem. Abstracts, **54**, 604 (1960).

89. Zinner, H., G. Sych, and F. Schneider, Chem. Ber., **93**, 468 (1960).

CHAPTER 2

C$_2$OS$_2$ RING SYSTEMS

These ring systems involve primarily the cyclic anhydrides of 1, 2-disulfonic acids and are indexed in Chemical Abstracts under the parent acids.

I. 1, 2, 5-OXADITHIA COMPOUNDS

A. C$_2$OS$_2$ 1, 2, 5-OXADITHIOLANE (1)

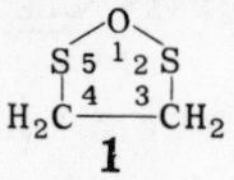

1

(RRI 102)

The sole representative of this ring system is 1, 2-ethanedisulfonic anhydride (**2**). It can be prepared in 66% yield by heating the acid at 190-200° *in vacuo* or, more readily, by refluxing the acid with thionyl chloride.[9]

2

The anhydride melts at 145-146°; it is hygroscopic and dissolves readily in cold water.

B. C$_2$OS$_2$-C$_4$S THIENO[3, 4-*c*][1, 2, 5]OXADITHIOLE (3)

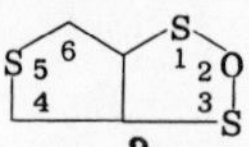

3

(RRI 866)

These compounds are anhydrides of 3, 4-thiophenedisulfonic acids. Their preparation from substituted thiophenes and fuming sulfuric acid is straightforward; the compounds are listed in Table 1.

All the anhydrides are fairly stable to water and hydrolyze with hot caustic. Steinkopf[12] reported that 2-bromo-5-methyl-3, 4-thiophenedisulfonic anhydride (**4**) yields two acid chlorides. One, melting at 174°,

62

TABLE 1. Anhydrides of 3, 4-Thiophenedisulfonic Acids

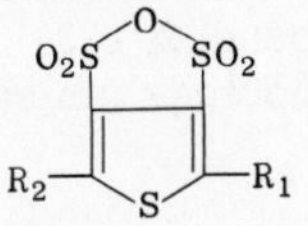

R_1	R_2	Yield (%)	M.p. (°C)		Ref.
Br	Br		darkens dec.	>150° >200°	8, 10
CH_3-	CH_3-	55	darkens dec.	170° 200°	11
CH_3-	Br	28	darkens dec.	185° 210°	12

reacts readily with aniline, while the other, melting at 189°, reacts only slowly. By analogy with the isomeric phthalyl chlorides he assigned structure **5** to the low-melting isomer and **6** or **7** to the high-melting isomer.

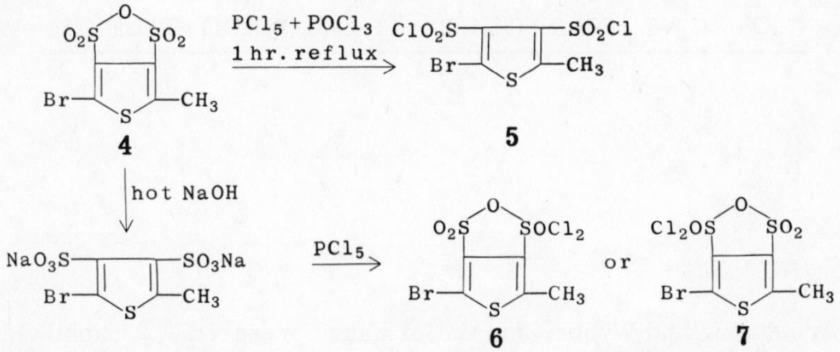

Steinkopf[11] claimed that the other anhydrides yield only one acid chloride.

Although some doubt has been raised as to the structures of thiophenesulfonic acids,[5] these appear to be on a reasonably firm basis.

C. C_2OS_2-C_6 2, 1, 3-BENZOXADITHIOLE **(8)**

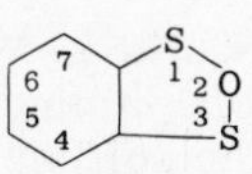

8
(RRI 1099)

[For references, see p. 66.]

An alternative name for this ring system is 2-oxa-1, 3-dithiindan. The system is represented by the anhydrides of o-benzenedisulfonic acids. Hurtley and Smiles[7] prepared the parent compound, 2, 1, 3-benzoxadithiole 1, 1, 3, 3-tetroxide (9), by heating the dipotassium salt with chlorosulfonic acid.

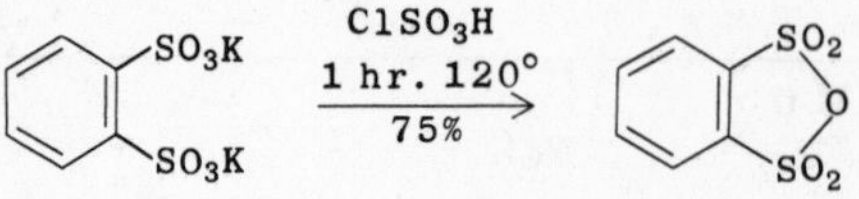

9

The anhydride, m.p. 180°, is attacked slowly by cold water. Holleman and Choufoer[6] used phosphorus pentachloride to prepare the 4, 7-dimethyl analog (10), m.p. 189-190°.

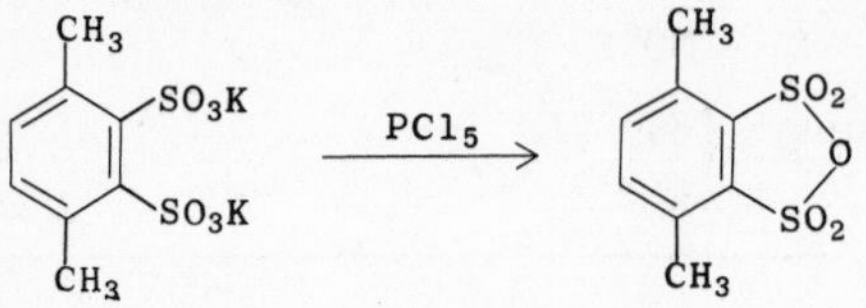

10

In both cases the disulfonic acids were prepared by diazotization of the aminosulfonic acid, conversion to the mercaptosulfonic acid, and oxidation.

D. C_2OS_2-C_6-C_6 NAPHTH[1, 2-c][1, 2, 5]OXADITHIOLE (11)

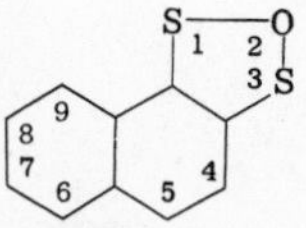

11

(RRI 2652)

Armstrong and Wynne[1] and Gattermann[4] prepared 1, 2-naphthalenedisulfonic anhydride (12), m.p. 198-199°, by ring closure with phosphorus pentachloride.

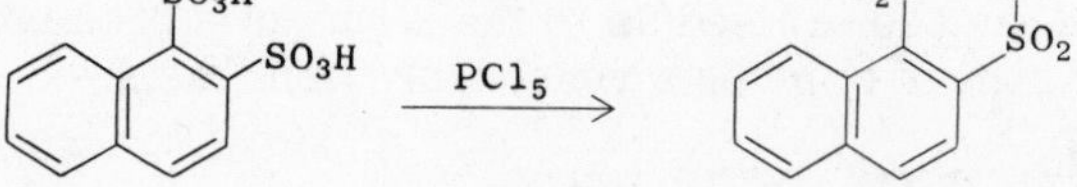

12

The latter prepared the disulfonic acid by diazotization of 1-amino-2-naphthalenesulfonic acid with subsequent conversion to the sulfinic sulfonic acid and oxidation with permanganate.

II. 1, 3, 4-OXADITHIA COMPOUNDS

C_2OS_2 1, 3, 4-OXADITHIOLANE (13)

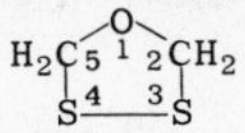

13

Davis[2,3] claimed that reaction of α, α'-dichlorodimethyl ether with sodium tetrasulfide in the presence of base yields a polymer. Steam distillation of the polymer yielded monomeric 1, 3, 4-oxadithiolane, whose properties were not described. Treatment of the monomer with sodium methoxide gave rapid polymerization.

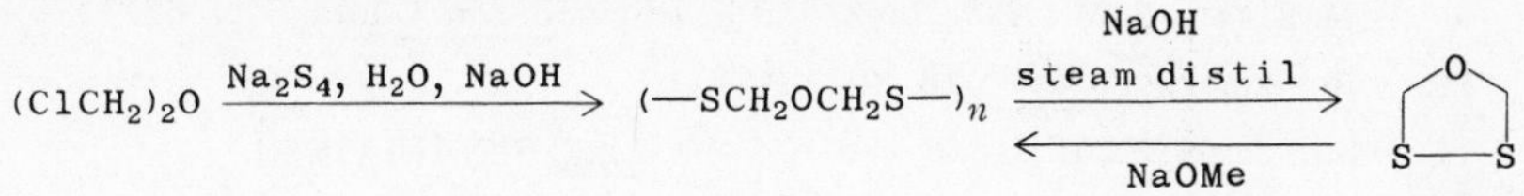

$$(ClCH_2)_2O \xrightarrow{\ Na_2S_4,\ H_2O,\ NaOH\ } (-SCH_2OCH_2S-)_n \underset{NaOMe}{\overset{\substack{NaOH \\ steam\ distil}}{\rightleftarrows}}$$

13

[For references, see p. 66.]

Chapter 2

REFERENCES

1. Armstrong, H. E., and W. P. Wynne, Chem. News, **67**, 298 (1893); Chem. Zentr., **1893**, II, 274.

2. Davis, F. O. (to Thiokol Chemical Corp.), U. S. Patent 2, 657, 198 (1953).

3. Davis, F. O. (to Thiokol Chemical Corp.), U.S. Patent 2, 715, 635 (1955).

4. Gattermann, L., Ber., **32**, 1156 (1899).

5. Hartough, H. D., Thiophene and its Derivatives, Interscience Publishers,Inc., New York, 1952, p. 420.

6. Holleman, A. F., and H. J. Choufoer, Rec. trav. chim., 48, 1075 (1929).

7. Hurtley, W. R. H., and S. Smiles, J. Chem. Soc.. **1926**, 1821.

8. Langer, J., Ber., **17**, 1566 (1884).

9. McElvain, S. M., A. Jelinek, and K. Rorig, J. Am. Chem. Soc., **67**, 1578 (1945).

10. Rosenberg, J., Ber., **18**, 3027 (1885).

11. Steinkopf, W., H. Jacob, and H. Penz, Ann., **512**, 136 (1934).

12. Steinkopf, W., Ann., **513**, 281 (1934).

CHAPTER 3

C₂S₃ RING SYSTEMS

I. 1, 2, 3-TRITHIA COMPOUNDS

A. C_2S_3 1, 2, 3-TRITHIOLE (1)

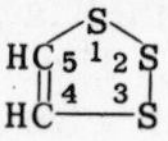

(RRI 115)

In 1958 Bähr[2b] reported that treatment of carbon disulfide with sodium cyanide led to the formation of the disodium salt of 2, 3-dimercapto-maleonitrile (2, M = Na). Treatment of the corresponding silver salt (2, M = Ag) with thionyl chloride yielded 4, 5-dicyano-1, 2, 3-trithiole 2-oxide (3).

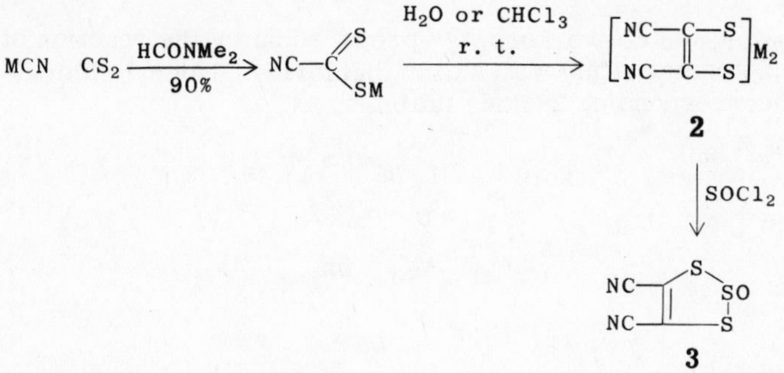

Although the details of Bähr's work are unavailable, it has been confirmed in general in several laboratories[17a],[19a] (see chapter 12, section III A-2a).

The dihydro ring system, 1, 2, 3-trithiolane, was suggested as being present in dibenzophenone trisulfide, but this has since been proved to be incorrect (see section II A). No other examples are known.

B. C_2S_3-C_6 BENZOTRITHIOLE (4)

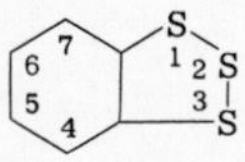

4

(RRI 1107)

[For references, see p. 75.]   67

Only one example of this ring system has been reported. Guha and Chakladar[12] reacted the dipotassium salt of 4-bromothiocatechol with thionyl chloride and obtained a compound which they formulated as 5-bromobenzotrithiole 2-oxide (5).

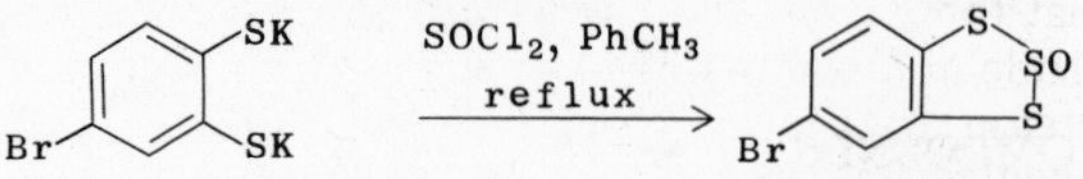

The compound was isolated as an amorphous yellow powder, melting at 220° with decomposition and insoluble in all organic solvents. These properties are more in accord with a polymeric material than with the structure assigned, and the existence of this ring system is in doubt.

C. C_2S_3-C_4N_2-C_6 TRITHIOLO[4, 5-b]QUINOXALINE (5a)

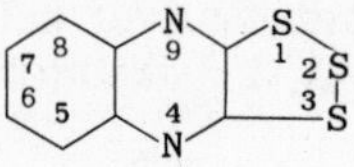

5a

Sasse, Wegler, and co-workers,[15a] prepared **5a** by the reaction of 2, 3-dimercaptoquinoxaline with sulfur dichloride. Thionyl chloride yielded the corresponding 2-oxide (**5b**).

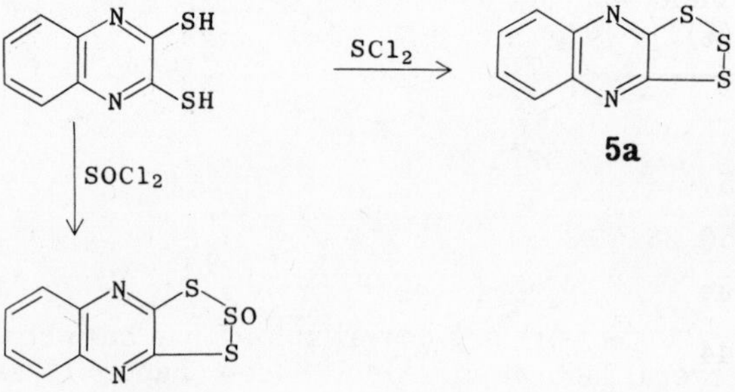

Both **5a** and **5b** have been reported to be active acaricides.

II. 1, 2, 4-TRITHIA COMPOUNDS

A. C_2S_3 1, 2, 4-TRITHIOLANE (6)

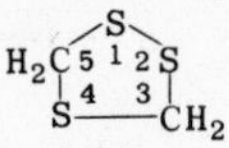

6

(RRI 116)

Chemical Abstracts indexes this ring system as indicated above. Other names have been used, such as dimethylene trisulfide and 1, 2, 4-trithiacyclopentane; the compounds are also known as trithio-ozonides. The compounds reported are listed in Table 1.

Davis[8,9] claimed that the parent compound (6) could be prepared from bis(chloromethyl) sulfide and sodium tetrasulfide. A polymer was first formed and this, on steam distillation in the presence of base, yielded the monomer. Conversely, treatment of the monomer with base led to rapid polymerization. However, no properties of the monomer were described, and its instability does not agree with the reported stability of other 1, 2, 4-trithiolanes (*vide infra*).

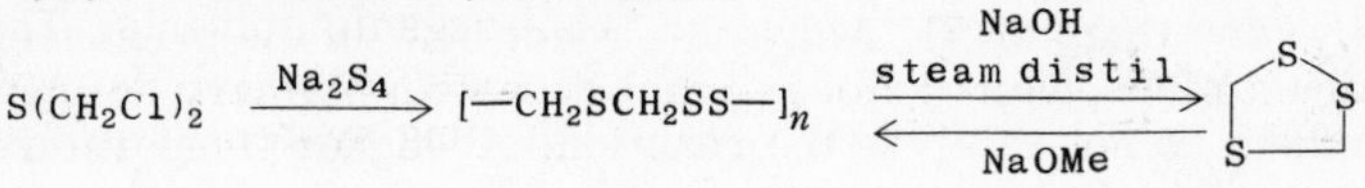

$$S(CH_2Cl)_2 \xrightarrow{Na_2S_4} [-CH_2SCH_2SS-]_n \underset{NaOMe}{\overset{\substack{NaOH \\ steam\ distil}}{\rightleftarrows}} $$

6

TABLE 1. 1, 2, 4-Trithiolanes

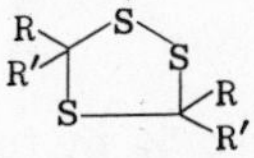

R	R'	Yield (%)	M.p (°C)	B. p. (°C)	(mm)	n_D^{20}	Ref.
H	H						8, 9
CH$_3$-	H	5		38	0. 3	1. 597	2a
C$_2$H$_5$-	H	50, 38		77	1	1. 567	2, 2a
n-C$_3$H$_7$-	H	47		86	0. 4	1. 549	2, 2a
CH$_3$-	CH$_3$-	44		34	0. 4		2
				75	10	1. 546	2a
CH$_3$-	C$_2$H$_5$-	81		70	0. 6	1. 542	2a
CH$_3$-	n-C$_3$H$_7$-	80, 75		84	0. 3	1. 533	2a
C$_2$H$_5$-	C$_2$H$_5$-	87		84	0.'2		2, 2a
		92		103	0. 8	1. 541	2a
C$_6$H$_5$-	C$_6$H$_5$-	52	dec. 124				15-18

Asinger and co-workers[1,2,2a] reported a more general synthesis of 1, 2, 4-trithiolanes (7) involving the reaction of an aldehyde or ketone at

[For references, see p. 75.]

0° with a solution of sulfur in an amine solvent saturated with hydrogen sulfide.

$$R-\overset{O}{\underset{||}{C}}-R' + H_2S + S \xrightarrow{0°} \begin{array}{c} R \\ R' \end{array}\!\!\!\!\begin{array}{c} S \\ S \\ S \end{array}\!\!\!\!\begin{array}{c} R \\ R' \end{array}$$

7

The reaction gives good to excellent yields with a number of aldehydes and ketones; it fails with formaldehyde, acetophenone, and benzophenone. With certain ketones the corresponding tetrathianes are formed simultaneously (see Chapter 7). Aldehydes react best in the presence of secondary amines, while ketones react best with primary amines; tertiary amines do not catalyze the reaction. At higher temperatures the reaction takes a different course.

The authors formulated the reaction as taking place by a series of condensations, as illustrated with acetone, X being O or RN.

$$(CH_3)_2C=X \xrightarrow{H_2S} (CH_3)_2C\!\!\!\begin{array}{c}XH \\ SH\end{array} \xrightarrow[-H_2S]{+S} (CH_3)_2\overset{XH\ HX}{\underset{S-S}{\bigtriangleup}}C(CH_3)_2$$

$$\xrightarrow{H_2S} (CH_3)_2\overset{SH\ HX}{\underset{S-S}{\bigtriangleup}}C(CH_3)_2 \xrightarrow{-H_2X} (CH_3)_2\overset{S}{\underset{S-S}{\bigtriangleup}}C(CH_3)_2$$

These reactions are reversible. Treatment of the 1, 2, 4-trithiolane with a primary amine yields the Schiff base, while treatment of the Schiff base with sulfur and H_2S yields the trithiolane. Ketones form enamines rather than Schiff bases with secondary amines, and these too were shown to yield trithiolanes.

1, 2, 4-Trithiolanes derived from ketones are remarkably stable. They do not react with aqueous acids and bases, heavy metal salts, mercury, triethyl phosphite, or triphenylphosphine. Reduction to mercaptan with lithium aluminum hydride and cleavage to ketone with methanolic potassium hydroxide confirmed the assigned structure.

$$\begin{array}{c} R \\ R' \end{array}\!\!\!\!\begin{array}{c} S \\ S \\ S \end{array}\!\!\!\!\begin{array}{c} R \\ R' \end{array} \xrightarrow[95\%]{LiAlH_4} \begin{array}{c} R \\ R' \end{array}\!\!\!>\!CHSH + H_2S$$

$$\downarrow \begin{array}{c} KOH,\ MeOH \\ r.\ t. \end{array}$$

$$\begin{array}{c} R \\ R' \end{array}\!\!\!>\!C=O + K_2S$$

Mann and Pope[15] reacted sulfur monochloride with α-2, 4, 6-trimethyl-s-trithiane (**8**). α, α'-Dichlorodiethyl sulfide (**9**) was formed in 45% yield; a by-product, diethylidene trisulfide (**10**), was formed as well (see Chapter 10, section II A-3d). Although this compound might be formulated as 3, 5-dimethyl-1, 2, 4-trithiolane (11), its properties are not in very good accord with this structure.

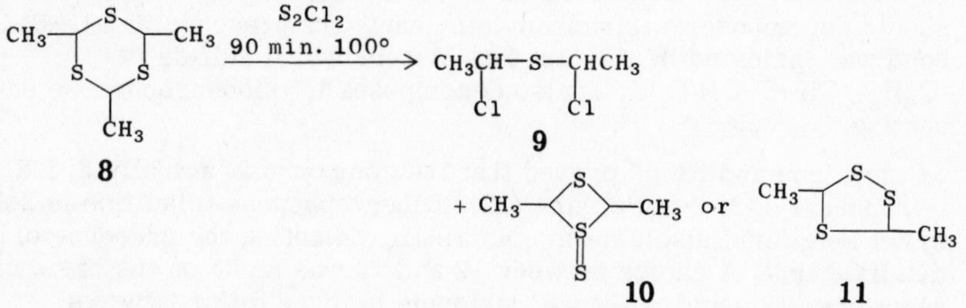

Thus, it was reported to be a pale green liquid boiling at 89-90° at 14 mm; this boiling point appears to be too low for a 1, 2, 4-trithiolane, and Asinger and co-workers[2a] report trithiolanes to be colorless or pale yellow liquids.

It had been known for many years that thiobenzophenone reacts rapidly with air.[11] The reaction was investigated at about the same time by Schönberg[16] and by Staudinger.[18] Schönberg and co-workers[16] found that the blue crystals of thiobenzophenone melt on exposure to air, and then resolidify. From this was isolated a colorless crystalline product which decomposed to a blue product above 100°. Its solutions were colorless or pale blue at room temperature, but they became deep blue on heating. Staudinger and Freudenberger[18] were the first to report that a trisulfide, decomposing at 124°, is formed in the reaction, as well as benzophenone, sulfur, and sulfur dioxide. By carrying out the oxidation very slowly at room temperature they obtained a 52% yield of trisulfide.[19]

$$6(C_6H_5)_2C{=}S + O_2 \longrightarrow 2(C_6H_5)_2C{=}O + 2[(C_6H_5)_2C]_2S_3$$

More rapid reactions gave more benzophenone and less trisulfide. The trisulfide decomposed almost quantitatively to thiobenzophenone and sulfur at 130°.

More recently Kambara, Okita, and Higuchi[14] claimed that the same compound is formed in good yield by reacting benzophenone with hydrogen sulfide and hydrogen chloride.

$$(C_6H_5)_2C{=}O \xrightarrow[\text{EtOH}]{\text{HCl, H}_2\text{S}} [(C_6H_5)_2C]_2S_3$$

According to these authors the compound is unaffected by hydrogen peroxide in acetic or sulfuric acid at room temperature.

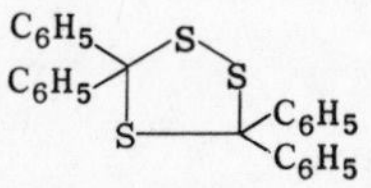

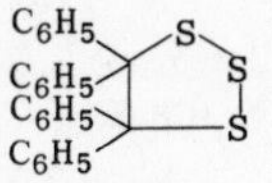

Chapter 3

Staudinger and Freudenberger[19] suggested two alternative structures, 12 and 13, for the trisulfide but preferred Structure 12. Schönberg and co-workers[17] also preferred 12 on the reasonable assumption that 13 should decompose to tetraphenylethylene. The presence of a C–S–C bond was indicated by the fact that bisbenzhydryl sulfide, $(C_6H_5)_2CH-S-CH(C_6H_5)_2$, also decomposes to thiobenzophenone on heating.

Campaigne and Reid[6] proved that the compound is actually 3, 3, 5, 5-tetraphenyl-1-2, 4-trithiolane (12). Dibenzophenone trisulfide is soluble in hot alkali and insoluble in cold alkali, indicating the presence of a disulfide link. A choice between 12 and 13 was made on the basis of two reactions. 12 could react with chlorine in three different ways:

(1) $12 + 9\,Cl_2 + 9\,H_2O \longrightarrow (C_6H_5)_2C(SO_2Cl)_2 + (C_6H_5)_2CO + H_2SO_4$
$+ 16\,HCl$

(2) $12 + 10\,Cl_2 + 11\,H_2O \longrightarrow (C_6H_5)_2C{\overset{Cl}{\underset{SO_2Cl}{<}}} + (C_6H_5)_2CO + 2\,H_2SO_4$
$+ 18\,HCl$

(3) $12 + 11\,Cl_2 + 12\,H_2O \longrightarrow 2\,(C_6H_5)_2CCl_2 + 3\,H_2SO_4 + 18\,HCl$

13 would presumably react in two different ways, equation (5) being more likely because of the known instability of 1, 2-disulfonyl chlorides.

(4) $13 + 8\,Cl_2 + 8\,H_2O \longrightarrow C_6H_5CH{-}CHC_6H_5 + H_2SO_4 + 14\,HCl$
$\quad\quad\quad\quad\quad\quad\quad\quad SO_2Cl\ SO_2Cl$

(5) $13 + 10\,Cl_2 + 12\,H_2O \longrightarrow C_6H_5CH{-}CHC_6H_5 + 3\,H_2SO_4 + 18\,HCl$
$\quad\quad\quad\quad\quad\quad\quad\quad Cl\quad Cl$

When the trisulfide was treated with chlorine and water in glacial acetic acid, 1. 96 moles of benzophenone dichloride and 2. 94 moles of sulfuric acid per mole of trisulfide were isolated. Thus, the reaction followed equation (3) and indicated the correctness of Structure 12. However, since the possibility exists that 13 might react with chlorine to give benzophenone dichloride, the structure was proved unequivocally by desulfurizing the compound with Raney nickel. Diphenylmethane was isolated in 85% yield, whereas 13 would give 1, 2-diphenylethane.

In 1895 Freund and Asbrand[10] claimed that 2, 5-bis(methylimino)-1, 2, 4-trithiolane (15) was formed by rearrangement of 3-methylimino-4-methyl-1, 2, 4-dithiazolidine-5-thione (14).

14   15

72

Hantzsch and Wolvekamp[13] believed that the rearrangement involved the formation of 2,4-dimethyl-1,2,4-thiadiazolidine-3,5-dithione (16).

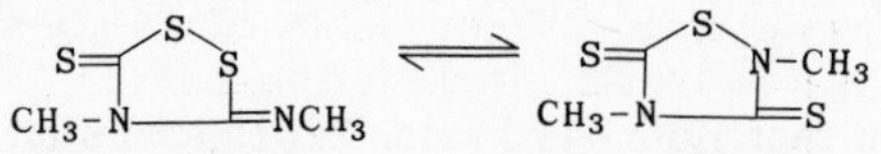

14   **16**

Bradsher, Brown, and co-workers,[4] have confirmed this latter interpretation, since the infrared spectrum of the rearrangement product showed the absence of imino groups. Thus, the product must be 16 and not 15.

B. SPIRO DERIVATIVES OF 1, 2, 4-TRITHIOLANE

Asinger and co-workers[1,2,2a] found that cyclohexanone condenses with sulfur and hydrogen sulfide in the presence of an amine to give 7,14,15-trithiadispiro [5.1.5.2]pentadecane (17), m.p. 50°, plus the corresponding tetrathiane (see Chapter 7). The chemistry of 17 is similar to that of other 1, 2, 4-trithiolanes.

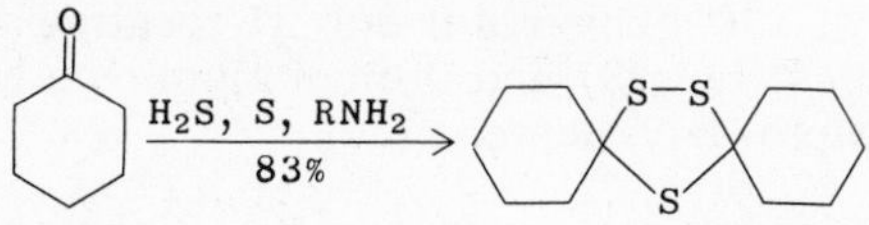

17

Although ammonium polysulfide usually yields a tetrathiane, Magnusson[14b] found that with certain ketones 1, 2, 4-trithiolanes are the major product. Thus, thiolan-3-one (18) formed 2, 6, 9, 12, 13-pentathiadispiro [4.1.4.2]tridecane (19) and *m*-dithian-5-one (20) (see Chapter 12, section II A-1) formed 2, 4, 7, 10, 12, 14, 15-heptathiadispiro [5.1.5.2]pentadecane (21). The properties of these derivatives have not been reported.

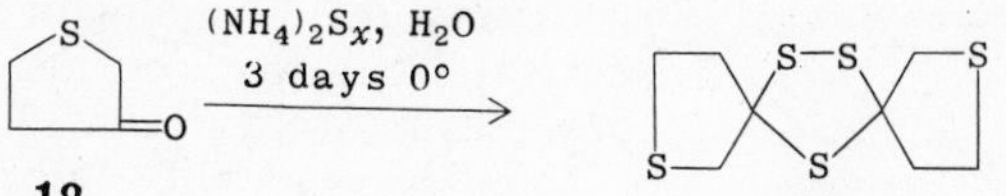

18   **19**

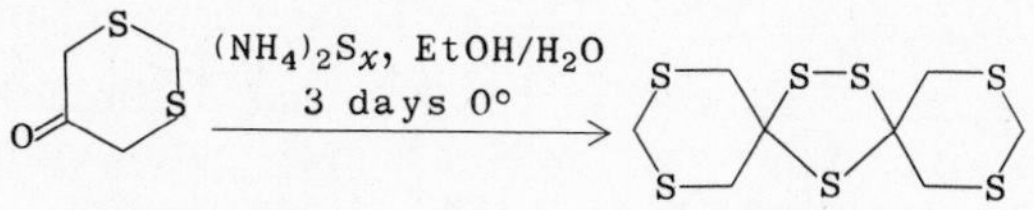

20   **21**

Campaigne and Moss[1] found that monomeric 3-phenylindanethione (22) reacts with air to give a trisulfide, m.p. 88-91°, which they formulated as 3, 3″-diphenyldispiro[indane-1, 3′-[1, 2, 4]trithiolane-5′, 1″-indane] (23).

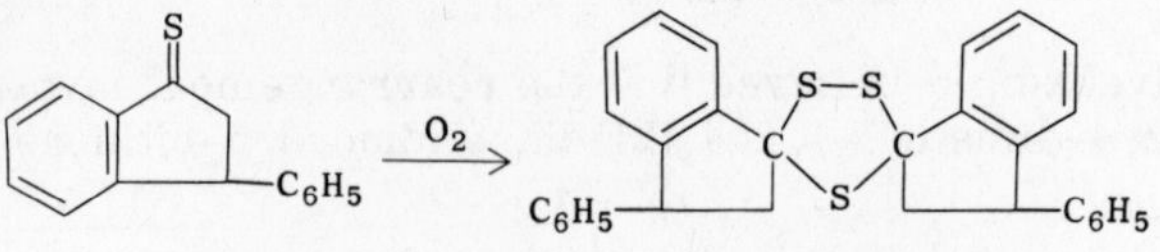

Campaigne and Reid[5] showed that fluorenethione (24) reacts similarly to give dispiro[fluorene-9, 3'-[1, 2, 4]trithiolane-5', 9"-fluorene] (25, RRI 7107). The structure was proved by the same reactions used in proving the structure of dibenzophenone trisulfide.

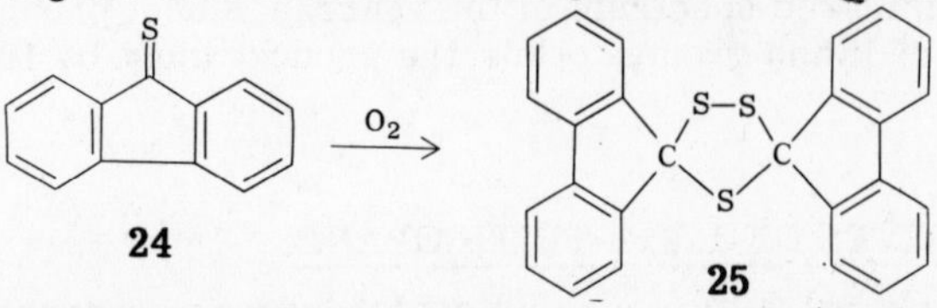

Bourdon[3] prepared 4-cholestene-3-thione (27) by treating 4-cholestenone (26) with hydrogen chloride and hydrogen sulfide. As a by-product he isolated in 5-10% yield a trisulfide, instantaneous melting point 198°, $[\alpha]_D^{20}$ —209°, which he formulated as dispiro[cholest-4-ene-3, 3'-[1, 2, 4]trithiolane-5', 3"-cholest-4"-ene] (28). Evidence for the assigned structure were: heating 28 at 130° converts it into 27, treatment with Raney nickel yields 4-cholestene (29), and lithium aluminum hydride reduction gives 3β-mercapto-4-cholestene (30).

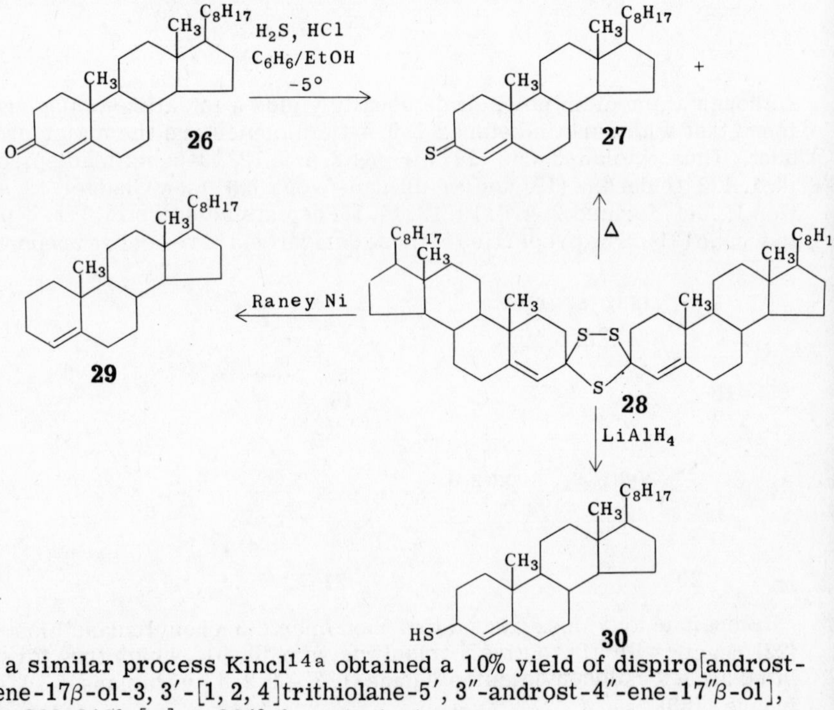

By a similar process Kincl[14a] obtained a 10% yield of dispiro[androst-4-ene-17β-ol-3, 3'-[1, 2, 4]trithiolane-5', 3"-androst-4"-ene-17"β-ol], m.p. 209-210°, $[\alpha]_D$ —204°, from testosterone.

REFERENCES

1.   Asinger, F., M. Thiel, G. Lipfert, R. E. Plessmann, and J. Mennig, Angew. Chem., **70**, 372 (1958).

2.   Asinger, F., and M. Thiel, Angew. Chem., **70**, 667 (1958).

2a. Asinger, F., M. Thiel, and G. Lipfert, Ann., **627**, 195 (1959).

2b. Bähr, G., Angew. Chem., **70**, 606 (1958).

3.   Bourdon, R., Bull. soc. chim. France, **1958**, 722.

4.   Bradsher, C. K., F. C. Brown, E. E. Sinclair, and S. T. Webster, J. Am. Chem. Soc., **80**, 414 (1958).

5.   Campaigne, E., and W. B. Reid, Jr., J. Am. Chem. Soc., **68**, 769 (1946).

6.   Campaigne, E., and W. B. Reid, Jr., J. Org. Chem., **12**, 807 (1947).

7.   Campaigne, E., and R. D. Moss, J. Am. Chem. Soc., **76**, 1269 (1954).

8.   Davis, F. O. (to Thiokol Chemical Corp.), U.S. Patent 2,657,198 (1953).

9.   Davis, F. O. (to Thiokol Chemical Corp.), U.S. Patent 2,715,635 (1955).

10. Freund, M., and E. Asbrand, Ann., **285**, 179 (1895).

11. Gattermann, L., and H. Schulze, Ber., **29**, 2944 (1896).

12. Guha, P. C., and M. N. Chakladar, Quart. J. Indian Chem. Soc., **2**, 318 (1925); Chem. Abstracts, **20**, 1797 (1926).

13. Hantzsch, A., and M. Wolvekamp, Ann., **331**, 280 (1904).

14. Kambara, S., K. Okita, and H. Higuchi, J. Soc. Rubber Ind. Japan, **24**, 281 (1951); Chem. Abstracts, **48**, 4246 (1954).

14a. Kincl, F. A., Chem. Ber., **93**, 1043 (1960).

14b. Magnusson, B., Acta Chem. Scand., **13**, 1031 (1959).

15. Mann, F. G., and W. J. Pope, J. Chem. Soc., **123**, 1172 (1923).

15a. Sasse, K., R. Wegler, G. Unterstenhöfer, and F. Grewe, Angew. Chem., **72**, 973 (1960).

16. Schönberg, A., O. Schütz, and S. Nickel, Ber., **61B**, 1375 (1928).

17. Schönberg, A., O. Schütz, and S. Nickel, Ber., **61B**, 2175 (1928).

17a. Simmons, Jr., H. E., E. I. du Pont de Nemours and Co., private communication. See J. Am. Chem. Soc., **84**, 4746, 4756, 4772, 4782 (1962).

18. Staudinger, H., and H. Freudenberger, Ber., **61B**, 1576 (1928).

19. Staudinger, H., and H. Freudenberger, Ber., **61B**, 1836 (1928).

19a. Wolf, W., E. Degener, and S. Petersen, Angew. Chem., **72**, 963 (1960).

C₃OS RING SYSTEMS

I. 1, 2-OXATHIA COMPOUNDS

A. C_3OS 5H-1, 2-OXATHIOLE (1), 3H-1, 2-OXATHIOLE (2), AND
    1, 2-OXATHIOLANE (3)

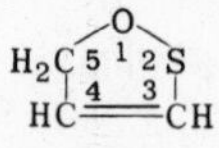

1	2	3
(RRI 132)		(RRI 133)

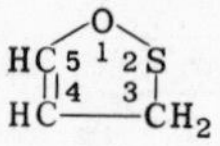

There is some question in the literature as to whether any 3H-1, 2-oxathiole (2) has been prepared. Chemical Abstracts has indexed the reported preparations of this ring under 1, 2, 5-thioxole, the nomenclature also mostly used in the literature. Only the 2, 2-dioxide of 5H-1, 2-oxathiole (1) has been reported, and this in only trace amounts.[307]

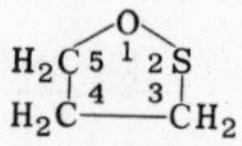

1, 2-Oxathiolane (3) is unknown. It is well represented, however, by two types of derivatives: the cyclic esters of γ-hydroxysulfonic acids (4) and the cyclic anhydrides of β-sulfocarboxylic acids (5).

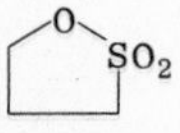

4	5

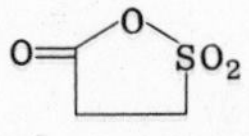

The cyclic esters are commonly called sultones of the 3-hydroxyalkanesulfonic acids and Chemical Abstracts has used this nomenclature for indexing. The cyclic anhydrides are commonly called β-sulfocarboxylic acid anhydrides, which is also the nomenclature Chemical Abstracts has used for indexing. A cross is made in Chemical Abstracts from the 1, 2-oxathiolane nomenclature.

1. 3H-1, 2-Oxathiole (2)

Staudinger and Siegwart[447] in 1920 reported the preparation of a product from the reaction of phenylbenzoyldiazomethane with thiophosgene to which they assigned the structure 3, 3-dichloro-4, 5-diphenyl-1, 2, 3H-oxathiole (6). Reasoning from analogy with the action of diazoalkanes with o-quinones, Schönberg, Mustafa, Awad, and Moussa[424] suggested that the reaction should lead to 2, 2-dichloro-4, 5-diphenyl-2H-1, 3-oxathiole (7) and not to the 3H-1, 2-oxathiole (6).

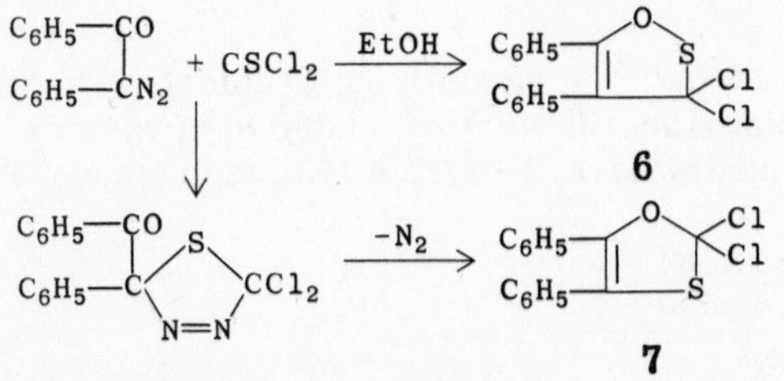

$$\begin{array}{c} C_6H_5\text{—CO} \\ C_6H_5\text{—CN}_2 \end{array} + CSCl_2 \xrightarrow{EtOH}$$

6

$$\begin{array}{c} C_6H_5\text{—CO} \\ C_6H_5\text{—C} \\ \quad \diagdown N{=}N \end{array} CCl_2 \xrightarrow{-N_2}$$

7

The product (**6** or **7**)·melted at 55-57°. It was sensitive to water and was easily hydrolyzed to the keto derivative (**8** or **9**), melting at 76-78°, which Staudinger and Siegwart prepared directly by conducting the re-action of phenylbenzoyldiazomethane with thiophosgene in aqueous methanol. The keto derivative (**8** or **9**) was a stable compound. Treat-ment with nitric acid decomposed it to dibenzyl. On heating with alco-holic potassium hydroxide, the keto derivative was hydrolyzed to des-oxybenzoin. Staudinger and Siegwart rejected the 2H-1, 3-oxathiole structure because they obtained only desoxybenzoin and no thiobenzoin in the alkaline hydrolysis. Schönberg and co-workers, however, point out that thiobenzoin is easily hydrolyzed by alkali to desoxybenzoin. Schönberg and co-workers suggested that the 2H-1, 3-oxathiole struc-ture more reasonably accounts for the ready hydrolysis of the geminal dichloro to the keto derivative.

Staudinger and Siegwart also reported the preparation of the anil de-rivative (**10** or **11**), melting at 129-130°, from the reaction of the dichloro compound with aniline.

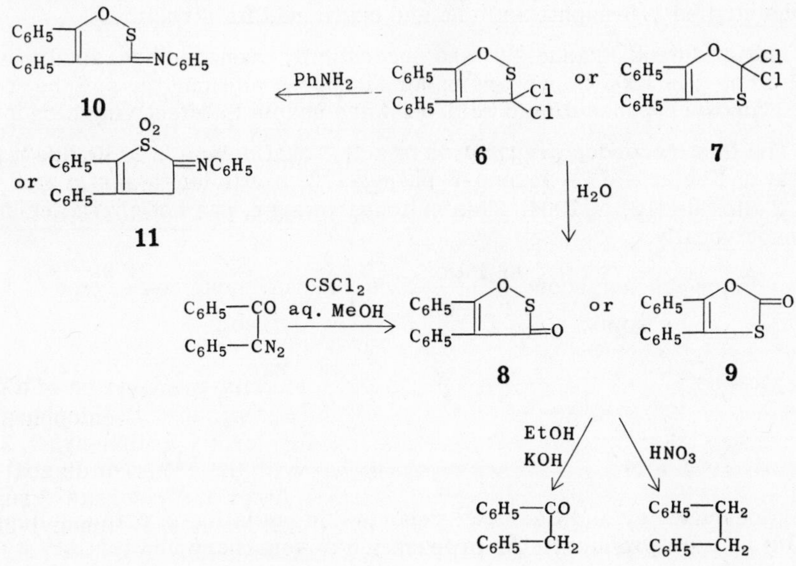

10

11

$\xleftarrow{PhNH_2}$

6

or

7

$\Big\downarrow H_2O$

$$\begin{array}{c} C_6H_5\text{—CO} \\ C_6H_5\text{—CN}_2 \end{array} \xrightarrow[aq.\ MeOH]{CSCl_2}$$

8

or

9

EtOH / KOH

HNO$_3$

$$\begin{array}{c} C_6H_5\text{—CO} \\ C_6H_5\text{—CH}_2 \end{array}$$

$$\begin{array}{c} C_6H_5\text{—CH}_2 \\ C_6H_5\text{—CH}_2 \end{array}$$

2. 5H-1, 2-Oxathiole (1)

Manecke, Danhäuser, and Reich,[307] on saponifying 3-chloro-2-hydroxypropanesulfonic acid and distilling the mixture under high vacuum obtained a trace of 5H-1, 2-oxathiole-2, 2-dioxide (12), melting at 78°.

1) aq. NaOH
2) vacuum distn.

$ClCH_2CH(OH)CH_2SO_3H$ $\xrightarrow{\text{1) aq. NaOH, 2) vacuum distn.}}$

12

The structure of this heterocycle (12) has yet to be proved, although there is no apparent reason for doubting its existence.

3. 1, 2-Oxathiolane (3)

It is convenient to differentiate the 1, 2-oxathiolanes into two classes, cyclic esters (4) and cyclic anhydrides (5), as the preparative methods and the chemical properties of these two types are quite different. This chapter, therefore, treats these two types of 1, 2-oxathiolanes separately.

a. 1, 2-Oxathiolane 2, 2-Dioxide (4)

1, 2-Oxathiolane 2, 2-dioxides are commonly called alkanesultones or cyclic esters. As cyclic esters or sultones of γ-hydoxyalkanesulfonic acids they are analogous to the cyclic esters or lactones of γ-hydroxyalkanecarboxylic acids. Whereas the lactones have been known for many years, the analogous sultones have been known for only a relatively short time. 1, 8-Naphthosultone was first characterized in 1887 by Schultz,[427] and the term sultone was introduced in 1888 by Erdmann,[117] who studied 1, 8-naphthosultone and confirmed its structure.

Markwald and Frahne,[308] who successfully prepared benzylsultone, attempted in 1898 to prepare under similar conditions the sultone from γ-hydroxypropanesulfonic acid, but were unable to effect ring closure.

The first recorded preparation of a 1, 2-oxathiolane 2, 2-dioxide was that of Kohler's[269] 4-bromo-5-phenyl-1, 2-oxathiolan-3-acetic acid 2, 2-dioxide (13) in 1904. This sultone, however, was not characterized unequivocally.

$C_6H_5CH=CHCHCH_2COOH$ $\xrightarrow{Br_2, H_2O}$ $C_6H_5CHBrCHBrCHCH_2COOH$ $\xrightarrow{-HBr}$

13

Baldeschweiler and Cassar[31] reported the isolation of octanesultone (14) as a by-product in the preparation of secondary and tertiary alcohols from the hydration of olefin fractions with sulfuric acid. The product was assumed to have occurred through the formation of an intermediate sulfate. The reported melting point for this sultone is decidedly out of line, in comparison to the melting points of other 5-alkyl-1,2-oxathiolane 2,2-dioxides listed in Table 1, and it is questionable whether the product was a 1,2-oxathiolane. Shriner, Rendleman, and Berger[436] attempted to synthesize octanesultone (14), but were unable to cyclize octan-3-ol-1-sulfonic acid.

$$CH_3(CH_2)_4MgBr + ClCH_2CH_2CHO \longrightarrow CH_3(CH_2)_4\underset{\underset{OMgBr}{|}}{C}HCH_2CH_2Cl \xrightarrow[\substack{1) H_2O \\ 2) KI \\ 3) K_2SO_3}]{}$$

$$CH_3(CH_2)_4\underset{\underset{OH}{|}}{C}HCH_2CH_2SO_3H \xrightarrow[\,]{-H_2O} \quad CH_3(CH_2)_4 \overset{O}{\boxed{}}SO_2$$

14

(1) Preparation

Except for the two 1,2-oxathiolane 2,2-dioxides, **13** and **14**, mentioned above, the compounds listed in Table 1 have been reported since 1942.[186] There are two basic methods for the preparation of 1,2-oxathiolane 2,2-dioxides: the elimination of water from γ-hydroxyalkanesulfonic acids or the elimination of hydrogen halide from γ-haloalkanesulfonic acids.[336,510]

$$R\underset{\underset{OH}{|}}{C}HCH_2CH_2SO_3H \xrightarrow{-H_2O}$$

$$R\underset{\underset{Cl}{|}}{C}HCH_2CH_2SO_3H \xrightarrow{-HCl} \quad R\overset{O}{\boxed{}}SO_2$$

Preparative methods for 1,2-oxathiolane 2,2-dioxides were thus contingent upon preparative methods for γ-hydroxyalkanesulfonic acids and γ-haloalkanesulfonic acids and methods for their ring closure. A third method for the preparation of 1,2-oxathiolane 2,2-dioxides involves the sulfonation of olefins with dioxane-sulfur trioxide complex.

(a) From 3-chloroalkanesulfonic acids. Chlorosulfonation of alkyl chlorides as adopted and developed by Helberger[186,187,190,196] is based on Reed's initial discovery in 1936[375a] and Kharasch and Reads's[258a] extension in 1939. In this reaction, the alkyl chloride is chlorosulfonated with sulfur dioxide and chlorine under irradiation to chloroalkanesulfonyl chloride, which, in turn, is converted to chloroalkanesulfonic acid. Dehydrohalogenation of the chloralkanesulfonic acid gives the sultone. Thus, the reaction of propyl chloride with sulfur dioxide and chlorine gives 3-chloropropanesulfonyl chloride from which 1,2-oxathiolane 2,2-dioxide (15) is prepared.

[For references, see pp. 289-312.]

$$CH_3CH_2CH_2Cl \xrightarrow[\text{light}]{SO_2, \; Cl_2} ClCH_2CH_2CH_2SO_2Cl \xrightarrow{H_2O}$$

$$ClCH_2CH_2CH_2SO_3H \xrightarrow[-HCl]{200-210°} \quad \overset{O}{\underset{}{\diagup}}SO_2$$

15

The methyl group in propyl chloride is chlorosulfonated with difficulty, and the main product is 1-chloropropane-2-sulfonyl chloride; only a small amount of 3-chloropropanesulfonyl chloride is obtained. The chlorosulfonation of butyl chloride proceeds much more easily without chlorosulfonation on the 2-carbon. In this case, however, a mixture is produced as the result of chlorosulfonation on the 3- and 4-carbons and some chlorination on the 2-carbon.[13b,186,187,190]

$$CH_3(CH_2)_3Cl \xrightarrow[\text{light}]{SO_2, \; Cl_2} \underset{\underset{SO_2Cl}{|}}{CH_3}CH(CH_2)_2Cl + Cl(CH_2)_4SO_2Cl +$$

$$CH_3(CH_2)_2CHClCH_2Cl \xrightarrow[\text{2) }H_2O]{\text{1) distn.}}$$

$$\underset{\underset{SO_3H}{|}}{CH_3}CH(CH_2)_2Cl + Cl(CH_2)_4SO_3H \xrightarrow[65\%]{150-210°} \quad \overset{O}{\underset{-CH_3}{\diagup}}SO_2 \; + \; \overset{O}{\underset{}{\diagup}}SO_2 \underset{\Delta}{\overset{MeOH}{\rightleftharpoons}}$$

16   **17**

$$\underset{\underset{SO_3H}{|}}{CH_3}CH(CH_2)_2OCH_3 + CH_3O(CH_2)_4SO_3H$$

The chlorobutanesulfonyl chloride mixture is separated from 1, 2-dichlorobutane by distillation. The sultone mixture, 3-methyl-1, 2-oxathiolane 2, 2-dioxide (16) and 1, 2-oxathiane 2, 2-dioxide (17), is separated into its components by virtue of the difference in their methanolysis reaction rates, 16 reacting with methanol ten times faster than 17. Distillation of the methoxybutanesulfonic acid gives the sultone. From a 25 g mixture of the sultones, Helberger, Heyden, and Winter[196] obtained 13. 6 g 16 and 4. 5 g 17 by this method.

The chlorosulfonation of isobutyl chloride led to 3-chloro-2-methylpropane-1-sulfonic acid which was dehydrohalogenated to 4-methyl-1, 2-oxathiolane 2, 2-dioxide (18).[19]

$$(CH_3)_2CHCH_2Cl \xrightarrow[92\%]{SO_2, \; Cl_2 \atop \text{light}} \underset{\underset{CH_3}{|}}{ClCH_2}CHCH_2SO_2Cl \xrightarrow[63\%]{\text{1) }H^+, H_2O \atop \text{2) }\Delta} \quad CH_3-\overset{O}{\underset{}{\diagup}}SO_2$$

18

The chlorosulfonation of isoamyl chloride[186, 187,190] proceeded to give 3, 3-dimethyl-1, 2-oxathiolane 2, 2-dioxide (19). Chlorosulfonation of 2-chloro-4-methylpentane[187] (from mesityl oxide) gave a mixture of 58% 3,3,5-trimethyl-1,2-oxathiolane 2,2-dioxide (20) and 4,6-dimethyl-1,2-oxathiane 2,2-dioxide (21).

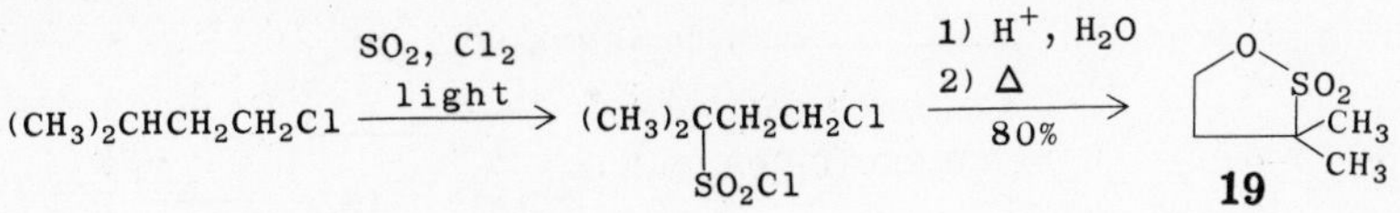

$$(CH_3)_2CHCH_2CH_2Cl \xrightarrow[\text{light}]{SO_2,\ Cl_2} (CH_3)_2CCH_2CH_2Cl \xrightarrow[\text{80\%}]{\substack{1)\ H^+,\ H_2O \\ 2)\ \Delta}}$$

with SO_2Cl substituent on the central carbon. Structure **19**.

$$(CH_3)_2CHCH_2CHClCH_3 \xrightarrow{\substack{1)\ SO_2,\ Cl_2,\ light \\ 2)\ H^+,\ H_2O \\ 3)\ \Delta}} \mathbf{20} + \mathbf{21}$$

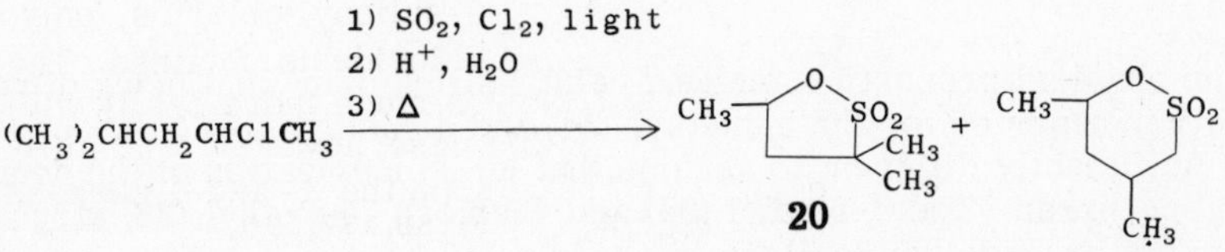

Scott[429a] was unable to obtain a 1,2-oxathiolane from chlorosulfonated neopentyl chloride. In the chlorosulfonation of neopentane, Scott and McLeod[430] obtained 2,2-dimethylpropanesulfonyl chloride and 17% of 3-chloro-2,2-dimethylpropanesulfonyl chloride which was cyclized to 4,4-dimethyl-1,2-oxathiolane 2,2-dioxide (22).

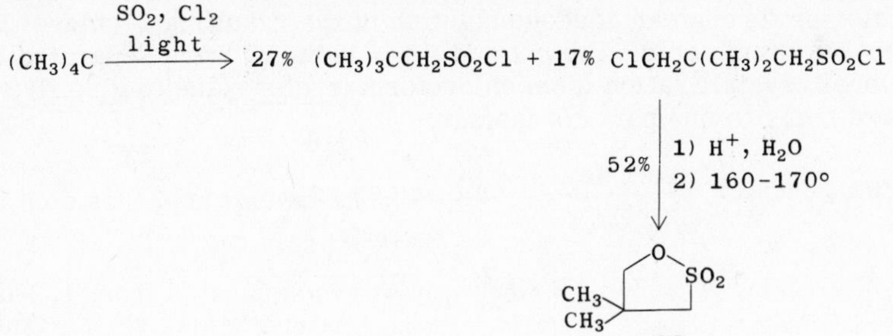

$$(CH_3)_4C \xrightarrow[\text{light}]{SO_2,\ Cl_2} 27\%\ (CH_3)_3CCH_2SO_2Cl\ +\ 17\%\ ClCH_2C(CH_3)_2CH_2SO_2Cl$$

$$\xrightarrow[52\%]{\substack{1)\ H^+,\ H_2O \\ 2)\ 160-170°}} \mathbf{22}$$

Helberger and Benecke[192] prepared 4-bromo- and 4-chloro-5-methyl-1,2-oxathiolane 2,2-dioxide (23) by treating crotyl chloride with aqueous sodium sulfite, brominating or chlorinating the 2-butene-1-sulfonic acid, and eliminating hydrogen halide.

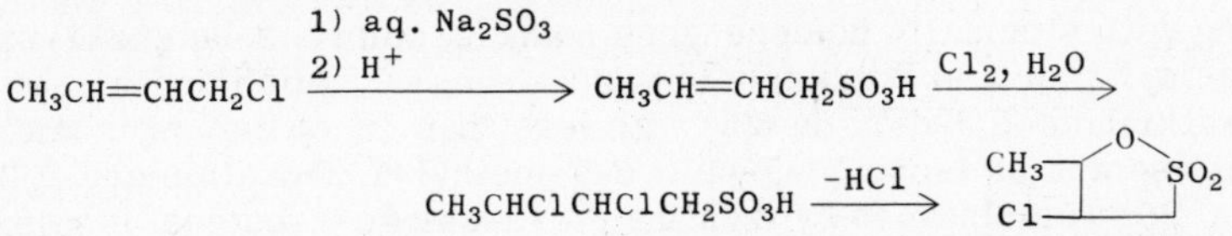

$$CH_3CH{=}CHCH_2Cl \xrightarrow{\substack{1)\ aq.\ Na_2SO_3 \\ 2)\ H^+}} CH_3CH{=}CHCH_2SO_3H \xrightarrow{Cl_2,\ H_2O}$$

$$CH_3CHClCHClCH_2SO_3H \xrightarrow{-HCl} \mathbf{23}$$

Broderick[65] found that potassium bromide catalyzes the reaction between crotyl chloride and sodium sulfite. On treating the resulting 2-butene-1-sulfonic acid with hydrogen chloride gas and distilling the reaction product, Broderick obtained 5-methyl-1, 2-oxathiolane 2, 2-dioxide (**24**).

$$CH_3CH{=}CHCH_2Cl \xrightarrow[\text{KBr}]{\text{aq. Na}_2SO_3} CH_3CH{=}CHCH_2SO_3Na \xrightarrow{\text{HCl gas}}$$

$$CH_3CHClCH_2CH_2SO_3H \xrightarrow[46\%]{\Delta}$$

24

The physical properties, melting point, boiling point, and index of re-fraction, reported for the 5-methyl (**24**) and 3-methyl (**16**) compounds are sufficiently different to assume that no isomerization of the double bond occurred. The 5-methyl (**24**) and 4-chloro-5-methyl (**23**) structures were not proved chemically.

Exner and Wichterle[123] found that β,γ-unsaturated sulfonic acids were halogenated by a specific *trans* addition. The configuration of the resulting sultones were assigned on the basis of dipole moment meas-urements. Thus *cis*- and *trans*-4, 5-dichloro-5-methyl-1, 2-oxathio-lane 2, 2-dioxide (**25**) were prepared by treating 1, 3-dichloro-2-butene with aqueous sodium hydroxide saturated with sulfur dioxide, and pass-ing chlorine through an aqueous solution of the resulting 3-chloro-2-butene-1-sulfonic acid. The *cis* and *trans* isomers were separated by fractional crystallization from chloroform-cyclohexane to give five parts of *trans* to one part *cis* isomer.

25   **26**   **27**

Starting with sterically homogeneous *trans*-3-chloro-2-butene-1-sul-fonic acid, Exner and Wichterle obtained *trans*-4, 5-dichloro-5-methyl-1, 2-oxathiolane 2, 2-dioxide (**25**) with less than 1% of the *cis* isomer. The *cis* isomer of 4-bromo-5-chloro-5-methyl-1, 2-oxathiolane 2, 2-dioxide (**26**) was obtained by treating *cis*-3-chloro-2-butene-1-sulfonic acid with bromine water. 5-Chloro-4-iodo-5-methyl-1, 2-oxathiolane 2, 2-dioxide (**27**) was obtained by treating aqueous *cis*-3-chloro-2-butene-1-sulfonic acid with iodine chloride.

On reacting epichlorohydrin with sodium bisulfite and vacuum dis-tilling the 3-chloro-2-hydroxypropane-1-sulfonic acid, Manecke, Danhäuser, and Reich[307] obtained a 1% yield of 4-chloro-1, 2-oxathiolane 2, 2-dioxide (28), and none of the expected 4-hydroxy-1, 2-oxathiolane 2, 2-dioxide.

$$ClCH_2\underset{O}{CHCH_2} \xrightarrow{NaHSO_3} ClCH_2\underset{OH}{CHCH_2}SO_3Na \xrightarrow[1\%]{\substack{1)\ H^+ \\ 2)\ \Delta}} \quad \mathbf{28}$$

That 4-chloro-1, 2-oxathiolane 2, 2-dioxide (28) was the product was shown by its preparation through the chlorination of 2-propene-1-sulfonic acid and vacuum distillation of the resulting 2, 3-dichloropropane-sulfonic acid. Hydrolysis of 4-chloro-1, 2-oxathiolane with water yielded 2-chloro-3-hydroxypropane-1-sulfonic acid and with alkali 2, 3-dihydroxypropane-1-sulfonic acid.

$$CH_2{=}CHCH_2SO_3H \xrightarrow[60\%]{Cl_2} ClCH_2CHClCH_2SO_3H \xrightarrow[30\%]{\Delta} \quad \mathbf{28}$$

$$\text{aq. NaOH} \swarrow \qquad \searrow H_2O$$

$$HOCH_2CHOHCH_2SO_3H \qquad HOCH_2CHClCH_2SO_3H$$

Asinger, Geissler, and Hoppe[19] obtained 4-methyl-1, 2-oxathiolane 2, 2-dioxide (29) from 3-chloro-2-methylpropanesulfonic acid, which they prepared from methallyl chloride through a series of reactions.

$$CH_2{=}\underset{CH_3}{C}CH_2Cl \xrightarrow[\quad]{\substack{HBr,\ H_2O \\ PhCO_3H}} ClCH_2\underset{CH_3}{C}HCH_2Br \xrightarrow{KSCN}$$

$$ClCH_2\underset{CH_3}{C}HCH_2SCN \xrightarrow[\quad]{\substack{1)\ Cl_2,\ H_2O \\ 2)\ H^+,\ H_2O}} ClCH_2\underset{CH_3}{C}HCH_2SO_3H \xrightarrow[69\%]{\Delta} \quad \mathbf{29}$$

They obtained 3, 3-dimethyl-1, 2-oxathiolane 2, 2-dioxide (30) from 1-chlorobutane-2-sulfonic acid, which was prepared from ethyl β-chloro-propionate.[19]

$$ClCH_2CH_2COOC_2H_5 \xrightarrow{MeMgCl} ClCH_2CH_2\underset{OH}{C}(CH_3)_2 \xrightarrow{HBr,\ H_2O}$$

$$ClCH_2CH_2\underset{Br}{C}(CH_3)_2 \xrightarrow[\quad]{\substack{1)\ CS(NH_2)_2 \\ 2)\ aq.\ NaOH}} ClCH_2CH_2\underset{SH}{C}(CH_3)_2 \xrightarrow{[O]}$$

$$ClCH_2CH_2\underset{SO_3H}{C}(CH_3)_2 \xrightarrow[71\%]{\Delta} \quad \mathbf{30}$$

Cyclization of 3-chloroalkane-1-sulfonic acids proceeds relatively easily, in general, by heating or distilling at reduced pressure. A German patent by Helberger[189a] claims an improved process for the dehydrochlorination of chlorosulfonic acids by heating at 150-160° in the presence of copper oxide.

(b) From 3-Hydroxyalkanesulfonic Acids. Markwald and Frahne's[308] unsuccessful attempt in 1898 to prepare propanesultone was noteworthy in that they did obtain 1-hydroxypropane-3-sulfonic acid by the addition of potassium bisulfite to allyl alcohol. The validity of their proposed preparative method was confirmed in 1942 by Helberger[186] who found that the sultone (15) is readily obtained by distilling the hydroxy acid under vacuum.

$$CH_2{=}CHCH_2OH \xrightarrow{\ KHSO_3\ } \underset{\underset{SO_3K}{|}}{CH_2CH_2CH_2OH} \xrightarrow[\text{2) }\Delta]{\text{1) }H^+} \boxed{}SO_2$$

15

In a series of experiments, Kharasch, May, and Mayo[256] established that the addition of bisulfite to ethylenic compounds is best interpreted on the basis of a free radical mechanism. In agreement with this, they found that oxidizing agents, such as oxygen, which are capable of producing free radicals from bisulfite, are essential for the addition reaction. In the absence of an oxidizing agent, no addition occurred; and in the presence of an antioxidant, such as hydroquinone, no addition occurred. These facts may explain the poor yields of addition product obtained by earlier workers.

Smith, Norton, and Ballard[442] obtained a 52% yield of 4-methyl-1, 2-oxathiolane 2, 2-dioxide (29) (based on methallyl alcohol) from the acidified addition product of the reaction of methallyl alcohol and sodium bisulfite, in a molar ratio of 2 : 1, in the presence of 2, 2-bis (tert-butylperoxy)-butane at 130° for one hour. By the same procedure only a 5% yield of 1, 2-oxathiolane 2, 2-dioxide (15) was obtained from the addition product of allyl alcohol and sodium bisulfite.

Whereas Kharasch and co-workers reported a yield of 65% of addition product on reacting allyl alcohol with bisulfite, H. M. Fischer, as recorded by Helberger,[197] was unable to obtain yields higher than 30-40%. Fischer's main product was an amorphous salt which could not be converted to the sultone. In an attempt to improve the yield of addition product, Helberger[197,203] found that an increase in the amount of oxygen decreased the reaction time considerably, and involved the autoxidation of bisulfite to sulfate with a change in pH towards the alkaline side. By reacting allyl alcohol with a solution of potassium bisulfite and potassium sulfite (in a molar ratio of 2 : 1) in the presence of oxygen at 55-60°, yields of 90% and better of the addition product were obtained.[50,197] Apparently the addition and oxidation reactions occur in the following stoichiometric ratio:

$$KHSO_3 + \tfrac{1}{2}K_2SO_3 + CH_2{=}CHCH_2OH + \tfrac{1}{4}O_2 \longrightarrow$$
$$HOCH_2CH_2CH_2SO_3K + \tfrac{1}{2}K_2SO_4$$

Cationic exchange resins have been used to convert the hydroxyalkane-sulfonic acid salt to the acid.[53] The hydroxypropanesulfonic acid was cyclized to the sultone in yields of 89-92% by heating at 140-200° *in vacuo*.

Willems[512] obtained 47-53% yields of the allyl alcohol addition product under the Kharasch conditions. When *tert*-butyl perbenzoate was used as the catalyst, a yield of 75% was obtained. Willems extended this reaction to a series of α, β-unsaturated alcohols, and obtained yields of 40-83% of 3-hydroxyalkanesulfonic acids from which sultones could be obtained. A British patent describes the preparation of 1-hydroxybutane-3-sulfonic acid from crotyl alcohol[52] by the Helberger method.[197]

Smith, Norton, and Ballard[442] obtained a 73% yield of 4-methyl-1, 2-oxathiolane 2, 2-dioxide (29) on reacting an aqueous solution of sodium bisulfite with a 2% excess of methacrolein, hydrogenating the resulting sulfonated aldehyde to the corresponding alcohol, and cyclizing the sulfoalcohol by distillation.

A 16% yield of 1, 2-oxathiolane 2, 2-dioxide was obtained from acrolein by the same procedure.

In a study of the addition of bisulfite to α, β-unsaturated carbonyl compounds, Willems[511,512] found that the optimum pH lay in the range of from 4 to 7, and that the reactivity of the α, β-unsaturated carbonyl decreases with an increase in molecular weight. For a series of α, β-unsaturated aldehydes and ketones, Willems obtained yields of 52-100% of addition product. The addition products were converted to the corresponding 3-hydroxyalkanesulfonates by hydrogenation in the presence of Raney nickel at 100-150 atm. and 60-100°, or by reduction with sodium amalgam in a neutral aqueous solution.

[For references, see pp. 289-312.]

$$(CH_3)_2C=CHCOCH_3 \xrightarrow{NaHSO_3} (CH_3)_2\underset{SO_3Na}{C}CH_2COCH_3 \xrightarrow[2)\ H_2,\ Ni]{1)\ H^+}$$

$$(CH_3)_2\underset{SO_3H}{C}CH_2CHOHCH_3 \xrightarrow[70\%]{\Delta} CH_3\underset{}{\overset{O}{\diagup}}SO_2\overset{CH_3}{\underset{CH_3}{\diagdown}}$$

20

The reaction of ethyl acetoacetate with the bisulfite addition product of formaldehyde, acetaldehyde, or propionaldehyde in the presence of sodium hydroxide, was used by Willems[512] for the preparation of several β-sulfo ketones, which he converted to the hydroxyalkanesulfonic acids by hydrogenation and in turn to the 1, 2-oxathiolane 2, 2-dioxides (**31**), where R = —H, —CH$_3$, and —(CH$_2$)$_2$CH$_3$, in yields of 87, 72, and 75%, respectively.

$$CH_3COCH_2COOC_2H_5 + R\underset{OH}{C}HSO_3K \xrightarrow{NaOH} CH_3CO\underset{RCHSO_3K}{C}HCOOC_2H_5 \xrightarrow{H_2SO_4}$$

$$CH_3COCH_2\underset{R}{C}HSO_3K \xrightarrow[2)\ H_2,\ Ni]{1)\ H^+} CH_3CHOHCH_2\underset{R}{C}HSO_3H \xrightarrow{\Delta} CH_3\underset{}{\overset{O}{\diagup}}SO_2\diagdown R$$

31

Another method used by Willems[512] for the preparation of several β-sulfo-ketones was the addition of bisulfite to alkylidene acylacetic acid esters by the procedure he used for the addition to α, β-unsaturated carbonyl compounds.

$$CH_3COCH_2COOC_2H_5 + RCHO \longrightarrow CH_3CO\underset{CHR}{\overset{\|}{C}}COOC_2H_5 \xrightarrow[90-100\%]{NaHSO_3}$$

$$CH_3CO\underset{RCHSO_3Na}{C}HCOOC_2H_5 \xrightarrow[52-86\%]{} CH_3COCH_2\underset{R}{C}HSO_3Na$$

R = H—, CH$_3$—, CH$_3$(CH$_2$)$_2$—, CH$_3$(CH$_2$)$_5$ —

In general, the hydroxyalkanesulfonic acids have been converted to the corresponding sultones by distillation of their solutions, e.g., in alcohol, at atmospheric or reduced pressures. Yields have not always been good, particularly for the higher molecular weight hydroxyalkanesulfonic acids, because of thermal decomposition. This fact prompted Willems[513] to seek less drastic methods for the cyclization reaction. Dehydrating agents, such as zinc chloride, phosphorous pentachloride, or phosphorous oxychloride, were found to be without effect. The use of diluting agents, azeotropic with water, with boiling points near the dehydration temperature, 150°C, and which are miscible with the sultones, was found to be particularly effective. The use of butyl cellosolve in this manner not only improved the cyclization yields, but resulted in cyclizations otherwise not obtainable. Xylene, which forms a ternary azeotrope with water and the ethyl alcohol usually used as a solvent for the hydroxyalkanesulfonic acid, was a convenient and effective agent for the cyclization reaction. Cyclization yields in the xylene method ranged from 25-91% and were consistently higher than for the butyl cellosolve method, which, in turn, gave higher yields than by distillation without the addition of a higher boiling solvent.

(c) From Olefins. A general method for the preparation of alkyl or aryl substituted 5, 5-dialkyl-1, 2-oxathiolane dioxides has been thoroughly studied by Bordwell and co-workers.[55, 57-59] In studying the reaction of dioxane-sulfur trioxide with various olefins, it was found that γ- branched olefins, such as 3-methyl-1-butene, underwent sulfonation in ethylene chloride to give good yields of 1, 2-oxathiolanes. It was postulated that the mechanism involves a dioxane-solvated carbonium ion (32) with a hydride (R = H) or methide (R = alkyl) shift, which in the case of 3-methyl-1-butene yields 5, 5-dimethyl-1, 2-oxathiolane 2, 2-dioxide (34, R = H).

The 1, 2-oxathiolane 2, 2-dioxides which have been reported are listed in Table 1.

(2) Properties, Reactions, and Uses

The 1, 2-oxathiolane 2, 2-dioxides listed in Table 1 are crystalline substances of relatively low melting points and rather high boiling points. For the most part, they are stable and can be distilled under reduced pressure without decomposition, although the distillation temperature should be under 200° to avoid pyrolysis. The 1, 2-oxathiolanes are colorless and odorless when pure. They are insoluble in cold water, but are hydrolyzed to the corresponding hydroxysulfonic acids by warm water or warm alkaline solutions.

In his doctoral thesis, Hoerger[220] pointed out that the six-membered ring sultones are more stable than are the five-membered ring sultones. Qualitatively, this is borne out by the greater ease of dehydra-

[For references, see pp. 289-312.]

TABLE 1. 1, 2-Oxathiolane 2, 2-Dioxides

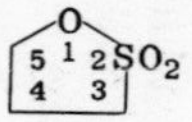

Substituent	Yield (%)	M.p. (°C)	B.p. (°C)	(mm)	n_D/°C	d_4/°C	Ref.
None	40-50	31	121	1			513
	60	–	140	8			190
	90	31	130	1			197
	–	31	155-157	14			187
	16	29-30	95-100	1	1.4585/20		442
	97	–	–				53
3-CH$_3$-	60	–14	150	12		1.310/18	196
			124	15	1.4525/25	1.3004/25	190
4-CH$_3$-	73	28.8-29.3	89-91	<0.5	1.4518/30	1.2931/30	442
	69	29	137-138	5	1.4520/20	1.2932/30	19
5-CH$_3$-	50-76		124	2	1.4500/25	1.2929/25	190
			157.5	14			153, 190
	46	–9	123-129	0.8	1.4512/25		65
			146-149	5			65
	87						512

Substituents	Yield (%)	M.p. (°C)	B.p. (°C)	mm	n_D	d	Ref.
5-[CH₃(CH₂)₃-]	60		141	2			513
5-[CH₃(CH₂)₄-]	42	129					31
5-[CH₃(CH₂)₇-]	59		160-163	0.5			513
5-[CH₃(CH₂)₁₅-]	46	81					513
5-[(CH₃)₂CH(CH₂)₂-]	30		130	1.5			513
4-Cl-	80	42					307
3,3-(CH₃-)₂	71		154-158	15	1.4600/23		187
3,5-(CH₃-)₂	47		158-161	15	1.4536/20	1.2170/20	19
	72		129	1	1.4511/25	1.2220/25	513
4,4-(CH₃-)₂	52	51.5-52.0					512
5,5-(CH₃-)₂	53	70-71					430
3-[CH₃(CH₂)₂]-5-CH₃-	73		150-160	18-20			59
	75		143	4.2	1.4520/25	1.3359/25	153, 513
3-[CH₃(CH₂)₅]-5-CH₃-	75		145	0.6			512
3-[CH₃(CH₂)₁₃]-5-CH₃-	63						513
3-C₆H₅-5-CH₃-	91	106					513
4-Br-3-CH₃-							192
4-Cl-3-CH₃-							192
4-Br-5-CH₃-		54					192
4-Cl-5-CH₃-		49					192

[For references, see pp. 289-312.]

TABLE 1. 1,2-Oxathiolane 2,2-Dioxides (contd.)

Substituent	Yield (%)	M.p. (°C)	B.p. (°C)	(mm)	n_D/°C	d_4/°C	Ref.
3,3,5-(CH$_3$-)$_3$	58	45					187
3,5,5-(CH$_3$-)$_3$	70	50	160	16			511, 513
4,5,5-(CH$_3$-)$_3$	82	Unstable					59
4,5,5-(CH$_3$-)$_3$	71	61.3					59
3-[CH$_3$(CH$_2$)$_2$]-4,5-(CH$_3$-)$_2$	52		128	1.5			513
3-[CH$_3$(CH$_2$)$_5$]-4,5-(CH$_3$-)$_2$	56		155	1.5			513
3-CH$_2$COOH-4-Br-5-C$_6$H$_5$-							269
4-Br-4-CH$_3$-5-C$_6$H$_5$-	100	113-114					55, 188
4,5-(Cl-)$_2$-5-CH$_3$-	58	112 (*trans*)					123
		118 (*cis*)					123
4-Br-5-Cl-5-CH$_3$-	70	142 (dec.)					123
4-I-5-Cl-5-CH$_3$-	36	111 (dec.)					123
3,4,5,5-(CH$_3$-)$_4$	51	76-77					59
4,4,5,5-(CH$_3$-)$_4$	76	145-146					59
		140-143					58
4,5,5-(CH$_3$-)$_3$-4-C$_6$H$_5$-	73	132-133					59
4,4,5-(CH$_3$-)$_3$-5-BrCH$_2$-	89	135-135.5					59

tion of 4-hydroxy-1-butanesulfonic acid relative to that of 3-hydroxy-1-propanesulfonic acid to their sultones. Helberger's methanolysis studies[196] were cited as quantitative evidence that the five-membered ring sultones undergo methanolysis much more rapidly than the corresponding six-membered ring sultones. Asinger, Geisler, and Hoppe[19] reported a methanolysis rate in 0.1 N NaOH at 100° of 1.25 × 10^{-4} sec^{-1} for 5-methyl-1,2-oxathiolane 2,2-dioxide and 0.292 × 10^{-4} sec^{-1} for 5-methyl-1,2-oxathiane 2,2-dioxide. Helberger's work further showed that the five-membered ring sultones react faster than the six-membered ring sultones with nucleophilic reagents, such as ammonia, pyridine, aniline, dimethylaniline, potassium cyanide, potassium iodide, sodium phenolate, and others. Hoerger thus concluded that the six-membered ring sultone exists in a staggered chair-type structure (36), and the five-membered ring sultone in an essentially planar structure. This must be a relative difference as it is well known that the cyclopentane ring is not planar. There is evidence that 1,2-oxathiolane 2,2-dioxide, which is a larger ring than cyclopentane, exists in a puckered form (35).[60]

35   **36**

The effect of substituents on the stability of the 1,2-oxathiolane 2,2-dioxide ring is well illustrated by the hydrolysis studies of Bordwell, Osborne, and Chapman.[60] Table 1a shows the relative enhancement or retardation of the hydrolysis as affected by the substitution of methyl groups in positions 3, 4, and 5 of the sultone.

TABLE 1a. Hydrolysis of 1,2-Oxathiolane 2,2-Dioxides

1,2-Oxathiolane 2,2-dioxide	Relative rate at 40°C
No substituent	1.0
4-CH$_3$-	0.21
4,4-(CH$_3$-)$_2$	0.0035
3-CH$_3$-	1.4
5-CH$_3$-	1.3
3,3,5-(CH$_3$-)$_3$	0.7
5,5-(CH$_3$-)$_2$	3100
4,5,5-(CH$_3$-)$_3$	18
3,4,5,5-(CH$_3$-)$_4$	3.7
4,5,5-(CH$_3$-)$_3$-4-C$_6$H$_5$-	6.3

Substitution of methyl groups on position 4 results in a striking re-tardation effect: the 4-methyl shows about twice the effect on the sul-tone as for an open chain sulfonate ester and the 4, 4-dimethyl about thirty times that of an open chain analog. The effect of 5-methyl sub-stitution in the sultone results in an enhancement of 1. 3 instead of the expected ten-fold increase exhibited by the open chain analog. Likewise the enhancement of 5, 5-dimethyl relative to the 5-methyl of 2×10^3 is much less than the 10^5 enhancement shown by open chain sulfonate esters. Substitution of a 4-methyl group into the 5, 5-dimethyl deriva-tive results in a marked retardation; this is unexpected from the be-havior of open chain analogs which show a slight enhancement. Intro-duction of a 3-methyl group into the 4, 5, 5-trimethyl derivative causes a sharp decrease in hydrolysis rate. The effect of a 4-methyl and a 3-methyl is greater than that of a 4, 4-dimethyl by a factor of about five.

Inasmuch as methyl substitution causes retardation of the hydrolysis rate, it is reasonable to picture 1, 2-oxathiolane 2, 2-dioxides as being puckered and not planar. Whereas the ions of the ion pair formed on cleavage of the C—O bond may separate linearly in the solvolysis of open-chain compounds, ring-opening solvolysis, in which the C—O bond is cleaved, is accomplished by rotation around the bond. This concept may explain how the methyl groups may sterically retard the rate of ring-opening.

The hydrolysis of 4, 5, 5-trimethyl-4-phenyl-1, 2-oxathiolane 2, 2-dioxide (**35**) involves a phenyl migration during hydrolysis.

$$
\begin{array}{c}
CH_3 \\
CH_3 \\
CH_3 \\
C_6H_5
\end{array}
\underset{\textbf{35}}{\overset{O}{\diagdown}} SO_2 \xrightarrow{H_2O}
C_6H_5\overset{CH_3}{\underset{CH_3}{C}}-\overset{CH_3}{C}=CHSO_3H
$$

In the hydrolysis of 4, 4, 5, 5-tetramethyl-1, 2-oxathiolane 2, 2-dioxide (**36**)[59] the major product is an unsaturated sulfonic acid (62%).

$$
\begin{array}{c}
CH_3 \\
CH_3 \\
CH_3 \\
CH_3
\end{array}
\underset{\textbf{36}}{\overset{O}{\diagdown}} SO_2 \xrightarrow{H_2O}
(CH_3)_2C\underset{OH}{\overset{CH_3}{\underset{|}{C}}}CCH_2SO_3H + CH_2=C\underset{CH_3}{\overset{CH_3}{\underset{|}{C}}}CCH_2SO_3H
$$

Manecke and Hetterich[306a] prepared 3-hydroxypropane-1-sulfonic acid in 60% yield by reducing 1, 2-oxathiolane 2, 2-dioxide with lithium aluminum hydride in ethyl ether.

The reaction of 1, 2-oxathiolane 2, 2-dioxides with nucleophilic rea-gents undoubtedly proceeds by an $S_N 2$ mechanism. They resemble open-chain sulfates and sulfonates rather than analogous lactones. Their reaction with nucleophilic reagents may be generalized by the following equation, in which R is H, alkyl, aromatic, halogen, etc., M is

H, K, Na, etc., and X is a basic group such as NH_2, CN, SCN, halogen, carboxylate, amido, alkoxy, alkyl, etc.[36, 54, 65, 93, 137, 139, 139a, 153, 166, 167, 172, 186, 188, 189, 193-196, 198, 199, 201, 202, 204, 205, 220, 513]

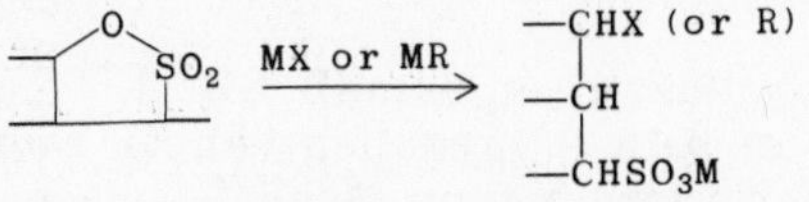

Thus, whereas lactones are acylating agents, 1, 2-oxathiolane 2, 2-dioxides are alkylating agents. This behavior has led to many patents in which 1, 2-oxathiolane 2, 2-dioxides are used to introduce water dispersible or solubilizing groups into a variety of compounds in excellent yields.

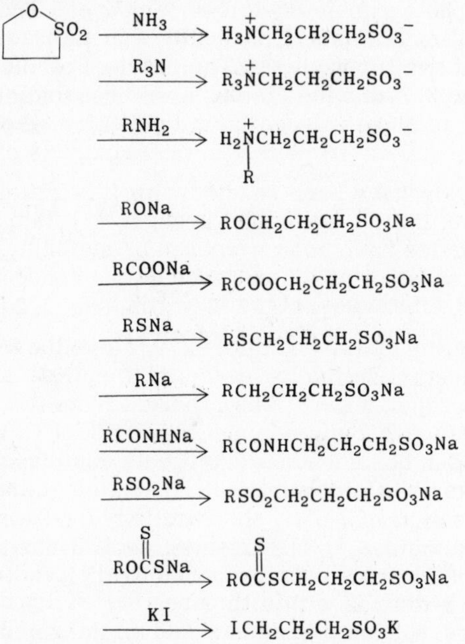

The reaction between 3-methyl-1, 2-oxathiolane 2, 2-dioxide and ammonia takes place at 0° to give yields of 87-89% of the aminoalkane-sulfonic acid[186] which on heating at 230° is converted to a water-soluble, ethanol-insoluble polymer.[188] The condensation derivatives of p-phenylenediamine with a 1, 2-oxathiolane 2, 2-dioxide have been described as photographic color developing agents.[153] 3-Anilinopropane-sulfonic acid, from the reaction of aniline and 1, 2-oxathiolane 2, 2-dioxide, yields a red dye when coupled with p-nitroaniline which is suitable for acetate rayon.[138] Water-soluble fluorescent compounds have been prepared from water-insoluble fluorescent amines by reaction with 4-methyl-1, 2-oxathiolane 2, 2-dioxide.[36] The reaction of 1, 2-oxathiolane 2, 2-dioxides with tertiary amines to give the sulfobetaine is

[For references, see pp. 289-312.]

quantiative and has been used as an identification method [188, 207, 513] Polymers having the group $\geqslant \overset{+}{N}$-$(CH_2SO_3^-$ have been prepared by reacting 1, 2-oxathiolane 2, 2-dioxides with a polymer or copolymer of vinylpyridine.[154]

Although 1, 2-oxathiolane 2, 2-dioxides react with KI, KBr, KCN, and KSCN by merely heating on a water bath, the reaction with KF requires heating at higher temperatures for a longer time.[188, 194]

The products from the reaction of 1, 2-oxathiolane 2, 2-dioxides with acid amides,[66b,188,198] sulfonamides,[202] alcohols or phenols,[93,167,204] hydrocarbons containing an active hydrogen or halogenated hydrocarbons,[193,201] sulfinic acids,[199] etc., are water-soluble compounds useful as detergents, dispersing agents, and intermediates for the manufacture of pharmaceuticals, photographic chemicals, and dyes. The product from the reaction of 1, 2-oxathiolane 2, 2-dioxide and anthraquinone was found to be a fluorescent dye for wool.[137] The reaction of alkali cellulose and 1, 2-oxathiolane 2, 2-dioxide yielded a water-soluble or -dispersable cellulose ether of some interest as a thickening agent or as a size.[186]

Synthetic fibers, such as nylon, have been reacted with 1, 2-oxathiolane 2, 2-dioxides to incorporate 0. 1-0. 5% sulfoalkyl groups.[161a] Depot carriers for therapeutical agents have been prepared by sulfoalkylation with 1, 2-oxathiolane 2, 2-dioxides of polymers, such as the condensation product from adipic acid and triethylenetetramine.[360b]

The products from the reaction of 1, 2-oxathiolane 2, 2-dioxide with thioethers, such as dodecyl methyl sulfide or di-(i-amyl) sulfide, show good foaming and detergent properties.[205] The products from the reaction of 5-methyl-1, 2-oxathiolane 2, 2-dioxide and NaSH, KSCN, C_6H_5SNa, and alkyl mercaptans have been described as detergents and dispersing, emulsifying, or wetting agents.[189] Compounds with insecticidal and fungicidal properties have been prepared by the reaction of 1, 2-oxathiolane 2, 2-dioxide with thioacetamides.[172] Isothiourea derivatives, useful as pharmaceutical intermediates, have been prepared by the reaction of 5-methyl-1, 2-oxathiolane 2, 2-dioxide with a thiourea.[54,167] Products useful as corrosion inhibitors, vulcanizing agents, and as intermediates for the preparation of fungicides have been prepared by the reaction of 1, 2-oxathiolane 2, 2-dioxide with carbon disulfide and with xanthates.[166, 167]

Haas[169-171] reacted 1, 2-oxathiolane 2, 2-dioxide with alkyl phosphites and phosphines to obtain products useful as insecticides and fungicides. Gaertner[139a-139b] reacted 1, 2-oxathiolane 2, 2-dioxide with various phosphites at 130–165° to obtain products useful as insecticides (especially against mites), surfactive agents, and plasticizers.

$$\text{(structure)} \; SO_2 + (C_2H_5O)_3P \xrightarrow[56\%]{155-165°} (C_2H_5O)_2\overset{O}{\overset{\|}{P}}CH_2CH_2CH_2SO_3C_2H_5$$

This is essentially a Michaelis-Arbuzov reaction and undoubtedly proceeds through the formation of $(C_2H_5O)_3\overset{+}{P}CH_2CH_2CH_2SO_3$, and subsequent rearrangement to the sulfonate. The reaction proceeds readily at atmospheric pressure and catalysts, such as triphenylamine, may be used in the reaction of aryl phosphites. The reaction is generally complete within a relatively short time. The sulfonate ester group may be removed through pyrolysis to give the phosphonoalkanesulfonic acid. The ester group is pyrolyzed off as an olefin.

Runge, El-Hewehi, Jenner, and Taeger,[405c] on reacting 4-phenyl-1, 3-dithiole-2-thione (**36a**) and 1, 2-oxathiolane 2, 2-dioxide, obtained 4-phenyl-5-sulfopropyl-1, 3-dithiole-2-thione (**36b**) as an amorphous violet powder.

36a　　　　　　　　　　**36b**

b.　1, 2-Oxathiolan-5-one 2, 2-Dioxide

1, 2-Oxathiolan-5-one 2, 2-dioxides are commonly called cyclic anhydrides of β-sulfocarboxylic acids and have been indexed in Chemical Abstracts under the carboxylic acid name. Although the inner anhydrides of o-sulfobenzoic acids have been known for a long time, the aliphatic homolog was unknown until 1940, when Kharasch and his students[256-258a] reported the results of their studies on sulfonation reactions with sulfuryl chloride. Earlier work[258a,375a] had demonstrated that sulfuryl chloride is a sulfonating or a chlorinating agent depending upon conditions and the type of compound undergoing reaction. In the presence of light, aliphatic acids undergo a photochemical reaction with sulfuryl chloride to β-sulfocarboxylic anhydrides.[256,257]

Unless the starting materials are dry and moisture is excluded from the reaction, the β-sulfocarboxylic acid is obtained instead of the anhydride. In addition to the anhydride, the chlorinated carboxylic acids are also obtained in this photochemical sulfonation reaction. The photosulfonation of n-butyric acid undoubtedly gives the sulfoanhydride, but Kharasch, Chao, and Brown[258] obtained an oil which could not be distilled without extensive decomposition. The photosulfonation of higher aliphatic acids, such as isovaleric and lauric acids, yielded a mixture containing a large number of isomers.

[For references, see pp. 289-312.]

β-Sulfocarboxylic acid anhydrides have been prepared from the corresponding β-sulfocarboxylic acids by treatment with thionyl chloride. [258, 268]

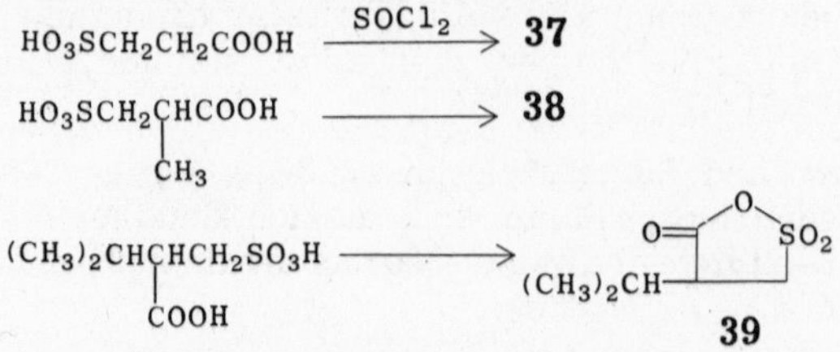

$$HO_3SCH_2CH_2COOH \xrightarrow{\text{SOCl}_2} \textbf{37}$$

$$HO_3SCH_2\underset{\underset{CH_3}{|}}{C}HCOOH \longrightarrow \textbf{38}$$

$$(CH_3)_2CH\underset{\underset{COOH}{|}}{C}HCH_2SO_3H \longrightarrow$$

$$(CH_3)_2CH{-}\quad \textbf{39}$$

1, 2-Oxathiolane-5-one 2, 2-dioxide (**37**) is a white crystalline solid which melts at 76-77°. The 4-methyl derivative (**38**) is an oil, b.p. 135-145° at 3-5 mm, $d^{22.5}$ 1.442. The reactions of these inner sulfocarboxylic anhydrides are similar to the o-sulfobenzoic acid anhydrides. Reaction with methanol yields the monomethyl carboxylate; the pH of the ester from 1, 2-oxathiolane-5-one 2, 2-dioxide showed a high degree of dissociation indicating a free sulfonic acid group.[258] Reaction with aniline yielded an aniline salt of the sulfocarboxylic acid anilide; similarly, ammonia gave the corresponding ammonium salt of the amide.[258] Refluxing 1, 2-oxathiolan-5-one 2, 2-dioxide with lithium aluminum hydride in ether yielded 3-hydroxypropanesulfonic acid.[306]

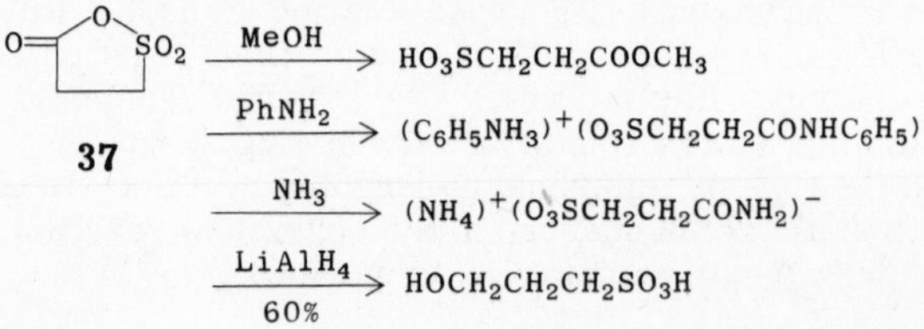

37

$$\xrightarrow{\text{MeOH}} HO_3SCH_2CH_2COOCH_3$$

$$\xrightarrow{\text{PhNH}_2} (C_6H_5NH_3)^+(O_3SCH_2CH_2CONHC_6H_5)^-$$

$$\xrightarrow{\text{NH}_3} (NH_4)^+(O_3SCH_2CH_2CONH_2)^-$$

$$\xrightarrow[\text{60\%}]{\text{LiAlH}_4} HOCH_2CH_2CH_2SO_3H$$

B. $\underline{C_3OS\text{-}C_6}$

1. $3H$-1, 2-Benzoxathiole (**40**)

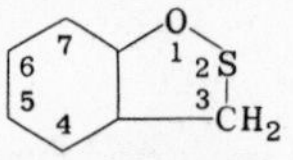

40

(RRI 1220)

The parent compound is unknown. Its 2, 2-dioxide derivative and substituted 2, 2-dioxides have been prepared and are listed in Table 2. $3H$-1, 2-Benzoxathioles are more commonly known as benzylsultones. They are indexed in <u>Chemical Abstracts</u> as derivatives of o-toluenesulfonic or methanesulfonic acid, to which headings they are crossed from 3H-1, 2-benzoxathiole.

Marckwald and Frahne[308] were prompted to prepare 3H-1, 2-benz-oxathiole 2, 2-dioxide by Schulz's[472] preparation of naphthosultone and Remsen and Saunders'[383] preparation of toluenesultone. Thus, Marckwald and Frahne prepared 3H-1, 2-benzoxathiole 2, 2-dioxide (41) by hydrolyzing the diazonium chloride from o-amino-α-toluenesulfonic acid. They also prepared 3H-1, 2-benzoxathiole 2, 2-dioxide by treating o-hydroxy-α-toluenesulfonic acid with phosphorus pentachloride.[308] They were unable to convert o-hydroxy-α-toluenesulfonic acid to 3H-1, 2-benzoxathiole 2, 2-dioxide by heating.

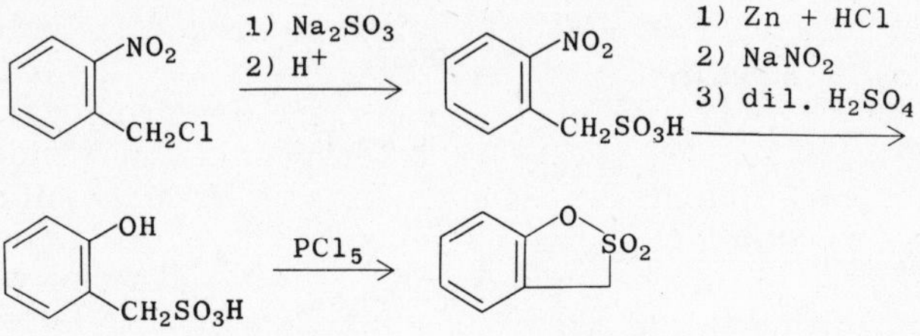

41

Shearing and Smiles[435] prepared 3H-1, 2-benzoxathiole 2, 2-dioxide and its 5-methyl (42) and 5, 7-dimethyl derivatives by treatment of an o-hydroxybenzyl alcohol with aqueous sodium bisulfite and ring closure of the resulting o-hydroxy-α-toluenesulfonic acid with phosphorus pentachloride.

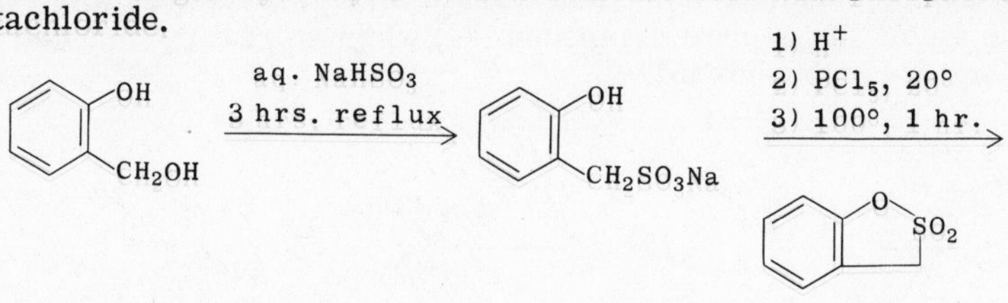

41

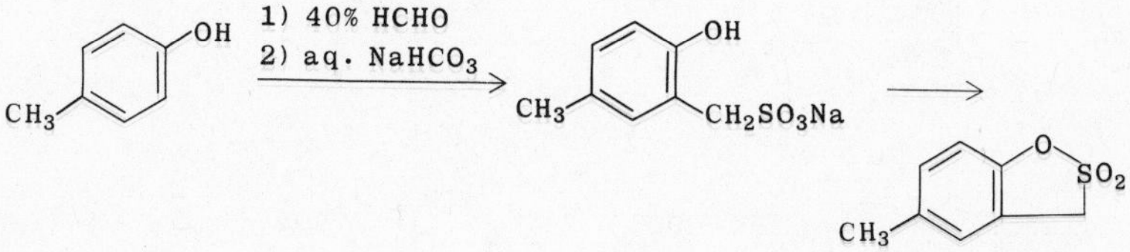

42

Erdtman[118,119] prepared 5-methyl-5H-1, 2-benzoxathiole 2, 2-dioxide (42) by treating N,N-dimethyl-2-hydroxy-5-methylbenzylamine with aqueous sodium sulfite.

[For references, see pp. 289-312.]

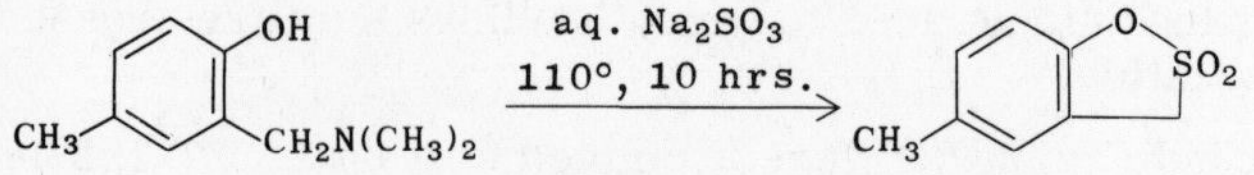

Chapter 4

42

3*H*-1, 2-Benzoxathiole 2, 2-dioxides are crystalline compounds with well-defined melting points. 3*H*-1, 2-Benzoxathiole 2, 2-dioxide is insoluble in cold water and moderately soluble in hot water; it is recrystallized best from hot water or benzene. It reacts readily with alkali, ammonium hydroxide, and barium hydroxide.[308]

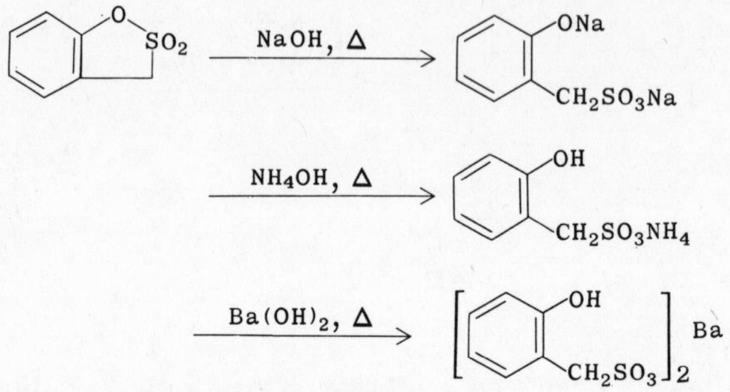

3*H*-1, 2-Benzoxathiole 2, 2-dioxide reacts slowly with bromine to give the 5-bromo derivative (**43**). Nitration of 3*H*-1, 2-benzoxathiole 2, 2-dioxide yields the 5-nitro compound (**44**) which is readily reduced to the 5-amino compound (**45**).[308]

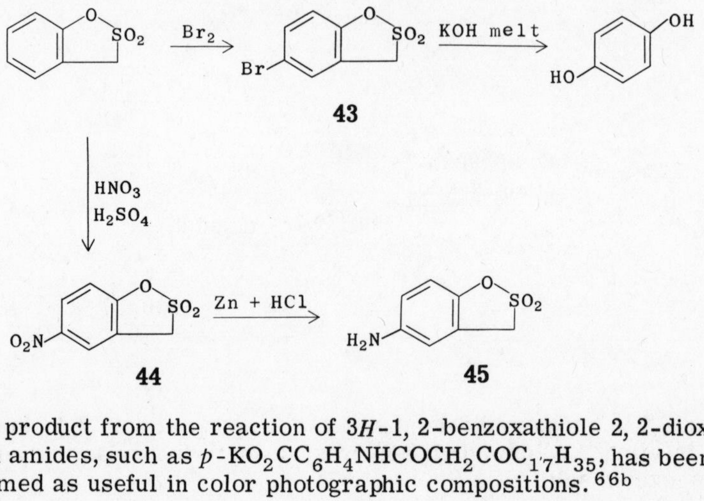

43

44   **45**

The product from the reaction of 3*H*-1, 2-benzoxathiole 2, 2-dioxide with amides, such as *p*-$KO_2CC_6H_4NHCOCH_2COC_{17}H_{35}$, has been claimed as useful in color photographic compositions.[66b]

98

TABLE 2.   3H-1, 2-Benzoxathiole 2, 2-Dioxides

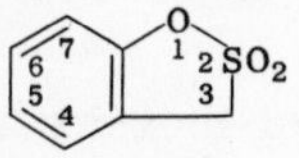

Substituent	M.p. (°C)	Ref.
None	86	308, 435
5-CH$_3$-	91. 5	118, 119, 435
5, 7-(CH$_3$-)$_2$	92. 5	435
5-Br-	147	308
5-NO$_2$-	148	308
5-NH$_2$-	138	308

2. 3H-2, 1-Benzoxathiole (46)

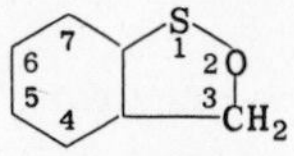

46
(RRI 1222)

   The study of this ring system had its beginning in 1884, when Ira Remsen[376] wondered whether o-sulfobenzoic acids would behave analogously to phthalic acids in their reactions to give phthaleins. The products he obtained from o-sulfobenzoic acids and phenols were similar to the phthaleins, and consequently he introduced the name sulfonephthalein. Following this lead, subsequent experiments by Remsen and his students resulted in many papers for the next twenty or so years. Much of Remsen's scientific fame rests on this work.

   3H-2, 1-Benzoxathiole is unknown. Two derivatives of this ring system, however, have been investigated extensively. They are 3H-2, 1-benzoxathiole 1, 1-dioxide and 3H-2, 1-benzoxathiole-3-one 1, 1-dioxide, which are considered as the sultone of α-hydroxy-o-toluenesulfonic acid and the anhydride of o-sulfobenzoic acid, respectively. The sultone and anhydride names have been the ones most used in the literature except for the 3, 3-phenol derivatives, for which the sulfonephthalein name is widely used. The more common sulfonephthaleins are better known by common names such as phenol red, bromophenol blue, etc. Other names used for derivatives of 3H-2, 1-benzoxathioles were 3-benzisothioxole and o-sulfobenzoic acid endoanhydrides. Chemical Abstracts indexes compounds in this ring system under toluenesulfonic

[For references, see pp. 289-312.]

acid sultone, benzoic acid *o*-sulfocyclic anhydride, or under the sulfone-phthalein indicator name; 3*H*-2, 1-benzoxathiole is crossed to these names.

Table 3 lists the various 3*H*-2, 1-benzoxathiole 1, 1-dioxides and Table 4 the sulfonephthaleins which have been reported.

a. 3*H*-2, 1-Benzoxathiole 1, 1-Dioxide

(1) Preparation

Jones[242] in 1894 reported the preparation of 3*H*-2, 1-benzoxathiole 1, 1-dioxide (**47**) by the reduction of the chloride obtained from the reaction of the ammonium salt of *o*-sulfobenzoic acid with phosphorus pentachloride. The melting point he observed, 287-289° with decomposition, makes it unlikely that he had the benzoxathiole; he did obtain *o*-sulfobenzoic acid, however, on oxidizing the product with concentrated nitric acid.

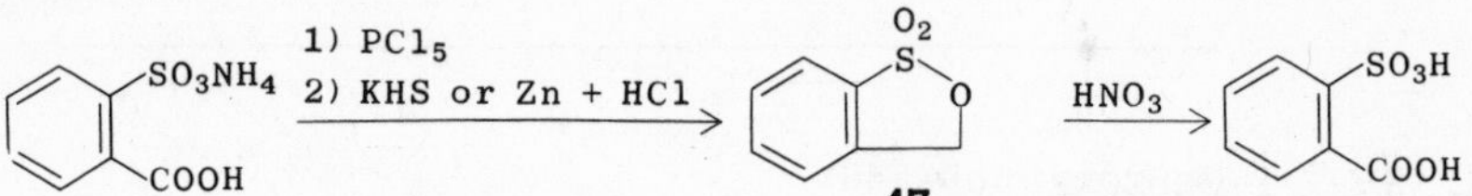

Because of its structural similarity to phthalide, 3*H*-2, 1-benzoxathiole 1, 1-dioxide was called "sulphonphthalide".

On treating an ether solution of the symmetrical chloride of *o*-sulfobenzoic acid with zinc and hydrochloric acid, List and Stein[292] in 1898 obtained 3*H*-2, 1-benzoxathiole 1, 1-dioxide (**47**). Another method used by List and Stein involved the reduction of 3-chloro-3*H*-2, 1-benzoxathiole 1, 1-dioxide (**48**) with zinc and hydrochloric acid, a procedure which has given 90% yields.[188]

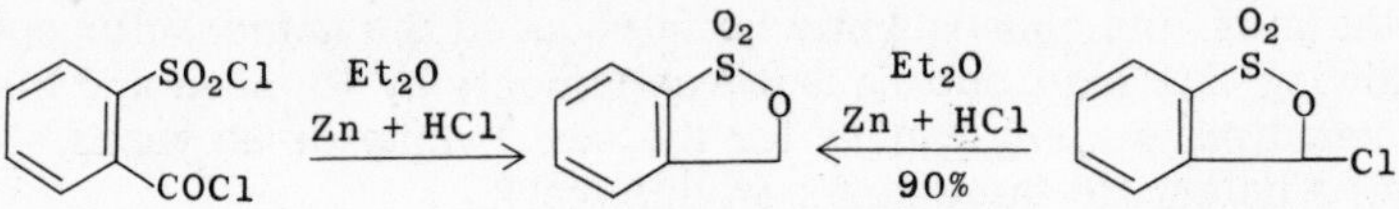

List and Stein used the name "sulfobenzide" for 3*H*-2, 1-benzoxathiole 1, 1-dioxide to mark its analogy to phthalides in reactions. Goldberger[162] prepared 3*H*-2, 1-benzoxathiole 1, 1-dioxide by heating the sodium salt of *o*-sulfobenzaldehyde with dimethyl sulfate. This reaction is suspect as it requires that dimethyl sulfate act as a reducing agent.

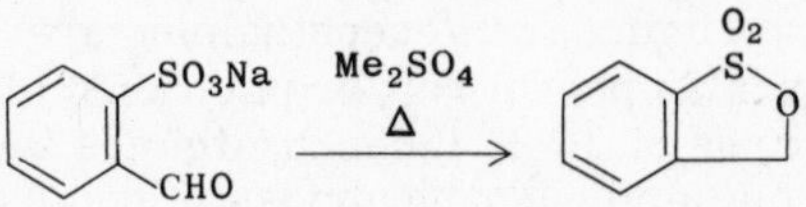

100

Davies and Dick[90] obtained a 25% yield of 3H-2,1-benzoxathiole 1,1-dioxide on treating o-iodomethylbenzenesulfonyl fluoride with silver oxide in aqueous ethanol; the major product in this reaction was hydroxymethylbenzenesulfonyl fluoride.

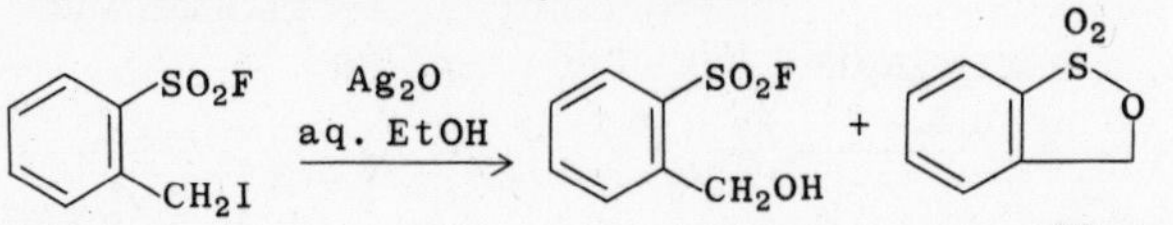

47

Relatively few 3-monosubstituted 3H-2,1-benzoxathiole 1,1-dioxides have been reported. The 3-chloro derivative (**48**) has been prepared by treating o-sulfobenzaldehyde or its sodium salt with PCl$_5$ or PCl$_5$–POCl$_3$.[160,162,188,292]

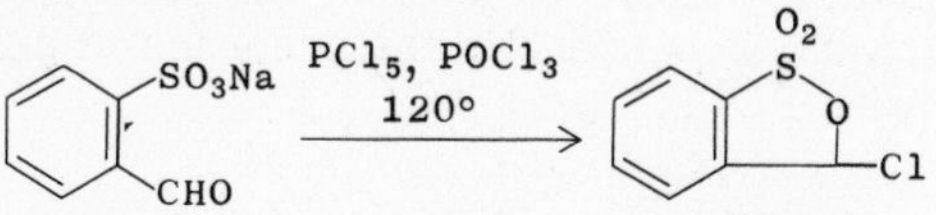

48

Freeman and Ritchie [133a] postulated a tautomeric structure (**49**) for o-sulfobenzaldehyde to account for the reported difficulty of preparing the free acid and of oxidizing the free acid. They prepared 3-chloro-3H-2,1-benzoxathiole 1,1-dioxide by treatment of o-sulfobenzaldehyde with PCl$_5$ and confirmed the structure by means of infrared. Their attempt to prepare the 3-carboxylic acid derivative by treatment of the 3-chloro compound with KCN followed by hydrolysis was inconclusive.

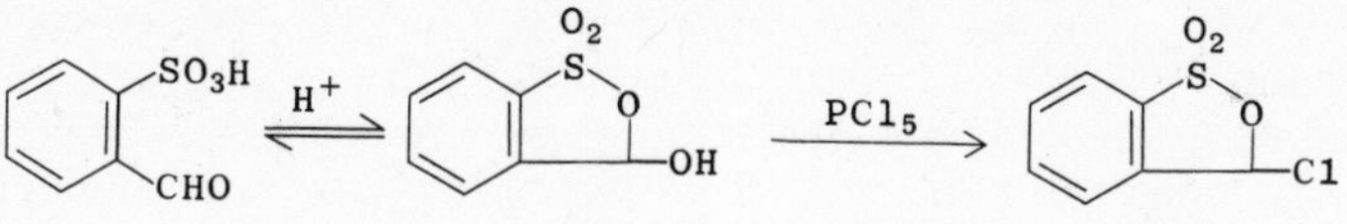

49   **48**

Hinsberg and Meyer[213,214] obtained 3-aminomethyl-5,6,7-trihydroxy-3H-2,1-benzoxathiole 1,1-dioxide (**50**), a water-soluble compound, on sulfonation of pyrogallol, reaction of the sulfonated pyrogallol with aminoacetaldehyde acetal, and dehydration.

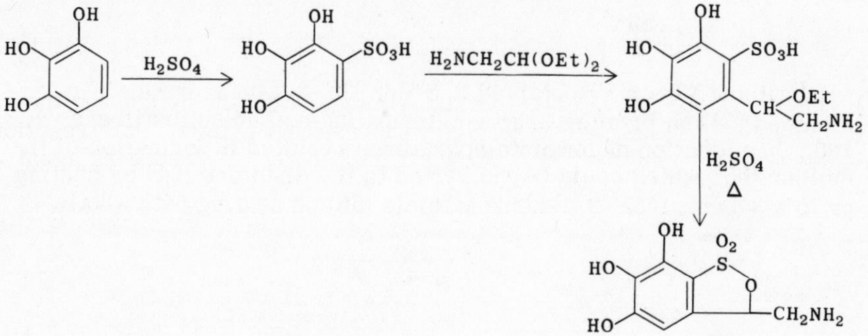

50

A French patent[234] describes the condensation of o-sulfobenzaldehyde with 2, 4, 6-trichlorophenol to 3-(2, 4, 6-trichloro-3-hydroxyphenyl)-
3H-2, 1-benzoxathiole 1, 1-dioxide (51).

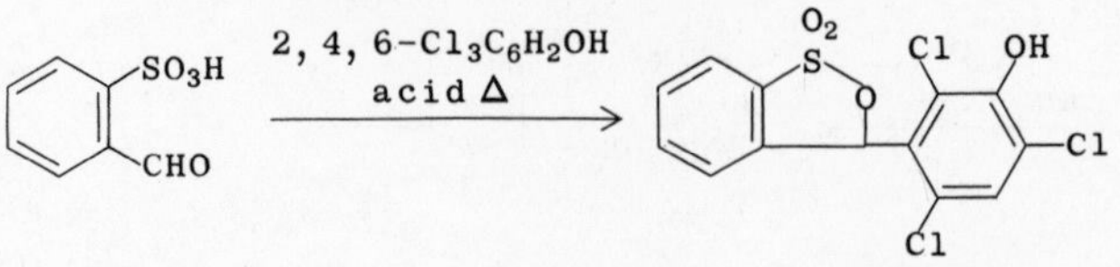

51

Farrar, [125a] in a study of mothproofing agents, prepared several chloro
derivatives by the condensation of o-sulfobenzaldehydes with chloro-
phenols in the presence of fuming sulfuric acid or by the condensation
of o-sulfobenzaldehyde with a chlorobenzene in the presence of sulfuric
acid followed by treatment with $POCl_3$.

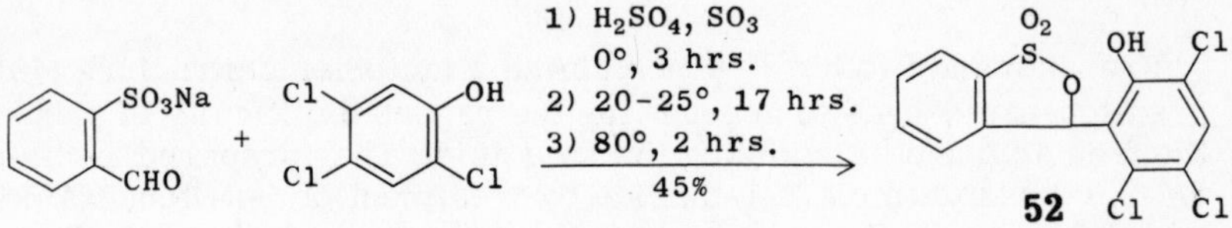

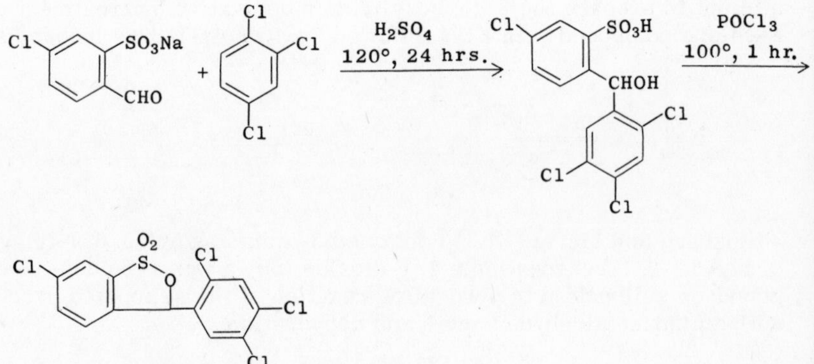

Ruggli and Peyer [405] obtained 3, 3'-bis-3H-2, 1-benzoxathiole 1, 1-
dioxides (54) on brominating or chlorinating o, o'-disulfostilbenes at
100°; bromination at lower temperatures resulted in formation of the
sultone (55), which could be converted to the disultone (54) by heating
or to a 3-benzal-3H-2, 1-benzoxathiole (56) on heating with alkali.

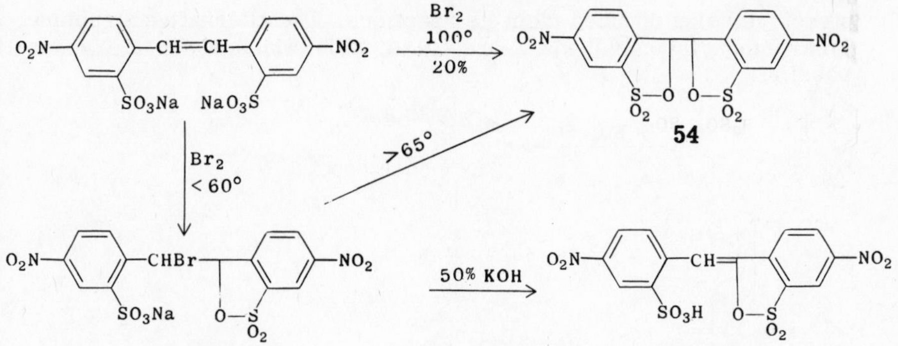

54

55

56

Sachs, Wolff, and Ludwig[410] prepared 3, 3-dimethyl-3H-2, 1-benzoxa-thiole 1, 1-dioxide (**57**) by the treatment of N-ethyl-o-(2-hydroxy-2-propyl)benzenesulfonamide with fuming hydrochloric acid. They called the product dimethylbenzylsultone.

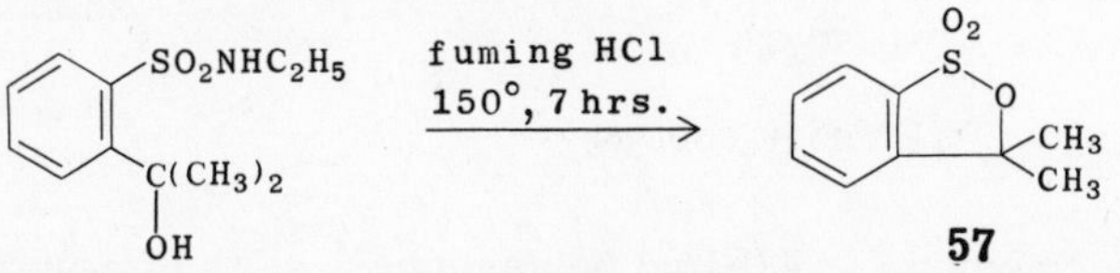

57

Mustafa and Hilny[334] obtained 3, 3-diphenyl-3H-2, 1-benzoxathiole 1, 1-dioxide (**58**), to which they assigned the name sulfonylide, by elimination of aniline from α-hydroxy-α, α-diphenyl-o-toluenesulfonanilide by treatment with sulfuric acid.

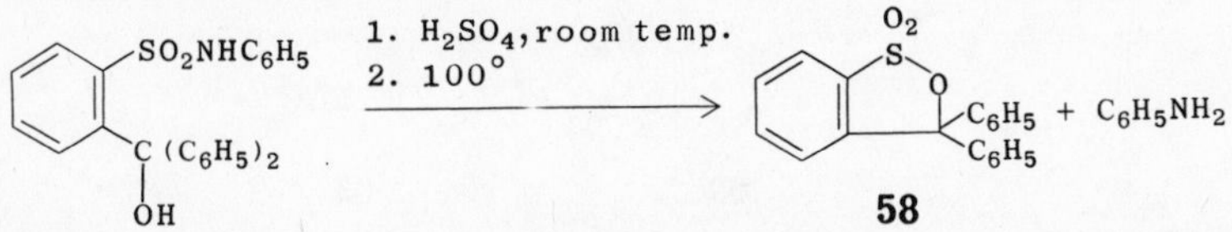

58

A similar reaction carried out by Oddo and Mingoia,[341] in which α-hydroxy-α, α-dianilino-o-toluenesulfonamide was treated with acetic anhydride, led to the preparation of 3, 3-dianilino-3H-2, 1-benzoxathiole 1, 1-dioxide (**59**).

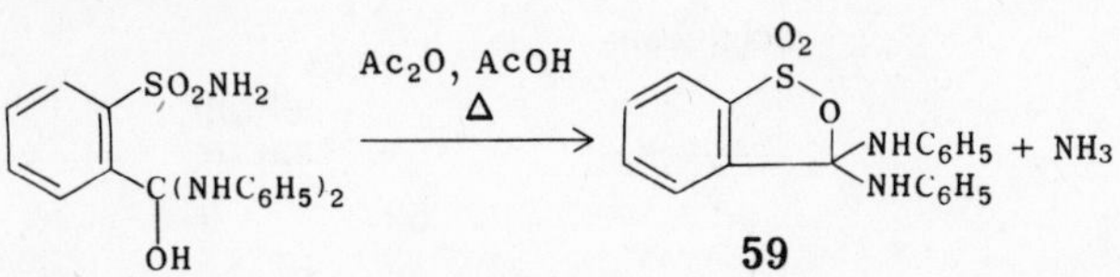

59

Feist, Pauschardt, and Dibbern,[126] in their studies of the transformation of benzoylacetic acid esters by fuming sulfuric acid, obtained o-sulfobenzoylacetic acid, which in the enol form underwent ring closure to 3-carbethoxymethylidene-3H-2, 1-benzoxathiole 1, 1-dioxide (**60**), the structure being deduced from its reactions. The alternative structure, 2-carbethoxythianaphthene-3-one 1,1-dioxide (61), is a strong possibility.

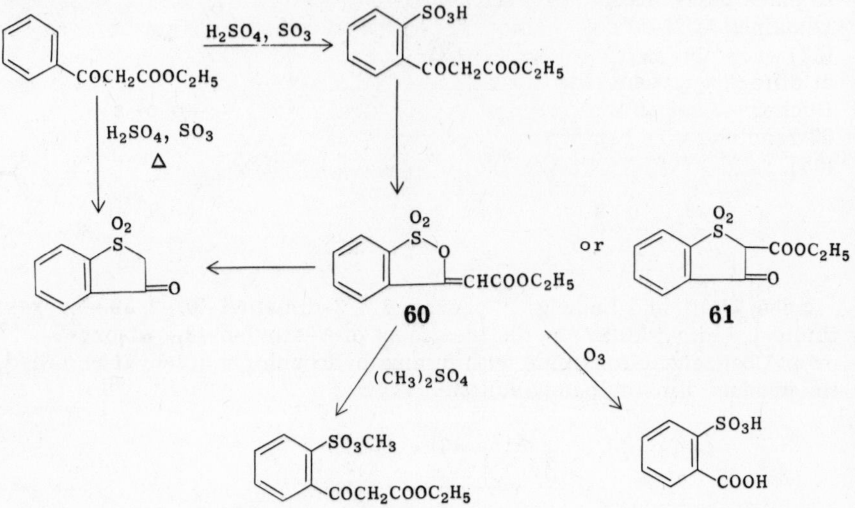

H_2SO_4, SO_3

SO_3H

$COCH_2COOC_2H_5$

H_2SO_4, SO_3
Δ

O_2

60   or   **61**

$(CH_3)_2SO_4$

O_3

SO_3CH_3
$COCH_2COOC_2H_5$

SO_3H
$COOH$

That the acid ammonium[242,379] and potassium[252] salts of o-sulfo-benzoic acid yield a mixture of isomeric chlorides on treatment with phosphorus pentachloride was not realized until Remsen[380] postulated this reaction course to account for the two products obtained on reacting the mixed chlorides with aniline.

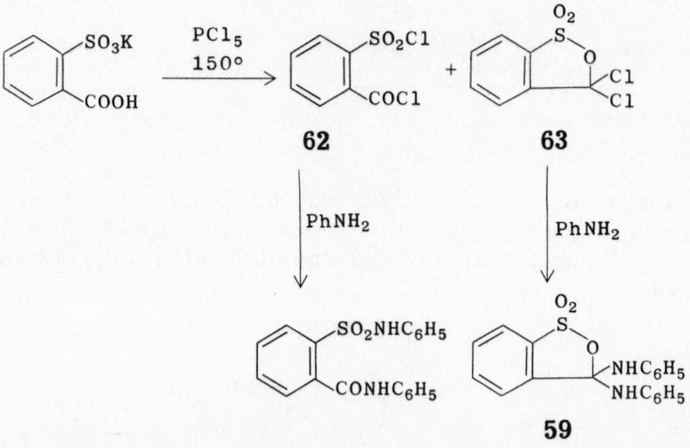

SO_3K PCl_5 SO_2Cl O_2
$COOH$ $150°$ $COCl$

62   **63**

$PhNH_2$ $PhNH_2$

$SO_2NHC_6H_5$ O_2
$CONHC_6H_5$ NHC_6H_5
NHC_6H_5

59

The acid chloride (62) which melts at 76° was called the symmetrical chloride and 3,3-dichloro-3H-2,1-benzoxathiole 1,1-dioxide (63) which melts at 21.5-22.5° was called the unsymmetrical chloride. The two chlorides are extremely difficult to separate, particularly without the availability of refrigeration. It was fortuitous that the winter where

Saunders[383] was working on the separation was exceptionally cold and particularly favorable for the separation of the two chlorides by crystallization from ether and chloroform. The method Saunders used was to place the solution out of doors for several days. If the temperature remained at 0° or below fine crystals of the lower melting chloride (63) were obtained. This method was tedious. The two chlorides react at different rates and give different products, 64 and 65, with ammonia. Bucher[67] used this difference for preparing large samples of 62, as 63 reacted more rapidly to give ammonium o-cyanobenzenesulfonate (65).

In extending their studies, Remsen and Gray[388] treated the acid potassium salt of p-nitro-o-sulfobenzoic acid with phosphorus pentachloride and obtained a good yield of 3, 3-dichloro-6-nitro-3H-2, 1-benzoxathiole 1, 1-dioxide (66) which was

easily separated from the higher melting or symmetrical chloride. This product undoubtedly was also obtained by Kastle [252] but not so characterized. This reaction was also studied by Hollis,[222] Henderson,[209] and Holmes.[226] Hollis reported a quantitative yield of 66 by this reaction. Holmes ran the reaction with POCl$_3$ in a sealed tube at 135° and obtained a 50% yield of 3, 3-dichloro-6-nitro-3H-2, 1-benzoxathiole 1, 1-dioxide (66). Henderson was concerned with getting good yields of the symmetrical chloride for the preparation of sulfonephthaleins.

Because List and Stein[292] stated that the mixed chlorides were a case of tautomerism and in view of the great difficulty in obtaining the pure unsymmetrical chloride for chemical characterization, Blanchard[47] investigated the preparation of the chlorides from p-bromo-o-sulfobenzoic acid. He was successful in converting the acid potassium salt to 6-bromo-3, 3-dichloro-3H-2, 1-benzoxathiole 1, 1-dioxide only by treatment with phosphorus oxychloride at 130° for 15 hours in a sealed tube. The symmetrical chloride was obtained by treating the acid potassium salt with phosphorus pentachloride on a water bath for one hour, and then destroying the unsymmetrical chloride with ammonia leaving only the symmetrical chloride.

Cobb[74] studied various reactions of the two chlorides with ethanol, hydrochloric acid, methanol, ammonium hydroxide, water, and others to help characterize the differences between the symmetrical and unsymmetrical chlorides. He was able to show that phosphorus pentachloride reacts with o-sulfobenzoic acid or anhydride to give a mixture and that phosphorus oxychoride gives only the unsymmetrical chloride. Phosphorus oxychloride also reacts with $3H$-2, 1-benzoxathiol-3-one 1, 1-dioxide to give only the unsymmetrical chloride.

Karslake and Bond, [249] on treating the acid potassium salt of 4-nitro-5-methyl-2-sulfobenzoic acid with a little phosphorus oxychloride and slightly more than the calculated amount of phosphorus pentachloride under reflux for about one-half hour, obtained the two chlorides. The symmetrical chloride was easily separated, but the unsymmetrical chloride was difficultly separated in a pure form. Karslake and Bond[250] found that if a pure acid potassium salt were used, the unsymmetrical chloride could be separated easily by fractional crystallization. The formation of the unsymmetrical chloride is favored by the presence of phosphorus oxychloride.

Scheiber and Knothe, [415] as a result of their absorption spectra studies, considered the symmetrical chloride to be the one melting at 40° and the unsymmetrical chloride to be the one melting at 79°. Recently, Rozina, Nesterenko, and Vainshtein[404a] compared the half-way potentials of these two dichlorides with those of o-phthalic acid and concluded that Scheiber and Knothe were correct. The bulk of the chemical evidence as discussed in the next section favors the result of Remsen and co-workers.

The $3H$-2, 1-benzoxathiole 1, 1-dioxides described in the literature are listed in Table 3.

C$_3$OS Ring Systems

TABLE 3.   3H-2, 1-Benzoxathiole 1, 1-Dioxides

Substituent	Yield (%)	M.p. (°C)	Ref.
None	25	112-113	90, 292
	—	113	162
	90	—	188
3-Cl-	—	114	160, 292
	—	114-115. 5	162
	—	—	133a
3-H$_2$N-	—	—	160, 265
3-(3-HO-2, 4, 6-Cl$_3$C$_6$H-)	—	—	234
	—	243-244	125a
3-(2-HO-3, 5, 6-Cl$_3$C$_6$H-)	—	233 (dec.)	125a
3-(HN=)	—	—	387
3-(C$_2$H$_5$OCOCH=)	—	140	126
3-(2, 4, 5-Cl$_3$C$_6$H$_2$-)-6-Cl-	—	230	125a
3, 3-(Cl-)$_2$	50	—	226
	—	38	299
	—	40	292, 518
	—	21. 5-22. 5	380, 389
3, 3-(CH$_3$-)$_2$	—	106-107	410
3, 3-(C$_2$H$_5$-)$_2$	—	91	410
3, 3-(C$_6$H$_5$-)$_2$	—	161-162	292
	—	162-163	74, 136, 334
	—	210	410
3, 3-(CH$_3$NH-)$_2$	—	>330	390
3, 3-(C$_2$H$_5$NH-)$_2$	—	276	341
3, 3-(C$_6$H$_5$NH-)$_2$	—	315	341
		270-280 (dec.)	292
3, 3-(o-CH$_3$C$_6$H$_4$NH-)$_2$	—	278	341

[For references, see pp. 289-312.]

Chapter 4

TABLE 3. $3H$-2, 1-Benzoxathiole 1, 1-Dioxides (contd)

Substituent	Yield (%)	M.p. (°C)	Ref.
$3, 3\text{-}(2\text{-HO-}3, 5\text{-Cl}_2\text{C}_6\text{H}_2\text{-})_2$		235-240 (dec.)	125a
$3\text{-}(O_2N$— [benzo ring] —$CH\text{-})\text{-}6\text{-}O_2N\text{-}$ (S, O, O_2)	20	290 (dec.)	405
$3\text{-}(O_2N$— [benzo ring] —$CH=)\text{-}6\text{-}O_2N\text{-}$ (SO_3CH_3)	—	179-180	405
$3\text{-}(O_2N$— [benzo ring] —$CHBr\text{-})\text{-}6\text{-}O_2N\text{-}$ (SO_3Na)	—	234-237 (dec.)	405
$3\text{-}(O_2N$— [benzo ring] —$CHCl\text{-})\text{-}6\text{-}O_2N\text{-}$ (SO_3Na)	—	—	405
$3, 3\text{-}(Cl\text{-})_2\text{-}5\text{-Br-}$	50	89-90	47, 48
$3, 3\text{-}(Cl\text{-})_2\text{-}6\text{-}O_2N\text{-}$	50	—	226
	90	56-57	388
	100	57	69, 222
$3, 3\text{-}(C_6H_5NH\text{-})_2\text{-}6\text{-Br-}$	—	—	47, 48
$3, 3\text{-}[p\text{-}(CH_3)_2NC_6H_4\text{-}]_2\text{-}7\text{-}CH_3\text{-}$	—	—	266
$3, 3\text{-}(2\text{-HO-}3, 5\text{-Cl}_2\text{C}_6\text{H}_2\text{-})_2\text{-}6\text{-Cl}$	—	255-265 (dec.)	125a
$3, 3\text{-}(Cl\text{-})_2\text{-}5\text{-}CH_3\text{-}6\text{-}O_2N\text{-}$	46	83 (b.p. 212/10 mm.)	250
	—	90	249
$3, 3\text{-}(C_6H_5NH\text{-})_2\text{-}5\text{-}CH_3\text{-}6\text{-}O_2N\text{-}$	—	195	250
$3\text{-}H_2NCH_2\text{-}5, 6, 7\text{-}(HO\text{-})_3$	35	—	213

(2) Properties and Reactions

$3H$-2, 1-Benzoxathiole 1, 1-dioxides are crystalline, sharp-melting, colorless compounds. The 3, 3-dichloro-substituted compounds are the lowest melting of this group. The low melting point of 3, 3-dichloro-$3H$-2, 1-benzoxathiole 1, 1-dioxide contributed to the difficulty experienced at the turn of the century in its isolation and characterization. Zirn-

108

giebl[518] reported that the 3, 3-dichloride crystals are rhombic; Scheiber and Knothe[415] studied its ultraviolet absorption spectrum.

3H-2, 1-Benzoxathiole 1, 1-dioxide (47) is easily hydrolyzed by hot water or alkaline media to o-sulfobenzyl alcohol.[292] It is converted to benzoic acid on heating with alkali; on fusion with potassium hydroxide, some o-cresol is produced along with benzoic acid.[164]

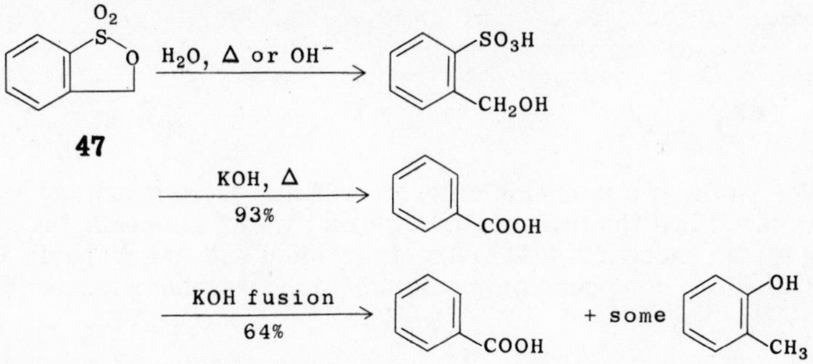

3H-2, 1-Benzoxathiole 1, 1-dioxide is an alkylating agent towards salts, phenolates, amides, amines, etc.[188,194,202,204,220,291]

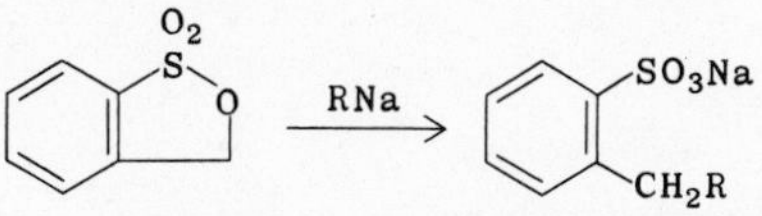

R = β-C$_{10}$H$_7$O—, C$_6$H$_5$CH$_2$COO—, C$_{18}$H$_{35}$COO—, CH$_3$CONH—, HS—, C$_{18}$H$_{37}$NH—, etc.

3-Chloro-3H-2, 1-benzoxathiole 1, 1-dioxide (48) is hydrolyzed with hot water to o-sulfobenzaldehyde.[162] Treatment of 3-chloro-3H-2, 1-benzoxathiole 1, 1-dioxide with ammonium hydroxide gives saccharin (64) and with ammonia in an autoclave the 3-amino compound (67), which is easily air oxidized to saccharin.[160]

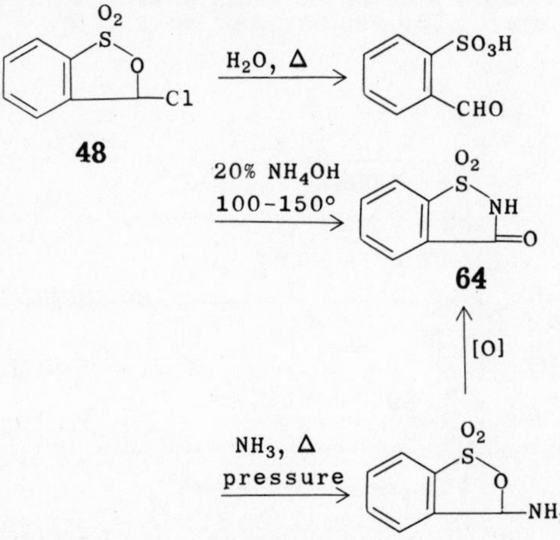

3, 3-Dichloro-3*H*-2, 1-benzoxathiole 1, 1-dioxide (**63**) reacts with water about three times as rapidly as its higher melting isomer (**62**) to give *o*-sulfobenzoic acid.[380] The 3, 3-dichloro derivative, however, is not particularly sensitive to water. Hydrolysis in boiling water is complete within five to ten minutes, but in cold water hydrolysis is quite slow.[383]

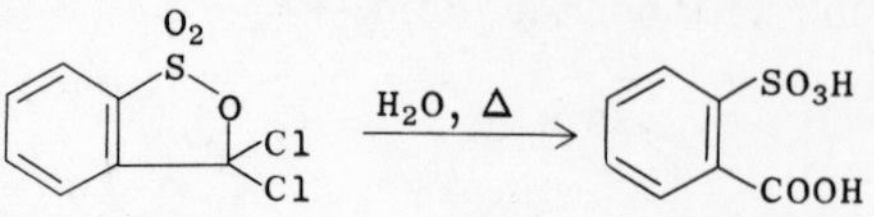

In studies on the two isomeric chlorides, **62** and **63**, Remsen and his students found that the two reacted differently with ammonia, the higher melting giving saccharin (**64**) or the ammonium salt of saccharin and the 3, 3-dichloro compound ammonium *o*-cyanobenzenesulfonate (**68**). [47, 250,292,380,384,385]

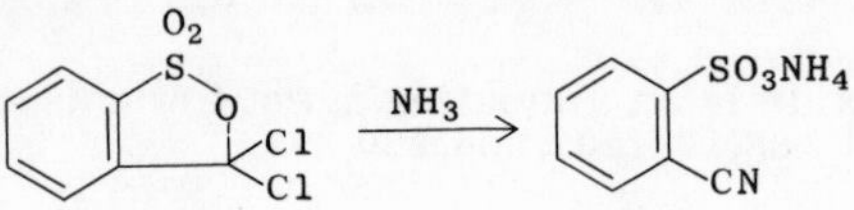

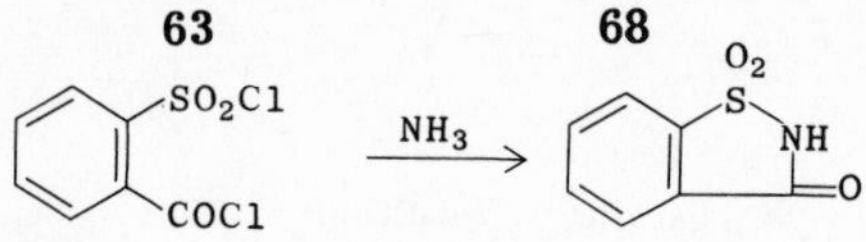

Reaction with ammonium hydroxide, which proceeds slowly, gives the same products. [176,385,387–389,391] Remsen and his students devoted considerable attention to the reaction of the two isomeric chlorides with aniline, using this reaction as well as the reaction with ammonia to elucidate the structures. [47,48,209,250,292,380–382,389,392,452]

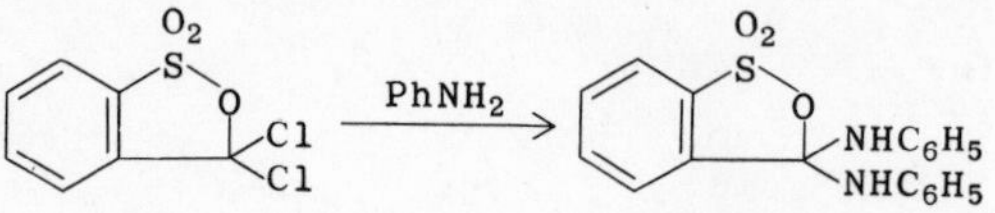

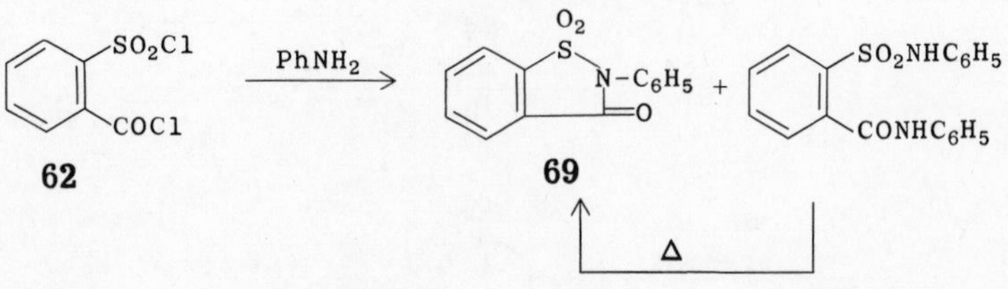

The 3, 3-dianilino derivative (**59**) on fusion with potassium hydroxide is converted to salicylic acid and aniline; on refluxing with 20% potassium hydroxide in a dilute alcohol solution, it is hydrolyzed to α, α-dianilino-o-sulfobenzyl alcohol; it is not affected by prolonged boiling with 0.5 N sodium hydroxide.[341]

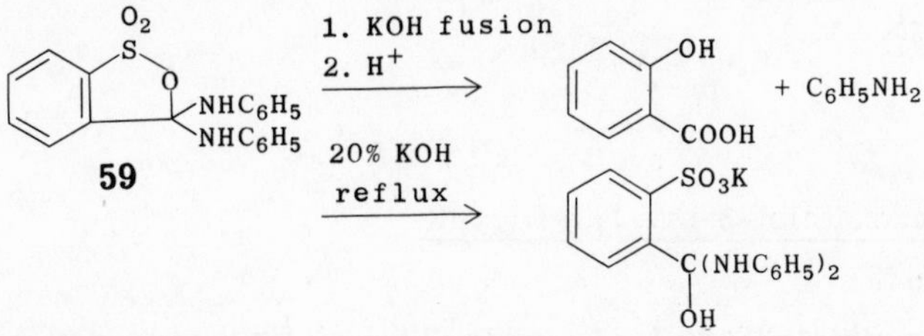

Remsen[389] and Remsen and Clark[390,393] reacted the two chlorides with methylamine and ethylamine with similar results; the 3,3-dichloro compound reaction proceeded at a lower temperature.

The 3,3-dichloro compound reacts readily with alcohols to give the 3,3-dialkoxy derivative (70), which is readily hydrolyzed to o-chloro-sulfonylbenzoates.[69,74,250,383,389]

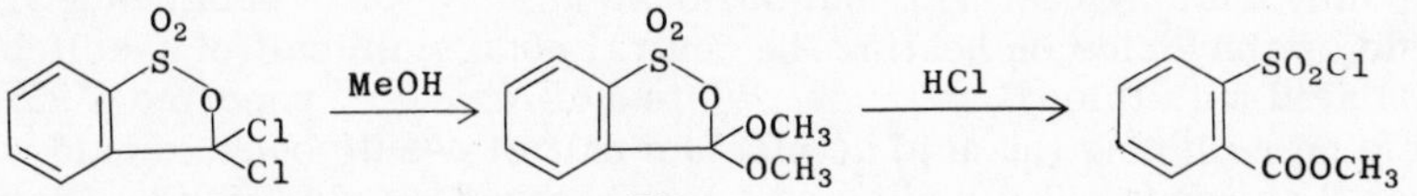

Phenols react similarly,[69,383,394] although unless a base is present a sulfonephthalein (71) is formed.[250]

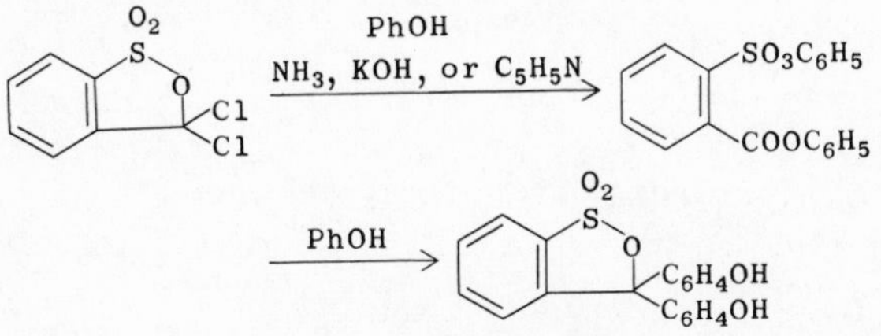

3,3-Dichloro-3H-2,1-benzoxathiole 1,1-dioxide reacts with benzene in the presence of aluminum chloride to give the 3,3-diphenyl derivative (58); the final product on continued reaction is o-phenylsulfonebenzophenone (72).[136,222,292,380,383,385]

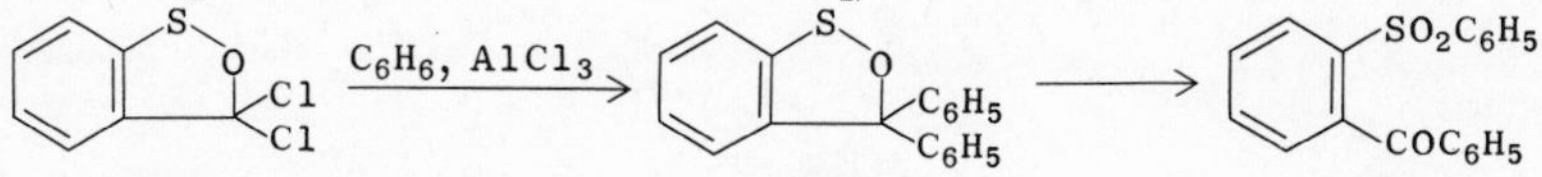

[For references, see pp. 289-312.]

Delisle[95] obtained *o*-mercaptobenzoic acid on reducing the 3, 3-dichloro compound with zinc and sulfuric acid.

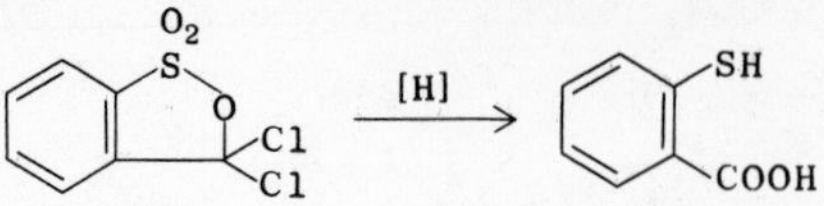

63

b.   3*H*-2, 1-Benzoxathiol-3-one 1, 1-Dioxide

(1) Preparation

    3*H*-2, 1-Benzoxathiol-3-one 1, 1-dioxide (**73**) was first prepared in 1889 by Remsen and Dohme,[175] who treated *o*-sulfobenzoic acid with phosphorus pentoxide at 130°, and by Fahlberg and Barge,[125] who treated *o*-sulfobenzoic acid with acetyl chloride with warming and the neutral potassium salt of *o*-sulfobenzoic acid with phosphorus pentachloride with warming. Sohon[444] prepared the anhydride by heating the acid potassium salt of *o*-sulfobenzoic acid with phosphorus pentachloride and phosphoryl chloride. Mathews[311] and Taverne[455] obtained the anhydride by heating *o*-sulfobenzoic acid. Cobb[74] obtained a 31% yield of anhydride on heating the neutral potassium salt of *o*-sulfobenzoic acid with thionyl chloride; White and Acree[506] reported a 93% yield on refluxing the acid ammonium salt of *o*-sulfobenzoic acid with thionyl chloride. The White and Acree method, as modified by Clarke and Dreger,[73] is a convenient method for the preparation. Vodák and Leminger[481, 483] obtained an 85% yield of anhydride by refluxing the acid ammonium salt of *o*-sulfobenzoic acid with phosphorus trichloride in benzene.

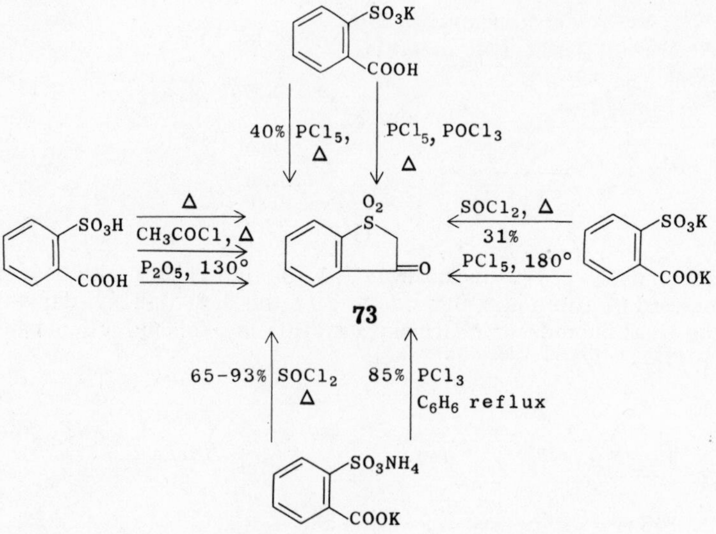

73

In an attempt to prepare the symmetrical acid fluoride of o-sulfobenzoic acid or 3, 3-difluoro-3H-2, 1-benzoxathiole 1, 1-dioxide by heating the symmetrical acid chloride of o-sulfobenzoic acid with zinc fluoride, Davies and Dick[90] obtained instead a small amount of the anhydride.

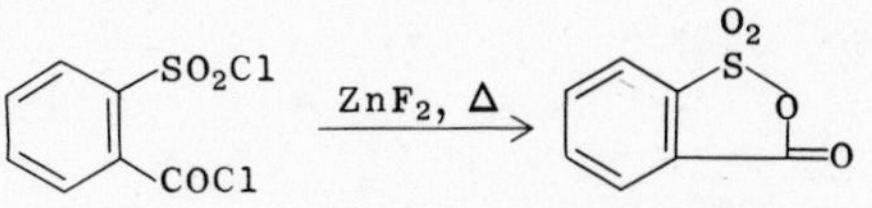

73

o-Sulfobenzoic acid undergoes dehydration and simultaneous substitution when treated with concentrated or fuming sulfuric acid and nitric acid or a halogen. Thus, Stubbs[452] obtained 5-nitro-3H-2, 1-benzoxathiol-3-one 1, 1-dioxide (74) on heating o-sulfobenzoic acid with a mixture of sulfuric and nitric acids.

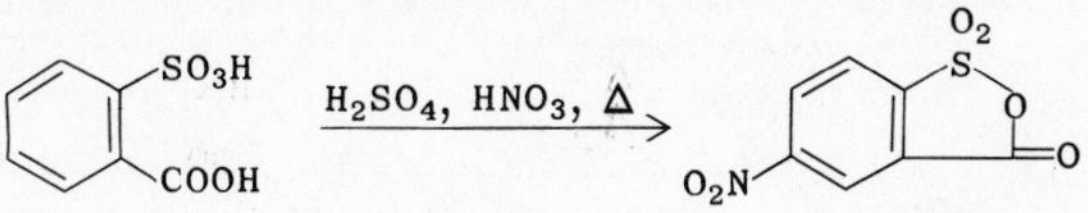

74

Twiss[465] and Twiss and Farinholt[466] prepared halogenated 3H-2, 1-benzoxathiol-3-one 1, 1-dioxides in good yields by treating o-sulfobenzoic acid with 60% fuming sulfuric acid and a halogen. The temperature of the reaction determined the degree of halogenation; a trace of iodine catalyzed the reaction. It is difficult to account for the orientation in 76 and 77.

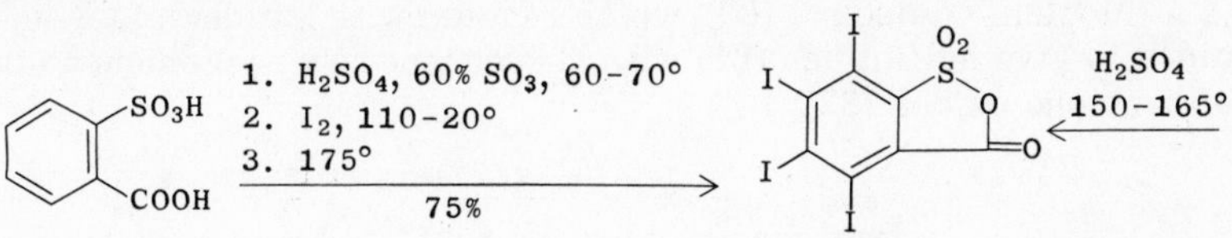

75

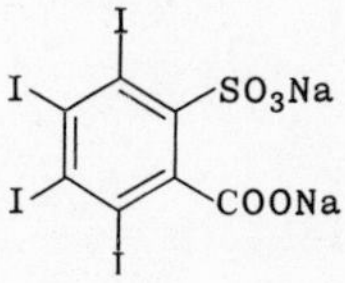

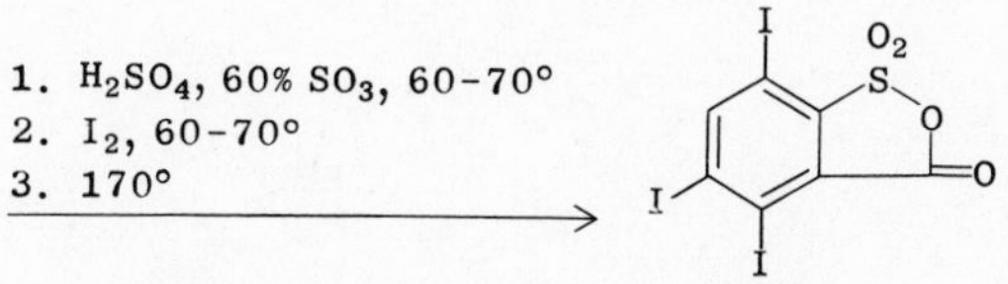

76

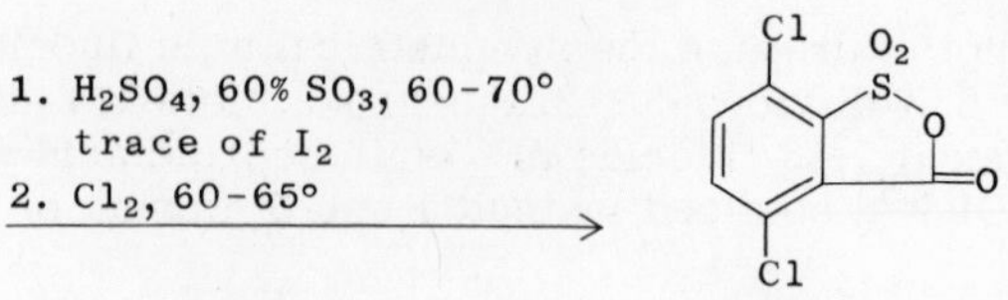
1. H_2SO_4, 60% SO_3, 60-70°
trace of I_2
2. Cl_2, 60-65°
Cl
O_2
S
O
O
Cl

77

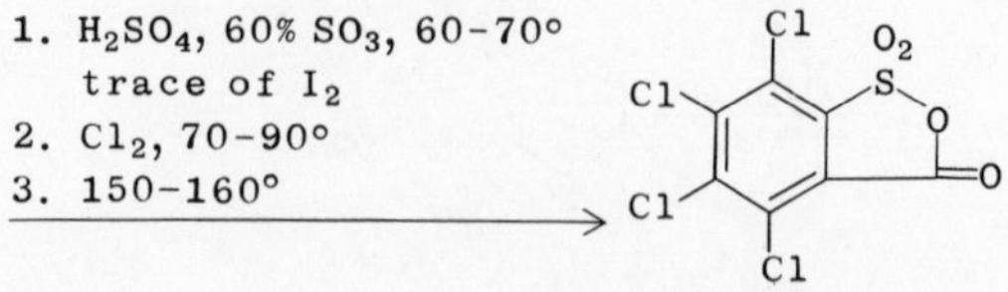
1. H_2SO_4, 60% SO_3, 60-70°
trace of I_2
2. Cl_2, 70-90°
3. 150-160°
Cl
O_2
S
O
Cl
Cl
O
Cl

78

Price and Smiles[364] reported the preparation of 1,1-dichloro-3*H*-2,1-benzoxathiol-3-one (**79**), which may be considered as a derivative of the anhydride of *o*-carboxybenzenesulfinic acid. They obtained good yields of this compound by the action of chlorine on *o*-mercaptobenzoic acid.

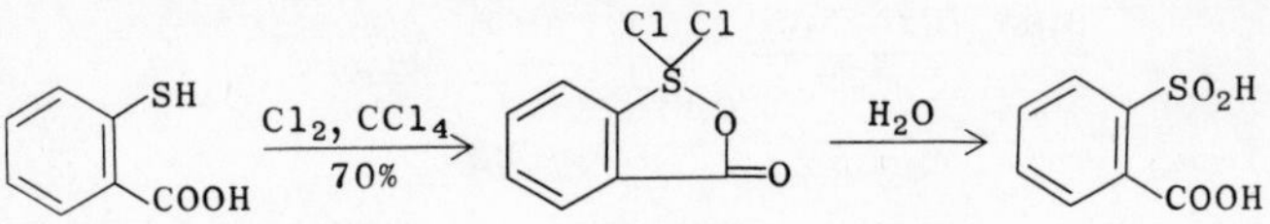
SH
COOH
Cl_2, CCl_4
70%
Cl Cl
S
O
O
H_2O
SO_2H
COOH

79

The 1,1-dichloro compound (**79**) was not isolated, and the evidence for its existence was deduced from its reaction with water, phenol, and *p*-nitrophenol. Hart, McClelland, and Fowkes[180a,183] reacted *o*-mercaptobenzoic acid with chlorine in the presence of ferric chloride and presumably obtained the same product. They suggested that the product was a thionium compound (**80**), which reacted with sulfonamides and amides to give sulfimines (**81**) with subsequent rearrangement to benzisothiazolone oxides (**82**).

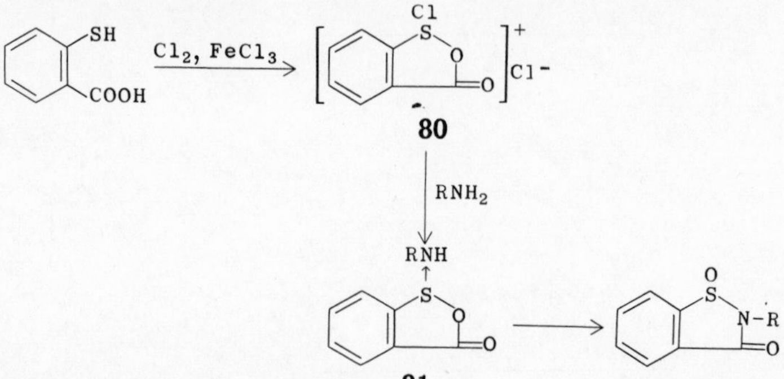
SH
COOH
Cl_2, $FeCl_3$
Cl
S
O
O
+
Cl^-
80
RNH_2
RNH
S
O
O
O
S
N-R
O

81 **82**

Douglas and Farah,[108a] from their study of this reaction, suggest that the Price and Smiles product was probably *o*-chlorosulfinylbenzoyl chloride, and not **79**.

TABLE 4. 3H-2,1-Benzoxathiol-3-one 1,1-Dioxides

Substituent	Yield (%)	M.p. (°C)	Ref.
None	65	126-127 (b.p. 184-186/18 mm)	73
	85	123-126	481, 483
	93	—	506
	31	—	74, 185
	80	—	110
	—	118-119	125
	—	124-125	90
	—	128	379
	—	129.5	444
	—	130	311, 456
6-CH$_3$-	—	97	496
5-O$_2$N-	—	212	452
5,6-Br$_2$	—	—	465
4,7-Br$_2$	80	167-168	466
4,7-Cl$_2$	45	121-122	466
5,6-I$_2$	—	—	465
4,7-I$_2$	55	243-245	466
4,6,7-I$_3$	65	287-288	466
4,5,6,7-Br$_4$	75	216-217	465, 466
4,5,6,7-Cl$_4$	67	158-159	465, 466
4,5,6,7-I$_4$	75	300 (dec.)	465, 466

[For references, see pp. 289-312.]

D'Silva and McClelland[96a] postulated 3H-2, 1-benzoxathiol-3-one (83) as an intermediate in the disproportionation of 2, 2′-dithiobenzoic acid in the presence of acetic anhydride and potassium acetate. The final product was 3-hydroxy-2-acetyl-1-thianaphthene (86).

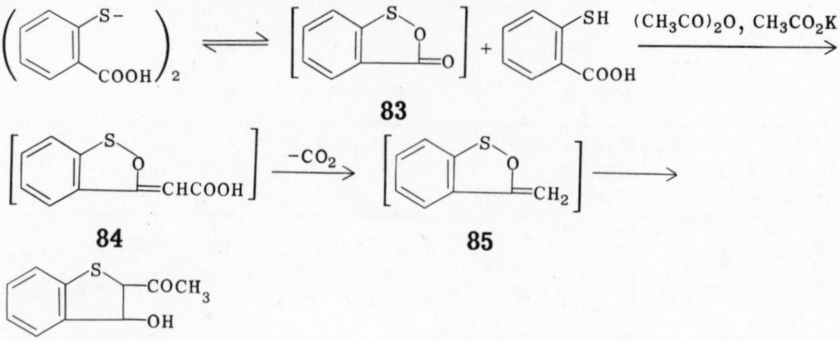

83

84   **85**

86

Schönberg, Rupp, and Gumlich[424a] cited this reaction as evidence for free radical formation involving a mercaptyl radical. There is no evidence, however, that 3H-2, 1-benzoxathiol-3-one (83) was formed.

The 3H-2, 1-benzoxathiol-3-one 1, 1-dioxides described in the literature are listed in Table 4.

(2) Properties and Reactions

3H-2, 1-Benzoxathiol-3-one 1, 1-dioxides are crystalline, sharp-melting, colorless compounds. They have higher melting points than the 3-unsubstituted, the 3-chloro, or the 3, 3-dichloro compounds. Although these compounds are analogous to saccharin, they do not have a sweet taste; actually 3H-2, 1-benzoxathiol-3-one 1, 1-dioxide has a bitter taste.[262]

The 3-one derivatives are quite sensitive to water.[73,110,379,444, 452,465,466] Moist air converts 3H-2, 1-benzoxathiol-3-one 1, 1-dioxide to o-sulfobenzoic acid;[73,379] the reaction is violent when heat is applied to its mixture with water.[110]

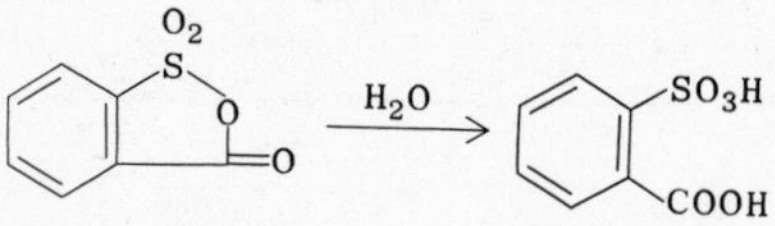

Ammonia reacts with 3H-2, 1-benzoxathiol-3-one 1, 1-dioxide in ether[444] or benzene[125,456] to give ammonium o-sulfobenzamide. The same product is obtained in low yields along with products of decomposition when the melted 3-one is treated with dry ammonia.[125] Reaction with methylamine[456] and anilines[444] in benzene give the N-substituted-o-sulfobenzamides.

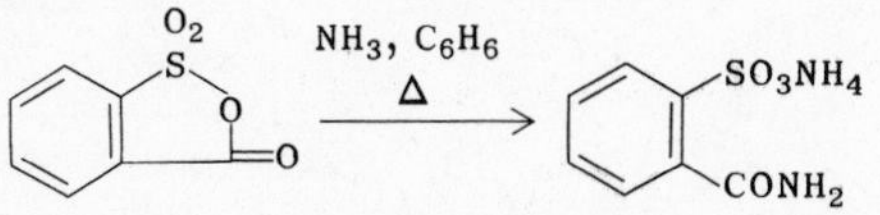

3H-2,1-Benzoxathiol-3-one 1,1-dioxide reacts readily with alcohols,[110, 161, 444] such as methanol, ethanol, and 2-ethylhexanol, to give the corresponding o-sulfobenzoate. 2-Ethylhexyl o-sulfobenzoate is claimed to be useful as a dentrifice detergent.[161]

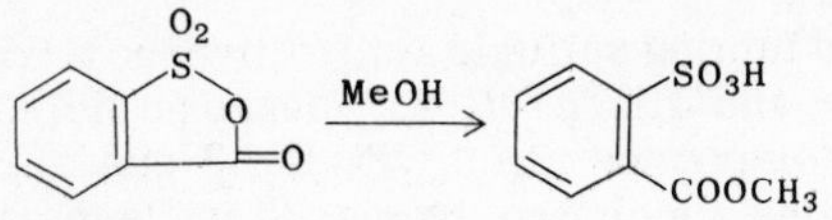

According to Sohon,[444] benzamide reacts with the 3-one compound to give o-sulfobenzoic acid and benzonitrile.

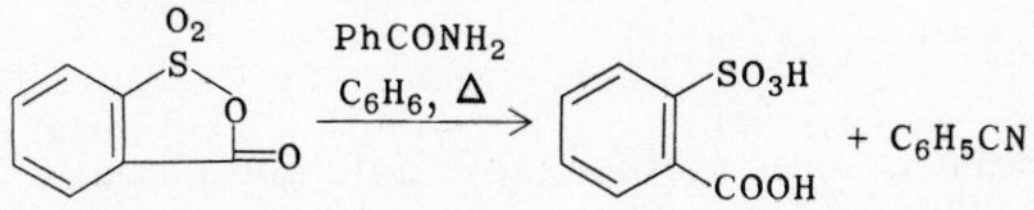

Phenylmagnesium bromide reacts with the 3-one to give α,α-diphenyl-o-sulfobenzyl alcohol.[74]

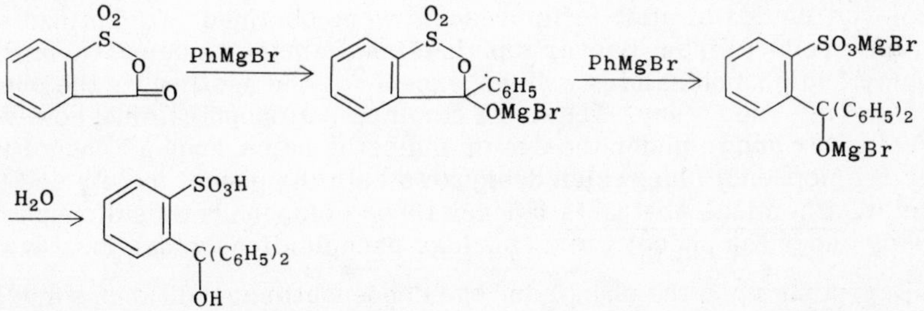

According to a German patent,[330] the 3-one combines with alkylenediamines, phenylenediamines, o-aminophenols, and o-aminothiophenols to yield imidazoles, oxazoles, or thiazoles, which are intermediates for dyes and pharmaceuticals.

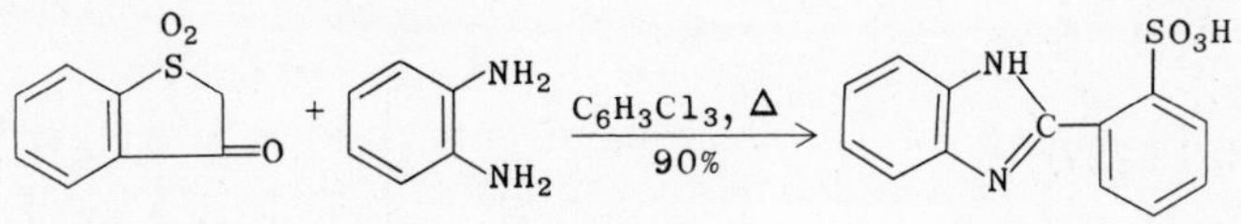

[For references, see pp. 289-312.]

$3H$-2, 1-Benzoxathiol-3-one 1, 1-dioxide reacts with PCl_5 to give a mixture of the two chlorides and with $POCl_3$ to give a low yield of the 3, 3-dichloro derivative.[74,136,444] Its reaction with PCl_5 in a sealed tube at 170° gives only the symmetrical chloride.[136]

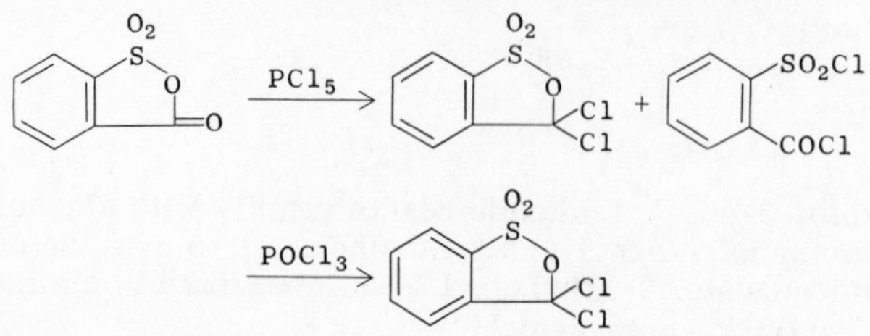

The 3-one has been halogenated in fuming sulfuric acid to give the tetra-chloro-, tetrabromo-, tetraiodo-, and diiodo-$3H$-2, 1-benzoxathiol-3-one 1, 1-dioxides.[465] Phenolic compounds react with the 3-one, splitting out water, to give sulfonephthaleins which are discussed in the next section. In alkaline media, however, phenolic compounds react like alcohols to open the ring.[185]

c. Sulfonephthaleins

The structural analogy between o-sulfobenzoic acid and phthalic acid prompted Remsen in 1884[376] to begin his studies on the reaction of o-sulfobenzoic acid and its derivatives with a variety of phenolic compounds. In a preliminary investigation, in which resorcinol was heated with potassium o-sulfobenzoate, saccharin, or 4-nitro- or 4-bromo-2-sulfobenzoic acid in the presence of concentrated sulfuric acid, dark-colored liquids similar to fluorescein were obtained. To distinguish these products from Baeyer's phthaleins, Remsen assigned them the name "sulphonphthaleins", which, except for the spelling, is the one commonly used today. The more common sulfonephthaleins, however, are better known under the dye or indicator name, such as phenol red or bromophenol blue, which designates both the phenol moiety and the color. Chemical Abstracts indéxes these compounds as sulfonephthaleins under the phenol name; such as phenolsulfonephthalein.

Depending upon the phenol and the condensation conditions, some sulfonephthaleins have the spiro(3H-2, 1-benzoxathiole-3, 9′-xanthene) structure (**87**).

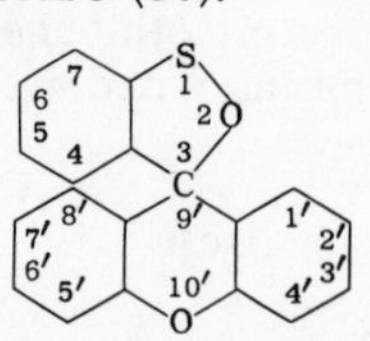

87 (RRI 5827)

Evidence is lacking in practically every reported preparation to allow one to specify whether or not the xanthene structure was obtained.

The various sulfonephthaleins whose preparations have been described in the literature are listed in Table 6. Because the nomenclature for substituted sulfonephthaleins is somewhat confusing, the sulfonephthaleins in Table 6 are specified by the phenol reactant, the substitution in the 3H-2, 1-benzoxathiole moiety, and ester, ether, oxide, or salt formation. Thus, the benzoate of bromophenol blue (from 3H-2, 1-benzoxathiol-3-one 1, 1-dioxide and 2, 6-dibromophenol) is listed as 2′, 6′-dibromophenol-, dibenzoate (88).

88

(1) Preparation

(a) Phenolsulfonephthalein (Phenol Red) (89). Remsen and Saunders[383] in 1895 and List and Stein[292] in 1898 prepared phenolsulfonephthalein (89) by heating phenol with the dichlorides of o-sulfobenzoic acid (62 and 63). Sohon[444] prepared it in a relatively pure state by heating 3H-2, 1-benzoxathiol-3-one 1, 1-dioxide (73) with phenol. Under relatively mild conditions, phenol and other phenolic compounds react with the dichlorides or anhydride of o-sulfobenzoic acid to give the phenyl esters of o-sulfobenzoic acid.[69,185,385,394] The unsymmetrical chloride (63) reacts faster than does the symmetrical chloride (62). At a sufficiently high temperature, phenolsulfonephthalein is obtained. Particularly in the presence of base, potassium hydroxide or pyridine, the two dichlorides yield the diphenyl ester; in the absence of base the two dichlorides, such as from 5-methyl-4-nitro-2-sulfobenzoic acid,[250] yield the phenolsulfonephthalein.

The reaction between the anhydride and phenol is best carried out at 130—140° [295,367,444,506] or fusion temperatures[437] for 6—24 hours. According to Freas and Provine,[132] the best conditions for the reaction between saccharin (64) and phenol are a temperature of 120°, a reaction time of up to 48 hours, the use of sulfuric acid as the condensing agent, and a ratio of reactants of 1 : 5 : 4 of saccharin : phenol : sulfuric acid; the yield of phenolsulfonephthalein is 25%. A recent French patent[360a] claims the preparation of phenolsulfonephthalein and of o-cresolsulfonephthalein by the condensation of saccharin with oleum (20-25% SO$_3$) at 130° and subsequent reaction of the reaction mixture with the phenol in the presence of ZnCl$_2$ for 2–3 hours at 130-140°. Lubs and Clarke on condensing phenol with the symmetrical chloride used ZnCl$_2$ as the condensing agent.[294] Orndorff and Sherwood,[393] on

[For references, see pp. 289-312.]

the other hand, prepared the sulfonephthalein in 50% yield by heating the symmetrical chloride with an excess of phenol at 135-140°; the use of $ZnCl_2$, although not increasing the yield, did allow a shorter heating time.

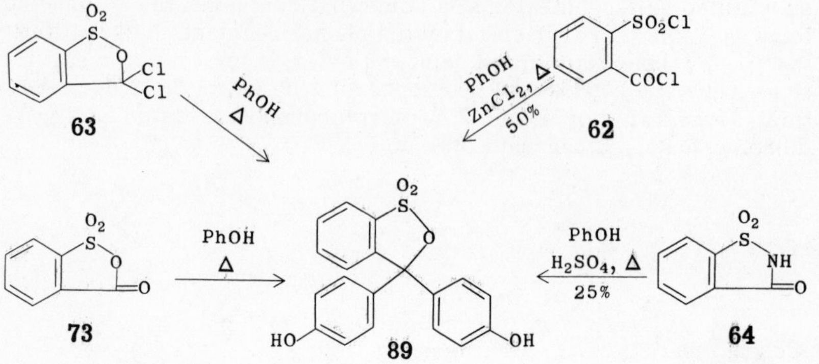

(b) Cresolsulfonephthaleins (o-Cresol Red (90) and m-Cresol Purple (91 or 92)). o-Cresolsulfonephthalein (90) has been prepared under essentially the same conditions as used for phenolsulfonephthalein - a reaction temperature of 130-140° without a catalyst[77,367,444] or at 105-123° with $ZnCl_2$[294,349,348] and a reaction time of up to 24 hours.

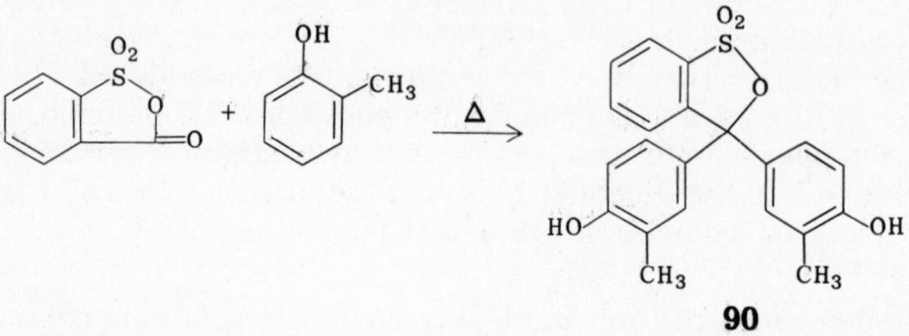

The product was described as carmine-red, green reflecting crystals, whose alkaline solutions are red and whose neutral or acid solutions are yellow. A similar product was obtained on using p-cresol. This sulfonephthalein also has been prepared[240] in a yield of 12% through the condensation of saccharin with o-cresol in the presence of sulfuric acid at 130-140°; under similar conditions, m-cresol did not yield a sulfonephthalein.

Orndorff and Purdy,[348] on reacting m-cresol with 3H-2,1-benzoxathiol-3-one, obtained two different products 91 or 92, depending upon the condensation temperature.

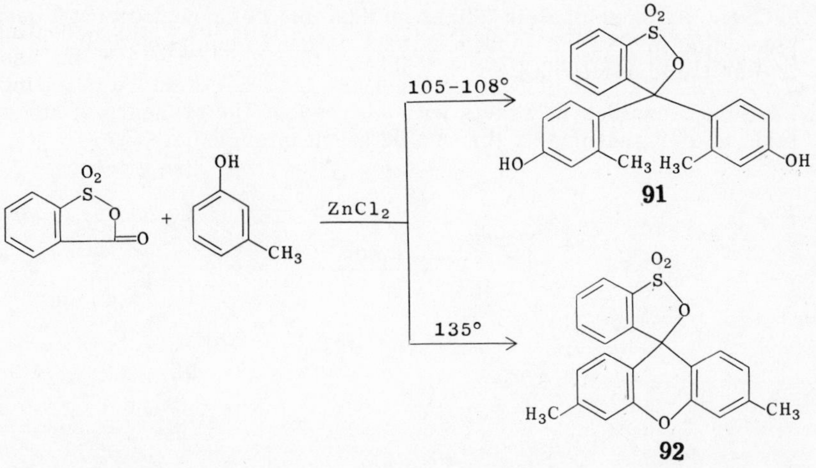

91

92

Cohen[77] called *m*-cresolsulfonephthalein meta-cresol purple. Orndorff and Beach[349] obtained a 20% yield of sulfonephthalein (**93**) from the reaction of *p*-cresol with 3*H*-2,1-benzoxathiol-3-one.

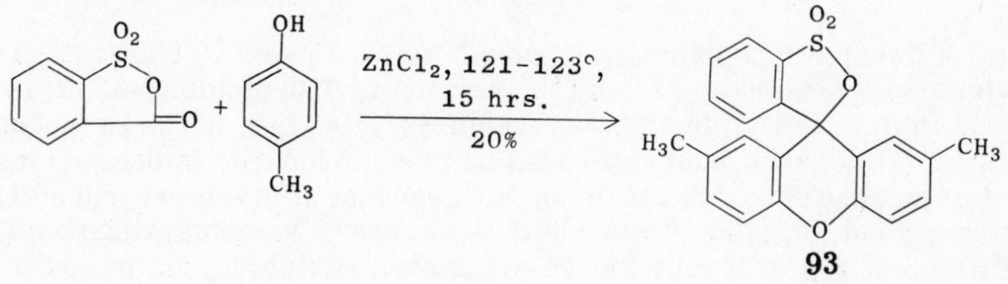

93

On reacting *p*-cresol with the symmetrical chloride in the presence of base, they obtained di-(*p*-cresyl)-*o*-sulfobenzoate (**94**) which on heating at 170° in the presence of ZnCl$_2$ gave 9-(*o*-sulfophenyl)xanthydrol (**95**) which lost water on treatment with concentrated hydrochloric acid to give *p*-cresolsulfonephthalein (**93**).

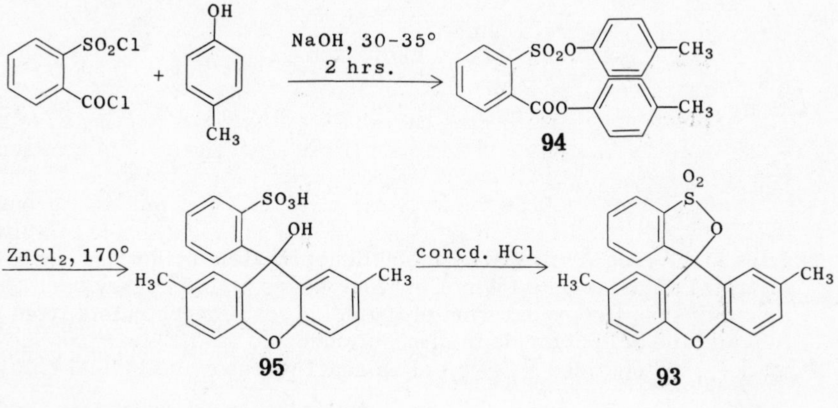

94

95

93

[For references, see pp. 289-312.]

121

p-Cresolsulfonephthalein (**93**) is an unstable compound, giving a deep blue color in alkaline solutions and a yellow to colorless color in neutral and acid solutions.

o-Sulfobenzaldehyde reacts with o-cresol in the presence of 20% sulfuric acid[96] presumably through **96** as an intermediate.

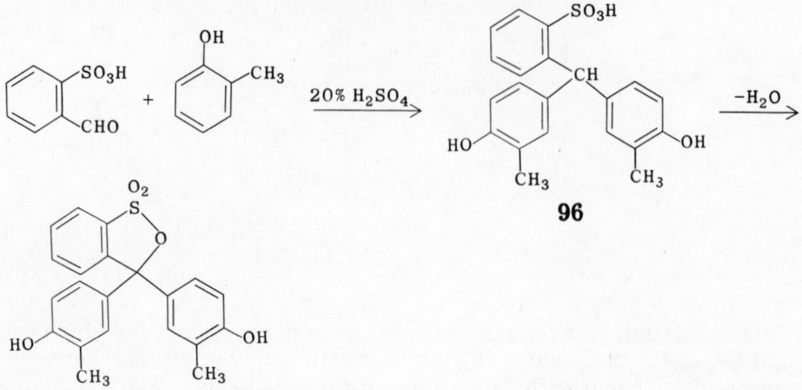

96

90

(c) <u>Xylenolsulfonephthalein (Xylenol Blue)</u>. Cohen[76] obtained 3,4-xylenolsulfonephthalein from the reaction of 3,3-dichloro-3H-2,1-benzoxathiole 1,1-dioxide with 3,4-xylenol at 105-110° in the presence of ZnCl$_2$. This sulfonephthalein also has been prepared in poor yields (8%) from the reaction of 3,4-xylenol with saccharin in the presence of sulfuric acid at 130-140°.[240] A yield of 17.5%[240] was obtained from the reaction of 3,4-xylenol with the symmetrical chloride in the presence of ZnCl$_2$ at 100-110°. It has been prepared also from 3,4-xylenol and 3H-2,1-benzoxathiol-3-one 1,1-dioxide.[77]

(d) <u>Thymolsulfonephthalein (**97**) (Thymol Blue)</u>. Lubs and Clarke[294] prepared thymolsulfonephthalein (**97**) by heating thymol and the symmetrical chloride in the presence of ZnCl$_2$.

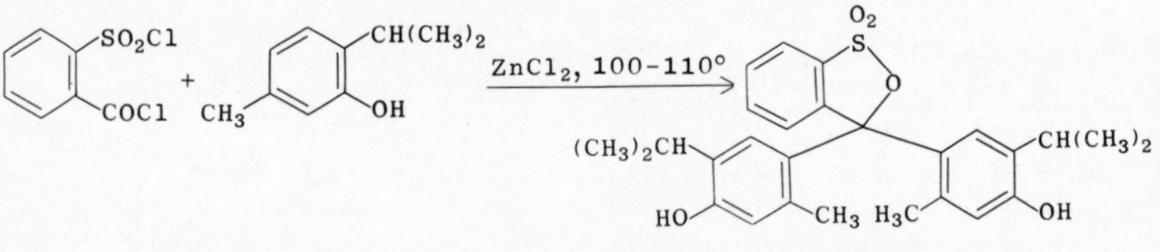

97

Lubs and Acree[295] prepared the sulfonephthalein by heating the symmetrical chloride with thymol for four hours at 140°. They used ZnCl$_2$ as catalyst in the preparation of thymolnitrosulfonephthalein from thymol and the acid chloride of nitrosulfobenzoic acid. Javery and co-workers[240] obtained a 34% yield on reacting the symmetrical chloride with thymol in the presence of ZnCl$_2$ at 100-110° for up to 8 hours. They obtained only 5% yields from the reaction of saccharin and thymol in the presence of sulfuric acid for 8-10 hours at 130-140°.

According to Orndorff and Cornwell[346] the formation of thymolsulfonephthalein from thymol and the anhydride occurs in two stages.

The intermediate acid, 4'-hydroxy-5'-isopropyl-2'-methylbenzoylbenzene-2-sulfonic acid (98), or its sultone form (99), then reacts with another molecule of thymol at 85° in the presence of ZnCl$_2$ to give the sulfonephthalein. The tautomeric nature of the intermediate was established by making various derivatives of both the ketone (98) and the sultone (99). The position of attachment of the thymol ring was determined by fusion of the intermediate with potassium hydroxide and identification of p-thymotic acid. The intermediate, on heating above 150°, decomposed to give thymolsulfonephthalein, o-sulfobenzoic acid, and water; in the presence of ZnCl$_2$, the decomposition occurred at 135°.

Orndorff and Cornwell studied the effect of ZnCl$_2$ on the reaction of 3H-2, 1-benzoxathiol-3-one 1, 1-dioxide with thymol. A 55% yield was obtained when the reaction was carried out at 105-110° in the presence of ZnCl$_2$. At lower temperatures and at 120-125°, the yields were 30-35%; above 125°, the product was a green tar. Without the ZnCl$_2$, only 4% thymolsulfonephthalein was obtained. Condensations of thymol with the chlorides of o-sulfobenzoic acid without condensing agents and with ZnCl$_2$ and AlCl$_3$ at 100-110° gave mainly dithymyl o-sulfobenzoate and 10-15% thymolsulfonephthalein; at higher temperatures, only tars were obtained. It was not possible to convert dithymyl o-sulfobenzoate to thymolsulfonephthalein by warming with an equivalent amount of either AlCl$_3$ or SnCl$_4$.

An 80% yield of thymolsulfonephthalein was obtained by Chrzaszczewski, Koziński, and Wroński[71] by the condensation of the ammonium salt of o-sulfobenzoic acid with thymol in the presence of P$_2$O$_5$ at 130-140° for not more than 4 hours and steam distilling the thymol at the end of the reaction.

(e) <u>Hydroquinonesulfonephthalein.</u> Sohon[444] described the condensation product of hydroquinone and $3H$-2, 1-benzoxathiol-3-one 1, 1-dioxide obtained on heating the mixture at 130-135° as a dark brown mass whose alkaline solutions were brown-yellow. Henderson,[209] on the other hand, was able to isolate only the ester from the reaction of hydroquinone with 4-nitro-2-chlorosulfonylbenzoyl chloride at 120-135°. Orndorff and Shapiro[350] questioned whether Sohon actually isolated hydroquinonesulfonephthalein. In their studies of the condensation of the 3-one and hydroquinone, a 20% yield was obtained by heating at 130° for 18-24 hours; in the presence of $ZnCl_2$ the yield was only 5%; in the presence of H_2SO_4, H_3BO_3, or $SnCl_4$ only tarry material was obtained. Its alkaline solutions were colored blue-purple and its neutral solutions orange-red.

(f) <u>Resorcinolsulfonephthalein</u> (**100**). Remsen and Hays[377] reported the preparation of resorcinolsulfonephthalein (**100**) which they called "sulfonfluorescein", by the condensation of the 3-one with resorcinol.

100

In a later paper Remsen and Linn[378] stated that the product was not as believed but the intermediate o-(2, 4-dihydroxybenzoyl)benzenesulfonic acid (**101**), which they were able to prepare in a rather pure form by condensing resorcinol with ammonium o-sulfobenzoate at 175-185°. The intermediate, on being heated at 160-170°, yielded resorcinolsulfonephthalein (**100**).

101   **100**

Fahlberg and Barge,[125] on repeating the work of Remsen and Hayes, but using o-sulfobenzoic acid or its ammonium salt, obtained the sulfonephthalein as red crystals and proposed various formulas for the product. Blackshear[46] obtained a 32% yield of sulfonephthalein on heating the intermediate (**101**) of Remsen and Linn at 160-180°. White[502] also reported the conversion of the intermediate (**101**) to the sulfone-

phthalein, but on condensing resorcinol with o-sulfobenzoic acid at 140°
he obtained products which could not be characterized. Jones[243] similarly reported the conversion of 6-(2, 4-dihydroxybenzoyl)-3-methyl-
benzenesulfonic acid to the corresponding sulfonephthalein, which he
called "p-methylsulfonfluorescein", and noted the difficulty of chara-
terizing the condensation products from resorcinol and 4-methyl-2-
sulfobenzoic acid.

Orndorff and Vose,[344] on the other hand,reported that resorcinolsulfonephthalein is readily formed on heating the intermediate (101) at
160-170° for 2 hours; it was also obtained by heating the intermediate
with resorcinol at 160-170°.

Contrary to Fahlberg and Barge,[125] and White,[502] Sohon[444] and
Orndorff and Vose[344] obtained the sulfonephthalein by heating 3H-2, 1-
benzoxathiol-3-one 1, 1-dioxide with resorcinol at 130-140°.

Moale[329] condensed resorcinol with 4-methoxy-2-sulfobenzoic acid
at 110-115° to the corresponding resorcinolmethoxysulfonephthalein
which he called "p-methoxysulfonefluorescein".

Sisley[439] prepared resorcinolsulfonephthalein by heating saccharin
and resorcinol at 150-180° with sulfuric acid. Monnet and Koetschet[331]
on hydrolyzing "resorcinolsaccharein" (102), obtained resorcinolsulfonephthalein (100), which they called "sulfurein".

102   **100**

Orndorff and Vose[344] obtained a 52% yield of resorcinolsulfonephthalein on heating saccharin and resorcinol with sulfuric acid at 135-140°
for seven hours.

Henderson[209] prepared a sulfonephthalein by heating 4-nitro-2-
sulfobenzoic acid dichloride with resorcinol at 125°. Orndorff and
Vose,[344] on heating o-sulfobenzoic acid dichloride with resorcinol at
100° for 12 hours, obtained a 41% yield of the sulfonephthalein. On heating the dichloride with 4-ethylresorcinol at 100-110° for 7-8 hours in
the presence of ZnCl$_2$, Javery and co-workers[240] reported a 60% yield
of sulfonephthalein.

(g) Pyrocatecholsulfonephthalein (103 or 104) (Pyrocatechol Violet
and Pyrocatechol Green). Vodak and Leminger[482,484] prepared pyrocatecholsulfonephthalein by fusing pyrocatechol and 3H-2, 1-benzoxa-
thiol-3-one 1, 1-dioxide at 100-110°.

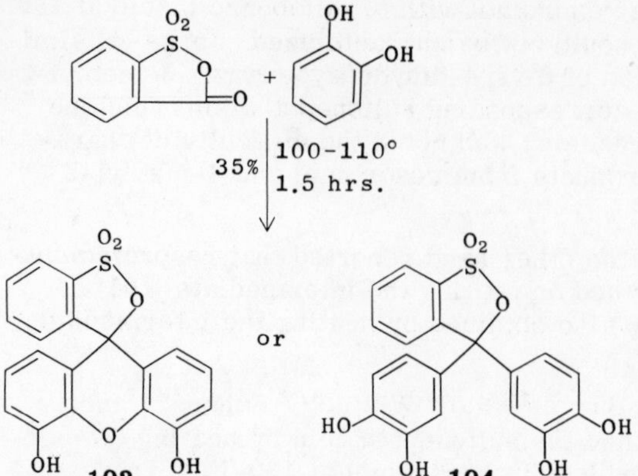

It is not known whether the condensation occurs ortho or para to the phenolic hydroxyls. This is an area which requires more evidence than presently available. It would not be surprising if a mixture of both were actually formed.

(h) Pyrogallolsulfonephthalein (**105** and **106**). Henderson [209] reported that six moles of pyrogallol react with 4-nitro-2-sulfobenzoic acid dichloride. Orndorff and Fuchs[347] obtained the sulfonephthalein in a series of reactions from ammonium o-sulfobenzoic acid and pyrogallol.

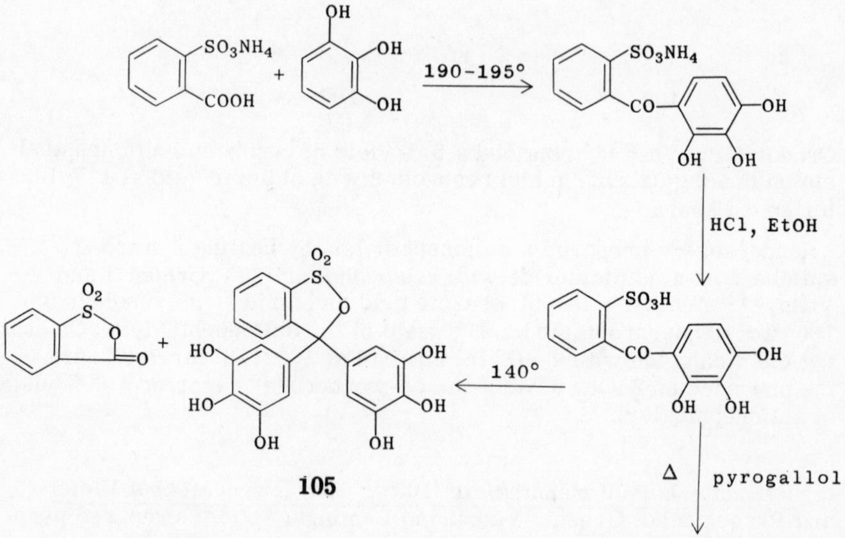

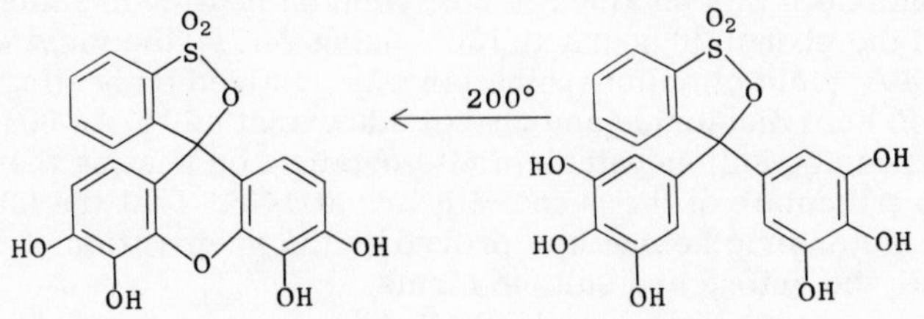

106   105

On heating 3H-2, 1-benzoxathiol-3-one 1, 1-dioxide and pyrogallol at 130-135°, Orndorff and Fuchs obtained a 51% yield of sulfonephthalein both with and without ZnCl$_2$; on heating the dichloride and pyrogallol they obtained only the diester; on heating saccharin and pyrogallol with concentrated sulfuric acid, a 20% yield of sulfonephthalein was obtained.

Whereas Sohon[444] postulated the xanthene structure, (106), for the product he obtained on heating the anhydride with pyrogallol, Orndorff and Fuchs believed that this structure, which they called "sulfonegallein", occurred on heating pyrogallolsulfonephthalein, (105), at 200° and was easily converted to the sulfonephthalein in the presence of moisture.

Vodák and Leminger[487] prepared pyrogallolsulfonephthalein by azeotropic condensation of 3H-2, 1-benzoxathiol-3-one 1, 1-dioxide with pyrogallol using xylene. Adsorption spectra indicated the xanthene structure (106).

(i) Hydroxyhydroquinonesulfonephthalein (108). Orndorff and Willard[351] postulated that the formation of this sulfonephthalein (108) occurs through the benzoyl intermediate (107) step they had observed for other sulfonephthaleins.

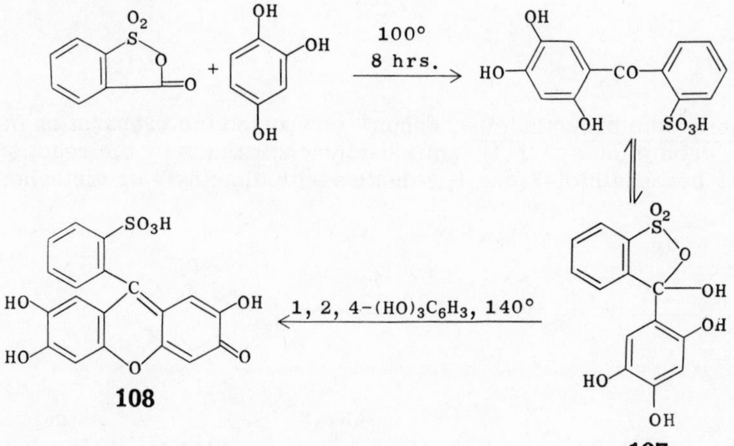

108   107

The sulfonephthalein was obtained in 30% yield on heating o-sulfoben-zoic acid and the phenol 30 hours at 130°; using $ZnCl_2$, the yield was only 15%. A 40% yield of sulfonephthalein was obtained on heating the o-sulfobenzoic acid dichloride and phenol 3 hours at 120°. An 80% yield of the corresponding sulfonephthalein was obtained on heating the anhy-dride and the triacetate of the phenol 8 hours at 140°. That the inter-mediate is a tautomeric ketone was proved by the preparation of deri-vatives of both the ketone and sultone forms.

(j) α-Naphtholsulfonephthalein (**109**). Lubs and Clark[294] reported the preparation of α-naphtholsulfonephthalein (**109**) by the reaction of α-naphthol with the dichloride.

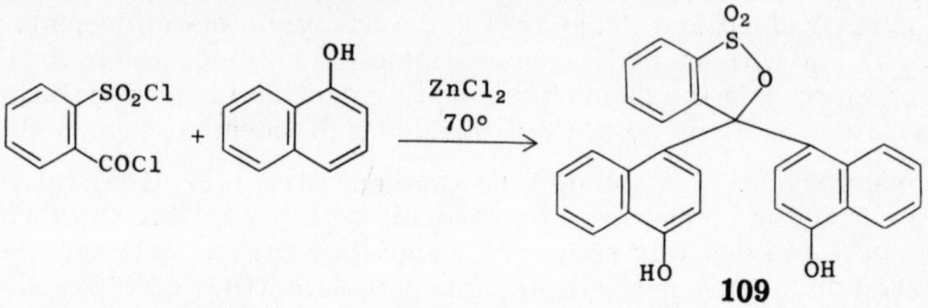

(k) Salicylsulfonephthalein (**110**) (Salicyl Red). Harden[175] studied the reaction of $3H$-2, 1-benzoxathiol-3-one 1, 1-dioxide with salicylic acid in the presence of $SnCl_4$ and concentrated sulfuric acid to give salicyl-sulfonephthalein (**110**). It is likely that the xanthene compound was formed.

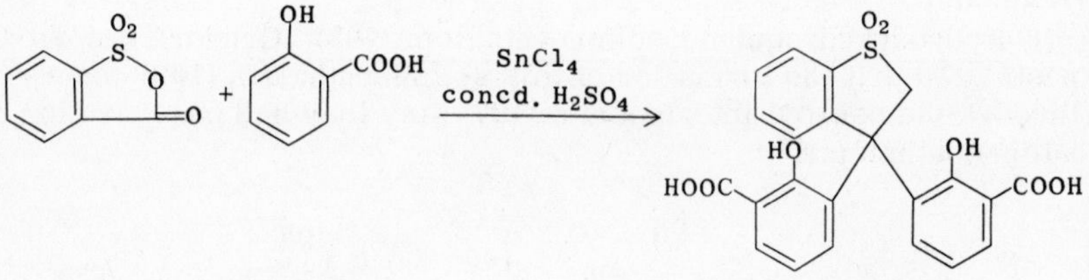

(l) Anilinosulfonephthaleins. Sohon[443] reported the preparation of diethyl- and dimethyl (**111**) -anilinosulfonephthaleins by the reaction of $3H$-2, 1-benzoxathiol-3-one 1, 1-dioxide with dimethyl- or diethylani-line.

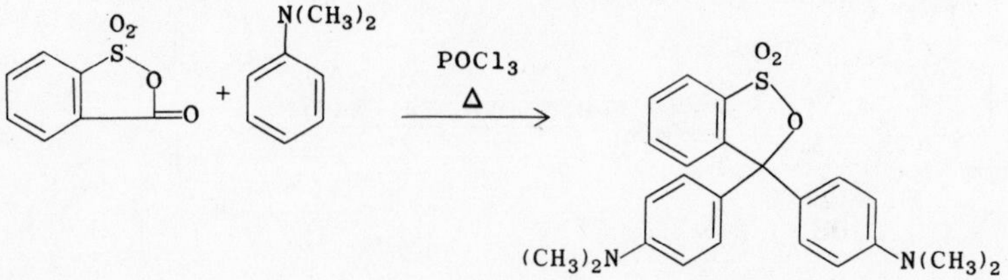

The reaction with *m*-aminophenol was assumed to proceed to the xanthene structure (**112**).[444]

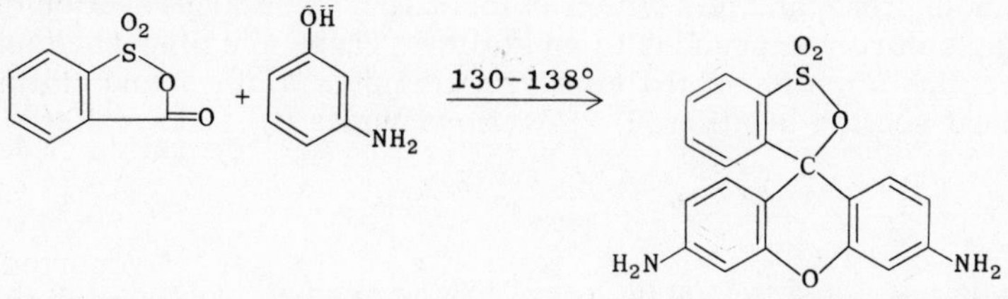

112

Sandmeyer's[412] successive oxidation of sulfonated tetramethyldiaminodiphenylmethane and condensation of the hydrol with dimethylaniline may have led to a sulfonephthalein (**113**).

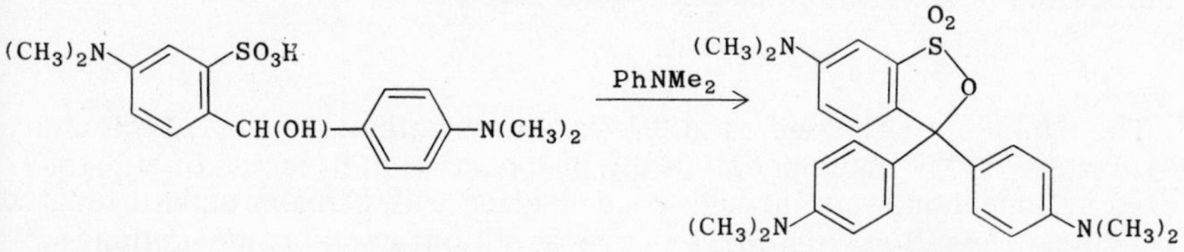

113

He did not assign a sulfonephthalein structure to the product which he characterized as a dye, nor did Knecht and Hibbert[266] who used it as an indicator.

Kuhn and DeAngelis[276] described the reaction of 3, 3-dichloro-3H-2, 1-benzoxathiole 1, 1-dioxide with benzalmethylphenylhydrazone as giving a dye which contains a functional group reactive with aldehydes with change of color and demonstrated its use for the qualitative determination of aldehydes.

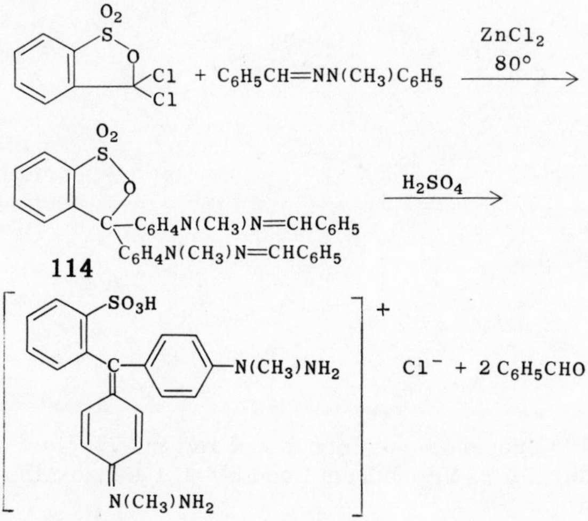

114

Most of the anilinosulfonephthaleins have been prepared by the reaction of sulfonephthaleins, which is discussed in section IB-2c(2d), affects resorcinolsulfonephthalein with a chlorinating agent and reaction of the resulting chloro compound with an aniline. These are discussed under the reactions of sulfonephthaleins with ammonia, amines, and anilines in the next section [section (2). Reactions, under (f)] and are listed in Table 7.

(m) Halogenated Sulfonephthaleins. There are two methods for the preparation of halogenated sulfonephthaleins: halogenation of sulfonephthaleins and condensation of moieties containing halogen. Halogenation of sulfonephthaleins, which is discussed in section I B-2c(2d), affects only the phenolic moiety. Vigorous halogenation destroys the molecule before the benzoxathiole can be halogenated.

The synthesis of halogenated $3H$-2, 1-benzoxathiol-3-one 1, 1-dioxide by Twiss[465,466] made possible the preparation of a series of halogenated sulfonephthaleins through condensation with phenols or halogenated phenols. Thus, Boyd and Rowe[61] prepared iodo- and bromo-sulfonephthaleins through the iodination or chlorination of $3H$-2, 1-benzoxathiol-3-one 1, 1-dioxide and condensation of the halogenated benzoxathiole with a phenol.

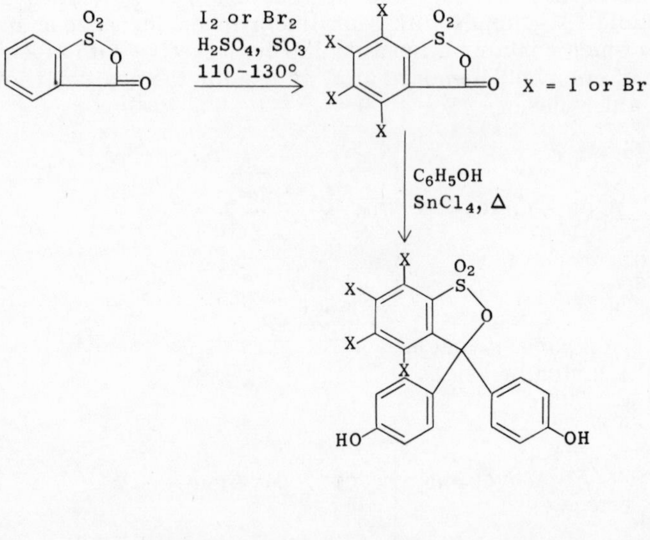

Leminger and Vodák[284] prepared o-chlorophenol red in 37% yield by heating a molten mixture of o-chlorophenol and $3H$-2, 1-benzoxathiol-3-one 1, 1-dioxide.

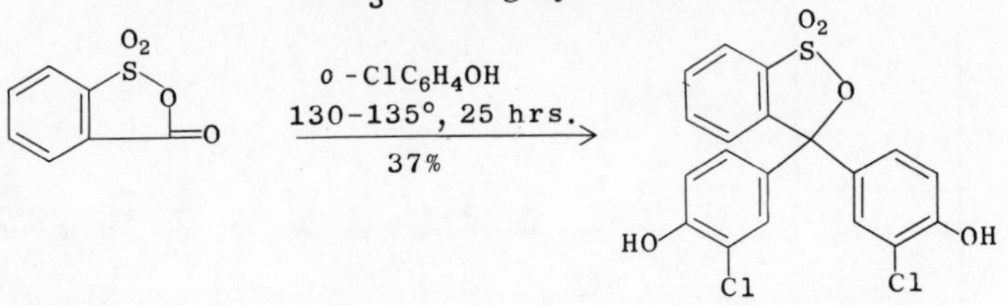

C₃OS Ring Systems

$$o\text{-}ClC_6H_4OH$$
$$130\text{-}135°,\ 25\ hrs.$$
$$37\%$$

The halogenated sulfonephthaleins prepared by a condensation reaction are listed in Table 5.

(2) Reactions

The use of sulfonephthaleins as acid-base indicators represents the most important reaction which they undergo. This reaction is discussed in section I B-2c(3), as it is the basis for elucidating the structure and properties of sulfonephthaleins.

(a) Salt Formation. Phenolsulfonephthalein reacts with sodium hydroxide to give the monosodium salt; the disodium salt is prepared by reaction with ethanol and sodium. [343] The monoammonium and barium salts of m-cresolsulfonephthalein have been prepared[348] as well as the mono- and disodium salts of tetrabromophenolsulfonephthalein. [348]

The monosodium salt of thymolsulfonephthalein, a brick-red compound, is prepared by treating thymolsulfonephthalein with aqueous sodium bicarbonate; the disodium salt, a dark-blue compound, is prepared using sodium and ethanol. [346] The zinc salt, prepared by using zinc carbonate, is soluble in water, the solution having a red color.

Treatment of hydroquinonesulfonephthalein with sodium alcoholate gives the disodium salt; treatment with barium carbonate gives the barium salt. [350]

Hydroxyhydroquinonesulfonephthalein forms a red monoammonium salt, a barium salt, a bright orange zinc salt, and a reddish potassium salt. [351]

Pyrogallolsulfonephthalein forms a deep red monosodium and a blue disodium salt. [347]

Pyrocatecholsulfonephthalein forms metal complexes with magnesium, calcium, and zinc (115) in alkaline media. [481]

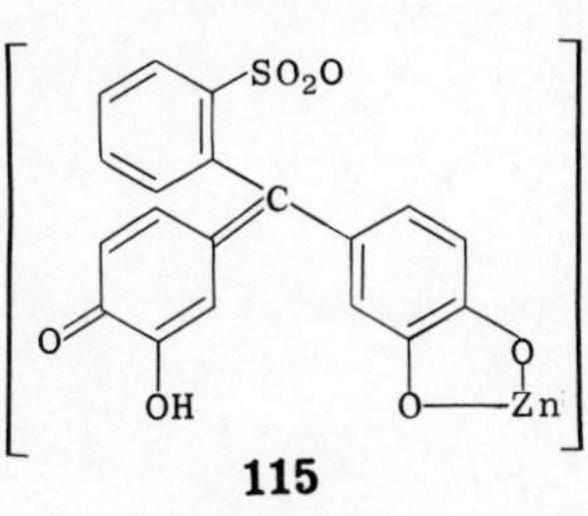

115

[For references, see pp. 289-312.]

TABLE 5. Preparation of Halogenated Sulfonephthaleins by a Condensation Reaction

$3H$-2,1-Benzoxathiol-3-one 1,1-dioxide	Phenol	Condensation Catalyst	Temperature (°C)	Time (hrs)	Sulfonephthalein yield (%)	Ref.
Unsubstituted	o-ClC$_6$H$_4$OH	None	130–135	25	37	283, 284
4,5,6,7-Tetrachloro-	Phenol	SnCl$_4$	120–130°	8	45	176
	o-Cresol	SnCl$_4$	120–130°	2	73	176
	Resorcinol					111
6-Bromo-	Phenol	SnCl$_4$				457
4,5,6-Tribromo-	Phenol	SnCl$_4$				61, 178, 457
4,5,6,7-Tetrabromo-	Phenol	SnCl$_4$	130–140°	7	60	176
	o-BrC$_6$H$_4$OH	SnCl$_4$	120–130°			176
	Br$_4$C$_6$HOH	SnCl$_4$		8		61
	o-Cresol	SnCl$_4$			82	176
	Resorcinol	NaOH	110–120	80		111
	Resorcinol	SnCl$_4$		8		61
6-Iodo-	Phenol	SnCl$_4$				457
4,6-Diiodo-	Phenol	ZnCl$_2$ or H$_2$SO$_4$	120–170°			178

4, 5, 6-Triiodo-	Phenol	SnCl$_4$			457
4, 5, 6, 7-Tetraiodo-	Phenol	SnCl$_4$		8	61
	Cl$_2$C$_6$H$_3$OH	ZnCl$_2$ or H$_2$SO$_4$	120-170°		178
	Br$_4$C$_6$HOH	ZnCl$_2$ or H$_2$SO$_4$			178
	Br$_4$C$_6$HOH	SnCl$_4$		8	61
4, 5, 6, 7-Tetraiodo-	I$_4$C$_6$HOH	SnCl$_4$		8	61
	(NO$_2$)$_4$C$_6$HOH	SnCl$_4$		8	61
	(CH$_3$CO)$_2$C$_6$H$_3$OH	SnCl$_4$		8	61
	o-Cresol	SnCl$_4$		8	61
	Resorcinol				111
	I$_2$C$_6$H$_2$(OH)$_2$	ZnCl$_2$ or H$_2$SO$_4$	120-170°		178
	Salicylic Acid	SnCl$_4$		8	61

TABLE 6. Sulfonephthaleins

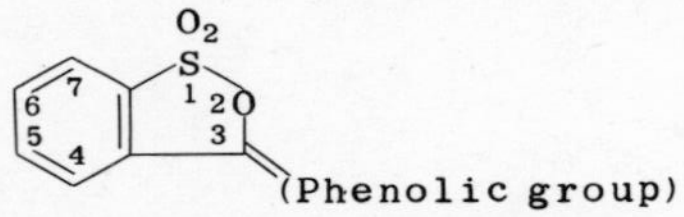

(Phenolic group)

Phenolic group	Substituents Benzoxathiole group	Common name	Yield (%)	M.p. (°C)	Ref.
Phenol		Phenol red	25		96, 132, 283, 294, 295, 343, 367, 385, 437, 444, 506
			26		360a
Phenol diacetate				165	343
Phenol dibenzoate				185–186 (dec.)	343
Phenol monomethyl ether				178	343
Phenol dimethyl ether			78	178	345
Phenol monoethyl ether				171	343
Phenol diethyl ether			34	131–132	345
Phenol di (ethylmercury oxide)			87	118–121	181
Phenol	6-CH$_3$				298
Phenol	6-OCH$_3$				329
Phenol	6-NO$_2$				209
Phenol	7-NO$_2$				457

Compound	Substituent			References
Phenol	7-NH$_2$			457
Phenol	6-Br			457
Phenol	6-I			457
Phenol	5-CH$_3$-6-NO$_2$			250
Phenol	4,6-I$_2$			457
Phenol	4,5,6-Br$_3$			457
Phenol	4,5,6-I$_3$			457
Phenol	4,5,6,7-Br$_4$	60	—	176, 178
		—	—	61
Phenol	4,5,6,7-Cl$_4$	45	—	176
Phenol	4,5,6,7-I$_4$	45	—	176, 178
		—	—	61
Phenol diacetate	4,5,6,7-I$_4$	—	136 (dec.)	61
o-Cresol	Cresol red	50	—	295
		12	—	240
		—	—	283, 294, 367, 444
		30		71a
		25		360a
o-Cresol di (ethylmercury oxide)		80	128–131	181
o-Cresol	6-NO$_2$	—	—	209
o-Cresol	4,5,6,7-Br$_4$	82	—	176, 178
o-Cresol	4,5,6,7-Cl$_4$	73	—	176, 178

TABLE 6. Sulfonephthaleins (contd)

Phenolic group	Substituents — Benzoxathiole group	Common name	Yield (%)	M.p. (°C)	Ref.
o-Cresol	4, 5, 6, 7-I$_4$		—	—	61, 176, 178
m-Cresol		m-Cresol purple	20	—	77, 348
m-Cresol	4, 5, 6, 7-Br$_4$		20	—	328
p-Cresol			20	—	349
p-Cresol			—	—	444
p-Cresol	6-NO$_2$		—	—	209
3, 4-Xylenol			17.5	—	240
2, 5-Xylenol			—	—	76
2, 6-Xylenol		Xylenol blue	—	253-254	77
Thymol		Thymol blue	80	—	71
			78	—	71a
			55	—	346
			34	—	95
			—	—	283, 294, 295
Thymol di (ethylmercury oxide)			78	145-155	181
Thymol	6-NO$_2$		—	—	295
o-Bromophenol		Bromophenol red	—	230	77
			—	—	444

Compound	Substituents / Indicator		M.p.	References
o-Bromophenol	4, 5, 6, 7-Br$_4$	—	—	176, 178
o-Chlorophenol-	Chlorophenol red	37	—	284
m-Chlorophenol		—	261–262	77
		—	—	218
2, 6-Dibromophenol	Bromophenol blue	—	270–271	295, 506
		—	279	343
		—	—	283, 294
2, 6-Dibromophenol diacetate		—	234	343
2, 6-Dibromophenol dibenzoate		—	—	343
2, 6-Dibromophenol	4, 5, 6, 7-Br$_4$	—	—	61, 176, 178
2, 6-Dibromophenol	4, 5, 6, 7-Cl$_4$	81	—	176, 178
2, 6-Dibromophenol	4, 5, 6, 7-I$_4$	—	—	61
2-Bromo-6-chlorophenol		—	250–251	77
2, 6-Dichlorophenol		—	—	283
2, 3, 5, 6-Tetrabromophenol	4, 5, 6, 7-Br$_4$	—	—	61
2, 3, 5, 6-Tetrabromophenol	4, 5, 6, 7-I$_4$	—	—	61, 178
2, 3, 5, 6-Tetraiodophenol	4, 5, 6, 7-I$_4$	—	—	61
o-(H$_2$O$_3$As—N=N)-Phenol		—	—	70
m-Nitrophenol		—	187–188	338
Dinitrophenol		—	>240	506
		—	292–294	338
Tetranitrophenol	4, 5, 6, 7-I$_4$	—	190 (dec.)	61

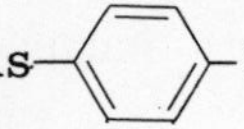

TABLE 6. Sulfonephthaleins (contd)

Phenolic group	Benzoxathiole group	Common name	Yield (%)	M.p. (°C)	Ref.
m-Aminophenol			—	—	444
p-Aminophenol			—	—	444
Bromo-o-cresol		Bromophenol purple	—	—	283
Bromo-o-cresol	4, 5, 6, 7-Br$_4$		—	—	176, 178
Bromo-o-cresol	4, 5, 6, 7-Cl$_4$		—	—	176, 178
Dibromo-m-cresol		Bromocresol green	20	—	283, 328
Dichloro-m-cresol			—	217–218	77
			—	200–201	77
Bromothymol		Bromothymol blue	—	—	283, 294, 295
2-[(NaOOCCH$_2$)$_2$NCH$_2$-]Thymol			87	ca. 300 (dec.)	275
			20	—	350
Hydroquinone			—	—	444
Hydroquinone	6-CH$_3$		—	—	298
Hydroquinone	6-NO$_2$		—	—	209
Resorcinol			50	—	253, 344
			32	—	46
			—	—	125, 331, 377, 378, 385, 439, 444, 502

Compound	Substituent		m.p.	References
Resorcinol-, diacetate		—	—	344
Resorcinol-, mercuri derivs.		—	—	111
Resorcinol	6-CH$_3$	—	—	243, 298
Resorcinol	6-OCH$_3$	—	—	329
Resorcinol	6-NO$_2$	—	—	209
Resorcinol	4, 5, 6, 7-Br$_4$	—	—	61
Resorcinol	4, 5, 6, 7-Cl$_4$	—	—	111
Resorcinol	4, 5, 6, 7-I$_4$	—	—	61
4-Ethylresorcinol		—	80	111
5, 6-Dimethylresorcinol		—	60	240
5-Methyl-6-methoxyresorcinol		—	50	298
Bromoresorcinol		—	—	329
Chlororesorcinol		—	65	111, 344
Iodoresorcinol		—	—	111
Dibromoresorcinol		—	—	344
Pyrocatechol	Pyrocatechol violet	—	34.5	283, 481, 482, 482a
	Pyrocatechol green	—	—	439
6-Methylpyrocatechol		—	—	298
Pyrogallol		—	51	347, 487
		—	—	283, 444

TABLE 6. Sulfonephthaleins (contd.)

Substituents		Common name	Yield (%)	M.p. (°C)	Ref.
Phenolic group	Benzoxathiole group				
Pyrogallol hydrate			54	>300	487
6-Methylpyrogallol			—	—	298
Bromopyrogallol			—	—	283, 347
Hydroxyhydroquinone			80	—	351
Bromohydroxyhydroquinone			—	—	351
Salicylic Acid		Salicyl red	—	—	175
Monohydroxymercuri Salicylic Acid			—	—	175
Salicylic Acid	$4,5,6,7\text{-}I_4$		—	—	61
Dibromosalicylic Acid			—	—	175
α-Naphthol			—	—	294

(b) Esterification. Acetylation of phenolsulfonephthalein occurs at the phenolic hydroxyls on refluxing with acetic anhydride. [343,429] Refluxing phenolsulfonephthalein with acetyl chloride and phosphorus pentachloride gives the phosphate. [429] The diacetate is easily hydrolyzed. [343] The acetates which have been prepared are listed in Table 6. These acetates are colorless compounds and have relatively sharp melting points. The benzoates, prepared from benzoyl chloride, are also colorless compounds with relatively sharp melting points.

(c) Etherification. Phenolic ethers of sulfonephthaleins have been prepared by reaction with boiling methanol or ethanol containing hydrochloric or sulfuric acid or by boiling for a long time with the alcohol,[345] by reacting with methanol in the presence of methyl iodide and sodium methylate[347] and by reaction with diazomethane.[506]

The dimethyl and diethyl ethers of phenolsulfonephthalein are sharp-melting compounds, colorless until heated above their melting points; the colored ethers are unstable and revert to the colorless form when treated with methanol.[345]

(d) Halogenation. Direct halogenation of sulfonephthaleins affects only the phenolic moiety. Practically all the known sulfonephthaleins have been subjected to halogenation. The usual names for these sulfonephthaleins designate whether the halogen is in the benzoxathiole part or in the phenolic part. When the halogen name follows the phenol and precedes the sulfonephthalein, it is in the benzoxathiole part; when it precedes the phenol name, it is in the phenolic part. Several examples of this nomenclature are as follows:

116
Tetrabromophenol-
sulfonephthalein

117
Phenoltetrabromo-
sulfonephthalein

118
Tetrabromophenoltetra-
bromosulfonephthalein

Halogenation is carried out by treating the sulfonephthalein with halogen in glacial acetic acid[175,176,243,294,295,346,377,502,506] or in ethanol.[132,347,439] Kosheleva and Zimakova[275c,275d] chlorinated phenol red with sodium hypochlorite in the presence of boric acid and brominated phenol red with sodium hypobromite in alkaline medium; the products in these two cases were dichloro- and dibromophenol-sulfonephthalein, respectively.

According to Burger and Loo, [67a] the uterus of pregnant dogfish converts phenol red to bromophenol blue. This is the first example of biological bromination observed in a vertebrate.

Bromination of phenolsulfonephthalein yields tetrabromophenolsulfonephthalein,[132,294,295,343,506] more commonly known as bromphenol blue (**119**).

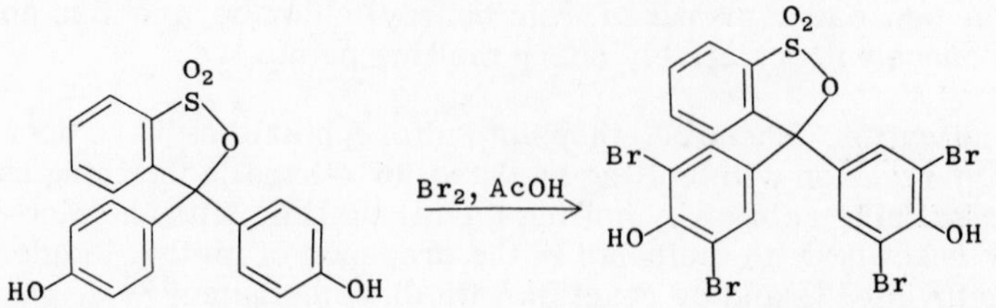

119

The tetrabromo derivative (**119**) readily forms a mono- and disodium salt, a monomethyl ether with methanol, a dimethyl ether with diazomethane, and a dibenzoate; it does not react with aniline; it is hydrolyzed with aqueous hydrochloric acid, the hetero ring opening, to give the sulfonate.[343,506]

Bromination of phenoltetrachlorosulfonephthalein and of phenoltetrabromosulfonephthalein gives good yields of the corresponding tetrabromophenol derivative.[167] Dichlorophenol- and tetrabromophenoltetraiodosulfonephthalein and dibromo-o-cresol-tetrachloro- and tetrabromosulfonephthalein have been prepared similarly.[176,178] Cohen[77] reported the preparation of tetrachloro- and tetrabromo-o-cresolsulfonephthalein and dibromodichlorophenolsulfonephthalein. Sirokman and Otvos[438a] reported the preparation of bromocresol green (tetrabromo-m-cresolsulfonephthalein) in 5% yield based on benzoxathiol-3-one by bromination of m-cresolsulfonephthalein with bromine in acetic acid. Bromination of resorcinolsulfonephthalein gives a dibromo derivative[243,377,502] and no tetrabromo derivative as Sisley postulated.[439] The orientation of the bromine in **120** was not verified.

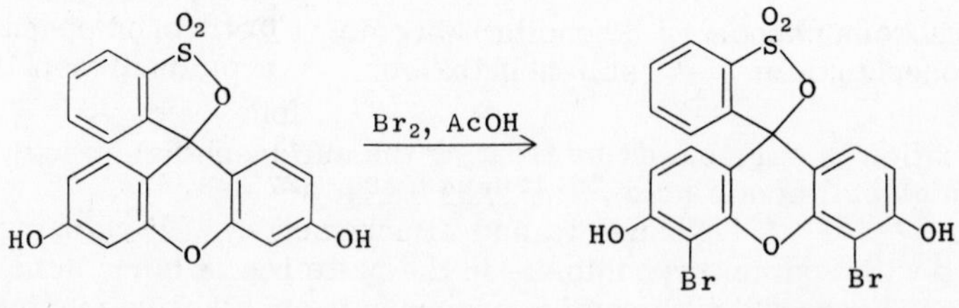

120

Iodination similarly gives the diodo derivative.[344] The diodo and dibromo derivatives form a diacetate on treatment with acetic anhydride.[344]

142

Treatment of resorcinolsulfonephthalein with phosphorus pentachloride yields a dichloride (**121**)[344] or tetrachloride (**122**).[243]

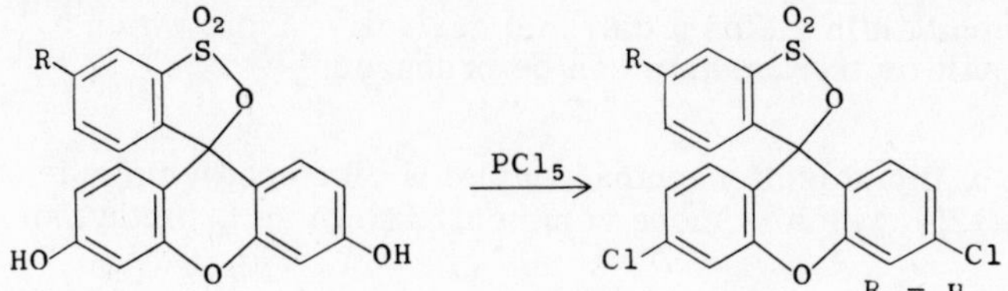

121   R = H

122   R = CH$_3$

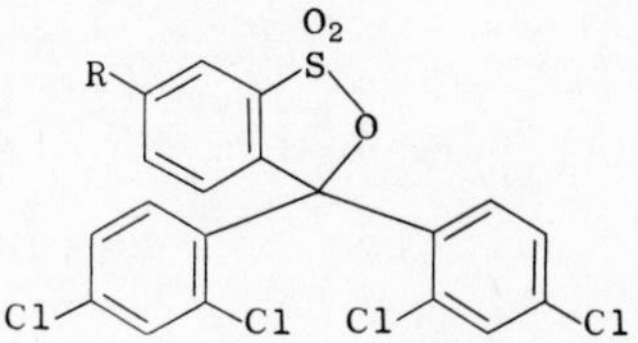

The dichlorodiphenyl compound (**121**) was also obtained on treating resorcinolsulfonephthalein with benzoyl chloride.[344] Diiodoresorcinol-tetraiodosulfonephthalein also has been reported.[178] The dichloro derivative is a colorless compound; the chlorine atoms are not removed on boiling with 20% sodium hydroxide, although both colored (**123**) and colorless (**124**) salts were formed.[344]

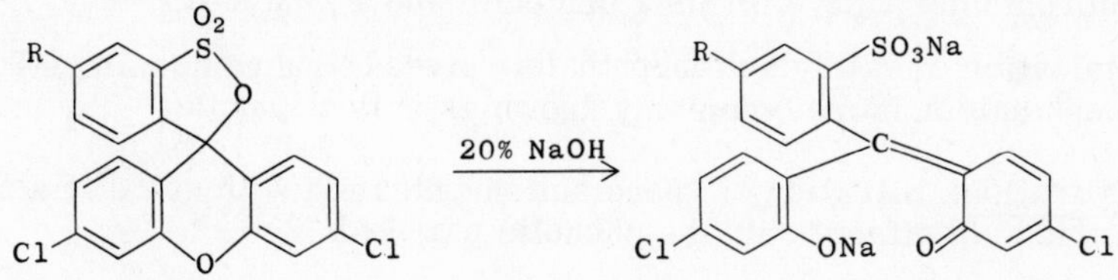

121

123   colored salt

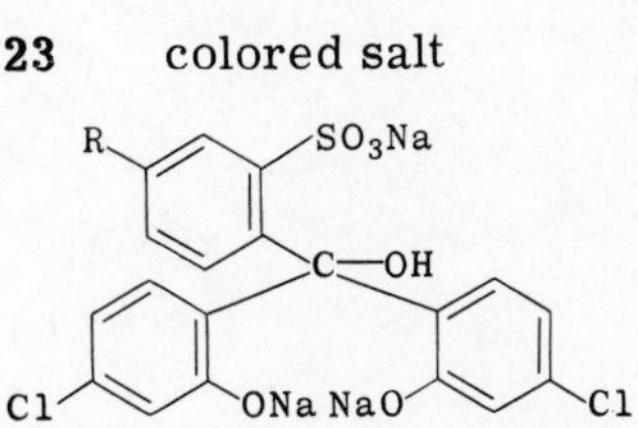

124   colorless salt

The dichloro- and diodosulfonephthaleins form essentially colorless diacetates which probably have the sultone structure.[344]

Bromination of pyrogallolsulfonephthalein yields a dibromo derivative, which on reaction with benzoyl chloride gives a tetrabenzoate of dibromopyrogallolsulfonephthalein.[347] Bromination of hydroxyhydroquinonesulfonephthalein yields a dibromo derivative from which a triammonium salt or tetraacetate can be prepared.[351]

Bromination of thymolsulfonephthalein yields dibromothymolsulfonephthalein (**125**), which is more commonly known as bromthymol blue.[346,349]

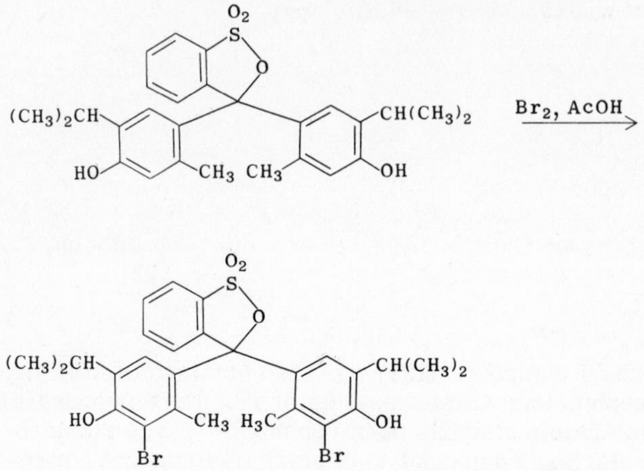

125

The dibromo derivative forms a diacetate and a zinc salt.[346]

Bromination of salicylsulfonephthalein gives tetrabromosalicylsulfonephthalein, more commonly known as salicyl purple.[175]

(e) <u>Nitration.</u> Nitration of phenolsulfonephthalein with sulfuric acid and nitric acid affects only the phenolic part.[294,295,338,506]

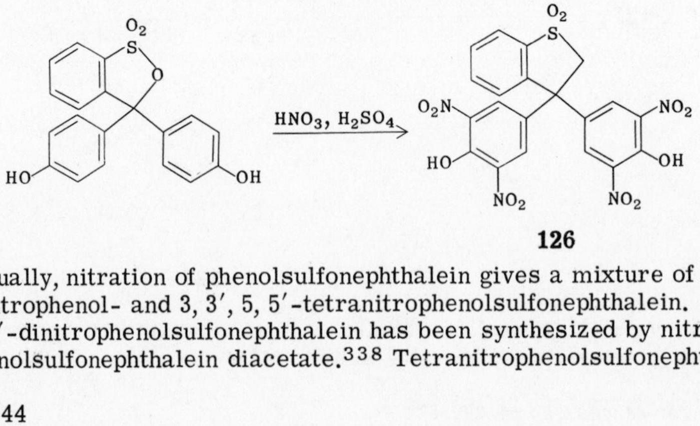

126

Actually, nitration of phenolsulfonephthalein gives a mixture of 3, 3'-dinitrophenol- and 3, 3', 5, 5'-tetranitrophenolsulfonephthalein. Pure 3, 3'-dinitrophenolsulfonephthalein has been synthesized by nitration of phenolsulfonephthalein diacetate.[338] Tetranitrophenolsulfonephthalein

144

(126) is isolated as canary-yellow flakes which change to a shellac-like material on heating above 200°. Its diammonium salt, however, is stable.

Phenolnitrosulfonephthalein has been prepared by condensing 7-nitro-3H-2, 1-benzoxathiol-3-one 1, 1-dioxide with phenol.[457]

(f) Reaction with Ammonia, Amines, and Anilines. Phenolsulfonephthal-ein absorbs two moles of ammonia to give the diammonium salt, a dark red product whose aqueous solution is purple, but which is un-stable and loses ammonia to give the monoammonium salt, a brownish red product whose aqueous solution is orange-red.[343] The phenolic hydroxyl group is replaced by ammonia on heating phenolsulfonephthal-ein in a sealed tube at 150° for 24 hours giving a 50% yield of anilinosul-fonephthalein.[428,429] Bromination of anilinosulfonephthalein in glacial acetic acid yields the tetrabromoanilinosulfonephthalein; refluxing the anilinosulfonephthalein with acetic anhydride gives the N-acetyl deriva-tive; treatment of anilinosulfonephthalein with benzenesulfonyl chloride in pyridine gives phenylsulfanilidosulfonephthalein.[429]

Phenolsulfonephthalein similarly reacts with amines on heating in a sealed tube at 150° for 24 hours to give 65% yields of the corresponding N-alkylanilinosulfonephthalein, such as the N-methyl and N-ethyl from methylamine and ethylamine. Yields of 40-70% of N-substituted anilino-sulfonephthaleins were obtained by heating the phosphate of phenolsul-fonephthalein at 100° for 12 hours in a sealed tube with propylamine, isobutylamine, benzylamine, ethanolamine, m- and p-aminophenol,p-phenylenediamine, and o-bromoaniline.[429]

Phenolsulfonephthalein acetylated with acetyl chloride reacts with 2, 4-dichloroaniline, m-aminoacetophenone, p-aminodiphenyl, and ben-zoylhydrazine in ethanol on heating 12 hours in a sealed tube at 100°; the reaction with $(CH_3)_2NNH_2$ was carried out at 80° for one hour; the reaction with ethyl glycinate, giving N-(carbethoxymethyl)- anilinosul-fonephthalein, was carried out at 100° for 10 hours.[249]

The reaction between phenolsulfonephthalein and aniline carried out by refluxing the mixture gave a 96% yield of diphenylaminosulfone-phthalein. Refluxing phenolsulfonephthalein with o-toluidine, 2, 4-xylidine, 2, 4, 5-trimethylaniline, p-anisidine, and p-phenetidine gave 80-90% yields of the corresponding diphenylaminosulfonephthalein.[429]

127

[For references, see pp. 289-312.]

TABLE 7. Amino- and Anilinosulfonephthaleins

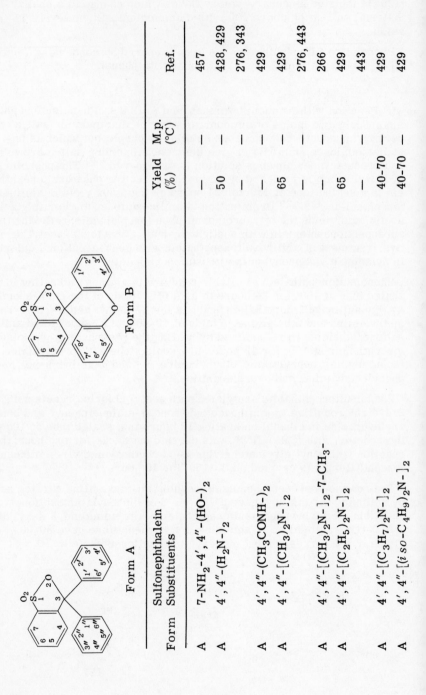

Form A   Form B

Form	Sulfonephthalein Substituents	Yield (%)	M.p. (°C)	Ref.
A	7-NH_2-4',4''-$(HO-)_2$	—	—	457
A	4',4''-$(H_2N-)_2$	50	—	428, 429
A	4',4''-$(CH_3CONH-)_2$	—	—	276, 343
A	4',4''-$[(CH_3)_2N-]_2$	65	—	429
A	4',4''-$[(CH_3)_2N-]_2$-7-CH_3-	—	—	276, 443
A	4',4''-$[(C_2H_5)_2N-]_2$	65	—	266
A	4',4''-$[(C_3H_7)_2N-]_2$	40-70	—	429
A	4',4''-$[(iso\text{-}C_4H_9)_2N-]_2$	40-70	—	429

A	4′,4″-(C$_6$H$_5$CH$_2$NH-)$_2$	40–70	—	429
A	4′,4″-[(CH$_3$)$_2$NCH$_2$CH$_2$NH-]$_2$	40	—	429
A	4′,4″-(C$_2$H$_5$O$_2$CCH$_2$NH-)$_2$	—	—	429
A	4′,4″-(HOCH$_2$CH$_2$NH-)$_2$	40–70	—	429
A	4′,4″-(C$_6$H$_5$SO$_2$NH-)$_2$	—	—	429
A	4′,4″-(C$_6$H$_5$NH-)$_2$	96	—	429
		—	>315	343
A	4′,4″-(o-CH$_3$C$_6$H$_4$NH-)$_2$	80–90	—	429
A	4′,4″-(m-HOC$_6$H$_4$NH-)$_2$	40–70	—	429
A	4′,4″-(p-HOC$_6$H$_4$NH-)$_2$	40–70	—	429
A	4′,4″-(m-CH$_3$CO$_2$C$_6$H$_4$NH-)$_2$	—	—	429
A	4′,4″-(p-CH$_3$OC$_6$H$_4$NH-)$_2$	80–90	—	429
A	4′,4″-(p-C$_2$H$_5$OC$_6$H$_4$NH-)$_2$	80–90	—	429
A	4′,4″-(o-BrC$_6$H$_4$NH-)$_2$	40–70	—	429
A	4′,4″-(p-H$_2$NC$_6$H$_4$NH-)$_2$	40–70	—	429
A	4′,4″-(p-C$_6$H$_5$-C$_6$H$_4$NH-)$_2$	—	—	429
A	4′,4″-[2,4-(CH$_3$)$_2$C$_6$H$_3$NH-]$_2$	80–90	—	429
A	4′,4″-[2,4,5-(CH$_3$)$_3$C$_6$H$_2$NH-]$_2$	80–90	—	429
A	4′,4″-[2,4-Cl$_2$C$_6$H$_3$NH-]$_2$	—	—	429
A	3′,3′,5′,5″-Br$_4$-4′,4″-(H$_2$N-)$_2$	—	—	429
A	3′,3″-(iso-C$_3$H$_7$-)$_2$-4′,4″-(C$_6$H$_5$NH-)$_2$-6′,6″-(CH$_3$-)$_2$	—	—	346

TABLE 7. Amino- and Anilinosulfonephthaleins (contd)

Form	Sulfonephthalein Substituents	Yield (%)	M.p. (°C)	Ref.
A	$3', 3''-(iso-C_3H_7-)_2-4', 4''-(HO-)_2-5', 5''-[(NaO_2CCH_2)_2NCH_2-]_2-6', 6''-(CH_3-)_2$	87	300°(dec.)	275
A	$6, 4', 4''-[(CH_3)_2N-]_3$	—	—	412
A	$4', 4''-[(CH_3)_2NNH-]_2$	—	—	429
A	$4', 4''-(C_6H_5NHNH-)_2$	—	—	276, 429
A	$4', 4''-[C_6H_5CH=N-N(CH_3)-]$	—	—	276
B	$3'-Cl-6'-C_6H_5NH-$	—	—	218a
B	$3'-Cl-6'-[C_6H_5N(C_2H_5)-]$	—	—	218a
B	$3'-Cl-6'-[C_6H_5N(C_4H_9)-]$	—	—	218a
B	$3'-Cl-6'-[2-CH_3C_6H_4N(CH_3)-]$	—	—	218a
B	$3'-Cl-6'-[2-CH_3C_6H_4N(C_2H_5)-]$	—	—	218a
B	$3'-Cl-6'-(2-F_3CC_6H_4NH-)$	—	—	218a
B	$3'-Cl-6'-(p-CH_3OC_6H_4NH-)$	—	—	218a
B	$3'-Cl-6'-(p-O_2NC_6H_4NH-)$	—	—	218a
B	$3'-Cl-6'-(p-CH_3CONHC_6H_4NH-)$	—	—	218a
B	$3'-Cl-6'-(p-HOCH_2CH_2SO_2C_6H_4NH-)$	—	—	218a
B	$3'-Cl-6'-(3-NaO_3SC_6H_4NH-)$	—	—	218a
B	$3'-Cl-6'-[2,5-(CH_3)_2C_6H_3N(CH_3)-]$	—	—	218a
B	$3'-Cl-6'-(2-CH_3-6-ClC_6H_3NH-)$	—	—	218a

B	3'-Cl-6'-(2-CH$_3$-4-C$_6$H$_{11}$C$_6$H$_3$NH-)	—	—	218a
B	3'-Cl-6'-[2-CH$_3$-4-(o-CH$_3$C$_6$H$_4$N=N-)C$_6$H$_3$NH-]	—	—	218a
P.	3'-Cl-6'-[2,6-(CH$_3$)$_2$C$_6$H$_3$NH-]	—	—	218a
B	3'-Cl-6'-[2,4,6-(CH$_3$)$_3$C$_6$H$_2$NH-]	—	—	218a
B	3'-Cl-6'-(2-O$_2$N-4-CH$_3$C$_6$H$_3$NH-)	—	—	218a
B	3'-Cl-6'-[2-CH$_3$O-5-(C$_2$H$_5$)$_2$NHSO$_2$C$_6$H$_3$NH-]	—	—	218a
B	3'-Cl-6'-(2-CH$_3$O-5-HOCH$_2$CH$_2$SO$_2$C$_6$H$_3$NH-)	—	—	218a
B	3'-Cl-6'-[2,6-(CH$_3$)$_2$-4-HOCH$_2$CH$_2$SO$_2$C$_6$H$_2$NH-)	—	—	218a
B	3'-Cl-6'-(2-HO-3-HO$_2$CC$_6$H$_3$NH-)	—	—	218a
B	3'-Cl-6'-(4-C$_6$H$_5$-2-NH$_4$O$_3$SC$_6$H$_3$NH-)	—	—	218a
B	3'-Cl-6'- 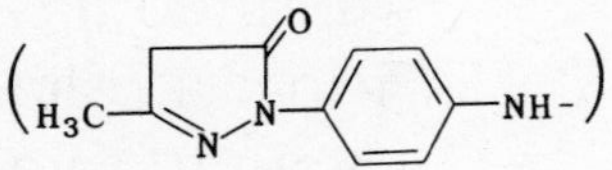	—	—	218a
B	3'-Cl-6'- 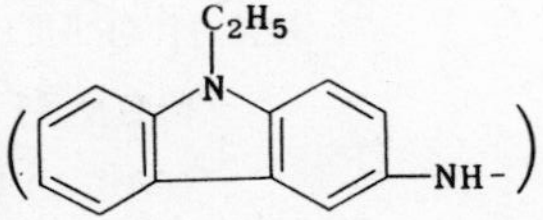	—	—	218a
B	6-HO$_3$S-3'-Cl-6'-C$_6$H$_5$NH-	—	—	218a
B	6-HO$_3$S-3'-Cl-6'-[2-CH$_3$C$_6$H$_4$N(CH$_3$)-]	—	—	218a
B	6-HO$_3$S-3'-Cl-6'-[2,4,6-(CH$_3$)$_3$C$_6$H$_2$NH-]	—	—	218a
B	6-CH$_3$O-3'-Cl-6'-(p-CH$_3$C$_6$H$_4$NH-)	—	—	218a
B	6-HO$_2$C-3'-Cl-6'-(p-C$_2$H$_5$OC$_6$H$_4$NH-)	—	—	218a

TABLE 7. Amino- and Anilinosulfonephthaleins (contd)

Form	Sulfonephthalein Substituents	Yield (%)	M.p. (°C)	Ref.
B	$6,3'-Cl_2-6'-[C_6H_5N(C_2H_5)-]$	—	—	218a
B	$3',6-Cl_2-6'-(2-NaO_3S-4-C_6H_5C_6H_3NH-)$	—	—	218a
B	$3',6'-(H_2N-)_2$	—	—	444
B	$3',6'-(HOCH_2CH_2NH-)_2$	—	—	218
B	$3',6'-(piperidino)_2$	—	—	218
B	$3',6'-(C_6H_5NH-)_2$	—	—	218, 344
B	$3',6'-(o-CH_3C_6H_4NH-)_2$	—	—	218
B	$3',6'-[2-CH_3C_6H_4N(CH_3)-]_2$	—	—	218
B	$3',6'-[2-CH_3C_6H_4N(C_2H_5)-]_2$	—	—	218
B	$3',6'-(4-C_2H_5OC_6H_4NH-)_2$	—	—	218
B	$3',6'-(2-HO_3SC_6H_4NH-)_2$	—	—	218
B	$3',6'-(3-ClC_6H_4NH-)_2$	—	—	218
B	$3',6'-(2-CH_3OC_6H_4NH-)_2$	—	—	218
B	$3',6'-(2-C_2H_5OC_6H_4NH-)_2$	—	—	218
B	$3',6'-[4-(2-NaO_3SC_6H_4O)C_6H_4NH-]_2$	—	—	218
B	$3',6'-[2,4-(CH_3)_2C_6H_3NH-]_2$	—	—	218
B	$3',6'-[2,6-(CH_3)_2C_6H_3NH-]_2$	—	—	218
B	$3',6'-[2,5-(CH_3)_2C_6H_3N(CH_3)-]_2$	—	—	218
B	$3',6'-(2-C_6H_5O-5-ClC_6H_3NH-]_2$	—	—	218
B	$3',6'-(2-HO-3-HO_2CC_6H_3NH-)_2$	—	—	218

B	3',6'-(2-HO-3-HO$_3$S-5-HO$_2$CC$_6$H$_2$NH-)$_2$	—	—	218
B	3'-(p-CH$_3$OC$_6$H$_4$NH-)-6'-(3-NaO$_3$S-4-CH$_3$OC$_6$H$_3$NH-)	—	—	219
B	3'-(2-F$_3$CC$_6$H$_4$NH-)-6'-[NaO$_3$SCH$_2$CH$_2$N(CH$_3$)-]	—	—	219
B	3'-(2-F$_3$CC$_6$H$_4$NH-)-6'-[2,6-(CH$_3$)$_2$C$_6$H$_3$NH-]	—	—	219
B	[9-ethylcarbazol-NH- structure] 3'-(... NH-)-6'-(p-C$_6$H$_{11}$C$_6$H$_4$NH-)	—	—	219
B	[9-ethylcarbazol-NH- structure] 3'-(... NH-)-6'-(2-HO-3-HO$_2$C-5-HO$_3$SC$_6$H$_2$NH-)	—	—	219
B	3'-(2-HO-3-HO$_2$CC$_6$H$_3$NH-)-6'-(2-HO$_3$S-4-C$_6$H$_5$C$_6$H$_3$NH-)	—	—	219
B	3'-(3-HO$_2$C-4-HOC$_6$H$_3$NH-)-6'-(2-HO-3-HO$_2$C-5-HO$_3$SC$_6$H$_2$NH-)	—	—	219
B	3'-(2-HO-3-HO$_2$C-5-HO$_3$SC$_6$H$_2$NH-)-6'-(2-HO-3-HO$_2$CC$_6$H$_3$NH-)	—	—	219
B	3'-(2-HO-3-HO$_2$C-5-HO$_3$SC$_6$H$_2$NH-)-6'-(4-C$_2$H$_5$OC$_6$H$_4$NH-)	—	—	219
B	6-Cl-3'-[C$_6$H$_5$N(C$_2$H$_5$)-]-6'-(2-NaO$_3$SC$_6$H$_4$NH-)	—	—	219
B	6-Cl-3'-(4-C$_2$H$_5$OC$_6$H$_4$NH-)-6'-(2-NaO$_3$S-4-C$_6$H$_5$OC$_6$H$_3$NH-)	—	—	219
B	6-HO$_2$C-3'-[2,4,6-(H$_3$C)$_3$C$_6$H$_2$NH-]-6'-(3-HO$_3$S-4-H$_3$CC$_6$H$_3$NH-)	—	—	219
B	6-HO$_3$S-3'-[o-H$_3$CC$_6$H$_4$N(CH$_3$)-]-6'-(3-NaO$_3$S-4-HOC$_6$H$_3$NH-)	—	—	219
B	6-HO$_3$S-3'-[o-H$_3$CC$_6$H$_4$N(CH$_3$)-]-6'-(3-NaO$_3$S-4-H$_3$CC$_6$H$_3$NH-)	—	—	219
B	6-HO$_3$S-3'-[o-H$_3$CC$_6$H$_4$N(CH$_3$)-]-6'-(3-NaO$_2$C-4-HOC$_6$H$_3$NH-)	—	—	219
B	6-HO$_3$S-3'-(C$_6$H$_5$NH-)-6'-(3-NaO$_3$S-4-HOC$_6$H$_3$NH-)	—	—	219

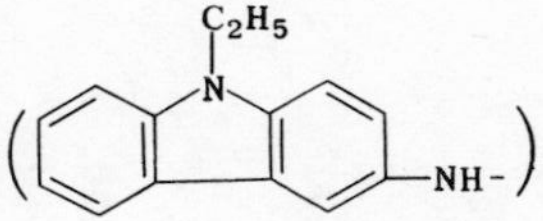

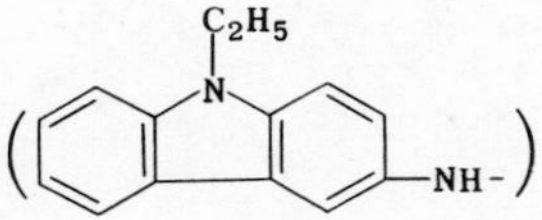

Heating phenolsulfonephthalein with $(C_2H_5)_2NCH_2CH_2NH_2$ for 3 hours at 100° gave a 40% yield of N-(N'-diethylaminoethyl)-anilinosulfone-phthalein. [429]

Orndorff and Sherwood[343] prepared anilinosulfonephthalein by heating phenolsulfonephthalein with aniline 2 hours at 140-150°; dimethylaniline did not undergo the reaction. Resorcinolsulfonephthalein similarly reacts with aniline. [343]

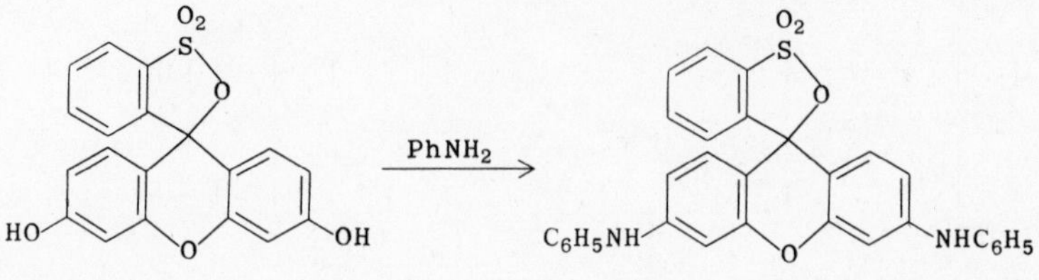

128

A series of diamino derivatives from resorcinolsulfonephthalein are described in three British patents.[218,218a,219] These were prepared by heating resorcinolsulfonephthalein with $POCl_3$ to give the dichloro derivative (**129**) which in turn was treated with amines or anilines. The diamino derivatives (**130** and **132**) on sulfonation yielded sulfonated dyes which impart red to blue tints to wool and silk.

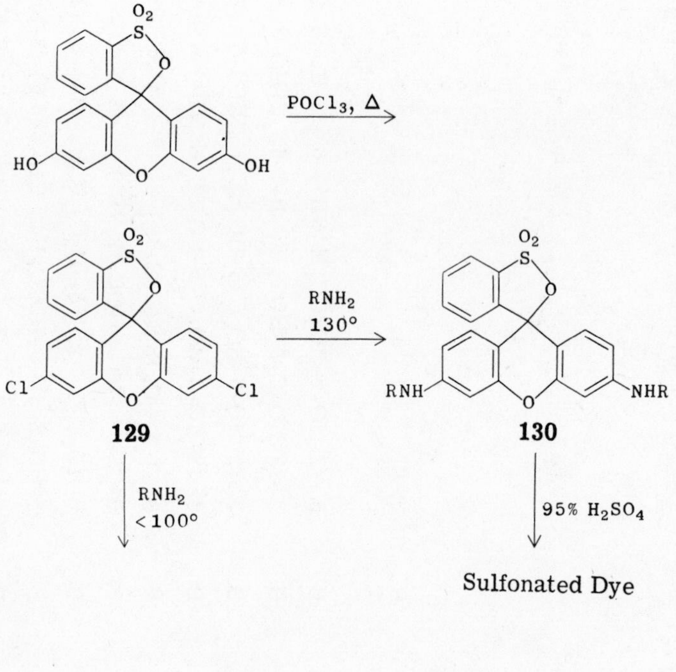

129   **130**

Sulfonated Dye

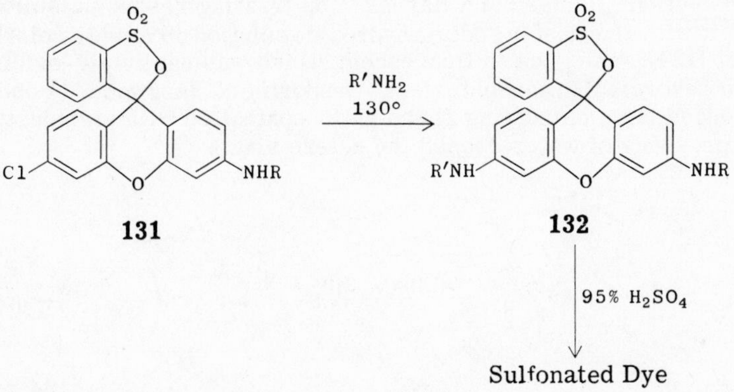

131   **132**

Sulfonated Dye

Pyrogallolsulfonephthalein absorbs four moles of ammonia to give a product which on heating at 200° gives a monoammonium salt. Pyrogallolsulfonephthalein reacts quantitatively with aniline to give a red product whose empirical formula was given as $C_{19}H_{11}O_8S(C_6H_5NH_3)$. This salt was insoluble in the usual organic solvents but slightly soluble in water and in alcohols.[347]

Hydroquinonesulfonephthalein absorbs three moles of ammonia, the product yielding a monoammonium salt.[350] Thymolsulfonephthalein absorbs one mole of ammonia to give a monoammonium salt and reacts with aniline on heating to give an aniline salt.[346] Thymolsulfonephthalein is converted to an indicator (**133**) for chelatometric titration by treating with sodium iminodiacetate and formalin.[275]

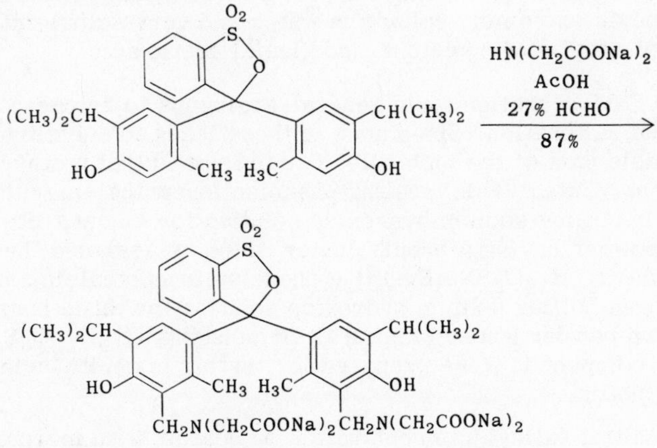

133

[For references, see pp. 289-312.]

Condensation of 7-amino-3H-2, 1-benzoxathiol-3-one 1, 1-dioxide with phenol gives phenolaminosulfonephthalein.[457] The amino- and anilino-sulfonephthaleins which have been reported are listed in Table 7.

(g) Reduction. Remsen and Hayes[377] on treating resorcinolsulfonephthalein with zinc dust in sodium hydroxide solution obtained a colorless product (134), analogous to fluorescein, which was easily air-oxidized back to resorcinolsulfonephthalein. Orndorff and Sherwood[343] obtained the reduced form on heating phenolsulfonephthalein with zinc dust, which in the presence of water opened the hetero ring.

134

Treatment of hydroxyhydroquinonesulfonephthalein with boiling formic acid and zinc dust gave the reduced form which was called hydroxyhydroquinonesulfonephthalein.[351] The reduced form, which has an ocher-yellow color, is oxidized by air and becomes red; the tetraacetate and silver salts of the reduced form are colorless and also are easily oxidized. Pyrogallolsulfonephthalein reacts with zinc dust and boiling water to give the zinc salt of pyrogallosulfonephthalein, which is easily oxidized by air, and which on being heated at 200° gives the zinc salt of sulfonegallein.[347]

Thymolsulfonephthalein similarly on treatment with zinc dust and boiling water gives the colorless zinc salt of thymolsulfonephthalein, which is slowly oxidized by exposure to sunlight or by bubbling oxygen through it to give the zinc salt of thymolsulfonephthalein.[346] Thymolsulfonephthalein, obtained by treating the zinc salt with concentrated hydrochloric acid, is extremely soluble in water and very soluble in methanol, ethanol, ethyl ether, acetone, and glacial acetic acid.

(h) Mercuration. Mercuration is, in general, analogous to halogenation, nitration, and sulfonation. Since none of these leads to substitution in the benzoxathiole part of the molecule, it is presumed that neither does mercuration. White,[508] on treating phenolsulfonephthalein with mercuric oxide in boiling sodium hydroxide solution for 4 hours, obtained a purple powder having a bronze luster which he assigned the empirical formula $C_{19}H_{10}O_5SNa(HgOH)_3$; phenolsulfonephthalein and mercuric acetate in boiling sodium hydroxide solution for three hours gave a dark brown powder whose empirical formula was $C_{19}H_{10}O_5S$ $(HgOH)_4$. These compounds were prepared for testing in genito-urinary infections and syphilis.

The disodium salt of salicylsulfonephthalein on heating with mercury acetate yielded monohydroxymercuri-salicylsulfonephthalein,[175] a compound which showed germicidal activity against *B. typhosus* and *Staphylococcus aureus*.

Dunning and Farinholt[111] prepared the mono- and dihydroxymercuri derivatives of resorcinolsulfonephthalein and its halogenated derivatives. These mercury compounds were insoluble in water and organic solvents. The mono- and disodium salts were readily formed and their solutions showed only a slight fluorescence as compared to the parent sulfone-phthalein before mercuration.

Ethylmercury derivatives of phenol-, *o*-cresol-, and thymolsulfone-phthalein were prepared in 78-87% yield by treating the sulfonephthalein with ethylmercuri hydroxide. These three mercury derivatives exhibit-ed bacteriostatic activity against *Staphylococcus aureus*.[181]

(i) Preparation of Arsenates. Christiansen[70] prepared *p*-arsenoben-zeneazophenolsulfonephthalein (**135** and **136**) by reacting diazotized ar-sanilic acid with phenolsulfonephthalein.

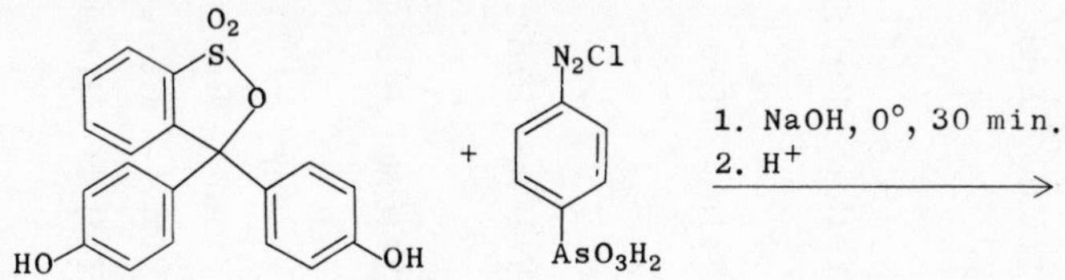

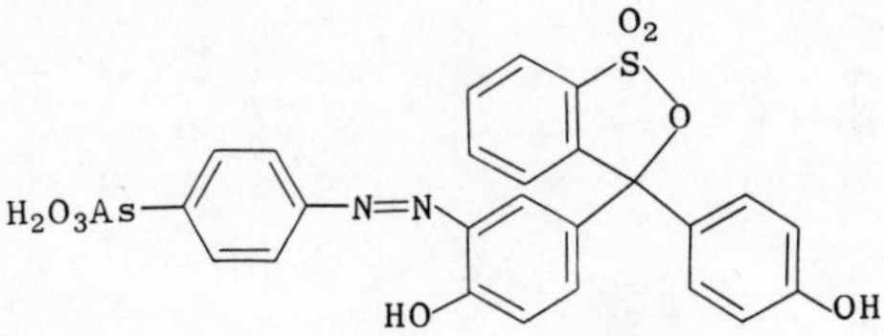

1. NaOH, 0°, 30 min.
2. H$^+$

135

and

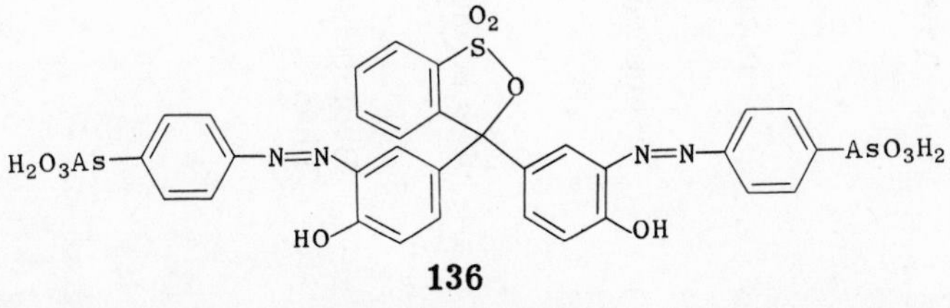

136

The product mixture was readily soluble in water, methanol, ethanol; fairly soluble in acetone and glacial acetic acid; and insoluble in ethyl ether. Its alkaline solution was red and its acid solution deep orange. The product had low *trypanocidal* toxicity.

(3) Structure and Properties

Many studies have been directed to the elucidation of the structure of sulfonephthaleins. The definitive study has yet to be made. The neutral form of sulfonephthaleins is generally assigned the 3*H*-2,1-benzoxa-thiole structure. The effect of pH on the neutral structure has been

[For references, see pp. 289-312.]

TABLE 8. Sulfonephthaleins: pH Range, Color Change, and Indicator Constant

Chemical name	Common name	pH range	Color Acid	Color Alkaline	Ionization constant, pK	Ref.
Phenol-	Phenol red	6.8-8.6	Yellow	Red	7.90	43, 64, 72, 75, 79, 159, 176, 227, 270-273, 295, 309, 327, 459, 514
Dibromophenol-	Bromphenol red	5.2-6.8	Yellow	Red	6.16	77
		5.4-7.0				275c
Tetrabromophenol-	Bromphenol blue	2.8-4.6	Yellow	Blue	4.05	64, 72, 75, 79, 98, 159, 176, 259, 270-272, 295, 309, 339, 408, 480, 514
Dichlorophenol-	Chlorophenol red	4.8-6.4	Yellow	Red	5.98	77, 272
		4.6-6.6				275d
Dibromodichlorophenol-	Bromochlorophenol blue	3.0-4.6	Yellow	Blue	3.98	77
Dinitrophenol-		2.6-3.9	Yellow	Violet-red		338
		11.5-14	Violet	Red-yellow		
Tetranitrophenol-		9.5-11.0	Violet	Red-yellow		338
Tetrabromophenoltetrachloro-		2.6-4.4	Yellow	Green-blue	3.56	180
		3.0-4.6				176
Tetrabromophenoltetrabromo-	Tetrabromophenol	2.6-4.4	Yellow	Green-blue	3.56	180
		3.0-4.6				176, 177

Compound	Trivial name	pH range	Acid color	Base color	pK	References
Phenoltetrabromo-		5.8-7.7	Yellow	Violet	7.03	180
Phenoltetrachloro-		6.6-8.2	Yellow	Purple		176
Phenoltetraiodo-		5.8-7.7	Yellow	Violet	7.04	180
		6.6-8.2	Yellow	Purple		176
		6.4-8.0	Yellow	Red		176
Dibromophenoltetrabromo-		5.6-7.2	Yellow	Purple		176
o-Cresol-	Cresol red	7.2-8.8	Yellow	Red	8.20	64, 72, 75, 159, 176, 271, 273, 327, 409, 459, 480
Dibromo-o-cresol-	Bromcresol purple	5.2-6.8	Yellow	Purple	6.30	64, 72, 75, 79, 159, 176, 271, 459
o-Cresoltetrachloro-		6.6-8.3	Yellow	Purple	7.51	180
		7.2-8.8	Yellow	Violet-purple		176
o-Cresoltetrabromo-		6.6-8.3	Yellow	Purple	7.53	180
		7.2-8.8	Yellow	Violet-purple		176
o-Cresoltetraiodo-		7.0-8.6	Yellow	Purple		176
		0.2-1.8	Red	Yellow		272, 303
Dibromo-o-cresoltetrachloro-		4.8-6.6	Yellow	Green-blue	5.64	180
		5.2-6.8	Yellow	Green-violet		176
Dibromo-o-cresoltetrabromo-		5.2-6.8	Yellow	Green-blue		176
m-Cresol-	m-Cresol purple	1.2-2.8	Red	Yellow	1.51	77, 79
		7.4-9.0	Yellow	Purple	8.32	77
p-Cresol-		9.6-10.0	Yellow	Colorless		349

157

TABLE 8. Sulfonephthaleins: pH Range, Color Change, and Indicator Constant (contd)

Chemical name (Sulfonephthalein)	Common name	pH range	Color Acid	Color Alkaline	Ionization constant, pK	Ref.
Tetrabromo-m-cresol-	Bromcresol green	3.8-5.4	Yellow	Blue	4.67	77, 79, 228, 259, 270-273, 309, 310, 339, 514
Tetrachloro-m-cresol-	Chlorocresol green	4.0-5.6	Yellow	Blue	4.8	77
Xylenol-	Xylenol blue	1.2-2.8	Red	Yellow	8.6	77
Thymol-	Thymol blue	8.0-9.6	Yellow	Blue	8.9	29, 43, 64, 72, 75, 159, 228, 271-273, 295, 459
		1.2-2.8	Red	Yellow	1.7	72, 75, 79, 407
		1.2-3.4			1.75	64, 271
Dibromothymol-	Bromothymol blue	5.8-8.4	Yellow	Blue	7.10	64, 159, 271-273, 295, 409, 459
		6.0-7.6	Yellow	Blue	7.0	43, 72, 75, 79, 168, 407
Hydroxyquinone-		8.6-10	Red	Blue-purple		350
Hydroxyhydroquinone-		7.2-12.0	Yellow	Red		351
Salicyl-	Salicyl red	6.6-8.2	Yellow	Bluish-red		175
Tetrabromosalicyl-	Salicyl purple	3.2-4.6	Brown-purple	Clear purple		175

described as involving an equilibrium between the sultone and quinone forms or as involving resonating structures or as involving carbonium and oxonium forms. These studies arose from the use of sulfonephthaleins as acid-base indicators and the theories were developed mostly from experiments with the phthaleins.

The most important property of sulfonephthaleins is the color change they undergo with change in pH. This property is usually expressed by the Ostwald ionization or dissociation equilibrium of the sulfonephthalein which is pictured as behaving as a weak acid.

$$HI \rightleftharpoons H^+ + I^-$$

Undissociated sulfonephthalein $\rightleftharpoons$ dissociated sulfonephthalein

Although this misrepresents the color change mechanism, it is a convenient tool for assigning a numerical quantity to the color transformation by means of the well-known ionization constant, K, and the indicator constant, pK, which is the negative logarithm of the ionization constant.

$$\frac{[H^+]\,[I^-]}{HI} = K = \text{ionization constant}$$

$$- \log K = pK = \text{indicator constant}$$

The pH range in which the color change occurs, the color transformation and the indicator constant are given in Table 8.

Between 1916 and 1919, Lubs and Acree,[295] White,[502] and White and Acree[505,506] advanced the quinone-phenolate theory to explain the behavior of sulfonephthaleins under varying conditions of pH. This theory pictured the color change as arising through the formation of a quinone group and a phenolate group or its ion. Phenolsulfonephthalein thus was considered to involve equilibria with **137**, **138**, and **139**.

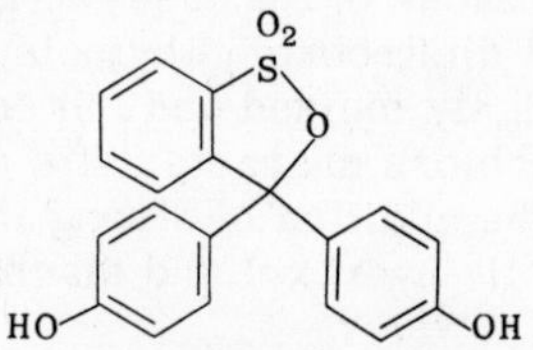

colorless, weak acid
sultone (lactoid) form

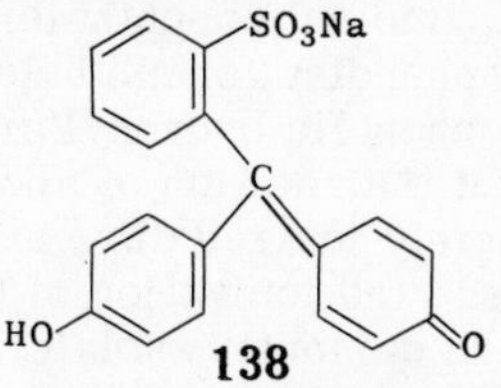

138
yellow, monobasic salt

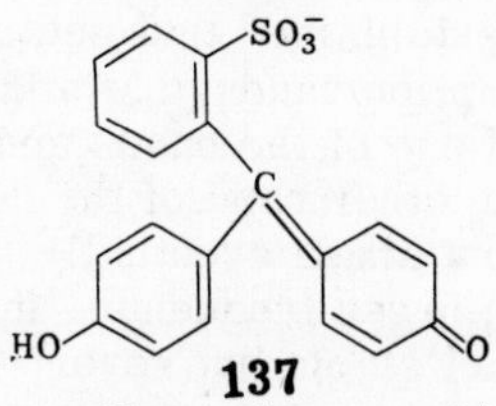

137
yellow, strong acid
quinoid form

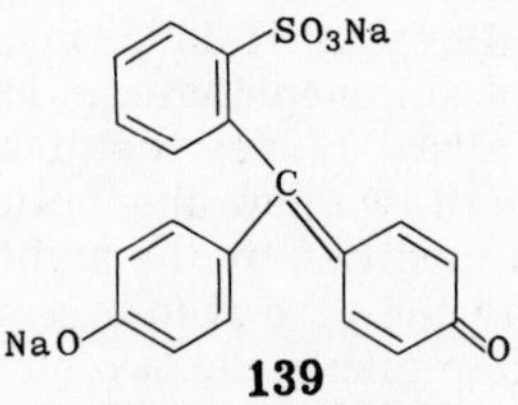

139
deeply colored
dibasic salt

[For references, see pp. 289-312.]

Chapter 4

Conductivity measurements by White[504] substantiated the quinoid form and according to these data phenolsulfonephthalein and the tetrabromo- and tetranitro- derivatives have at least 65% quinoidal form.

In contrast to the phenolphthaleins, which are weak acids, the sulfonephthaleins are strong acids. In the case of phenolsulfonephthalein, the weak phenol group is suppressed by the ionization of the strong sulfonic group whose acidity is nearly as great as a mineral acid. The yellow color, which is characteristic of phenolsulfonephthalein solutions, is not perceptibly altered by the addition of alkali up to 75% of a molecular equivalent. The addition of 95% molecular equivalent or more of alkali neutralizes the sulfonic acid group and results in a tautomeric rearrangement in which the alkali is neutralized by the phenolic hydrogen ions until the deeply colored dibasic sodium salt appears.

The amount of alkali necessary to produce a sharp change in color in phenolsulfonephthalein is about 85-87% molecular equivalent and in thymolsulfonephthalein about 98%. This is interpreted to be dependent on the constant for the equilibrium between the sultone and quinoidal structures and on the relative acidity strengths of the sulfonic and phenolic groups. Thus, the substitution of negative bromo or nitro groups in the $-C_6H_4SO_3H$ residue confers an increased acidity on the sulfonic group while not affecting that of the phenolic hydroxyl or the pH range of the color change. The substitution of negative bromo or nitro groups in the phenol residue greatly increases the acidity (ionization) of the phenolic hydroxyl and the color change occurs at a lower pH. The substitution of methyl, isopropyl, or amino groups in the phenol part lowers the ionization of the phenolic hydroxyl and raises the pH from 6. 8-8. 4 for phenolsulfonephthalein to 7. 2-8. 8 for o-cresolsulfonephthalein, and 8. 0-9. 6 for thymolsulfonephthalein. In solutions of the free tetrabromo- and tetranitrophenolsulfonephthalein and of dinitrobromothymolsulfonephthalein, the phenolic hydroxyl group is highly ionized and the compounds, without the addition of alkali, have colors characteristic of the nearly completely ionized dibasic salts. The addition of strong mineral acid suppresses the ionization of the phenolic hydroxyl and discharges the color of the quinonephenolate ion.[43,295,505,506]

The similarity of the absorption spectra of the alkaline solutions of sulfonephthaleins, phenolpthaleins, aurines, fluoresceins, and related compounds was advanced by White and Acree[230,505] as evidence that the deep color in all of these arises from the quinonephenolate ion. Additional confirmation was given by the absorption spectra studies of o-cresolsulfonephthalein[342] in which it was established that neutral solutions of sulfonephthaleins have two absorption bands, that addition of acid or alkali causes the disappearance of one of the bands and the appearance of two new absorption bands. The other band of the neutral solution is modified by the addition of acid, but alkali eventually makes it disappear and give rise to a new band with lower frequency. In the case of dilute alkali, the two new bands are not stable but revert to the two bands of the neutral solution.

Vodák and Leminger[481] reported that pyrocatechol violet has a yellow-orange color in water, violet-red in alkaline solution. They explained these color changes by equilibria of the undissociated sultone structure (140) with a quinoid anion (141) and a carbonium ion (142). Pyrocatechol violet was converted to pyrocatechol green (143) through a rearrangement and dehydration reaction.

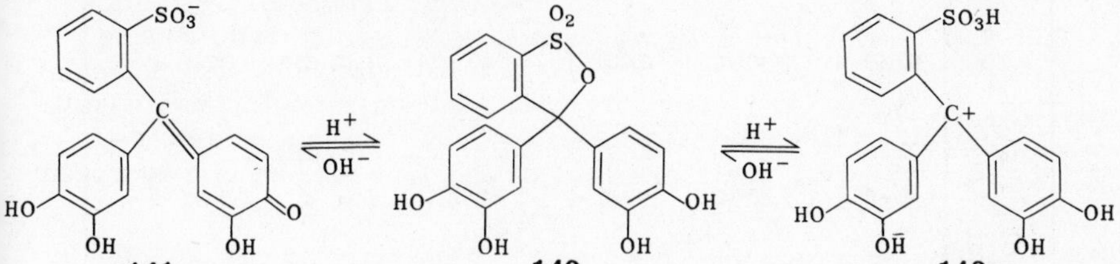

141
Violet anion

·140
Yellow sultone structure

142
Red carbonium ion

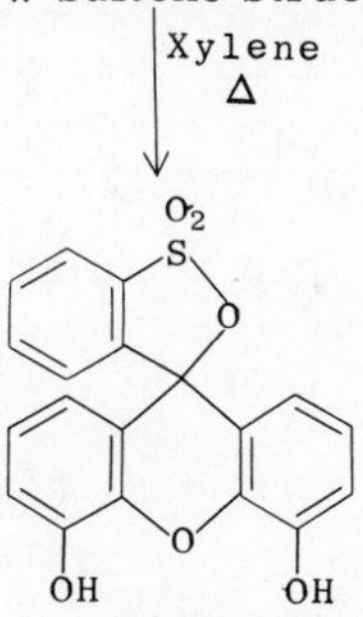

Xylene
Δ

143

Pyrocatechol green (143) dissolves in water with a brown color. Its alkaline solution is intense green and its acid solution yellow. It does not form metal complexes.

In a series of absorption spectra studies of sulfonephthaleins, Ramart-Lucas[368-375] postulated equilibria of the sultone form (144) with a quinoid structure (146) and a carbinol form (145).

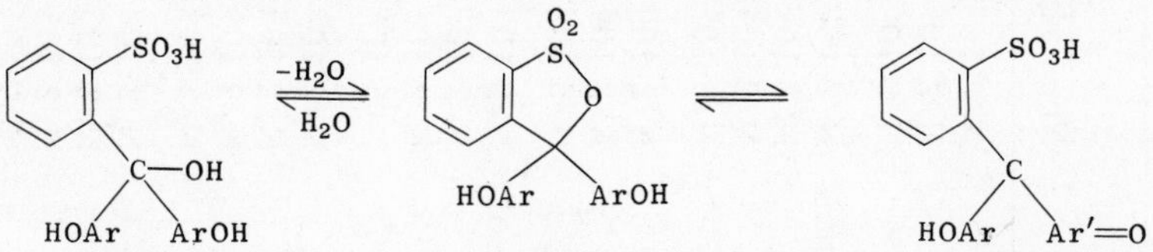

145
Carbinol form

144
Sultone form

146
Three quinoid forms:
A, B and B'

The three desmotropic forms occur as follows: 146A in neutral water, alcohol, and benzene media, and sometimes in acid media, but never in alkaline media; 146B in neutral (water and alcohol), acid (dilute acetic acid), and in alkaline media: this form is prevalent in the brominated products; 146B only in certain neutral solutions (alcohol and water) and in the presence of hydrochloric and acetic acid. Because of the

[For references, see pp. 289-312.]

TABLE 9. Structures of Sulfonephthaleins

Sulfonephthalein	Normality	Aqueous solution Neutral	Aqueous solution AcOH	Aqueous solution AcONa	Alcohol solution 5% NaOH	Alcohol solution Neutral	Alcohol solution AcOH	Alcohol solution HCl	Benzene Solution
Phenol-	N/2 10^3	A	A	B	B	A+B′	A+B′	B′	Insol.
	N/2 10^4	A	A	B	B	A+B′	A	B′	—
	N/5 10^5	A	—	—	—	A	—	—	—
Tetrabromophenol-	N/2 10^2	Insol.	Insol.	—	—	A	—	—	Insol.
	N/2 10^3	A+B	A+B	B	B+C	A	A	A+C	**144**
	N/2 10^4	A+B	A+B	B	B+B′	A	A	A+C	**144**
	N/5 10^4	B	—	—	—	A	—	—	—
o-Cresol-	N/2 10^3	A	Insol.	B	B	A+B′	A+B′	B′	Insol.
	N/2 10^4	A	Insol.	B	B	A+B′	A+B′	B′	—
	N/5 10^4	A	Insol.	—	—	A	—	—	—
Dibromo-*o*-cresol-	N/2 10^2	Insol.	Insol.	—	—	A	—	—	Insol.
	N/2 10^3	A	A	B	B	A	A	—	**144**
	N/2 10^4	A	A	B	B	A	A	—	**144**
	N/5 10^4	A	—	—	—	A	—	—	—
Thymol-	N/2 10^2	Insol.	Insol.	—	—	A+B′	—	—	Insol.
	N/2 10^3	—	—	B	B	A+B′	A+B′	B′	—
	N/2 10^4	—	—	B	B	A+B′	A+B′	B′	—
	N/5 10^4	—	—	—	—	A	—	—	—
Dibromothymol-	N/2 10^2	Insol.	Insol.	—	—	A	—	—	—
	N/2 10^3	A	—	B	B	A	A	A+B′	**144**
	N/2 10^4	A	—	B	B	A	A	A	**144**
	N/5 10^4	A	—	—	—	A	—	—	—

small difference in spectra of B and B′, B′ was found in alkaline solutions only at very high concentrations. Table 9 lists various sulfonephthaleins studied and their postulated structures, A, B, or B′, for various media.

There apparently is no question concerning the quinoid structure of A. The structures of B and B′ are postulated to be due to alterations in valence angles or spatial relations within the molecule and are affected by the electrical charges of the substituents. There also appears to be no question of the prevalence of the sultone structure in benzene.

Other spectra studies also have been reported.[5-7,54a,64,78,87,180,275b,275c,275d,276,309,321,397,398,458,459,471,474,480,520]

Schwarzenbach and co-workers[428] explained the color changes of phenolsulfonephthalein from red to yellow at pH 1.5 as a change from a symmetrical to an unsymmetrical resonance, and vice versa. The sulfonephthaleins were regarded as resonance systems in which two or more auxochrome groups with free electron pairs are attached to an unsaturated carbon chromophore residue in such a way that the double bonds can be displaced without affecting the molecular stability.

SO$_3^-$ C$^+$ HO   **147**   OH
Red

pH 1.5 ⇌

SO$_3^-$ C$^+$ HO   **148**   O
Yellow

pH 7.9 ⇌

SO$_3^-$ C$^+$ O   **149**   O   2−
Red

Kolthoff and Guss,[274] in their studies on the ionization constants of various sulfonephthaleins, visualized a similar change. Colichman[78] also attributed the two colored forms of bromophenol blue to this ionization equilibrium.

There has been considerable discussion and controversy on the fading phenomenon of sulfonephthaleins.[3-7,278,355,411,474] Fading is regarded to occur by the addition of hydroxyl ion to a colored form to give a colorless carbinol. The fading is a reversible process and depends upon the alkali concentration. Chen and Laidler[69a] studied the effect of pressure and temperature on the kinetics of the alkaline fading of bromophenol blue. They found that pressure has essentially no effect on

[For references, see pp. 289-312.]

the rate constants and concluded that, in reactions of bromophenol blue, the quinoid form may be structurally somewhat larger (relative to the carbinol form) so that the fading reaction involves a decrease in volume; they suggest that electrostriction effects in bromophenol blue may also contribute some effect.

One of the more exhaustive studies on the structural changes of sulfonephthaleins is that of Davis, Schukmann, and Lovelace.[88] The relation between the color and the pH of the solution of sulfonephthaleins was summarized by the following equilibria:

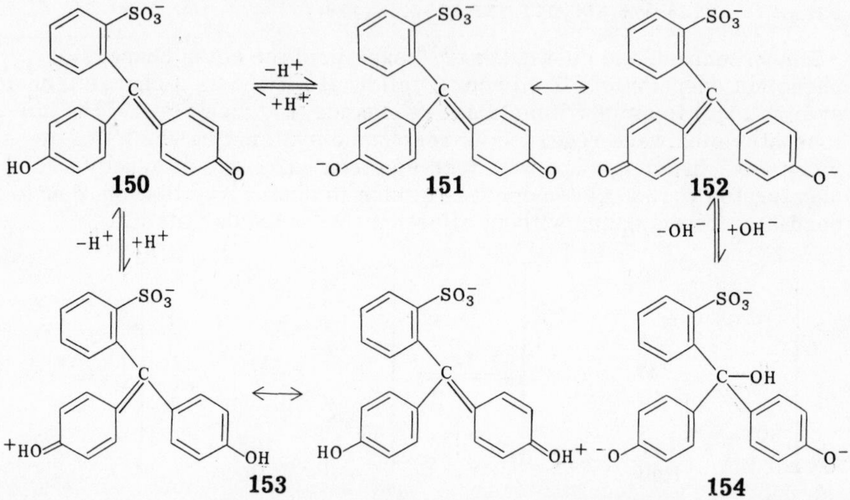

Thus, in aqueous medium, three colored forms and one colorless form are known to exist: **150** (yellow form), a univalent ion which contains a quinoid group, absorbs in the violet region of the spectrum; the bivalent anion, **151** and **152**, formed by removal of a phenolic hydroxyl proton, is of deeper color and absorbs light of longer wavelengths; the amphion, **153**, arising from the attachment of a proton to the phenolic hydroxyl, is deeply colored. The colors of the bivalent anions and the amphions are similar but not identical. The colorless form, **154**, absorbs ultraviolet but not visible light. The colorless form of the solid, on the other hand, is believed to have a sultone structure which can be easily converted to the deeply colored hydrate (solid amphion of **153**). The sultone structure probably does not occur in aqueous medium, at least not for long, because of the ease of hydration. Its solution in dry benzene, on the other hand, is colorless and is present as the sultone; deeply colored sulfonephthaleins are insoluble in benzene.

Blow and Rich[50a] described the effect of pH on bromophenol blue by the following series of structural changes:

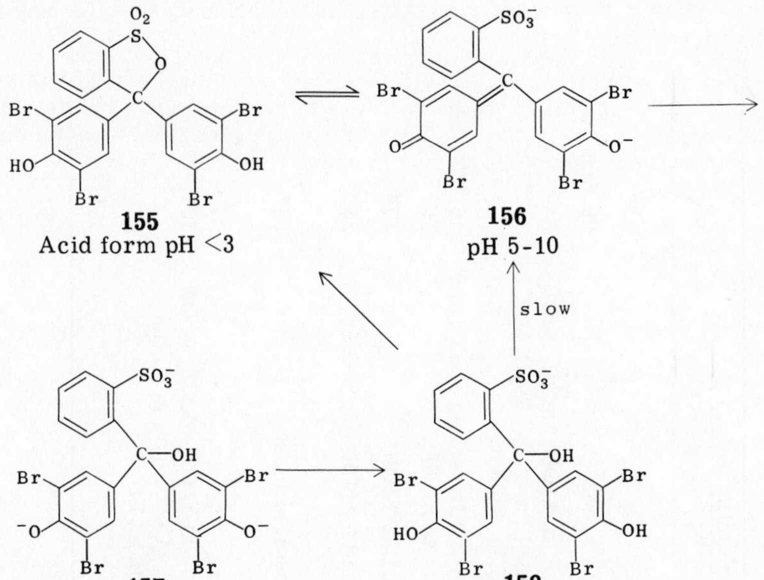

155
Acid form pH <3

156
pH 5-10

slow

157
pH 10-14

158
pH 5-10

According to this, the acid form (**155**) has a sultone ring and exists as an unchanged molecule with a yellow color which persists over the pH range of 3. 0-4. 6. This gradually changes to the blue quinoid form (**156**) on addition of hydroxyl ions and this divalent structure, with its resonance modifications, is stable between pH 4. 6 and 10. Above pH 10, the quinoid structure is slowly converted to a trivalent ion (**157**). On neutralizing the alkaline form, little change is observed as the colorless monovalent ion (**158**) is formed. This, being unstable, reverts to the blue form (**156**) within a day or to the yellow form (**155**) within a few hours if the pH is lowered below 5.

Table 10 lists the solubility of sulfonephthaleins in water and in organic solvents.

In addition to the properties discussed in various sections of this chapter, such as adsorption spectra, two others are of some interest. Taira, Yamatodani, and Fujii[454] separated the following sulfonephthaleins (R_f values in parenthesis) by paper chromatography using 3% sodium chloride solution as the developing agent: thymol blue (0. 37), bromothymol blue (0. 37), phenol red (0. 73), bromophenol blue (0. 57), bromocresol purple (0. 58), bromocresol purple (0. 73), and phenol red (0. 74).

Patti[358] irradiated phenol red, bromocresol purple, and bromophenol

[For references, see pp. 289-312.]

TABLE 10. Solubility of Sulfonephthaleins

Sulfonephthalein	Solubility in water	Solubility in organic solvents	Ref.
Phenol-	0. 03 g/100 g		506
Tetrabromophenol-	0. 7 g/l	10^{-4} mols/l. C_6H_6	89, 506
m-Cresol-	sl. sol.	sol. in EtOH, MeOH, AcOH; insol. in C_6H_6, Et_2O, $CHCl_3$, CCl_4, AcOEt	348
Resorcinol-	sl. sol. in hot	Difficulty sol. in AcOH and in hot EtOH	46, 377, 439, 502
Tetrabromoresorcinol-		sol. in EtOH	439
Hydroquinone-	0. 117 g/100 ml at 22°	0. 012 g/100 ml. EtOH	350
Pyrogallol-	1 g/20 l. cold 3 g/20 l. in boiling	insol. in most	347
Hydroxyhydroquinone-	difficulty sol.	sol. in EtOH, MeOH, AcOH, Me_2CO; insol. in C_6H_6, PhMe, Et_2O	351
Dibromohydroxyhydroquinone-	sol.		351

blue aqueous solutions with gamma rays and established by means of paper chromatography and electrophoresis that the phenol red and bromocresol solutions decolorized with the formation of two compounds and bromophenol blue changed from blue to yellow with the formation of two compounds. He postulated the splitting of the chromophoric group with formation of phenol.

Franglen[131] investigated the purity of sulfonephthalein dyes with paper chromatography and electrophoresis under normal light and ultraviolet light. The sulfonephthalein dyes were readily distinguished from each other, although chromatography was more effective than electrophoresis. This study is important particularly for showing that the majority of sulfonephthalein samples had appreciable quantities of impurities which could be of importance in their use for pH determinations. Thus, paper chromatography showed that six other components were present in chlorophenol red as impurities.

The relative degree of chromatographic adsorption of the following sulfonephthaleins on Silene EF-Celite 535 was studied by Karabinos and Hyde:[248] bromophenol blue, bromocresol green, chlorophenol red, bromocresol purple, m-cresol purple, thymol blue, cresol red, and bromothymol blue. Elemental flowers of sulfur has been shown to be a suitable hydrophobic adsorbent in chromatography for the separation of sulfonephthaleins.[296] Bromophenol blue has been successfully determined by virtue of the sharp thin blue line it gives in an ionographic isoelectric apparatus.[304]

According to Doss and Gupta[108b] bromocresol purple and thymol blue have relatively large heats of adsorption.

During work on the uptake of bromocresol green by serum proteins, Franglen and Gosselin[131a] noticed that the quinoid form of bromocresol green appeared to be polymerized. Thus, in dialysis experiments on the acid side of the dye, 4.7 (phenol form), equilibrium was reached within two days; on the alkaline side (quinoid form), equilibrium was not reached until after two weeks. On electrophoresis in starch gel, the quinoid form split into two separate components, presumed to be a mixture of two polymers or groups of polymers.

(4) Uses and Applications

(a) Analytical. White[503-505] and Lubs, Acree, and Clark[72,295] showed that sulfonephthaleins and their derivatives constitute an excellent series of acidimetric indicators with sharp color changes and with readily distinguishable colors. The first series of sulfonephthalein indicators introduced by Clark and Lubs[72] was extended by Cohen,[75-77] Hardin,[177,178] and others.[62,64,293,300,305,343-345,413,429,506]

In the preparation of indicator solutions of sulfonephthaleins, if the indicator is too insoluble in water, enough sodium hydroxide is added to neutralize the sulfonic acid group. Stock solutions of these indicators generally contain from 0.5 to 1 g of indicator per liter of solvent. Alcohol is sometimes used to increase the solubility of the indicator.

[For references, see pp. 289-312.]

Usually one to three drops of the indicator stock solution is used per 10 ml solution in hydrogen ion determinations.

The more important sulfonephthalein acid-base indicators are thymol blue, bromophenol blue, bromocresol green, chlorophenol red, bromothymol blue, phenol red, and cresol purple. Of these tetrabromophenol blue, bromocresol green, and chlorophenol red have enjoyed the widest use. Some of the sulfonephthaleins are not satisfactory indicators because of their marked dichromatism during transformation.

Bromocresol green, cresol red, and thymol blue have been used in mixed indicators.[515] Bromothymol blue, thymol blue, bromocresol green, and bromocresol purple have been used in the preparation of universal indicators which cover the range pH 1. 2—12. 7.

Cresol red, thymol blue, bromophenol blue, and bromocresol purple have been recommended as indicators for the determination of hydrogen ion in colored and cloudy solutions.[251]

In addition to their use in acidimetry, the sulfonephthaleins have found use as adsorption, complexometric, and chelatometric indicators, such as for the titration of thiocyanate ions with silver ions and tellurium ions with iodide ions.[275,277,317-320,340,482] A specific test for silver ions is the gold-yellow colors or spots on filter paper obtained with addition of 0. 1% pyrogallolsulfonephthalein or its dibromo derivative in ethanol solution.[488] Pyrocatechol violet forms colored complexes with various cations, such as bismuth, thorium, aluminum, iron, zirconium, vanadium, etc., and is a suitable reagent for their detection on paper electropherograms in amounts as small as 0. 1 microgram.[301] Tetrabromophenol blue[312] and iodophenol blue have been used in the potentiometric titration of the halogens with $Hg_2(NO_3)_2$. Sulfonephthalein dyes, such as bromothymol blue and bromophenol blue, combine with organic bases, such as cetyltrimethylammonium bromide or ephedrine hydrochloride, to form complex addition compounds in colorimetric determinations.[24, 229, 519] Auerbach[19a] used bromothymol blue as a dye anion in the colorimetric determination of germicidal quaternary ammonium salts in dilute solution and for the determination of alkaloids.

Körbl, Svoboda, and Terzijska[275a] reported a new series of metallochromic indicators from the condensation of sulfonephthaleins, such as pyrocatechol violet, pyrogallol red, cresol red, thymol blue, and xylenol blue with formaldehyde, β, β'-iminodipropionic acid, or N-(2-carboxyethyl)glycine. These derivatives exhibit hypochromic minimums at about pH 12, in which region they form complexes with alkaline earth metals.

The use of p-hydrazinophenylsulfonephthalein for the determination of aldehydes[276] has been noted. The sulfonephthaleins have found wide use in biochemical analyses.[68a,69b,94,182,184,209a,212,215,258d,324,434,509] Phenol red has been used in the determination of the depth of penetration of sodium fluoride into wood.[479] Many other analytical uses are mentioned in the literature,[165a,165b,305a,401a] but they are of minor importance compared to the use in acidimitry.

(b) Dyes. According to three British patents granted to Farbwerke Hoechst,[218,218a,219] sulfonated aminosulfonephthaleins are useful red to blue wool and silk dyes having good fastness to light and alkalies. These dyes are prepared by treating resorcinolsulfonephthalein (**159**) with $POCl_3$ to give the 3′, 6′-dichloro derivative (**160**), which on reaction with an aromatic amine, e.g., aniline, yields a dye (**162**) whose solubility properties are improved by sulfonation.

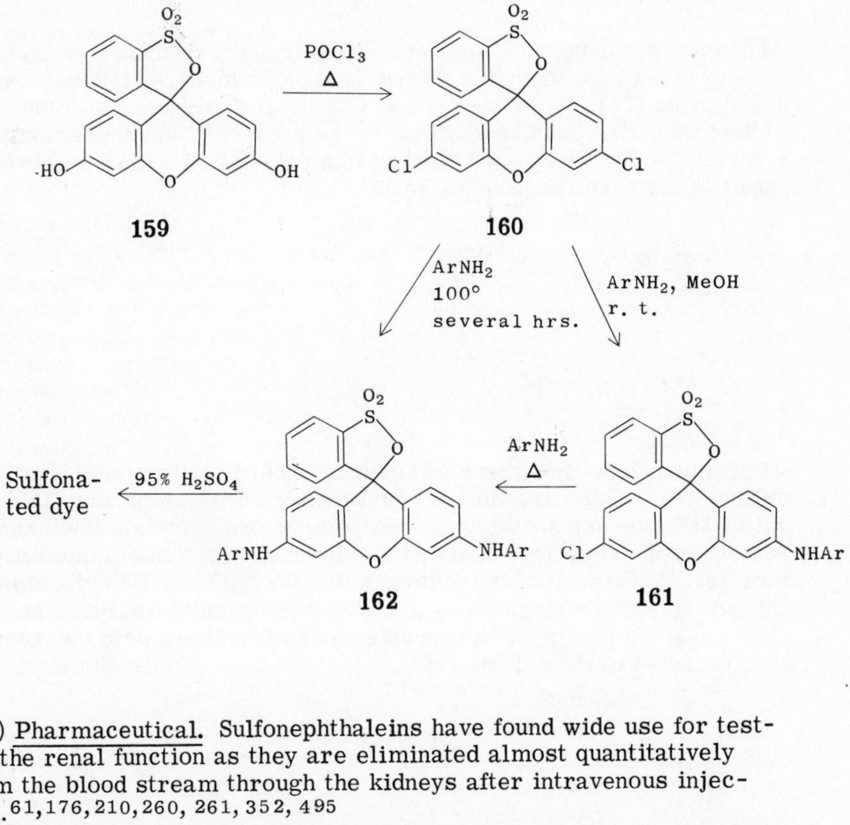
O2
S
O
HO
OH
O
159
POCl3
Δ
O2
S
O
Cl
Cl
O
160
ArNH2
100°
several hrs.
ArNH2, MeOH
r. t.
Sulfonated dye
95% H2SO4
O2
S
O
ArNH
NHAr
O
162
ArNH2
Δ
O2
S
O
Cl
NHAr
O
161

(c) Pharmaceutical. Sulfonephthaleins have found wide use for testing the renal function as they are eliminated almost quantitatively from the blood stream through the kidneys after intravenous injection.[61,176,210,260,261,352,495]

Because phenol red is not absorbed from the stomach nor altered chemically by the gastric secretions, it has been used as a dilution indicator for gastric analysis.[359,360] It has found use in the study of muscle,[314] hypertension,[128] general paresis[8], and the spleen.[235]

Mercury derivatives of sulfonephthaleins have shown bacteriostatic activity against *B. typhosus* and *S. aureus*.[70,175,181]

C. $C_3OS-C_5-C_5$

1. 4, 7-Methano-3H-1, 2-benzoxathiole (163)

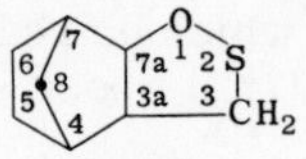

163
(RRI 2222)

The parent compound is unknown. The primary compound of this ring system is 3a, 7a-dimethyl-4, 7-methano-hexahydro-3H-1, 2-benzoxathiole 2, 2-dioxide (**164**), the name used in <u>Chemical Abstracts</u>. It is more commonly called camphenehydrato-π-sulfolactone or camphenesultone. A variety of derivatives substituted in position 4 or 5 have been prepared. These are listed in Table 11.

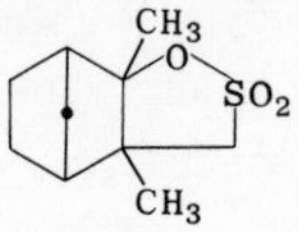

164

a. Structure

For quite some time there was doubt concerning the structure of this sultone (**164**). Lipp and Holl,[289] on treating active camphene (**165**) with sulfur trioxide and acetic acid, obtained isobornyl acetate (**166**) and a residue from which they isolated a sultone to which they assigned structure 167. Treatment of the sultone with 10% NaOH or Ba(OH)$_2$ solution opened the sultone ring to give 2-hydroxycamphane-ω-sulfonic acid (**168**) which on heating with concentrated hydrochloric acid and acetic acid reverted to the sultone (**167**).

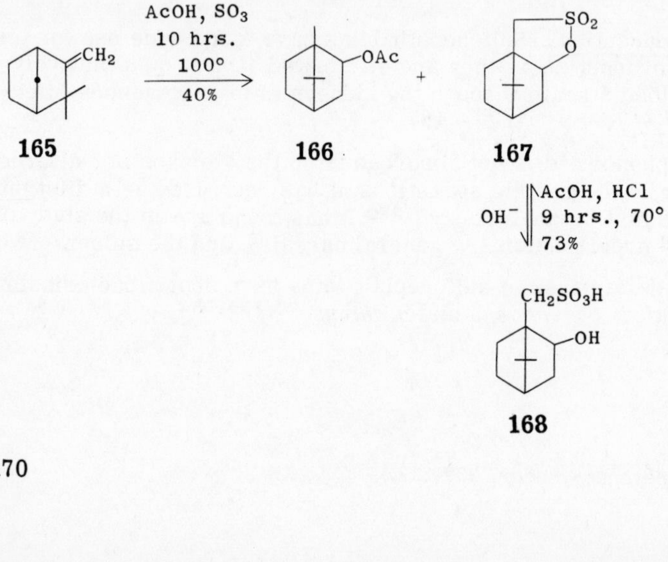

165   **166**   **167**

AcOH, HCl
OH⁻ 9 hrs., 70°
73%

CH$_2$SO$_3$H
OH

168

Lipp and Holl were not able to oxidize 2-hydroxycamphane-ω-sulfonic acid to Reychler's[394a] camphorsulfonic acid (169), although they found the inverse reaction readily yielded two stereoisomeric 2-hydroxycamphane-ω-sulfonic acids, an *endo* form (168a) and an *exo* form (168b), from which they obtained the sultone.

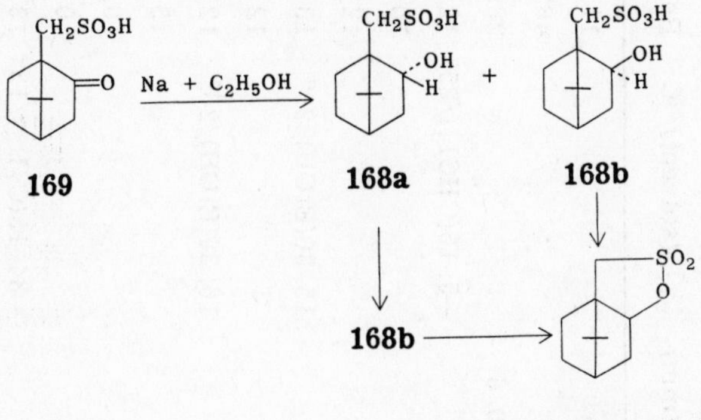

Apparently there is no doubt that Lipp and Holl obtained the sultone, although they assigned to it an incorrect structure. More recently Asahino, Sano, and Mayekawa[11] have shown that the formation of the inactive sultone from active 2-hydroxycamphane-ω-sulfonic acid is understandable only on the assumption that tricyclene-ω-sulfonic acid (170) is formed as an intermediate.

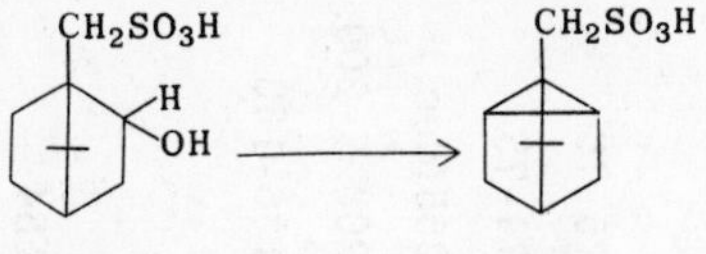

The tricyclene, through hydrolytic cleavage, is converted to camphene-hydrato-π-sulfonic acid (171) in two optically active forms which, on lactonization, yield the inactive sultone (164).

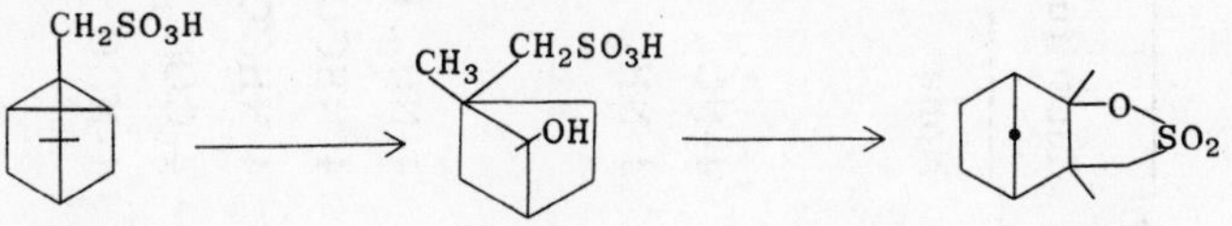

It is not possible to designate the sultone configuration. Its formation from active 2-hydroxycamphane-π-sulfonic acid may be explained through the Wagner-Nametkin rearrangement.[438] According to Asahino, Sano, and Mayekawa it it unlikely that camphene-π-sulfonic acid (172)

TABLE 11. 3a,7a-Dimethyl-4,7-methano-hexahydro-1,2,3H-benzoxathiole 2,2-Dioxides

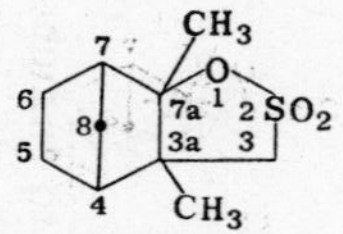

Substituent	Yield (%)	M.p. (°C)	B.p. (°C)	(mm)	$[\alpha]_D$ (solvent)/°C	Ref.
None	50	133				11, 12a
	55	133				462
	73	133	147.5-148.0	0.6		289
4-NO_2		258			$-5.15(CHCl_3)/25°$	12
4-NH_2		75-76				10
		74-75				12
4-$NH_2 \cdot HCl$		255(dec.)			$15.30(EtOH)/25°$	13
4-$NHCOC_6H_5$		208.5-209.0				12
4-$NHCO_2CH_3$		136-138			$16.34(EtOH)/26°$	12, 13
4-CON_3						13
4-NCO		184				12
						10, 13
					$-34.15(C_6H_6)/13°$	10
						13

4-CN	25	236		−58/16°	13
4-COOH	23	189			13
4-COCl		199–200			13
4-CONH$_2$		191–192	10.03(EtOH)/15°		13
4-CO$_2$CH$_3$	100	179–180	−16.18(C$_6$H$_6$)/13°		13
4-CO$_2$C$_2$H$_5$		85			13
4-OH	40				12
4-OCOCH$_3$		178			11
		186	28.30(CHCl$_3$)/24°		12a
5-NO$_2$	19	168			12
5-NH$_2$					12
5-NHCOC$_6$H$_5$		190			12
5,6-H$_2$		197			12

(a) Ref. (12) prepared it from the 5-NO$_2$-derivative through the amino- and diazotized-derivatives but cited a m.p. of 168°. The m.p. of the 5-NO$_2$-derivative was cited as 133-4°. Presumably these two m.p.'s were interchanged accidentally.

stereoisomers are intermediates, as in this case the sultone would be a mixture of diastereomeric *endo* and *exo* forms and not racemic

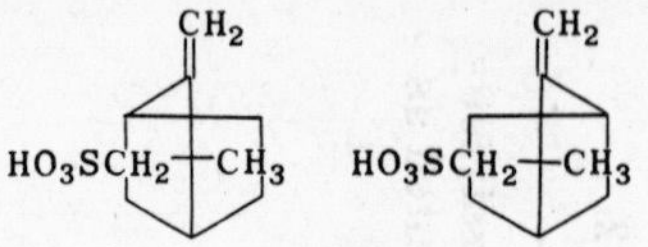

172

Asahino, Sano, and Mayekawa further concluded that the saponification product of the sultone is not 2-hydroxycamphane-ω-sulfonic acid (**168**) for the following three reasons: (a) the product is unsaturated and contains two hydrogens and one oxygen less than Lipp and Holl[290] supposed; (b) the product is optically inactive although prepared from optically active camphene; and (c) the same sultone is obtained from 2-hydroxy-camphane-π-sulfonic acid.

Frèrejacque,[131a] in preparing Reychler's acid (**169**), recovered from the mother liquor two isomeric neutral compounds which he believed were mixed camphor acetylsulfates. Asahino, Sano, and Mayekawa postulated that the compounds were probably stereoisomeric acetoxysultones arising from the formation of camphor diacetate (**174**) which undergoes a Wagner rearrangement to give 1-acetoxycamphene (**175**) with subsequent ring isomerization to the camphane skeleton and sultone (**177**).

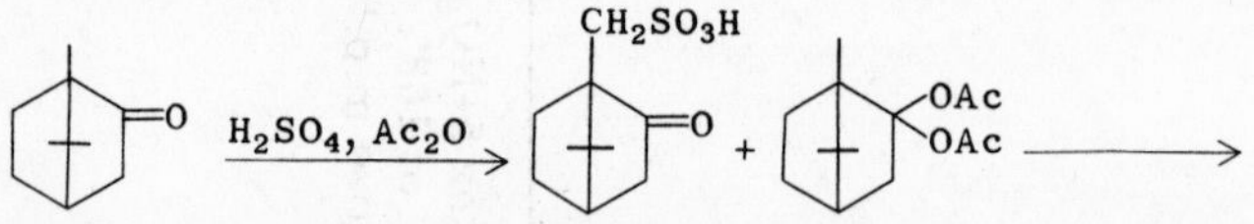

173   H$_2$SO$_4$, Ac$_2$O   **169**   +   **174**

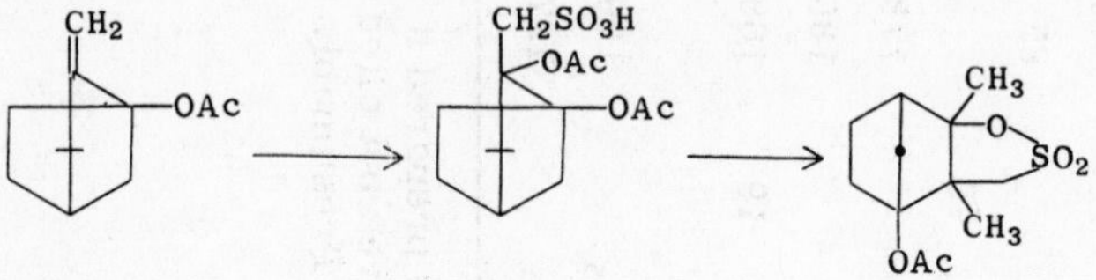

175   **176**   **177**

b. Preparation

(1) Sulfonation of Camphor

The sulfonation of camphor (**173**) by Reychler's method with sulfuric acid in acetic anhydride, as already discussed, yields a small amount of neutral by-product characterized as the 4-acetoxysultone (**177**).[11,131b] The reduction of Reychler's acid (**169**) with sodium in alcoholic solution by Lipp and Holl[289] gave 2-hydroxycamphane-ω-sulfonic acid (**168**) from which they obtained the sultone (**164**) in 73% yield by treatment with acetic acid and concentrated hydrochloric acid at 70° for 9 hours.

(2) Sulfonation of Camphene

Lipp and Holl[289] obtained a 4% yield of sultone (164) as a by-product from the action of sulfur trioxide in acetic acid on active camphene (165); the major product was isobornyl acetate (166). Asahino, Sano, and Mayekawa[11] considerably improved the yields, up to 50%, of sultone (164) by treating inactive camphene with sulfuric acid and acetic anhydride.

The action of sulfuric acid and acetic anhydride on nitrocamphenes (178 and 179) is analogous to that on camphene.[12]

O$_2$N—[structure] CH$_2$ $\xrightarrow[\text{19\%}]{\begin{array}{c}\text{H}_2\text{SO}_4,\ \text{Ac}_2\text{O}\\ 20°\end{array}}$ O$_2$N—[structure]—O—SO$_2$

178   **179**

[structure]—CH$_2$, NO$_2$ $\xrightarrow[\text{48\%}]{\begin{array}{c}\text{H}_2\text{SO}_4,\ \text{Ac}_2\text{O}\\ 20°\end{array}}$ [structure]—O—SO$_2$, NO$_2$

180   **181**

This reaction of nitrocamphene to give the nitrocamphenehydrato-π-sulfolactone (179 and 181) is probably accompanied by a rearrangement similar to that observed for the hydration of camphene and probably proceeds through 182 and 183 involving a methyl shift and ring closure.

O$_2$N—[structure] CH$_2$ $\xrightarrow{\text{H}_2\text{SO}_4}$ O$_2$N—[structure]$^+$CH$_2$SO$_3$H $\xrightarrow{\text{CH}_3\ \text{shift}}$

178   **182**

O$_2$N—[structure] CH$_2$SO$_3$H, $^+$ $\longrightarrow$ O$_2$N—[structure]—O—SO$_2$

183   **179**

The preparation of the sultone from nitrocamphene may be cited as confirmation of Asahino and co-workers[11-13] postulate that camphenehydrato-π-sulfonic acid (172) is the precursor of the sultone.

Treatment of camphene-4-carboxylic acid (184) with sulfuric acid and acetic anhydride, as was done with camphene and nitrocamphene, yielded isobornylaceto-4-carboxylic-ω-sulfonic acid (185) and no sultone.[13]

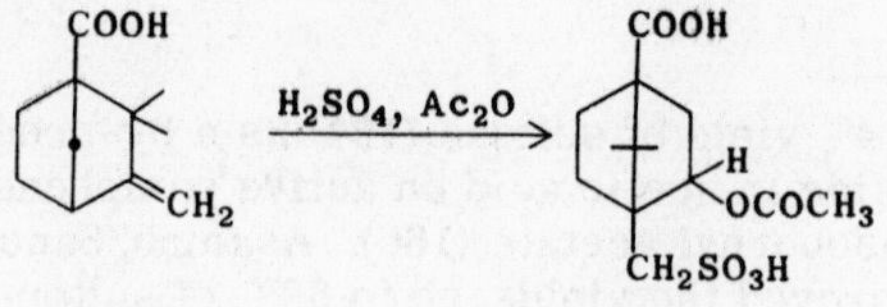

184 → **185**

On the other hand, active camphene-1-carboxylic acid (**186**), under the same conditions, gave 23% of sultone (**187**), whose methyl and ethyl esters had a measurable rotation.[13]

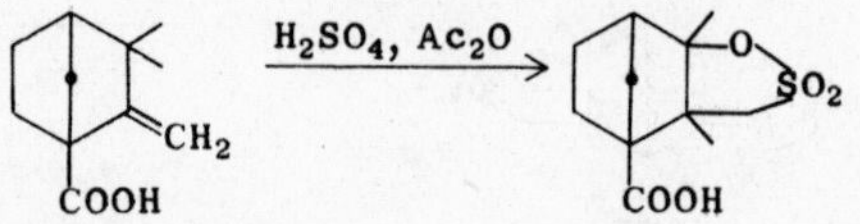

186 → **187**

The conversion of camphene-1-carboxylic acid (**186**) to the sultone (**187**) whereas camphene-4-carboxylic acid (**184**) undergoes the Wagner rearrangement is in agreement with the behavior of α- and β-methyl-camphenes towards acids.[438] In general, 1-substituted camphenes undergo the Nametkin rearrangement and 4-substituted camphenes undergo the Wagner rearrangement. A possible exception to this generalization is the conversion of camphene-1-carboxamide (**188**), on treatment with sulfuric acid and acetic anhydride, to camphene-4-carboxamide-π-sulfonic acid (**189**).[13]

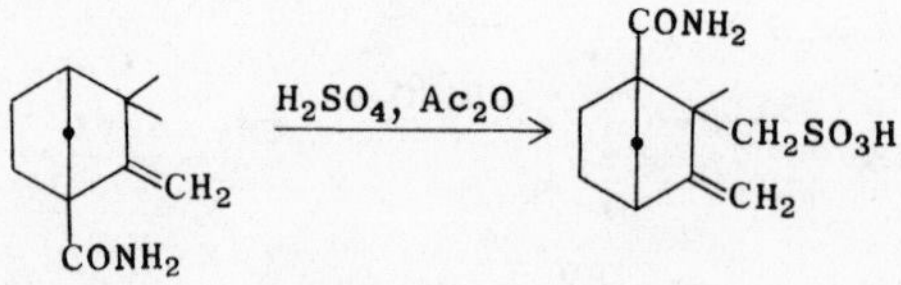

188 → **189**

(3) Sulfonation of Isoborneol and Borneol

Treibs and Lorenz[462] obtained camphenesultone (**164**) in 55% yield by the sulfonation of isoborneol (**190**) by Reychler's method. A similar treatment of borneol (**190**) gave a 7.6% yield of sultone. It was assumed that borneol or isoborneol was first converted to camphene (**165**) with racemization through formation of a carbonium ion intermediate (**192**).

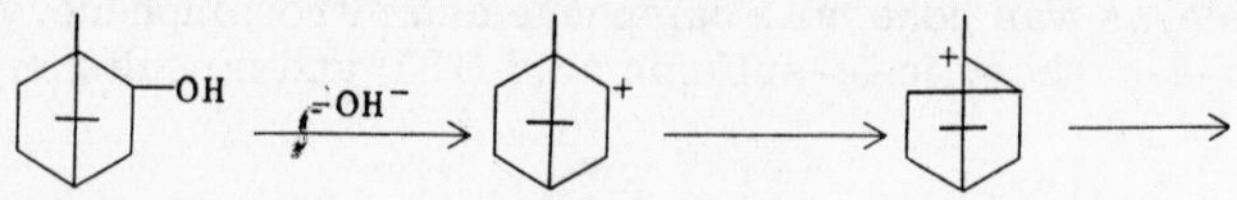

190 → **191** → **192**

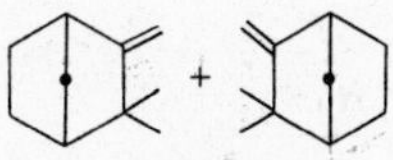

165

c. Reactions

Treatment of camphenesultone with 10% NaOH or Ba(OH)$_2$ solution opens the sultone ring to give 2-hydroxycamphene-π-sulfonic acid (193).[11,289]

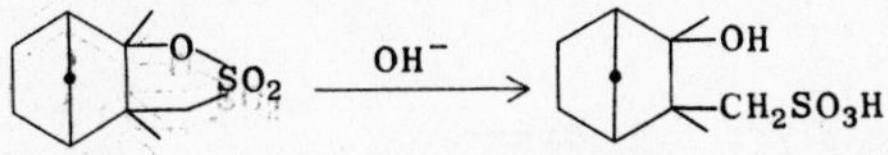

194   **193**

Sulfur dioxide evolves on thermally decomposing the sultone in the presence of zinc oxide to give camphene.[462]

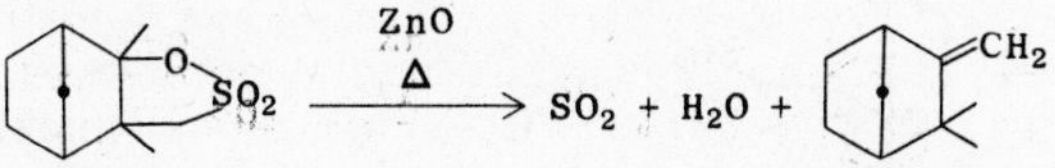

194   **165**

In heated concentrated hydrochloric acid, the 4-aminosultone (195) is attacked at the sultone ring to give 4-aminocamphene-π-sulfonic acid (195a).[12]

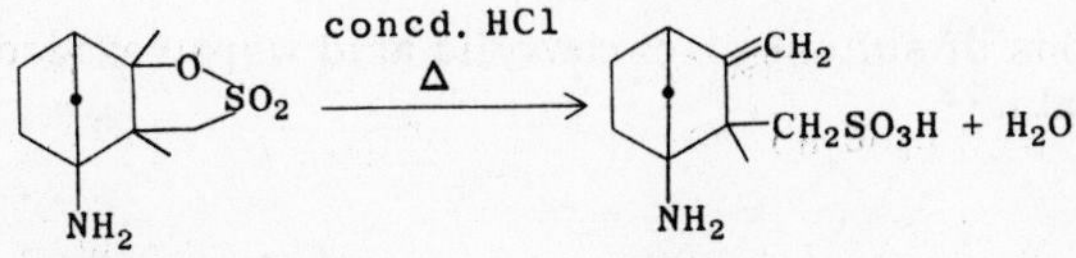

195   **195a**

Helberger and Manecke,[194] on treatment of the sultone with potassium iodide in refluxing methyl ethyl ketone, found that the ring opened to give 2-iodocamphene-π-sulfonic acid (196) in good yield.

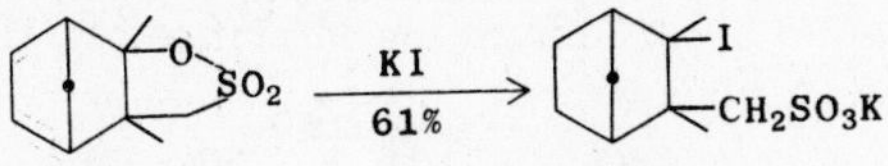

194   **196**

The following reactions of the 4- and 5-nitrosultones (197 and 181) were carried out by Asahino and Yamagucki.[12]

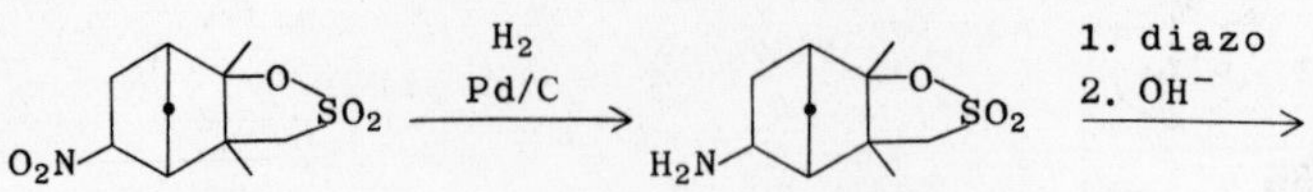

The reaction of primary amines with nitrous acid ordinarily goes by way of a carbonium ion intermediate. At bridgehead carbons, however, the reaction goes with great ease, and some other path may be involved.[10] Thus the difference between the diazotization products of the 4- and 5-aminosultones (198 and 200).

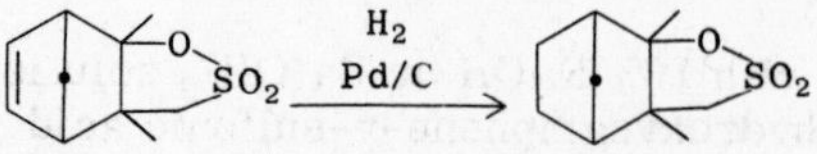

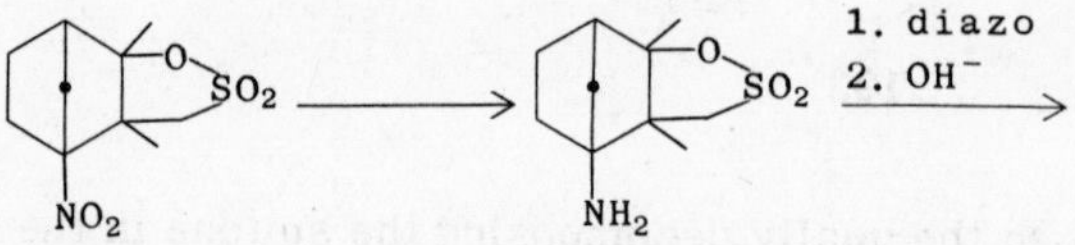

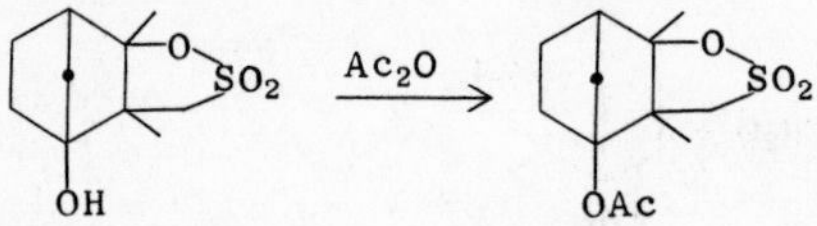

The following reactions of sultone-4-carboxylic acid were carried out by Asahino and Kawahata.[13]

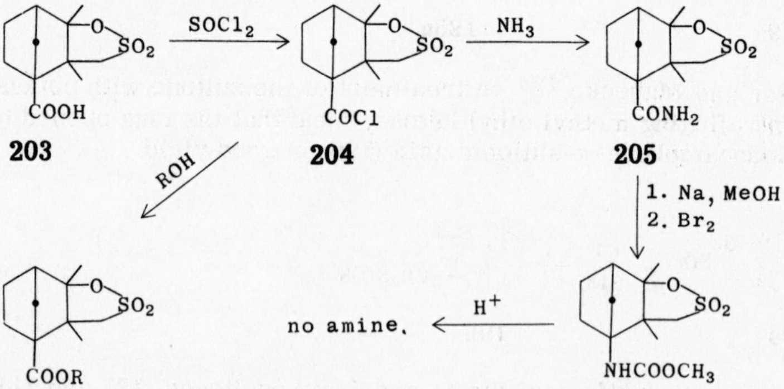

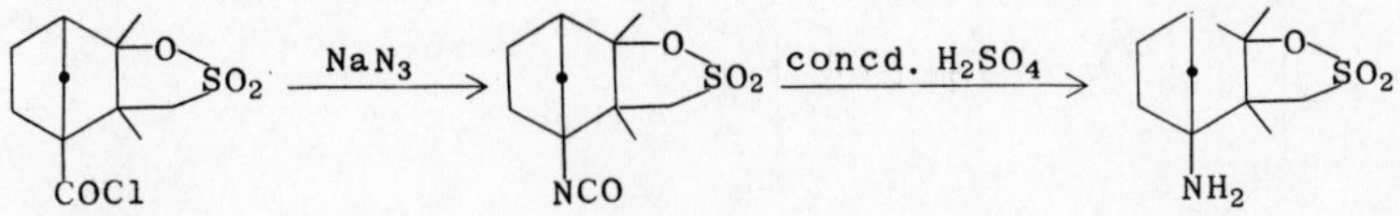

204   **209**   **200**

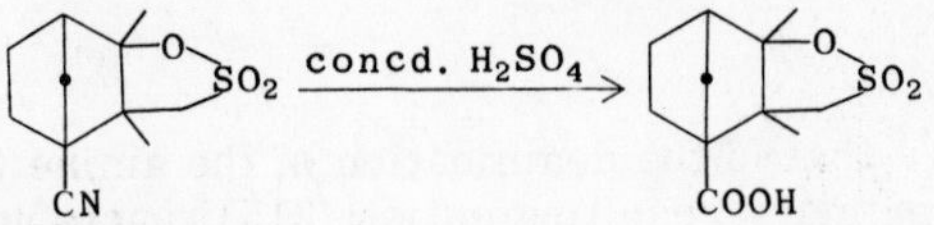

210   **203**

2. 5, 7a-Methano-7aH-1, 2 Benzoxathiole (211)

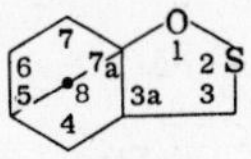

211
(RRI 2223)

The only representatives of this ring system are the 4-substituted-3a-methyl-5, 7a-methano-hexahydro-7aH-1, 2-benzoxathiole 2, 2-dioxides listed in Table 12. In addition to this nomenclature, Chemical Abstracts has called them sultones of 4-hydroxy-9-camphenesulfonic acid.

TABLE 12.   3a-Methyl-5, 7a-methano-hexahydro-7aH-benzoxathiole 2, 2-Dioxides.

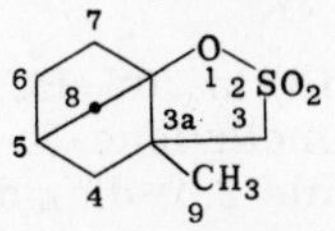

Substituent	Yield	M.p. (°C)	$[\alpha]_D$	Ref.
4-(=CH$_2$)	55	115–116	−12. 86(EtOH)/22°	12
4-(=O)	50	171. 2	47. 25(C$_6$H$_6$)/30°	12
4-(=NNHC$_6$H$_4$-p-NO$_2$)		230		12
4-CH$_3$	100	143 and 147	4. 93(EtOH)/25°	12

Asahino and Yamaguchi[12] obtained these sultones (**214**) on boiling 4-amino-3a, 7a-dimethyl-4, 7-methano-hexahydro-1, 2, 3H-benzoxathiole 2, 2-dioxide (**212**) with 10% HCl solution, and diazotizing the resulting 4-aminocamphene-π-sulfonic acid (**213**).

[For references, see pp. 289-312.]

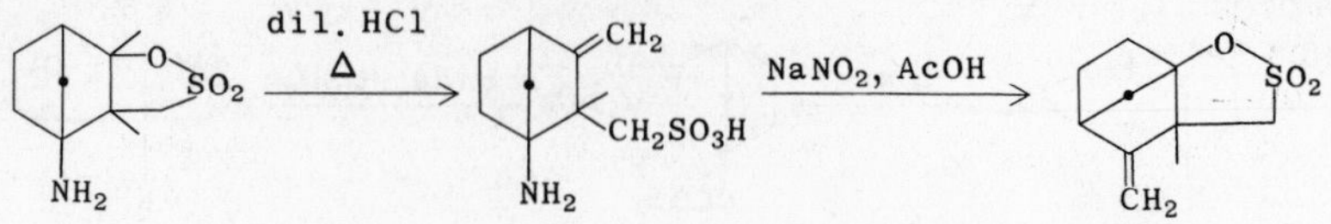

212 → **213** → **214**

Schöllkopf[423b] pointed out that in the deamination of the amine (**213**) through diazotization, the primary resulting cation (**215**) reacts not only with a water molecule but also with the favorably positioned oxygen of the sulfonic acid hydroxyl.

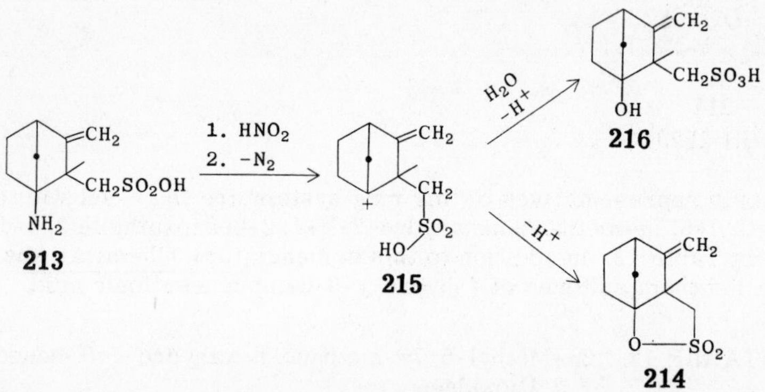

213 → **215** → **216**, **214**

Treatment of the 4-aminosultone (**212**) in 30% HCl solution with sodium nitrite gave a hydrochloride of the 4-methylene-3a-methyl-5, 7a-methano-hexahydro-7aH-1, 2-benzoxathiole 2, 2-dioxide, although there is some question as to the structure of the sultone. The chloride is removed by catalytic hydrogenation or by reduction with zinc and acetic acid.

The 4-methylenesultone (**214**) in acetic acid absorbed hydrogen over a Pd—C catalyst to give two stereoisomeric 4-methylsultones (**217**), melting at 143° and 147°.

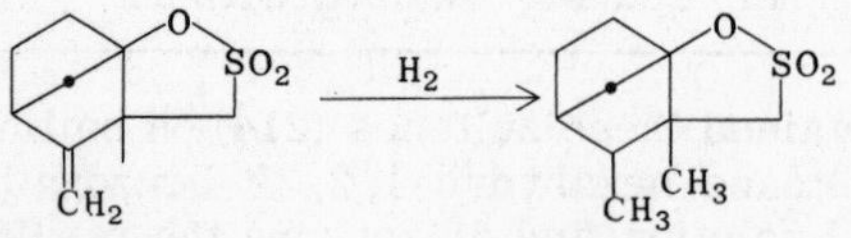

214 → **217**

On ozonolysis, the 4-methylenesultone (214) cleaved into formaldehyde and a ketosultone.

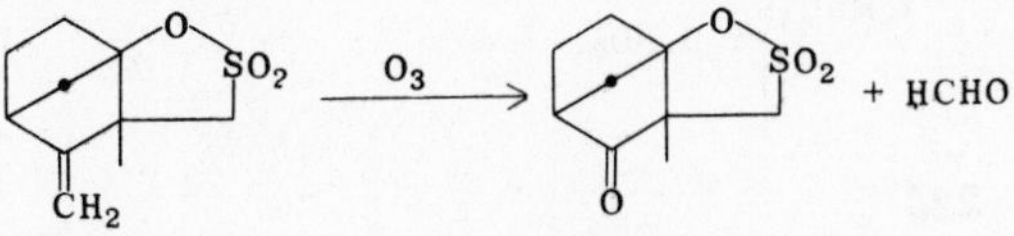

214   213   + HCHO

p-O$_2$NC$_6$H$_4$NHNH$_2$

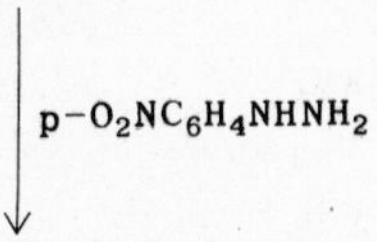

p-Nitrophenylhydrazone

3. 3, 5-Methanocyclopent[*c*][1, 2]oxathiole (219) or
    6-Oxa-7-thiatricyclo[3. 2. 1. 1$^{3, 8}$]nonane (220)

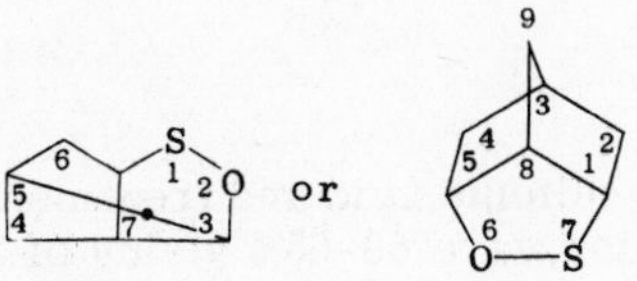

219   220

(RRI 2224)

Chemical Abstracts uses the tricyclo name for indexing. Compounds in this ring system also have been called [2. 2. 1]bicycloheptane-3, 5-sultones.

In the course of investigating the Diels-Alder reaction of cyclopentadiene with several phenylethene-1-sulfonates, Rondestvedt and Wygant[399] treated the adducts with potassium tribromide to give the bromosultone in order to estimate the composition of the stereoisomeric adduct mixture. Thus, when methyl 2-*p*-nitrophenylethene-1-sulfonate (221) was refluxed with cyclopentadiene in bromobenzene for one hour, 68% of an adduct was obtained. This adduct, characterized as methyl 6-*p*-nitrophenyl-2, 5-endomethylene-1, 2, 5, 6-tetrahydrobenzenesulfonate, was a mixture of two stereoisomers (222 and 223).

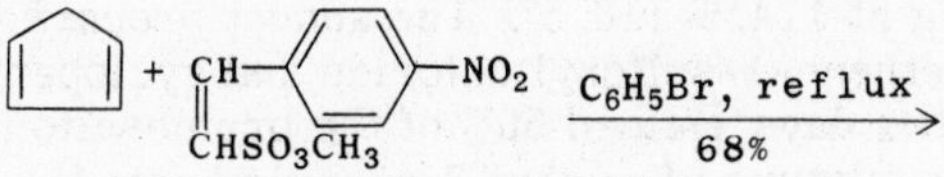

221

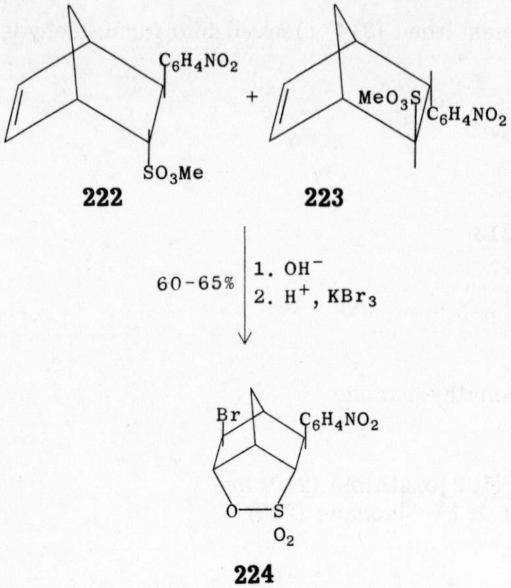

C6H4NO2

+

MeO3S C6H4NO2

SO3Me

222   **223**

60-65%   1. OH⁻
         2. H⁺, KBr₃

Br   C6H4NO2

O——S
    O₂

224

The adduct mixture, on hydrolysis to the sulfonic acid and treatment of the acid with potassium tribromide solution, gave 60-65% yields of 2-p-nitrophenyl-6-bromobicyclo [2. 2. 1] heptane-3, 5-sultone (**224**), melting at 206-208°.

On recrystallizing the adduct 14 times, the yield of bromosultone was 93%. It was therefore concluded that the crude adduct contained approximately 65% of isomer **222**, in which the position of the sulfo group is favorable for sultone formation.

The basis for this conclusion was the quantitative yield of 2-bromo-2-methyl-3-phenylpropene-1, 3-sultone obtained by Bordwell, Suter, and Webber[60a] on treating 2-methyl-3-phenyl-2-propene-1-sulfonic acid with bromine water (section I A-3a(1c)). The ease of formation of the propane sultone and the bromosultone of **222** indicated that sultone formation may be used to estimate certain β, γ-or γ, δ-unsaturated sulfonic acids in mixtures. Rondestvedt and Wygant[399] point out, however, that the reaction is not completely general for these classes of unsaturated acids, as bromosultones can be prepared from β, γ-unsaturated acids only if a phenyl group is in the γ-position.

The adduct prepared by refluxing cyclopentadiene with methyl 2-phenylethene-1-sultonate yielded only 9% of 2-phenyl-6-bromobicyclo [2. 2. 1] heptane-3, 5-sultone, melting at 114. 5-116. 5°. The adduct prepared from a mixture of 2-phenylethene-1-sulfonyl chloride and cyclopentadiene in toluene at 45° for 3¹/₂ days yielded 59% of the bromosultone.[400] The adduct prepared from a mixture of methyl 2-phenylethene-1-sulfonate and cyclopentadiene in toluene at 45° for 3 days yielded only 1% of the bromosultone.[400] The adduct prepared from a mixture of 2-*p*-nitro-phenylethene-1-sulfonyl chloride and cyclopentadiene in toluene at 45° for 3^{1}/$_2$ days yielded 74% of the bromosultone (224).[400]

D. C$_3$OS-C$_6$-C$_6$

1. Naphth[1, 8-*cd*]-1, 2-oxathiole (225)

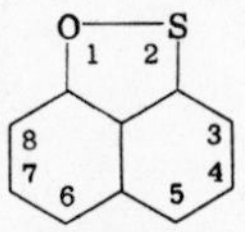

225

(RRI 2800)

The parent compound is unknown. It is well represented, however, by numerous derivatives of its 2, 2-dioxide, commonly known as naphtho-sultone, the cyclic ester of 1-naphthol-8-sulfonic acid. These compounds have been indexed in Chemical Abstracts under 1-naphthol-8-sulfonic acid sultone.

Naphthosultone (226) was first prepared by Mensching[322] in 1885. It was first characterized by Schultz[427] in 1887 and the term "sultone" was introduced by Erdmann[117] in 1888. The various naphthosultones which have been reported are listed in Table 13.

a. Preparation

(1) From 1-Naphthylamine-8-sulfonic Acids

The most general procedure for preparing naphthosultones has been by heating or refluxing diazotized solutions of 1-naphthylamine-8-sul-fonic acids with water, alcohol, or dilute acids.[33, 41, 42, 85, 86, 117, 122, 135, 140, 236, 267, 322, 427, 448, 475, 476]

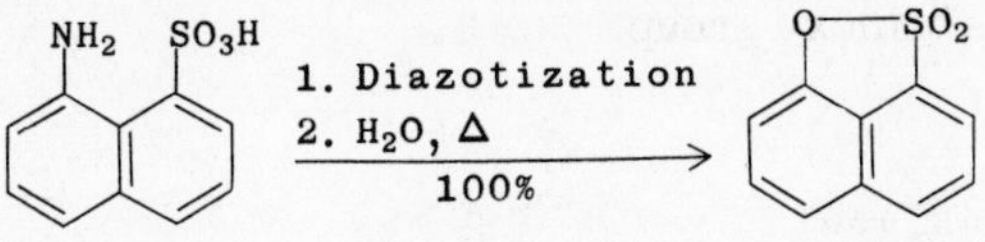

226

The mechanism of this reaction is not known. There is reason to believe that the diazo compound is not converted to the naptholsulfonic acid as an intermediate, in view of the difficulty of dehydrating this to the sultone. An interesting mechanistic lead is that the sultone was obtained by Cumming and Muir[85] on pouring diazotized 1-naphthylamine-8-sulfonic acid into boiling hydrogen iodide rather than the iodo compound one would expect from the Sandmeyer reaction. This observation by Cumming and Muir was cited by Hodgson, Birtwell, and Walker[217] as

Chapter 4

an exception to their interpretation of the Sandmeyer reaction. It seems reasonable to postulate that the reaction involves an internal displacement of nitrogen by the sulfonate oxygen in the diazonium zwitterion to account for the ease of ring closure.

(2) From 1, 8-Naphtholsulfonic Acids

The literature does not disclose any case in which naphthosultone was obtained by heating 1, 8-naphtholsulfonic acid. An early German patent[35] implies that the sultone was obtained as an intermediate on heating naphtholsulfonic acid at high temperatures with sulfur and alkali sulfides; however, the claimed product was a brown dye stated to be useful for dyeing wool.

Two early German patents[26,27] claimed the preparation of naphthosultone sulfonic acids by treating naphtholsulfonic acid with concentrated sulfuric acid at 100°, fuming sulfuric acid in the cold, or with phosphorus pentoxide or oxychloride. Schetty[417] converted 4-substituted sodium 1-naphthol-8-sulfonates to 6-substituted naphthosultones by treatment with boiling phosphorus oxychloride.

In studies on the chlorosulfonating action of chlorosulfonic acid on naphtholdisulfonic acids, Gebauer-Fuelnegg and Haemmerle[141] obtained naphthosultone-7-sulfonyl chloride (227) on treating 1-napthol-3, 8-disulfonic acid with chlorosulfonic acid; naphthosultone-6-sulfonyl chloride was obtained analogously from 1-naphthol-4, 8-disulfonic acid. In attempting to prepare carbethoxy-1-naphthol-4, 8-disulfonyl chlorides, naphthosultone-6-sulfonyl chloride was obtained if traces of moisture were not excluded during the reaction of the carbethoxy 1-naphthol-4, 8-disulfonic acid with PCl$_5$ as well as in the recrystallization step by the splitting off of the carbethoxy group.

227

Spryskov and Aparyeva[446] on chlorosulfonating 1-naphthol-4, 8-disulfonic acid at 20° for 24 hours obtained 43-64% yields of naphthosultone-6-sulfonyl chloride. They prepared the naphthosultone-7-sulfonic acid by heating sodium 1-naphthol-3, 8-disulfonate with sulfuric acid; the sultone was converted to the corresponding sulfonyl chloride by treatment with chlorosulfonic acid at room temperature for 24 hours.

The sulfonyl chlorides are important for the identification and purification of aromatic sulfonic acids as well as for the preparation of a variety of derivatives. In general, phosphorus pentachloride is not an effective agent for converting sulfonic acid to sulfonyl chloride; rather, phosphorus pentachloride displaces the phenolic hydroxyl with chlorine. In the treatment of 1, 8-napholsulfonic acids with chlorosulfonic acid, there is little doubt that the first stage is the chlorination of the sulfonic group to give the sulfonyl chloride. The mechanism, however, for elimination of hydrogen chloride from the intermediate 1-naphthol-8-sulfonyl chloride is not known.

Schirmacher and Langbein, [421] on treating sodium 1-naphthol-4, 8-disulfonate with chlorine and concentrated hydrochloric acid at 30-80° for half an hour, obtained a 90% yield of 6-chloronaphthosultone (228); the bromo compound was prepared analogously. The treatment of sodium 1-naphthol-6, 8-disulfonate with sodium chlorate in dilute hydrochloric acid at 30-80° yielded 6-chloronaphthosultone-4-sulfonic acid (229). The mechanisms of these two reactions are not obvious.

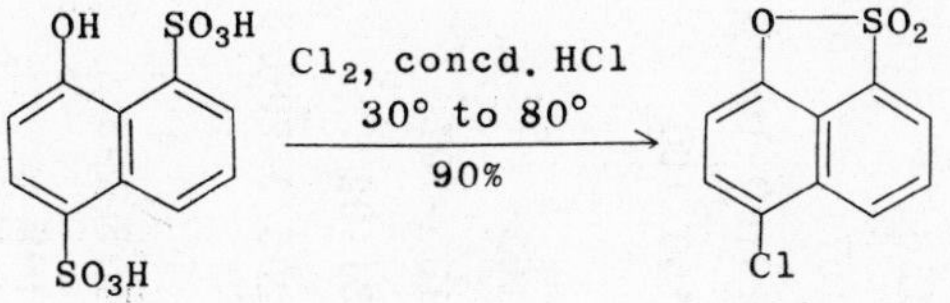

228

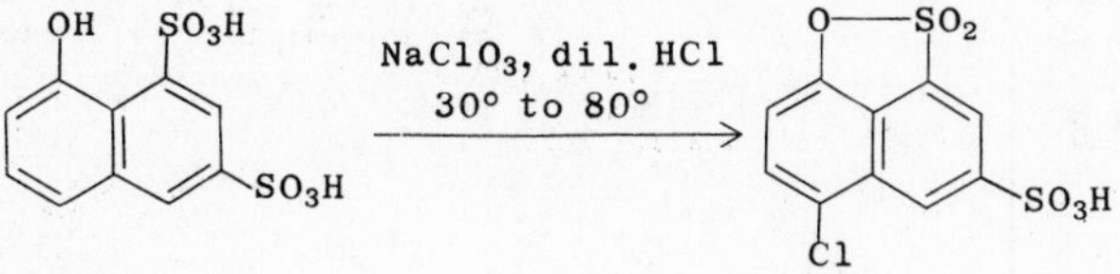

229

b. **Properties**

The naphthosultones listed in Table 13 are colorless, well crystallized compounds of relatively high melting point. The oxathiolane ring structure is stable towards heat and is not readily broken; thus naphthosultone at its atmospheric boiling point, 360°, undergoes only slight decomposition.

c. **Reactions**[336]

(1) **Hydrolysis**

Naphthosultones are relatively stable to alkalies in the cold; prolonged treatment with aqueous sodium carbonate or sodium hydroxide in the cold is without effect. Naphthosultone is only scarcely attacked by boiling aqueous ammonia. [117]

TABLE 13. Naphthosultones

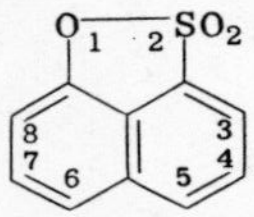

Substituent	Yield (%)	M.p. (°C)	B.p. (°C)	(mm)	Ref.
None	100	154	360 (dec.)		117, 217, 322, 427
		156			85
		157	190	2-3	417
5-CH₃-		161.0-161.5			448
		159-160			475, 476
					333, 337
6-CH₃-	84	162			148, 418, 420
6-C₂H₅-	37	106-107			417
6-C₃H₇-	18	81-82			417
6-I	81	205.5-206.5			2a
5-Br					337
6-Br	88	196-198			421
		199			308
		140			151

Substituents	Yield (%)	M.p., °C	References
x-Cl			117
5-Cl		184	135
6-Cl	90	176–178	421
		178	135, 151
		181–183	247
5-BrCH$_2$-			337
6-BrCH$_2$-	85	145–146	418, 420
5-ClCH$_2$-			337
6-ClCH$_2$-	90	144–145	146, 418, 420
6-HOCH$_2$-	79	143–144	418, 420
6-C$_6$H$_5$CH$_2$-	40	96–98	417
		110–111	147, 418, 420
6-(2-HOC$_6$H$_4$CH$_2$-)	13	167–169	418
6-(4-HOC$_6$H$_4$CH$_2$-)	56	89–91	418
6-(2-CH$_3$CO$_2$C$_6$H$_4$CH$_2$-)		141–142	420
6-(4-CH$_3$CO$_2$C$_6$H$_4$CH$_2$-)		124–125	418
6-(2-HO-5-CH$_3$C$_6$H$_3$CH$_2$-)		174–176	418
6-[2-HO-3,5-(CH$_2$)$_2$C$_6$H$_3$CH$_2$-]			418
6-[2-CH$_3$CO$_2$-3,5-(CH$_3$)$_2$C$_6$H$_2$CH$_2$-]		171–172	418
6-(3-HOOC-4-HOC$_6$H$_3$CH$_2$-)			418
			420

TABLE 13. Naphthosultones (contd)

Substituent	Yield (%)	M.p. (°C)	B.p. (°C)	(mm)	Ref.
6-(3-CH$_3$OOC-4-HOC$_6$H$_3$CH$_2$-)		177-178			418
6-(3-CH$_3$OOC-4-CH$_3$COOC$_6$H$_3$CH$_2$-)		146-147			418
6-(1-piperidylmethyl-)					420
6-HOOC-	62	263-264			418
6-HCO-					418
6-ClCO-		173-174			418
6-CH$_3$CO-	74	172-173			417
6-ClCH$_2$CO-		164-166			417
6-C$_2$H$_5$CO-	80	160-161			417
6-C$_3$H$_7$CO-	70	131-132			417
6-(CH$_3$)$_2$CHCH$_2$CO-	36	121.5-122.5			144, 416, 417
6-C$_6$H$_{11}$CO-	0.5	134-135			417
6-C$_6$H$_5$CO-	90	158-159			417
		156-159			144, 416
6-(3-O$_2$NC$_6$H$_4$CO-)	76	236-237			417
6-(4-O$_2$NC$_6$H$_4$CO-)	79	231-232.5			144, 416, 417
6-(3-O$_2$N-4-ClC$_6$H$_3$CO-)	55	218-219			416, 417
6-(2,4-Cl$_2$C$_6$H$_3$CO-)	76	171-172			417

Substituent		M.p., °C	References
6-CH₃NHCO-		255-256	418
6-(C₂H₅)₂NCO-		156-158	418
6-C₆H₅NHCO-		273-275	418
6-(CH₃)(C₆H₅)NCO-		147-148	418
	29	146-147	417
6-(C₂H₅)(C₆H₅)NCO-		169-170.5	418
6-(C₆H₅)₂NCO-		178-179.5	417
6-(o-CH₃C₆H₄)NHCO-		242.5-243.5	418
6-(1-C₁₀H₇)NHCO-		293-295	418
6-(2-C₁₀H₇)NHCO-		272.5-273.5	418
6-C₆H₅NHN=C(CH₃)-		159.5-160.5	417
6-C₆H₅NHN=C(CH₂Cl)-			417
6-C₆H₅NHN=C(C₂H₅)-		151-152	417
6-C₆H₅NHN=C(C₃H₇)-		188-189.5	417
6-C₆H₅NHN=C[CH₂CH(CH₃)₂]-		177-178	417
6-(m-ClC₆H₄)NHN=C(CH₃)-		212-213	417
5-HO₃S-			140
6-HO₃S-		240	27, 33, 42
7-HO₃S-		241	446
			122
			26, 41

TABLE 13. Naphthosultones (contd)

Substituent	Yield (%)	M.p. (°C)	B.p. (°C)	(mm)	Ref.
6-ClSO$_2$-	64	197			446
		195			141
		194			246
7-ClSO$_2$-	86	187-188			446
		190-191			141
		186-187			246
6-CH$_3$SO$_2$-					420
6-C$_6$H$_5$SO$_2$-	61	206-207			417
					333
6-(p-CH$_3$C$_6$H$_4$SO$_2$-)	95	215-216.5			145, 416-420
					333
6-(3,4-Cl$_2$C$_6$H$_3$SO$_2$-)	17	197.0-197.5			417
6-(3-HOOC-4-HOC$_6$H$_3$SO$_2$-)	3	247-248			417
6-C$_6$H$_5$NHSO$_2$-	40	145			446
		146-147			246
7-C$_6$H$_5$NHSO$_2$-		212-213			246, 446
4,7-(HO$_3$S-)$_2$					267

4,7-(ClSO₂-)₂	163		246
4-HO₃S-6-Cl			421
6-HO₃S-8-O₂N-			152
6,6'-	24	289-290	2a
6,6'-CH₂-		288-289	420
6,6'-[2,5-(HO)₂C₆H₂-1,3-(CH₂-)]₂		290 (dec.)	418
6,6'-SO₂	75	292-293	417

[For references, see pp. 289-312]

Treatment of naphthosultones with hot solutions of alkali or alcoholic alkali yields the corresponding 1, 8-naphtholsulfonate salt.[26,42,117,135,147,148,247,308,475]

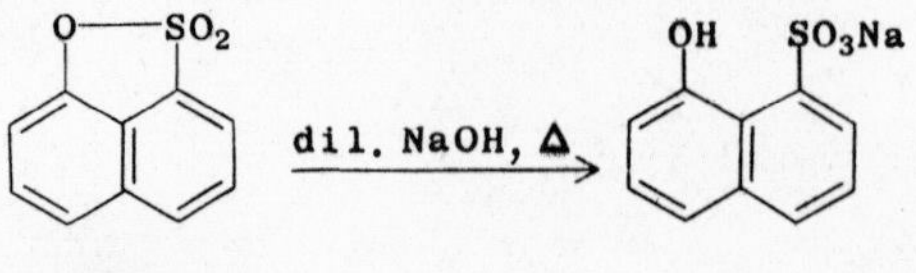

226

Heating naphthosultone with ethyl alcohol and dilute ammonium hydroxide half an hour at 130° gives ammonium 1, 8-naphtholsulfonate. [117]

Alkali fusion of naphthosultonesulfonic acid (**230**) at 170-220° yields the corresponding 1, 8-dihydroxynaphthalenesulfonic acid.[34,216]

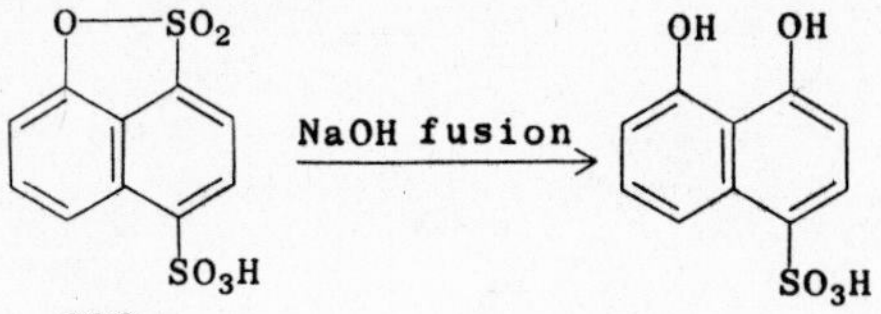

230

Treatment of naphthosultone with dilute sulfuric acid opens the sultone ring to give the corresponding 1. 8-naphtholsulfonic acid.[26]

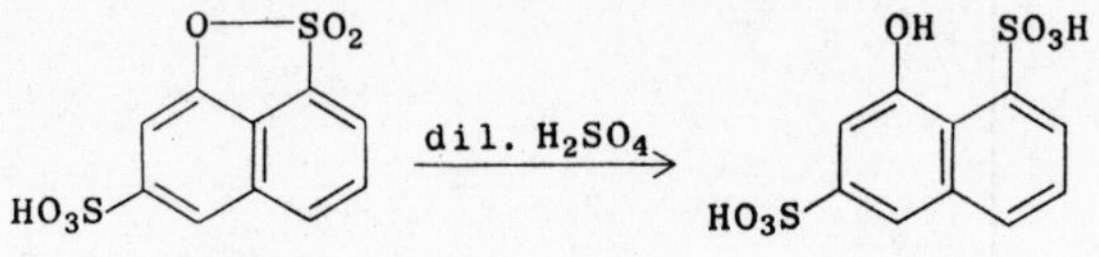

227

On the other hand, treatment of naphthosultone with 98% sulfuric acid gives 1-naphthol-4, 8-disulfonic acid[236] and treatment with fuming sulfuric acid (25% SO_3) over several days gives 1-naphthol-2, 4, 8-trisulfonic acid. [109]

(2) Halogenation

Bromination of naphthosultone in cold acetic acid yields 6-bromonaphthosultone (**231**).[308] Sodium naphthosultone-6-sulfonate and disodium 1-naphthol-4, 8-disulfonate afford the same product on treating their aqueous solutions acidified with sulfuric acid with bromine in acetic acid. The latter involves an unusual ring closure.

192

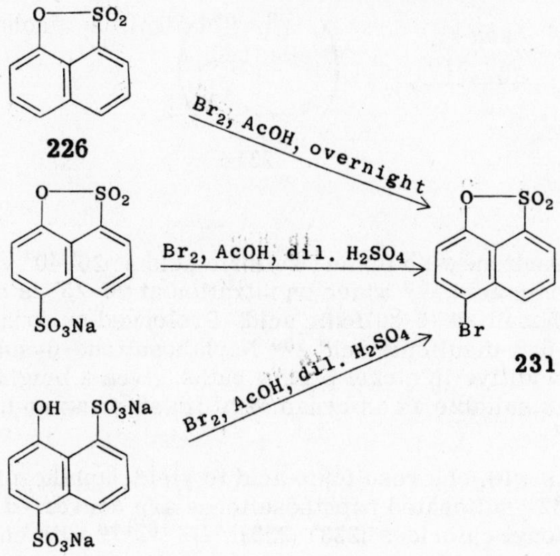

According to a German patent,[151] bromination of naphthosultone with bromine over a long period in the cold also gives 6-bromonaphthosultone.

Chlorination of naphthosultone with hydrochloric acid and sodium chlorate[247] with heating gives 6-chloronaphthoquinone. The product is also obtained by chlorination with hydrochloric acid and manganese dioxide at 80-90° or with chlorine in the presence of iron powder at 160-200°.[151]

Treatment of naphthosultone with phosphorus pentachloride by Erdmann[117] yielded a chloronaphthosultone which was not characterized. The reaction is somewhat ambiguous.

Allport and Bu'Lock[2a] prepared 6-iodonaphthosultone (231a) in 81% yield by treating a mixture of naphthosultone, acetic acid, sulfuric acid, and iodine with nitric acid added dropwise. Heating 231a with copper bronze yielded 6, 6'-bis (naphthosultone) (231b) which, on heating with sodium hydroxide, gave the tetrahydroxy-1, 1'-binaphthyl (231c), the chromogen of *Daldinia concentrica,* a fungus parasite found on ash.

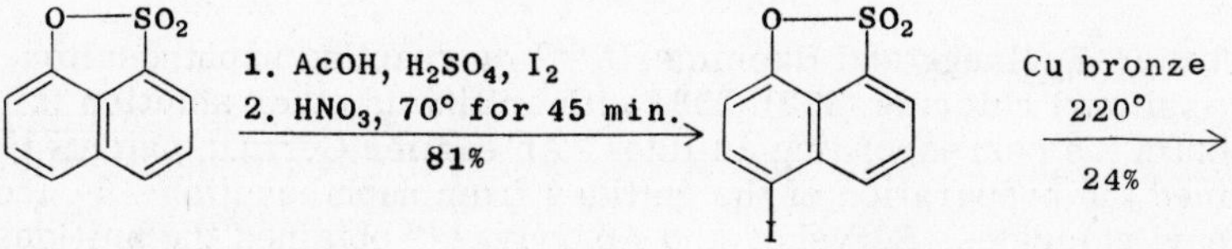

[For references, see pp. 289-312.]

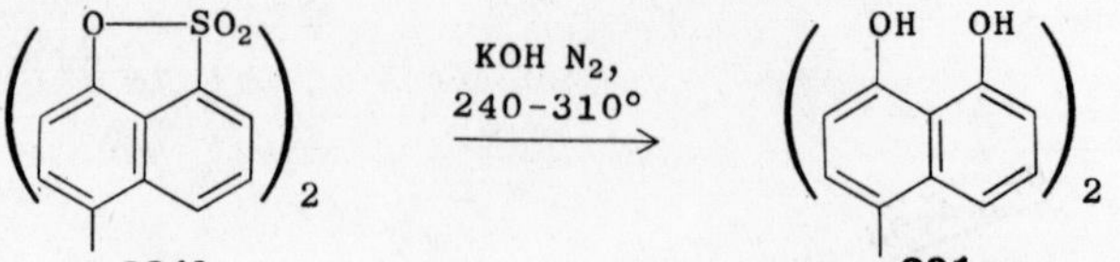

231b → **231c**

KOH N$_2$,
240-310°

(3) Sulfonation

Treatment of naphthosultone with fuming sulfuric acid at 20-40° yields naphthosultone-6-sulfonic acid,[152] which on nitration at 20-25° is converted to 8-nitronaphthosultone-6-sulfonic acid. Prolonged sulfonation yields naphthosultone-6, 8-disulfonic acid.[109] Naphthosultone-6-sulfonic acid, when used as an additive in nickel plating baths, gives a bright deposit of nickel that is suitable as an ornamental finish or as an undercoat for chromium.[221]

Naphthosultone reacts with chlorosulfonic acid to yield naphthosultone-6-sulfonyl chloride (232); sulfonated naphthosultones are converted to the corresponding sulfonyl chlorides (233) (235)[141,246,446] with chlorosulfonic acid.

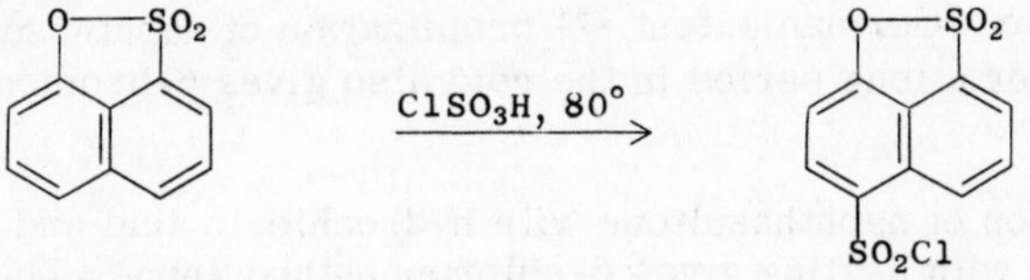

226 → **232**

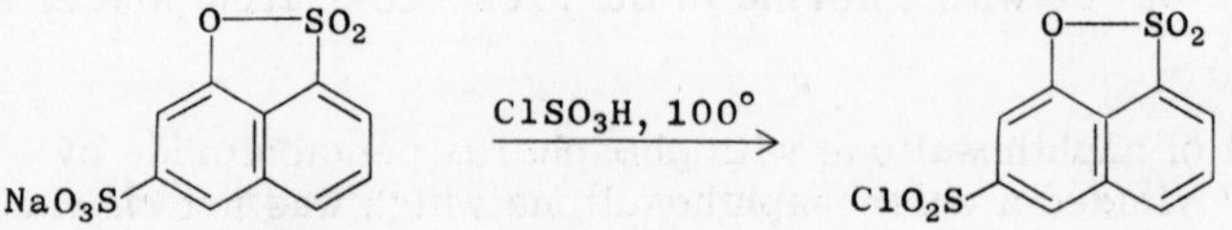

ClSO$_3$H, 80°

227 → **233**

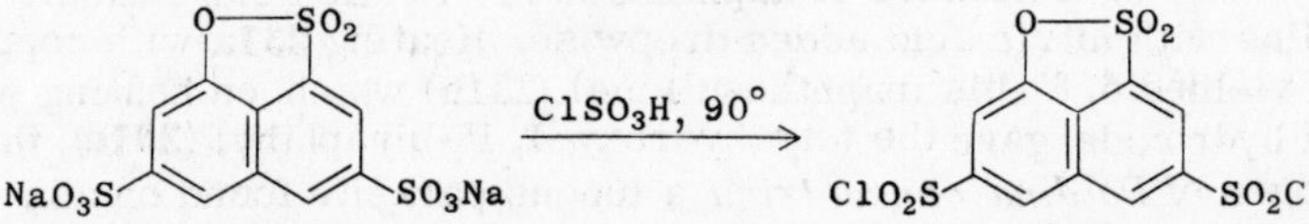

ClSO$_3$H, 100°

234 → **235**

ClSO$_3$H, 90°

Gebauer-Fuelnegg and Haemmerle[141] on reacting naphthosultone-6 or 7-sulfonyl chloride (232) (233) with aniline in ether solution failed to obtain the corresponding anilides. An earlier German patent[246] claimed the preparation of the anilides from naphthosultone-6- and 7-sulfonyl chlorides. Spryskov and Aparylva[446] obtained the anilides by heating the sulfonyl chlorides with excess aniline in benzene solution.

(4) With Ammonia

Treatment of naphthosultone with ammonia, aqueous ammonia, or aqueous ammonium carbonate yields 1-naphthol-8-sulfonamide.[150] Similarly, naphthosultone sulfonic acids react to give the corresponding 1-naphthol-8-sulfonamide sulfonic acids.[25,28,41,42,150,152,267,418]

Naphthosultonesulfonyl chlorides react with dry ammonia in benzene to give the corresponding 1-naphthol-3 (or 4), 8-disulfonamide.[63,246,446] Treatment of naphthosultone-6-sulfonyl chloride (**232**) with ammonium hydroxide for two days at room temperature yielded diammonium 1-naphthol-4, 8-disolfonate.[446]

The rate of reaction of naphthosultones with cold, aqueous ammonia[418] is influenced by substitution in the 6-position. The sultone bridge in naphthosultone is under the influence of the strong electron attraction of the sulfone group and of the tendency for a pair of electrons to shift from the oxygen atom to the electrophilic naphthalene ring. An electron-donating substituent, such as a methyl group, would reverse the electron shift. An electrophilic substituent would enhance the electron shift of naphthosultone.

226   **236**   **227**

The reaction, however, is similar to that of the cleavage of aromatic sulfonates with ammonia. Thus, phenyl benzenesulfonate reacts slowly with alcoholic ammonia at 200° to give the sulfonamide; aryl sulfonates substituted with electron-attracting groups cleave with considerable ease as do the similarly substituted naphthosultones.[452]

(5) The Friedel-Crafts Reaction

Schetty acylated, aroylated, and sulfonated naphthosultone by a Friedel-Crafts reaction to yield the corresponding 6-substituted derivative, which is useful as a dye intermediate.[143-145,233,417] The following types of halides were investigated: alkyl halides, aralkyl halides, aliphatic and aromatic acid and sulfonyl halides, and substituted carbamyl halides. Alkyl halides did not undergo the reaction. Benzyl chloride yielded mixtures containing 6-benzylnaphthosultone, which could not be separated. The Friedel-Crafts reaction of naphthosultone with aliphatic (unbranched) and aromatic acid chlorides gave good yields of 6-acyl- or aroylnaphthosultones. Branched aliphatic acid chlorides did not readily acylate naphthosultone and tended to form a resin. Aromatic acid chlorides substituted with electron-attracting groups reacted more slowly and poorly than the unsubstituted.

Diphenylcarbamyl chloride undergoes the Friedel-Crafts reaction with naphthosultone to give the amide (237) with some resin formation.

$$O{-\!\!\!-}SO_2 \text{ (226)} + (C_6H_5)_2NCOCl \xrightarrow[55\%]{AlCl_3,\ 135°} O{-\!\!\!-}SO_2 \text{ (237)}$$

$(C_6H_5)_2NCO$

226   **237**

At temperatures above 135° the resinous material increases. Phenylmethylcarbamyl chloride reacts under the same conditions somewhat less readily, but without resin formation.

Aliphatic sulfonyl chlorides do not undergo the Friedel-Crafts reaction as do the aromatic sulfonyl chlorides, which react more sluggishly than the analogous carboxylic acid chlorides. At higher temperatures, the sulfonyl chlorides react to give good yields of 6-arylsulfonylnaphthosultones without side reactions. Aromatic sulfonyl chlorides substituted with electron-attracting groups are considerably less reactive or nonreactive; those substituted with electron-donating groups, such as a methyl group, are more reactive.

These 6-keto-, sulfonyl-, or amidonaphthosultones are easily saponified with aqueous alkali solutions to the corresponding substituted 1-naphthol-8-sulfonic acid. Treatment of these 6-substituted naphthosultones with ammonia yields the corresponding 1-naphthol-8-sulfonamide. The sultones, indifferent towards ammonia in the cold, react on heating.

(6) With Grignard Reagents, Phenyllithium, and Lithium Aluminum
   Hydride

Mustafa and co-workers[332-337] have shown that Grignard reagents react with naphthosultone and its derivatives to open the sultone ring. The reaction provides a method for preparation of perihydroxydiarylsulfones.[238]

$$O{-\!\!\!-}SO_2 \text{ (226)} \xrightarrow{RMgX} OH \quad SO_2R \text{ (238)}$$

226   **238**

A 75% yield of 8-*t*-butylsulfonyl-1-naphthol was obtained by refluxing naphthosultone and *t*-butylmagnesium chloride in benzene solution four hours and letting stand overnight.

Mustafa and co-workers[337] found that phenyllithium, like organomagnesium compounds, could effect the opening of hetero rings. Thus, naphthosultone reacted with phenyllithium to give 8-phenylsulfonyl-1-naphthol. Lithium aluminum hydride, similarly to the Grignard reagents, opened the hetero ring of naphthosultone and its derivatives. Treatment of naphthosultone with lithium aluminum hydride, followed by hydrolysis, gave 1, 1'-dihydroxy-8, 8'- dinaphthyldisulfide (239).

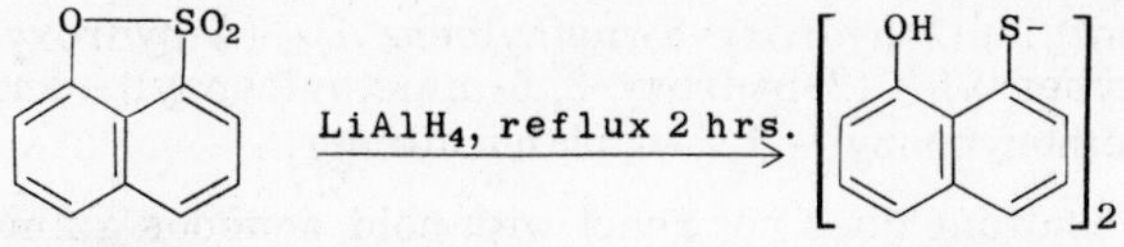

226   LiAlH$_4$, reflux 2 hrs.   239

(7) With Sodium Amalgam

Sodium amalgam, similar to phenyllithium and organomagnesium compounds, effects the opening of the hetero ring.[140]

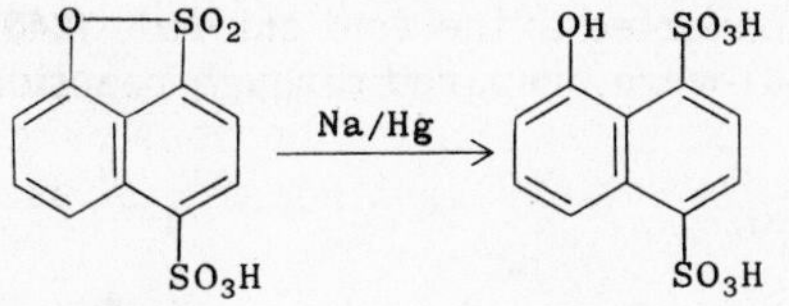

240

(8) Halomethylation[146,418,420]

Treatment of naphthosultone with paraformaldehyde and hydrogen chloride or bromide in acetic acid in the presence of zinc chloride at 70-80° gives excellent yields of 6-chloro- or bromomethylnaphthosultone. No reaction occurs in the absence of zinc chloride. The halomethylation is strongly dependent on the substitution in the naphthalene ring. Electron-attracting substituents hinder or retard the reaction and electron-donating substituents assist, but often to the extent as to yield diarylmethanes.

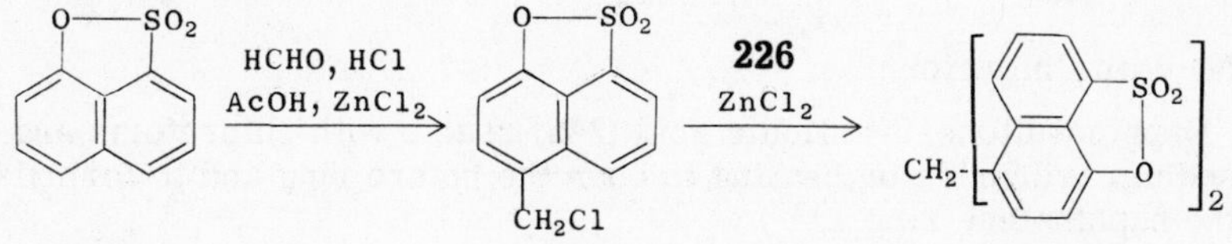

226   241   242

Chloromethylnaphthosultone (241) condenses with naphthosultone in the presence of zinc chloride to give the dinaphthylmethane-4, 5, 4', 5'-disultone (242). This condensation occurs extremely easily, particularly at low hydrogen ion concentrations. The excess hydrogen halide used in the preparation of the halomethylnaphthosultone suppresses the condensation side reaction.

[For references, see pp. 289-312.]

Halomethylnaphthosultone is converted to 6-methylnaphthosultone by treatment with zinc dust in hydrochloric acid and ethyl alcohol; further reaction of 6-methylnaphthosultone with sodium hydroxide solution gives 4-methyl-1, 8-naphtholsulfonic acid.

The halogen in halomethylnaphthosultone is easily replaced by a variety of groups. Thus, Schetty[417] prepared 6-(p-tolylsulfonylmethyl)-hydroxymethyl-, benzyl-, (2-hydroxy-5-methylbenzyl)-, (4-hydroxy-benzyl)-, (2-hydroxybenzyl)-, (2-hydroxy-3, 5-dimethylbenzyl)-, and (4-hydroxy-3-carbomethoxybenzyl)- 1, 8-naphthosultone.

Halomethylnaphthosultone does not react with cold, aqueous ammonia. This inactivity is explained in section I D-1c(4). Alkali acetate, sulfite. alcoholate, phenolate, sodiomalonic acid, or potassium phthalimide do not react without splitting the sultone ring.

The oxidation of 6-hydroxymethylnaphthosultone (**242a**) with chromic acid at room temperature yielded 6-formyl-1, 8-naphthosultone and 1, 8-naphthosultone-6-carboxylic acid. The 6-carboxylic acid, on treatment with thionyl chloride, is readily converted to the acid chloride (**243**) from which various 6-amides (**244**) were prepared through reaction with amines.[418]

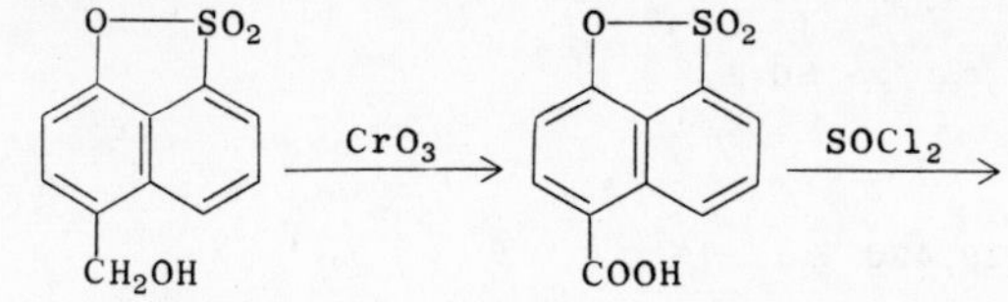

242a

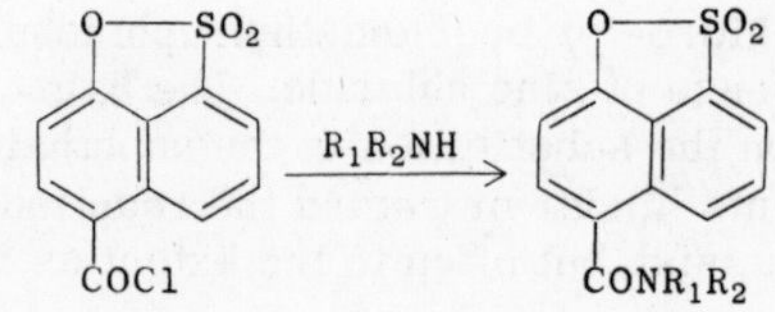

243   **244**

(9) With Chloroform

Naphthosultone-6-sulfonic acid (**245**) reacts with chloroform and sodium hydroxide on heating to open the hetero ring and to formylate the naphthalene ring.[142]

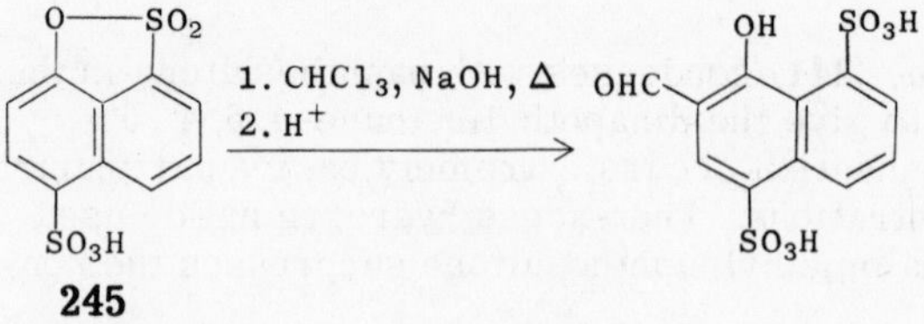

245

2. Naphth [1, 2-*c*]-3*H*-2, 1-oxathiole (246) and Naphth [2, 1-*c*]-1*H*-2, 3-oxathiole (247)

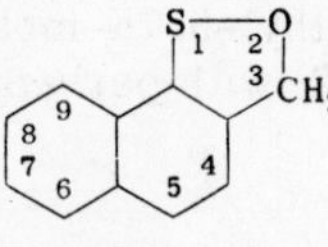

246 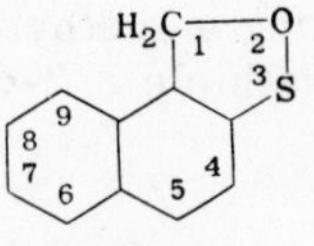   **247**

Kaufmann and Zobel[253] described a single derivative of each of these ring systems in 1922. They were prepared by the reaction of the corresponding naphthosaccharin (**248a** and **b**) with resorcinol.

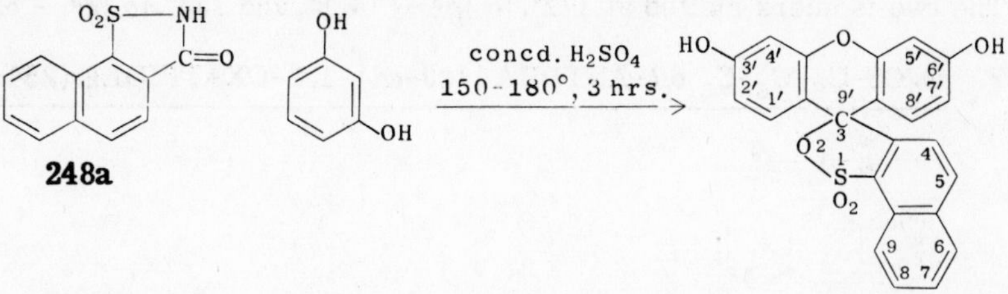

248a

249

248b

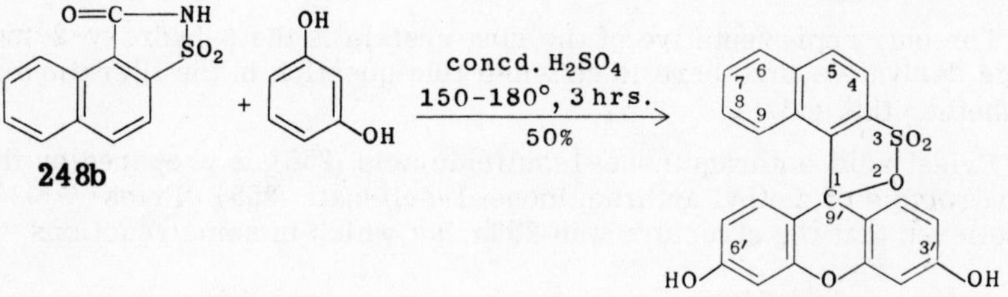

250

Both of these derivatives are analogous to the sulfonephthaleins. Spiro (naphth [2, 1]-1*H*-2, 3-oxathiole-1, 9'-[3', 6'-dihydroxyxanthene]) (**250**) was described as having a red color and green fluorescence.

Neither of these two ring systems has an entry in the Revised Index.

E.   C$_2$O-C$_3$OS-C$_5$-C$_5$ SPIRO [5, 7*a*-METHANO-7*aH*-1, 2-BENZ-

OXATHIOLE-4(5*H*), 2'-OXIRANE (251)

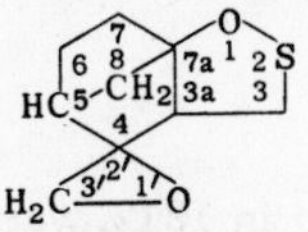

251

(RRI 3957)

[For references, see pp. 289-312.]

The only representative of this ring system is spiro [3a-methyl-5, 7a-methanohexahydro-7aH-1, 2-benzoxathiole-4(5H), 2'-oxirane] 2, 2-dioxide (253) which Asahina and Yamaguti[12] obtained in 46% yield as two stereoisomers on treating 4-methylene-3a-methyl-5, 7a-methano-hexahydro-7aH-1, 2-benzoxathiole 2, 2-dioxide (252) with perbenzoic acid.

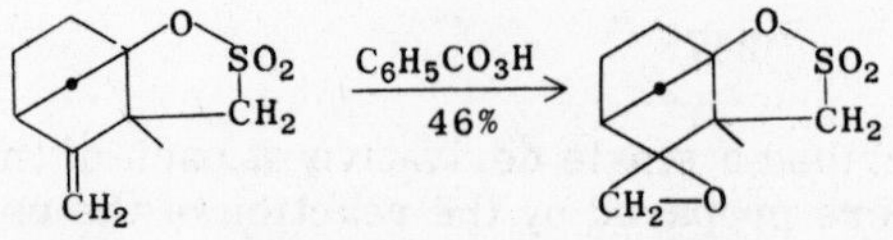

252   **253**

The two isomers melted at 172°, $[\alpha]_D^{23} - 14.8°$, and 153°, $[\alpha]_D^{25} - 8.5°$.

F. C_3OS-C_6-C_6-C_6 6H-ANTHRA [1, 9-cd]-1, 2-OXATHIOLE (254)

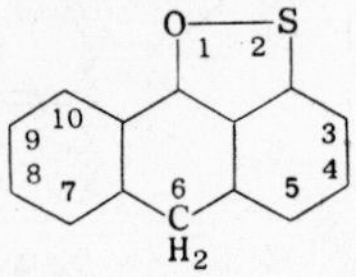

254

The only representative of the ring system is the 6-hydroxy-2-monoxide derivative, and there is considerable question in the literature as to whether this exists.

Fries' acid, anthraquinone-1-sulfenic acid (256), is prepared by the hydrolysis of methyl anthraquinone-1-sulfenate (255). Fries[135a, 135b] believed that the structure was 256a, but which in some reactions

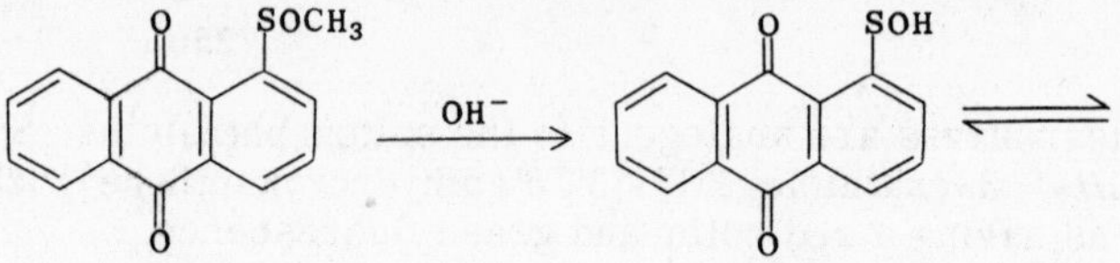

255   **256a**

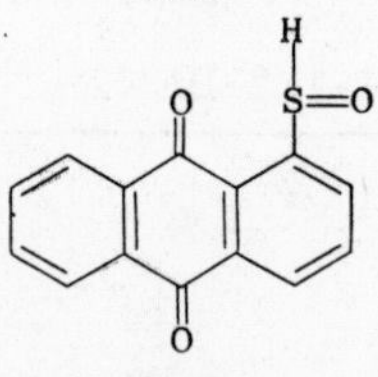

256b

behaved as though it were **256b**. Fries' acid, prepared in 1912, was the only sulfenic acid known until Bruice and Markiw[66a] prepared anthraquinone-1, 4-disulfenic acid, which was verified by Jenny[241] who also

prepared anthraquinone-1, 5-disulfenic acid. There are many references in the literature describing attempts to prepare other aryl sulfenic
acids.

Because anthraquinone-1-sulfenic acid appears to possess an unusual
stability, its structure has been studied in order to find an explanation
for its uniqueness and for the failure to prepare other analogs of Fries'
acid. These studies are relatively important when one considers that
over five hundred references have proposed sulfenic acids as intermediates.[258b]

Kharasch and co-workers[258a,258b] suggested that the sulfenic acid
group in anthraquinone-1-sulfenic acid was stabilized through hydrogen
bonding (257). This explains the stability of anthraquinone-1-sulfenic
acid relative to the 2-sulfenic acid analog.

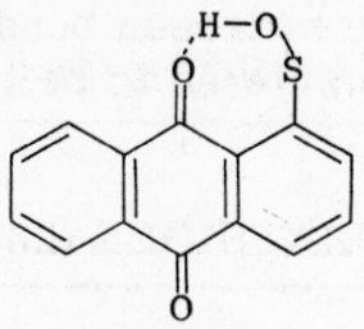

257

It does not explain, however, the failure to prepare fluorenone-1-sulfenic
acid (258) by Kharasch and Bruice.[258c]

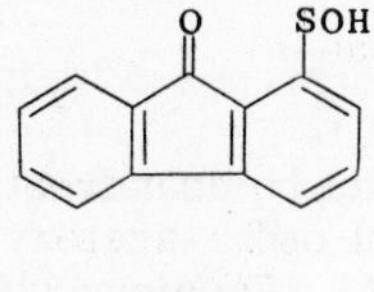

258

Lecher and Hardy[282] suggested that anthraquinone-1-sulfenic acid was
stabilized through the formation of the tetracyclic structure, 6-hydroxy-
anthra [1, 9-cd]-1, 2-oxathiole 2-monoxide (259).

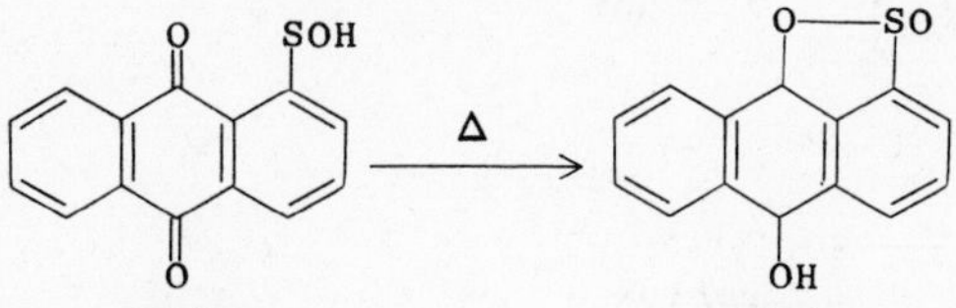

256a   **259**

Barltrop and Morgan,[32] however, believed that the structure proposed
by Lecher and Hardy was untenable inasmuch as the infrared spectrum
of Fries' acid showed both carbonyl and hydroxyl absorption. Barltrop

and Morgan's infrared data also precluded the tautomeric oxanthrone structure (260) proposed by Rylander.[406]

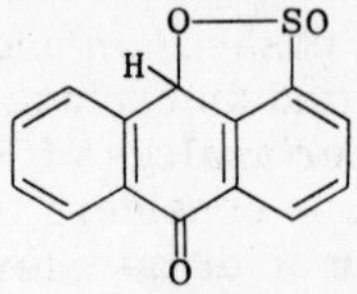

260

Bruice and Sayigh,[66] on the basis of quantitative infrared spectra for the carbonyl bands of methyl anthraquinone-1-sulfenate, dimethyl anthraquinone-1, 4-disulfenate, and methyl fluorenone-1-sulfenate in comparison with anthrone, anthraquinone, fluorenone, and 1-hydroxy and 1, 4-dihydroxy-anthraquinones, concluded that the structure Fries originally proposed for the sulfenic acid is correct. The hydrogen bonded structure of Kharasch and co-workers was also considered to be tenable with the spectral evidence.

G. $C_3OS-C_6-C_6-C_6-C_6$ CHRYSENO [3, 4-c]-1, 2-OXATHIOLE (261)

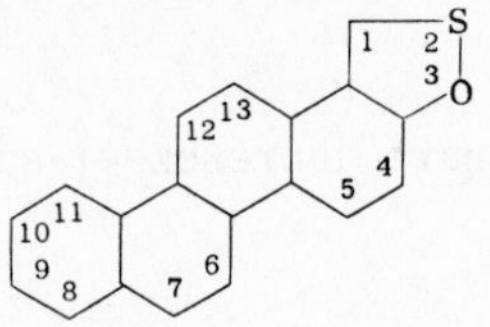

261

Wendler and Taub[497a] reported the preparation of the homoandrostane derivative of 1, 2-oxathiolane (263) by the treatment of 3α-acetoxy-17α-hydroxy-17β-methyl-D-homo-5β-androstane-11, 17a-dione (262) with methanesulfonyl chloride in pyridine.

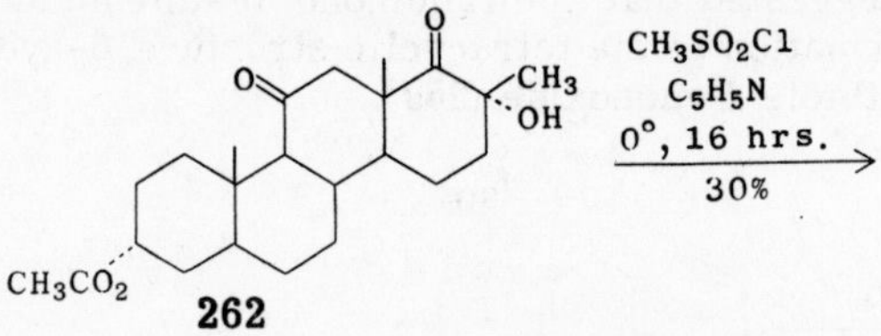

262

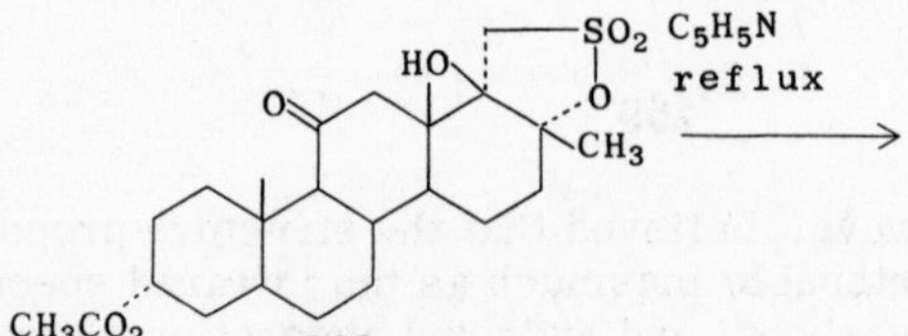

263

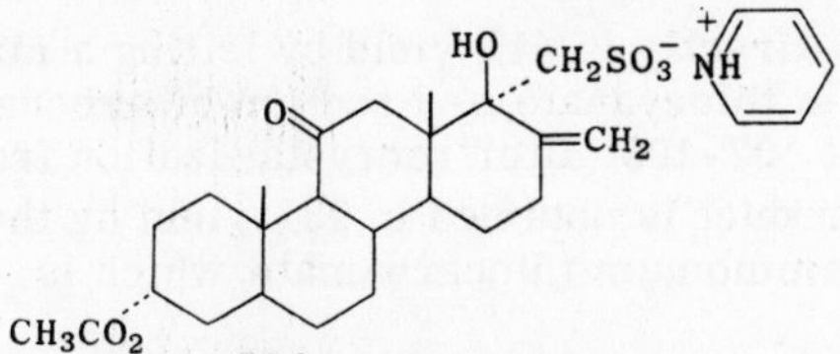

264

This compound, melting at 142-144° with decomposition, reacted with refluxing pyridine to open the 1, 2-oxathiolane ring, giving **264**.

II. 1, 3-OXATHIA COMPOUNDS

A. C$_3$OS 2H-1, 3-OXATHIOLE (265) AND 1, 3-OXATHIOLANE (266)

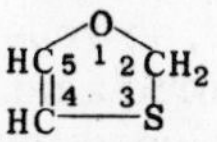

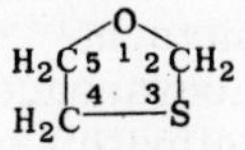

265   (RRI 133)   **266**

1. 2H-1, 3-Oxathiole

The parent compound is unknown. Schatzmann[414] prepared the first derivative in 1891 by refluxing S-phenacylthiocarbamic acid with dilute nitric acid.

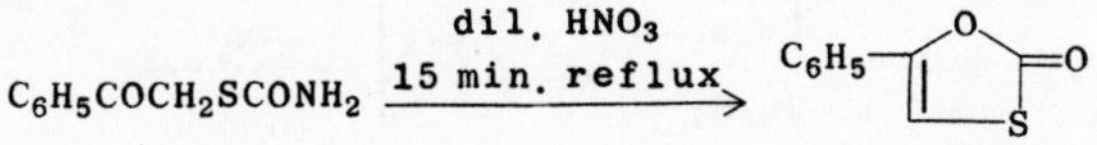

267

The 5-phenyl-2H-1, 3-oxathiol-2-one (**267**) was characterized as yellow scales, melting at 75°, and having an intense carmine-red color in sulfuric acid. The compounds have been called 1, 3-thioxoles in the literature. Chemical Abstracts uses the 1, 3-oxathiole nomenclature.

Tscherniac,[463] on reacting sodium thiocyanate and chloroacetone, obtained a small yield of thiocyanoacetone. On treating this with hydrochloric acid he obtained what he called "hydroxymethylthiazole" or "α-methylrhodin" as a by-product.

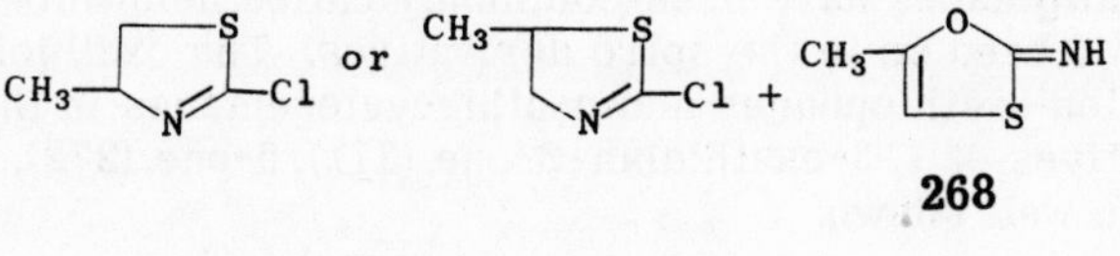

268

[For references, see pp. 289-312.]

He also obtained the compound directly in 41% yield by letting a mixture of chloroacetone, potassium thiocyanate, and sodium bicarbonate stand for ten days. It melted at 102-103° after recrystallization from water. It was stated that the product is obtained in 93% yield by the reaction of chloroacetone and ammonium thiocarbamate, which is characterized as violent.

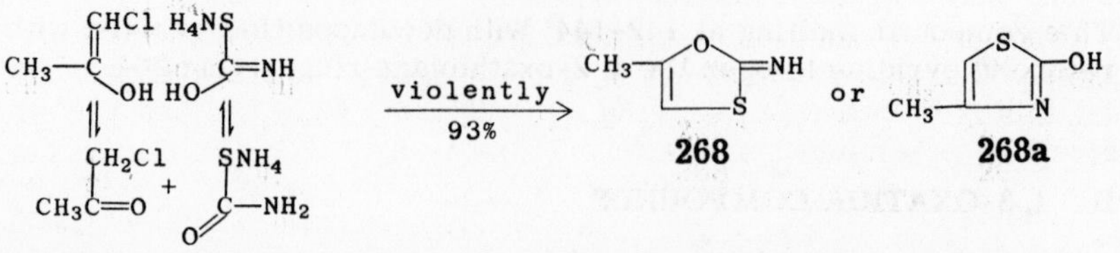

Tscherniac[463,463a] suggested that the hydroxymethylthiazole, first described by Hantzsch and Weber[174b] in 1887, is really 5-methyl-1, 3-oxathiol-2-imine (268). Hantzsch,[174a] on the other hand, on repeating Tscherniac's treatment of thiocyanoacetate with hydrochloric acid, obtained only 2-hydroxy-4-methylthiazole (268a). He concluded that the 1, 3-oxathiole is not produced by this reaction. Subsequent work by others[97] supports Hantzsch.

In disagreement with Staudinger and Siegwart,[447] Schönberg, Mustafa, Awad, and Moussa[424] suggest that the reaction of phenylbenzoyldiazomethane with thiophosgene leads to the 1, 3-oxathiole (270) rather than to the 1, 2-oxathiole.

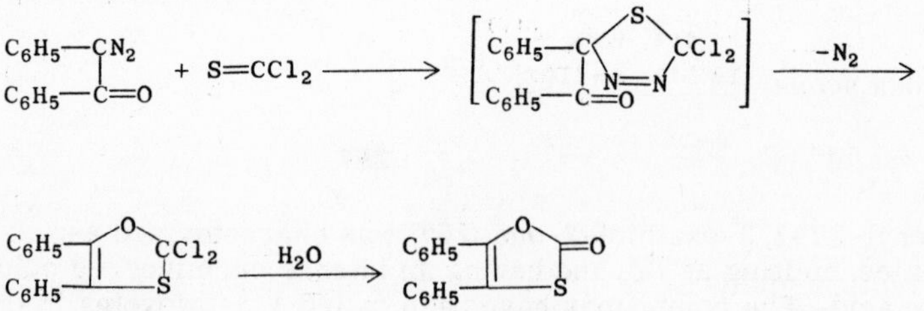

2. 1, 3-Oxathiolane

Many derivatives of 1, 3-oxathiolane (266) are known. These are listed in Tables 14, 15, 16, and 17. Oxathiolanes are the 4, 5-dihydro form of 1, 3-oxathiole, or, as frequently called, 1, 3-thioxole. The earlier volumes of Chemical Abstracts used the thioxole nomenclature but more recent volumes use the oxathiole and oxathiolane nomenclatures. The 2, 2-substituted oxathiolanes have been commonly called hemithioketals, particularly has this been so in the spiro derivatives. The oxathiolanes also have been called oxathiophanes and oxathiacyclopentanes in the literature. Derivatives of 1, 3-oxathiolan-3-one (271), 5-one (272), and 2, 5-dione (273) are well known.

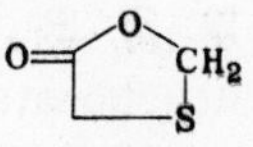

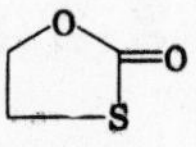

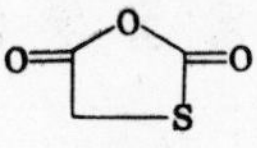

272　　　**271**　　　**273**

The 2-one has been called thioethylene carbonate; the 2, 5-dione anhydro-(carboxythio) acid or anhydrocarboxy-2-mercaptoacetic acid; and the 5-one oxathiophanone and thiolactone.

Although 1, 3-oxathiolanes are not found in nature, Schneider and Urede[423] isolated merosinigrin (275), which they postulated as containing this ring system, on treating sinigrin (274), a natural product, with alcoholic potassium hydroxide.

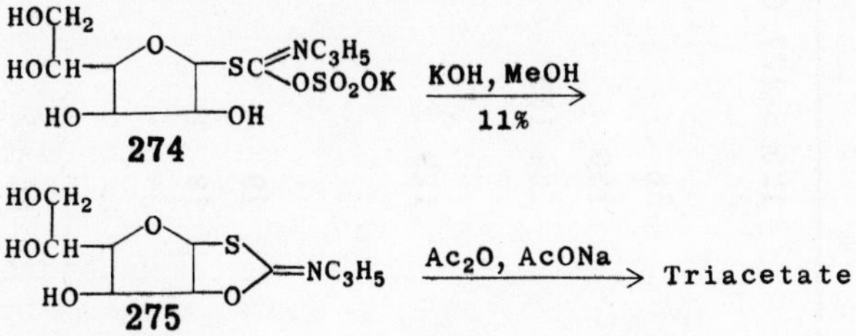

a. Preparation

(1) 1, 3-Oxathiolanes

(a) By Reaction of Ketones or Aldehydes with β-Mercaptoalcohols. Sjöberg[440,441] prepared 1, 3-oxathiolanes by reacting acetone with a β-mercaptoalcohol in the presence of P$_2$O$_5$.

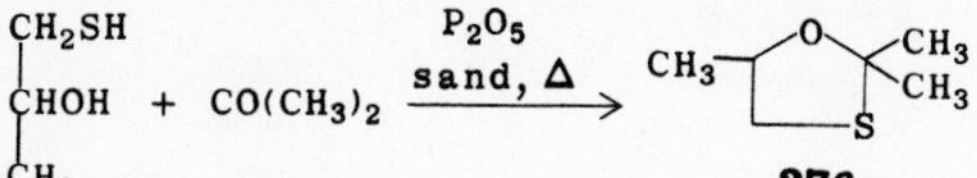

By this reaction, yields of 38-65% of oxathiolane derivatives, *viz.*, 2, 2, 5-trimethyl- (276), 2, 2-dimethyl-5-hydroxymethyl-, and 2, 2-dimethyl-5-chloromethyl-1, 3-oxathiolanes, were obtained.

1, 3-Oxathiolanes are conveniently prepared by the reaction of a 2-mercaptoalcohol and an aldehyde or ketone in the presence of an acid catalyst under refluxing conditions with a large excess of an azeotropic agent for taking off the water of reaction. Kipnis and Ornfelt[263] employed a trace of hydrochloric acid as catalyst and benzene as the azeotropic agent in their preparation of 2-substituted-1, 3-oxathiolanes (277) from mercaptoethanol and an aldehyde.

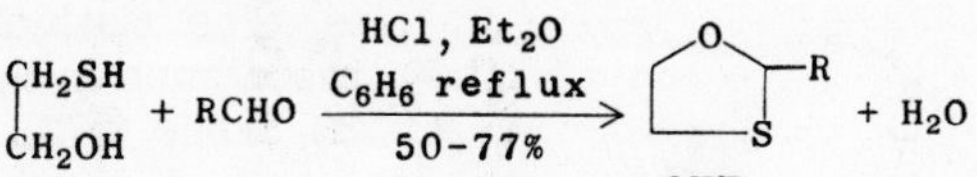

[For references, see pp. 289-312.]

TABLE 14. 1,3-Oxathiolanes

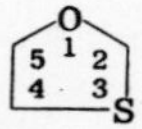

Substituent	Yield (%)	M.p. (°C)	B.p. (°C)	(mm)	n_D and d_4	Ref.
None	70		126.5–127.0	745	n 1.5035/27.5	96b
					d 1.1565/27.5	96b
2-CH_3-	80		58	53	n 1.4867/20	149
			130	752	d 1.069/20	149
	43		134–135	744	n 1.4872/20	96b
					d 1.048/20	96b
5-CH_3-			129	760		80, 81
2-C_2H_5-						96b
2-$(CH_3)_2CH$-	60		29	2.5		96b
2-$HOOCCH_2$-	43		78–81	1.0		263
2-Cl_3C-		70–85			n 1.4838/20	83, 84
					d 1.181/20	83, 84
2-C_6H_5-	77		86–87	5.0		309a
2-p-ClC_6H_4-			124	0.9		263
						309a

Compound / substituent	Yield (%)	M.p.	B.p.	mm	Constants	Ref.
2-o-ClC₆H₄-			123	1.0		309a
2-p-O₂NC₆H₄-		73–77				309a
2-p-CH₃SO₂C₆H₄-		102				309a
2- 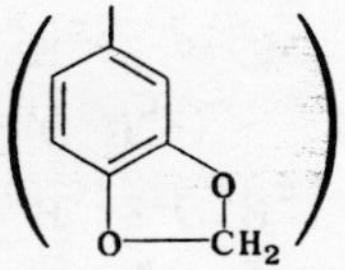	50		118	1.5		263
Allo-7-pregnen-3β-acetoxy-20-one 20-[1,3-Oxathiolane]	78	180.6–182.4			$[\alpha]_D^{25}$ −1.2	2
Allo-7,9(11)-pregnadiene-3β-acetoxy-20-one 20-[1,3-Oxathiolane]		120–125				2
Allopregnane-3β-acetoxy-20-one 20-[1,3-Oxathiolane]	86	207–209			$[\alpha]_D^{20}$ 3	402
Allopregnane-3β-acetoxy-11,20-dione 20-[1,3-Oxathiolane]	85	191–193	70	65	$[\alpha]_D^{20}$ 35	102
2,2-(CH₃-)₂					n^{24} 1.4724, d^{24} 1.0105	103
	78		96	2	n^{24} 1.5663, d^{24} 1.1232	103
2-CH₃-2-C₂H₅-	79		42	8	n^{24} 1.4751, d^{24} 0.9776	103
2-CH₃-2-(CH₃)₂CHCH₂-	70		41	2	n^{24} 1.4730, d^{24} 0.9696	103

TABLE 14. 1,3-Oxathiolanes (contd.)

Substituent	Yield (%)	M.p. (°C)	B.p. (°C)	(mm)	n_D and d_4	Ref.
2-CH₃-2-CH₃COCH(CH₃)-	49		56	0.1	n^{23} 1.4860	68b
2-CH₃-2-C₂H₅O₂CCH₂-	77		117	20	n^{24} 1.4790	103
					d^{24} 1.1118	103
2-CH₃-2-C₆H₅-	59		132–133	16	n^{17} 1.610	362
2-CH₃-2-C₆H₅- 3,3-dioxide	34	56–57				309a
2-CH₃-2-p-ClC₆H₄-			113	1.5	n^{23} 1.5757	309a
2-CH₃-2-p-CH₃OC₆H₄-			132	1.1	n^{20} 1.5680	309a
2-CH₃-2-p-O₂NC₆H₄-		50–52				309a
2-CH₃-2-(2, 4-Cl₂C₆H₃-)			135	1.5	n^{23} 1.5930	309a
2-CH₃-2-(2, 5-Cl₂C₆H₃-)			136	0.25		309a
2, 2-(ClF₂C-)₂	33		76	9	n_D^{25} 1.4414	437b
2-C₂H₅-2-C₆H₅-			107	2.4	n^{21} 1.5610	309a
2, 2-(C₆H₅-)₂	28	52				309a
2-C₆H₅-2-p-ClC₆H₄-		28				309a
2-C₆H₅-2-C₆H₅CH₂-		42–43.5				309a
2-C₆H₅-2-p-ClC₆H₄CH₂-		60–63				309a

Substituent	Yield (%)	m.p.	b.p.	mm	n_D / d	Ref.
2-C_6H_5-2-$C_6H_5CH(OH)$-	13	95-96				309a
2,2-(p-ClC_6H_4-)$_2$		36				309a
2,2-($C_6H_5CH_2$-)$_2$	90	42-43				103
2-(p-ClC_6H_4-)-2-(2,4-$Cl_2C_6H_3$-)		65-68				309a
2-$(CH_3)_2CHCH_2$-4-$HSCH_2$-						40
2-(3-$CH_3OC_6H_4$-)-2-[2-H_2N-3,4,5-$(OCH_3)_3$-$C_6HCH_2CH_2$-]	98	74-75				509a
2-(3-$CH_3OC_6H_4$-)-2-[2-O_2N-3,4,5-$(OCH_3)_3$-$C_6HCH_2CH_2$-]	63	76-78				509a
2,2,5-$(CH_3$-)$_3$	55		72	80	n^{20} 1.4645	441
			141	760	d^{20} 0.9782	441
2,2-$(CH_3$-)$_2$-5-$HOCH_2$-	65		58-60	0.8	n^{20} 1.4987	441
			95-105	12	d^{20} 1.1232	441
2,2-$(CH_3$-)$_2$-5-$ClCH_2$-	38		74-75	15	n^{20} 1.4940	440
2-CH_3-2-C_2H_5-5-C_6H_5-	32	104-105				105
2,2-$(CH_3$-)$_2$-5- (spiro dioxolane–dithiolane structure)	100	78 and 145 92-93 and 103-104				121
2,2-$(CH_3$-)$_2$-5- 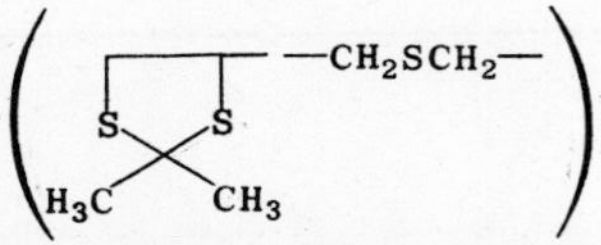 (spiro dithiolane $-CH_2SCH_2-$ structure)	19	132				130 325

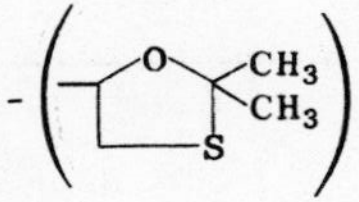

209

TABLE 15. 1,3-Oxathiolan-5-ones

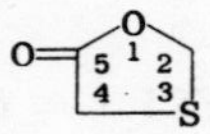

Substituent	Yield (%)	M.p. (°C)	B.p. (°C)	(mm)	Other	Ref.
2-C$_6$H$_5$-	69	56-57				223, 224
2-C$_6$H$_5$CH$_2$-	43		110-112	0.45	d_4^{20} 1.2331	225
2-C$_6$H$_5$CO-		93-94				426
2-C$_6$H$_5$CH=CH-		111-112				224
2-[3,4-(CH$_3$O)$_2$C$_6$H$_3$-]		110-111.5				224
2-(3,4-methylenedioxyphenyl)		65-66				224
2-HOOC-		144-145				224, 245, 279, 281
2-Cl$_3$C-			92-93	0.15	n_D^{20} 1.5472	297
2-CH$_3$-2-C$_6$H$_5$-	66		96-99	0.5		225
2-C$_6$H$_5$-4-CH$_3$-		77-78				224
4,4-(C$_6$H$_5$-)$_2$	81	99-100				44
2,2-(ClF$_2$C-)$_2$	98		120	50	n_D^{25} 1.4388	437a, 437b
					d_4^{25} 1.7064	437a, 473b
2-CH$_3$-2-HOOC-		137				245, 280, 281
2-HOOC-4-CH$_3$-						245

Compound	Yield	M.p.	Ref.
2,4-$(CH_3-)_2$-2-HOOC-		108	245, 281
2,4-$(C_2H_5-)_2$-2-HOOC-		81	245, 281
2-CH_3-4,4-$(C_6H_5-)_2$		89-91	44
2-Cl_3C-4,4-$(C_6H_5-)_2$		107	44
2-$(C_6H_5CH=CH-)$-4,4-$(C_6H_5-)_2$		156-157	44
2,4,4-$(C_6H_5-)_3$	98	94-96	44, 403a
2-$(o\text{-}ClC_6H_4-)$-4,4-$(C_6H_5-)_2$	100	105.5	45
2-$(m\text{-}ClC_6H_4-)$-4,4-$(C_6H_5-)_2$	100	83-84	45
2-$(p\text{-}ClC_6H_4-)$-4,4-$(C_6H_5-)_2$		125-126	44
2-$(p\text{-}CH_3C_6H_4-)$-4,4-$(C_6H_5-)_2$	96	100-100.5	45
2-$[p\text{-}(CH_3)_2CHC_6H_4-]$-4,4-$(C_6H_5-)_2$		100.100.5	45
2-$(o\text{-}HOC_6H_4-)$-4,4-$(C_6H_5-)_2$	92	147 (dec.)	44
2-$(p\text{-}CH_3OC_6H_4-)$-4,4-$(C_6H_5-)_2$	90	102-104	44
2-$(m\text{-}O_2NC_6H_4-)$-4,4-$(C_6H_5-)_2$	100	132-133	44
2-$(p\text{-}O_2NC_6H_4-)$-4,4-$(C_6H_5-)_2$	100	116.117.5	44
2-(9-anthryl-)-4,4-$(C_6H_5-)_2$	79	157-159	403a
2-(2,3-tetramethylene-9-anthryl-)-4,4-$(C_6H_5-)_2$		159-160	403a
2,2-$(CH_3-)_2$-4,4-$(C_6H_5-)_2$	62	119.5-120.5	44
2-CH_3-3-$HOOCCH_2$-4,4-$(C_6H_5-)_2$		65.0-66.5	44
2-CH_3-2-$C_2H_5OOCCH_2$-4,4-$(C_6H_5-)_2$	56	65.0-65.6	44

TABLE 15. 1,3-Oxathiolan-5-ones (contd.)

Substituent	Yield (%)	M.p. (°C)	B.p. (°C) (mm)	Other	Ref.
2-CH$_3$-2-HOOC-4,4-(C$_6$H$_5$-)$_2$	85	160.5-162.0			44
2,2-(CH$_3$-)$_2$-4-(...)(CH$_3$)$_2$ ... CH$_2$CH$_2$— ... -4,4-(C$_6$H$_5$-)$_2$ 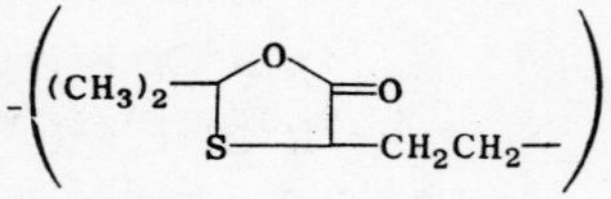	39	138.9-139.5			133
2-(...)(C$_6$H$_5$)$_2$ 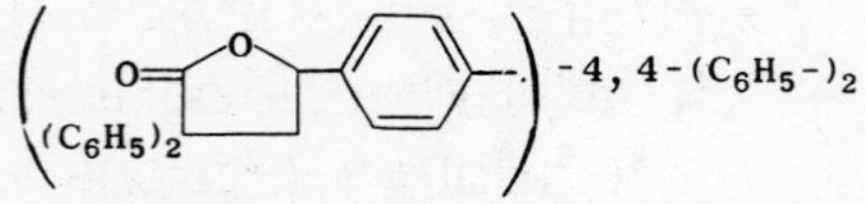		195-196(dec.)			45

Dermer,[96b] in reacting merecaptoethanol with formaldehyde in the presence of concentrated hydrochloric acid, obtained a 70% yield of 1,3-oxathiolane. He described this reaction as practically immediate and quite exothermic. Evans, Fraser, and Owen[121] obtained a quantitative yield of a bis-1,3-oxathiolane, one melting at 78° (**278**) and the other at 145° (**279**), on condensing acetone with *dl*-1,4-dithiothreitol (**280**) or with 1,4-dithioerythritol (**281**), respectively.

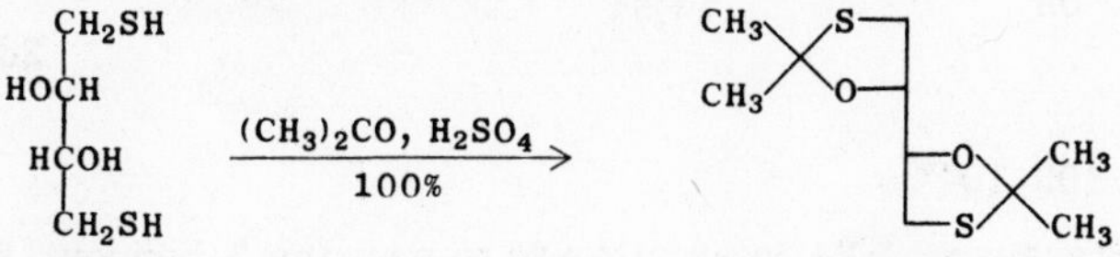

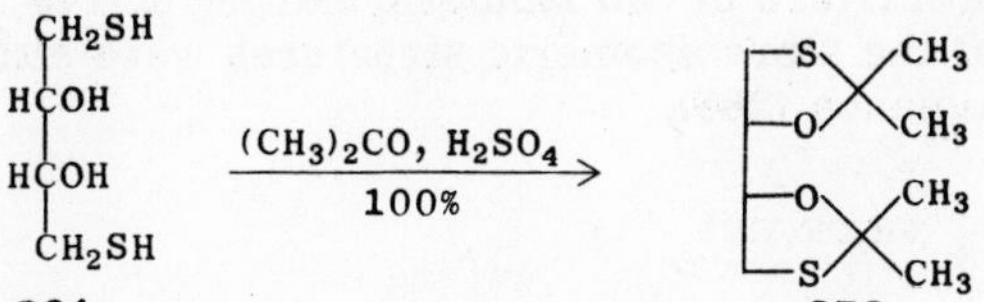

The similarity of imidazolidines, dioxolanes, oxazolidines, and oxathiolanes in structure was shown by infrared absorption spectra by Bergmann, Meeron, Hirshberg, and Pinchas,[40] who used the condensation product of methyl isobutyl ketone and mercaptoethanol in their study. The condensation of 2,3-dimercaptopropanol with the ketone involved the hydroxyl and the adjacent mercapto group and not the two vicinal mercapto groups as proved by the strongly positive reaction of nitrous acid with the free -SH and by the characteristic -SH band.

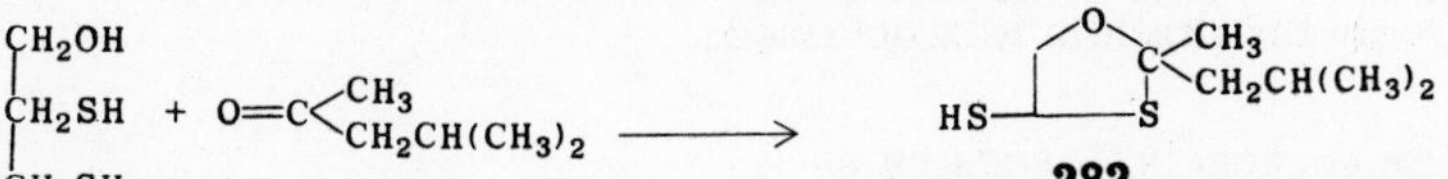

On passing hydrogen chloride gas for one minute through a mixture of 3-hydroxy-2,2′,3′-trimercaptodipropyl sulfide and acetone, Miles and Owen[325] obtained the oxathiolane (**283**) in about 19% yield.

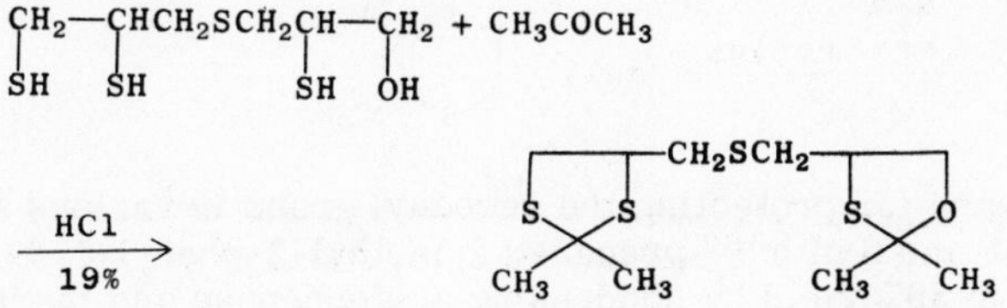

[For references, see pp. 289-312.]

On letting a mixture of 2, 3-dimercaptobutane-1, 4-diol and acetone stand for one week in the presence of concentrated hydrochloric acid, Flitt and Owen[130] obtained a small yield of 4, 4'-bis(2, 2-dimethyl-1, 3-oxathiolane) (284) as a mixture of two isomers, one melting at 92-93°

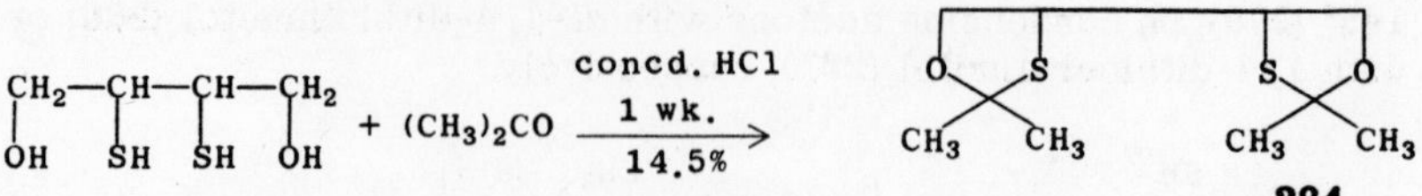

$$
\begin{array}{c}
CH_2-CH-CH-CH_2 \\
| \quad\;\; | \quad\;\; | \quad\;\; | \\
OH \quad SH \quad SH \quad OH
\end{array}
+ (CH_3)_2CO \xrightarrow[\substack{1 \text{ wk.} \\ 14.5\%}]{\text{concd. HCl}}
$$

284

and the other at 103-104°.

Marshall and Stevenson,[309a] in an attempt to prepare 2-benzoyl-2-phenyl-1, 3-oxathiolane by the condensation of benzil with mercaptoethanol obtained instead a mixture of two isomers, melting at 149° and 212°. They postulated that the stereoisomeric structures were either oxathianes (285) or oxathiolanes (286).

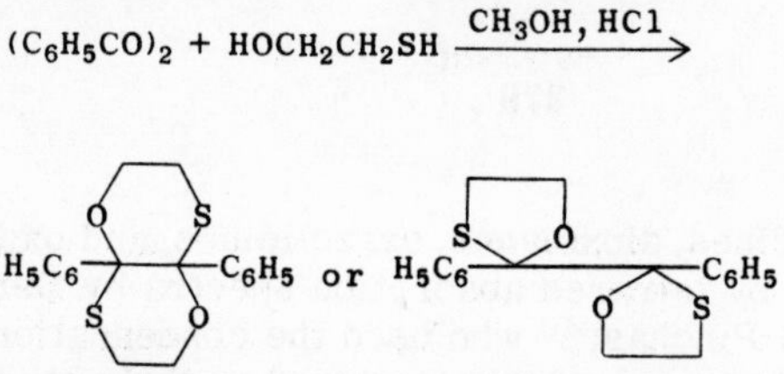

$$(C_6H_5CO)_2 + HOCH_2CH_2SH \xrightarrow{CH_3OH, HCl}$$

285 or 286

On condensing benzoin with mercaptoethanol, Marshall and Stevenson[309a] obtained a mixture of 2, 3-diphenyl-5, 6-dihydro-*p*-oxathiin (287) and 2-phenyl-2-phenylhydroxymethyl-1, 3-oxathiolane (288); on prolonged reflux, only the oxathiin was obtained.

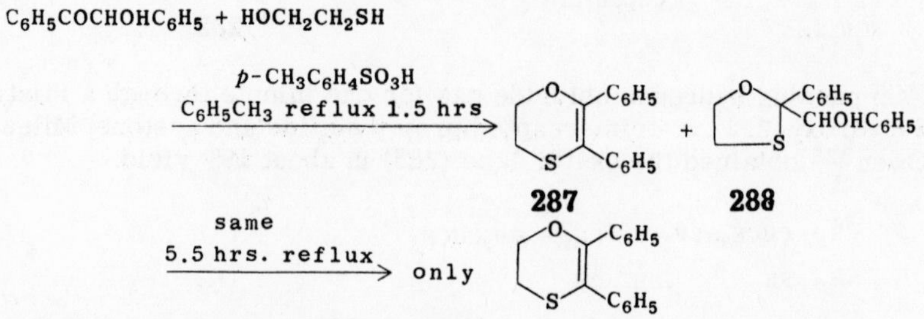

$$C_6H_5COCHOHC_6H_5 + HOCH_2CH_2SH$$

$$\xrightarrow[\substack{C_6H_5CH_3 \text{ reflux } 1.5 \text{ hrs}}]{p\text{-}CH_3C_6H_4SO_3H}$$ 287 + 288

$$\xrightarrow[\substack{5.5 \text{ hrs. reflux}}]{\text{same}} only$$ 287

In studies on means for protecting the carbonyl group in various acetophenones, Pinder and Smith[362] prepared 2-methyl-2-phenyl-1, 3-oxathiolane (289) in 59% yield by condensing acetophenone and mercaptoethanol in dioxane with zinc chloride and anhydrous sodium sulfate.

$$\begin{array}{c} CH_2OH \\ | \\ CH_2SH \end{array} + O=C \begin{array}{c} CH_3 \\ C_6H_5 \end{array} \xrightarrow[\substack{24 \text{ hrs. r. t.} \\ 59\%}]{Na_2SO_4, \ ZnCl_2} $$

289

Djerassi and Gorman[103] condensed various ketones with β-mercapto-ethanol in benzene solution in the presence of p-toluenesulfonic acid. This method, which has found wide use in the analogous preparation of ketals from ethylene glycol and carbonyl compounds, gave yields of up to 90% for the reaction of mercaptoethanol with ketones, such as acetone and dibenzyl ketone.

Whereas Djerassi and Gorman were unable to condense benzophenone with mercaptoethanol in the presence of p-toluenesulfonic acid and using benzene for azeotroping off the water of reaction, Marshall and Stevenson[309a] found that the reaction is successful if toluene is used instead of benzene. The diphenyloxathiolanes, however, tended to decompose to the corresponding benzophenone in refluxing toluene.

(b) By Other Reactions. Copenhaver[80,81] prepared 2-methyl-1,3-oxathiolane (**290**) by the reaction of mercaptoethanol and methyl vinyl ether in the presence of p-toluenesulfonic acid. Presumably this reaction occurs through addition of the mercaptan group across the double bond followed by release of methanol and ring formation.

$$HSCH_2CH_2OH + CH_2=CHOCH_3 \xrightarrow{H^+}$$

$$\begin{array}{c} OCH_3 \\ OH | \\ H_2C \quad CHCH_3 \\ | \\ H_2C——S \end{array} \xrightarrow{-CH_3OH} $$

290

Mercaptoethanol has been reacted with certain β-alkoxyacrylic esters in the presence of bisulfate[83,84] to give 1,3-oxathiolane-2-acetic acid esters (**291**) presumably through transetherification.

$$(C_2H_5O)_2CHCH_2COOC_2H_5$$

$$EtOH \updownarrow -EtOH$$

$$C_2H_5OCH=CHCOOC_2H_5 \quad + HSCH_2CH_2OH \xrightarrow{NaHSO_4} \begin{bmatrix} CH_2COOC_2H_5 \\ | \\ CHOC_2H_5 \\ | \\ SCH_2CH_2OH \end{bmatrix}$$

$$\xrightarrow[-C_2H_5OH]{\Delta}$$

291

In the reaction of epichlorohydrin with thioacetic acid, 5-chloromethyl-2-hydroxy-2-methyl-1,3-oxathiolane (**292**) is believed to be an intermediate[440] leading to β-acetylthiochlorohydrin.

[For references, see pp. 289-312.]

215

$$\begin{array}{c} CH_2 \\ | \\ CH \end{array}\!\!\!>\!O \;+\; CH_3COSH \xrightarrow[12 \text{ hrs.}]{60^\circ} \begin{array}{c} CH_2SCOCH_3 \\ | \\ CHOH \\ | \\ CH_2Cl \end{array} \xrightarrow{60^\circ}$$

ClCH₂ — O — OH — CH₃ — S   **292**

$$\begin{array}{c} CH_2SH \\ | \\ CHOCOCH_3 \\ | \\ CH_2Cl \end{array}$$

In treating bis(2-hydroxyethyl) sulfide with potassium hydroxide at high temperatures in a nitrogen atmosphere, Georgieff and Dupré[149] obtained a mixture of 36% divinyl sulfide, 9-10% 2-methyl-1, 3-oxathiolane (290), 7-8% *p*-oxathiane (293), and 3.5% 2-hydroxyethyl vinyl sulfide.

$$S(CH_2CH_2OH)_2 \xrightarrow[\substack{N_2}]{\substack{KOH \\ 195-230^\circ}} (CH_2\!\!=\!\!CH)_2S \;+\; \begin{array}{c} O \\ \diagup \quad \diagdown CH_3 \\ S \end{array}$$

290

$$+ \begin{array}{c} O \\ \diagup \quad \diagdown \\ S \end{array} \;+\; \begin{array}{c} HOCH_2CH_2 \\ CH\!\!=\!\!CH \end{array}\!\!\!>\!\!S$$

293

These products were identified by means of infrared spectra and the 2-methyl-1, 3-oxathiolane (290) also was found to be identical with that prepared by the reaction of mercaptoethanol and acetaldehyde in the presence of 0.7 *N* HCl in ether using benzene to azeotrope off the water of reaction.

(2) 1, 3-Oxathiolan-2-ones

1, 3-Oxathiolan-2-one (294) is conveniently prepared by reacting mercaptoethanol with phosgene in an ether solution at 0° and then at room temperature for three days.[23]

$$\begin{array}{c} CH_2OH \\ | \\ CH_2SH \end{array} \;+\; COCl_2 \xrightarrow[56\%]{\substack{EtOH \\ r.\,t.,\,3\text{ days}}} \begin{array}{c} O \\ \diagup \quad \diagdown \!\!=\!\!O \\ S \end{array}$$

294

Reynolds[395,396] carried the reaction out at -15° using ethyl acetate as the solvent and pyridine to take up the evolved hydrogen chloride. The tetramer, (-CH₂CH₂SCOO-)₄, was a by-product.

Reynolds, Fields, and Johnson[396b] reported the synthesis of 1, 3-oxathiolan-2-one in 70-77% yields by the acid-catalyzed intramolecular transesterification of ethyl 2-hydroxyethythiolcarbonate.

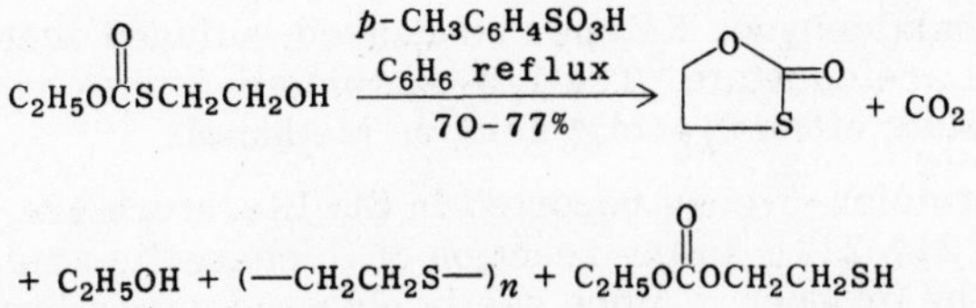

$$\text{C}_2\text{H}_5\text{O}\overset{\text{O}}{\overset{\|}{\text{C}}}\text{SCH}_2\text{CH}_2\text{OH} \xrightarrow[\substack{70\text{-}77\%}]{\substack{p\text{-}\text{CH}_3\text{C}_6\text{H}_4\text{SO}_3\text{H} \\ \text{C}_6\text{H}_6 \ \text{reflux}}} \left[\overset{\text{O}}{\underset{\text{S}}{\bigcirc}}{=}\text{O}\right] + \text{CO}_2$$

$$+ \ \text{C}_2\text{H}_5\text{OH} + (\text{—CH}_2\text{CH}_2\text{S—})_n + \text{C}_2\text{H}_5\text{O}\overset{\text{O}}{\overset{\|}{\text{C}}}\text{OCH}_2\text{CH}_2\text{SH}$$

The following physical properties of 1,3-oxathiolan-2-one have been reported: melting point, —20°; boiling point 47-50° at 0.08, 73° at 2, and 105° at 14 mm, n_D^{25} 1.5104. No derivative has been reported.

In the liquid phase reaction of ethylene oxide with carbon disulfide at 150° in the presence of an amine catalyst, Durden, Stansbury, and Catlette[112a] postulated that 1,3-oxathiolan-2-one (294) or 2-thione (295) is an intermediate in the formation of 1,3-dithiolane-2-thione. The 2-one presumably could form from the carbon oxysulfide released by the 2-thione.

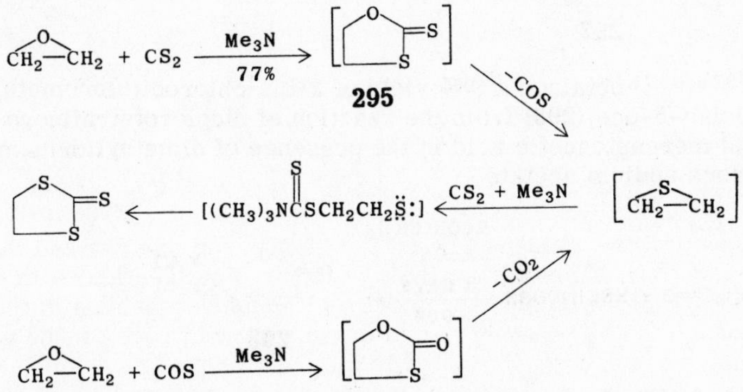

(3) 1,3-Oxathiolan-5-ones

Bistrzycki with Brenken[44] and with Traub[45] extensively studied the reaction of thiobenzilic acid with a variety of aldehydes and ketones for the preparation of 1,3-oxathiolan-5-ones (296). The reaction mixture in acetic acid was heated or refluxed for half an hour to several hours while dry hydrogen chloride was passed through. Excellent yields, in many case quantitative, were obtained.

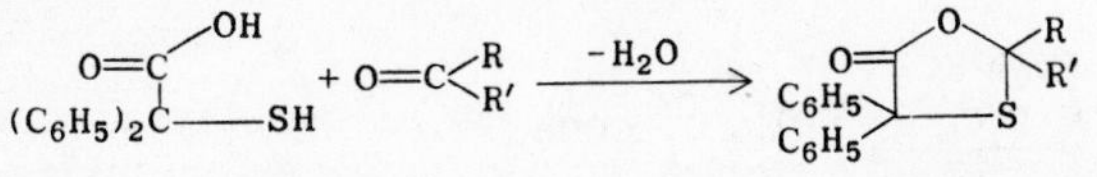

Aldehydes condensed included formaldehyde, acetaldehyde, chloral, benzaldehyde, p-chlorobenzaldehyde, o- and m-nitrobenzaldehyde, salicylaldehyde, anisaldehyde, cinnamic aldehyde, tolualdehyde, cumylaldehyde, piperonal, and terephthalaldehyde. Ketones condensed included acetone, pyruvic acid, and ethyl acetoacetate. The 1, 3-oxathiolan-5-ones were recrystallized from dilute ethanol, acetic acid, or methanol.

The various 1, 3-oxathiolan-5-ones reported in the literature are listed in Table 15 (pp. 210-212). In the reaction of thiobenzilic acid with salicylaldehyde, the product is more easily obtained pure when benzene is used as the solvent in place of acetic acid.

Schubert[426] obtained 2-benzoyl-1, 3-oxathiolan-5-one (297) on reacting mercaptoacetic acid with phenylglyoxal in acetic anhydride and sodium acetate at room temperature.

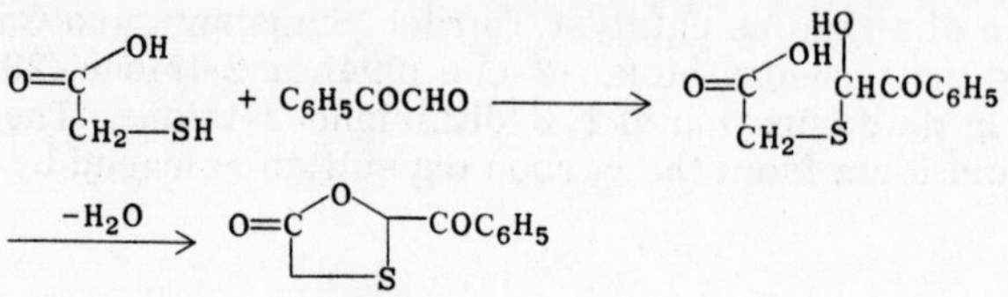

297

Simmons[437a, 437b] obtained a 98% yield of 2-bis(chlorodifluoromethyl)-1, 3-oxathiolan-5-one (298) from the reaction of dichlorotetrafluoroacetone and mercaptoacetic acid in the presence of dimethylformamide and anhydrous sodium acetate.

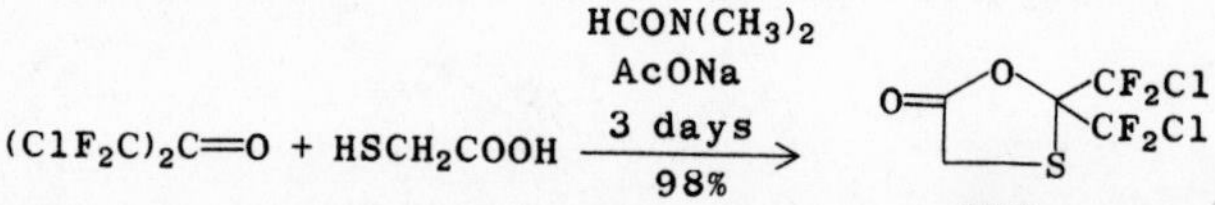

298

This method of preparation is similar to that used by Jönsson, whose starting reactant was thiodiglycollic acid. This underwent oxidation and ring closure[244,245] to give **299** on standing in a vacuum dessicator with bromine.

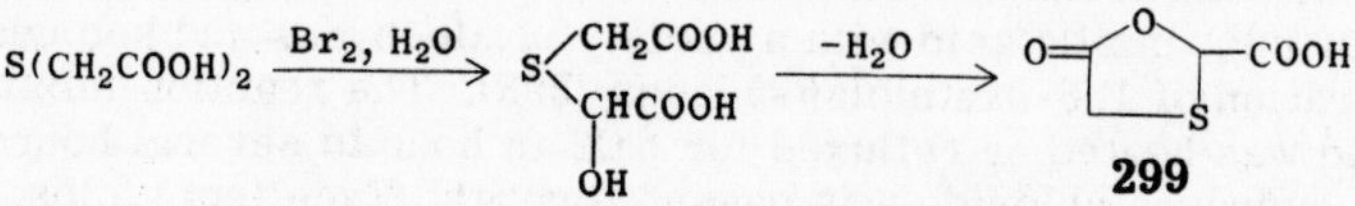

299

Larsson[279,280] similarly started from the thioether to prepare the oxathiolan-5-one (**300**).

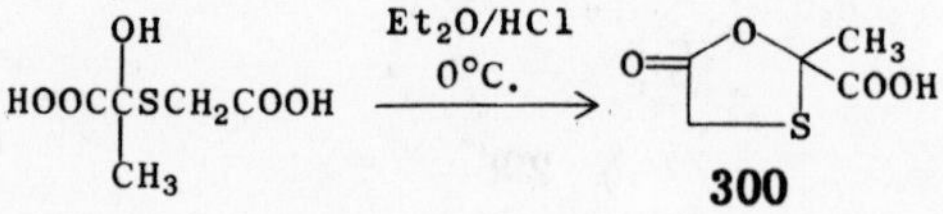

300

However, ring closure was not favored in the reaction of mercaptoacetic acid with pyruvic acid.

218

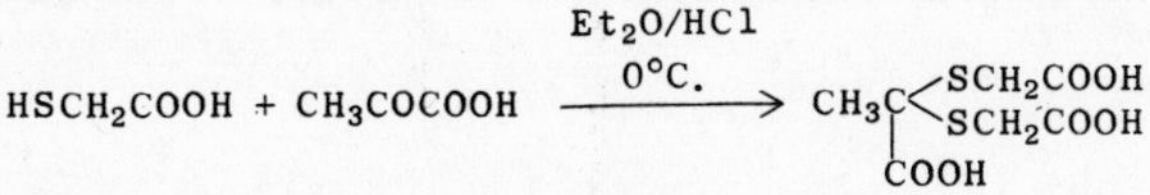

$$\text{HSCH}_2\text{COOH} + \text{CH}_3\text{COCOOH} \xrightarrow[\text{0°C.}]{\text{Et}_2\text{O/HCl}} \text{CH}_3\text{C}\underset{\text{COOH}}{\overset{\text{SCH}_2\text{COOH}}{<}}\text{SCH}_2\text{COOH}$$

Fredga[133] condensed *meso*-dimercaptoadipic acid and acetone in the presence of dry hydrogen chloride to obtain 29% of the bis(1, 3-oxathiolan-5-one) (301).

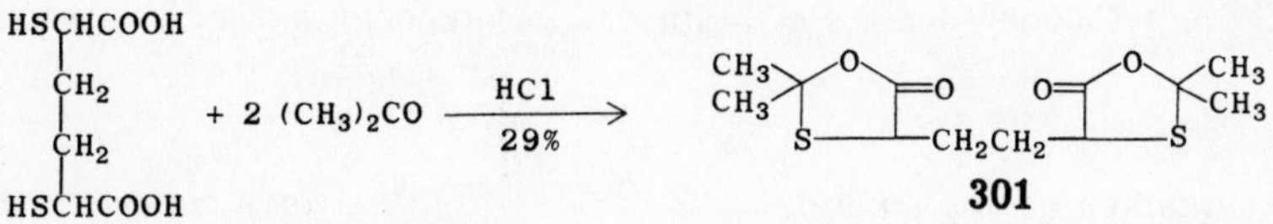

$$\begin{array}{c}\text{HSCHCOOH}\\|\\\text{CH}_2\\|\\\text{CH}_2\\|\\\text{HSCHCOOH}\end{array} + 2 \ (\text{CH}_3)_2\text{CO} \xrightarrow[29\%]{\text{HCl}}$$

301

The racemic bis(1, 3-oxathiolan-5-one) was obtained in 10. 5% yield from racemic dimercaptoadipic acid.

Lüttringhaus and Prinzbach[297] obtained a 90% yield of 2-trichloro-methyl-1, 3-oxathiolan-5-one (302) by the Dieckmann condensation of ethyl thioglycolate with chloral and benzene as solvent in the presence of concentrated H_2SO_4.

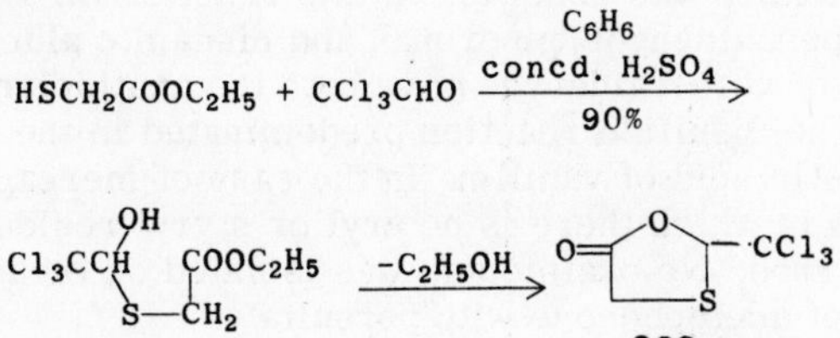

$$\text{HSCH}_2\text{COOC}_2\text{H}_5 + \text{CCl}_3\text{CHO} \xrightarrow[90\%]{\overset{\text{C}_6\text{H}_6}{\text{concd. H}_2\text{SO}_4}}$$

$$\underset{\text{S—CH}_2}{\overset{\text{OH}}{\text{Cl}_3\text{CC}\underset{|}{\text{H}}\ \text{COOC}_2\text{H}_5}} \xrightarrow{-\text{C}_2\text{H}_5\text{OH}}$$

302

Essentially these reactions, which involve the formation of hemimercaptals or hemimercaptols, yield the oxathiolane through an acid catalyzed inner esterification. In the preparation of oxathiolanes by Holmberg[223-225], it is quite likely that the mechanism involves a nucleophilic displacement leading to ring closure. Holmberg, on treating various mercaptals and mercaptols with potassium persulfate and 1 N sodium hydroxide for three hours in the cold, obtained oxathiolan-5-ones (303).

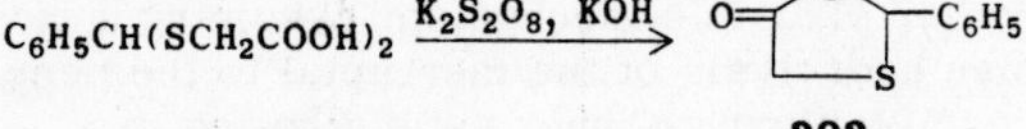

$$\text{C}_6\text{H}_5\text{CH(SCH}_2\text{COOH)}_2 \xrightarrow{\text{K}_2\text{S}_2\text{O}_8, \ \text{KOH}}$$

303

He postulated that the intermediate product in this reaction was **304**.

$$C_6H_5\underset{\underset{OSO_3Na}{|}}{C}HSCH_2COONa$$

304

He further postulated that the reaction could occur by one or more of the following courses in neutral solution.

$$\underset{R_2}{\overset{R_1}{>}}C(SCH_2COOH)_2 + 2\ K_2S_2O_8 + 2\ H_2O \longrightarrow (KOOCCH_2\overset{\overset{O}{\|}}{S}-)_2C\underset{R_2}{\overset{R_1}{<}} + 4\ KHSO_4$$

$$C_6H_5CH(SCH_2COOH)_2 + K_2S_2O_8 \longrightarrow \overset{O=\overset{O}{\underset{S}{\boxed{\quad}}}-C_6H_5}{} + (SCH_2COOK)_2 + 2\ K_2SO_4$$

303

$$\underset{R_2}{\overset{R_1}{>}}C(SCH_2COOH)_2 + K_2S_2O_8 + H_2O \longrightarrow (-SCH_2COOK)_2 + \underset{R_2}{\overset{R_1}{>}}C=O + 2\ KHSO_4$$

Thus, Holmberg reasoned, if the oxidation occurs to give oxathiolane there would be no change in the pH of the reaction mixture. An increase in acidity would indicate sulfone or disulfide (and aldehyde or ketone) formation. No change in acidity was observed in this reaction for the mercaptalacetic acids of benzaldehyde, piperonal, and cinnamic aldehyde. The mercaptalacetic acid of veratraldehyde gave both the oxathiolane and disulfide reactions. The disulfide reaction predominated in the oxidation of the mercaptalacetic acid of vanillin. In the case of mercaptal- and mercaptolacetic acids in which there is no aryl or styryl residue, the sulfonyl reaction occurred. No oxathiolane was isolated on treating the mercaptalacetic acid of acetophenone with persulfate.

Rather than attributing oxathiolane formation to oxidation, the following course appears to be more likely.

$$C_6H_5\underset{\diagdown SCH_2C=O}{\overset{\diagup SCH_2COOH}{CH \longleftarrow OH}} \rightleftharpoons \overset{O=\overset{O}{\underset{S}{\boxed{\quad}}}-C_6H_5}{} + HSCH_2COOH$$

303 $\downarrow$ [O]

$$(-SCH_2COOH)_2$$

This mechanism does not involve a change in pH and the oxidation of mercaptoacetic acid to the disulfide favors the forward course of this reversible reaction. Another plausible mechanism, assuming a reversible reaction, may involve hydrolysis of the mercaptal to the hemimercaptal which then could cyclize through inner esterification.

220

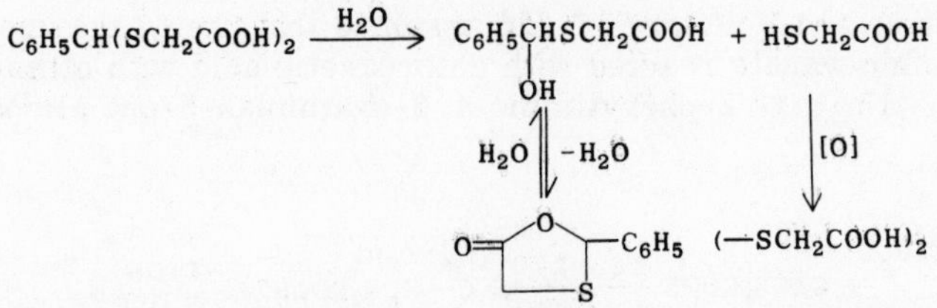

$$C_6H_5CH(SCH_2COOH)_2 \xrightarrow{H_2O} C_6H_5\underset{\underset{OH}{|}}{C}HSCH_2COOH + HSCH_2COOH$$

$$H_2O \Updownarrow -H_2O \qquad\qquad \downarrow [O]$$

303

$$O=\!\!<\!\!\overset{O}{\underset{S}{}}\!\!>\!\!-C_6H_5 \qquad (-SCH_2COOH)_2$$

The nucleophilic attack of the carboxylic hydroxyl and displacement of mercaptoacetic acid appears to be a reasonable course.

Holmberg obtained 2-methyl-2-phenyl-1,3-oxathiolan-5-one from the mercaptolacetic acid of acetophenone on heating.

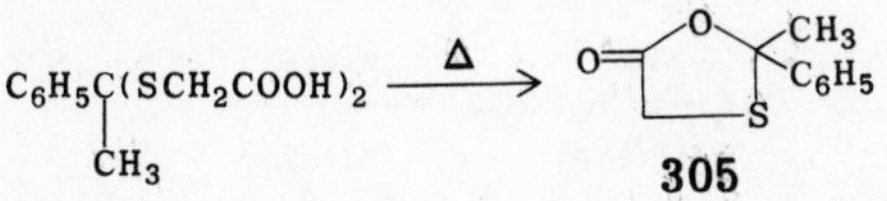

$$C_6H_5\underset{\underset{CH_3}{|}}{C}(SCH_2COOH)_2 \xrightarrow{\Delta} O=\!\!<\!\!\overset{O}{\underset{S}{}}\!\!>\!\!\overset{CH_3}{\underset{C_6H_5}{<}}$$

305

Holmberg[225] obtained 2-benzyl-1,3-oxathiolan-5-one also by heating the mercaptalacetic acid of phenylacetaldehyde.

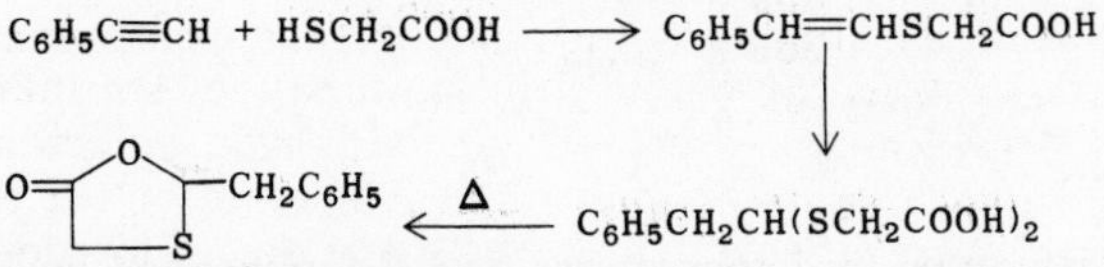

$$C_6H_5C\equiv CH + HSCH_2COOH \longrightarrow C_6H_5CH=CHSCH_2COOH$$

$$\downarrow$$

$$O=\!\!<\!\!\overset{O}{\underset{S}{}}\!\!>\!\!-CH_2C_6H_5 \xleftarrow{\Delta} C_6H_5CH_2CH(SCH_2COOH)_2$$

The thermal reaction is best explained by the nucleophilic displacement mechanism suggested above.

(4) 1,3-Oxathiolan-2,5-dione (**306**)

Analogously to the preparation of 1,3-oxathiolan-2-one, the 2,5-dione, which melts at 68-70° with decomposition, is conveniently prepared by the reaction of phosgene with mercaptoacetic acid.[91,92,423a]

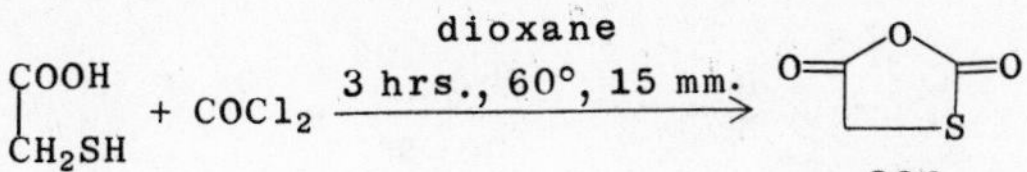

$$\underset{CH_2SH}{\overset{COOH}{|}} + COCl_2 \xrightarrow[\text{3 hrs., 60°, 15 mm.}]{\text{dioxane}} O=\!\!<\!\!\overset{O}{\underset{S}{}}\!\!>\!\!=O$$

306

No derivative has been reported.

(5) 1,3-Oxathiolan-2-imines

The 1,3-oxathiolan-2-imines reported in the literature are listed in Table 16. All of these compounds were prepared by the reaction of an epoxide with a thiocyanate.

[For references, see pp. 289-312.]

Liebermann and Voltzkow[288,489] assumed that phenyl thiourethan or phenyl isothiocyanate reacted with chloroacetic acid with elimination of ethyl alcohol to give 2-phenylimino-1, 3-oxathiolan-5-one almost quantitatively.

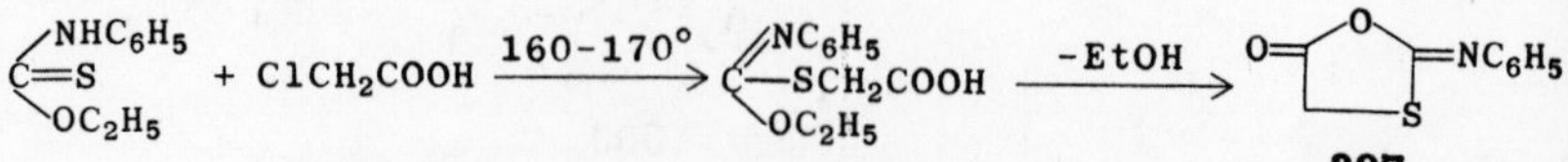

Meyer,[323] on the other hand, preferred to think of the reaction as taking place with elimination of ethyl chloride. This was shown to be the case by Wheeler, Barnes, and Johnson.[500,501] Thus, the thiazole (308 or 309) is the product of this reaction, not the oxathiolane (307).

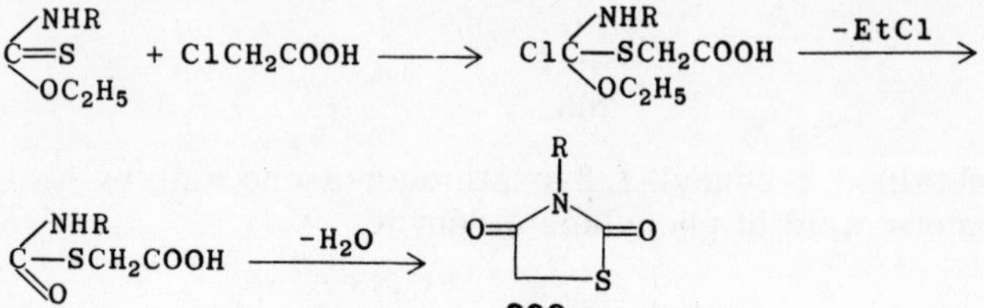

308 R = H
309 R = C_6H_5

The melting points reported by Liebermann and Voltzkow and by Wheeler, Barnes, and Johnson were identical.

The reaction of epoxides with thiocyanate ion in the preparation of episulfide has received considerable attention, particularly in the cyclopentane and cyclohexane series. Ostensibly the mechanism[120,363] of this reaction is:

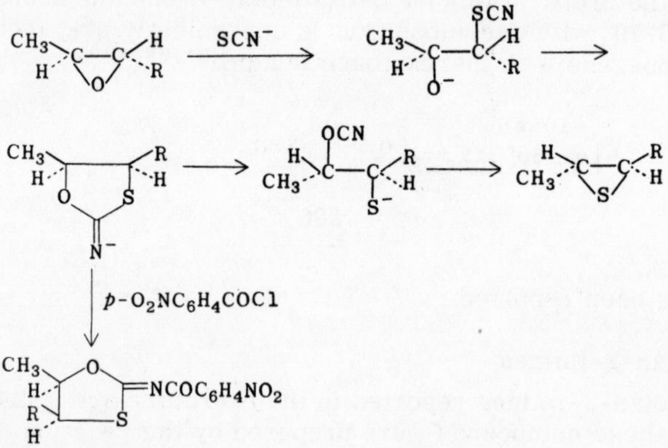

310

Sergeev and Kolychev[431,432] showed that ethylene oxide reacts with thiocyanic acid to form β-thiocyanoethanol, which, on treatment with hydrochloric acid, yields the hydrochloride of 1,3-oxathiolan-2-imine (311).

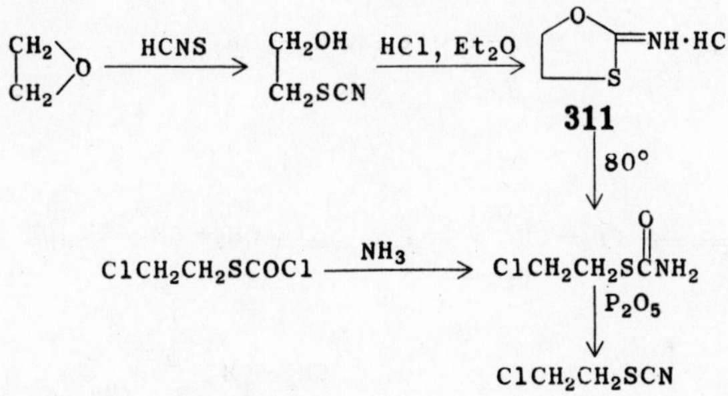

Proof that this product was isolated was established by the fact that β-chloroethylthiourethan, obtained on heating the 3-oxathiolan-2-imine at 80° and also obtained from the reaction of ClCH$_2$CH$_2$SCOCl and NH$_3$, gave β-chloroethyl thiocyanate on heating with phosphorus pentoxide.

Price and Kirk,[363] on reacting propylene oxide with thiocyanic acid by the method of Wagner-Jauregg[491a] obtained a small amount of needle like crystals which was shown to be N-carbamyl-5-methyl-1,3-oxathiolan-2-imine (312). Wagner-Jauregg and Häring[492] somewhat later reported yields of 40-80% of 1,3-oxathiolan-2-imines in the reaction of the β-hydroxy thiocyanate with hydrochloric acid and yields of 80-90% of the corresponding N-carbamyls on treating the 2-imines with potassium cyanate.

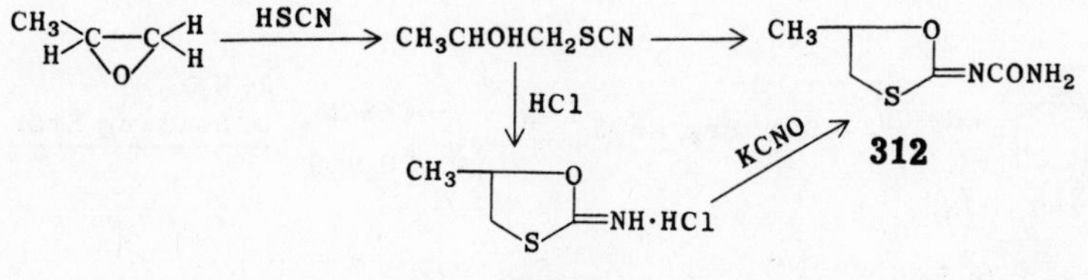

In their studies on the reaction of epoxides with thiourea, Bordwell and Anderson[56] postulated an oxathiolane intermediate (314) to explain the formation of episulfides.

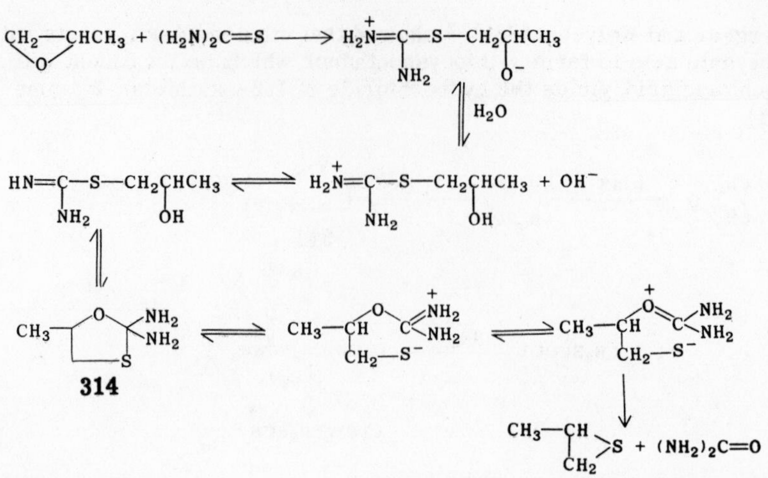

Emerson and Patrick[114,115] treated 2-vinylthiophene (**315**) with potassium thiocyanate and bromine in glacial acetic acid and obtained a product which they believed to be 5-(2'-thienyl)-1,3-oxathiolan-2-imine (**316**) for which they reported no yield. Inasmuch as they reported a yield of 57% of 2-vinylthiophene dithiocyanate from the reaction of 2-vinylthiophene with thiocyanogen, it is reasonable to postulate that the dithiocyanate on mild hydrolysis would lead to the oxathiolane. It is also reasonable to expect the 5-(2'-thienyl)-1,3-oxathiolane rather than the 4-(2'-thienyl)-1,3-oxathiolane as the allylic nature would favor elimination at the carbon attached to the thiophene ring over that of the carbon atom β to the thiophene ring. Using 5-chloro-2-vinylthiophene, Emerson and Patrick obtained a mixture of 18% dithiocyanate and 32% 5-(5'-chloro-2'-thienyl)-1,3-oxathiolan-2-imine. Neither of the oxathiolan-2-imines was characterized.

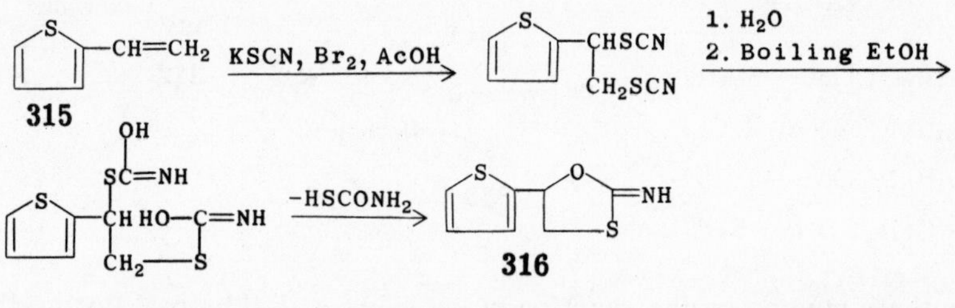

In the reaction of ethyl 2,3-epoxy-3-methylvalerate in acid media with thiourea, Durden and Stansbury[113] postulated the formation of an isothiouronium salt which, on treatment with base, is cyclized to the 2,2-diamino-1,3-oxathiolane (**317**) which was not isolated but decomposed to form the episulfide.

$$
\begin{array}{c}
\text{C}_2\text{H}_5\text{OCO---CH} \\
\text{CH}_3 \diagup \triangleright\!\!-\!\!\text{O} \\
\text{C}_2\text{H}_5 \diagdown \text{C}
\end{array}
\xrightarrow{\text{H}^+}
\begin{array}{c}
\text{C}_2\text{H}_5\text{OCO---CH} \\
\text{CH}_3 \diagup \triangleright\!\!-\!\!\text{OH}^+ \\
\text{C}_2\text{H}_5 \diagdown \text{C}
\end{array}
\longrightarrow
\begin{array}{c}
\text{C}_2\text{H}_5\text{OCOCHOH} \\
\text{CH}_3 \diagdown \\
\text{C}_2\text{H}_5 \diagup \text{C}+
\end{array}
\quad (\text{NH}_2)_2\text{C}{=}\text{S} \xrightarrow{}
$$

$$
\begin{array}{c}
\text{C}_2\text{H}_5\text{OCOCHOH} \\
\text{CH}_3 \diagdown \\
\text{C}_2\text{H}_5 \diagup \text{CSC}{=}\text{NH} \\
\text{NH}_2
\end{array}
\xrightarrow{\text{OH}^-}
\begin{array}{c}
\text{C}_2\text{H}_5\text{OCO---} \overset{\text{CH}_3}{\underset{\text{S}}{\diagdown \text{C}_2\text{H}_5}} \\
\text{O} \diagdown \diagup \\
\text{H}_2\text{N} \diagup \diagdown \text{NH}_2
\end{array}
\longrightarrow
\begin{array}{c}
\text{C}_2\text{H}_5\text{OCO---CH} \\
\text{CH}_3 \diagup \triangleright\!\!-\!\!\text{S} \\
\text{C}_2\text{H}_5 \diagdown \text{C}
\end{array}
$$

317

TABLE 16. 1, 3-Oxathiolan-2-imines

Substituent	Yield (%)	M. p. (°C)	Ref.
2-(HCl . HN=)		121. 5	431, 432
		114-115	492
2-(HCl . HN=)-5-CH$_3$-		112-115	363
		108-110	492
2-(HCl . HN=)-5-ClCH$_2$-			492
2-(HCl . HN=)-4-C$_6$H$_5$-		110-111	492
2-(HN=)-5-(2-thienyl)-		140-141	114, 115
2-(HN=)-5-(5-Cl-2-thienyl)-	32	145	114, 115
2-(HCl . HN=)-4-CH$_3$-5-C$_2$H$_5$-			492
2-(H$_2$NCON=)-5-CH$_3$-		173-174	363
2-(H$_2$NCON=)-5-ClCH$_2$-		144. 5-146. 5	492
2-(H$_2$NCON=)-5-C$_6$H$_5$-		133-135	492
2-(H$_2$NCON=)-4-C$_2$H$_5$-5-CH$_3$-		156	492
2-(C$_6$H$_5$CON=)-5-CH$_3$-		126	363
2-(p-O$_2$NC$_6$H$_4$CON=)-5-CH$_3$-	16	158 and 171	363

(6) Spiro-1, 3-oxathiolanes

The various 2, 2-spiro-1, 3-oxathiolanes reported in the literature are listed in Table 17. Cyclohexanone and mercaptoethanol react in the presence of p-toluenesulfonic acid to give 62-70% yields of the spiro-1, 3-

[For references, see pp. 289-312.]

TABLE 17. 2,2-Spiro-1,3-oxathiolanes

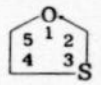

Spiro Compound Ketone	Ketone position	1,3-Oxathiolane substituents	Yield (%)	M.p. (°C)	B.p. (°C)	(mm)	Other properties	Ref.
Cyclohexanone	1		70		111	22	n_D^{21} 1.5108	39
							d_4^{21} 1.085	39
			42		51-53	0.55	n_D^{25} 1.5119	79
							d_4^{25} 1.0781	79
			62		47	0.6	n_D^{24} 1.5155	103
							d_4^{24} 1.0811	103
2-HO-cyclohexanone	1				80	0.15		238
2-(3,5-dinitrobenzoxy)-cyclohexanone	1			144				238
2-C_2H_5-2-HO-cyclohexanone	1				100	0.1		238
2-(HC≡C)-2-HO-cyclohexanone	1	two isomers		68 / 109-111				237, 239
2-CH_3CO-3-C_2H_5O-cyclohexanone	1			119.5				239
2-CH_3CHOH-3-C_2H_5O-cyclohexanone	1			135				239
2-(HC≡C-)-3-C_2H_5O-cyclohexanone	1	two isomers		95 / 118				239
2-(HC≡C-)-cyclohex-3-enone	1			59				237, 239
Cyclohexanone	1	5-C_6H_5-	73	36-37				105
Cyclohexanone	1	4,5-(C_6H_5-)$_2$	87	98-99				105
Cyclohexanone	1	5-(C_6H_5)$_2$CH-	73	96-97				105
Cyclohexanone	1	4,4-(C_6H_5-)$_2$-5-one	68	80-82				403a
Cycloheptanone	1	4,4-(C_6H_5-)$_2$-5-one	21	112-113				403a
Isatin	3	4,4-(C_6H_5-)$_2$-5-one	35	210-211				403a
Cyclohexane-1,2-dione	1	Dinitrophenylhydrazone	40	178	78-82	0.3		237, 238
Cyclohexane-1,2-dione	1, 2	two isomers		135	130	0.2		238

Compound	Positions	Substituent / Note	No.	mp	bp	$[\alpha]$	Ref.
Cyclohexane-1,2-dione	1,2	4,4-(C$_6$H$_5$-)$_2$-5-one	37	108-110			403a
Cyclohexane-1,3-dione	1		22		130-135 12		362a
Cyclohexane-1,4-dione	1,4			87-99			362a
Octahydroanthraquinone	9,10		99	252-256			212b
1-(-CH$_2$COCH$_3$-2-[-CH$_2$C(CH$_3$)=CH$_2$]-2,4b-(CH$_3$-)$_2$-1,2,3,4,4a,4b,5,6,7,9,10,10a dodecahydrophenanthrene-4,7-dione	7						10a, 10b
Androstan-17-one	17		90	119-121		$[\alpha]_D^{20} -40°$	103
Androstan-17-one	17	3,3-dioxide		199-200			104
Androstan-17β-ol-3-one acetate	3		72	164-167		$[\alpha]_D^{20} 20$	402
Androstan-17β-acetoxy-3-one	3	4,4-(C$_6$H$_5$-)$_2$-5-one	73	179-181		$[\alpha]_D^{20} 7.5$	403a
D-Homo-5β-androstan-3α-actoxy-11,17a-dione	11,17a			229-236		$[\alpha]_D^{25} 51.5$	449
Androstane-3,17-dione	3,17	(RRI 6575)	56	203-206		$[\alpha]_D^{25} -40.7$	211
			23	202-204		$[\alpha]_D^{20} -60$	402
Androst-5-en-3β-acetoxy-17-one	17		90	172-174		$[\alpha]_D^{20} -99$	103
				174-176		$[\alpha]_D^{20} -86.7$	402
				198-200		$[\alpha]_D^{20} -63$	403
			87	183-184		$[\alpha]_D^{25} -99.5$	127
Androst-4-en-3,17-dione	3,17		70	192-193		$[\alpha]_D^{25} 46$	402
			41	190-193			404
			2	167-170		$[\alpha]_D^{25} 271$	211
D-Homo-5β-androstane-3α,11β-diol-17a-one	17a			207-208		$[\alpha]_D^{25} 32.4$	449
Cholan-24-ol-3,7,12-trione	12	(RRI 5564)		182-183		$[\alpha]_D 57.5$	314, 316
Cholan-24-ol-3,7,12-trione	7,12	(RRI 6576)	41	212-214		$[\alpha]_D 43$	315, 316
Cholan-24-ol-3,7,12-trione	3,7,12	(RRI 7091)	98	233-235		$[\alpha]_D 95$	315, 316
Etiocholane-17β-acetoxy-3-one	3		60	163-165		$[\alpha]_D 24.5$	402
Dehydrocholic acid	3,7,12		30	155		$[\alpha]_D 92$	315, 316
Methyl Dehydrocholate	3,7,12		99	183		$[\alpha]_D 90$	315, 316
Cholestan-3-one	3		89	135-136		$[\alpha]_D 25$	103
			82	133-134		$[\alpha]_D 24.8$	127

TABLE 17. 2,2-Spiro-1,3-oxathiolanes (contd)

Spiro Compound (Ketone)	Ketone position	1,3-Oxathiolane substituents	Yield (%)	M.p. (°C)	B.p. (°C) (mm)	Other properties	Ref.
Cholestan-3-one	3	4-C_6H_5-	20	158-160		$[\alpha]_D^{20}$ 12.8	105
Cholestan-3-one	3	5-C_6H_5-	37	164-166		$[\alpha]_D^{20}$ 45.7	105
Cholestan-3-one	3	5-$C_6H_5CH_2$-	36	149-150		$[\alpha]_D^{20}$ 25.3	105
Cholestan-3-one	3	5-$[(C_6H_5)_2CH-]$	8	152-153		$[\alpha]_D^{25}$ 2.8	104,107
			10	172-173		$[\alpha]_D^{25}$ -9.7	
			18	193-194		$[\alpha]_D^{25}$ 60	
Cholest-5-en-3-one	3		18	136-137		$[\alpha]_D$ -19.6	127
Estrone	17			181-183		$[\alpha]_D^{20}$ 57	403
Estrone acetate	17		83	162		$[\alpha]_D^{20}$ 0	402
Pregnan-3β-acetoxy-12,20-dione	12			175-177		$[\alpha]_D^{24}$ 112	1
Pregn-4-en-20β-acetoxy-3-one	3		30	183-185		$[\alpha]_D^{20}$ -31	103
Pregn-4-en-3-ol-20-one	20		78	156-158		$[\alpha]_D^{20}$ 36	402
Pregn-5-en-3β-acetoxy-20-one	20		72	186-188		$[\alpha]_D^{20}$ -34	402
Progesterone	20		60	190-192.5		$[\alpha]_D^{20}$ 77.4	402
				175-177		$[\alpha]_D^{24}$ 112	1
22a-5α-Spirostan-3β-acetoxy-12-one	12		62	224-225		$[\alpha]_D^{20}$ -77	103
22a-Spirost-4-en-3-one	3		65	240-242		$[\alpha]_D^{20}$ -146	103
Testosterone	3		22	192-194		$[\alpha]_D^{20}$ -30	103
			18	192-193		$[\alpha]_D^{20}$ -19	402
Testosterone acetate	3		15	200-202		$[\alpha]_D^{20}$ -15	402
Dihydrotestosterone acetate	3			188-192		$[\alpha]_D^{20}$ 0	402
D-Homoetiocholan-3α-acetoxy-11,17α-dione	17α		35	229.2-236.2		$[\alpha]_D$ 51.5	73a,73b
D-Homoetiocholan-3α-ol-11,17α-dione	17α		67	207.0-207.8		$[\alpha]_D$ 32.4	73a,73b
2-Ethoxycarbonylethyl-des-A-androstan-5,17-dione	5,17		75	113-115		$[\alpha]_D^{18}$ 0	398a

oxathiolane (**318**) when benzene is used to azeotrope off the water of reaction.[39,102] Using zinc chloride and anhydrous sodium sulfate at room temperature results in a 42% yield.[79]

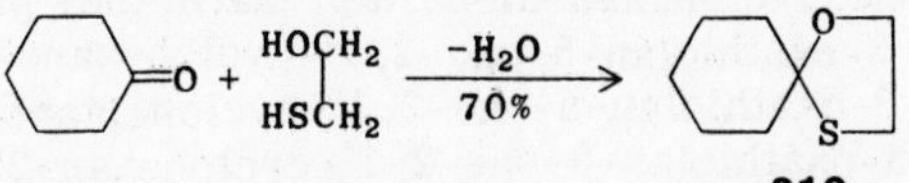

318
(RRI 1224)

The Chemical Abstracts name for this particular compound is 1-oxa-4-thiaspiro[4.5]decane. Other names given to this compound have been 2-pentamethylen-1,3-thioxolane,[39] cyclohexane-1-spiro-2'-(1',3'-oxathiolane),[238] and cyclohexanone ethylene hemithioketal.[103]

Jaeger and Smith[237-239] studied the reaction of cyclohexanone-1,2-dione with mercaptoethanol using p-toluenesulfonic acid and azeotroping off the water of reaction with benzene. They obtained the mono- (**319**) and di- (**320**) spiro-1,3-oxathiolane.

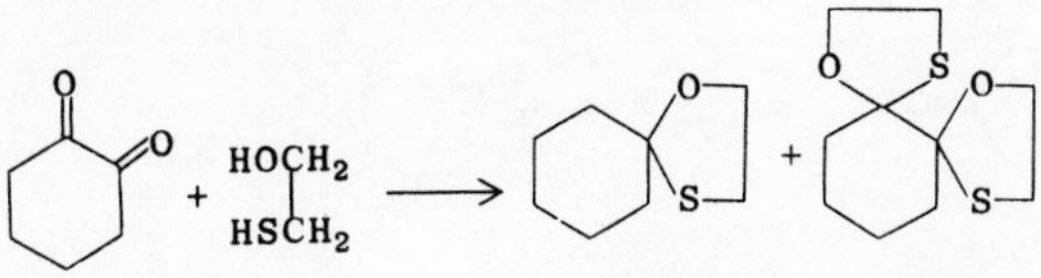

319   **320**

(RRI 2402)

The dispiro, or 1,7-dioxa-4,10-dithiaspiro [4.0.4.4]tetradecane (**320**), was obtained as two isomers.

Plieninger and Grasshof[362a] prepared the bis(ethylene hemithioketal) of 1,4-cyclohexadione by heating the diketone with mercaptoethanol for twelve hours in the presence of p-toluenesulfonic acid; under reflux and with shorter heating, they obtained the mono(ethylene hemithioketal).

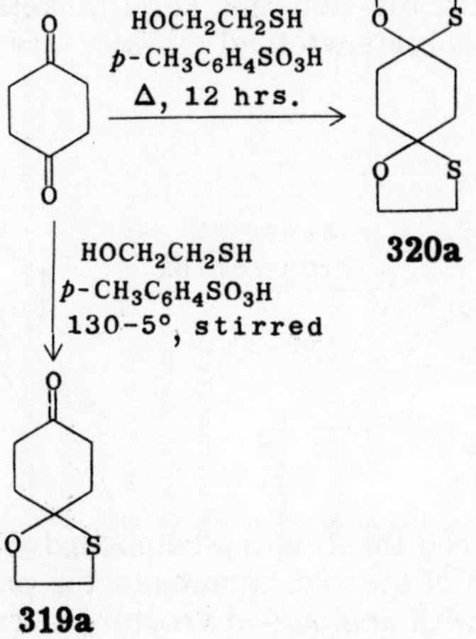

320a

319a

[For references, see pp. 289-312.]

Romo de Vivar and Romo[403a] prepared several spiro-1, 3-oxathiolan-5-ones by reacting a cyclic ketone with α-mercaptodiphenylacetic acid in refluxing benzene using p-toluenesulfonic acid as the catalyst. From cyclohexanone, cycloheptanone, cyclohexanedione, and isatin they prepared spiro(4, 4-diphenyl-1, 3-oxathiolan-5-one-2, 1'-cyclohexane) (321), spiro(4, 4-diphenyl-1, 3-oxathiolan-5-one-2, 1'-cycloheptanone) (322), spiro(4, 4-diphenyl-1,3-oxathiolan-5-one-2, 1'-cyclohexan-2'-one) (323), and spiro(4, 4-diphenyl-1, 3-oxathiolan-5-one-2, 3'-oxindol) (324).

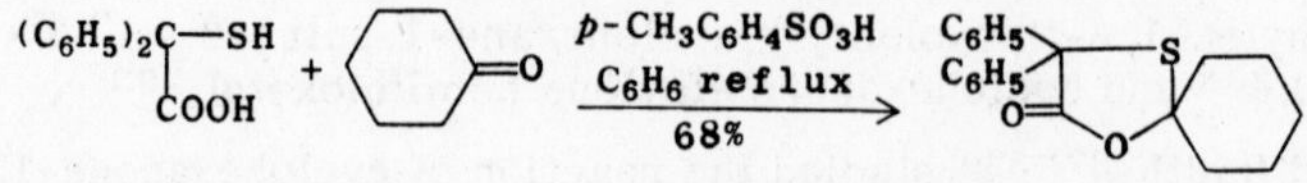

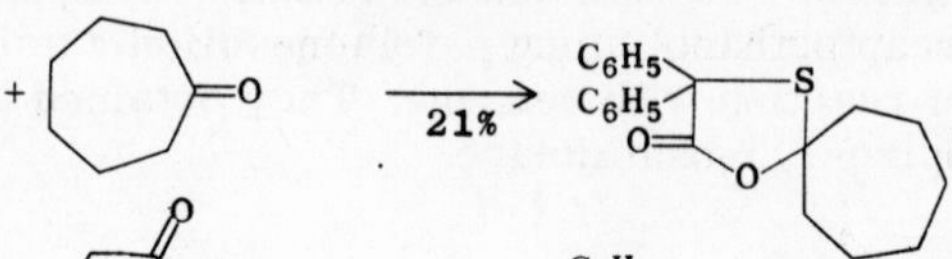

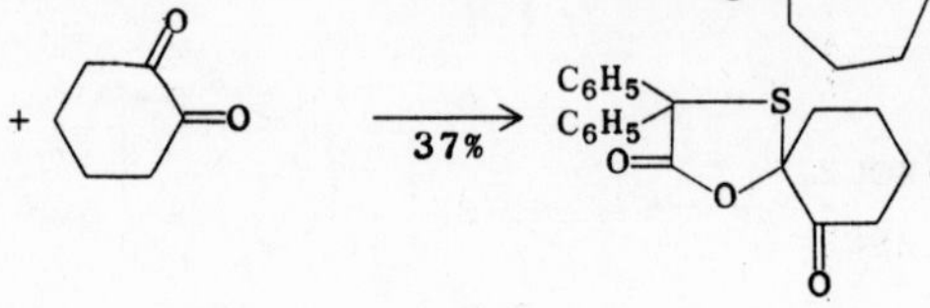

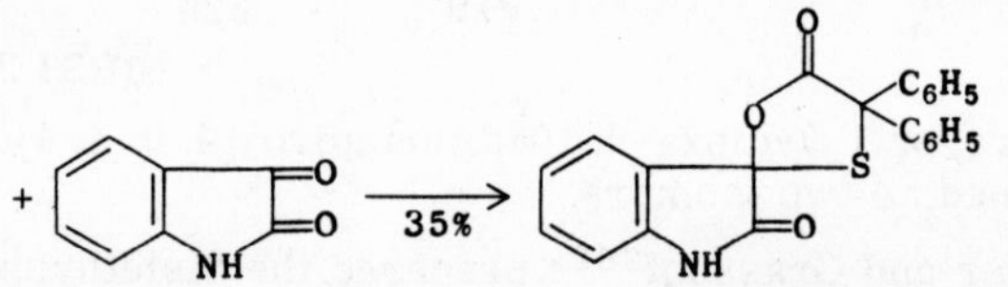

Hill, Martin, and Stouch,[212b] in a study of the stereochemistry of hydroanthracenes, reacted mercaptoethanol with *cis-anti-cis* adduct of p-benzoquinone and butadiene to give the bis-ethylene hemithioketal (324a), which, on Raney nickel hydrogenolysis, yielded *cis-anti-cis* perhydroanthraquinone.

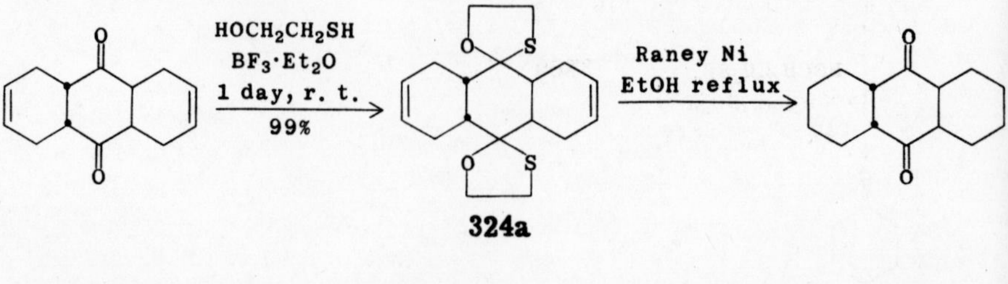

324a

Arth, Poos, and Sarrett[10a,10b] prepared the 7-spiro compound (324b) as an intermediate for the preparation of steroid hormones; the parent diketone was recovered by treatment with acetone-hydrochloric acid.

324b

Rosenkranz, Kaufmann, and Romo[404], analogously to the reaction of steroids with ethylene glycol and with dimercaptoethanol, reacted androst-4-ene-3, 17-dione (**325**) with mercaptoethanol to form the 17-cyclic hemithioketal (**326**).

325

$$+ \quad \begin{matrix} CH_2OH \\ CH_2SH \end{matrix} \quad \xrightarrow{-H_2O}$$

326
(RRI 5565)

Romo, Rosenkranz, and Djerassi[402] in a rather general study of this reaction found that mercaptoethanol reacts readily in the presence of zinc chloride with unconjugated carbonyl groups to give the corresponding cyclic ethylenehemithioketals. The 3-ketosteroids and 20-keto-steroids, regardless of the configuration of C-5, such as androstan-17β-ol-3-one acetate, etiocholan-17β-ol-3-one acetate, estrone acetate, androst-5-en-3β-ol-17-one acetate, allopregnan-3β-ol-20-one acetate, and pregn-5-en-3β-ol-20-one acetate, underwent this reaction. In the presence of the Δ^4-3-keto moiety, a saturated carbonyl group, such as at C-17 or C-20, could be attacked selectively when zinc chloride was used as the condensing agent. Using p-toluenesulfonic acid, which is a more drastic condensing agent, the bis(ethylenehemithioketal) was formed, although in poor yield, from androst-4-ene-3, 17-dione. Testosterone or its acetate was converted to the hemithioketal in less than 20% yield. This reaction thus affords a means of protecting an unconjugated carbonyl group in the presence of a Δ^4-3-keto moiety.

Romo, Rosenkranz, and Djerassi[402] assumed that the reaction of mercaptoethanol with a Δ^4-3-ketosteroid proceeded with least alteration of structure. Treatment with ethylene glycol apparently shifts the double bond; treatment with dimercaptoethane, on the other hand, does not cause the double bond to shift. Whether or not hemithioketal formation from a Δ^4-3-ketosteroid is accompanied by a shift of the double bond was

[For references, see pp. 289-312.]

Chapter 4

considered unsolved in 1952.[9] In the following year Djerassi and Gorman,[103] on the basis of earlier observations of Fernholz[126a] which indicated a shift of the double bond from the 4, 5-position to the 5, 6-position, concluded that a shift does occur.

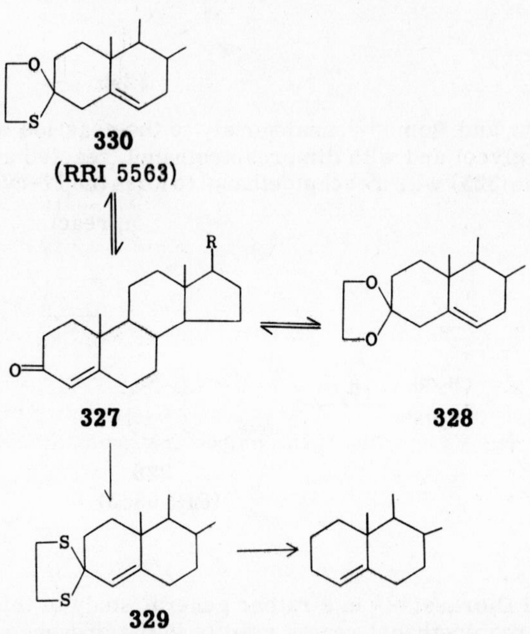

330
(RRI 5563)

327   **328**

329

Their consideration of the molecular rotations in the cholest-4-en-3-one series (**327**) showed a positive change in molecular rotation on going to the thioketal (**329**), a strongly negative change on going to the ketal (**328**), and an even more strongly negative change on going to the hemithioketal (**330**). A strongly negative change is characteristic of a shift of the double bond from 4, 5 to 5, 6. To explain this difference in the shift of the double bond, Djerassi and Gorman postulated **332** as the intermediate for hemithioketal formation through nucleophilic attack by the primary hydroxyl group to give **331** without a shift of the double bond or through dehydration to **333** followed by 1, 2-addition to the 3, 4-double bond to give **330**. They preferred the latter process.

232

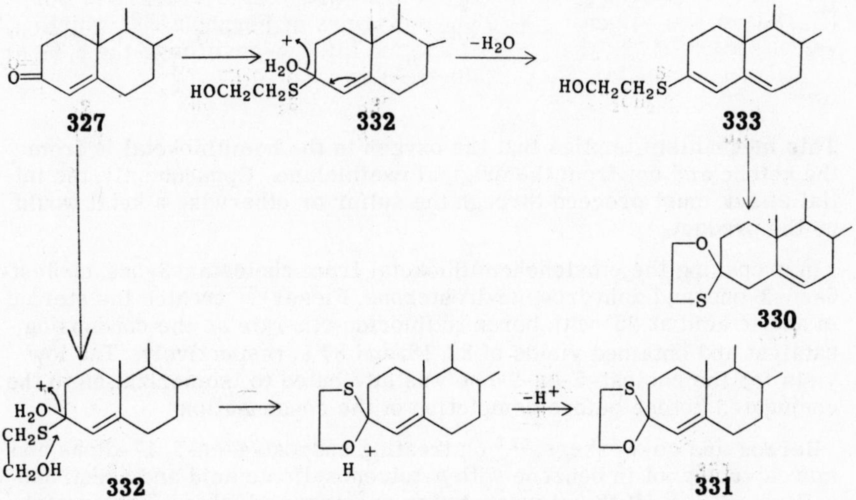

In the case of the mercaptole 329, on the other hand, the S$_N$2 reaction predominates over dehydration by virtue of the more strongly nucleophilic sulfur.

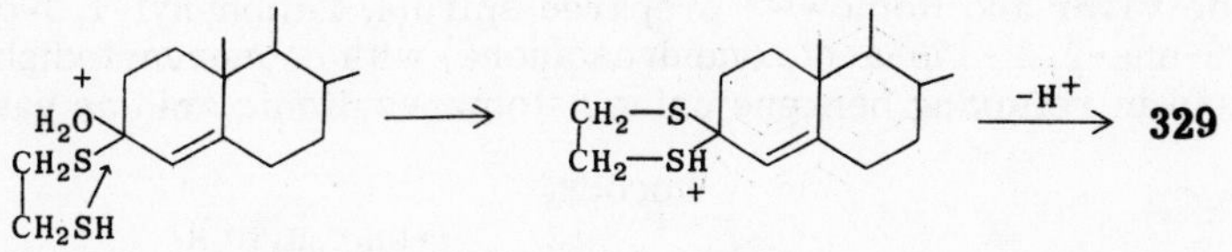

Another method for the preparation of these ethylene hemithioketals was Djerassi and Gorman's[103] adaptation of the exchange method developed for ketals ("trans-ketalization") in which a nonvolatile ketone is refluxed in benzene with 2, 2-dimethyl-1, 3-oxathiolane (334).

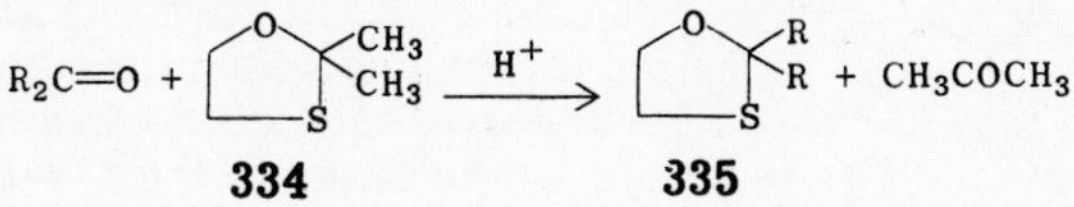

This method in general did not work with steroids and the ethylene mercaptal of acetone. In the case of androstan-17-one, androst-5-en-3β-ol-17-one acetate, and 22a-spirost-4-en-3-one, yields of 90, 85, and 34%, respectively, of the hemithioketals were obtained as compared with 93, 90, and 65%, respectively, by the benzene—p-toluenesulfonic acid method.

Djerassi and Gorman[103] suggested the following mechanism for the exchange reaction:

[For references, see pp. 289-312.]   233

$$R_2C{=}O \;+\; \left[\begin{array}{c} O{-}C{<}^{CH_3}_{CH_3} \\ \quad\quad S \end{array}\right] \xrightarrow{H^+} \quad \begin{array}{c} O{\curvearrowright}C{<}^{CH_3}_{CH_3} \\ CH_2 \quad S^+ \\ CH_2 \\ H\overset{|}{O}{-}CR_2 \end{array} \xrightarrow{-H^+} \left[\begin{array}{c} O \quad S \\ \;\; R_2 \end{array}\right] + O{=}C{<}^{CH_3}_{CH_3}$$

This mechanism implies that the oxygen in the hemithioketal is from the ketone and not from the original oxathiolane. Consequently, the initial attack must proceed through the sulfur or otherwise a ketal would be the product.

In preparing the ethylenehemithioketal from cholestan-3-one, cholest-5-en-3-one, and dehydroepiandrosterone, Fieser[127] treated the steroid in acetic acid at 25° with boron trifluoride etherate as the condensing catalyst and obtained yields of 82, 18, and 87%, respectively. The low yield for the cholest-5-en-3-one was attributed to isomerization to the conjugated ketone before completion of the condensation.

Herzog and co-workers,[211] on treating androst-4-en-3, 17-dione and mercaptoethanol in benzene with p-toluenesulfonic acid and azeotropically distilling off the benzene-water azeotrope, obtained four crystalline fractions including a 2% yield of androst-4-en-3, 17-dione-3-oxathiolane. Starting with androstane-3, 17-dione, and following a similar procedure, they obtained a 56% yield of androstane-3, 17-dione-bis-(oxathiolane).

Romo de Vivar and Romo[403a] prepared spiro(4, 4-diphenyl-1, 3-oxathiolan-5-one-2, 3′-17β-acetoxyandrostanone) with α-mercaptodiphenylacetic acid in refluxing benzene using p-toluenesulfonic acid as catalyst.

$$(C_6H_5)_2\underset{\underset{SH}{|}}{C}COOH \;+\; \text{[steroid]} \xrightarrow[\substack{C_6H_6 \text{ reflux} \\ 73\%}]{p{-}CH_3C_6H_4SO_3H} \text{[336]}$$

336

b. Properties, Reactions, and Uses

(1) 1, 3-Oxathiolanes

The simpler, monosubstituted 1, 3-oxathiolanes are liquids with fresh, aromatic aromas. They are insoluble in water and soluble in most organic solvents. They are fairly stable to bases, but are completely hydrolyzed to the starting mercaptoalcohol and carbonyl compounds by dilute acids.[263]

The structural similarity among imidazolidines, dioxolanes, oxazolidines, and oxathiolanes as expressed by the infrared absorption spectrum has been pointed out.[40] The condensation product from methyl isobutyl ketone and 2-mercaptoethanol showed maxima at 1074, 1130, 1157, and 1186 cm^{-1}. In the condensation product of the same ketone with 2,3-dimercaptopropanol, bands were observed at 1072, 1125, 1160, and 1199 cm^{-1}. Thus, the condensation involved the hydroxyl and adjacent mercapto and not the two vicinal mercapto groups. The presence of the free mercapto group in this condensation product was proved by the positive reaction with nitrous acid and by the 2500 cm^{-1} band, which are characteristic for a free mercapto group.

Only one chloromethyloxathiolane has been reported, although two have been postulated to be intermediates in reactions which conceivably could have led to their preparations. This might imply the chloromethyloxathiolanes are intrinsically unstable or that they are not reasonable intermediates. Thus, in the reaction of epichlorohydrin with thiolacetic acid, Sjoberg[440] obtained the acetate of 1-chloro-2-mercapto-2-propanol, which, he believed, resulted from the intermediate oxathiolane (337).

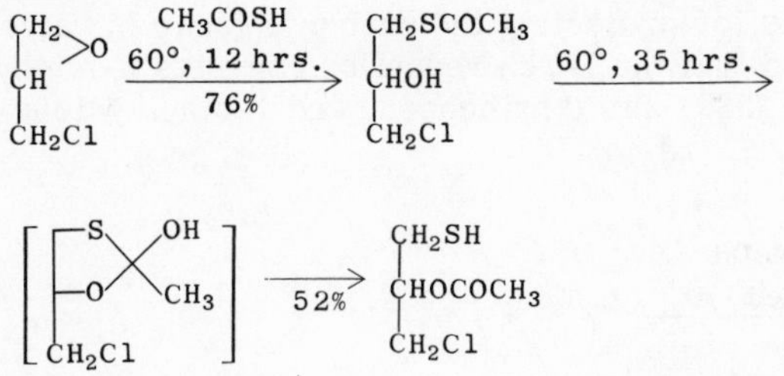

337

Sjoberg,[440] on the other hand, prepared 5-chloromethyl-2,2-dimethyl-1,3-oxathiolane, which he distilled twice at 74-75° and 15 mm pressure. Consequently, if 337 is an intermediate, its instability must be due to the tertiary hydroxyl group.

Parham, Heberling, and Wynberg[357] postulated that 2-chloromethyl-1,3-oxathiolane (338) is an intermediate in the reaction of chloroacetal and 2-mercaptoethanol to give dihydro-p-oxathiin (see Chapter 11, section III A-6).

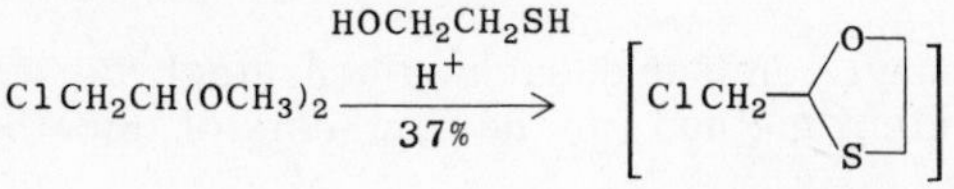

338

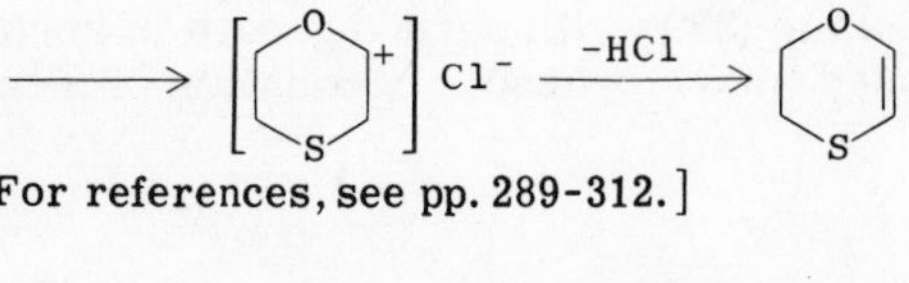

Although this is a likely mechanism, other equally reasonable mechanisms could be postulated which do not require the oxathiolane to be an intermediate, as in the following.

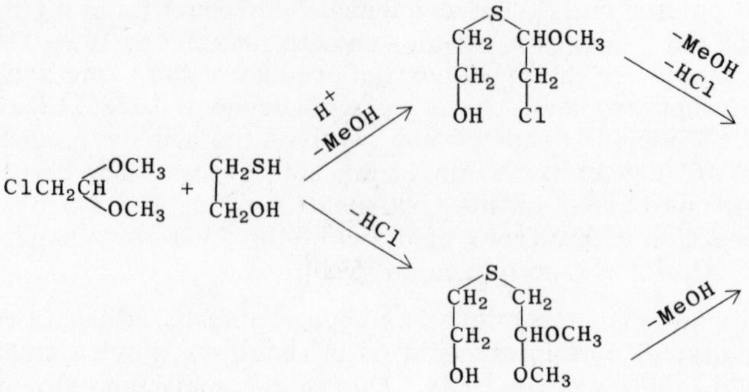

According to Marshall and Stevenson,[309a] 2-trichloromethyl-1,3-oxathiolane decomposes on distillation at 1 mm pressure and slowly deliquesces on exposure to the atmosphere.

Pinder and Smith,[362] who studied the formation of dioxolanes and oxathiolanes as a means for protecting the carbonyl group in various acetophenones, observed that the Birch reduction converts 2-methyl-2-phenyl-1,3-oxathiolane (**339**) into ethylbenzene and 1-ethylcyclohexa-1,4-diene (**340**).

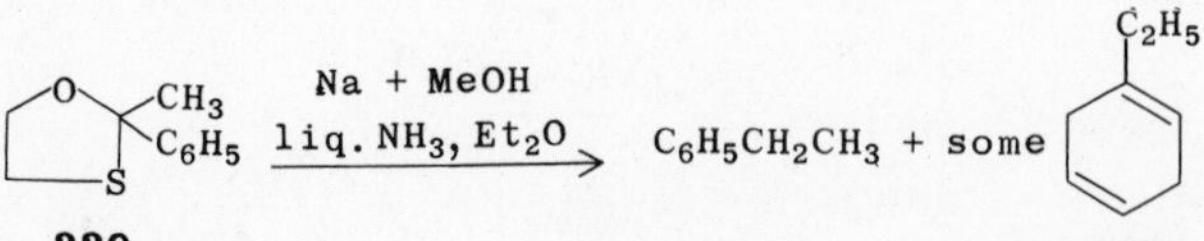

339   **340**

Eliel and Badding,[113a] on treating 2-phenyl-1,3-oxathiolane (**341**) with lithium aluminum hydride and aluminum chloride, obtained the thioether (**342**).

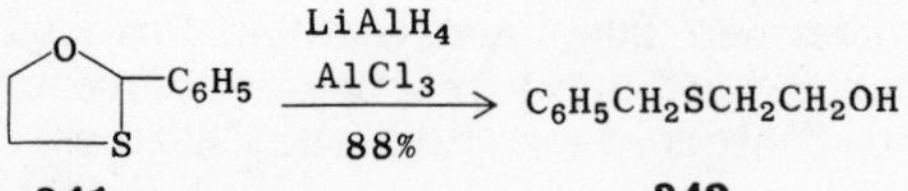

341   **342**

Thus, the reaction of a carbonyl compound, such as benzaldehyde, with a mercaptoethanol is a convenient method for the synthesis of thioethers through the 1,3-oxathiolane.

Marshall and Stevenson[309a] obtained the dioxide (**343**) on treating 2-methyl-2-phenyl-1,3-oxathiolane (**339**) with permanganate in acetone. The dioxide slowly decomposed to acetophenone. Oxidation of 2-methyl-

2-phenyl-1,3-oxathiolane with hydrogen peroxide yielded only aceto-phenone.

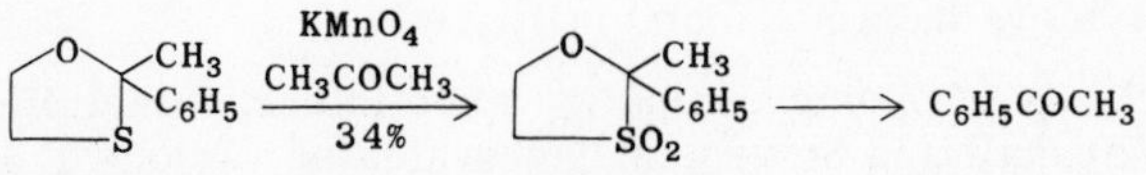

339   **343**

Djerassi and Gorman[103] investigated the scope and mechanism of the protection of carbonyls by formation of the corresponding hemithioketal and the removal of the hemithioketal group under essentially neutral conditions with Raney nickel. They postulated a 1,4-diradical (**344**) mechanism.

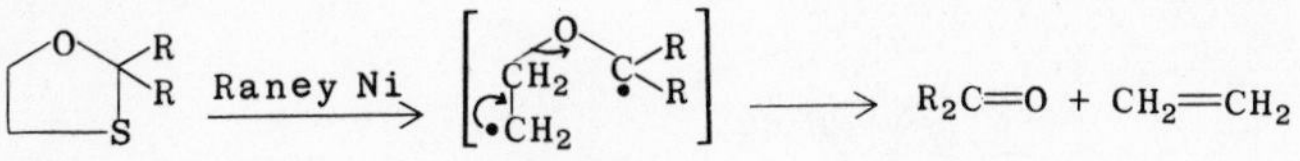

344

Dermer[96b] reported that treatment of 1,3-oxathiolane with acids gives a viscous polymer having a molecular weight of about 1500. It was postulated that the polymerization proceeds through the cleavage of the oxygen-carbon bond.

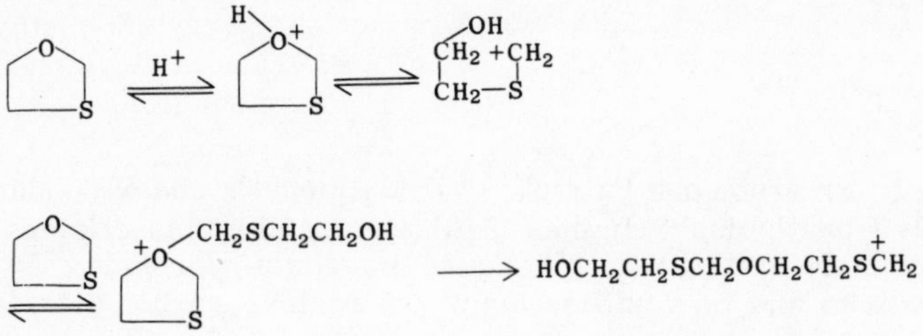

That the oxygen in preference to the sulfur is attacked by acid is indi-cated by the rapid polymerization of 1,3-dioxolane and the slow poly-merization of 1,3-dithiolane relative to that of 1,3-oxathiolane. Where-as 5-methyl-1,3-oxathiolane polymerizes, the 2-substituted oxathiolanes decompose with elimination of an aldehyde or ketone and formation of polyethylene sulfide. The behavior of 2-substituted oxathiolanes with acid may be attributed to the inductive effect of substituents.

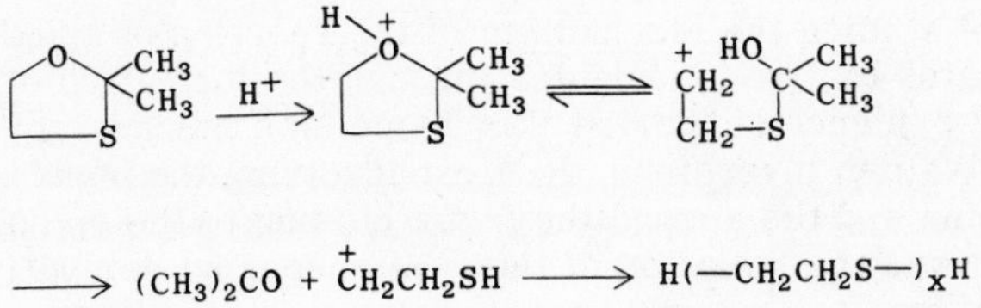

[For references, see pp. 289-312.]   237

Copolymers of 1, 3-oxathiolane with 1, 3-dioxolane, ethylene oxide, ethylene sulfide, and formaldehyde have been prepared by similarly heating the mixture with sulfuric acid at 70° for several days. The polymers and copolymers have not found utility.[96b]

Because of the activity of phenoxathiins as insecticides, anthelmintics, and bactericides, Marshall and Stevenson[309a] evaluated various 1, 3-oxathiolanes. They were found to be inactive.

(2) 1, 3-Oxathiolan-2-imines

1, 3-Oxathiolan-2-imine hydrochloride (**345**) is a solid which decomposes on melting. On treating with alkali, Sergeev and Kolychev[431] obtained ethylene sulfide polymers.

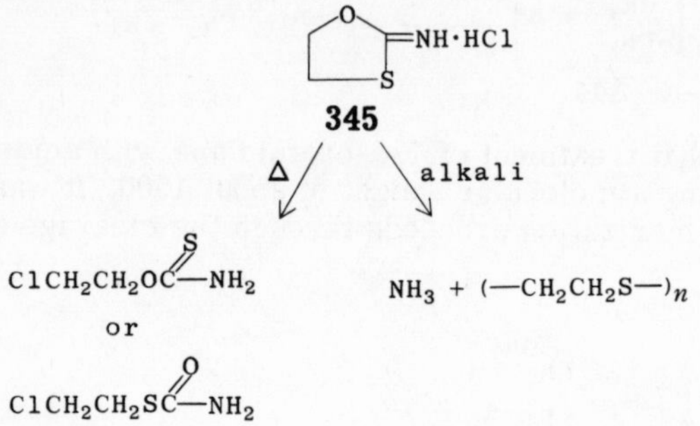

345

Δ / \ alkali

$ClCH_2CH_2OC\overset{S}{\Vert}{-}NH_2$

or

$ClCH_2CH_2SC\overset{O}{\Vert}{-}NH_2$

$NH_3 + (-CH_2CH_2S-)_n$

According to Emerson and Patrick[115] 5-(2-thienyl)- and 5-(5-chloro-2-thienyl)-1, 3-oxathiolan-2-imines (**346**) are useful as insecticides and fungicides. On boiling with 25% aqueous sodium hydroxide,[114] ammonia evolves, and, on acidification of the residue, carbon dioxide evolves.

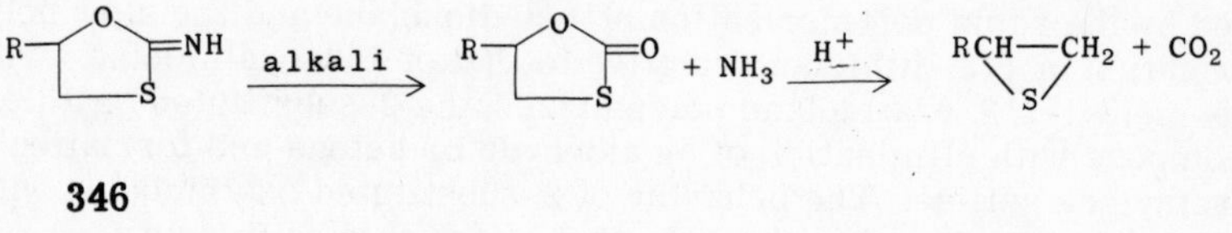

346

Price and Kirk[363] studied the mechanism of the reaction of epoxides with alkali thiocyanates to give episulfides through the formation of oxathiolanes. Their evidence supported Van Tamelen's mechanism,[473] which involves two Walden inversions, the first involving the *trans* opening of the epoxide ring and the second the *trans* closing to the episulfide ring. This evidence was the isolation of the *p*-nitrobenzoyl derivative of the oxathiolane-2-imine.

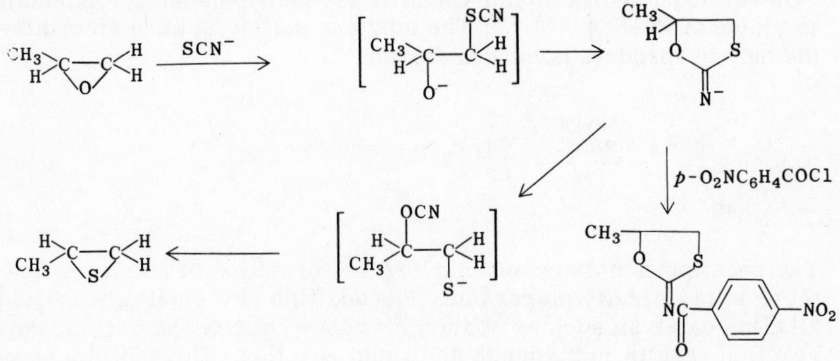

Wagner-Juaregg and Häring,[492] in their studies of the reaction of epoxides with HSCN, reported the following reactions of the several 1,3-oxathiolan-3-imines they prepared.

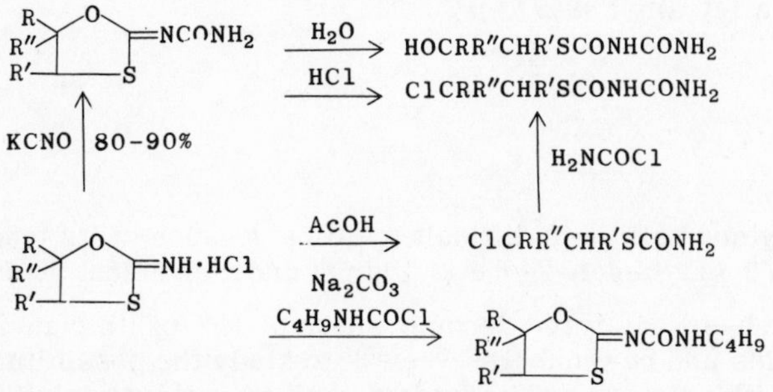

The 2,2-diamino-1,3-oxathiolane (347) which Durden, Stansbury, and Catlette[113] considered to result from the reaction of ethyl 2,3-epoxy-3-methylvalerate and thiourea could not be isolated because of its ready decomposition to the episulfide and urea.

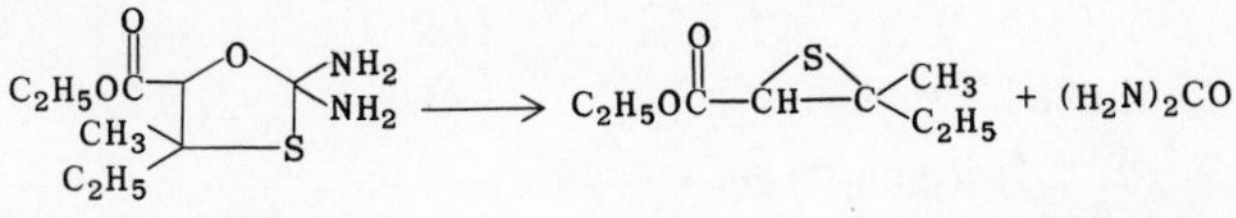

347

(3) 1,3-Oxathiolan-2-one

1,3-Oxathiolan-2-one (348) is a high boiling, stable liquid. On treatment with 2N sodium hydroxide, it forms a polymer; with a trace of sulfuric acid in benzene solution it is converted to p-dithiane; with hydrogen peroxide in acetic acid solution it reacts to give carbon dioxide and sulfuric acid.[23]

On heating **1, 3**-oxathiolan-2-one at 200°, ethylene sulfide is obtained in yields of 80-88%.[395,396] The ethylene sulfide is pure as obtained and the only by-product is carbon dioxide.

$$\text{348} \quad \xrightarrow[83\%]{\substack{Na_2CO_3 \\ 200°}} \quad \begin{matrix} CH_2 \\ | \\ CH_2 \end{matrix} \hspace{-2pt} > \hspace{-2pt} S \; + \; CO_2$$

348

The reaction is not accompanied by the formation of polymers and there is practically no residue. The addition of a small amount of an alkaline catalyst, such as sodium carbonate, during the decomposition reaction results in a smooth and rapid reaction. The addition of an acid catalyst, such as p-toluenesulfonic acid, inhibits the decomposition.

However, if the sodium carbonate is added in larger quantity (1% is optimum), the decomposition is too rapid and polymerization occurs. The polymer formed in the normal preparation from mercaptoethanol and phosgene is a tetramer (**349**).

$$(-CH_2CH_2S\overset{O}{\overset{\|}{C}}-O-)_4$$

349

Inasmuch as ethylene sulfide is difficult to store because of its tendency to polymerize, 1, 3-oxathiolan-2-one is a quick and convenient source.

The ease of the base-catalyzed decomposition of 1, 3-oxathiolan-2-one prompted Reynolds and co-workers[396a,396b] to study the possibilities of the reaction with primary and secondary amines without isolation of the ethylene sulfide. This was realized for moderately to strongly basic organic amines. The procedure consists of refluxing overnight 1, 3-oxathiolan-2-one with a two-fold excess of amine in a nonpolar solvent such as benzene or toluene; the yields are comparable to those reported for the direct reaction of the amines with ethylene sulfide.

$$\text{348} \quad \xrightarrow[33-83\%]{\substack{R_2NH, \; PhMe \\ \Delta}} \quad R_2NCH_2CH_2SH \; + \; CO_2$$

348

Amines used in this reaction include $(C_2H_5)_2NH$, $(n\text{-}C_4H_9)_2NH$, $n\text{-}C_4H_9NH_2$, $C_6H_5CH_2NH_2$, piperidine, N-methylpiperazine, morpholine, and cyclohexylamine. In the reaction with several primary amines, such as n-butyl-, allyl-, and cyclohexylamine, by reaction of two moles **348** per mole amine, the product was the 2-mercaptoethyl carbamate from n-butyl- and allylamines and the ethylmercaptoethanethiol from cyclohexylamine.

$$\text{348} \quad \xrightarrow{\text{C}_4\text{H}_9\text{NH}_2} \text{C}_4\text{H}_9\text{NHCO}_2\text{CH}_2\text{CH}_2\text{SH}$$

$$\xrightarrow{\text{C}_6\text{H}_{11}\text{NH}_2} \quad \text{—NHCH}_2\text{CH}_2\text{SCH}_2\text{CH}_2\text{SH}$$

In the presence of an ionizing solvent, such as dioxane or water, the products were low-molecular-weight polyethylene sulfides of the general formulas, $R_2N(CH_2CH_2S)_nH$ and $R_2NCO_2(CH_2CH_2S)_nH$.

(4) 1, 3-Oxathiolan-5-one

1, 3-Oxathiolan-5-ones are colorless solids, in general, the alkyl derivatives being lower melting than the functional derivatives. They are insoluble in water and soluble in the usual organic solvents, such as benzene, chloroform, acetone, and warm methanol and acetic acid. They are rather easily hydrolyzed,[245,280] particularly by alkaline media.

Bistrzycki with Brenken[44] and with Traub,[45] who prepared a variety of 1, 3-oxathiolan-5-ones, reported the following reactions (illustrated with 4, 4-diphenyl-1, 3-oxathiolan-5-one (**350**).

$$\text{350} \quad \xrightarrow[\text{10 hrs. in tube}]{\text{25\% NH}_4\text{OH, 100°}} \quad (\text{C}_6\text{H}_5)_2\text{CHCONH}_2$$

$$\xrightarrow[\Delta]{\text{5\% NaOH}} \quad (\text{C}_6\text{H}_5)_2\text{CCOOH} \quad \overset{|}{\text{SH}}$$

$$\xrightarrow[\Delta]{\text{Zn + AcOH}} \quad (\text{C}_6\text{H}_5)_2\text{CHCOOH}$$

$$\xrightarrow[\Delta]{\text{CrO}_3/\text{AcOH}} \quad \text{351}$$

The 4, 4-diphenyl-1, 3-oxathiolan-5-ones are colorless prisms, flakes or tablets, and are crystallized from dilute alcohol or dilute acetic acid. The color reaction with concentrated sulfuric acid is general, and usually involves several color changes. It is to be noted that the reaction with ammonia involves a reduction. The sulfone obtained by chromate oxidation also gives the concentrated sulfuric acid color reaction. On hydrolyzing with alkaline solutions, the products are the original ketone or aldehyde and thiobenzilic acid.

According to Bistrzycki and Traub,[45] 2-aryl-4, 4-phenyl-1, 3-oxathiolan-5-ones, such as **352**, yield 9, 10-epithioanthracenes (**353**) on treatment with concentrated sulfuric acid. Bistrzycki and Brenken,[44] who also observed this reaction, suggested that acid hydrolysis occurred, followed by loss of carbon monoxide and then dehydration to give the epithioanthracene.

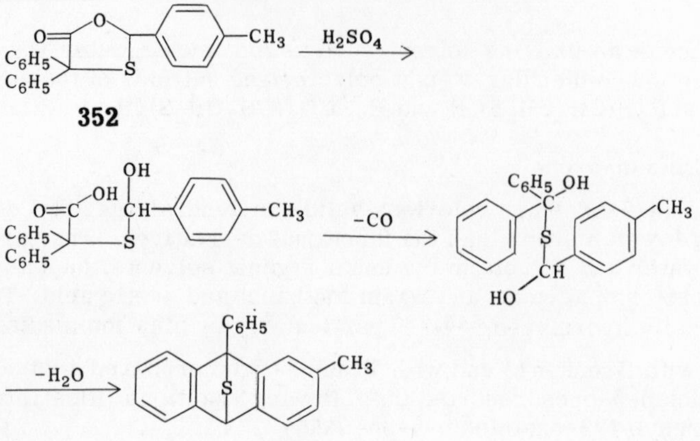

352

353

These compounds are strongly triboluminescent, i.e., luminescent when subjected to friction.

Larsson[280,281] studied the alkaline hydrolysis of several substituted 5-oxo-1, 3-oxathiolane-2-carboxylic acids (**354**). In the first stage of hydrolysis, they give hydroxyacids, which, in the second stage, decompose to keto and mercapto acids.

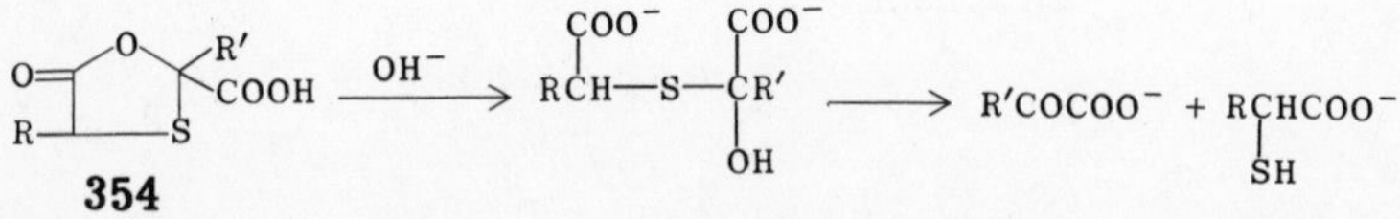

354

The first stage of the hydrolysis is the rate-determining step. The reaction rate constants (k) of the alkaline hydrolysis at 20.0° for various oxathiolanes are given in Table 18.

The reaction of 2-phenyl-1, 3-oxathiolan-5-one (**355**) with mercapto-acetic acid reported by Holmberg[23] illustrates the ease with which it reverts to the reactants from which it had been prepared.

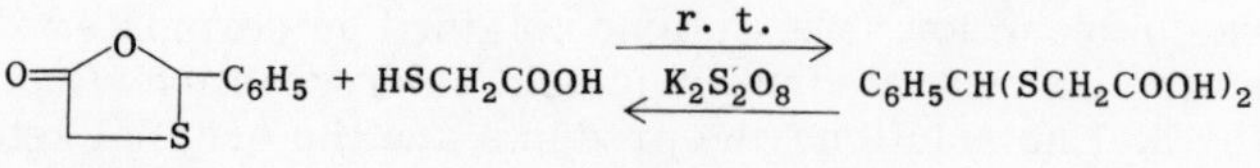

355

Simmons[437a] described 2, 2-bis (chlorodifluoromethyl)-1, 3-oxathiolan-5-one as a clear, colorless liquid having a high chemical stability. It is

TABLE 18.   Alkaline Hydrolysis of Oxathiolan-5-ones at 20. 0°

Oxathiolan-5-one-2-carboxylic acid	k
Unsubstd.	large
2-CH$_3$	92
	90
	118
2, 4-(CH$_3$)$_2$	41
	38
	48
	50
2, 4-(C$_2$H$_5$)$_2$	19
	18
	22

particularly stable towards hydrolysis and thermal and oxidative degradation. It is therefore suggested as potentially useful as a transformer fluid. It is also suggested as being useful as a systemic fungicide for the control of bean rust.

(5) 1, 3-Oxathiolane-2, 5-dione

1, 3-Oxathiolane-2, 5-dione (**356**) is quite water sensitive and must be stored in a dry atmosphere. It hydrolyzes readily with evolution of carbon dioxide. On treatment with aniline in dioxane at 10°, carbon dioxide is evolved in an exothermic reaction.[21,22]

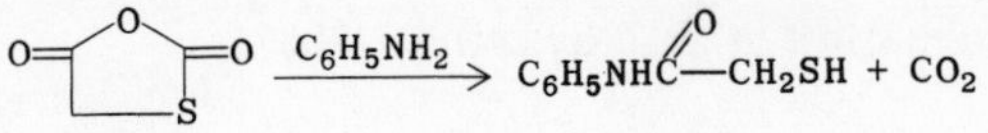

356

1, 3-Oxathiolane-2, 5-dione loses carbon dioxide quantitatively in the presence of polymerization initiators, such as pyridine, to give a white, powdery polymer (**357**) melting at 130-140° or 147-157°C. Block polymerization is carried out near the melting point of 1, 3-oxathiolane-2, 5-dione. [423a]

[For references, see pp. 289-312.]   243

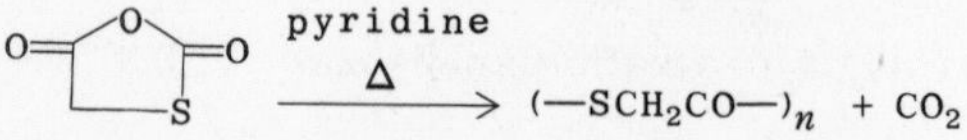

$$(-SCH_2CO-)_n + CO_2$$

357

(6) Spiro 1,3-oxathiolanes (from cyclohexanones)

As Djerassi and Gorman[103] pointed out, the ease of removing the hemithioketal group under essentially neutral conditions with Raney nickel is a potentially useful tool in organic synthesis for protecting a carbonyl group. It was postulated that the desulfurization proceeded through a 1,4-diradical mechanism (**358**).[103,106,402,403a]

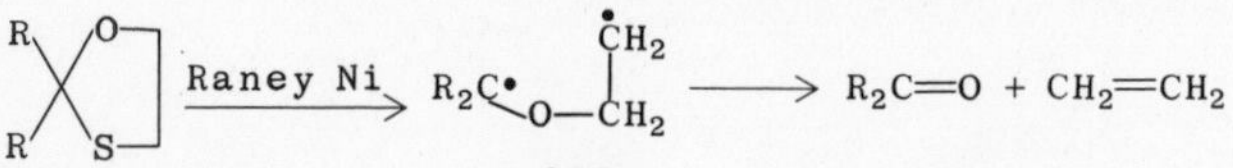

$$R_2C=O + CH_2=CH_2$$

358

This reaction has found extensive use in the steroid series.

The normal course of Raney nickel desulfurization of hemithioketals (**359**), in acetone, as postulated by Djerassi, Gorman, and Henry,[106] involves the formation of predominantly or exclusively the original ketone and an alcohol derived from the mercaptoethanol moiety.

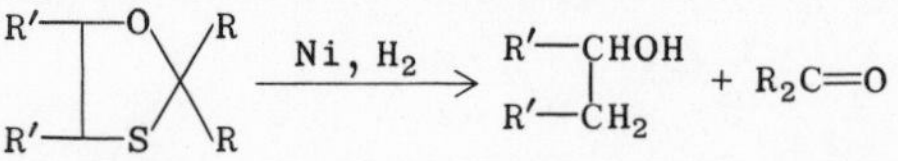

$$+ R_2C=O$$

359

Jaeger and Smith[238] reported that while Raney nickel desulfurization in acetone may occur to regenerate the ketone (**361**),

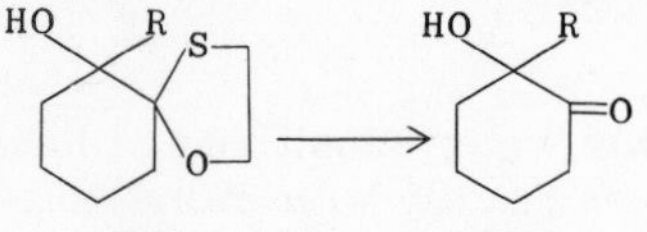

360   **361**

(R = H or C_2H_5)

it may occur also with formation of an ethyl ether (**363**).

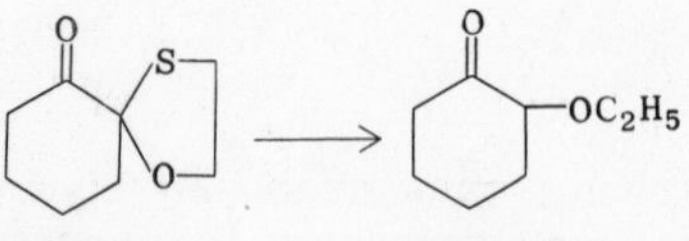

362   **363**

Desulfurization of the dihemithioketal **364** from cyclohexanedione led predominantly to the cyclohexadiol.

244

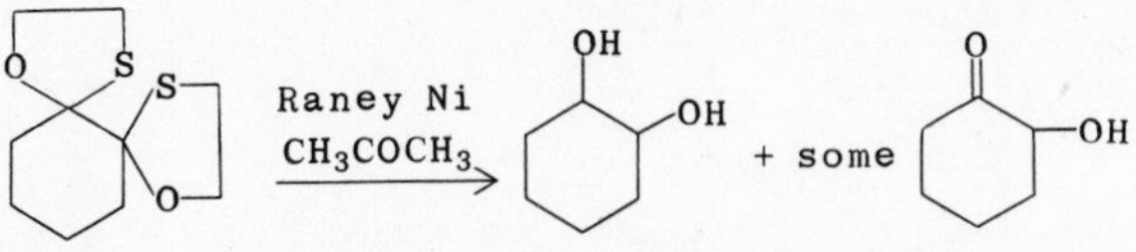

364

There is also a third path by which desulfurization can occur. Employing an atmosphere of nitrogen in the absence of water and oxygen-containing solvents, ketones and hydrocarbons were obtained,[106] the hydrocarbons probably arising from the β-mercaptoethanol part of the molecule. The production of hydrocarbons was also observed on heating the oxathiolane (**365**) in acetone.

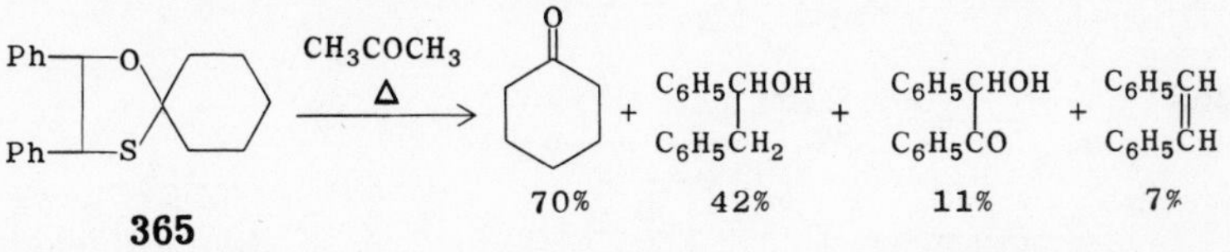

365

To explain some of the products they obtained on Raney Ni desulfurization in ethanol, acetone, or benzene, Romo de Vivar and Romo[403a] postulated that the 1, 4-biradical (**366**) proceeds by formation of a 1, 2-biradical to diphenylketene (**367**). The solvent did not appear to have an important effect on the reaction mechanism.

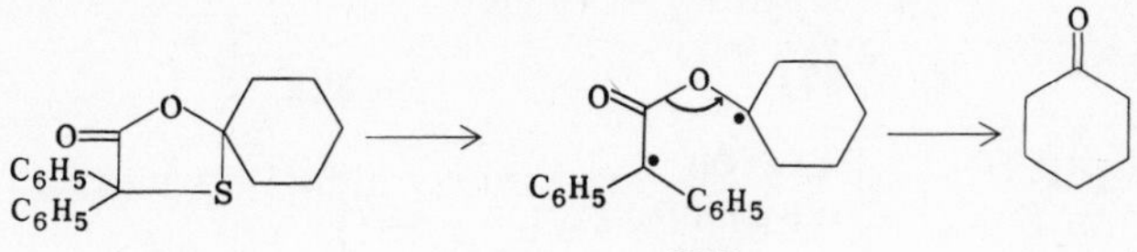

366

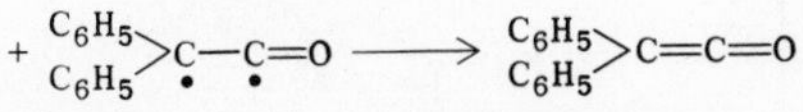

367

Table 19 lists the products from the desulfurization of 4, 4-diphenyl-1, 3-oxathiolan-5-ones.

Cope and Farkas[79] catalytically hydrogenolized the hemithioketal (**368**) of cyclohexanone with molybdenum sulfide at 240-260° to obtain cyclohexane and cyclohexanethiol (also obtained when ruthenium was used).

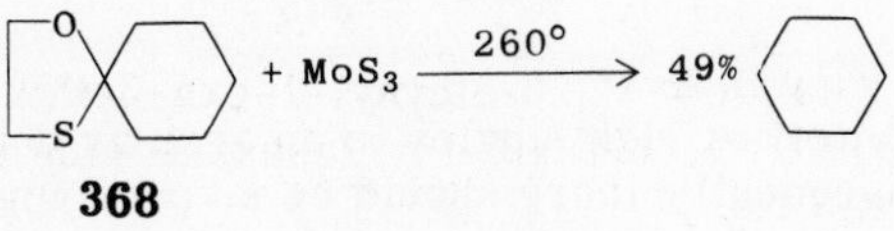

368

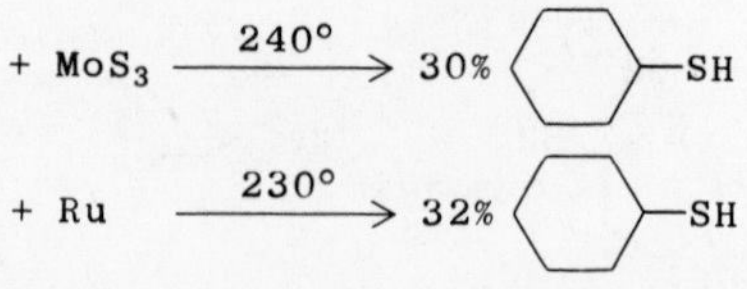

$$+ \; MoS_3 \xrightarrow{240°} 30\% \; \text{⬡—SH}$$

$$+ \; Ru \xrightarrow{230°} 32\% \; \text{⬡—SH}$$

Bergmann, Lavie, and Pinchas[39] found that lithium aluminum hydride does not cleave the hemithioketal of cyclohexanone. Jaeger and Smith[237,238] consequently considered cyclohexane-1,2-dione as a potential intermediate for the synthesis of steroids through the protection of the carbonyl group against anionoid reagents.

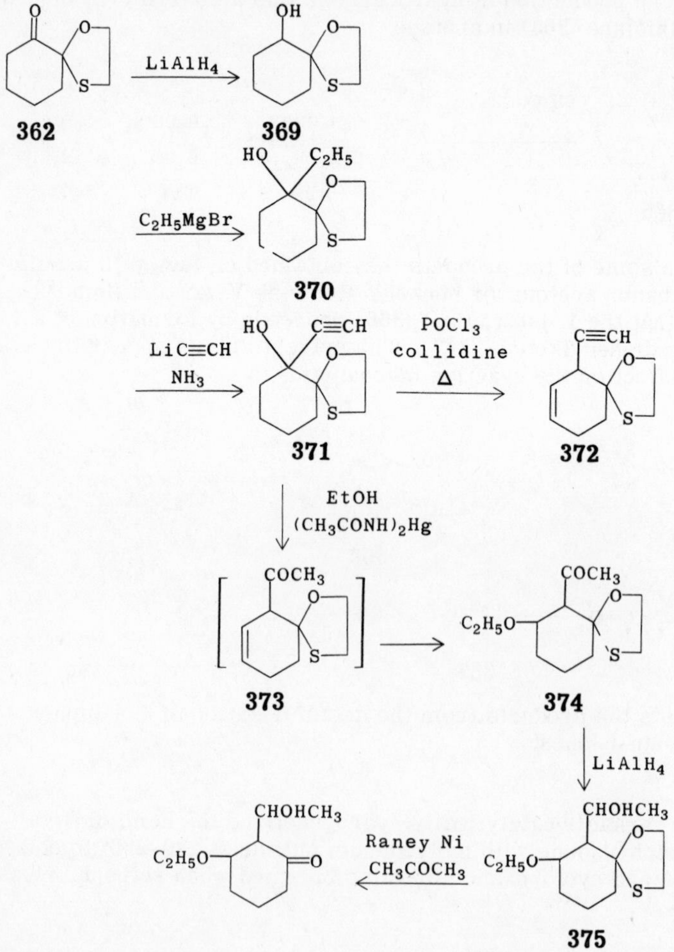

The plane of the oxathiolane ring in $\Delta^{7,8}$-6-ethynyl-1-oxa-3-thiaspiro-[4.5]decane (**372**) is approximately at right angles to an annular double bond in the α,β-position. Consequently, there should be no pronounced

TABLE 19. Desulfurization of 4, 4-Diphenyl-1, 3-oxathiolan-5-ones

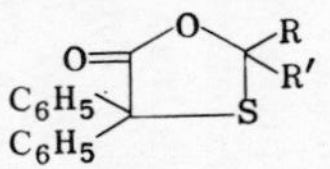

Oxathiolane	Solvent	Time (hrs.)	Products (% yield)
R = H, R' = C$_6$H$_5$-	C$_2$H$_5$OH	5	(C$_6$H$_5$)$_2$CHCOOH (2%)
	(CH$_3$)$_2$CO	4	(C$_6$H$_5$)$_2$CHCO$_2$C$_2$H$_5$ (61%)
	C$_6$H$_6$	5	(C$_6$H$_5$)$_2$CHCOOH (7%)
			C$_6$H$_5$CHO (2.1%)
R, R' 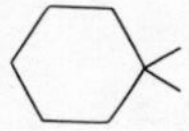 =	C$_2$H$_5$OH	4	(C$_6$H$_5$)$_2$CHCO$_2$C$_2$H$_5$ (35%)
			(C$_6$H$_5$)$_2$CHCH$_2$OH (4.9%)
	(CH$_3$)$_2$CO	4	(C$_6$H$_5$)$_2$CHCOOH (13.7%)
			cyclohexanone (98%)
	C$_6$H$_6$	5	(C$_6$H$_5$)$_2$CHCOOH (0.5%)
			(C$_6$H$_5$)$_2$CHCH$_2$OH (14%)
			cyclohexanone (42.5%)
	C$_6$H$_6$/C$_6$H$_5$NH$_2$	5	(C$_6$H$_5$)$_2$CHCONHC$_6$H$_5$ (43.3%)
			cyclohexanone (21.2%)
R, R' 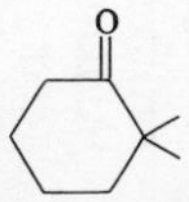 =	C$_2$H$_5$OH	5	cyclohexanediol diphenyl acetate (< 1%)

electronic interaction between the two functions. Jaeger and Smith[237] rationalized the dehydration in terms of steric strains. Assuming a planar oxathiolane ring and an unstrained tetrahedral angle (109. 5°) for the carbons, and ignoring the requirements of bond distances, they calculated the O-C-S angle to be 103. 5°, which is a relatively large deformation compared to dithiolane (S-C-S calculated to be 108°). The strain in the oxathiolane moiety can be reduced with consequent stabilization by migration of the double bond in **372** from α, β- to β, γ- (with respect to the oxathiolane), although the presence of the ethynyl group tends to hold the double bond in conjugation. This could explain why the double bond shifts in the oxathiolane series and not in the dithiolane, as observed also for the oxathiolanes of the Δ^4-3-oxosteroids in which the double bond shifts to the 5, 6-position and for the dithiolanes in which the double bond remains in the 4, 5-position.

Eliel and Badding[113a] reported that the hemithioketal of cyclohexanone, on treatment with lithium aluminum hydride and aluminum chloride, is converted to the thioether in good yields.

(7) Spiro 1, 3-oxathiolanes (from steroids)

The chemical properties and reactions discussed for spiro 1, 3-oxathiolanes of cyclohexanones also holds true for those of the steroids. Most important, of course, is the protection the 1, 3-oxathiolane affords to the ketone group of the steroid while other groups of the molecule are altered. The protected ketone is regenerated by acid hydrolysis or treatment with Raney nickel[103, 106, 402, 449] of the 1, 3-oxathiolane moiety. The 1, 3-oxathiolane grouping is not affected by dilute bases and is resistant toward reduction with lithium aluminum hydride,[402, 403] the two reagents commonly used to alter groups in the steroid molecule.

Thus, estrone acetate 17-ethylenehemithioketal is hydrolyzed by refluxing with potassium bicarbonate solution in ethanol in 83% yield to estrone 17-ethylenehemithioketal, which is converted by acid hydrolysis (ethanolic hydrochloric acid) to estrone in 67% yield.[402] Oppenauer oxidation of androst-5-en-3β-ol-17-one-17-ethylenehemithioketal (treatment with aluminum t-butoxide in cyclohexanone and toluene with reflux) gives a 70% yield of androst-4-ene-3, 17-dione-17-ethylenehemithioketal.[402] The treatment with Raney nickel does not always lead to good yields of the parent ketone: androst-4-ene-3, 17-dione-3, 17-bis (ethylenehemithioketal) is converted to androst-4-ene-3, 17-dione in only 22% yield by this treatment whereas acid hydrolysis gives a 60% yield.[402] Hydrolysis also has been carried out in the presence of a mixture of cadmium carbonate-mercuric chloride.[402]

Djerassi, Batres, Romo, and Rosenkraz[102] converted allopregnan-3β-ol-11, 20-dione acetate (**376**) to the 20-hemithioketal (**377**), reduced this with lithium aluminum hydride to the hemithioketal (**378**) of allo-

pregnane-3β, 11β-diol-20-one, which on treatment with Raney nickel in
ethanol gave allopregnane-3β, 11β-diol-20-one (379), which they considered as a potential starting material for the synthesis of 17α-hy-
droxycorticosterone (Kendall's compound F).

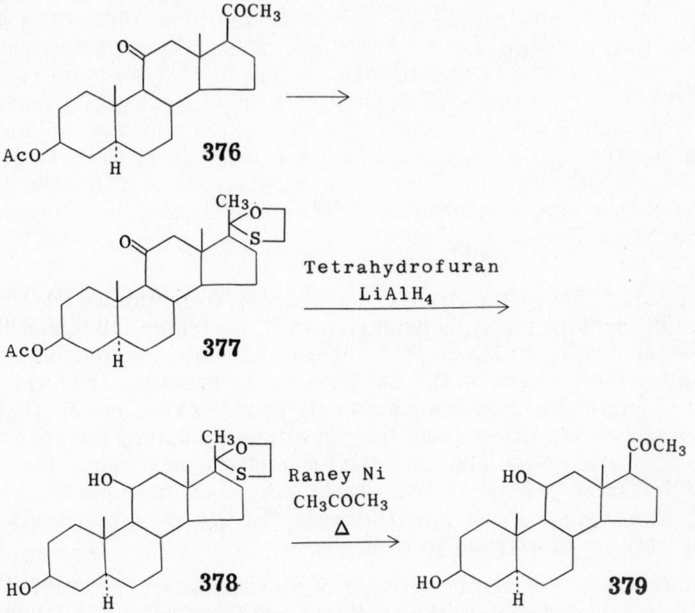

Another series of reactions in which the steroid oxo group was protected by the 1, 3-oxathiolane moiety is that reported by Mazur[315,316]
for dehydrocholic acid (380).

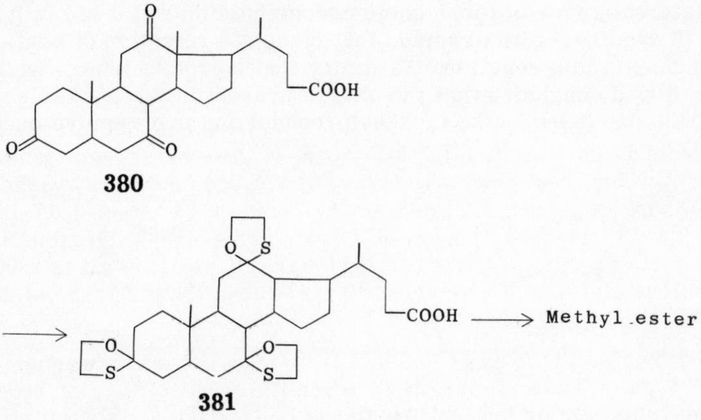

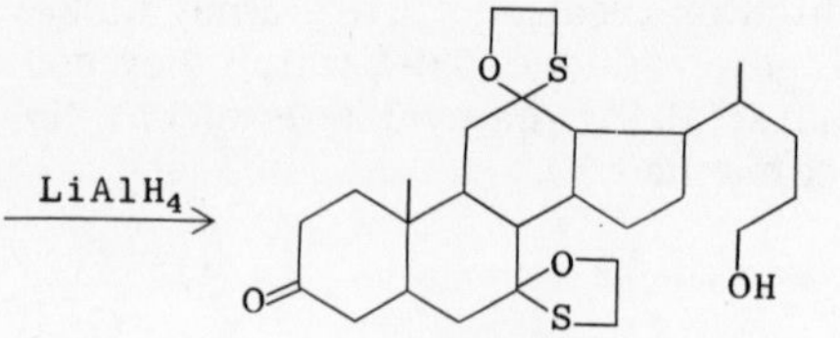

382

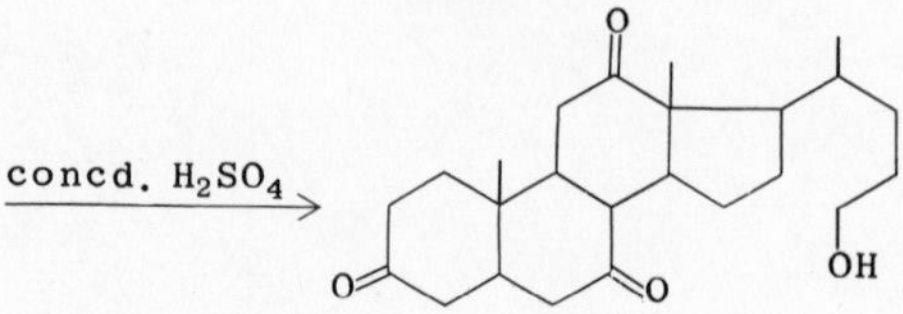

383

The final product, hexadecahydro-17-(5-hydroxy-α-methylbutyl)-10, 13-dimethyl-15H-cyclopenta[a]phenanthrene-3, 7, 12-trione (**383**), and its derivatives, according to Mazur,[316] possess valuable pharmacological properties for their effect on the cardiovascular system. They are said to be of particular importance as anti-hypertensive agents; they show a myotropic activity without testoid stimulation; they possess a desirable chloretic action and have the property of increasing the volume of bile from the liver. Estrone 17-ethylenehemithioketal, according to Romo, Rosenkranz, and Djerassi, [402] has about one-tenth the estrogenic activity of estrone in rats.

The desulfurization of hemithioketals of steroids has been studied by Djerassi, Gorman, and Henry, [106] Djerassi and Grossman, [107] Djerassi, Shamma, and Kan, [108] and Romo de Vivar and Romo. [403] Desulfurization of spiro(5-diphenylmethyl-1, 3-oxathiolane)-2, 3'-cholestane (**384**), prepared from optically active mercapto-alcohol, in ethyl methyl ketone by refluxing with Raney nickel for 24 hours led to 52% yield of 1, 1-diphenylpropan-2-ol and over 80% 3-cholestanone (**385**) and 3-cholestanol. The diphenylpropanol was optically active and the desulfurization of the diastereoisomer of the 3-cholestanone hemithioketal led to its antipode. It was therefore assumed that complete retention of configuration occurs in this reaction. Assuming that complete inversion does not occur, it was concluded that the oxygen present in the oxathiolane moiety is the one found in the diphenylpropanol and that rupture occurs at the C-O bond.

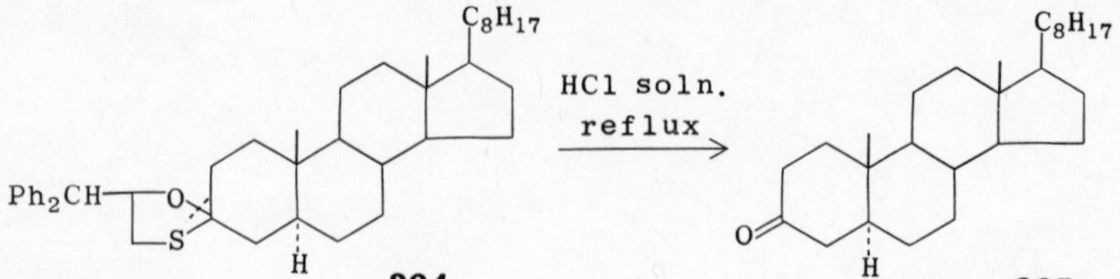

+ Ph$_2$CHCHOHCH$_2$SH or [Ph$_2$CHCHOHCH$_2$S—]$_2$

Desulfurization of these spiro-1, 3-oxathiolanes of steroids in hydrolytic solvents, such as alcohols and ketones, thus yields chiefly the parent steroid and the alcohol of the original β-mercaptoethanol. In a nonpolar solvent, such as benzene, however, the main products of desulfurization are the parent steroid and the hydrocarbon derived from the original β-mercaptoethanol.[108]

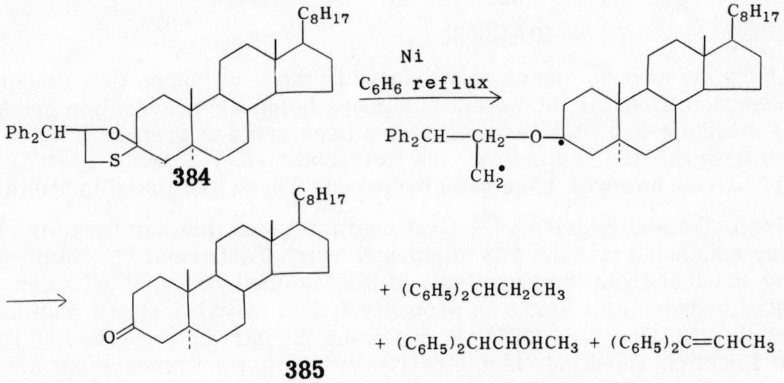

$$\text{Ph}_2\text{CH} - \text{O} \quad \mathbf{384} \xrightarrow[\text{C}_6\text{H}_6 \text{ reflux}]{\text{Ni}} \quad \text{Ph}_2\text{CH} - \text{CH}_2 - \text{O}$$

$$\longrightarrow \quad \mathbf{385}$$

$$+ (\text{C}_6\text{H}_5)_2\text{CHCH}_2\text{CH}_3$$

$$+ (\text{C}_6\text{H}_5)_2\text{CHCHOHCH}_3 + (\text{C}_6\text{H}_5)_2\text{C}=\text{CHCH}_3$$

Fieser,[127] in his studies on the preparation of spiro-oxathiolanes of three steroid ketones, compared the molecular rotations of their spiro-dioxolanes, -oxothiolanes, and -dithiolanes (increments are given in parentheses in Table 20).

TABLE 20.   Molecular Rotations of Steroid Ketones and Spiro-Derivatives

Steroid	$\rangle$C=O	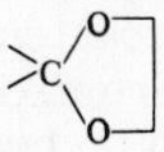 $\rangle$C(O-O)	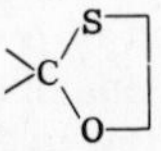 $\rangle$C(S-O)	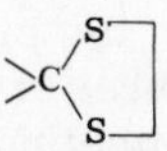 $\rangle$C(S-S)
Dehydroepiandro-sterone acetate	−23	−313(−290)	−389(−366)	−351(−328)
Cholestanone	158		111(−47)	148(−10)
Cholest-5-en-3-one	−18	−135	−87(−69)	

Steroids with a double bond between C-5 and C-6 give a color reaction when treated with ferric chloride in glacial acetic acid-sulfuric acid solution. Zak, Moss, Boyle, and Zlatkis[516] observed a similar color reaction for the spiro-oxathiolanes. Thus, spiro [3H-cyclopenta [a] phenanthrene-3, 2'-(1, 3-oxathiolane)] gave a blue-violet color.

[For references, see pp. 289-312.]

B. $C_3OS\text{-}C_3OS$ 7-OXA-2, 5-DITHIABICYCLO [2. 2. 1] HEPTANE (386)

or

386

(RRI 952)

These compounds are closely related to the p-dithianes (see Chapter 12, section III A-1j), the parent compound being the dehydration product of p-dithiane-2, 5-diol. Attempts have been made to prepare it by dehydrating the diol, but only resins were obtained.[232c] Quite a few alkyl derivatives, however, have been prepared. These are listed in Table 21.

Hromatka and Engel[231,232] first characterized this heterocyclic class. They concluded that the oily compound which Tscherniac[463] obtained as a by-product from the hydrolysis of his "isomethylrhodin" with concentrated hydrochloric acid was probably 1, 4-dimethyl-7-oxa-2, 5-dithiabicyclo[2. 2. 1]heptane (**387**). In repeating the earlier work, Hromatka and Engel obtained the "isomethylrhodin" from thiocyanoacetone and potassium bisulfite; on treatment with 2NHCl, 1, 4-dimethyl-7-oxa-2, 5-dithia-bicyclo[2. 2. 1]heptane was obtained; on treatment with concentrated acid, however, only higher boiling fractions were obtained.

Chemical Abstracts uses the Baeyer bicyclic nomenclature. Most of the workers in the field have used the 2, 5-endoxy-p-dithiane nomenclature.

1. Preparation

This class of heterocyclic compounds was discovered through studies of the preparation of α-mercaptoketones and elucidation of the structures of the resulting products. Hromatka and Engel[231] obtained the 1, 4-dimethyl derivative in 35% yield on heating dimeric mercaptoacetone at 100° for 3 hours.

387

Schotte[425] believed that the mercaptoacetone dimer exists in two polymorphic forms, and dehydration of one of the dimeric forms gives **387**. Bacchetti, Sartori and Fiecchi[21] looked upon the cyclization of the α-mercaptoketone as involving first a dimerization and secondly a dehy-

252

dration, although in many cases the dimeric ketone cannot be isolated. The ease of formation was considered to be dependent on the reactivity of the carbonyl group and on the nature and size of the radicals in the ketone.

It is pertinent that Hromatka and Haber[232c] obtained a 61% yield of dihydroxy-p-dithiane from the reaction of chloroacetaldehyde and sodium bisulfide at 0°, but were unable to convert it to the bicyclic compound. Böhme, Freimuth, and Mudlas,[51] in studying the solvolysis of acetylmercaptoacetone with alcoholic hydrochloric acid, did not obtain the expected thioacetic acid; instead, the reaction resulted in a 78% yield of **387**.

$$CH_3COCH_3 + CH_3COSCl \longrightarrow CH_3COCH_2SCOCH_3 \xrightarrow[\text{r. t., 1 day}]{\text{EtOH, HCl}} \textbf{387}$$

On treating 2, 5-dimethyl-7-phenyl-2, 5-dithia-7-aza[2. 2. 1] heptane (**388**) with 10% hydrochloric acid, Bacchetti and Ferrati[22a] obtained a small amount of **387**.

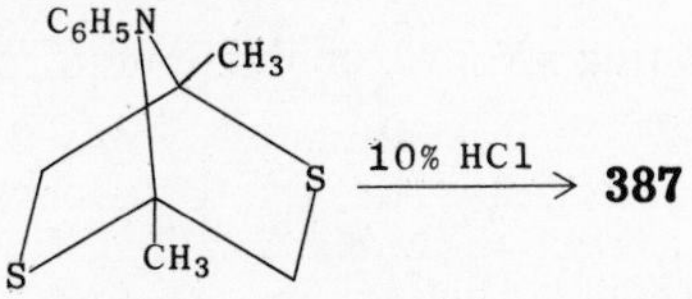

388

Thiel, Schäfer, and Asinger,[461] on treating 2, 2, 4-trimethyl-3-thiazoline with butyllithium in absolute ether, obtained a 6% yield of **387**.

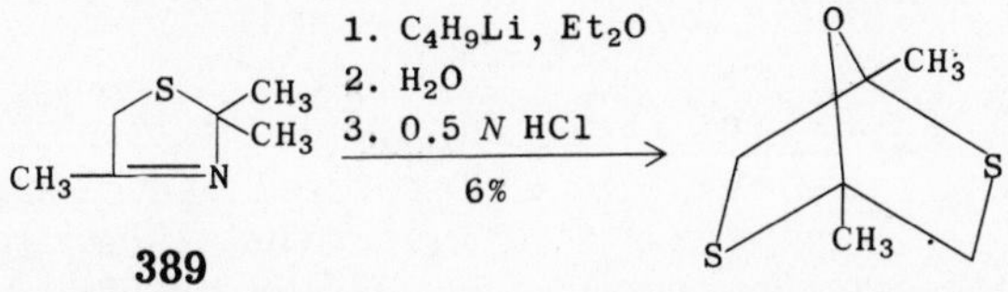

389

Whereas these heterocyclic compounds have been obtained in reasonably good yields by heating α-mercaptoketones, excellent yields are obtained on treating the α-mercaptoketone with dry HCl at room temperature[14,17,18a] or by refluxing it in 15% hydrochloric acid for one hour.[14,18] Using phosphorus pentachloride in the cold gave lower yields.[14]

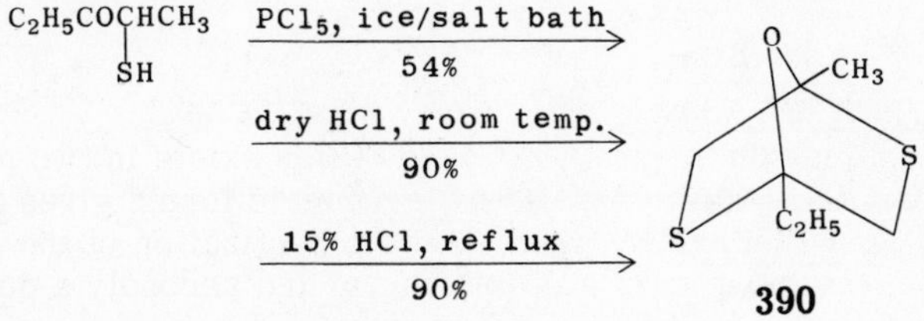

390

[For references, see pp. 289-312.]

Asinger, Thiel, and Sedlak[18a] obtained two mercaptoketones from 2-methylpentanone-3 which led to two different 7-oxa-2,5-dithia bicyloheptanes (**391** and **392**) on treatment with HCl gas followed by heating.

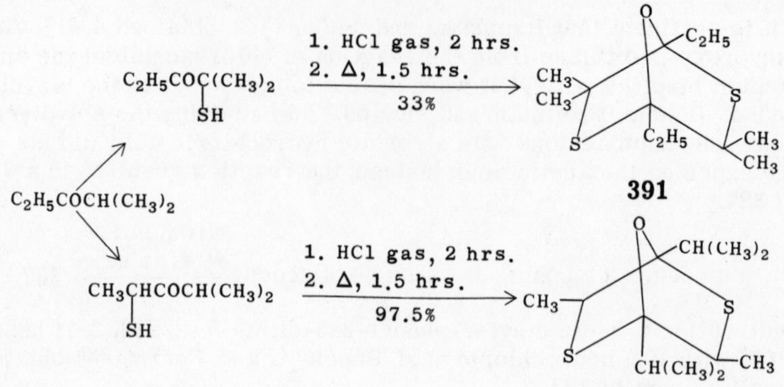

$C_2H_5COC(CH_3)_2$ — SH

1. HCl gas, 2 hrs.
2. Δ, 1.5 hrs.
33%

391

$C_2H_5COCH(CH_3)_2$

$CH_3CHCOCH(CH_3)_2$ — SH

1. HCl gas, 2 hrs.
2. Δ, 1.5 hrs.
97.5%

392

Excellent yields are also obtained on using 4N hydrochloric acid.[460]

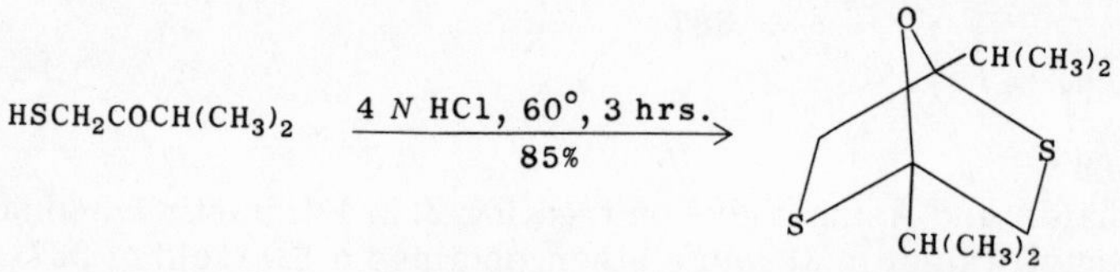

$HSCH_2COCH(CH_3)_2$

4 N HCl, 60°, 3 hrs.
85%

393

$(CH_3)_2CCOCH_3$ — SH

4 N HCl, 60°, 3 hrs.
89%

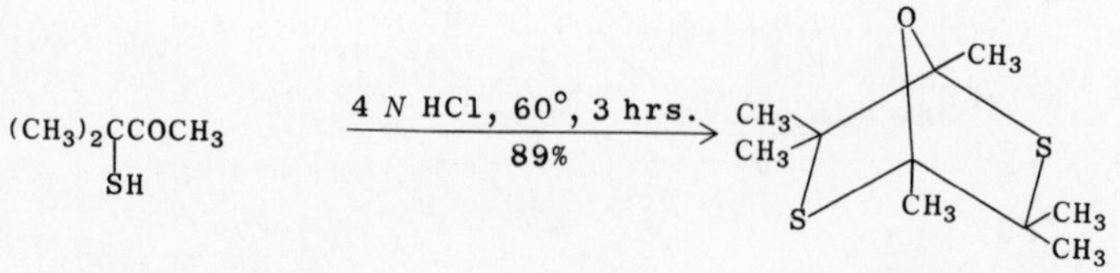

394

Rühlmann, Schräpler, and Grames,[405b] in their studies on the addition of α-mercaptoketones to allyl halides, found that 7-oxa-2,5-dithiabicyclcoheptanes resulted rather than addition when benzoyl peroxide was used as the catalyst; when potassium carbonate was used, the bicyclo compound was also obtained, but in lower yields. This dehydration in basic medium is unusual.

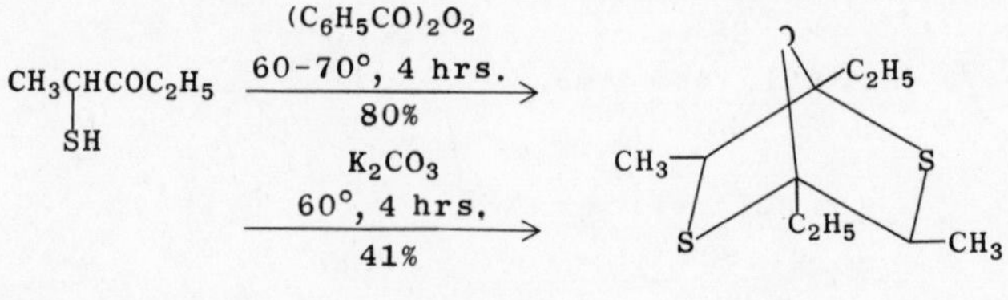

$CH_3CHCOC_2H_5$ — SH

$(C_6H_5CO)_2O_2$
60–70°, 4 hrs.
80%

K_2CO_3
60°, 4 hrs.
41%

Asinger and Thiel,[16,460] in studies on the reaction of ketones with sulfur and ammonia, obtained alkyl thiazolines, which, on treatment with 2 N hydrochloric acid gave good yields of 7-oxa-2, 5-dithiabicyclohep-tanes. Undoubtedly the Δ³-thiazoline hydrolyzes to the α-mercaptoketone, which then undergoes dimerization and dehydration in the presence of acid.

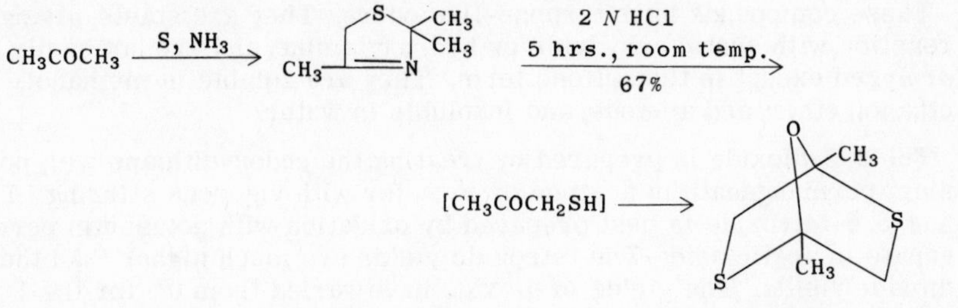

$$CH_3COCH_3 \xrightarrow{S,\ NH_3} \text{[thiazoline]} \xrightarrow[67\%]{2\ N\ HCl \atop 5\ hrs.,\ room\ temp.}$$

$$[CH_3COCH_2SH] \longrightarrow \text{(387)}$$

387

$$CH_3COC_2H_5 \xrightarrow{S,\ NH_3} \text{[thiazoline]} \xrightarrow{86\%}$$

$$\underset{SH}{[CH_3CO\overset{|}{C}HCH_3]} \longrightarrow \text{(395)}$$

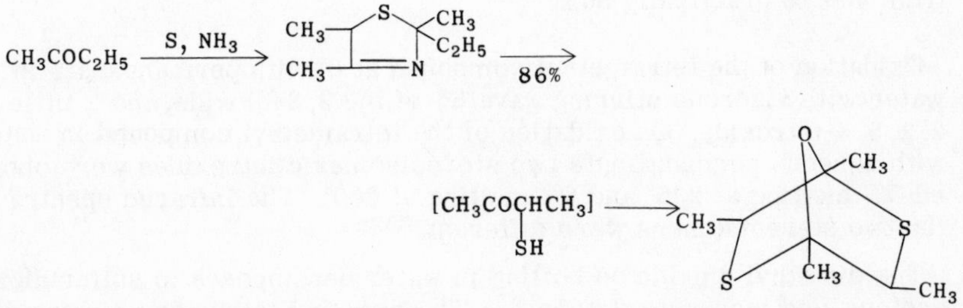

395

Treatment of 3-mercaptobutanone-2 with $2N$ hydrochloric acid at 70-75° for 5 hours gave an 83% yield of the tetramethyl compound (**395**). Asinger and Thiel[16a] obtained **395** in low yield along with 2, 4, 5-tri-methyl-2-ethyl-Δ³-thiazoline on stirring a mixture of 3-mercaptobutan-one-2, butanone, 10% acetic acid, and aqueous ammonia at room tempera-ture for 6 hours.

2. Structure

According to Hromatka and Haberl,[232a] the endoxydithiane is in the boat form. The chair form for the dithiane ring is not possible. Three isomers then may exist for a 3, 6-disubstituted endoxydithiane.

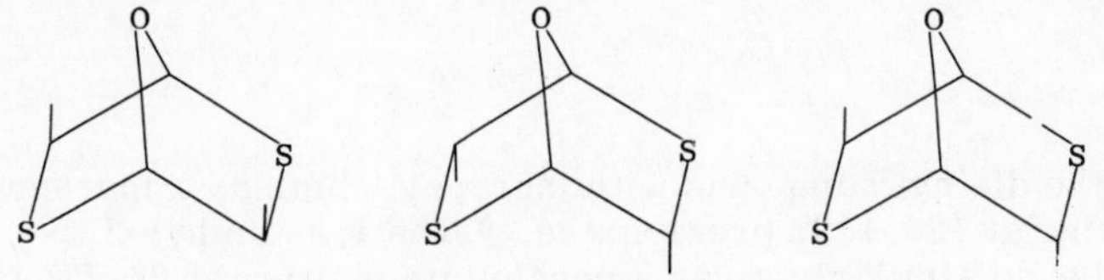

[For references, see pp. 289-312.]

The 2, 2-dioxide, however, has four possible isomers. The 2, 2, 5, 5-tetroxide, on the other hand, being symmetrical, has only three possible isomers.

3. Properties and Reactions

These compounds have terpene-like odors. They are stable, giving no reaction with acetic anhydride or hydroxylamine, and are not easily hydrolyzed except in the sulfone form. They are soluble in methanol, ethanol, ether, and acetone, and insoluble in water.

The 2, 2-dioxide is prepared by treating the endoxydithiane with potassium permanganate in acetone or in water with vigorous stirring. The 2, 2, 5, 5-tetroxide is best prepared by oxidation with potassium permanganate in acetic acid. The tetroxide yields are much higher than the dioxide yields. The yields of dioxide have varied from 0% for the 1, 4-diethyl to 53% for the 1, 2-dimethyl; the yields of tetroxide have varied from 40% to practically 90%.

Oxidation of the tetramethyl compound at 0° with permanganate in water with vigorous stirring gave 8% of the 2, 2-dioxide, and a little 2, 2, 5, 5-tetroxide. On oxidation of the tetramethyl compound in water with aqueous permanganate two stereoisomeric tetroxides were obtained: 7% melting at 236° and 6% melting at 260°. The infrared spectra of the two stereoisomers were different.[232a]

The dimethyl dioxide on boiling in water decomposes to sulfur dioxide, acetone, and mercaptoacetone.[231] The dimethyl tetroxide remains unchanged on boiling in water, but in cold sodium hydroxide gives sulfur dioxide and two moles acetone.[231] The dioxide does not react with methyl iodide at room temperature. On refluxing the dioxide with hydroxylamine, the oxime of mercaptoacetone is obtained.[232]

On treating the diethyl compound with mercuric chloride a mercury complex, melting at 129-130°, precipitates.[16] The 1, 4-diethyl-3, 6-dimethyl compound similarly gives a precipitate melting at 66-72°.[16]

C. C$_3$OS-C$_4$O Furo[2, 3-d]-2H-1, 3-oxathiole (396)

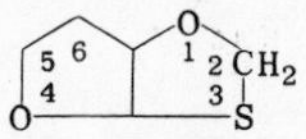

396

Only a tetrahydro derivative of this ring system has been reported. Schneider and Urede,[423] in studies on the constitution of sinigrins, treated sinigrin (397) with methanolic potassium hydroxide and isolated in 11% yield the furo[2, 3-d]-1, 3-oxathiole derivative (398) which they called merosinigrin, melting at 192°. Treatment of merosinigrin with acetic anhydride yielded the triacetate (399), melting at 177°.

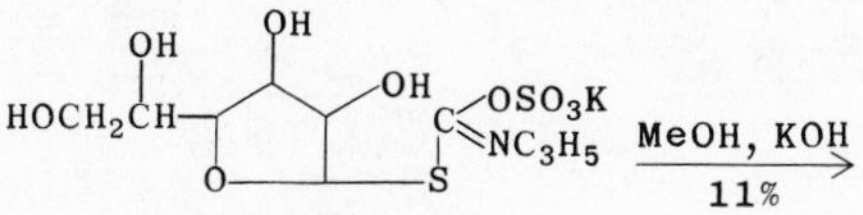

397

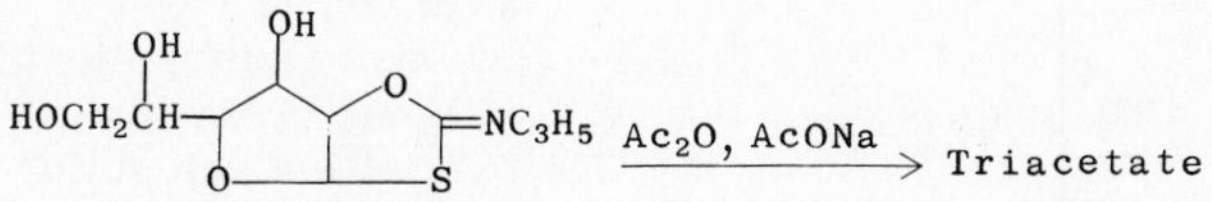

398   **399**

D. C$_3$OS-C$_5$ Cyclopenta-1, 3-oxathiolane (400)

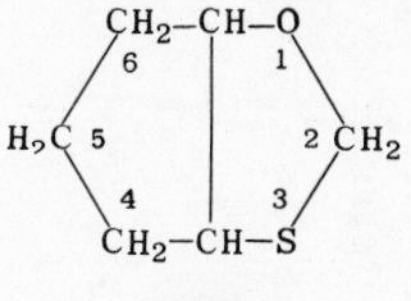

400

The only successful syntheses of members of this ring system are those reported by Goodman, Benitez, Anderson, and Baker[163] by the conversion of *trans*-1, 2-cyclopentanediol to *trans*-2-(phenylthiocarbamyloxy)-cyclopentanol, which on reaction with cold thionyl chloride gave the anil of *cis*-cyclopentano-1, 3-oxathiolane (401) with inversion.

TABLE 21. 7-Oxa-2,5-dithiabicyclo[2.2.1]heptanes

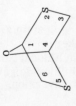

Derivative	Yield (%)	M.p. (°C)	B.p. (°C)	(mm)	Other properties	Ref.
1,4-$(CH_3-)_2$	78		50-55	0.01		22a, 425
	35	7-8	55-56	0.2	d^{20} 1.2158	51
			84	10	n_D^{25} 1.5488	231
	28					231
	67		70-72	5		459a
1,4-$(CH_3-)_2$ 2,2-dioxide	53	104-105				231, 232
1,4-$(CH_3-)_2$ 2,2,5,5-tetroxide	88	226-227				231, 232
	42	225				51
		223-226				461
1,4-$(C_2H_5-)_2$			124-125	15		21
	55	−23	106	10		232b
			108	15		16
1,4-$(C_2H_5-)_2$ 2,2,5,5-tetroxide	60	128-189				21

Compound	Yield (%)	M.p., °C	B.p., °C	Pressure, mm	Ref.
	50	194			232b
1,4-dicyclohexyl	67	192.5			16
1,4-dicyclohexyl 2,2,5,5-tetroxide		131–132			17
		228–232			17
1,4-$(C_2H_5-)_2$-3,6-$(CH_3-)_2$	90		131–133	16	14
1,4-$(C_2H_5-)_2$-3,6-$(CH_3-)_2$ 2,2,5,5-tetroxide	80		83–86	1.5	405a, 405b
1,3,4,6-$(CH_3-)_4$	85	106–107			14
	51		95–96	8	232a
1,3,4,6-$(CH_3-)_4$ 2,2-dioxide	86		84–85	5	16
			99–100	13	16
1,3,4,6-$(CH_3-)_4$ 2,2,5,5-tetroxide	8	114–116			232a
	65	236 and 260			232a
1,4-$[(CH_3)_2CH-]_2$	55	222			16
1,4-$[(CH_3)_2CH-]_2$ 2,2,5,5-tetroxide	85		91–92	2	460
	45	196.5–197.0			460
1,4-$(CH_3-)_2$-3,6-$[(CH_3)_2CH-]_2$	98		104–106	0.2	18a
1,3,3,4,6,6-$(CH_3-)_6$	89	60			460
1,3,3,4,6,6-$(CH_3-)_6$ 2,2,5,5-tetroxide	70	233–234			460
1,1,4,4-$(CH_3-)_4$-3,6-$(C_2H_5-)_2$	33	92		0.2	18a

[For references, see pp. 289-312.]

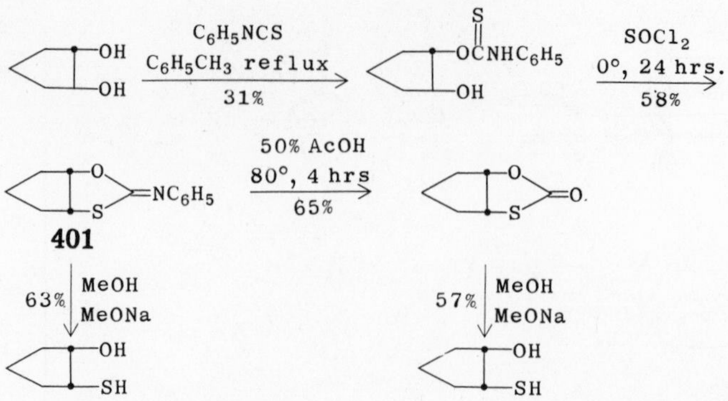

401

The anil melted at 55-61° and its picrate at 117-122°. The infrared absorption frequency of the C=N bond in the anil appeared at 6.12 μ whereas the C=ṄH absorption in its picrate and hydrochloride occurred at 6.15 μ. The anil was readily converted to *cis*-cyclopentano-1,3-oxathiolan-2-one, b.p. = 62-65° at 1 mm, n_D^{20} = 1.5264, which had a strong carbonyl band at 5.76 μ. The 2-one was converted to *cis*-2-mercaptocyclopentanol in 57% yield by treatment with methanolic sodium methoxide at room temperature; similar treatment of the anil gave the mercaptoalcohol in 63% yield.

Van Tamelen[473] was unsuccessful in his attempt to prepare cyclopentano-1,3-oxathiolane from cyclopentene oxide, whereas he was successful in preparing cyclohexano-1,3-oxathiolane from cyclohexene oxide. He attributed the failure to excessive strain in the five-membered fused rings. Harding and Owen[179] were unsuccessful in their attempt to prepare 2-mercaptocyclopentyl acetate by acid isomerization of S-acetyl-2-mercaptocyclopentanol, in which they postulated the likelihood of 2-hydroxy-2-methylcyclopentano-1,3-oxathiolane as the intermediate, similarly to the cyclohexane analog.

E. C_3OS-C_5O 4H-PYRANO[3,4-d]-2H-1,3-OXATHIOLE (402)

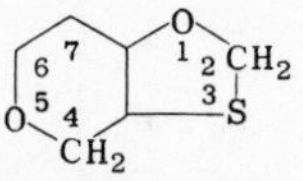

402

Baker, Hewson, Goodman, and Benitez,[30] on treating the thiourethan of methyl 4,6-O-benzylidene-α-D-glucopyranoside with thionyl chloride, obtained an oily product (**403**) that readily lost aniline to give another oil that was presumably the 1,3-oxathiolan-2-one (**404**). The presence of the 1,3-oxathiolan-2-anil and 2-one in the reaction mixtures was considered to be highly probable from the characteristic infrared absorption bands.

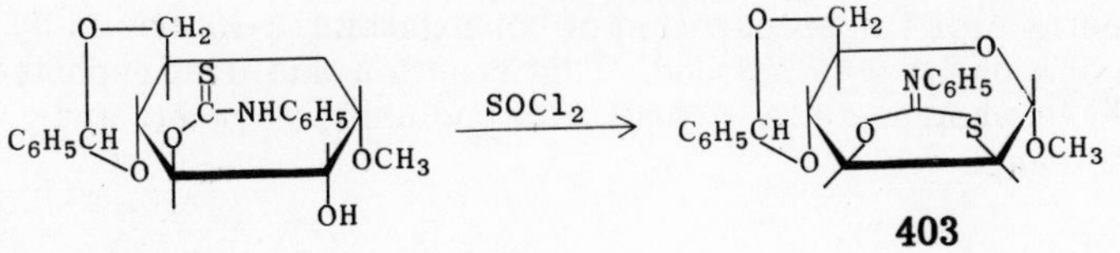

403

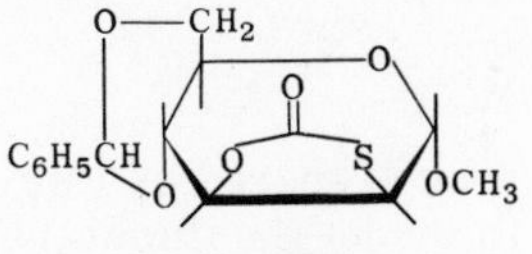

404

F. C$_3$OS-C$_6$

1. 2H-1, 3-Benzoxathiole (405)

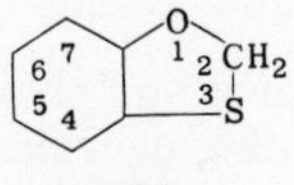

405

(RRI 1223)

Unsubstituted 2H-1, 3-benzoxathiole (405) has not been reported. This system is best known as the 2-one or 2-imino derivatives and substituted 1, 3-2H-benzoxathioles which are listed in Table 22.

Friedlander and Mauthner[134] prepared 2H-1, 3-benzoxathiol-2-imine in 1904. Zinke and Arnold[517] reported the preparation of 5-methyl-2H-1, 3-benzoxathiol-2-one in 1917, which was next repeated by Kaufmann and Weber[254a] in 1929; Kaufmann[254b] also reported the preparation of 5-methyl-2H-1, 3-benzoxathiole-2-imine. Activity in this ring system lay dormant until the forties and fifties.

This ring system has also been called benzothioxole and the 2-one compound benzothioxolone, benzoxathiolone, and thiocarbonate.

a. Preparation

The first benzoxathiole (406) was prepared by Friedlander and Mauthner[134] by diazotization of o-aminophenol and ring closure of the resulting diazonium compound with potassium ethyl xanthate.

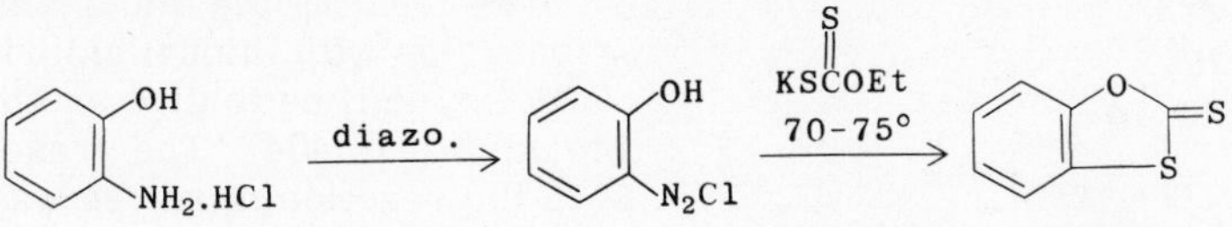

406

A general method for the preparation of benzoxathiol-2-imines is by thiocyanation of a phenolic compound. This reaction was first reported by Kaufmann[254b] who reacted p-cresol with sodium thiocyanate and bromine in methanol.

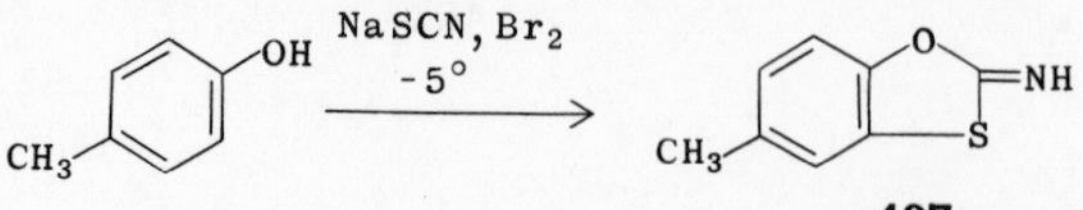

407

The unsubstituted benzoxathiol-2-imine could not be prepared by this method, as a substituent is needed in the phenol to direct the thiocyanation ortho to the phenolic hydroxyl.[254a] Acid hydrolysis converts the imino to the keto compound.[254b] Werner[298,499] thiocyanated resorcinol, phloroglucinol, orcinol, 4-chloro- and 4-bromoresorcinol, and 2, 6-dihydroxytoluene. He suggested that these substituted benzoxathiol-2-imines may be useful as intermediates in the manufacture of dyes or as disinfecting agents. The 2-imino and thio derivatives also have been said to stimulate plant growth.[497]

A French patent[129] describes the reaction of resorcinol and phloroglucinol with copper thiocyanate to give the corresponding benzoxathiol-2-imine, which, on treatment with dilute acid, was converted to the 2-one. Kaufmann[255] formulated the reaction as follows:

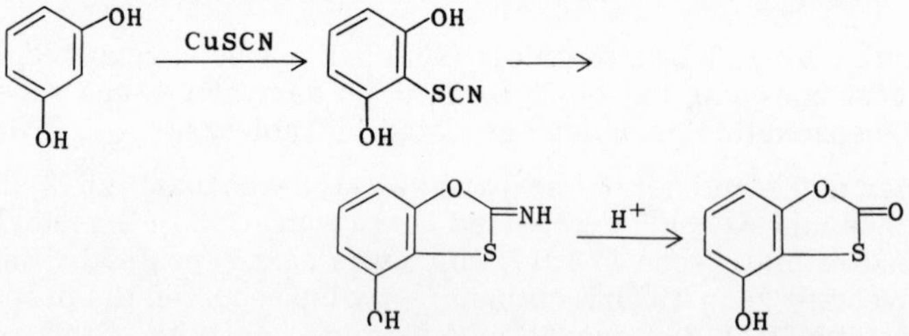

408   **409**

The French patent, on the other hand, assumed that thiocyanation occurred para to one of the phenolic hydroxyls. To clarify this, Pantlitschko and Benger[356] nitrated the hydroxybenzoxathiol-2-one (**409**).

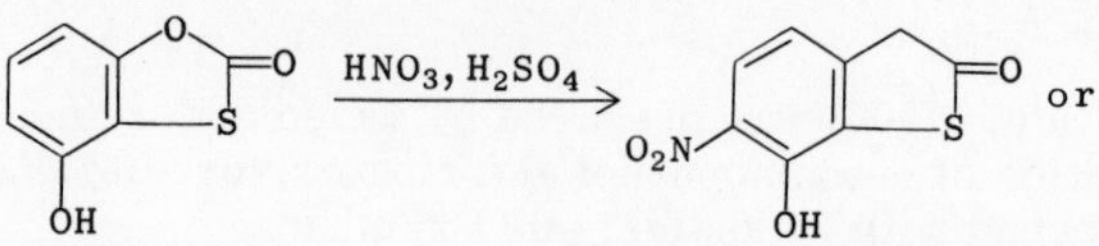

409   **410**

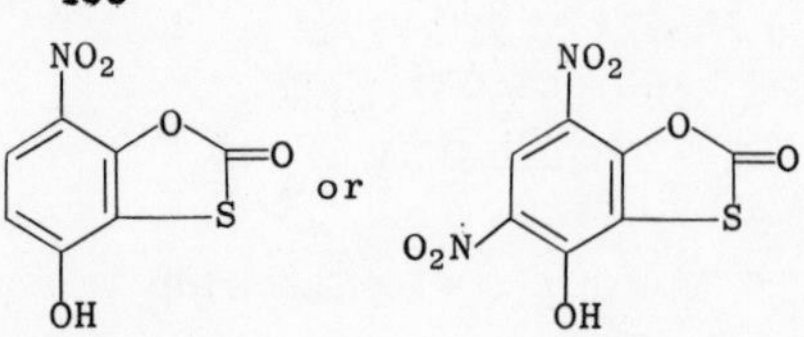

411   **412**

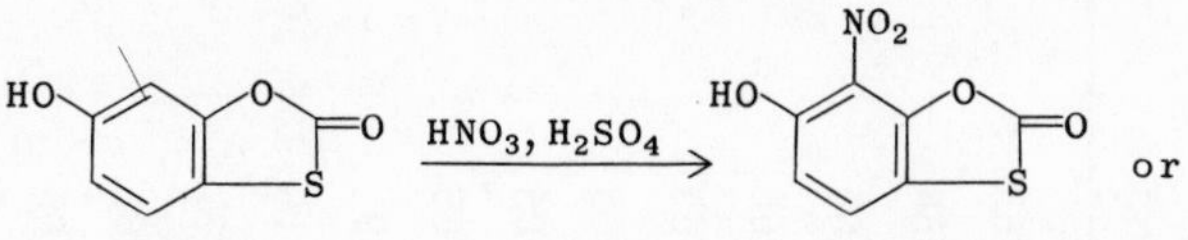

413 HNO$_3$, H$_2$SO$_4$ **414** or

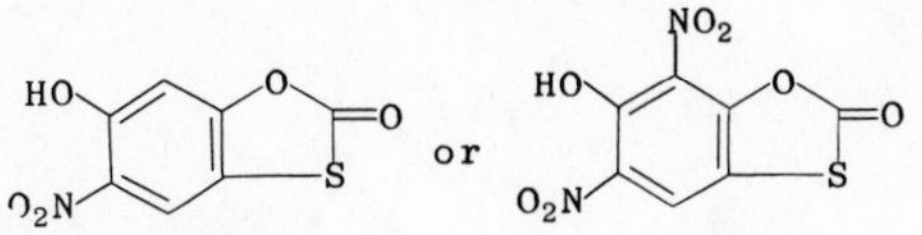

415 or **416**

Hydrolysis with sodium hydroxide and elimination of the sulfhydryl group with hydrogen iodide gave only 4,6-dinitroresorcinol from the dinitrohydroxybenzoxathiole (**412**) and only 4-nitroresorcinol from the mononitrohydroxybenzoxathiole (**410** or **411**). It was therefore concluded that thiocyanation of resorcinol occurred ortho to the two phenolic hydroxyls. The mononitrohydroxybenzoxathiole (**410**), on catalytic reduction followed by heating of the amino compound (**417**) with formic acid, and heating the resulting product under vacuum gave [1,3]-oxathiolo[5,4-g]benzoxazol-7-one (**419**). Thus, mononitration gives only **410**; no **411** could be isolated.

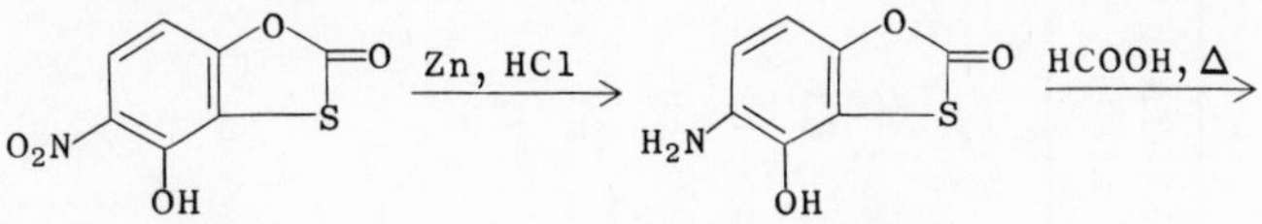

410 Zn, HCl **417** HCOOH, Δ

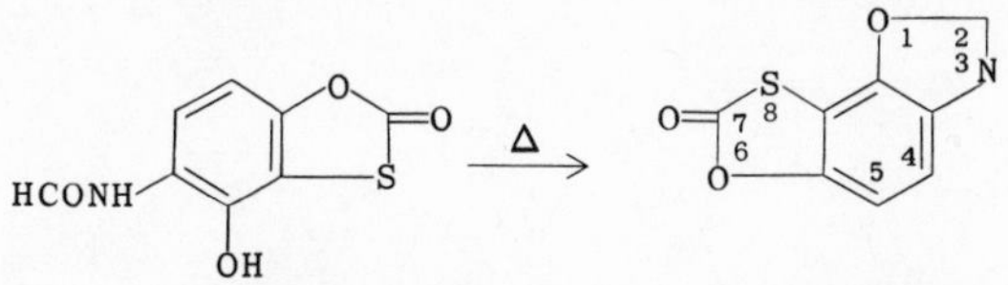

418 Δ **419**
(RRI 2316)

The reaction of β-resorcylic acid with copper thiocyanate was further proof of the position of thiocyanation.

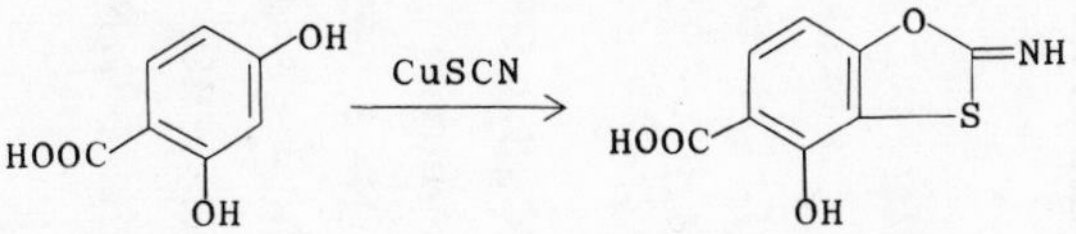

CuSCN **420**

Von Glahn and Stanley[490,491] prepared 6-hydroxy-2H-1,3-benzoxathiol-2-imine by thiocyanation of resorcinol with potassium thiocyanate in the presence of copper sulfate.

[For references, see pp. 289-312.]

263

TABLE 22. 2H-1,3-Benzoxathioles

Substituent	Yield (%)	M.p. (°C)	B.p. (°C)	(mm)	Other props.	Ref.
2-CH$_3$-	33		70-74	3		165
2,2-(CH$_3$-)$_2$	42		60	1.5		165
2,2-(CH$_3$-)$_2$ 3-oxide	63	38				165
2,2-(CH$_3$-)$_2$ 3,3-dioxide	17	75				165
2-CH$_3$-2-C$_2$H$_5$-	60		85	3		165
	67		77-78	2		105
2-CH$_3$-2-(C$_6$H$_5$)$_2$CH-	71	78-80				105
5-HO- 3,3-dioxide		145				366
5-HO-4-O$_2$N- 3,3-dioxide						99
4-H$_2$N-5-HO- 3,3-dioxide		186				116, 365, 366
4-ArCH$_2$NH-5-HO- 3,3-dioxide						37
4-H$_2$N-5-HO-4-O$_2$N 3,3-dioxide						366
2-(O=)	63	26	94	2		165
5-CH$_3$-2-(O=)						254a

Compound	Yield (%)	M.p. (°C)		Refs.
4-HO-2-(O=)	82			38, 356
4-CH$_3$O-2-(O=)		160	105	356
5-HO-2-(O=)	66	72	0.1	68
		170-171		468, 468a
5-CH$_3$CO$_2$-2-(O=)	70	173-174		68
6-HO-2-(O=)	100	88		490, 491
				469
5-H$_2$N- 3,3-dioxide	36	154.5-155.0		365a
5-H$_2$N-2-(O=)		160		468, 468a
5-H$_2$N-2-(O=) . HCl	67	124		468
5-O$_2$N-2-(O=)		248-249(dec.)		165
4-HO-5-Cl-2-(O=)	85	182-183		38
4-HO-5-H$_2$N-2-(O=)		156-158		356
4-HO-5-O$_2$N-2-(O=)				356
4-HO-5-H$_2$NCO-2-(O=)				356
4-HO-5-HOOC-2-(O=)				356
6-HO-4-Cl-2-(O=)				490, 491
5-H$_2$N-x-Cl- 3, 3-dioxide	47	210		365a
5-H$_2$N-6-CH$_3$-2-(O=)		164		468
4-HO-5, 7-(Cl-)$_2$-2-(O=)	95	180-182		38
4-HO-5, 7-(H$_2$N-)$_2$-2-(O=)				356

TABLE 22. $2H$-1, 3-Benzoxathioles (contd)

Substituent	Yield (%)	M.p. (°C)	B.p. (°C)	(mm)	Other props.	Ref.
4-HO-5, 7-$(O_2N-)_2$-2-(O=)	75	105				356
6-HO-4-CH_3-x-$[(CH_3)_2NCH_2CH_2-]$-2-(O=)						490, 491
2-(S=)		99.5				134
2-(S=)	20	97.8				165
4-HO-2-(S=)	70	124-127				38
4-CH_3O-2-(S=)		104-106				38
5-CH_3-2-(S=)		106-108				38
5-CH_3-2-(HN=)		105				254b
4-HO-2-(HN=)		158				498, 499
5-HO-2-(HN=)	88	118				68
4-HO-6-CH_3-2-(HN=)		140				498, 499
6-HO-7-CH_3-2-(HN=)						498, 499
4, 6-$(HO-)_2$-2-(HN=)		181				498, 499
4-HO-7-Cl-2-(HN=)		172				498, 499
4-HO-7-Br-2-(HN=)						498, 499
4-HO-5-HOOC-2-(HN=)						356
2-C_6H_5NHCH=	40	160				264
2-[2-(3-C_2H_5-2-benzothiazolinylidene)-$CH_2CH=$]	50	215-218				264

	Yield (%)	m.p.	$[\alpha]_D^{25}$	Ref.
2-[2-(3-C$_2$H$_5$-6-C$_2$H$_5$O-2-benzothiazolinylidene)-CH$_2$CH=]	68	237–238		264
2-[2-(3-C$_2$H$_5$-6-O$_2$N-2-benzothiazolinylidene)-CH$_2$CH=]	65	341–342		264
2-[2-[3-C$_2$H$_5$-6-(CH$_3$)$_2$N-2-benzothiazolinylidene]-CH$_2$CH=]	68	262		264
Spiro-(1,3-benzoxathiole-2,3'-androstan-17'β-ol-17'-acetate)	28	216	19	105
5,6-Cl$_2$-2-(S=)	80			233a
4,5,6,7-Cl$_4$-2-(S=)	46			233a
4,5,6,7-Cl$_4$-2-(C$_6$H$_5$N=)				233a

Greenwood and Stevenson[165] obtained a low yield of the 2-imine (421) from the thiocyanation of diazotized *o*-aminophenol with copper thiocyanate.

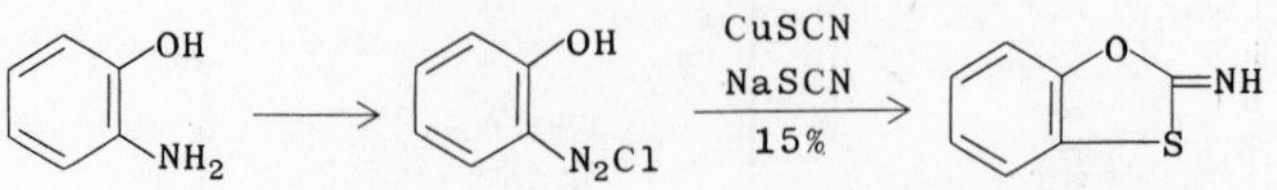

421

Greenwood and Stevenson[165] condensed aliphatic aldehydes and ketones with *o*-mercaptophenol in the presence of dry hydrogen chloride to give a 40% yield of 2,2-dimethyl- (422) and a 60% yield of 2-methyl-2-ethyl-2*H*-1,3-benzoxathiole from acetone and ethyl methyl ketone, respectively; with acetaldehyde, they obtained a 33% yield of 2-methyl-2*H*-1,3-benzoxathiole.

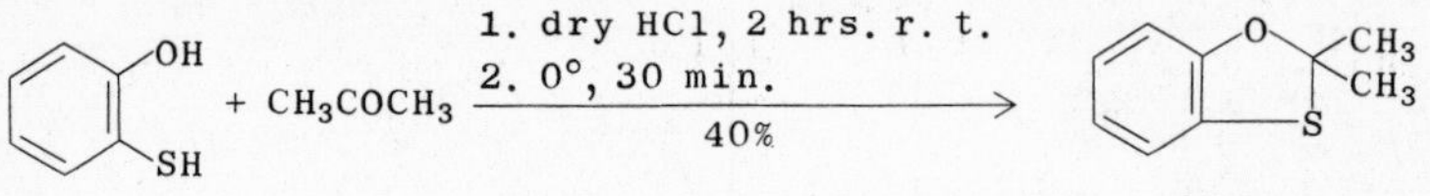

422

Attempts to extend this reaction to aromatic aldehydes and ketones did not yield pure 2-aryl-2*H*-1,3-benzoxathioles.

Djerassi, Gorman, Markley, and Oldenburg,[105] on treating *o*-mercaptophenol with ethyl methyl ketone for two days in the presence of zinc chloride, obtained a 67% yield of 2-methyl-2-ethyl-2*H*-1,3-benzoxathiole Similarly, they obtained a 71% yield of 2-methyl-2-diphenylmethyl-2*H*-1,3-benzoxathiole (423) from *o*-mercaptophenol and diphenylmethyl methyl ketone.

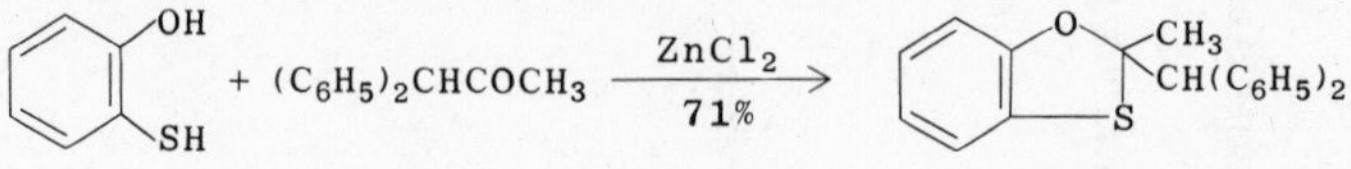

423

Spiro (1,3-benzoxathiole-2,3-androstan-17β-ol-17-acetate) (424) was prepared in 28% yield by the reaction of *o*-mercaptophenol and dihydrotestosterone acetate for two days at room temperature in the presence of zinc chloride and sodium sulfate.[105]

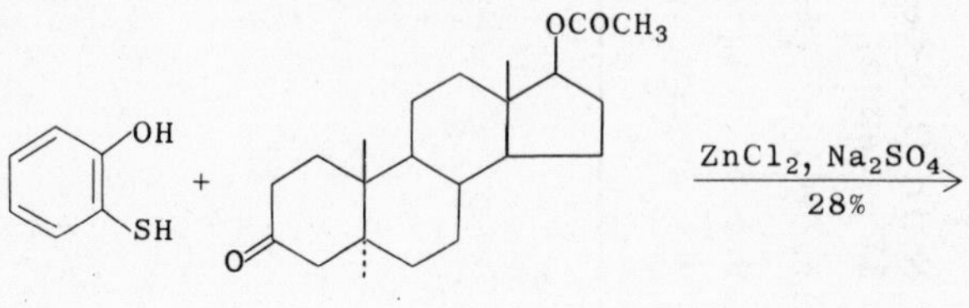

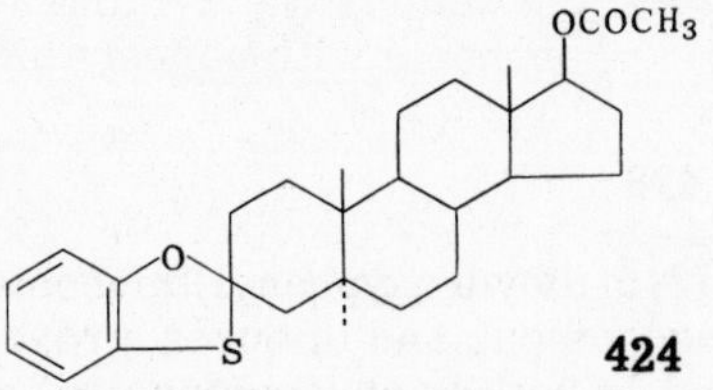

424

(RRI 6611)

Zinke and Arnold[517] attempted to prepare 2-mercapto-*p*-cresol by treating the carbethoxy compound of *p*-cresol-2-sulfonic acid with phosphorus pentachloride and reducing the resulting sulfonyl chloride with nascent hydrogen. A small amount of the desired product was obtained, but the major product, 70-80% yield, was 5-methyl-2*H*-1, 3-benzoxathiol-2-one (**425**).

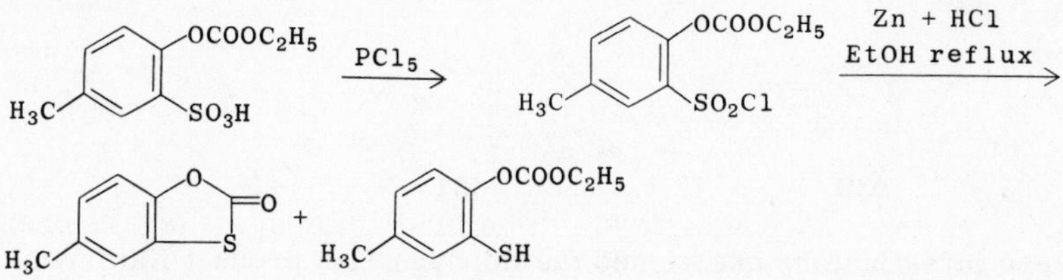

425

Kaufmann and Weber[254a], in attempting to prove the structure of the benzoxathiole (**426**) obtained from the thiocyanation of resorcinol, hydrolyzed the hetero ring with alkali, and treated the resulting mercaptoresorcinol with phosgene in an indifferent solvent. They obtained 4-hydroxy-2*H*-1, 3-benzoxathiol-2-one (**426**).

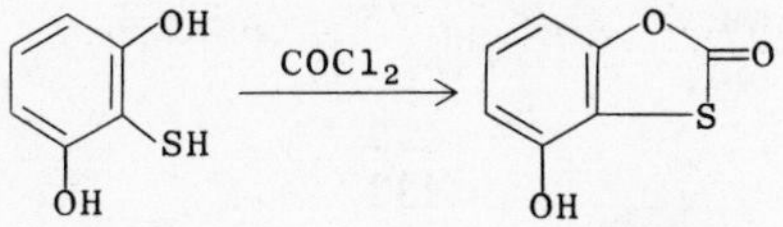

426

Greenwood and Stevenson[165] prepared 2*H*-1, 3-benzoxathiol-2-one (**427**) in 63% yield by treating *o*-mercaptophenol with carbonyl sulfide and the 2-thione (**428**) in 20% yield by treating *o*-mercaptophenol with CSCl₂.

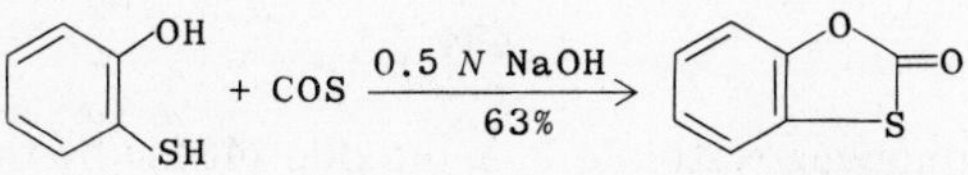

427

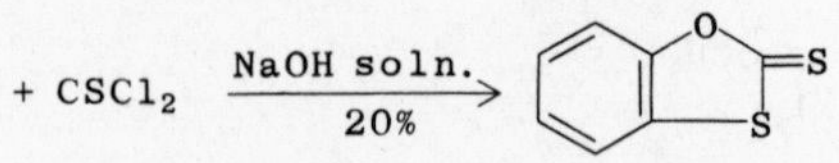

$$+ \ CSCl_2 \quad \xrightarrow[\ 20\% \ ]{\text{NaOH soln.}} \quad \textbf{428}$$

Burton and David,[68] who obtained S-(2, 5-dihydroxyphenyl)thiuronium chloride (**429**) from the reaction of benzoquinone and thiourea, proved the structure by hydrolyzing the product in boiling aqueous acetic acid. They obtained a good yield of 5-hydroxy-2H-1, 3-benzoxathiol-2-one (**431**), presumably by way of the dihydroxyphenyl thiocyanate.

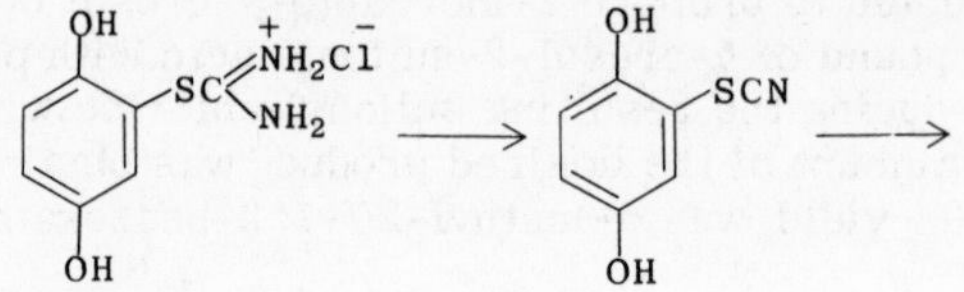

429

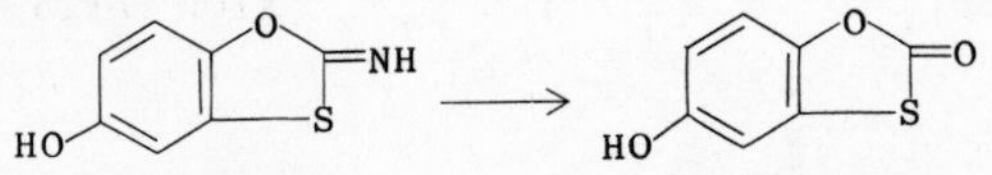

430   **431**

These investigators questioned the thiocyanation product Kaufmann obtained from resorcinol. It is their opinion that the thiocyanated resorcinol should give the 6-hydroxy- and not the 4-hydroxy-2H-1, 3-benzoxathiole.

In a study of merocyanine derivatives, Kiprianov and Timoshenko[264] obtained a benzoxathiole (**433**) on boiling for one hour an ethanol solution of diphenylformamidine and 3-hydroxythianaphthene-2-carboxylic acid (**432**). It is difficult to visualize how this reaction proceeds.

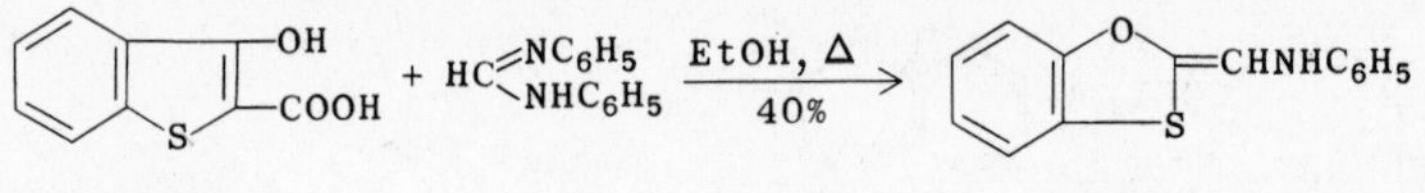

432   **433**

Dittmar, Pütter, and Suckfüll[99,100,365,366] prepared benzoxathiole 3, 3-dioxides by the reaction of benzoquinones with chloromethylsulfinic acid.

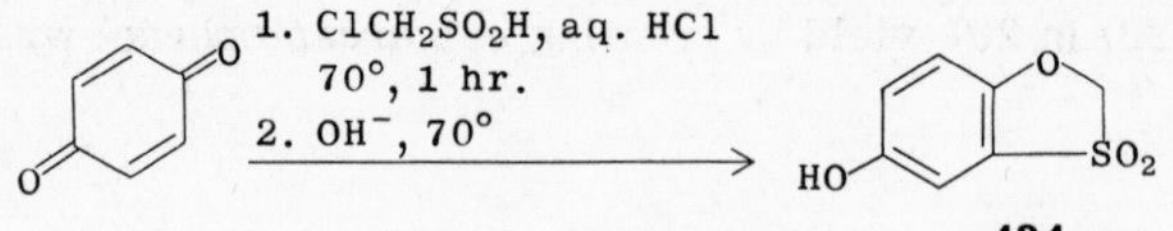

434

Pütter[365a] prepared 5-aminobenzoxathiole 3, 3-dioxide (**434a**) by the reaction of p-nitrosophenol with sodium chloromethanesulfinate.

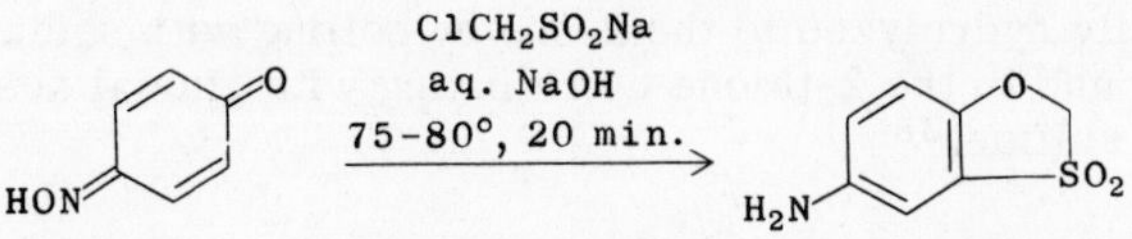

434a

Huisgen, König, Binsch, and Sturm[233a] reported the preparation of 2-thio- (**434c**) and 2-anilino- (**434b**) 4, 5, 6, 7-tetrachloro-2H-1, 3-benzoxa-thiole by the 1, 3-addition of carbon disulfide or phenyl isothiocyanate, respectively, to tetrachloro-o-quinonediazide at 130° or under photolysis.

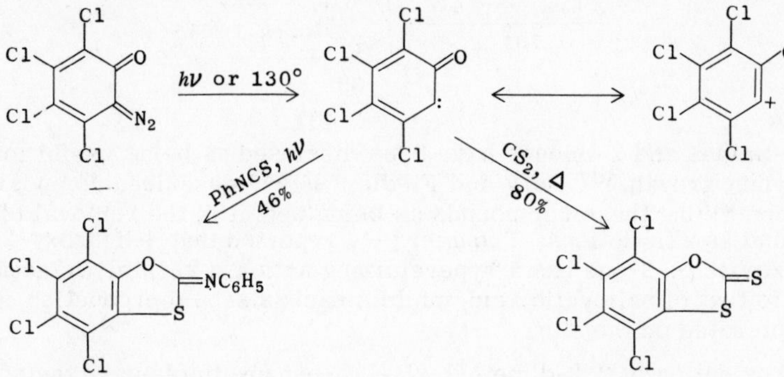

434b   **434c**

Hydrolysis of the 2-anilino compound (**434b**) gave 2-hydroxy-3, 4, 5, 6-tetrachlorothiophenol, aniline, and carbon dioxide. The thermolysis of 4, 6-dichloro-o-quinonediazide in the presence of CS$_2$ similarly yielded 5, 6-dichloro-2-thio-2H-1, 3-benzoxathiole.

b. Properties and Reactions

The 2H-1, 3-benzoxathioles listed in Table 22 are, in general, solids at room temperature and have relatively high boiling points. They are stable to acid media. Thus, boiling 5-hydroxy-2H-1, 3-benzoxathiol-2-one (**431**) in concentrated hydrochloric acid resulted in no change.[68] This compound was also stable to hot dilute sulfuric acid and to hydrogenation by treatment with zinc and dilute sulfuric acid. When boiled with oxygen-free 2 N NaOH solution in an atmosphere of nitrogen for one hour followed by acidification with 2 N H$_2$SO$_4$, a good yield of mercaptohydroquinone resulted.[68,468,469]

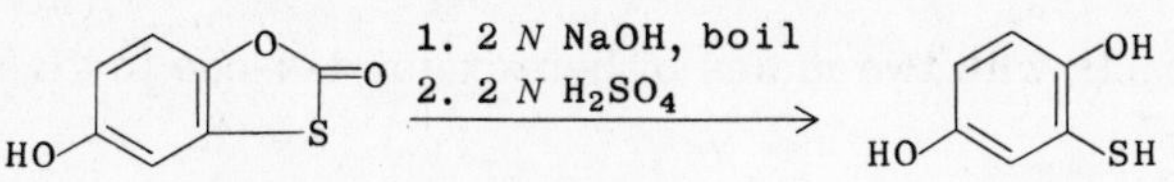

431

In the presence of air, the saponification reaction results in a dark brown solution. Alcoholic potassium hydroxide has also been used to convert the heterocyclic ring to the mercaptophenol.[134]

[For references, see pp. 289-312.]

Chapter 4

The 2-imine is readily hydrolyzed to the 2-one by boiling with sodium
carbonate solution[356] and to the 2-thione by refluxing with glacial acetic acid and hydrogen sulfide.[38]

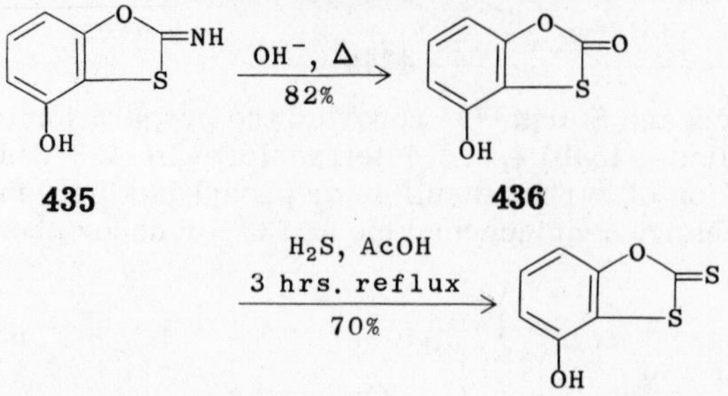

435   **436**

$\xrightarrow[\text{3 hrs. reflux}]{\text{H}_2\text{S, AcOH}}$ 70%

437

The 2-imines and 2-thiones have been disclosed as being useful to stimulate plant growth.[497] Berg and Fiedler[38a,38b] described compositions containing these compounds as being useful in the removal of dan-
druff and as skin lotions. Tronnier[462a] reported that 4-hydroxy-2H-1,
3-benzoxathiol-2-one has a hyperemizing action, a keratolytic action
equal to that of salicyclic acid, inhibits excess sebum production, and is
well tolerated on the skin.

Mild oxidation of 2, 2-dimethyl-2H-1, 3-benzoxathiole gave the sulfoxide
with hydrogen peroxide and the sulfone with neutral potassium permanganate.[165]

The 2H-1, 3-benzoxathiol-2-ones readily react with ammonia and primary and secondary amines to open the heterocyclic ring. Ouperoff-
Urne[353] conducted the reaction in aqueous medium or in an organic solvent such as acetone; an excess of ammonia or amine was used.

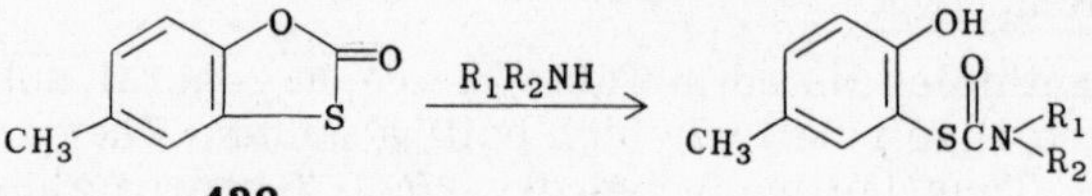

438

The steric effect of the alkyl group in the amine reactant is illustrated
in Table 23 for the reaction of 4-hydroxy-2H-1, 3-benzoxathiol-2-one
(436) with a two-fold excess of ammonia or amine in aqueous medium
at 30-35° (reaction time, 10 minutes). The effect of the hydroxyl group
in the benzene ring of 2H-1, 3-benzoxathiol-2-one is illustrated in
Table 24.

Piperazine reacts with two moles of benzoxathiol-2-one to give
thiolcarbamates.

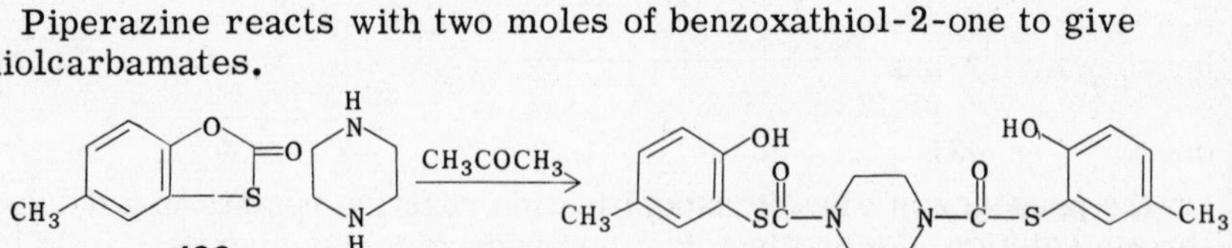

438

272

TABLE 23. Reaction of 4-Hydroxy-2H-1, 3-benzoxathiole with Amines

Amine	% Yield of thiolcarbamate
CH$_3$NH$_2$	100
C$_2$H$_5$NH$_2$	75
(CH$_3$)$_2$NH	100
(C$_2$H$_5$)$_2$NH	70

TABLE 24. Reaction of Hydroxy-benzoxathiol-2-ones with Amines

Benzoxathiol-2-one	Amine	% Yield of thiolcarbamate
5-CH$_3$	C$_2$H$_5$NH$_2$	100
5-CH$_3$	(C$_2$H$_5$)$_2$NH	85
4-OH	C$_2$H$_5$NH$_2$	75
4-OH	(C$_2$H$_5$)$_2$NH	70
4, 6-(OH)$_2$	C$_2$H$_5$NH$_2$	55
4, 6-(OH)$_2$	(C$_2$H$_5$)$_2$NH	30

The thiolcarbamates obtained are stated to be useful as coupling compounds in the preparation of azo dyes and in the diazotype photographic process for making heliographic papers of two components.[354]

The benzene ring of 2H-1, 3-benzoxathioles can be nitrated. Thus, nitration of the 2-one with nitric acid (density of 1. 14) under reflux for two and one-half hours gave what was believed to be 5-nitro-2H-1, 3-benzoxathiol-2-one.[165] Nitration of 4-hydroxy-2H-1, 3-benzoxathiol-2-one gave a 75% yield of 5, 7-dinitro-4-hydroxy-2H-1, 3-benzoxathiol-2-one.[356]

Treatment of 4-hydroxy-2H-1, 3-benzoxathiol-2-one (436) with chlorine in acetic acid gave a 95% yield of 5, 7-dichloro-4-hydroxy-2H-1, 3-benzoxathiol-2-one (439).[38] Treatment with concentrated hydrochloric acid in acetic acid and in the presence of perchloric acid yielded 5-chloro-4-hydroxy-$2H$-benzoxathiol-2-one (**440**).[38] These compounds are claimed to exhibit bactericidal and fungicidal activity.

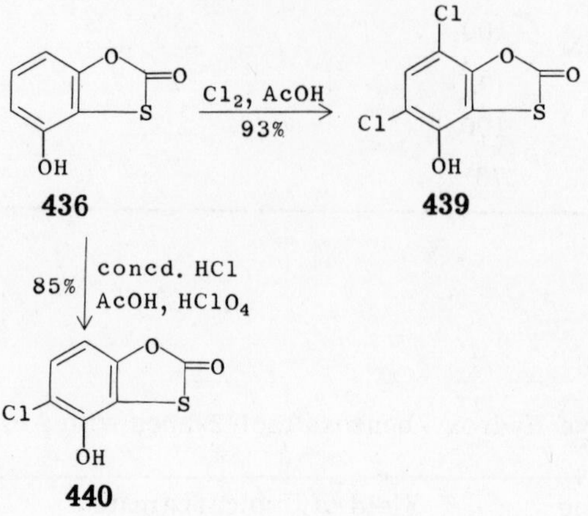

The hydroxy-$2H$-1, 3-benzoxathiol-2-ones can be methylated[356] with silver oxide and methyl iodide to give the corresponding methoxy-$2H$-1, 3-benzoxathiol-2-one or can be acetylated in almost quantitative yield with acetic anhydride and a little 72% perchloric acid[68,356] to the corresponding acetoxy-$2H$-1, 3-benzoxathiol-2-one.

According to a U.S. patent[490] 6-hydroxy-$2H$-1, 3-benzoxathiol-2-one undergoes the Mannich reaction with formaldehyde and dimethylamine, although the position of the dimethylaminomethyl group was not indicated.

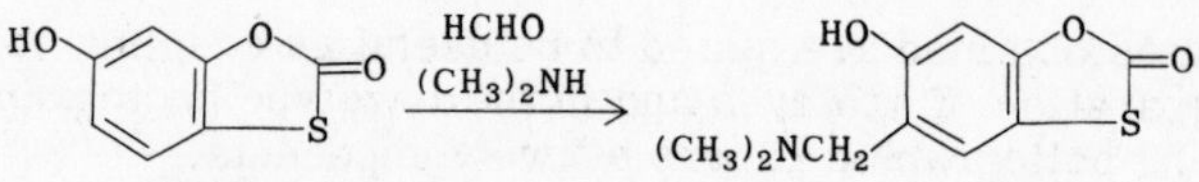

These compounds with diazonium salts are said to give two-component diazo dyes.

$2H$-1, 3-Benzoxathiol-2-anilinomethylidine, on reacting with various benzothioazoles yielded merocyanine dyes (**443**).

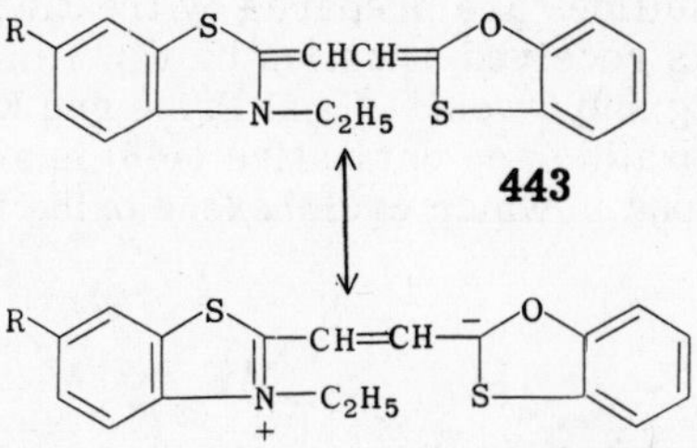

443

444

An electropositive R enhances the ionic structure (**444**) and shifts the color towards the red; an electronegative R has the opposite effect.[264]

According to a British patent,[37] chromium complexes of 4-arylmethyl-eneamino-5-hydroxy-2H-1, 3-benzoxathiole 3, 3-dioxides (**446**) dye wool yellow to red shades in neutral and weakly acidic baths. These dyes are prepared by reacting an aromatic aldehyde with 4-amino-5-hydroxy-2H-1, 3-benzoxathiole 3, 3-dioxide (**445**) in formamide in the presence of potassium dichromate and glucose.

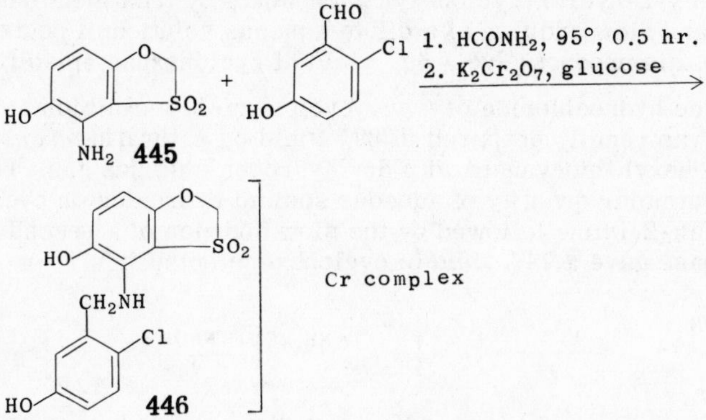

1. HCONH$_2$, 95°, 0.5 hr.
2. K$_2$Cr$_2$O$_7$, glucose

Cr complex

445

446

According to another British patent,[37b] also to Bayer & Co., chromium and cobalt complexes of diazo dyes from the reaction of diazotized 3-amino-4-hydroxybenzenesulfonamide and 5-(substituted 1-pyrazoyl)-2H-1, 3-benzoxathiole 3, 3-dioxide are wool dyes.

2. Hexahydro-2H-1, 3-benzoxathiole or Cyclohexa-1, 3-oxathiolane (447)

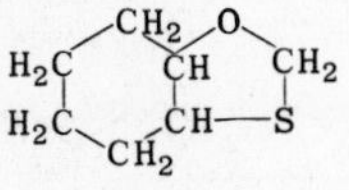

447

[For references, see pp. 289-312.]

The reaction through which episulfides are prepared by treating epoxides with alkali thiocyanates has received attention by van Tamelen,[473] Bordwell and Anderson,[56] Harding and Owen,[179] and Price and Kirk.[363] Van Tamelen postulated that the oxathiolane derivative (448) is an intermediate in the sequence of reactions in which cyclohexene oxide is converted to the sulfide.

448

This mechanism implies two Walden inversions; in the opening of the epoxide ring and in the closing of the episulfide ring.

In applying this reaction to cyclopentene oxide, van Tamelen was unable to isolate the oxathiolane intermediate. This ring system, in which two five-membered rings are fused in the *trans* sense, has been shown to involve considerable strain, and stereochemically should occur slowly, or not at all. On the other hand, cyclohexene oxide was readily converted to *trans*-2-hydroxycyclohexyl thiocyanate by treatment with thiocyanate and slow addition of a dilute aqueous solution of potassium hydroxide to this product gave a 69% yield of cyclohexene episulfide.

A crystalline hydrochloride of *trans*-cyclohexa-1, 3-oxathiolan-2-imine (449) was readily prepared in 89% yield by saturating *trans*-2-hydroxycyclohexyl thiocyanate with dry hydrogen chloride gas. The action of an equimolar quantity of aqueous sodium hydroxide on cyclohexa-1, 3-oxathiolan-2-imine followed by the slow addition of a second molar quantity of base gave a 74% yield of cyclohexene episulfide.[473]

449

The oxathiolane decomposes on heating above 220°. The free base spontaneously eliminates cyanic acid in ether solution at room temperature to give the episulfide.

Harding and Owen[179] in their investigations of this reaction, treated tosylated S-acetyl-2-mercaptocyclohexanol with calcium carbonate in moist dioxane and obtained only *trans*-2-mercaptocyclohexyl acetates. The elimination of the toluene-*p*-sulfonyloxy group apparently leads to the sulfonium structure rather than to 2-hydroxy-2-methylcyclohexa-1, 3-oxathiolane, which is the expected intermediate for the formation of the *cis*-monoacetyl derivative.

G. C_3OS-C_3NO-C_6 2H-1, 3-OXATHIOLO[5, 4-g]BENZOXAZOLE (450)

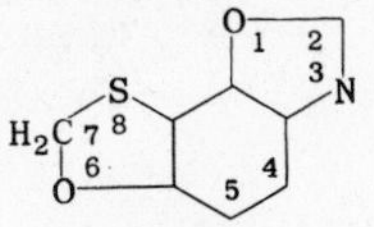

450

(RRI 2316)

Pantlitschko and Benger,[356] in studying the constitution of 4-hydroxy-2H-1, 3-benzoxathiol-2-one prepared by the thiocyanation of resorcinol, obtained 5-nitro-4-hydroxy-2H-1, 3-benzoxathiol-2-one on nitration. Catalytic reduction or hydrogenation with zinc and hydrochloric acid gave the corresponding amino compound which, on heating with formic acid, gave the N-formyl derivative (451). Heating the N-formyl derivative at 150° under vacuum gave [2H-1, 3]-oxathiolo[5, 4-g]benzoxazol-7-one (452), melting at 186°.

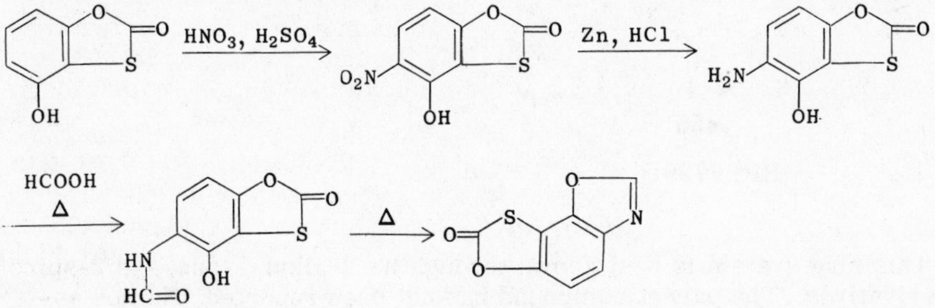

451   **452**

H. C_3OS-C_5O-C_6 7H-PYRANO[2, 3-g]-2H-1, 3-BENZOXATHIOLE (453)

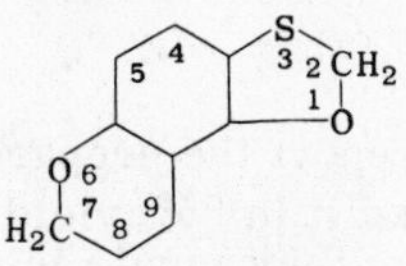

453

Ziegler and Schaar[516a] reported the preparation of 8-benzyl-9-hydroxypyrano[2, 3-g]-1, 3-benzoxathiol-2, 7-dione (454), melting at 236-240° (dec.), in 60% yield from the reaction of bis(2, 4-dichlorophenyl) benzylmalonate with 6-hydroxy-2H-1, 3-benzoxathiol-2-one at 280° for 90 minutes. The acetate of this compound melted at 219° (dec.).

[For references, see pp. 289-312.]   277

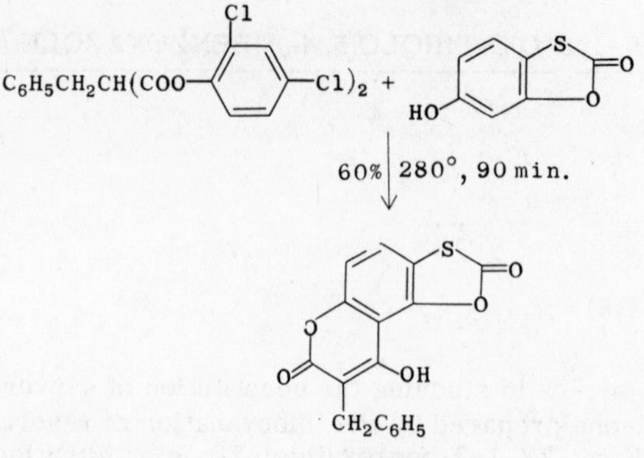

454

I. $C_3OS-C_6-C_6$

1. **Naphth[1, 2-d][1, 3]oxathiole (455)**

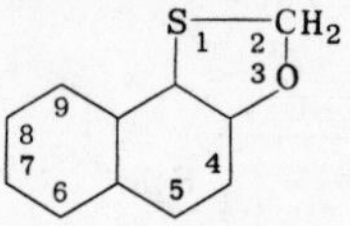

455

(RRI 2799)

This ring system is best known through its 2-alkyl, 2-one, and 2-spiro derivatives. The parent compound has not been reported. Names assigned to this ring system include naphtho[1, 2][1, 3]thioxole (Chemical Abstracts), 2-naphthylene-1-thiolcarbonate,[451] naphtho[1', 2'][1, 3]oxathiole,[165] thiolcarbonate of 2-hydroxynaphthalene.[464] Chemical Abstracts has been using naphth[1, 2][1, 3]oxathiole. The spiro compound, the first member of the ring system prepared, was first reported by Lesser and Gad in 1923. The early nomenclature for the spiro derivatives is quite confusing.

a. **Preparation**

Stevenson and Smiles,[451] who were the first to report the preparation of naphth[1, 2-d][1, 3]oxathiol-2-one **(456)**, prepared it in 85% yield from the reaction of β-naphthol with bromine and sodium thiocyanate in acetic acid and treatment of the resulting 1-thiocyano-2-naphthol with zinc dust or more conveniently by boiling the 1-thiocyano-2-naphthol in

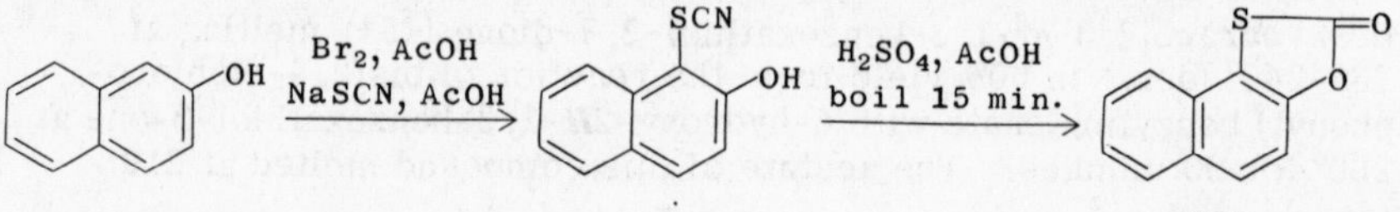

456

acetic acid with sulfuric acid for 15 minutes. McClelland and Smiles,[302] in preparing 7-bromonaphtho(1, 2-d)[1, 3]oxathiol-2--one from 6-bromo-1-thiocyano-2-naphthol, used zinc in acetic acid for ring closure.

Tsukamoto, Hamana, and Baba[464] obtained the 2-one in 85% yield from the reaction of 1-mercapto-2-naphthol with phosgene in alkaline solution.

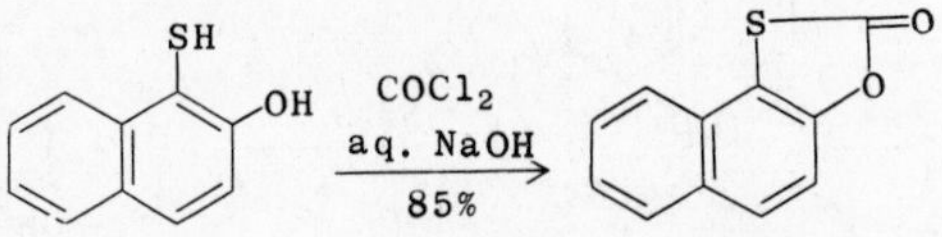

456

Greenwood and Stevenson[165] obtained 35% 2-methyl- and 42% 2, 2-dimethylnaphth[1, 2-d][1, 3] oxathiole (**457**) on condensing 1-mercapto-2-naphthol with acetaldehyde and acetone, respectively, in the presence of dry hydrogen chloride.

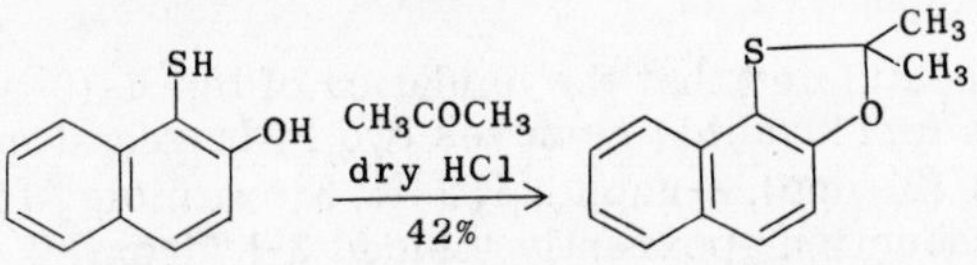

457

The chemistry of the spiro derivatives of naphth[1, 2-d][1, 3]oxathiole is somewhat ambiguous. Hinsberg[212a] noted during the period between 1914 and 1916 that oxidation of bis-1-(2-hydroxynaphthyl) sulfone with potassium ferricyanide produced a compound, called a "dehydrosulfone", which on reduction with sodium sulfide gave an isomer, called an "iso-sulfone", isomeric with the original sulfone. Hinsberg's "isosulfone" was shown by Warren and Smiles[493] in 1930 to be a sulfinic acid from the reduction of the spiro[naphthalene-1(2H), 2'-naphth[1', 2'-d][1', 3'] oxathiole] (**458**) as intermediate.

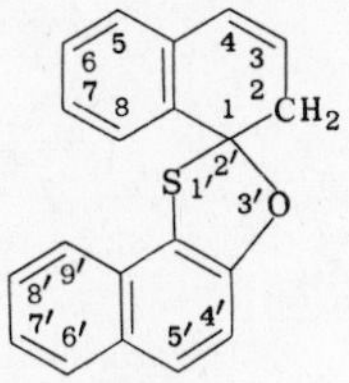

458

(RRI 5828)

Hinsberg's "dehydrosulfone" was apparently the 2'-one (**459**) derivative of the spiro sulfone and his "isosulfone" was the sulfinic acid (**460**).

[For references, see pp. 289-312.]

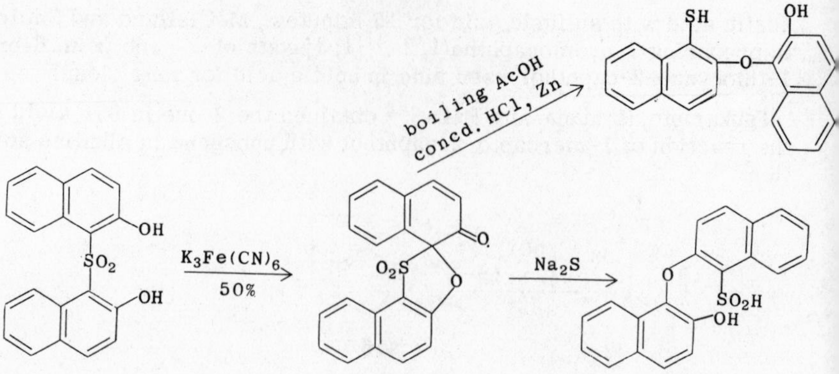

459   **460**

Warren and Smiles[493] postulated that the oxidation of bis-1-(2-naph-thol) sulfide with alkaline ferricyanide removes two hydrogen atoms to form spiro[naphthalene-1'(2'-one), 2-naphth[1,2][1,3]oxathiole] (461). The spiro compound on reduction apparently yielded 2-hydroxy-2'-mercapto-1,1'-bis(naphthyl) oxide and subsequent dehydration led to the formation of dinaphtha-1,4-oxathiin (462). (See Chapter 11, section III M).

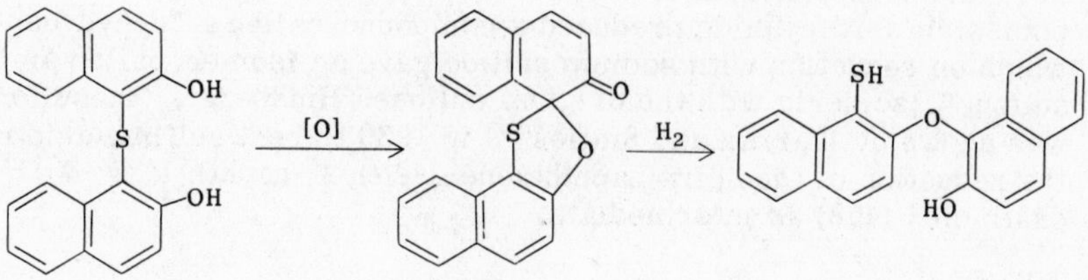

461

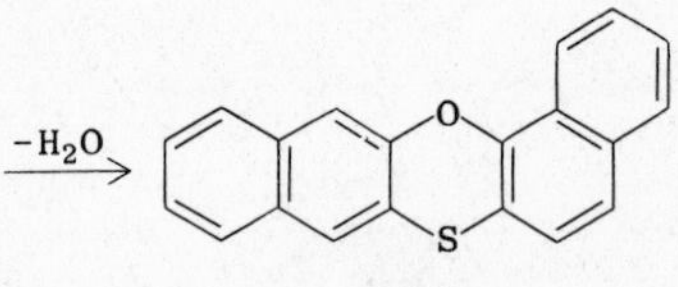

462

Lesser and Gad[285] treated bis-1-(3-carboxymethyl-2-naphthol) sulfide in alkali with bromine and obtained dark red, golden crystals which he identified as a "dehydrosulfide" and to which Beilstein assigned the spiro structure (463).

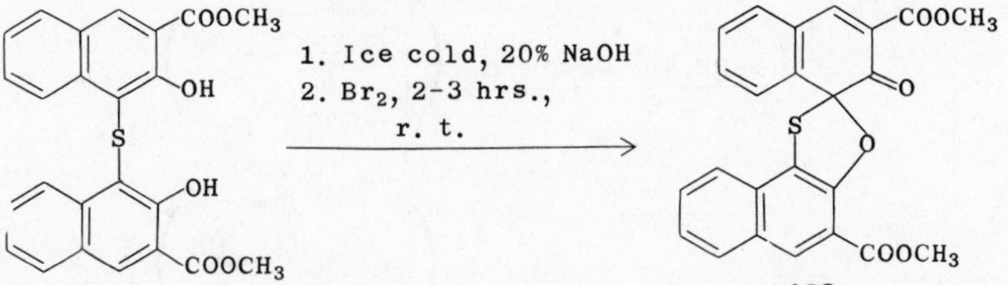

463

Stevenson and Smiles[451] prepared spiro[naphthalene-1'(2'-one), 2-naphth[1, 2][1, 3]oxathiole] in 30% yield by treating 1-mercapto-2-naphthol with bromine and reacting the resulting product with 1-bromo-2-naphthol in carbon tetrachloride followed by treatment with pyridine.

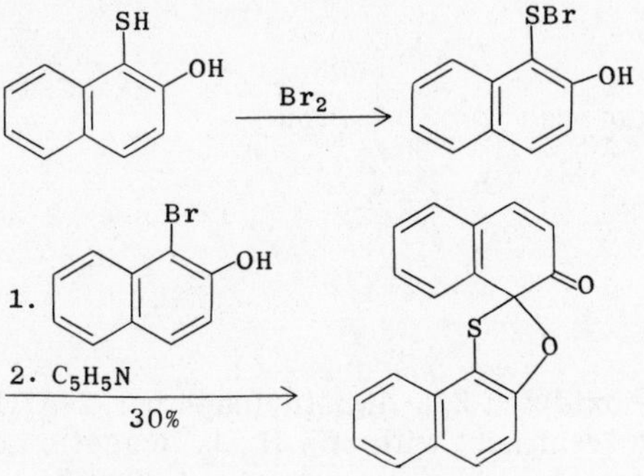

461

The various naphth[1, 2-d][1, 3]oxathioles which have been reported are listed in Table 25 and the spiro derivatives in Table 25a.

b. Reactions

Naphth[1, 2-d][1, 3]oxathiol-2-one (456) is easily hydrolyzed on heating with alkali to give bis-1-(2-naphthol) disulfide;[451,464] hydrolysis with methanolic sodium carbonate gives a mixture of the sulfide and disulfide of 2-naphthol;[464] it resists hydrolysis by acids.[451] On treatment with sodium alcoholate in alcohol, it yields ethyl 2-naphthol-1-thiolcarbonate.[451]

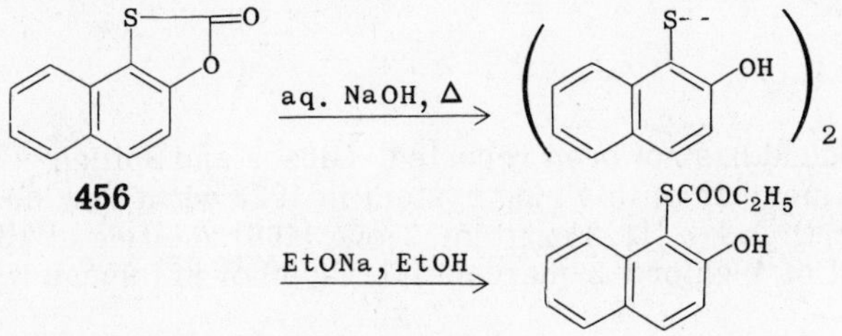

456

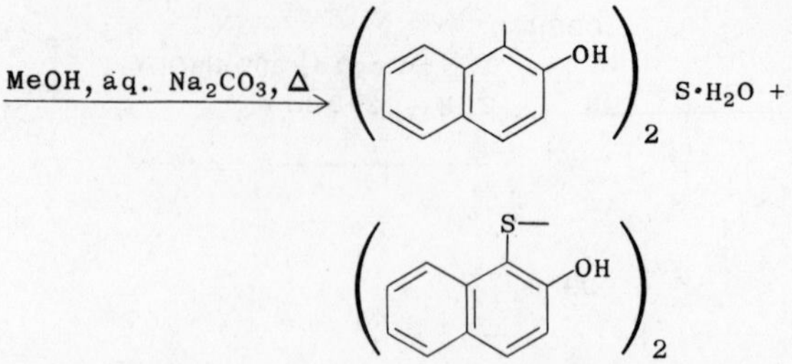

Oupéroff-Urné[353] prepared the thiolcarbamate from the reaction of 8-hydroxynaphth[1, 2-d][1, 3]oxathiol-2-one (464) with diethylamine, using an excess of amine in aqueous medium or in acetone.

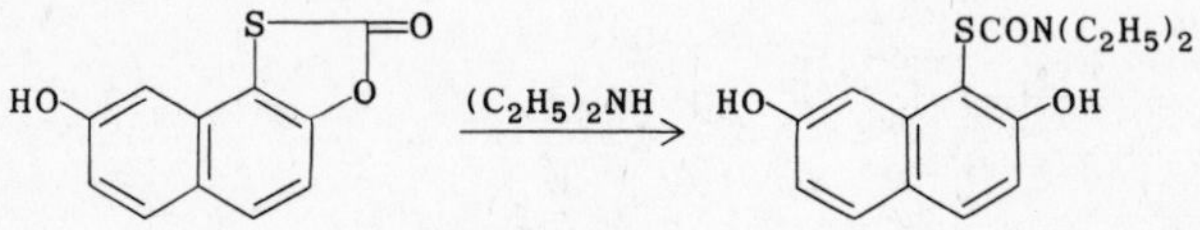

464

Greenwood and Stevenson[165] oxidized 2, 2-dimethylnaphth[1, 2-d][1, 3] oxathiole to the 1-monoxide by treatment with 30% H_2O_2 in acetic acid and to the 1, 1-dioxide by treatment with permanganate at 80-85°.

Reactions of the spiro compounds are given in the preceding section on preparation. Werner,[499] in a patent, stated that 4-hydroxynaphth-[1, 2-d][1, 3]oxathiol-2-one is useful as an azo dye component and as a disinfectant.

2. Naphth[2, 1-d][1, 3]oxathiole (465)

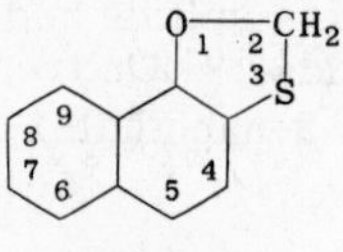

465

(RRI 2798)

The parent compound has not been reported. Gibson and Smiles[158] prepared the first member of this ring system in 1923 when they obtained 5-chloronaphth[2, 1-d][1, 3]oxathiol-2-one (466), melting at 132°, from the treatment of 4-chloro-2-mercapto-1-naphthol in toluene with phosgene.

C$_3$OS Ring Systems

TABLE 25. Naphth[1, 2][1, 3]oxathioles

Substituent	Yield (%)	M.p. (°C)	B.p. (°C)	(mm)	Ref.
2-(O=)	85	106			451
	85	107			464
7-Br-2-(O=)		167			302
4-HO-2-(O=)		199			498, 499
8-HO-2-(O=)		212			353
2-CH$_3$-	35		74	3	165
2, 2-(CH$_3$-)$_2$	42		136	2. 5	165
2, 2-(CH$_3$-)$_2$ 1-oxide		134			165
2, 2-(CH$_3$-)$_2$ 1, 1-dioxide		155			165

TABLE 25a. Spiro[naphthalene-1(2H), 2'-naphth[1', 2'-d][1', 3']oxathiolanes]

Substituent	Yield (%)	M.p. (°C)	Ref.
None	30	155	451
1', 1'-dioxide	50	245	494
3, 4'-(CH$_3$COO-)$_2$		245-246	285
4, 5'-(CH$_3$COO-)$_2$	78	188-189	287

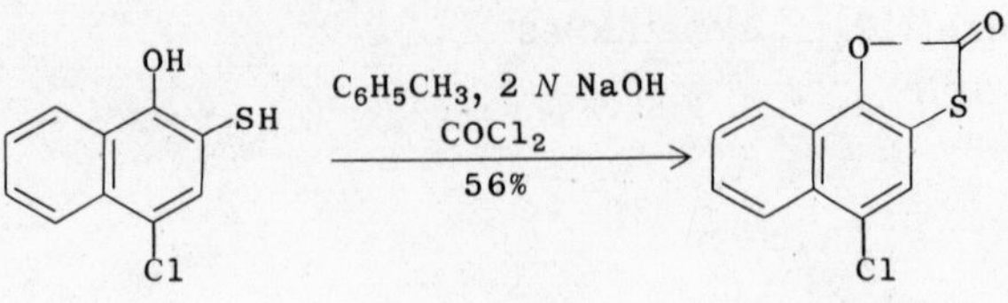

466

They called the product 4-chloro-1-naphthol-2-thiolcarbonate; Chemical Abstracts indexed it under 2-β-naphthothioxolone.

Huisgen, König, Binsch, and Sturn[233a] presumably prepared 2-thio-naphth[2, 1-d][1, 3]oxathiole (**466a**) by the thermolysis of naphthoquinone (1, 2)-2-diazide in the presence of carbon disulfide.

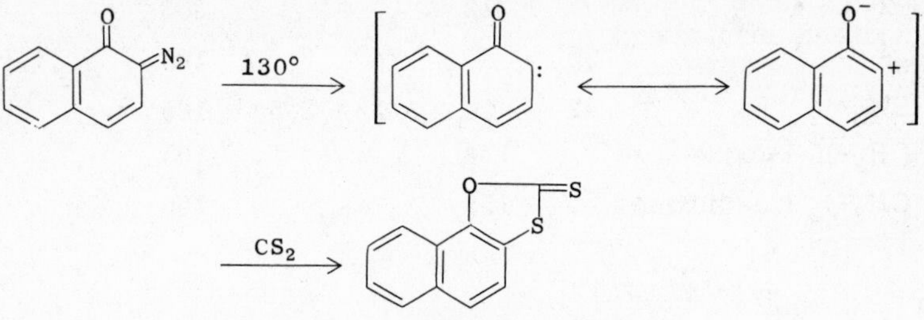

466a

Several patents assigned to Bayer[37, 99, 100, 365, 366] between 1954 and 1957 described the preparation of 5-hydroxynaphth[2, 1-d][1, 3]oxathiole 3, 3-dioxide (**467**), melting at 268°, from the reaction of 1, 4-naphthoquinone with chloromethylsulfinic acid.

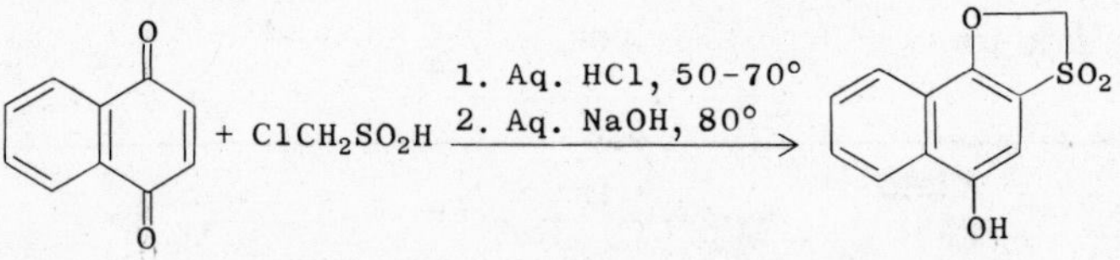

467

The product was described as being useful as a dye intermediate. In a 1958 British patent to Bayer,[37a] a chromium or cobalt complex suitable for dyeing and printing wool, silk, leather, nylon, and urethane fibers was prepared by reacting a diazotized sulfonamide with 5-hydroxynaphth-[2, 1-d][1, 3]oxathiole 3, 3-dioxide (**467**) and treating this product (**467a**) with a potassium dichromate-glucose alkaline solution.

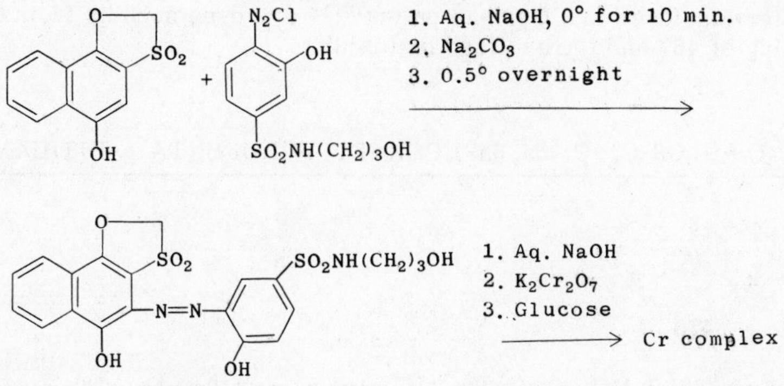

467a

1. Aq. NaOH
2. K₂Cr₂O₇
3. Glucose
⟶ Cr complex

On reaction with chloroform in aqueous alkali, the 4-carboxaldehyde (**468**), melting at 251°, was obtained; [37,422] this on reaction with the 4-methylsulfone of 2-aminophenol and with sodium potassium chrome salicylate in formamide yielded a chromium complex suitable as a yellow-red wool dye.

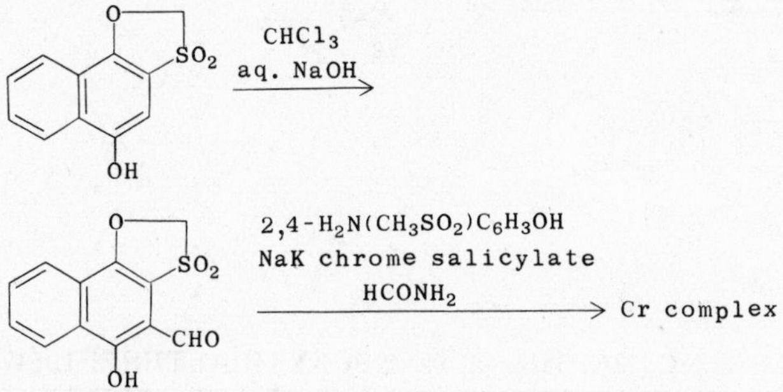

468

The coupling of 5-hydroxynaphth[2, 1-*d*][1, 3]oxathiole 3, 3-dioxide with various diazo compounds yielded azo derivatives whose chromium complexes were said to be suitable as dyes.

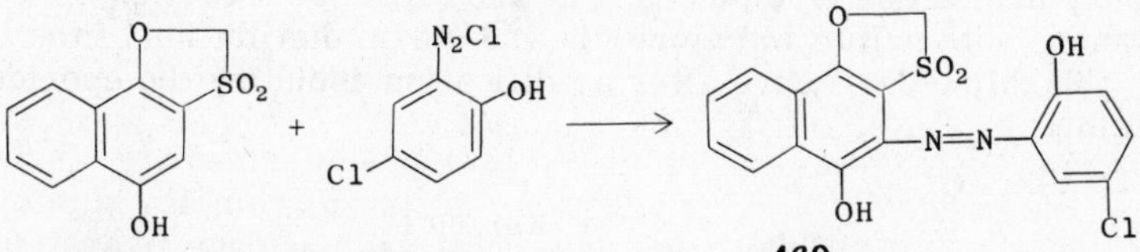

467   **469**

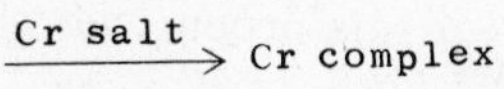

$\xrightarrow{\text{Cr salt}}$ Cr complex

[For references, see pp. 289-312.]   285

Müller disclosed in a German patent[331a] azo dyes such as from the coupling of **467** and tetrazotized bianisidine.

J $C_3OS-C_3OS-C_5-C_5$ 3a, 6a-EPOXYDICYCLOPENTA-p-DITHIANE

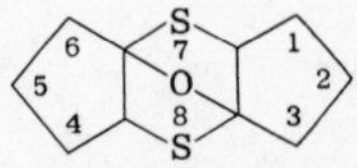

470

Asinger, Thiel, Usbeck, Gröbe, Grundmann, and Tränkner[18b] reported the preparation of 3a, 6a-epoxydicyclopenta-p-dithiane (**470**), boiling at 111-114°, 0. 05 mm, $n_D^{20} = 1.6086$, by the treatment of 2-mercaptocyclo-pentanone with 2 N HCl and distilling. On treatment of the epoxy compound with 2 N HCl at 70°, they obtained dicyclopenta-p-dithiin (**471**).

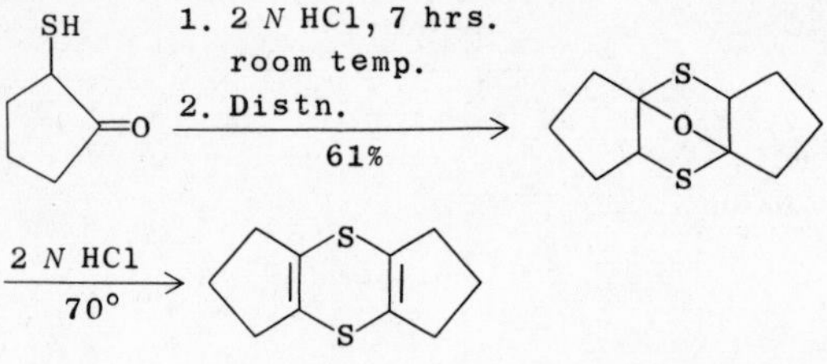

471

K. $C_3OS-C_3OS-C_6-C_6$ 2H, 5aH-4a, 9a-EPOXYTHIANTHRENE (472)

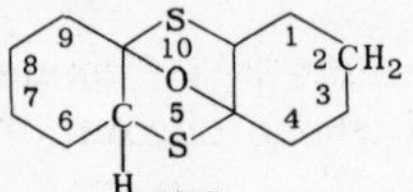

472

Asinger, Thiel, and Kaltwasser[15] reported the preparation of perhydro-4a, 9a-epoxythianthrene (**473**), melting at 196°, from the reaction of cyclohexanone with sulfur and ammonia and steam distillation of the resulting thiazoline derivative after acidification, isolating the epoxide in the residue.

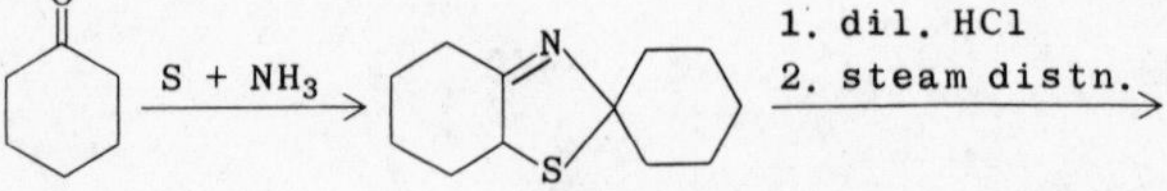

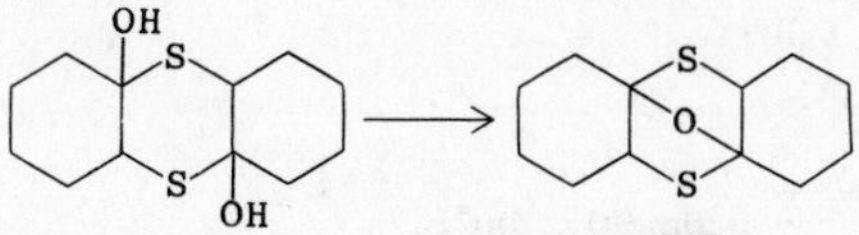

473

Asinger, Thiel, Usbeck, Gröbe, Grundmann, and Tränkner[18b] reported
the preparation of the perhydroepoxythianthrene (**473**), melting at
194-196° and boiling at 192-194°/10 mm, by heating 2-mercaptocyclo-
hexanone with hydrochloric acid and distilling. Prolonged heating of
perhydroepoxythianthrene with concentrated hydrochloric acid yielded
the dithiin (**474**); oxidation with potassium permanganate yielded the
disulfone (**475**); melting at 204-208°.

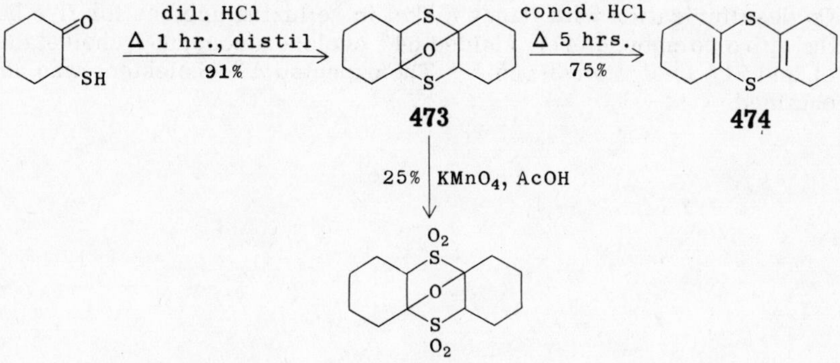

L. C$_3$OS-C$_5$-C$_6$-C$_6$-C$_6$ Spiro[cyclohexane-1, 8′-[1H]cyclopenta[7, 8]
    perhydrophenanthro[3, 2-d]-[1, 3]oxathiole] (**476**)

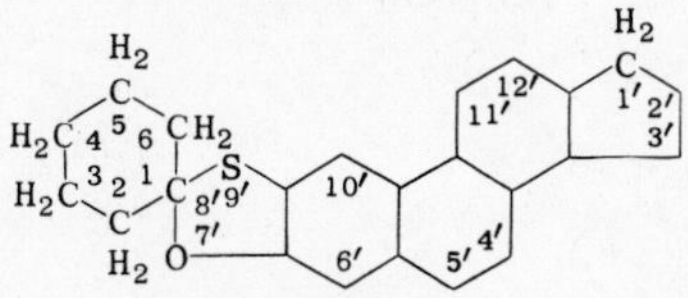

476

(RRI 6610)

Djerassi, Gorman, Henry, Markley, and Oldenburg[105,106] prepared the
spiro[cyclohexane-1, 8′-cyclopenta[7, 8]perhydrophenanthro [3, 2-d]-
[1, 3]oxathiolane (**477**), melting at 161-163°, [α]$_D^{25}$ = 65°, from the reaction of cyclohexanone with 2β-mercaptocholestan-3β-ol in the presence
of anhydrous sodium sulfate and freshly fused zinc chloride.

[For references, see pp. 289-312.]
                                                    287

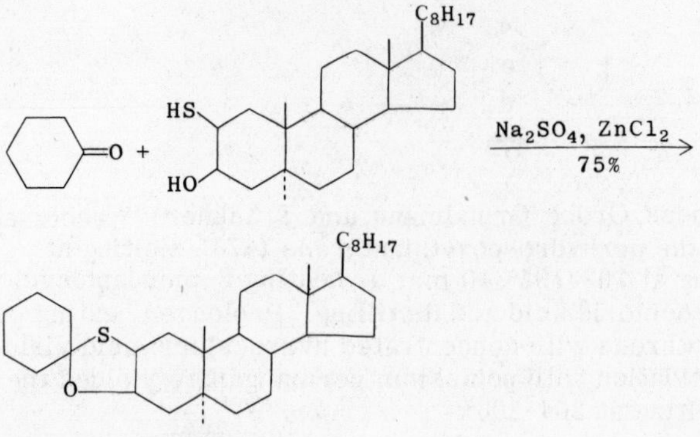

477

On desulfurization with Raney nickel in refluxing acetone for five hours, the spiro compound (477) yielded 64% cyclohexanone, 60% cholestan-3β-ol, and 21% cholestan-3-one.[106] The expected Δ²-cholestene was not obtained.

REFERENCES

1. Adams, W. J., D. N. Kirk, D. K. Patel, V. Petrow, and I. A. Stuart-Webb, J. Chem. Soc., **1954**, 2298.

2. Agnello, E. J., and G. D. Laubach (to Chas. Pfizer and Co.), U.S. Patent 2,773, 868 (1956).

2a. Allport, D. C., and J. D. Bu'Lock, J. Chem. Soc., **1958**, 4090.

3. Amis, E. S., and V. K. LaMer, Science, **90**, 90 (1939).

4. Amis, E. S., and V. K. LaMer, J. Am. Chem. Soc., **61**, 905 (1939).

5. Amis, E. S., and S. E. Cook, J. Am. Chem. Soc., **63**, 2621 (1941).

6. Amis, E. S., and J. B. Price, J. Phys. Chem., **47**, 338 (1943).

7. Amis, E. S., and R. T. Overmen, J. Am. Chem. Soc., **66**, 941 (1944).

8. Androp, S., H. E. Ratcliffe, and S. Katzenelbogen, Am. J. Med. Sci., **206**, 86 (1943); Chem. Abstracts, **37**, 5774 (1943).

9. Antonucci, R., S. Bernstein, R. Littell, K. J. Sax, and J. H. Williams, J. Org. Chem., **17**, 1341 (1952).

10. Applequist, D. E., and J. D. Roberts, Chem. Revs., **54**, 1065 (1954).

10a. Arth, G. E., G. I. Poos, and L. H. Sarett (to Merck and Co.), U.S. Patent 2, 864, 818 (1958).

10b. Arth, G. E., G. I. Poos, and L. H. Sarett (to Merck and Co.), U.S. Patent 2, 934, 532 (1960).

11. Asahina, Y., T. Sano, and T. Mayekawa, Ber., **71B**, 312 (1938).

12. Asahina, Y., and K. Yamaguti, Ber., **71B**, 318 (1938).

13. Asahina, Y., and H. Kawahata, Ber., **72B**, 1540 (1939).

13a. Asinger, F., and F. Ebeneder, Ber., **75**, 1344 (1942).

13b. Asinger, F., F. Ebeneder, and H. Eckoldt, PB 70183, Frame 893.

14. Asinger, F., M. Thiel, and E. Pallas, Ann., **602**, 37 (1957).

15. Asinger, F., M. Thiel, and H. Kaltwasser, Ann., **606**, 67 (1957).

16. Asinger, F., M. Thiel, and I. Kalzendorf, Ann., **610**, 25 (1957).

16a. Asinger, F., and M. Thiel, Ger. (East) Patent 14, 351 (1958); Chem. Abstracts, **53**, 10252 (1959).

17. Asinger, F., M. Thiel, G. Peschel, and K. H. Meinicke, Ann., **619**, 145 (1958).

18. Asinger, F., and M. Thiel, Angew. Chem., **70**, 667 (1958).

18a. Asinger, F., M. Thiel, and H. Sedlak, Ann., **634**, 164 (1960).

18b. Asinger, F., M. Thiel, H. Usbeck, K. H. Gröbe, H. Grundmann, and S. Tränkner, Ann., **634**, 144 (1960).

19. Asinger, F., G. Geiseler, and M. Hoppe, Ber., **91**, 2130 (1958).

19a.   Auerbach, M. E., Ind. Eng. Chem., Anal. Ed., 15, 492 (1943).

20.   Bacchetti, T., and A. Sartori, Gazz. chim. ital., 83, 655 (1953); Chem. Abstracts, 49, 845 (1955).

21.   Bacchetti, T., A. Sartori, and A. Fiecchi, Gazz. chim. ital., 83, 1031 (1953); Chem. Abstracts, 49, 8287 (1955).

22.   Bacchetti, T., Rend. ist. lombardo sci. Pt. I. Classe sci. mat. e nat., 91, 581 (1957); Chem. Abstracts, 52, 16191 (1958).

22a.   Bacchetti, T., and U. Ferrati, Gazz. chim. ital., 86, 722 (1956).

23.   Backer, H. J., and G. L. Wiggerink, Rec. trav. chim., 60, 453 (1941).

24.   Badinand, A., and J. Guiraud, Trav. soc. pharm. Montpellier, 14, No. 3, 119 (1954); Chem. Abstracts, 49, 8747 (1955).

25.   Badische Anilin- and Soda-Fabrik, Ger. Patent 53, 934 (1889).

26.   Badische Anilin- and Soda-Fabrik, Ger. Patent 55, 094 (1889).

27.   Badische Anilin- and Soda-Fabrik, Ger. Patent 57, 388 (1889).

28.   Badische Anilin- and Soda-Fabrik, Ger. Patent 57, 856 (1889).

29.   Baggesgaard-Rasmussen, H., and S. C. Jespersen, Compt. rend. trav. lab. Carsberg, Sēr. chim., 22, 54 (1938); Chem. Abstracts, 32, 6172 (1938).

30.   Baker, B. R., K. Hewson, L. Goodman, and A. Benitez, J. Am. Chem. Soc., 80, 6577 (1958).

31.   Baldeschwieler, E. L., and H. A. Cassar, J. Am. Chem. Soc., 51, 2969 (1929).

32.   Barltrop, J. A., and K. J. Morgan, J. Chem. Soc., 1956, 4245.

33.   Bayer and Co., Ger. Patent 70, 857 (1892).

34.   Bayer and Co., Ger. Patent 80, 667 (1892).

35.   Bayer and Co., Ger. Patent 95, 918 (1895); Chem. Zentr., 1898, II, 688

36.   Bayer and Co., Brit. Patent 748, 884 (1956); Chem. Abstracts, 50, 15246 (1956).

37.   Bayer and Co., Brit. Patent 759, 871 (1956); Chem. Abstracts, 51, 9171 (1957) - cf. ref. 422.

37a.   Bayer and Co., Brit. Patent 796, 759 (1958); Chem. Abstracts, 53, 2634 (1959).

37b.   Bayer and Co., Brit. Patent 806, 709 (1958); Chem. Abstracts, 53, 14527 (1959).

38.   Berg, A., and H. Fiedler (to Dr. Karl Thomae G.m.b.H.), U.S. Patent 2, 886, 488 (1959).

38a.   Berg, A., and H. Fiedler (to Dr. Karl Thomae G.m.b.H.), Ger. Patent 1, 023, 562 (1958).

38b.   Berg, A., and H. Fiedler (to Dr. Karl Thomae G.m.b.H.), Ger. Patent 1, 031, 471 (1958).

39. Bergmann, E. D., D. Lavie, and S. Pinchas, J. Am. Chem. Soc., **73**, 5662 (1951).

40. Bergmann, E. D., E. Meeron, Y. Hirshberg, and S. Pinchas, Rec. trav. chim., **71**, 200 (1952).

41. Bernthsen, A., Ber., **22**, 3327 (1889).

42. Bernthsen, A., Ber., **23**, 3088 (1890).

43. Birge, R. T., and S. F. Acree, J. Am. Chem. Soc., **41**, 1031 (1919).

44. Bistrzycki, A., and B. Brenken, Helv. Chim. Acta, **3**, 447 (1920).

45. Bistrzycki, A., and A. Traub, Helv. Chim. Acta, **7**, 935 (1924).

46. Blackshear, C. C., Am. Chem. J., **14**, 455 (1892).

47. Blanchard, W. M., Am. Chem. J., **30**, 485 (1903).

48. Blanchard, W. M., Am. Chem. J., **30**, 492 (1903).

49. Blaser, B., H. Haas, and J. H. Helberger (to Böhme Fettchemie), U.S. Patent 2, 793, 229 (1957), and Brit. Patent 756, 105 (1957).

50. Blaser, B., and H. Haas (to Böhme Fettchemie), U.S. Patent 2, 806, 876 (1957).

50a. Blow, D. M., and A. Rich, J. Am. Chem. Soc., **82**, 3572 (1960).

51. Böhme, H., F. Frimuth, and E. Mundlos, Ber., **87**, 1661 (1954).

52. Böhme Fettchemie, Brit. Patent 764, 340 (1956); Chem. Abstracts, **51**, 12956 (1957).

53. Böhme Fettchemie, Brit. Patent 774, 563 (1957); Chem. Abstracts, **51**, 16519 (1957).

54. Böhme Fettchemie, Brit. Patent 775, 026 (1957); Chem. Abstracts, **51**, 16534 (1957).

54a. Bol'shakova, A. A., Nauch. Doklady Vysshei Shkoly, Khim. i Khim, Tekhnol, **1958**, 696; Chem. Abstracts, **53**, 7731 (1959).

55. Bordwell, F. G., C. M. Suter, and A. J. Webber, J. Am. Chem. Soc., **67**, 827 (1945).

56. Bordwell, F. G., and H. M. Anderson, J. Am. Chem. Soc., **75**, 4959 (1953).

57. Bordwell, F. G., and G. W. Crosby, J. Am. Chem. Soc., **78**, 5367 (1956).

58. Bordwell, F. G., and C. E. Osborne, J. Am. Chem. Soc., **81**, 1995 (1959).

59. Bordwell, F. G., R. D. Chapman, and C. E. Osborne, J. Am. Chem. Soc., **81**, 2002 (1959).

60. Bordwell, F. G., C. E. Osborne, and R. D. Chapman, J. Am. Chem. Soc., **81**, 2698 (1959).

60a. Bordwell, F. G., C. M. Suter, and A. J. Webber, J. Am. Chem. Soc., **67**, 827 (1945).

61.   Boyd, W. C., and A. W. Rowe, J. Am. Chem. Soc., 52, 4954 (1930).

62.   Brightman, C. L., J. J. Hopfield, M. R. Meacham, and S. F. Acree, J. Am. Chem. Soc., 40, 1940 (1918).

63.   British Dyestuffs Corp., Ltd., Fr. Patent 653, 595 (1928); Chem. Abstracts, 23, 3816 (1929).

64.   Brode, W. R., J. Am. Chem. Soc., 46, 581 (1924).

65.   Broderick, E. (to Rohm and Haas), U.S. Patent 2, 900, 393 (1959).

66.   Bruice, T. C., and A. B. Sayigh, J. Am. Chem. Soc., 81, 3416 (1959).

66a. Bruice, T. C., and R. Markiw, J. Am. Chem. Soc., 79, 3150 (1957).

66b. Brunken, J., G. Bach, H. Pietrzok, W. Schlockermann, and W. Zeh, Ger. (East) Patent 11, 957 (1956); Chem. Abstracts, 53, 950 (1959).

67.   Bucher, J. E., [cf. I. Remsen and A. P. Saunders, Am. Chem. J., 17, 347 (1895)].

67a. Burger, J. W., and Ti-Li Loo, Science, 129, 778 (1959).

68.   Burton, H., and S. B. David, J. Chem. Soc., 1952, 2193.

68a. Butler, J. H., J. F. Jackson, J. B. Polya, and J. Tetlow, Enzymologia, 20, 119 (1959); Chem. Abstracts, 53, 22127 (1959).

68b. Carruthers, W., and J. D. Gray, J. Chem. Soc., 1958, 1280.

69.   Chambers, V. J., Am. Chem. J., 30, 373 (1903).

69a. Chen, D. T. Y., and K. J. Laidler, Can. J. Chem., 37, 599 (1959).

69b. Cheymol, J., F. Bovrillet, and H. Puppel, Therapie, 12, 72 (1957); Chem. Abstracts, 53, 1554 (1959).

70.   Christiansen, W. G., J. Am. Chem. Soc., 47, 2244 (1925).

71.   Chrzaszczewski, J., M. Kosiński, and M. Wroński, Przemsyl Chem., 12(35), 647 (1946); Chem. Abstracts, 52, 11785 (1958).

71a. Chrzaszczewski, J., and M. Kosiński, Zeszyty Nauk. Uniw. lódz, Ser. II Nauki Mat.-Przyrod., No. 3, 145 (1957).

72.   Clark, W. M., and H. H. Lubs, J. Wash. Acad. of Sciences, 6, 483 (1916).

73.   Clarke, H. T., and E. E. Dreger, Org. Syntheses, Coll. Vol., I, 2nd Ed., 495, John Wiley and Son, New York, 1941.

73a. Clinton, R. O., R. G. Christiansen, H. C. Newmann, and S. C. Laskowski, J. Am. Chem. Soc., 79, 6475 (1957).

73b. Clinton, R. O. (to Sterling Drug Inc.), U.S. Patent 2, 880, 233 (1959).

74.   Cobb, P. H., Am. Chem. J., 35, 486 (1906).

75.   Cohen, A., J. Am. Chem. Soc., 44, 1851 (1922).

76.   Cohen, A., Biochem. J., 16, 32 (1922).

77.   Cohen, A., Pub. Health Repts., 41, 3051 (1926).

78. Colichman, E. L., J. Am. Chem. Soc., 73, 3385 (1951).

79. Cope, A. C., and E. Farkas, J. Org. Chem., 19, 385 (1954).

80. Copenhaver, J. W. (to General Aniline and Film Corp.), Brit. Patent 642,253 (1950); Chem. Abstracts, 45, 4746 (1951).

81. Copenhaver, J. W., U.S. Patent 2, 551, 421 (1951).

82. Cray, F. M., and G. M. Westrip, Trans. Faraday Soc., 21, 326 (1925).

83. Croxall, W. J., J. O. VanHook, and R. Luckenbaugh, J. Am. Chem. Soc., 71, 2741 (1949).

84. Croxall, W. J., and J. O. VanHook, (to Rohm and Haas Co.), U.S. Patent 2, 500, 155 (1950); Chem. Abstracts, 44, 5395 (1950).

85. Cumming, W. M., and G. D. Muir, J. Roy. Tech. Coll. Glasgow, 3, 223 (1934); Chem. Abstracts, 28, 4410 (1934).

86. Cumming, W. M., and G. D. Muir, J. Roy. Tech. Coll., 3, 562 (1936); Chem. Abstracts, 30, 4491 (1936).

87. van Dam, H., Ing. chim., 24, 41 (1940); Chem. Abstracts, 36, 6878 (1942).

88. Davis, M. M., and P. Schuhmann, J. Research Natl. Bureau Standards, 39, 221 (1947).

89. Davis, M. M., P. J. Schuhmann, and M. E. Lovelace, J. Research Natl. Bureau Standards, 41, 27 (1948) (Research Paper No. 1900).

90. Davies, W., and J. H. Dick, J. Chem. Soc., 1932, 2042.

91. Davies, W. H., J. Chem. Soc., 1951, 1357.

92. Davies, W. H., (to Imperial Chemical Industries, Ltd.), Brit. Patent 650, 003 (1951); Chem. Abstracts, 45, 8033 (1951).

93. Dazzi, J., (to Monsanto), U.S. Patent 667, 506 (1954).

94. Delauney, A., Compt. rend. soc. biol., 138, 301 (1944); Chem. Abstracts, 39, 4393 (1945).

95. Delisle, A., Ber., 22, 2205 (1889).

96. Demont, P., Rev. gén. Mat. Col., 24, 66 (1920); Chem. Zentr., 1920 IV, 135.

96a. D'Silva, J. L., and E. W. McClelland, J. Chem. Soc., 1933, 2883.

96b. Dermer, O. C., Wright Air Development Center Tech. Rept. 55-447 (PB 121796) (June 1956).

97. DeStevens, G., A. Frutchey, A. Halamandaris, and H. A. Luts, J. Am. Chem. Soc., 79, 5263 (1957).

98. DiBella, L., Boll. soc. med-chiv. Modena, 48, 477 (1948); Chem. Abstracts, 45, 25 (1951).

99. Dittmar, G., R. Pütter, and F. Sückfull (to Bayer), U.S. Patent 2, 734, 052 (1956).

Chapter 4

100. Dittmar, G., R. Pütter, and F. Stückfull (to Bayer), Ger. Patent 940, 483 (1956).

102. Djerassi, C., E. Batres, J. Romo, and C. Rosenkranz, J. Am. Chem. Soc., 74, 3634 (1952).

103. Djerassi, C., and M. Gorman, J. Am. Chem. Soc., 75, 3704 (1953).

104. Djerassi, C., and R. R. Engle, J. Am. Chem. Soc., 75, 3838 (1953).

105. Djerassi, C., M. Gorman, F. X. Markley, and E. B. Oldenburg, J. Am. Chem. Soc., 77, 568 (1955).

106. Djerassi, C., M. Gorman, and J. A. Henry, J. Am. Chem. Soc., 77, 4647 (1955).

107. Djerassi, C., and J. Grossman, J. Am. Chem. Soc., 79, 2553 (1957).

108. Djerassi, C., M. Shamma, and T. Y. Kan, J. Am. Chem. Soc., 80, 4723 (1958).

108a. Douglas, I. B., and B. S. Farah, J. Org. Chem., 26, 351 (1961).

108b. Doss, K. S. G., and S. L. Gupta, Sci. and Culture (Calcutta), 22, 102 (1956); Chem. Abstracts, 53, 4856 (1959).

109. Dressel, O., and R. Kothe, Ber., 27, 2137 (1894).

110. van Duin, C. F., Rec. trav. chim., 40, 724 (1921).

111. Dunning, F., and L. H. Farinholt, J. Am. Chem. Soc., 51, 804 (1929).

112. Dunning, F., and A. E. Stickels (to Hynso, Westcott, and Dunning), U. S. Patent 1, 863, 241 (1932); Chem. Abstracts, 26, 4134 (1932).

112a. Durden, J. A., H. A. Stansbury, Jr., and W. H. Catlette, J. Am. Chem. Soc., 82, 3082 (1960).

113. Durden, J. A., H. A. Stansbury, Jr., and W. H. Catlette, J. Am. Chem. Soc., 81, 1943 (1959).

113a. Eliel, E. L., and V. G. Badding, J. Am. Chem. Soc., 81, 6087 (1959).

114. Emerson, W. S., and T. M. Patrick, Jr., J. Org. Chem., 13, 729 (1948).

115. Emerson, W. S., and T. M. Patrick, Jr., (to Monsanto), U.S. Patent 2, 503, 198 (1950); Chem. Abstracts, 40, 6440 (1950).

116. Enders, E., (to Bayer), Ger. Patent 951, 524 (1956); Chem. Abstracts, 51, 10067 (1957).

117. Erdmann, H., Ann., 247, 306 (1888).

118. Erdtman, H. G. H., (to Kärnbolaget Aktiebolag), Swedish Patent 130, 523 (1951); Chem. Abstracts, 45, 8555 (1951).

119. Erdtman, H. G. H., U.S. Patent 2, 623, 881 (1952); Chem. Abstracts, 48, 719 (1954).

120. Ettlinger, M. G., J. Am. Chem. Soc., 72, 4792 (1950).

121. Evans, R. M., J. B. Fraser, and L. N. Owen, J. Chem. Soc., 1949, 248.

122. Ewer and Pick, Ger. Patent 52, 724 (1888); Chem. Zentr., 1890, II, 896.

C$_3$OS Ring Systems

123. Exner, O., and O. Wichterle, Chem. Listy, 50, 922 (1956); Chem. Abstracts, 50, 16660 (1956).

124. Fahlberg, C., and A. List, Ger. Patent, 35, 717 (1886).

125. Fahlberg, C., and R. Barge, Ber., 22, 754 (1889).

125a. Farrar, W. V., J. Appl. Chem., 10, No. 5, 207 (1960).

126. Feist, F., H. Pauschardt, and H. Dibbern, Ber., 58B, 2311 (1925).

126a. Fernholz, E. (to E. R. Squibb and Sons); U.S. Patent 2, 356, 154 (1944) and U.S. Patent 2, 378, 918 (1945); Chem. Abstracts, 39, 1515, 5051 (1945).

127. Fieser, L. F., J. Am. Chem. Soc., 76, 1945 (1954).

128. Findley, T., J. C. Edwards, E. Clinton, and H. L. White, Arch. Internal Med., 70, 935 (1942); Chem. Abstracts, 37, 4460 (1943).

129. Firma Kalle and Co., Fr. Patent 852, 020 (1940).

130. Fitt, P. S., and L. N. Owen, J. Chem. Soc., 1957, 2240.

131. Franglen, G. T., Nature, 175, 134 (1954).

131a. Franglen, G., and C. Gosselin, Nature, 181, 1152 (1958).

131b. Frèrejacque, M., Compt. Rend., 196, 1513 (1933).

132. Freas, R., and E. A. Provine, J. Am. Chem. Soc., 50, 2014 (1928).

133. Fredga, A., Ber., 71B, 289 (1938).

133a. Freeman, K. A., and C. D. Ritchie, J. Assoc. Offic. Agr. Chemists, 40, 1108 (1957).

134. Friedländer, P., and F. Mauthner, Z. Farben-Textil-Chem., 3, 333 (1904); Chem. Zentr., 1904 II, 1176.

135. Friedländer, P., S. Karamessinis, and O. Schenk, Ber., 55B, 45 (1922).

135a. Fries, K., Ber., 45, 2965 (1912).

135b. Fries, K., and S. Shürman, Ber., 52, 2170 (1919).

136. Fritsch, P., Ber., 29, 2290 (1896).

137. Furukawa, K., T. Okada, I. Tamai, and R. Oda, Kôgyô Kagaku Zassi, 59, 221 (1956); Chem. Abstracts, 51, 10362 (1956).

138. Furukawa, K., I. Tamai, and R. Oda, Kôgyô Kagaku Zasshi, 59, 1028 (1956); Chem. Abstracts, 52, 10917 (1958).

139. Gaertner, V. R. (to Monsanto), U.S. Patent 2, 809, 973 (1957).

139a. Gaertner, V. R. (to Monsanto), U.S. Patent 2, 957, 905 (1960).

139b. Gaertner, V. R., and G. H. Birum (to Monsanto), U.S. Patent 2, 965, 665 (1960).

140. Gattermann, L., Ber., 32, 1136 (1899)

141. Gebauer-Fuelnegg, E., and E. Haemmerle, J. Am. Chem. Soc., 53, 2648 (1931).

142. Geigy, J. R., A.-G., Ger. Patent 98, 466 (1897); Chem. Zentr., 1898 II, 836.

143. Geigy, J. R., A.-G., Swiss Patent 236, 226 (1945); Chem. Abstracts, **43**, 5047 (1949).

144. Geigy, J. R., A.-G., Swiss Patent 240, 570 (1946); Chem. Abstracts, **43**, 4020 (1949).

145. Geigy, J. R., A.-G., Swiss Patent 251, 382 (1948); Chem. Abstracts, **44**, 664 (1950).

146. Giegy, J. R., A.-G., Swiss Patent 251, 640 (1948); Chem. Abstracts, **44**, 664 (1950).

147. Geigy, J. R., A.-G., Swiss Patent 254, 804 (1949); Chem. Abstracts, **44**, 1542 (1950).

148. Geigy, J. R., A.-G., Swiss Patent 256, 518 (1949); Chem. Abstracts, **44**, 663 (1950).

149. Georgieff, K. K., and A. Dupré, Canadian J. Chem., **37**, 1104 (1959).

150. Ges. für chem. Ind., Basel, Ger. Patent 407, 003 (1923); Chem. Zentr., **1925** I, 1244.

151. Ges. für chem. Ind., Basel, Ger. Patent 430, 551 (1925); Chem. Zentr., **1926** II, 1196.

152. Ges. für chem. Ind., Basel, Ger. Patent 467, 349 (1925); Chem. Abstracts, **23**, 1280 (1929).

153. Gevaert Photo-Producten N.V., Belg. Patent 535, 687-8 (1955); Chem. Abstracts, **51**, 17545 (1957).

154. Gevaert Photo-Producten N.V., Belg. Patent 561, 082 (1958).

155. Gibbs, R. C., and C. V. Shapiro, Proc. Natl. Acad. Sciences, Washington, **14**, 699 (1928); Chem. Zentr., **1928** II, 2624.

156. Gibbs, R. C., and C. V. Shapiro, J. Am. Chem. Soc., **50**, 1755 (1928).

156a. Gibbs, R. C., and C. V. Shapiro, J. Am. Chem. Soc., **51**, 1755 (1929).

157. Gibbs, R. C., and C. V. Shapiro, J. Am. Chem. Soc., **50**, 2798 (1928).

158. Gibson, D. T., and S. Smiles, J. Chem. Soc., **123**, 2388 (1923).

159. Gillespie, L. J., J. Am. Chem. Soc., **42**, 742 (1920).

160. Gilliard, Monnet, and Cartier, (to Société Chimique des Usines der Rhône), Ger. Patent 94, 948 (1896); Chem. Zentr., **1898** I, 540.

161. Gluesenkamp, E. W., and M. Kosmin (to Monsanto), U.S. Patent 2, 359, 291 (1944); Chem. Abstracts, **39**, 1259 (1945).

161a. Goldann, K. (to Böhme Fettchemie), Ger. Patent 1, 028, 527 (1958).

162. Goldberger, I., Monatsh., **37**, 125 (1916).

163. Goodman, L., A. Benitez, C. D. Anderson, and B. R. Baker, J. Am. Chem. Soc., **80**, 6582 (1958).

164. Graebe, C., and H. Kraft, Ber., **39**, 2507 (1906).

# C$_3$OS Ring Systems

165. Greenwood, D., and H. A. Stevenson, J. Chem. Soc., 1953, 1514.

165a. Gülübov, A., and M. Kitova, Sbornik Trudove, Visshiya Med. Inst., "I. P. Pavlov", 11, 145 (1958); Chem. Abstracts, 53, 16467 (1959).

165b. Gülübov, A., M. Kitova, and P. Petkov, Sbornik Trudove Visshiya Med. Inst. "I. P. Pavlov", 11, 151 (1958); Chem. Abstracts., 53, 16467 (1959).

166. Gündel, W., and H. Haas (to Böhme Fettchemie), Ger. Patent 1, 001, 676 (1957).

167. Gündel, W., and H. Haas (to Böhme Fettchemie), Ger. Patent 1, 016, 257 (1957).

168. Güntelberg, E., and E. Schiödt, Z. phys. Chem., 135, 393 (1928).

169. Haas, H. (to Böhme Fettchemie), Ger. Patent Appln. B 25, 970 (1955).

170. Haas, H. (to Böhme Fettchemie), Ger. Patent 937, 949 (1956); Chem. Abstracts, 50, 12109 (1956).

171. Haas, H. (to Böhme Fettchemie), Ger. Patent 938, 186 (1956); Chem. Abstracts, 50, 12096.

172. Haas, H., and W. Gündel (to Böhme Fettchemie), U.S. Patent 2, 822, 366 (1958); Chem. Abstracts, 32, 10155 (1958).

173. Haas, H. (to Böhme Fettchemie), U.S. Patent 2, 833, 781 (1958); see reference 54.

173a. Haberl, R., F. Grass, O. Hromatka, K. Brauner, and A. Preisinger, Monatsh., 86, 551 (1955).

174. Hantzsch, A., Ber., 60, 2537 (1927).

174a. Hantzsch, A., Ber., 61, 1776 (1928).

174b. Hantzsch, A., and J. H. Weber, Ber., 20, 3118 (1887).

175. Harden, W. C., J. Am. Chem. Soc., 49, 3139 (1927).

176. Harden, W. C., and N. L. Drake, J. Am. Chem. Soc., 51, 562 (1929).

177. Harden, W. C., and N. L. Drake, J. Am. Chem. Soc., 51, 2278 (1929).

178. Harden, W. C. (to Hynson, Westcott, and Dunning, Inc.), U.S. Patent 1, 786, 611 (1930); Chem. Abstracts, 25, 968 (1931).

179. Harding, J. S., and L. N. Owen, J. Chem. Soc., 1954, 1528.

180. Haring, M. M., and H. H. Heller, J. Am. Chem. Soc., 63, 1024 (1941).

180a. Hart, L. E., E. W. McClelland, and F. S. Fowkes, J. Chem. Soc., 1938, 2114.

181. Hart, M. C., and H. P. Anderson, J. Am. Chem. Soc., 56, 2752 (1934).

182. Hastings, A. B., and J. Sendroy, J. Biol. Chem., 61, 695 (1924).

183. Havlik, A. J., and N. Kharasch, J. Am. Chem. Soc., 77, 1150 (1955).

184. Haywood, C., V. C. Dickerson, and M. C. Collins, J. Cellular Comp. Physiol. 25, 145 (1945); Chem. Abstracts, 39, 4984 (1945).

185. Heitman, A. H. C., J. Am. Chem. Soc., 34, 1591 (1912).

186. Helberger, H. J., Reichsamt Wirtschaftsausbau, Chem. Ber., Prüf-Nr. 15 (PB 52013), 269 (1942); Chem. Abstracts 41, 4101 (1947).

187. Helberger, J. H., G. Manecke, and H. M. Fischer, Ann., 562, 23 (1949).

188. Helberger, J. H., G. Manecke, and R. Heyden, Ann., 565, 22 (1949).

189. Helberger, J. H., (to Henkel and Cie), Ger. Patent 823, 447 (1951).

189a. Helberger, J. H. (to Henkel and Cie), Ger. Patent 860, 637 (1952).

190. Helberger, J. H., G. Manecke, H. Lantermann, and H. M. Fischer (to Böhme Fettchemie), Ger. Patent 887, 341 (1953); Chem. Abstracts, 49, 3268 (1955).

192. Helberger, J. H., and H. Benecke (to Böhme Fettchemie), Ger. Patent 899,939 (1953); Chem. Abstracts, 49, 2512 (1955).

193. Helberger, J. H., and R. W. J. Heyden (to Böhme Fettchemie), Ger. Patent Appln. B 5804 (1953).

194. Helberger, J. H., and G. Manecke (to Böhme Fettchemie), Ger. Patent Appln. B 5805 (1953).

195. Helberger, J. H., and R. W. J. Heyden (to Böhme Fettchemie), Ger. Patent Appln. B 5899 (1953).

196. Helberger, J. H., J. R. Heyden, and H. Winter, Ann., 586, 147 (1954).

197. Helberger, J. H., Ann., 588, 71 (1959).

198. Helberger, J. H., R. Heyden, and G. Manecke, (to Böhme Fettchemie), Ger. Patent 901, 054 (1954); Chem. Abstracts, 49, 3248 (1955).

199. Helberger, J. H., and W. Grublewski (to Böhme Fettchemie), Ger. Patent 901, 288 (1954); Chem. Abstracts, 50, 9443 (1956)

200. Helberger, J. H., R. W. J. Heyden, and H. Lantermann (to Böhme Fettchemie), Ger. Patent 902, 615 (1954); Chem. Abstracts, 50, 9443 (1956).

201. Helberger, J. H., and R. W. J. Heyden (to Böhme Fettchemie), Ger. Patent 904, 894 (1954); Chem. Abstracts, 49, 3264 (1955).

202. Helberger, J. H., and R. W. J. Heyden, (to Böhme Fettchemie), Ger. Patent 907, 892 (1954); Chem. Abstracts, 49, 3249 (1955).

203. Helberger, J. H., Ger. Patent 915, 693 (1954); Chem. Abstracts, 49, 10357 (1955).

204. Helberger, J. H., and R. W. J. Heyden, (to Böhme Fettchemie), Ger. Patent 930, 687 (1955); Chem. Abstracts, 50, 10129 (1956).

205. Helberger, J. H., Ger. Patent 943, 830 (1956); Chem. Abstracts, 51, 4412 (1957).

206. Helberger, J. H. (to Böhme Fettchemie), Brit. Patent 782, 094 (1957); Chem. Abstracts, 52, 2895 (1958).

207. Helberger, J. H., and J. B. Niederl (to Böhme Fettchemie), Ger. Patent 1, 018, 421 (1947).

208. Heller, G., W. Eisenschmidt, R. Reichardt, and H. Wild, Z. angew. Chem., 41, 171 (1928).

209. Henderson, W. E., Am. Chem. J., 25, 1 (1901).

209a. Heremans, J., and J. P. Vaerman, Clin. Chim. Acta, 3, 430 (1958); Chem. Abstracts, 53, 3345 (1959).

210. Herrick, J. F., F. C. Mann, and H. L. Sheehan, J. Pharmacol., 66, 73, (1939); Chem. Abstracts, 33, 5507 (1939).

211. Herzog, H. L., M. A. Jernik, M. E. Tully, and E. B. Hershberg, J. Am. Chem. Soc., 75, 4425 (1953).

212. Hewitt, L. F., Biochem. J., 21, 1305 (1927).

212a. Hinsberg, O., J. prakt. chem., 90, 345 (1914); 91, 307 (1915); 93, 277 (1916).

212b. Hill, R. K., J. G. Martin, and W. H. Stouch, J. Am. Chem. Soc., 83, 4006 (1961).

213. Hinsberg, O., and R. Meyer, Ber., 60, 1914 (1927).

214. Hinsberg, O., and R. Meyer, Ber., 64B, 702 (1931).

215. Hirsch, E. F., J. Biol. Chem., 63, 55 (1925).

216. Höchster Farbw., Ger. Patent 67, 563 (1893).

217. Hodgson, H. H., S. Birtwell, and J. Walker, J. Chem. Soc., 1941, 770.

218. Hoechst, Brit. Patent 744, 972 (1956); Chem. Abstracts, 50, 14237 (1956).

218a. Hoechst, Brit. Patent 749, 908 (1956); Chem. Abstracts, 50, 17463 (1956).

219. Hoechst, Brit. Patent 749, 308 (1956); Chem. Abstracts, 50, 17464 (1956).

220. Hoerger, F. D., Ph.D. Thesis, Purdue Univ., Sept. 24, 1954.

221. Hoffman, R. A. (to Du Pont), U.S. Patent 2, 469, 727 (1949); Chem Abstracts, 43, 4964 (1949).

222. Hellis, F. S., Am. Chem. J., 23, 233 (1900).

223. Holmberg, B., Arkiv Kemi, Mineral. Geol., 12B, No. 2, 4 pp. (1935); Chem. Abstracts, 29, 6596 (1935).

224. Holmberg, B., Arkiv Kemi, Mineral. Geol., A15, No. 24, 8 pp. (1942); Chem. Abstracts, 38, 2944 (1944).

225. Holmberg, B., Arkiv Kemi, 2, 567 (1950); Chem. Abstracts, 46, 100 (1952).

226. Holmes, W. B., Am. Chem. J., 25, 202 (1901).

227. Holmes, W. C., J. Am. Chem. Soc., 46, 627 (1924).

228. Holmes, W. C., and E. F. Snyder, J. Am. Chem. Soc., 47, 221, 226 (1925).

229. Horioka, M., Yakugaku Zasshi, 77, 200 (1957); Chem. Abstracts, 51, 8367 (1957).

230. Howe, H. E., and K. S. Gibson, Phys. Rev., 10, 767 (1917).

231. Hromatka, O., and E. Engel, Monatsh., 78, 29 (1948).

232. Hromatka, O., and E. Engel, Montash., **78**, 38 (1948).

232a. Hromatka, O., and R. Haberl, Monatsh., **85**, 830 (1954).

232b. Hromatka, O., and R. Haberl, Monatsh., **85**, 1082 (1954).

232c. Hromatka, O., and R. Haberl, Monatsh., **85**, 1088 (1954).

233. Hughes, R. M., (to J. R. Geigy A. -G.), Brit. Patent 575, 285 (1946); Chem. Abstracts, **41**, 7763 (1947).

233a. Huisgen, R., H. König, G. Binsch, and H. S. Sturm, Angew. Chem., **73**, 368 (1961).

234. I. G. Farbenindustrie A. -G., Fr. Patent 732, 732 (1933); Chem. Abstracts, **27**, 1005 (1933).

235. Isitobi, K., Folia Endocrinol. Japan, **15**, 62 (1939); Chem. Abstracts, **36**, 2913 (1942).

236. Ito, H., (to Nippon Chemical Industries Co.), Japan Patent 4927 (1951); Chem. Abstracts, **47**, 9364 (1953).

237. Jaeger, R. H., and H. Smith, Chemistry and Industry, **1954**, 1106.

238. Jaeger, R. H., and H. Smith, J. Chem. Soc., **1955**, 160.

239. Jaeger, R. H., and H. Smith, J. Chem. Soc., **1955**, 646.

240. Javery, A. T., G. V. Jadhav, and R. C. Shah, J. Sci. Ind. Research (India), **11B**, 5 (1952); Chem. Abstracts, **47**, 6902 (1953).

241. Jenny, W., Helv. Chim. Acta, **41**, 317, 326 (1958).

242. Jones, W., Am. Chem. J., **16**, 366 (1894).

243. Jones, W., Am. Chem. J., **17**, 556 (1895).

244. Jönsson, K., Svensk Kem. Tidskr., **34**, 192 (1923); Chem. Zentr., **1923 III**, 1065.

245. Jönsson, K., Thesis, Lund University, 1929.

246. Kalle & Co., Ger. Patent 343, 056 (1921); Chem. Abstracts, **17**, 1247 (1923).

247. Kalle & Co., Ger. Patent 323, 147 (1921); Chem. Zentr., **1922 II**, 143

248. Karabinos, J. V., and P. M. Hyde, J. Am. Chem. Soc., **70**, 428 (1948).

249. Karslake, W. J., and P. A. Bond, J. Am. Chem. Soc., **31**, 405 (1909).

250. Karslake, W. J., and P. A. Bond, J. Am. Chem. Soc., **38**, 1338 (1916).

251. Karyakin, Yu. V., J. Applied Chem. (U.S.S.R.), **13**, 1713 (1940).

252. Kastle, J. H., Am. Chem. J., **11**, 177 (1889).

253. Kaufmann, H. P., and H. Zobel, Ber., **55**, 1499 (1922).

254a. Kaufmann, H. P., and E. Weber, Arch. Pharm., **267**, 192 (1929).

254b. Kaufmann, H. P., Arch. Pharm., **267**, 211 (1929).

255. Kaufmann, H. P., Z. angew. Chem., **54**, 168 (1941).

C$_3$OS Ring Systems

256. Kharasch, M. S. (to du Pont), U.S. Patent 2, 383, 320 (1945).

256a. Kharasch, M. S., E. M. May, and F. R. Mayo, J. Org. Chem., **3**, 175 (1938).

257. Kharasch, M. S., and H. C. Brown, J. Am. Chem. Soc., **62**, 925 (1940).

258. Kharasch, M. S., T. H. Chao, and H. C. Brown, J. Am. Chem. Soc., **62**, 2393 (1940).

258a. Kharasch, M. S., and A. T. Read, J. Am. Chem. Soc., **61**, 3089 (1939).

258b. Kharasch, N., S. J. Potempa, and H. L. Wehrmeister, Chem. Revs., **39**, 276 (1946).

258c. Kharasch, N., and T. C. Bruice, J. Am. Chem. Soc., **73**, 3240 (1951).

258d. Kilmer, T. H. (to Air Reduction Co.), U.S. Patent 2, 890, 177 (1959).

259. Kilpatrick, M., and W. H. Mears, J. Am. Chem. Soc., **62**, 3047, 3051 (1940).

260. Kimura, G., Oriental J. Diseases Infants, **28**, 15 (1940); Chem. Abstracts, **36**, 2915 (1942).

261. Kin, P., and K. Tei, J. Chosen Med. Assoc., **28**, 1565 (1938); Chem. Abstracts, **33**, 5442 (1939).

262. Kindler, K., Archiv. der Pharmazie, **1929**, 554.

263. Kipnis, F., and J. Ornfelt, J. Am. Chem. Soc., **71**, 3555 (1949).

264. Kiprianov, I., and E. S. Timoshenko, J. Gen. Chem. (U.S.S.R.), **17**, 1468 (1947); Chem. Abstracts, **42**, 8475 (1948).

265. Klarmann, B., Ber., **85**, 162 (1952).

266. Knecht, E., and E. Hibbert, Ber., **40**, 3819 (1907).

267. Koch, H., Ger. Patent 56, 058 (1890).

268. Kögl, F., J. H. Verbeek, H. Erxleben, and W. A. J. Borg, J. physiol. chem., **279**, 121 (1943); Chem. Abstracts, **38**, 1236, 3978 (1944).

269. Kohler, E. P., Am. Chem. J., **31**, 243 (1904).

270. Kolthoff, I. M., Rec. trav. chim., **40**, 775 (1921).

271. Kolthoff, I. M., Rec. trav. chim., **43**, 144 (1924).

272. Kolthoff, I. M., J. Phys. Chem., **34**, 1466 (1930).

273. Kolthoff, I. M., and L. S. Guss, Compt. rend. trav. lab. Carlsberg, Sér. chim., **22**, 264 (1938); Chem. Abstracts, **32**, 6135 (1938).

274. Kolthoff, I. M., and L. S. Guss, J. Am. Chem. Soc., **60**, 2516 (1938).

275. Körbl, J., Chem. listy, **51**, 1304 (1957); Chem. Abstracts, **51**, 17846 (1957).

275a. Körbl, J., V. Svodboda, and D. Terzijska, Chem. and Ind. (London), **1958**, 1232.

275b. Kosheleva, G. N., Trudy Vsesoyuz Nauch.-Issledovatel. Inst. Khim. Reaktivov, **1956**, No. 21, 54; Chem. Abstracts, **53**, 8919 (1959).

275c. Kosheleva, G. N., T. V. Zimakova, S. B. Petrovskaya, and K. N. Efimova, Russian Patent 127, 254 (1960); Chem. Abstracts, **54**, 19604 (1960).

275d. Kosheleva, G. N., T. V. Zimakova, V. V. Grushetskiï, and K. N. Efimova, Russian Patent 127, 264 (1960); Chem. Abstracts, **54**, 18204 (1960).

276. Kuhn, L. P., and L. DeAngelis, J. Am. Chem. Soc., **71**, 3084 (1949).

277. Kul'berg, L. M., Doklady Akad. Nauk S.S.S.R., **76**, 73 (1951); Chem. Abstracts, **45**, 5568 (1951).

278. LaMer, V. K., J. Franklin Inst., **225**, 709 (1938).

279. Larsson, E., Svensk Kem. Tid., **52**, 9 (1940); Chem. Abstracts, **34**, 4045 (1940).

280. Larsson, E., Svensk Kem. Tid., **53**, 241 (1941); Chem. Abstracts, **36**, 1607 (1942).

281. Larsson, E., Ber., **76B**, 912 (1943).

282. Lecher, H. Z., and E. M. Hardy, J. Org. Chem., **20**, 475 (1955).

283. Leminger, O., Chem. Prumysl., **5 (30)**, No. 1, 7 (1955); Chem. Abstracts, **49**, 11488 (1955).

284. Leminger, O., and I. Vodák, Czech. Patent 83, 863 (1955); Chem. Abstracts, **50**, 16124 (1956).

285. Lesser. R., and G. Gad, Ber., **56**, 963 (1923) and Beilstein's Handbuch, Vol. **19 II. 326.**

286. Lesser, R., and G. Gad, Ber., **56**, 1802 (1923).

287. Lesser, R., and G. Gad, Ber., **58**, 2551 (1925)

288. Liebermann, C., and M. Voeltzkow, Ber., **13**, 276 (1880); Ann., **207**, 137 (1881).

289. Lipp, P., and M. Holl, Ber., **62B**, 499 (1929).

290. Lipp, P., and H. Knapp, Ber., **73B**, 915 (1940).

291. Lisk, G. F., Ind. Eng. Chem., **42**, 1746 (1950); U.S. Dept. Commerce OTS Report, PB 44775 (frames 5769-71 of Fiat Reel 146, PB 19920).

292. List, R., and M. Stein, Ber., **31**, 1648 (1898).

293. Lizius, J. L., and N. Evers, Analyst, **47**, 333 (1922).

294. Lubs, H. A., and W. M. Clarke, J. Washington Acad., **5**, 609 (1915); Chem. Zentr., **1916 I**, 175.

295. Lubs, H. A., and S. F. Acree, J. Am. Chem. Soc., **38**, 2772 (1916).

296. Lüttringhaus, A., and J. Ruyssen, Angew. Chem., **67**, 305 (1955).

297. Lüttringhaus, A., and H. Prinzbach, Ann., **624**, 79 (1959).

298. Lyman, J. A., Am. Chem. J., **16**, 513 (1894).

299. Maarse, J., Rec. trav. chim., **33**, 207 (1914).

300. McBain, J. W., O. E. Dubois, and K. G. Hay, J. Gen. Physiol., **9**, 451 (1926); Chem. Zentr., **1926 II**, 71.

301. Macek, K., and L. Moravek, Nature, **178**, 102 (1956).

302. McClelland, J. A. C., and S. Smiles, J. Chem. Soc., **1933**, 786.

303. McCrumb, F. R., and W. R. Kenny, J. Am. Chem. Soc., **51**, 1458 (1929).

304. McDonald, H. J., and M. B. Williamson, Naturwissenschaften, **42**, 461 (1955).

305. McGil, W. J., J. Am. Chem. Soc., **44**, 2156 (1922).

305a. Mandl, R. H., Contribs. Boyce Thompson Inst., **19**, 461 (1958); Chem. Abstracts, **53**, 2941 (1949).

306. Mecke, G. (to Max-Planck-Gesellschaft), Ger. Patent Appln. M 25777 (1956).

306a. Manecke, G., and C. Hetterich (to Max-Planck Gesellschaft), Ger. Patent 960, 540 (1957); Chem. Abstracts, **53**, 14943 (1959).

307. Manecke, G., J. Danhäuser, and C. Reich, Angew. Chem., **70** 503 (1958).

308. Marckwald, W., and H. H. Frahne, Ber., **31**, 1854 (1898).

309. Marhkham, E. C., C. A. Glover, and S. B. Knight, J. Elisha Mitchel Sci. Soc., **67**, 261 (1951); Chem. Abstracts, **46**, 9388 (1952).

309a. Marshall, J. R., and H. A. Stevenson, J. Chem. Soc., **1959**, 2360

310. Mason, R. B., and M. Kilpatrick, J. Am. Chem. Soc., **59**, 572 (1937).

311. Mathews, J. A., J. Am. Chem. Soc., **20**, 648 (1898).

312. Matsuo, T., J. Chem. Soc. Japan, Ind. Chem. Sect., **57**, 808 (1954); Chem. Abstracts, **49**, 10798 (1955).

313. Matsuo, T., J. Chem. Soc. Japan, Ind. Chem. Sect., **57**, 811 (1954); Chem. Abstracts, **49**, 10798 (1955).

314. Maurer, F. W., J. Cellular Compt. Physiol., **12**, 379 (1938); Chem. Abstracts, **33**, 8789 (1939).

315. Mazur, R. H., and E. A. Brown, J. Am. Chem. Soc., **77**, 6670 (1955).

316. Mazur, R. H. (to G. D. Searle and Co.), U.S. Patent 2, 758, 992 (1956).

317. Mehrota, R. C., Anal. Chim. Acta, **3**, 69 (1949); Chem. Abstracts, **43**, 8300 (1949).

318. Mehrota, R. C., Anal. Chim. Acta, **3**, 73 (1949); Chem. Abstracts, **43**, 8300 (1949).

319. Mehrota, R. C., Z. anal. Chem., **130**, 390 (1950); Chem. Abstracts, **44**, 8824 (1950).

320. Mehrota, R. C., Anal. Chim. Acta, **4**, 38 (1950); Chem. Abstracts, **44**, 6347 (1950).

321. Mellon, M. G., and F. D. Martin, J. Phys. Chem., **31**, 161 (1927).

322. Mensching, C. (to Schöllkopf Aniline and Chemical Company), Ger. Patent 40, 571 (1885).

323. Meyer, P., Ber., **14**, 1663 (1881).

324. Meyers, D. B., M. V. Nadkarni, and L. C. Zopf, J. Am. Pharm. Assoc., **38**, 231 (1949); Chem. Abstracts, **43**, 8609 (2949).

325. Miles, L. W. C., and L. N. Owen, J. Chem. Soc., **1952**, 817.

326. Miolati, A., Ann., **262**, 61 (1891).

327. Mitchell, P. H., K. Buch, and N. W. Rakestraw, J. conseil intern. exploration mer, 11, 183 (1936); Chem. Abstracts, **31**, 308 (1937).

328. Miyagawa, I., K. Sakurayama, and K. Sawai, Research Rept. Nagoya Ind. Sci. Research Inst., No. 8, 31 (1955); Chem. Abstracts, **50**, 12446 (1956).

329. Moale, P. R., Am. Chem. J., 20, 285 (1898).

330. Moehrke, H., H. Koch, and H. V. Freyberg (to Farbwerke Hoechst), Ger. Patent 865, 305 (1953); Chem. Abstracts, **52**, 20201 (1958).

331. Monnet, P., and J. Koetschet, Bull. soc. chim., Paris (3) 17, 690, 1030 (1897); Chem. Zentr., **1897 II**, 521 and 1898 I, 239.

331a. Müller, G. (to Bayer), Ger. Patent 1, 011, 574 (1957).

332. Mustafa, A., and A. M. Gad, J. Chem. Soc., **1949**, 384.

333. Mustafa, A., J. Chem. Soc., **1949**, 2151.

334. Mustafa, A., and M. K. Hilmy, J. Chem. Soc., **1952**, 1339.

335. Mustafa, A., and O. H. Hishmat, J. Am. Chem. Soc., **75**, 4647 (1953).

336. Mustafa, A., Chem. Revs., **54**, 195 (1954).

337. Mustafa, A., W. Asker, O. H. Hishmat, A. F. A. Shalaby, and M. Kamel, J. Am. Chem. Soc., **76**, 5447 (1954).

338. Nagase, Y., U. Matsumoto, and Y. Satake, Ann. Proc. Gifu Coll. Pharm. No. 4, 44 (1954); Chem. Abstracts, **50**, 14648 (1956).

339. Nutten, A. J., Metallurgia, **42**, 216 (1950); Chem. Abstracts, **45**, 61 (1951).

340. Nutten, A. J., Metallurgia, **42**, 407 (1950); Chem. Abstracts, 45, 2361 (1951).

341. Oddo, B., and Q. Mingoia, Gazz. chim. ital., 61, 435 (1931); Chem. Abstracts, **26**, 123 (1932).

342. Orndorff, W. R., R. C. Gibbs, M Scott, and S. D. Jackson, Phys. Rev., 17, 437 (1921).

343. Orndorff, W. R., and F. W. Sherwood, J. Am. Chem. Soc., 45, 486 (1923).

344. Orndorff, W.R., and R.S. Vose, J. Am. Chem. Soc., **46**, 1896 (1924).

345. Orndorff, W. R., and C. V. Shapiro, J. Am. Chem. Soc., **46**, 2856 (1924).

346. Orndorff, W. R., and R. T. K. Cornwell, J. Am. Chem. Soc., **48**, 981 (1926).

347. Orndorff, W. R., and N. Fuchs, J. Am. Chem. Soc., **48**, 1939 (1926).

348. Orndorff, W. R., and A. C. Purdy, J. Am. Chem. Soc., **48**, 2212 (1926).

349. Orndorff, W. R., and L. T. Beach, J. Am. Chem. Soc., **50**, 1416 (1928).

350. Orndorff, W. R., and C. V. Shapiro, J. Am. Chem. Soc., **50**, 1730 (1928).

351. Orndorff, W. R., and M. L. Willard, J. Am. Chem. Soc., **51**, 1466 (1929).

352. Ota, H., Tôhuku J. Exptl. Med., **39**, 11 (1940); Chem. Abstracts, **35**, 787 (1941).

353. Oupéroff-Urné, V., Acta Chem. Scand., **4**, 1393 (1950).

354. Oupéroff-Urné, V. (to Laaketehdas Orion Oy), U.S. Patent 2, 650, 925 (1953).

355. Panepinto, F. W., and M. Kilpatrick, J. Am. Chem. Soc., **59**, 1871 (1937).

356. Pantlitschko, M., and H. Benger, Monatsh., **81**, 293 (1950).

357. Parham, W. E., J. Heberling, and H. Wynberg, J. Am. Chem. Soc., **77**, 1169 (1955).

358. Patti, F., Compt. rend., **242**, 357 (1956).

359. Penner, A., F. Hollander, and M. Saltzman, Am. J. Digestive Diseases Nutrition, **5**, 657 (1938); Chem. Abstracts, **33**, 5876 (1939).

360. Penner, A., F. Hollander, and A. Post, Am. J. Digestive Diseases Nutrition, **7**, 202 (1940); Hollander, F., and A. Penner, ibid., **7**, 199 (1940); Chem. Abstracts, **34**, 5104, 6966 (1940).

360a. Perrier, L. H., Fr. Patent 1, 108, 210 (1956); Chem. Abstracts, **53**, 11317 (1959).

360b. Pieper, G., O. Bayer, H. Kleiner, H. Weese, and W. Wirth (to Bayer), Ger. Patent 1, 020, 789 (1957).

362. Pinder, A. R., and H. Smith, J. Chem. Soc., **1954**, 113.

362a. Plieninger, H., and H. J. Grasshoff, Chem. Ber., **90**, 1973 (1957).

363. Price, C. C., and P. F. Kirk, J. Am. Chem. Soc., **75**, 2396 (1953).

364. Price, W. B., and S. Smiles, J. Chem. Soc., **1928**, 2858.

365. Pütter, R., and F. Sückfull (to Bayer), Ger. Patent 913, 177 (1954); Chem. Abstracts, **52**, 15597 (1958).

365a. Pütter, R. (to Bayer), Ger. Patent 920, 129 (1954); Chem. Abstracts, **53**, 293 (1959).

366. Pütter, R., and F. Suckfüll (to Bayer), U.S. Patent 2, 807, 627 (1957); Chem. Abstracts, **52**, 5484 (1958).

367. Rabinovich, P. N., N. L. Pridorogin, Yu. L. Pridorogin, and N. A. Kharitonov, Russian Patent 27, 052 (1931); Chem. Abstracts, **27**, 2164 (1933).

368. Ramart-Lucas, P., Compt. rend., **208**, 1312 (1939).

369. Ramart-Lucas, P., Compt. rend., **213**, 244 (1941).

370. Ramart-Lucas, P., Chimie and industrie, **45**, Special No., 285 (Mar. 1941); Chem. Zentr., **1942** II, 385; Chem. Abstracts, **37**, 4384 (1943).

371. Ramart-Lucas, P., Bull. soc. chim., **8**, 865 (1941).

372. Ramart-Lucas, P., Compt. rend., **217**, 24 (1943).

373. Ramart-Lucas, P., Bull. soc. chim., **10**, 127 (1943).

374. Ramart-Lucas, P., Bull. soc. chim., **10**, 282 (1943).

375.   Ramart-Lucas, P., Bull. soc. chim., **12**, 477 (1945).

375a. Reed, C. F., U.S. Patent 2,046,090 (1936); Chem. Abstracts, **30**, 5593 (1936).

376.   Remsen, I., Am. Chem. J., **6**, 180 (1884).

377.   Remsen, I., and C. W. Hayes, Am. Chem. J., **9**, 372 (1887).

378.   Remsen, I., and A. F. Linn, Am. Chem. J., **11**, 73 (1889).

379.   Remsen, I., and A. R. L. Dohme, Am. Chem. J., **11**, 332 (1889).

380.   Remsen, I., Am. Chem. J., **17**, 309 (1895).

381.   Remsen, I., and C. E. Coates, Jr., Am. Chem. J., **17**, 311 (1895).

382.   Remsen, I., and E. P. Kohler, Am. Chem. J., **17**, 330 (1895).

383.   Remsen, I., and A. P. Saunders, Am. Chem. J., **17**, 347 (1895).

384.   Remsen, I., Am. Chem. J., **18**, 791 (1896).

385.   Remsen, I., and S. R. McKee, Am. Chem. J., **18**, 794 (1896).

386.   Remsen, I., and J. R. Hunter, Am. Chem. J., **18**, 809 (1896).

387.   Remsen, I., and W. J. Karslake, Am. Chem. J., **18**, 819 (1896).

388.   Remsen, I., and G. W. Gray, Am. Chem. J., **19**, 496 (1897).

389.   Remsen, I., Am. Chem. J., **30**, 247 (1903).

390.   Remsen, I., and F. E. Clark, Am. Chem. J., **30**, 253 (1903).

391.   Remsen, I., and R. M. Bird, Am. Chem. J., **30**, 262 (1903).

392.   Remsen, I., and W. B. Holmes, Am. Chem. J., **30**, 273 (1903).

393.   Remsen, I., and F. E. Clark, Am. Chem. J., **30**, 277 (1903).

394.   Remsen, I., and R. E. Humphreys, Am. Chem. J., **30**, 294 (1903).

394a. Reychler, M. A., Bull. soc. chim. [3] **19**, 120 (1898).

395.   Reynolds, D. D., J. Am. Chem. Soc., **79**, 4951 (1957).

396.   Reynolds, D. D. (to Eastman Kodak), U.S. Patent 2,828,318 (1958).

396a. Reynolds, D. D., M. K. Massad, D. L. Fields, and D. L. Johnson, J. Org. Chem., **26**, 5109 (1961).

396b. Reynolds, D. D., D. L. Fields, and D. L. Johnson, J. Org. Chem., **26**, 5111, 5116, 5119, 5122, 5125, 5130 (1961).

397.   Ringer, A., Pharmazie, **5**, 269 (1950); Chem. Abstracts, **44**, 8771 (1950).

398.   Ringer, A., Pharmazie, **6**, 44, 103, 156 (1951); Chem. Abstracts, **45**, 10053 (1951).

398a. Robinson, M. J. T., J. Chem. Soc., **1958**, 2311.

399.   Rondestvedt, C. S., Jr., and J. C. Wygant, J. Am. Chem. Soc., **73**, 5785 (1951).

400.   Rondestvedt, C. S., Jr., and J. C. Wygant, J. Org. Chem., **17**, 975 (1952).

401. Romero, M., and J. Romo, Bol. inst. quím. univ. nacl. auton. Mex., **4**, 3 (1952) Chem. Abstracts, **47**, 10498 (1953).

401a. Romito, V. A. (to Aceptic Thermo Indicator Co.), U.S. Patent 2, 850, 393 (1958).

402. Romo, J., G. Rosenkranz, and C. Djerassi, J. Am. Chem. Soc., **73**, 4961 (1951)

403. Romo, J., and G. Contreras, Bol. inst. quim. univ. nacl. auton. Mex., **4**, 101 (1952); Chem. Abstracts, **48**, 9400 (1954).

403a. Romo de Vivar, A., and J. Romo, J. Org. Chem., **24**, 1490 (1959).

404. Rosenkranz, G., St. Kaufmann, and J. Romo, J. Am. Chem. Soc., **71**, 3689 (1949).

404a. Rozina, D. Sh., L. T. Nesterenko, and Yu. I. Vainshtein, J. Gen. Chem. (U.S.S.R.), **28**, 2904 (1958).

405. Ruggli, P., and E. Peyer, Helv. Chim. Acta, **9**, 929 (1926).

405a. Rühlmann, K., D. Gramer, D. Heuchel, and U. Schräpler, J. prakt. Chem., [4] **10**, 316 (1960).

405b. Rühlmann, K., U. Schräpler, and D. Gramer, J. prakt. Chem., [4] **10**, 325 (1960).

405c. Runge, F., Z. El-Hewehi, H. J. Renner, and E. Taeger, J. prakt. Chem., [4] **11**, 284 (1960).

406. Rylander, P. N., J. Org. Chem., **21**, 1296 (1956).

407. Sacconi, L., Gazz. chim. ital., **78**, 192 (1948); Chem. Abstracts, **42**, 7191 (1948)

408. Sacconi, L., Gazz. chim. ital., **78**, 303 (1948); Chem. Abstracts, **43**, 58 (1949).

409. Sacconi, L., Atti accad. nazl. Lincei, Classe sci. fis., mat. e nat., **8**, 376 (1950); Chem. Abstracts, **44**, 8776 (1950).

410. Sachs, F., F. von Wolff, and A. Ludwig, Ber., **37**, 3252 (1904).

411. Sager, E. E., A. A. Maryott, and M. R. Schooley, J. Am. Chem. Soc., **70**, 732 (1948).

412. Sandmeyer, T., J. Soc. Dyers and Colorists, **1896**, 155.

413. Scales, F. M., Science, **51**, 214 (1920).

414. Schatzmann, P., Ann., **261**, 19 (1891).

415. Schelber, J., and M. Knothe, Ber., **45**, 2252 (1912).

416. Schetty, G. (to J. R. Geigy A.-G.), U.S. Patent, 2, 359, 730 (1944); Chem. Abstracts, **39**, 1546 (1945).

417. Schetty, G., Helv. Chim. Acta, **20**, 1650 (1947).

418. Schetty, G., Helv. Chim. Acta, **31**, 1229 (1948).

420. Schetty, G., (to J. R. Geigy A. -G.), U.S. Patent 2, 451, 579 (1948); Chem. Abstracts, **43**, 2641 (1949).

421. Schirmacher, K. and W. Langbein (to I. G. Farbenind.), Ger. Patent 433, 527 (1924); Chem. Zentr., **1926 II**, 2497.

422. Schmidt, K., W. Müller, R. Pütter, F. Suckfüll, and G. Dittmar (to Bayer), U.S. Patent 2, 735, 344 (1956); Chem. Abstracts, 51, 7026 (1957).

423. Schnieder, W., and F. Wrede, Ber., **47**, 2225 (1914).

423a. Schöberl, A., IUPAC Symposium on Macromolecules, Wiesbaden, Germany Oct. 1959, Sect. IV B, paper 10.

423b. Schöllkopf, U., Angew. Chem., **72**, 147 (1960).

424. Schönberg, A., A. Mustafa, W. A. Awad, and G. E. M. Moussa, J. Am. Chem. Soc., **76**, 2273 (1954).

424a. Schönberg, A., E. Rupp, and W. Gumlich, Ber., **66**, 1932 (1933).

425. Schotte, L., Arkiv Kemi, **3**, 397 (1951).

426. Schubert, M. P., J. Biol. Chem., **121**, 539 (1937).

427. Schultz, G., Ber., **20**, 3158 (1887).

428. Schwarzenbach, G., M. Brandenberger, G. H. Ott, and O. Hagger, Helv. Chim. Acta, **20**, 490 (1937).

429. Schwarzenbach, G., G. H. Ott, and O. Hagger, Helv. Chim. Acta, **20**, 498 (1937).

429a. Scott, R. B., Doctoral Dissertation, University of Virginia (1949); PB 114389 [NR 055222 (N9 onr 96100)], Jan. 9, 1954.

430. Scott, R. B., and H. L. McLeod, J. Org. Chem., **21**, 388 (1956).

431. Sergeev, P. G., and B. S. Kolychev, J. Gen. Chem. (U.S.S.R.), **7**, 1390 (1937); Chem. Abstracts, **32**, 2534 (1938).

432. Sergeev, P. G., B. S. Kolychev, and V. S. Kolychev., J. Gen. Chem. (U.S.S.R.), **7**, 2963 (1937); Chem. Abstracts, **32**, 2940 (1938).

433. Shapiro, C. V., J. Am. Chem. Soc., **50**, 1772 (1928).

434. Shay, H., J. Gershon-Cohen, F. L. Munro, and H. Siplet, J. Lab. Clin. Med., **26**, 732 (1941); Chem. Abstracts, **35**, 1822 (1941).

435. Shearing, E. A., and S. Smiles, J. Chem. Soc., **1937**, 1348.

436. Shriner, R. L., H. A. Rendleman, and A. Berger, J. Org. Chem., **4**, 103 (1939).

437. Slagle, E. A., J. Pharmacol., **1**, 663 (1910); Chem. Abstracts, **4**, 2545 (1910).

437a. Simmons, Jr., H. E. (to du Pont), U.S. Patent 2, 911, 414 (1959).

437b. Simmons, Jr., H. E., and D. W. Wiley, J. Am. Chem. Soc., **82**, 2288 (1960).

438. Simonsen, J. L., and L. N. Owen, "The Terpenes", Vol. II, 2nd Edition, University Press, Cambridge, 1949.

438a. Sirokman, F., and L. Otvos, Acta Univ. Szegediensis, Acta Phys. et Chem. [N.S.] **4**, 73 (1958); Chem. Abstracts, **53**, 12225 (1959).

439. Sisley, P., Bull. soc. chim., [3] **17**, 821 (1897).

440. Sjöberg, B., Ber., **74B**, 64 (1941).

441. Sjöberg, B., Ber., **75B**, 13 (1942).

442. Smith, C. W., D. G. Norton, and S. A. Ballard, J. Am. Chem. Soc., **75**, 748 (1953).

443. Sohon, M. D., Am. Chem. J., **20**, 127 (1898).

444. Sohon, M. D., Am. Chem. J., **20**, 257 (1898).

445. Spryskov, A. A., and N. V. Aparyeva, J. Gen. Chem. (U.S.S.R.), **22**, 1667 (1952).

446. Spryskov, A. A., and N. V. Aparyeva, Zhur. Obshcheĭ Khim., **22**, 1624 (1952); Chem. Abstracts, **47**, 8710 (1953). See Ref. 445.

447. Staudinger, H., and J. Siegwart, Helv. Chim. Acta, **3**, 840 (1920).

448. Steiger, R. E., Helv. Chim. Acta, **13**, 173 (1930).

449. Sterling Drug, Brit. Patent 753, 724 (1956); Chem. Abstracts, **51**, 8819 (1957).

450. Stevens, P. G., and J. H. Richmond, J. Am. Chem. Soc., **63**, 3132 (1941).

451. Stevenson, H. A., and S. Smiles, J. Chem. Soc., **1930**, 1740.

452. Stubbs, M. B., Am. Chem. J., **50**, 193 (1913).

453. Suter, C. M., "The Organic Chemistry of Sulfur", p. 697, John Wiley and Sons, Inc., New York, 1944.

454. Taira, T., S. Yamatodani, and S. Fujii, J. Agr. Chem. Soc. Japan, **25**, 121 (1951-2); Chem. Abstracts. **47**, 6302 (1953).

455. Taverne, H. J., Rec. trav. chim., **25**, 50 (1905).

456. Taverne, H. J., Rec. trav. chim., **39**, 542 (1920).

457. Taylor, J. R., R. S. Rosenfeld, and J. W. Martin, Virginia J. Sci., **3**, 290 (1943); Chem. Abstracts, **38**, 695 (1944).

458. Thiel, A., A. Dassler, and F. Wülfken, Fortschr. Chem. Phys., **18**, No. 3, 1 (1924/26); Chem. Zentr., **1924 II**, 2227

459. Thiel, A., Monatsh., **53/54**, 1008 (1929).

459a. Thiel, M., and F. Asinger, Ann., **610**, 17 (1957).

460. Thiel, M., F. Asinger, and G. Reckling, Ann., **611**, 131 (1958)

461. Thiel, M., W. Scäfer, and F. Asinger, Ann., **613**, 128 (1958).

462. Treibs, W., and I. Lorenz, Ber., **84**, 666 (1951).

462a. Tronnier, H., Arzneimittel-Forsch., **8**, 647 (1958); Chem. Abstracts, **53**, 5519 (1959).

463. Tscherniac, J., J. Chem. Soc., **115**, 1071 (1919).

463a. Tscherniac, J., Ber., **61**, 574 (1928).

464. Tsukamoto, H., M. Hamana, and M. Baba, J. Pharm. Soc. Japan, **73**, 1083 (1953); Chem. Abstracts, **48**, 12053 (1954).

465. Twiss, D. (to Hynson, Westcott, and Dunning, Inc.), U.S. Patent 1,760,328 (1930); Chem. Abstracts, **24**, 3518 (1930).

466. Twiss, D., and L. H. Farinholt, J. Am. Chem. Soc., **58**, 1561 (1936).

467. Umemura, K., Igaku to Seibutsugaku (Medicine and Biology), **17**, 334 (1950); Chem. Abstracts, **46**, 1850 (1952).

468. Urbaschat, E. (to Bayer), Ger. Patent Appln. F 17,435 (1958).

468a. Urbschat, E. (to Bayer), Ger. Patent 1,022,596 (1958).

469. Urushibara, Y., and G. Koga, Bull. Chem. Soc. Japan, **29**, 419 (1956); Chem. Abstracts, **51**, 4357 (1957).

470. Usanovich, M., and K. Yatsimirskii, J. Gen. Chem. (U.S.S.R.), **11**, 954 (1941); Chem. Abstracts, **39**, 4540 (1945).

471. Uzumasa, Y., and M. Yamawaki, J. Chem. Soc. Japan, **58**, 721 (1937); Chem. Abstracts, **31**, 8375 (1937).

472. Venkataraman, K., "The Chemistry of Synthetic Dyes", Volumes I and II, Academic Press, New York, 1952.

473. Van Tamelen, E. E., J. Am. Chem. Soc., **73**, 3444 (1951).

474. Van Wyk, J. J., and W. M. Clark, J. Am. Chem. Soc., **69**, 1296 (1947).

475. Veselý, V., and A. Bubeník, Collection Czechoslov. Chem. Commun., **11**, 412 (1939); Chem. Abstracts, **34**, 6890 (1940).

476. Veselý, V., and A. Bubeník, Chem. Listy, **34**, 201 (1940); Chem. Zentr., **1942** II, 246.

477. Vieweg, H. F., J. Am. Chem. Soc., **46**, 2859 (1924).

478. Vinkler, E., and F. Klivényi, Folýairab, **61**, 103 (1955); Chem. Abstracts, **51**, 1125 (1957).

479. Vlasov, A. A., Stroitel. Prom., **19**, No. 3, 36 (1941); Chem. Zentr., **1942** II, 1868.

480. Vlès, F., Bull. soc. chim. France, [4] **37**, 558 (1925).

481. Vodák, Z., and O. Leminger, Collection Czechoslov. Chem. Commun., **19**, 925 (1954); Chem. Abstracts, **49**, 4576 (1955).

482. Vodák, Z., and O. Leminger, Czech. Patent 84,119 (1955); Chem. Abstracts, **51**, 2867 (1957).

482a. Vodák, Z., and O. Leminger, German Patent 1,061,328 (1959).

483. Vodák, Z., and O. Leminger, Czech. Patent 84,314 (1955); Chem. Abstracts, **50**, 7135 (1956).

484. Vodák, Z., and O. Leminger, U.S. Patent 2,772,290 (1956).

485. Vodák, Z., and O. Leminger, Brit. Patent, 754,367 (1956); Chem. Abstracts, **51**, 880 (1957).

486. Vodák, Z., and O. Leminger, Collection Czech. Chem. Communs., **21**, 1522 (1956); Chem. Abstracts, **51**, 12067 (1957).

487. Vodák, Z., and O. Leminger, Chem. Listy, **50**, 943 (1956); Chem. Abstracts, **50**, 16717 (1956).

488. Vodák, Z., and O. Leminger, Chem. Listy, **50**, 2028 (1956); Chem. Abstracts, **51**, 4203 (1957).

489. Voltzkow, M., Ber., **13**, 1579 (1880).

490. Von Glahn, W. H., and L. N. Stanley (to General Aniline and Film Corp.), U.S. Patent 2,547,843 (1951).

491. Von Glahn, W. H., and L. N. Stanley (to General Aniline and Film Corp.), Ger. Patent 821,759 (1951); Chem. Abstracts, **50**, 1506 (1956).

491a. Wagner-Jauregg, T., Ann., **561**, 87 (1949).

492. Wagner-Jauregg, T., and M. Häring, Helv. Chim. Acta, **41**, 377 (1958).

493. Warren, L. A., and S. Smiles, J. Chem. Soc., **1930**, 956.

494. Warren, L. A., and S. Smiles, J. Chem. Soc., **1930**, 1327.

495. Warthin, T. A., and C. B. Thomas, Bull. Johns Hopkins Hops., **72**, 203 (1943); Chem. Abstracts, **38**, 788 (1944).

496. Weber, O., Ber., **25**, 1737 (1892).

497. Wehnelt, B., and K. Bauer (to I. G. Farbenind.), Ger. Patent 701,960 (1941); Chem. Abstracts, **35**, 8194 (1941).

497a. Wendler, N. L., and D. Taub, J. Org. Chem., **25**, 1828 (1960).

498. Werner, G. (to Winthrop Chemical Co.), U.S. Patent 2,276,553 (1942): Chem. Abstracts, **36**, 4519 (1942).

499. Werner, G. (to Winthrop Chemical Co.), U.S. Patent 2,332,418 (1944); Chem. Abstracts, **38**, 1889 (1944).

500. Wheeler, H. L., and B. Barnes, Am. Chem. J., **24**, 60 (1901).

501. Wheeler, H. L., and T. B. Johnson, Am. Chem. J., **28**, 121 (1902).

502. White, Jr., J., Am. Chem. J., **17**, 545 (1895).

503. White, E. C., Science, **42**, 101 (1915).

504. White, E. C., J. Am. Chem. Soc., **39**, 648 (1917).

505. White, E. C., and S. F. Acree, J. Am. Chem. Soc., **40**, 1092 (1918).

506. White, E. C., and S. F. Acree, J. Am. Chem. Soc., **41**, 1190 (1919).

508. White, E. C., J. Am. Chem. Soc., **42**, 2355 (1920).

509. Wilhelmj, C. M., and D. E. Baca, J. Lab. clin. med., **24**, 207 (1938); Chem. Abstracts, **33**, 3408 (1939).

509a. Williams, K. I. H., S. E. Cremer, F. W. Kent, E. J. Sehm, and D. S. Tarbell, J. Am. Chem. Soc., **82**, 3982 (1960).

510. Willems, J., Ind. chim. belge, **19**, 905 (1954).

511. Willems, J., Compt. rend. 27^e congr. intern. chim. ind., Brussels, **1954**, 3; Industrie chim. belge, **20**, Spec. No., 666 (1955); Chem. Abstracts, **50**, 11952 (1956).

512. Willems, J., Bull. soc. chim. Belges, **64**, 409 (1955).

513. Willems, J., Bull. soc. chim. Belges, **64**, 747 (1955).

514. Wolff, J. P., Ann. chim. (Paris), **8**, 201 (1953); Chem. Abstracts, **48**, 7998 (1954).

515. Yagi, H., and H. Mori, Japan. Patent 176,521 (1948); Chem. Abstracts **45**, 5350 (1951).

516. Zak, B., N. Moss, A. J. Boyle, and A. Zlatkis, Anal. Chem., **26**, 776 (1954).

516a. Ziegler, E., and J. Schaar, Monatsh., **90**, 866 (1959).

517. Zincke, T., and K. Arnold, Ber., **50**, 116 (1917).

518. Zirngiebl, H., Z. Krystall., **36**, 117 (1902); Chem. Zentr., **1902 II**, 101

519. Zutrauen, H. A., and L. T. Minassian-Saraga, Compt. rend., **240**, 869 (1955).

520. Zutrauen, H. A., J. chim. Phys., **53**, 54 (1956).

CHAPTER 5

C_3S_2 RING SYSTEMS

The C_3S_2 ring is found in a variety of organic compounds. 1, 2-Dithiol-
··es are predominantly cyclic sulfides of 1, 3-dimercapto compounds,
chief of which is α-lipoic or thioctic acid. 1, 2-Dithiole-3-thiones, the
so-called "trithiones", have been the subject of numerous investigations.
Included in the 1, 3-dithiolane category are a large number of mercaptals and mercaptoles, derived from 1, 2-dimercaptoethane, and derivatives of trithiocarbonic acid. These systems are also known in condensed rings and as spiro compounds, and include a number of naturally
occurring products.

I. 1, 2-DITHIA COMPOUNDS

A. C_3S_2 1, 2-DITHIOLANE (**1**) AND 1, 2-DITHIOLE (**2**)

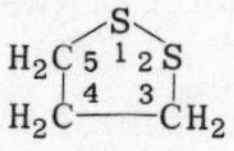

1 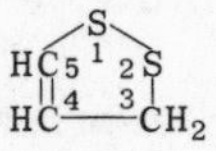   **2**

(RRI 137)

These compounds are now indexed in Chemical Abstracts as 1, 2-
dithiolane and 1, 2-dithiole. However, from 1907-1916 they were both
indexed under 1, 2-disulfole and from 1917-1936 they were both indexed under 1, 2-dithiole. The numbering has remained unchanged.
Alternative names for the saturated ring are 1, 2-dithiacyclopentane,
trimethylene disulfide, and propane α, γ-disulfide. The unsaturated
ring has been called 1, 2-dithia-4-cyclopentene. Böttcher and Lüttringhaus coined the unfortunate name "trithione" for 1, 2-dithiole-3-thione
and numbered the ring differently, first as in **3** and then as in **4** in con-
formity with Beilstein.

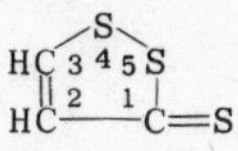

3 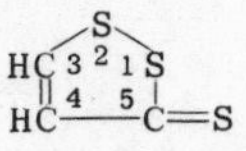   **4**

Spiro compounds in this ring system, as in others, are indexed in
Chemical Abstracts according to the Ring Index system for naming and
numbering spiro compounds. However, they are usually also cross-
indexed to the parent ring system.

[For references, see pp. 585-610.]   313

1. 1, 2-Dithiolane

a. 1, 2-Dithiolane and General Derivatives

(1) Preparation

Table 1 lists the 1, 2-dithiolanes reported in the literature. Hagelberg[234] was the first to attempt the preparation of the parent compound, 1, 2-dithiolane (1), using the following scheme:

$$NCS(CH_2)_3SCN \xrightarrow{KOH, \; EtOH} \quad \mathbf{1}$$

$$\Big\downarrow Zn + HCl \qquad \xrightarrow{Br_2}$$

$$HS(CH_2)_3SH$$

Both procedures yielded an insoluble white solid, m. p. 71°, and Hagelberg considered that this compound might be a dimer or higher polymer. Autenrieth and Wolff[20] obtained the same compound by treating 1, 3-dimercaptopropane with bromine in chloroform or with iodine in aqueous sodium hydroxide, and considered that their product too was polymeric. More recently, Brintzinger and co-workers[83] showed by molecular weight determinations that the hydrolysis product of the bis-(isothiocyanate) is a dimer.

In 1950 Affleck and Dougherty[8] attempted to prepare the compound by oxidizing the trimethylene Bunte salt (5) with iodine or hydrogen peroxide, but only polymeric disulfides were obtained. However, treatment of the Bunte salt with cupric chloride followed by steam distillation yielded a steam-distillable oil.

$$Br(CH_2)_3Br \xrightarrow{Na_2S_2O_3} NaO_3SS(CH_2)_3SSO_3Na \xrightarrow[60\%]{CuCl_2}$$

$$\mathbf{5}$$

The mechanism of this ring closure is obscure, but the authors did not feel that an oxidation was involved. Schöberl and Gräfje[472] have suggested that the ring closure involves a nucleophilic displacement of sulfite ion; presumably the copper salt would function to form the necessary mercaptide ion.

$$\mathbf{5} + H_2O \xrightarrow{Cu^{2+}} \quad \underset{CH_2-CH_2}{\overset{CH_2}{S}} \; S^- \curvearrowright SO_3^- \longrightarrow \quad + \; SO_3^{2-}$$

1, 2-Dithiolane was too unstable to be isolated as such, and it was obtained as a benzene solution. Even in solution the compound was unstable, and a molecular weight of 150 was found rather than the calculated value of 106. Barltrop, Hayes, and Calvin[36] were successful in preparing a solution of monomeric 1, 2-dithiolane in ethanol by reacting 1, 3-dibrompropane with sodium disulfide.

$$Br(CH_2)_3Br + Na_2S_2 \xrightarrow[\text{2. Distil}]{\text{1. EtOH, }\Delta} \quad \text{(ring)} + \text{dimer} + H_2\text{(ring)}$$

The desired compound was isolated in 9% yield. An additional amount was obtained by steam distilling the dimer in the presence of sodium disulfide and sodium hydroxide. A cryoscopic molecular weight determination in benzene showed the compound to be monomeric. Davis[143,144] used essentially the same procedure, substituting sodium tetrasulfide for the disulfide.

In contrast to the unsuccessful attempts of Hagelberg[234] and of Autenrieth and Wolff[20] to prepare monomeric 1, 2-dithiolane by the oxidation of 1, 3-dimercaptopropane, Barltrop, Hayes, and Calvin[36] were able to effect this synthesis in excellent to quantitative yields with a number of oxidizing agents: iodine in alcohol; air plus hydriodic acid, iodine presumably being an intermediate; air in the presence of alkali; and hydroxylamine in the presence of alkali. Ethyl t-butyl sulfenate, $(CH_3)_3CSOC_2H_5$, and di-t-butyl disulfide were also capable of oxidizing the dimercaptan to 1, 2-dithiolane in the presence of alkali, but yields were poor. These yields were determined spectroscopically and not by isolation of the product. Hellstrom[248] prepared 1, 2-dithiolane from 1, 3-dibromopropane and potassium xanthogenate, and reported physical properties for the compound. Unfortunately, no details are available.

Yur'ev and Levi[584] claimed that passage of thietane or a mixture of thietane and hydrogen sulfide over alumina at 250-350° gave a low yield of 1, 2-dithiolane, m.p. 76. 5-77. 5°. Their product was undoubtedly the same as Hagelberg's, although they claimed that molecular weight determination showed the compound to be monomeric. Bergson and Claeson[50] investigated the depolymerization of the polymer obtained from 1, 3-dibromopropane and sodium disulfide and found that some 1, 2-dithiolane is formed by heating the polymer in paraffin oil at 160°. They also found that the values obtained in a Rast molecular weight determination depend on the length of time the material is heated in camphor, which perhaps explains Yur'ev and Levi's claim that their material was monomeric.

Backer and Evenhuis[21] prepared 4, 4-dimethyl-1, 2-dithiolane (**6**) from 2, 2-dimethyl-1, 3-dibromopropane and potassium disulfide.

$$(CH_3)_2C(CH_2Br)_2 \xrightarrow[\text{55\%}]{\substack{K_2S_2,\ \text{EtOH} \\ \text{3 hrs. reflux}}} \quad \substack{CH_3 \\ CH_3}\text{(ring)}$$

6

This synthesis gave an impure product. It was improved by Backer and Tamsma[24] by using sodium tetrasulfide instead of the disulfide and treating the reaction mixture with copper in refluxing toluene. In these preparations a mixture of the 1, 2-dithiolane (**6**) with a trithio compound

TABLE 1. 1,2-Dithiolanes

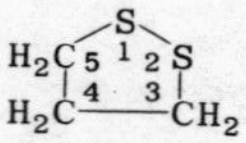

$H_2C\ 5\!-\!S\ 1$; $S\ 2$ — $H_2C\ 4\!-\!3\!-\!CH_2$ (1,2-dithiolane ring, positions 1–5)

Substituents	Yield (%)	M.p. (°C)	B.p. (°C)	(mm)	Other properties	Ref.
None	60					8
	9					36
(±)-3-(HO_2C-)	15	81–82	67–68	20	n_D^{20} 1.5402, d_{20} 1.1076	248
	66	80–82				131
(+)-3-(HO_2C-)	10	60–62			$[\alpha]_D^{25}$ + 158°	580
(±)-3-(HO_2CCH_2-)	16.5	37–39				131
4-(HO_2C-)		76.5–77.5				580
4-(HO_3S-), S-benzylthiouronium salt		90–92				487
3-($H_2NCONHN=$)		224				418a
3,3-(CH_3-)$_2$	50					480, 483
			68	14	n_D^{25} 1.5424	472

	Yield (%)	M.p.		Ref.
4,4-(CH$_3$-)$_2$	55	128-129	27	21
		84-86	17	24
		82-83	12	483
4,4-(CH$_3$-)$_2$ · HgCl$_2$		102		24
4,4-(HOCH$_2$-)$_2$	94	129-130		24, 417, 483
4,4-(HOCH$_2$-)$_2$ 1,1,2,2-tetroxide		242-244		24
(±)-3,5-(HO$_2$C-)$_2$	22	194-195		481, 485
	77			485
(+)- or (−)-3,5-(HO$_2$C-)$_2$		135-187		485
3,5-(C$_6$H$_5$N=)$_2$		154-155		449
3,5-(C$_6$H$_5$N=)$_2$ picrate	100	180(dec.)		464
3,5-(C$_6$H$_5$NHCO-)$_2$-4-(O=)		220		399
3,5-(o-CH$_3$C$_6$H$_4$NHCO-)$_2$-4-(O=)		225 (dec.)		399
3,5-(p-CH$_3$C$_6$H$_4$NHCO-)$_2$-4-(O=)		216-217		399
3,3,5,5-(CH$_3$-)$_4$		67-69	2 Impure	472
3-(O=)-4-(C$_6$H$_5$CONH-)-5,5-(CH$_3$-)$_2$	50	124-126		189
3-(O=)-4-(CH$_3$CONH-)-5,5-(CH$_3$-)$_2$		143		190
	11	146-147		190

was formed. Backer and co-workers[21,22,24] formulated the trithio compounds as thio-1, 2-dithiolanes (7), the coordinated sulfur being removed by the copper treatment.

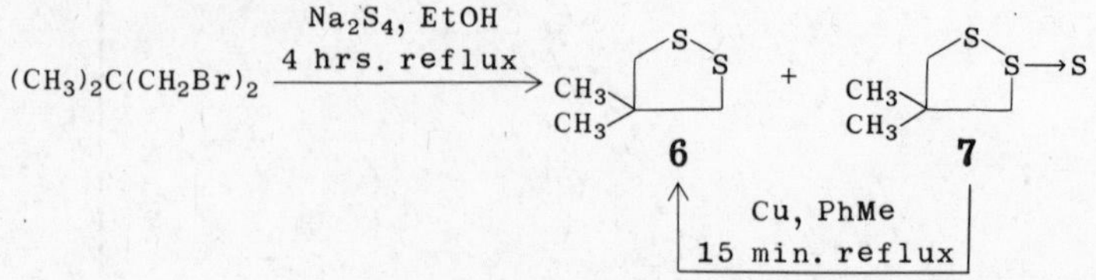

$(CH_3)_2C(CH_2Br)_2$ $\xrightarrow[\text{4 hrs. reflux}]{Na_2S_4,\ EtOH}$ **6** + **7**

Cu, PhMe
15 min. reflux

However, Schotte[484] has advanced the more reasonable explanation that these compounds are actually 1, 2, 3-trithianes (8) (see Chapter 10, section I). This might account for the improved yields obtained with sodium tetrasulfide, since six-membered rings form more readily than five-membered rings.

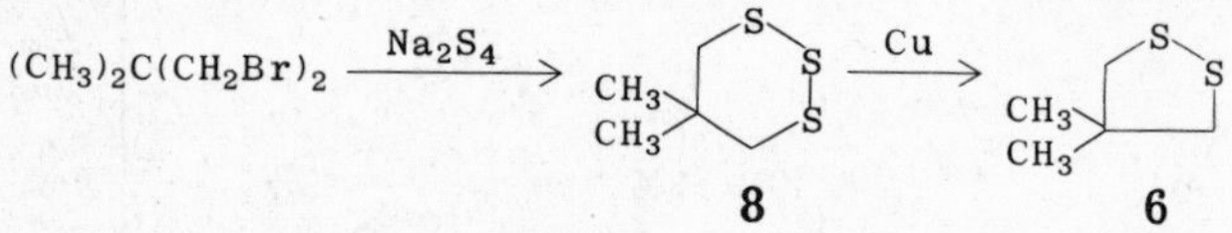

$(CH_3)_2C(CH_2Br)_2$ $\xrightarrow{Na_2S_4}$ **8** $\xrightarrow{Cu}$ **6**

It is rather interesting that 2, 2-bis(hydroxymethyl)-1, 3-dibromopropane with sodium tetrasulfide gave no trithio derivative,[24,417,483] the 1, 2, 3-trithiane, if formed, decomposing spontaneously to 4, 4-bis (hydroxymethyl)-1, 2-dithiolane (9). 9 was also prepared with sodium disulfide in 57% yield, and by oxidation of 2, 2-bis(hydroxymethyl)-1, 3-dimercaptopropane with iodine.[24]

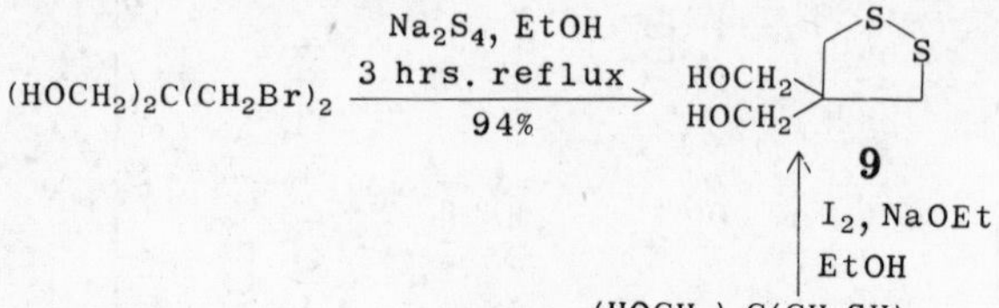

$(HOCH_2)_2C(CH_2Br)_2$ $\xrightarrow[\text{94\%}]{\substack{Na_2S_4,\ EtOH \\ 3\ hrs.\ reflux}}$ **9**

I_2, NaOEt
EtOH

$(HOCH_2)_2C(CH_2SH)_2$

Schöberl and Gräfje[472] prepared 3, 3-dimethyl-1, 2-dithiolane (10) and 3, 3, 5, 5-tetramethyl-1, 2-dithiolane (11) by oxidizing the corresponding dimercaptans with t-butyl hydroperoxide. Although yields were not high, no polymer was formed during the oxidation.

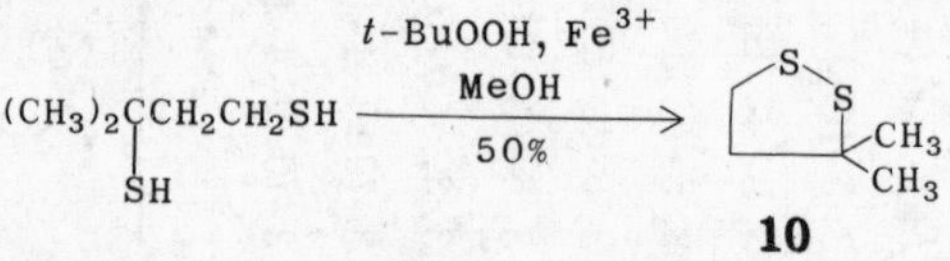

$(CH_3)_2CCH_2CH_2SH$, SH $\xrightarrow[\text{50\%}]{\substack{t-BuOOH,\ Fe^{3+} \\ MeOH}}$ **10**

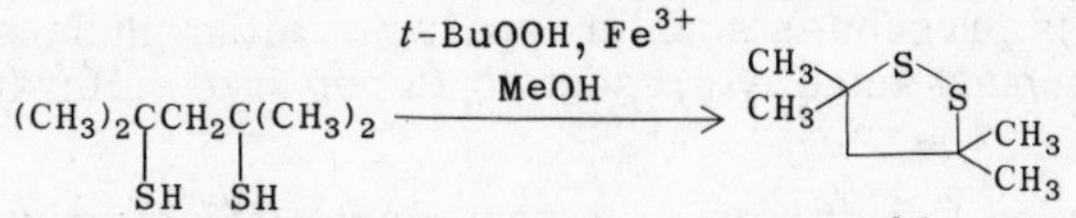

t-BuOOH, Fe^{3+}

MeOH

$(CH_3)_2CCH_2C(CH_3)_2$ $\xrightarrow{\hspace{1cm}}$

SH SH

11

Schotte[480] prepared 1,2-dithiolan-4-one (**12**) by the oxidation of 1,3-dimercaptoacetone.

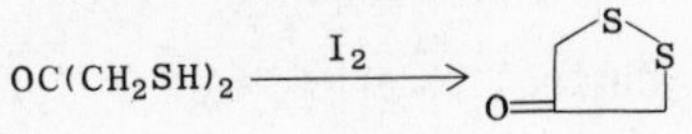

$OC(CH_2SH)_2 \xrightarrow{I_2}$

12

The compound was isolated as its crystalline semicarbazone.

Both possible 1,2-dithiolanecarboxylic acids have been prepared. Claeson[131] prepared the 3-carboxylic acid (**13**) by oxidizing the corresponding dimercaptan.

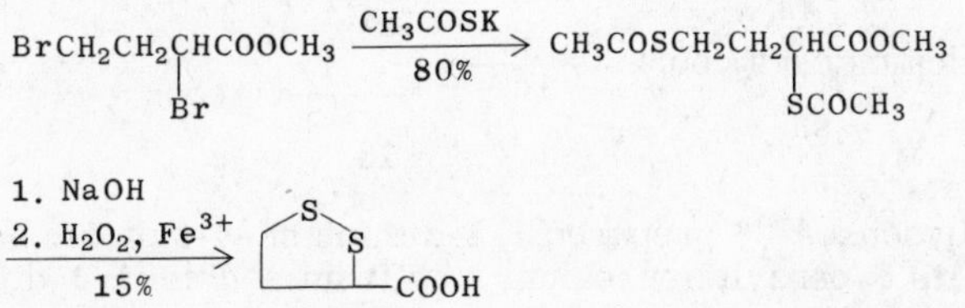

$BrCH_2CH_2CHCOOCH_3 \xrightarrow[80\%]{CH_3COSK} CH_3COSCH_2CH_2CHCOOCH_3$

Br | SCOCH$_3$

1. NaOH
2. H$_2$O$_2$, Fe^{3+}

$\xrightarrow[15\%]{}$ —COOH

13

The major product with several oxidizing agents was polymer. The *dl*-acid, m.p. 81-82°, was resolved, at least partially, via its cinchonidine salt, the (+)-acid having a m.p. of 60-62°, $[\alpha]_D^{25} + 158°$. More recently Wladislaw[580] reported the preparation of **13** in 66% yield by a modification of Claeson's synthesis.

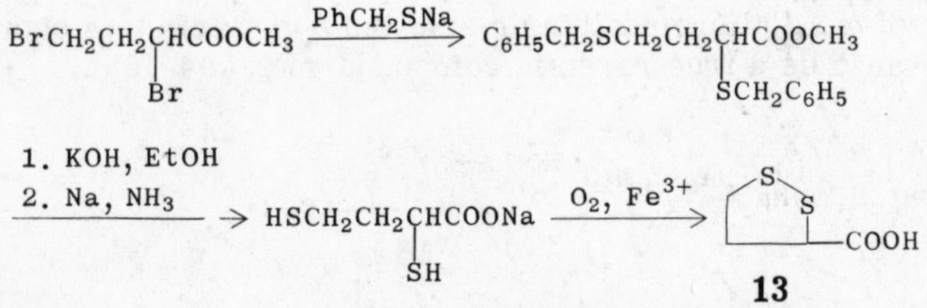

$BrCH_2CH_2CHCOOCH_3 \xrightarrow{PhCH_2SNa} C_6H_5CH_2SCH_2CH_2CHCOOCH_3$

Br | SCH$_2$C$_6$H$_5$

1. KOH, EtOH
2. Na, NH$_3$

$\longrightarrow HSCH_2CH_2CHCOONa \xrightarrow{O_2, Fe^{3+}}$ —COOH

SH

13

1,2-Dithiolane-4-carboxylic acid (**14**) was prepared by Schotte and Ström[487] by a similar procedure with an overall yield of 16.5%; **14** of course has no asymmetric carbon.

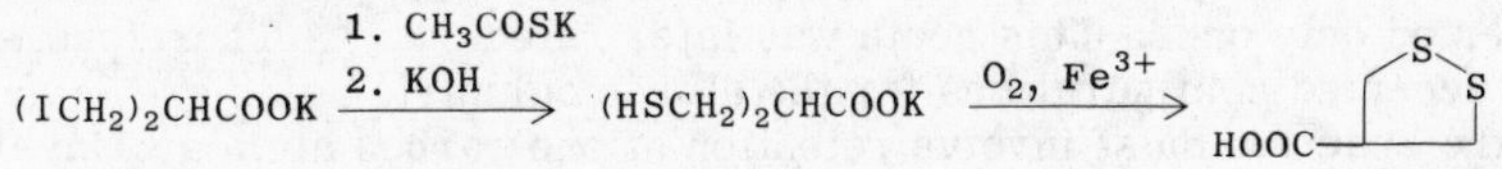

1. CH$_3$COSK
2. KOH

$(ICH_2)_2CHCOOK \xrightarrow{\hspace{1cm}} (HSCH_2)_2CHCOOK \xrightarrow{O_2, Fe^{3+}}$ HOOC—

14

They believe that **14** is present as such in asparagus, although Jansen[278] inferred that the compound actually present contained free sulfhydryl groups.

Wladislaw[580] prepared 1, 2-dithiolane-3-acetic acid (**15**), starting from acrolein. The low yield obtained in the ring closure step in this case illustrates the large effect which small structural variations have on the ease of closure to the 1, 2-dithiolane ring.

$$CH_2=CHCHO \xrightarrow{PhCH_2SH} C_6H_5CH_2SCH_2CH_2CH_2CHO$$

$$\xrightarrow[\text{piperidine}]{HOOCCH_2COOMe} C_6H_5CH_2SCH_2CH_2CH=CHCOOCH_3$$

$$\xrightarrow[\text{piperidine}]{PhCH_2SH} C_6H_5CH_2SCH_2CH_2\underset{\underset{SCH_2C_6H_5}{|}}{C}HCH_2COOCH_3$$

$$\xrightarrow[\text{2. Na, NH}_3]{\text{1. NaOH}} HSCH_2CH_2\underset{\underset{SH}{|}}{C}HCH_2COONa \xrightarrow[10\%]{O_2,\ Fe^{3+}}$$

15

Petrun'kin and Lysenko[418a] prepared 1, 2-dithiolane-4-sulfonic acid (**15a**), isolated as its S-benzylthiouronium salt, from sodium 1, 3-dimercaptopropane-2-sulfonate.

$$(HSCH_2)_2CHSO_3Na \xrightarrow{I_2,\ H_2O}$$

15a

Schotte[481,485] investigated thoroughly the preparation and resolution of 1, 2-dithiolane-3, 5-dicarboxylic acid (**16**). Starting with the high-melting form of α, α'-dibromoglutaric acid the *trans* acid was obtained. This was shown to be a true racemic compound, m.p. 194-195°.

$$NaOOC\underset{\underset{Br}{|}}{C}HCH_2\underset{\underset{Br}{|}}{C}HCOONa \xrightarrow[22\%]{Na_2S_2,\ H_2O}$$

16

Since the dibromo acid has been assigned the *meso* configuration, and since the reaction would be expected to take place without rearrangement, the formation of the *trans* acid is surprising. Schotte [481] considered first that possibly lactone formation occurred with inversion and that the ring was opened with inversion, while the other carbon was inverted only once. This route was later ruled out.[485] Therefore, either the accepted configurations for the dibromoglutaric acids are in error or the reaction must involve retention at one carbon atom and inversion at the other.[486] Several attempts to prepare *cis*-1, 2-dithiolane-3, 5-

dicarboxylic acid from the low-melting α, α'-dibromoglutaric acid were unsuccessful. Either it is unstable, rearranging readily to the *trans* acid, or steric factors unfavorable for ring closure are present.

The *trans* compound was also prepared by the oxidation of dl-α, α'-dimercaptoglutaric acid.

It is most interesting that the yield was so high, being essentially the same with iodine or hydrogen peroxide, and that no polymer was formed. The dicarboxylic acid was resolved with brucine, the (+)-acid being obtained from the acid brucine salt, $[\alpha]_D^{25} + 562°$, and the (−)- acid from the neutral brucine salt, $[\alpha]_D^{25} - 560°$, both melting at 185-187°. The rotation in aqueous solution depends on the pH, the disodium salt having a lower rotation than the free acid. Rather surprisingly, the acid racemized readily in hot water and the ultraviolet spectrum showed that this was not due to ring opening. The solid, on the other hand, did not racemize at 125°. The absolute configuration of these acids has been determined. [486]

Turning now to a different class of compounds, Naik[399] reported that the dianilide of acetonedicarboxylic acid reacts with sulfur monochloride to form 1, 2-dithiolan-4-one-3, 5-dicarboxanilide (17).

17

The same reaction was carried out with the *o*- and *p*-toluidides; the compounds are crystalline, and yellow or orange in color. Only one isomer has been isolated in each case.

Foldi [189] reacted 2-benzamido-3-mercapto-3-methylthiobutyric acid (18) with ferric chloride and isolated 4-benzamido-5, 5-dimethyl-1, 2-dithiolan-3-one (19) as a crystalline compound.

18   **19**

The corresponding acetamido derivative (21) was prepared similarly, [190] and also by addition of sodium hydrosulfide to the azlactone, 2-methyl-4-isopropylidene-2-oxazolin-5-one (20), but only in 11% yield. [190]

[For references, see pp. 585-610.]

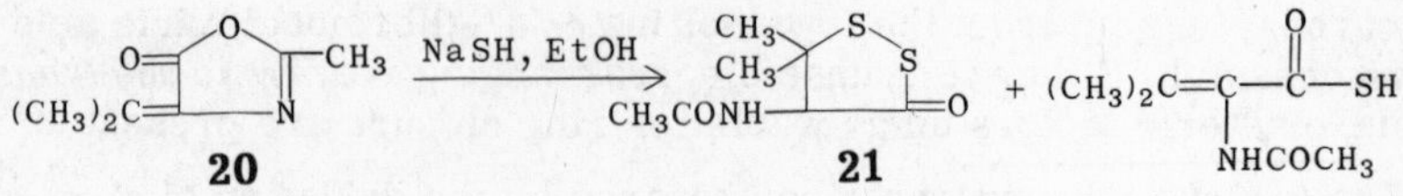

Presumably the mercaptothiobutyric acid is formed as an intermediate, air-oxidation converting it into the substituted 1, 2-dithiolane. Johnson[281] has claimed, unfortunately without experimental details, that the reaction of azlactones with hydrogen disulfide is a general synthesis for the above type of compound in good yield. The reaction is presumed to follow the course shown:

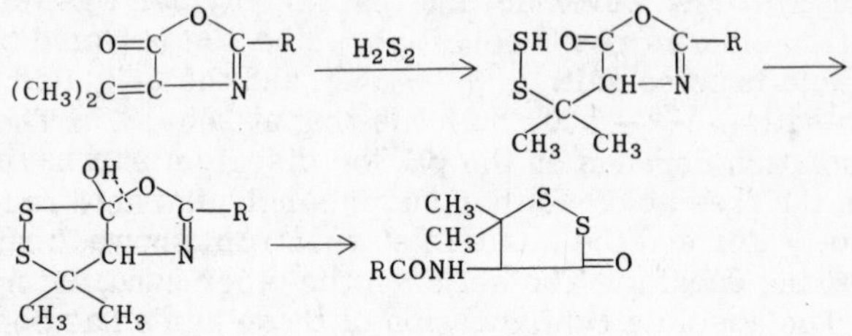

Reissert and Moré[449] reacted dithiomalonanilide (**22**) with concentrated sulfuric acid and obtained what they claimed to be 3, 5-bis(phenylimino)-1, 2-dithiolane (**23**). This ring closure involves the oxidation of the dienolic form. Schmidt[464] carried out the ring closure with iodine and isolated **23** as its picrate; unfortunately he did not compare his compound with that prepared by Reissert and Moré.

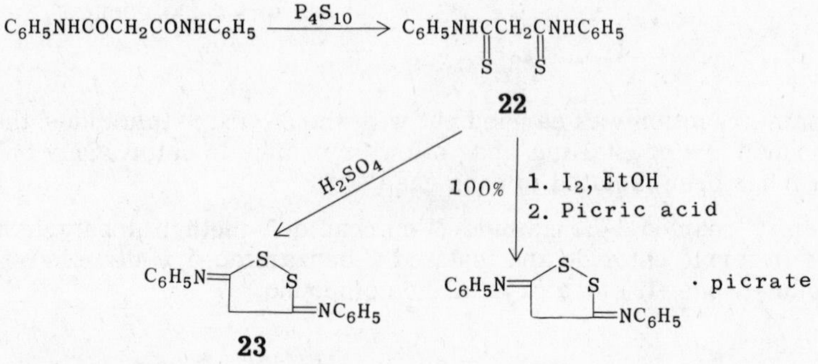

Other dithiomalonamides react similarly, but the products are obtained as 3, 5-diamino-1, 2-dithiolium salts (see section I A-2b). Reissert and Moré reacted **23** with hot 50% sulfuric acid to give another crystalline compound, $C_{30}H_{26}N_4S_6O_5$, m.p. 197° (dec.), which, on heating with aqueous caustic, liberated sulfuric acid and **22** and yielded another crystalline compound, m.p. 210°, which they formulated as **24**. However, Schmidt claimed this structure to be incorrect because of the known instability to base of the sulfur-sulfur bond in compounds of this type.

24

(2) Properties and Reactions

The physical and chemical properties of the 1, 2-dithiolane ring have been investigated quite thoroughly because of the interest in α-lipoic acid (see section I A-1b). Foss and co-workers[191, 192, 194], determined the molecular structure of 1, 2-dithiolane-4-carboxylic acid (**25**) crystallographically. The most important factor in the structure is the non-

25

planarity of the molecule, the CSS-SSC dihedral angle being 26.6°. The molecule is not symmetrical, and the S-S bond distance is longer than in linear disulfides (2.044 Å).

Probably the most important characteristic of the 1, 2-dithiolane ring is its instability under a variety of conditions. Thus, 1, 2-dithiolane itself is probably too unstable to be isolated in the pure state. Substituents on the ring in any position stabilize it to some extent, and, although many of the compounds still polymerize readily, they are stable enough to be isolated. Thus, according to Schöberl and Gräfje[472] 3, 3-dimethyl-1, 2-dithiolane (**10**) can be isolated, but it polymerizes after several hours at room temperature, while 3, 3, 5, 5-tetramethyl-1, 2-dithiolane (**11**) is stable indefinitely, and polymerizes only in the presence of a catalyst. This increased stability may be attributed to the well-known Thorpe-Ingold effect.[44]

Inasmuch as Calvin and co-workers[36,107-110,575] considered that α-lipoic acid might be involved in the primary quantum conversion act of photosynthesis, Barltrop, Hayes, and Calvin[36] attempted to calculate the ring strain in 1, 2-dithiolane by several methods. From spectroscopic measurements they arrived at a figure of 25-30 kcal/mole as the strain energy. Structural considerations carried out prior to Foss's determination of the structure of 1, 2-dithiolane-4-carboxylic acid led to a value of 11 kcal/mole. A more direct method was based on the fact that aliphatic thiols react with 1, 2-dithiolane reversibly, apparently in the following manner:

$$RSH + \text{[cyclic structure with S-S]} \rightleftharpoons RSS(CH_2)_3SH$$

$$RSS(CH_2)_3SH + \text{[cyclic structure with S-S]} \rightleftharpoons RSS(CH_2)_3SS(CH_2)_3SH, \text{ etc.}$$

Calculation of K for this series of equilibria gave a strain energy of 6. 3 kcal/mole.

Sunner[525,526] took exception to two of these methods, the spectroscopic one because he felt it was based on unrealistic assumptions and the equilibrium because of the ill-defined nature of the reaction, while Baltrop, Hayes, and Calvin themselves questioned the calculations based on conformational considerations. In order to arrive at a more reliable estimate, Sunner therefore studied the heat of oxidation of dimercaptans to disulfides with iodine, which he found to be a clean reaction. A comparison of 1, 3-dimercaptopropane with linear aliphatic mercaptans gave a strain energy for 1, 2-dithiolane of 4 kcal/mole. Since the ring is known to be highly strained, this is a surprisingly low value, and Sunner mentioned the possibility that the value was so low because the reactions were carried out in solution rather than in the vapor phase. Just as surprising was the fact that α-lipoic acid, essentially a 3-alkyl-1, 2-dithiolane, differed from 1, 2-dithiolane by only 0. 5 kcal, and yet it is considerably more stable.

Bergson and Schotte[52,53] recalculated the strain energy by conformational analysis based on the accurate determination of the structure of 1, 2-dithiolane-4-carboxylic acid by Foss and Tjomsland. [194] Assuming that the strain is composed of three components — stretching, bending, and torsion — they arrived at an estimate of 16-30 kcal/mole for the strain energy. Inasmuch as they estimated that the strain would have to be 20-25 kcal/mole for Calvin's hypothesis for the role of α-lipoic acid in photosynthesis to be correct, they arrived at the conclusion that Calvin's theory could not be ignored. They considered that the low results obtained by Barltrop, Hayes, and Calvin[36] and by Sunner[525,526] might have been caused by the presence of polymer in their samples of 1, 2-dithiolane.

Affleck and Dougherty[8] were the first to advance an explanation for the ring strain in 1, 2-dithiolane. Apparently the stable configuration about an S-S bond is one with a dihedral or azimuthal angle of 90°. [489,490] Since 1, 2-dithiolane, like all five-membered rings, would be only slightly puckered, the dihedral angle would be close to 0° and the system would therefore be highly strained. Barltrop, Hayes, and Calvin[36] suggested that the instability associated with the small dihedral angle is related to the repulsion between the two nonbonding pairs of p-electrons on the sulfur atoms.

Apparently all 1, 2-dithiolanes are yellow. 1, 2-Dithiolane itself has an absorption maximum in the ultraviolet at about 330 mμ, as does α-lipoic acid.[36,108] Schotte[482,483,486] made a thorough study of the effect of substituents on the absorption spectra of substituted 1, 2-dithiolanes. Aliphatic dialkyl disulfides have an absorption maximum at about 250 mμ, and Schotte attributed the shift to 330 mμ in 1, 2-dithiolane to the interaction between the nonbonding p-electrons on the sulfur atoms, this leading to excitation by less energy. Molecular orbital calculations carried out by Bergson[51] and by Kuboyama[311b] agree with this. In accord with this viewpoint, substituents in the 4-position have only a small effect on the absorption, a number of 4-substituted-1, 2-dithiolanes (semicarbazone, carboxylic acid, dialkyl, spiro compounds) all absorbing at 328-333 mμ. Only in 2, 6. 7-trithiaspiro [3. 4] octane, in which the four-membered ring might be expected to enhance the strain, is the maximum shifted appreciably (to 354 mμ). Alkyl groups in the 3-position have practically no effect on the absorption maximum, but carboxyl groups do. Thus, 1, 2-dithiolane-3-carboxylic acid has a maximum at 280 mμ[131,580] and *trans*-1, 2-dithiolane-3, 5-dicarboxylic acid at 250 mμ.[482,486] Whereas 1, 2-dithiolane-4-carboxylic acid and its sodium salt both have a maximum at 330 mμ, ionization of the 3, 5-dicarboxylic acid causes a considerable shift in the spectrum, the disodium salt having a weak maximum at 330 mμ. Since the dimethyl ester has the same maximum as the free acid, hydrogen bonding cannot be involved in the shift. A comparison of these compounds with linear disulfides and with other disulfide rings showed that the observed effects are rather specific for the five-membered ring.

Recently Claeson[132] investigated the spectra of 1, 2-dithiolane-3-carboxylic acid and 5-methyl-1, 2-dithiolane-3-carboxylic acid. In both cases he found, in addition to the strong maximum at 280 mμ reported by Schotte, a weak absorption at 330 mμ. In alkaline solution the 280 mμ peak disappeared, but the 330 mμ peak was intensified and sharpened somewhat. Thus, Schotte had observed not a shift but the disappearance of one absorption maximum. Claeson attributed this splitting of the disulfide absorption band to each sulfur atom acting independently, the unsymmetrical substitution leading to two peaks.

Schotte[482,483,486] also investigated the infrared spectra of substituted 1, 2-dithiolanes. The ring strain is indicated by the fact that the disulfide bands occur at higher frequencies than those of other disulfides, but further speculation appears to be unwarranted at present.

1, 2-Dithiolanes are cleaved to 1, 3-dimercaptans by a number of reducing agents. Thus, Barltrop, Hayes, and Calvin[36] cleaved 1, 2-dithiolane to 1, 3-dimercaptopropane quantitatively with zinc and dilute hydrochloric acid; however, the ring is stable to sodium borohydride. Schotte[487] cleaved 1, 2-dithiolane-4-carboxylic acid (14) to β, β'-dimercaptoisobutyric acid with zinc and ammonium hydroxide.

$$\text{HOOC}-\!\!\overset{\displaystyle S}{\underset{\displaystyle 14}{\boxed{}}}\!\!S \xrightarrow{\text{Zn, NH}_4\text{OH}} (\text{HSCH}_2)_2\text{CHCOOH}$$

The same reagent cleaves *trans*-1, 2-dithiolane-3, 5-dicarboxylic acid (**16**) to α, α'-dimercaptoglutaric acid, the (+)-acid giving the (−)-dimercaptan and *vice versa*. [485]

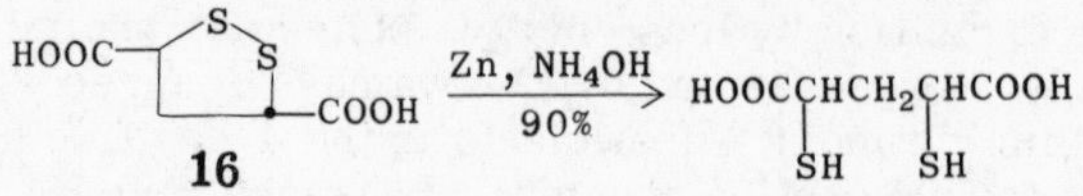

$$\text{16} \xrightarrow[90\%]{\text{Zn, NH}_4\text{OH}} \text{HOOCCHCH}_2\text{CHCOOH (SH SH)}$$

Backer and co-workers[23,24] reduced a number of their 1, 2-dithiolanes to the corresponding dimercaptans with sodium in liquid ammonia.

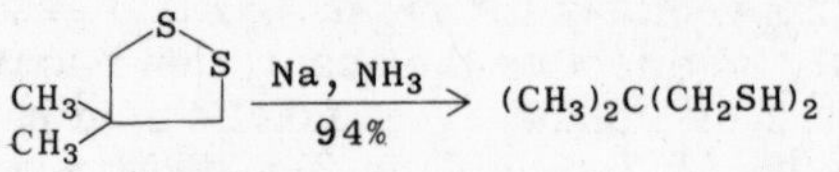

$$\text{6} \xrightarrow[94\%]{\text{Na, NH}_3} (\text{CH}_3)_2\text{C(CH}_2\text{SH})_2$$

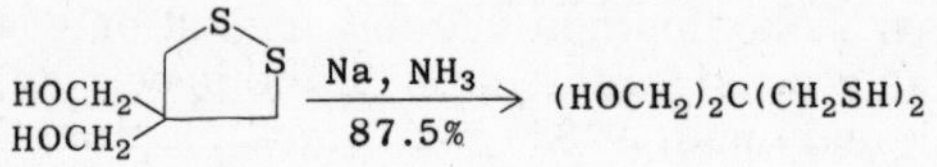

$$\text{9} \xrightarrow[87.5\%]{\text{Na, NH}_3} (\text{HOCH}_2)_2\text{C(CH}_2\text{SH})_2$$

Peppel and Signaigo[417] reduced **9** catalytically.

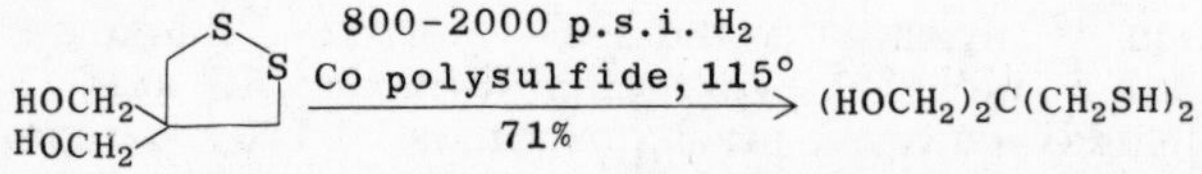

$$\text{9} \xrightarrow[71\%]{\substack{800-2000 \text{ p.s.i. H}_2 \\ \text{Co polysulfide, }115°}} (\text{HOCH}_2)_2\text{C(CH}_2\text{SH})_2$$

In many cases these reductions constitute the preferred method of preparation of the mercaptans.

Schotte and Nygård[407,486] investigated the polarographic reduction of a number of 1, 2-dithiolanes. At pH 2.2 all the derivatives gave good waves which were reversible in character. The wave heights indicated a two-electron reduction, presumably *via* the formation of mercury complexes formed on the drop at the rupture of the disulfide linkage.

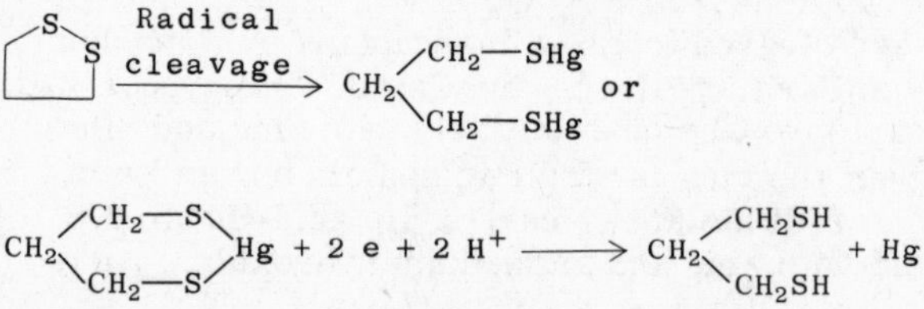

4-Substituted-1, 2-dithiolanes gave good waves over the pH range 2.2-9.2. *trans*-1, 2-Dithiolane-3, 5-dicarboxylic acid (**16**), on the other hand, gave a deformed wave at pH 7 and no wave at higher pH. Here, too, there is a difference between the free acid and the anion, just as there is in the ultraviolet spectrum.

Barltrop, Hayes, and Calvin[36] investigated the oxidation of 1,2-dithiolane. The compound was not oxidized by air alone, but was rapidly photo-oxidized in the presence of a photosensitizer, zinc tetraphenylporphin. Only one atom of oxygen per mole of 1,2-dithiolane was absorbed. The compound was not isolated but was assumed to be 1,2-dithiolane monoxide (26) because of the similarity of its ultraviolet absorption spectrum to that of the sulfoxide of thioctic acid (β-lipoic acid). Ammonium persulfate gave the same product. The sulfoxide is stable to acid in the cold but is destroyed rapidly by alkali. Schöberl and Gräfje[473] assumed that the same product is formed in the oxidation of 1,2-dithiolane with t-butyl hydroperoxide; 27 was formed by reaction with cysteine.

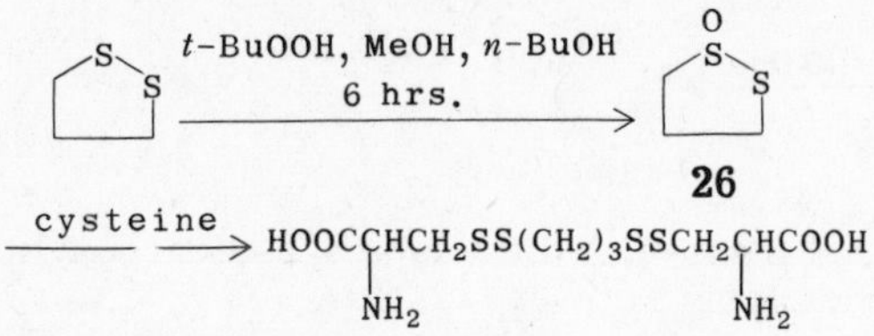

Backer and co-workers[21,22,24] studied the oxidation of substituted 1,2-dithiolane derivatives. A number of compounds were cleaved with hydrogen peroxide in acetic acid to the corresponding sulfonic acids.

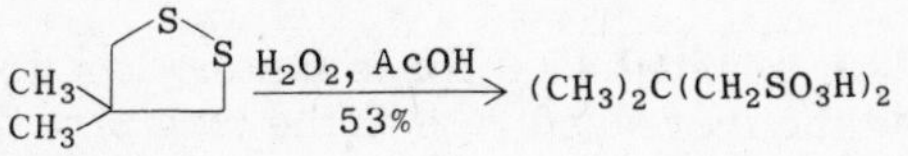

4,4-Bis(hydroxymethyl)-1,2-dithiolane (9) gave a 33% yield of the corresponding disulfonic acid and a small amount of disulfone, 4,4-bis-(hydroxymethyl)-1,2-dithiolane 1,1,2,2-tetroxide (28).

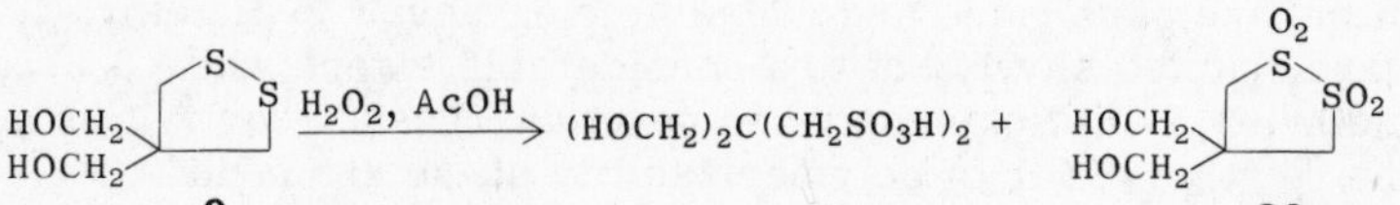

According to Backer and co-workers a number of substituted 1,2-dithiolanes form crystalline adducts with mercuric chloride and mercuric bromide; these are listed in Table 1.

Calvin and co-workers[36,108,575] studied the photolysis of 1,2-dithiolane intensively because of its relation to the role of α-lipoic acid in photosynthesis. Photolysis of 1,2-dithiolane in an ether-pentane-alcohol glass at $-196°$ gave a clear salmon-colored glass which became turbid on warming. However, over 50% of the starting material was still present, indicating that the reaction was following two paths.

[For references, see pp. 585-610.]

On the other hand, photolysis of 1, 2-dithiolane in ethanol containing hydrochloric acid yielded a clear solution from which no pure species could be isolated. One mercapto group per molecule was liberated and, on the basis of indirect reasoning, they reached the conclusion that the primary product is an unstable sulfenate ester (**29**), which under the reaction conditions is converted into other products.

29

Schotte[482, 485] has shown that *trans*-1, 2-dithiolane 3, 5-dicarboxylic acid is also destroyed by photolysis.

Further evidence of the instability of the 1, 2-dithiolane ring was presented by Fava, Iliceto, and Camera,[174] who studied the reaction of mercaptans with disulfides using labeled sulfur. They showed that the reaction involves the mercaptide ion.

$$RS^{*-} + RSSR \rightleftharpoons RS\overset{*}{S}R + RS^-$$

With $R = n$-butyl, 1, 2-dithiolane reacted 4500 times faster than di-n-butyl disulfide; they attributed the increased rate to the ring strain in 1, 2-dithiolane. Similarly, Schöberl and Gräfje[472] investigated the reaction of disulfides with cyanide ion, presumably to yield isothiocyanate and mercaptide ion.

$$RSSR + CN^- \longrightarrow RSCN + RS^-$$

1, 2-Dithiolane gave rapid and complete cleavage, 3, 3-dimethyl-1, 2-dithiolane reacted slowly but to a considerable extent, while 3, 3, 5, 5-tetramethyl-1, 2-dithiolane gave no reaction. These reactivities agree with the relative order of polymerizability of the compounds.

b. α-Lipoic Acid. 5-(1, 2-Dithiolan-3-yl)pentanoic Acid (**30**)

30

It would be hard to overestimate the importance of α-lipoic or thioctic acid in biological systems today. It has been reviewed in every volume of the <u>Annual Reviews of Biochemistry</u> since 1952, and numerous other reviews have been published.[222, 232, 298, 324, 325, 447, 447a, 526] A detailed description of its role in biological systems is beyond the scope of this book. Suffice it to say that, in addition to its essential role in the metabolism of many organisms, α-lipoic acid has been considered by Calvin and co-workers[36,107-110,575] to be involved in the primary quantum conversion act of photosynthesis.

In 1946 Guirard, Snell, and Williams[227,228] found that certain lactic acid bacteria require acetate for growth, and that, in the absence of acetate, growth was stimulated by certain crude yeast and liver preparations. Reed and co-workers[438,439] found that acid hydrolysis of liver yielded two so-called "acetate-replacing factors", and they isolated a very highly active oil. The material was an acid, unaffected in activity by esterification or by chemical reduction, but partially destroyed by oxidation with hydrogen peroxide, permanganate, and bromine, or by reduction with hydrogen and platinum.

In 1945 Kidder and Dewey[297] noticed that certain protozoa require a factor present in liver for growth. Stokstad and co-workers[516] investigated this factor and found that it existed in two forms, which they named Protogen A and B.

In 1947 O'Kane and Gunsalus[409,410] found that a "pyruvate oxidation factor" (POF), present in yeast and in liver, was required for the oxidative decarboxylation of pyruvate by resting cells of *Streptococcus faecalis*. In later work Gunsalus and co-workers[229,230] showed that the factor could exist in several forms, and the factor was concentrated.

Snell and Brohquist[498] were the first to suggest that these three factors might be identical, and showed that concentrates of pyruvate oxidation factor and of Protogen were highly active in promoting the growth of *Lactobacillus casei* in the absence of acetate. This was confirmed by Reed, DeBusk, Gunsalus, and Hornberger,[437] who isolated the active component from liver hydrolyzates in 1951. Ten tons of liver yielded 30 mg of crystalline material.[443] It was obtained as faint yellow platelets, m.p. 47.5-48.5°, and shown to be an acid with a pK_a of 4.76, which they named α-lipoic acid.

The structure of α-lipoic acid was elucidated almost simultaneously by Reed and co-workers[261,440,441,443] and by a group from the Lederle Laboratories of the American Cyanamid Company.[84,85,90,91,414,415] The compound analyzed as C$_8$H$_{14}$S$_2$O$_2$ and was shown to be a monocarboxylic acid. A negative nitroprusside test, which became positive after reduction, indicated the presence of a disulfide link, as did polarographic reduction; Sponar and Jirsa[508] found a two-electron reduction polarographically, and this was investigated in greater detail by Ke[288a] and by Asahi.[19b] Raney nickel desulfurization yielded *n*-octanoic acid, showing that the carbons were in a straight chain. The absence of a methyl band in the infrared spectrum indicated that one sulfur atom was on the terminal carbon, and the optical activity, $[\alpha]_D^{20}$ + 96.7°, showed the presence of at least one asymmetric center. The pK_a of 4.76 indicated that the other sulfur atom was not on C-2 or C-3, and polarographic reduc-

[For references, see pp. 585-610.]

tion made it seem likely that the compound was a six-membered cyclic disulfide rather than a five.[441]

A second compound, called β-lipoic acid and presumably identical with Protogen B, was isolated from liver hydrolyzates.[85,414,415,440] Its S-benzylthiouronium salt was crystalline, m.p. 143-144°.[90-92] It was considered to be a sulfoxide of α-lipoic acid, since it was formed by oxidation of α-lipoic acid and reduction converted it into α-lipoic acid.[85,415,440,444] The position of the oxygen has yet to be determined, and the compound is probably an artifact.[443]

Initial attempts to prove the structure of α-lipoic acid by synthesis were not too successful. Bullock, Brockman, Patterson, Pierce, and Stokstad[90] started with 4-(2-tetrahydrofuryl)butyric acid (**31**).

The cyclic disulfide was isolated as an oil and had some biological activity. However, they considered the synthesis equivocal because of the possibility of hydroxyl migration during the acid treatment.

Hornberger, Heitmiller, Gunsalus, Schnakenberg, and Reed,[216,262] repeated the synthesis and isolated a 10% yield of DL-α-lipoic acid, m.p. 59-60°, showing in the process that rearrangement did take place, both the valerolactone (**33**) and the butyrolactone (**34**) giving the same products. Makino and Koike[364] reported a 78% yield by the same procedure.

Bullock, Brockman, and co-workers,[91,92] showed that three compounds are formed in this reaction, the expected six-membered ring, which they called 5-thioctic acid (**32**), and minor quantities of the seven-membered ring, 4-thioctic acid, and of the five-membered ring, 6-thioctic acid (**30**). Biological potency showed without any doubt that α-lipoic or 6-thioctic acid is the naturally occurring product, its unequivocal synthesis being carried out as follows:

$$\underset{\textbf{35}}{Cl\overset{O}{\overset{\|}{C}}(CH_2)_4COOC_2H_5} \xrightarrow{C_2H_4,\ AlCl_3} \underset{\textbf{36}}{CH_2{=}CH\overset{O}{\overset{\|}{C}}(CH_2)_4COOC_2H_5} \xrightarrow[\substack{\text{3. NaOH}}]{\substack{\text{1. } CH_3COSH \\ \text{2. } NaBH_4}}$$

$$\underset{\underset{SH \quad\quad OH}{|\quad\quad\ |}}{CH_2CH_2CH(CH_2)_4COOH} \xrightarrow[\text{2. NaOH}]{\text{1. } S{=}C(NH_2)_2 + HI} \underset{\underset{SH \quad SH}{|\quad\ |}}{CH_2CH_2CH(CH_2)_4COOH}$$

$$\xrightarrow[\text{or } O_2 + Fe^{3+} \text{ on K salt}]{I_2 + CHCl_3 \text{ or } KI_3} \underset{\textbf{30}}{\overset{\text{[S-S ring]}}{\diagup}(CH_2)_4COOH}$$

Air oxidation in the presence of a trace of ferric ion was found superior to oxidation with iodine. This route has been patented,[96,98-101] and later work was carried out to improve the yields.[93]

The overall yield in the initial synthesis was quite low, and a number of variations were carried out to improve it, all starting with the addition of ethylene to the half ester-acid chloride of adipic acid (35). Thus, Soper, Buting, Cochran, and Pohland[503] added benzylmercaptan to the unsaturated keto-ester (36) and, by several different routes, converted the carbonyl group to either a benzylmercapto or a bis(benzylmercapto) group. Reduction with sodium in liquid ammonia removed the benzyl groups, and the dimercaptan was then oxidized to α-lipoic acid with iodine in potassium iodide. Nakano and Sano[400] used essentially the same procedure. Acker[1] added thioacetic acid to the double bond of the unsaturated keto-ester (36) and converted the carbonyl directly to a mercaptan by reduction with hydrogen and sulfur in the presence of cobalt polysulfide. Acker and Todd[2,3] showed that essentially the same yields are obtained by reducing the unsaturated keto-ester without first adding thioacetic acid or by adding a number of compounds, such as secondary amines, hydrogen cyanide, etc., to the double bond before reduction. This general route was investigated more thoroughly by Bullock, Hand, and Stokstad,[94] who found it the most convenient for preparation of large quantities of α-lipoic acid. Catalytic reduction of methyl 6-oxo-7-octenoate with sulfur and hydrogen, followed by hydrolysis and oxidation, gave a 30% yield of α-lipoic acid. Reduction of the thioacetic acid adduct gave a 39% yield, while reduction of the benzyl mercaptan adduct gave a 26% yield. Reduction of the benzyl mercaptan adduct by substituting benzyl mercaptan for sulfur was patented,[97] but the yield was only 20%.

Reed and Niu[446] modified the original synthesis still further, preparing a 6, 8-dihalooctanoic acid (37) by several different routes and reacting it with benzyl mercaptan. Their preferred procedure, which gave an overall yield of 36%, was as follows:

[For references, see pp. 585-610.]

$$Cl\overset{O}{\underset{\|}{C}}(CH_2)_4COOC_2H_5 \xrightarrow{C_2H_4,\ AlCl_3} ClCH_2CH_2\overset{O}{\underset{\|}{C}}(CH_2)_4COOC_2H_5$$

$$\xrightarrow[\text{2. SOCl}_2]{\text{1. NaBH}_4} \underset{\underset{Cl}{|}\ \ \underset{Cl}{|}}{CH_2CH_2CH(CH_2)_4COOC_2H_5} \xrightarrow[\text{2. KOH}]{\text{1. PhCH}_2\text{SNa}}$$

37

$$\underset{\underset{C_6H_5CH_2S}{|}\ \ \underset{SCH_2C_6H_5}{|}}{CH_2CH_2CH(CH_2)_4COOH} \xrightarrow{Na,\ NH_3}$$

$$\underset{\underset{SH}{|}\ \ \underset{SH}{|}}{CH_2CH_2CH(CH_2)_4COONa} \xrightarrow{O_2,\ Fe^{3+}} \alpha\text{-lipoic acid}$$

Essentially the same synthesis was used by Adams[6] and by Thomas and Reed[5,36] to prepare α-lipoic acid with labeled sulfur atoms. Acker and Wayne[4,5] simplified the synthesis considerably, obtaining α-lipoic acid in 68% yield by reacting **37** with sodium disulfide and hydrolyzing the product. The free acid of **37** gave a 46% yield and, by resolving the l-ephedrine salt of the free acid, they isolated pure $(+)$-α-lipoic acid. The use of radioactive sodium disulfide gave DL-α-lipoic acid-S$_2^{35}$. Hornberger[263,264] claimed excellent yields of α-lipoic acid by alkaline hydrolysis of the 6, 8-bis(isothiocyanate) of octanoic acid (**38**), but the difficulty of obtaining the bis(isothiocyanate) would appear to make this synthesis less convenient than that of Acker and Wayne. The ring closure method is interesting, however, probably involving partial hydrolysis followed by nucleophilic displacement of cyanide ion by mercaptide ion.

$$\underset{\underset{SCN}{|}\ \ \underset{SCN}{|}}{CH_2CH_2CH(CH_2)_4COOH} \xrightarrow{KOH,\ EtOH} \underset{\underset{S^-}{|}\ \ \underset{S-C N}{|}}{CH_2CH_2CH(CH_2)_4COOH}$$

$$\downarrow$$

$$\underset{(CH_2)_4COOH}{\overset{S\underset{|}{\diagup}\diagdown S}{\diagdown\diagup}} + CN^-$$

38

A different route was used by Braude, Linstead, and Woolridge.[80,81] They carried out a Prins reaction on 6-heptenoic acid. The mixture of dioxolane and diacetate was esterified with diazomethane, the acetyl groups were removed by treatment with methanol and sulfuric acid, and the resulting methyl 6, 8-dihydroxyoctanoate was converted to α-lipoic acid via the thiourea-hydrobromic acid route. The five-step synthesis gave yields of 20-30%.

$$CH_2{=}CH(CH_2)_4COOH \xrightarrow[\text{H}_2\text{SO}_4]{\text{HCHO, AcOH}} \underset{\underset{OCOCH_3}{|}\ \underset{OCOCH_3}{|}}{CH_2CH_2CH(CH_2)_4COOH} + \underset{\underset{O}{|}\ \ \underset{O}{|}}{CH_2CH_2CH(CH_2)_4COOH}$$

$$\xrightarrow[\text{2. MeOH, H}_2\text{SO}_4]{\text{1. CH}_2\text{N}_2} \underset{\overset{|}{\text{OH}}\quad\overset{|}{\text{OH}}}{\text{CH}_2\text{CH}_2\text{CH(CH}_2)_4\text{COOCH}_3} \xrightarrow{\quad\quad} \alpha\text{-lipoic acid}$$

Walton, Wagner, and co-workers,[563-567] were the first to synthesize (+)-α-lipoic acid, the following route being used:

$$\text{HOOCCH}{=}\text{CH(CH}_2)_4\text{COOC}_2\text{H}_5 \xrightarrow{\text{CH}_3\text{COSH}} \underset{\overset{|}{\text{SCOCH}_3}}{\text{HOOCCH}_2\text{CH(CH}_2)_4\text{COOC}_2\text{H}_5}$$

39

39 was resolved with l-ephedrine, the (+)-acid giving (+)-α-lipoic acid and the (−)-acid (−)-α-lipoic acid by a straightforward procedure.

$$\underset{\overset{|}{\text{SCOCH}_3}}{\text{HOOCCH}_2\text{CH(CH}_2)_4\text{COOC}_2\text{H}_5} \xrightarrow[\text{3. NaOH}]{\substack{\text{1. SOCl}_2 \\ \text{2. NaBH}_4}} \underset{\overset{|}{\text{OH}}\quad\overset{|}{\text{SH}}}{\text{CH}_2\text{CH}_2\text{CH(CH}_2)_4\text{COOH}}$$

40

α-Lipoic acid was obtained from the hydroxythiol (**40**) *via* the thiourea route. Alternatively, **40** was first oxidized to a disulfide, then treated with thiourea and hydrobromic acid, hydrolyzed, and oxidized to α-lipoic acid with iodine.[560] It is interesting that prior reduction of the disulfide (**41**) was not required, perhaps because it disproportionated.

$$\left(\underset{\overset{|}{\text{SH}}\quad\overset{|}{\text{S}{-}}}{\text{CH}_2\text{CH}_2\text{CH(CH}_2)_4\text{COOH}}\right)_2 \xrightarrow{\quad\quad} \underset{\overset{|}{\text{SH}}\quad\overset{|}{\text{SH}}}{\text{CH}_2\text{CH}_2\text{CH(CH}_2)_4\text{COOH}} + \alpha\text{-lipoic acid}$$

41

Several other syntheses have been reported. Starker and Cosulich[509] prepared 6-hydroxy-8-ethoxyoctanoic acid (**42**) by several different routes, perhaps the most interesting being the radical-catalyzed addition of β-ethoxypropionaldehyde to allylmalonic ester. The usual thiourea reaction was used to convert **42** into α-lipoic acid, but apparently the overall yield was not particularly impressive.

$$\text{CH}_2{=}\text{CHCH}_2\text{CH(COOC}_2\text{H}_5)_2 + \text{C}_2\text{H}_5\text{OCH}_2\text{CH}_2\text{CHO} \xrightarrow{(\text{C}_6\text{H}_5\text{COO})_2}$$

$$\text{C}_2\text{H}_5\text{OCH}_2\text{CH}_2\text{CO(CH}_2)_3\text{CH(COOC}_2\text{H}_5)_2 \xrightarrow[\text{2. Heat}]{\text{1. Aq. KOH}}$$

$$\text{C}_2\text{H}_5\text{OCH}_2\text{CH}_2\text{CO(CH}_2)_4\text{COOH} \xrightarrow{[\text{H}]} \underset{\overset{|}{\text{OH}}}{\text{C}_2\text{H}_5\text{OCH}_2\text{CH}_2\text{CH(CH}_2)_4\text{COOH}}$$

42

$$\xrightarrow[\substack{\text{2. Aq. NaOH} \\ \text{3. O}_2,\ \text{Fe}^{3+}}]{\text{1. SC(NH}_2)_2,\ \text{HI}} \alpha\text{-lipoic acid}$$

[For references, see pp. 585-610.]

Jones[285] prepared α-lipoic acid starting with an aldol condensation of acetaldehyde with δ-carbethoxyvaleraldehyde.

$$OHC(CH_2)_4COOC_2H_5 \xrightarrow[\text{Aq. NaOH}]{CH_3CHO} OHCCH_2\underset{\underset{HO}{|}}{C}H(CH_2)_4COOC_2H_5$$

$$\xrightarrow[\text{2. Aq. KOH}]{\text{1. NaBH}_4} HOCH_2CH_2\underset{\underset{HO}{|}}{C}H(CH_2)_4COOH \xrightarrow[\substack{\text{2. Aq. NaOH} \\ \text{3. KI}_3}]{\text{1. SC(NH}_2)_2, \text{HBr}} \alpha\text{-lipoic acid}$$

The novel feature of the synthesis devised by Segre, Viterbo, and Parisi[493] was a Baeyer-Villiger reaction on 2-(2-acetoxyethyl) cyclohexanone (43). The overall yield from cyclohexanone was 19%.

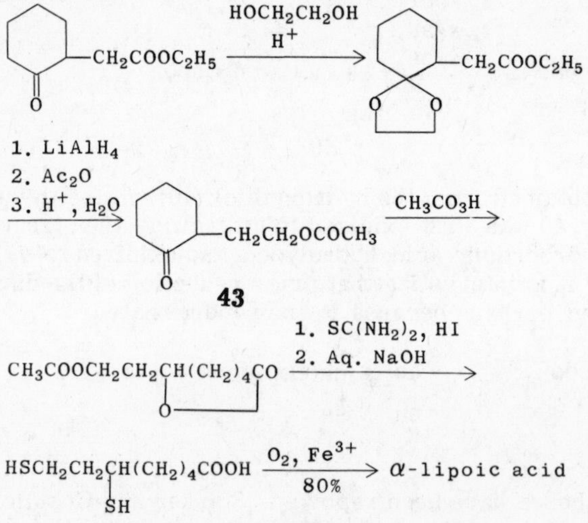

$$\xrightarrow[H^+]{HOCH_2CH_2OH}$$

$$\xrightarrow[\substack{\text{2. Ac}_2O \\ \text{3. H}^+, \text{H}_2O}]{\text{1. LiAlH}_4} \quad \text{—CH}_2CH_2OCOCH_3 \xrightarrow{CH_3CO_3H}$$

43

$$CH_3COOCH_2CH_2\underset{\underset{O}{|}}{C}H(CH_2)_4CO \xrightarrow[\text{2. Aq. NaOH}]{\text{1. SC(NH}_2)_2, \text{HI}}$$

$$HSCH_2CH_2\underset{\underset{SH}{|}}{C}H(CH_2)_4COOH \xrightarrow[80\%]{O_2, \text{Fe}^{3+}} \alpha\text{-lipoic acid}$$

Schmidt and Grafen[465] devised two syntheses of α-lipoic acid. One involved the reaction of the half ester-acid chloride of adipic acid (35) with acetylene instead of with ethylene, and gave an overall yield of 22%.

$$ClOC(CH_2)_4COOC_2H_5 \xrightarrow{C_2H_2, \text{AlCl}_3} ClCH=CHCO(CH_2)_4COOC_2H_5$$

35

$$\xrightarrow{MeOH, OH^-} (CH_3O)_2CHCH_2CO(CH_2)_4COOC_2H_5 \xrightarrow[\text{2. Ac}_2O]{\text{1. H}_2, \text{Ni}}$$

$$CH_3OCH_2CH_2\underset{\underset{OCOCH_3}{|}}{C}H(CH_2)_4COOC_2H_5 \xrightarrow[\substack{\text{2. Aq. NaOH} \\ \text{3. O}_2, \text{Fe}^{3+}}]{\text{1. SC(NH}_2)_2, \text{HI}} \alpha\text{-lipoic acid}$$

334

The second synthesis, which gave a 30% yield of α-lipoic acid, started from ethyl 6, 6-diethoxyhexanoate (44) and ethyl vinyl ether.

$$(C_2H_5O)_2CH(CH_2)_4COOC_2H_5 + CH_2\!\!=\!\!CHOC_2H_5 \xrightarrow{\ BF_3\ }$$

44

$$(C_2H_5O)_2CHCH_2\underset{\underset{OC_2H_5}{|}}{C}H(CH_2)_4COOC_2H_5 \xrightarrow{\ H_2,\ Ni\ }$$

$$C_2H_5OCH_2CH_2\underset{\underset{OC_2H_5}{|}}{C}H(CH_2)_4COOC_2H_5 \rightsquigarrow\!\!\!\longrightarrow \alpha\text{-lipoic acid}$$

Yurugi and co-workers[584a, 584b] developed a synthesis for the intermediate 8-alkoxy-6-oxooctanoic acid from an enamine.

$$\xrightarrow{\text{Aq. NaOH}} ROCH_2CH_2CO(CH_2)_4COOH$$

Deguchi[144a-144d] investigated several variations of these procedures, but none appears to have any outstanding advantage over those described here.

Mislow and Meluch[388,389] determined the absolute configuration of (+)-α-lipoic acid based on the Fredga method of melting point-composition diagrams.[197a] 3-Methylsuberic acid of known stereochemistry formed a continuous series of solid solutions with the 3-mercaptosuberic acid prepared by hydrolysis of (+)-3-acetylthio-7-carbethoxyheptanoic acid (37). They therefore have the same configuration. Since Walton, Wagner, and co-workers,[563,564] had shown that the (+)-isomer yields (+)-α-lipoic acid, the naturally occurring isomer was shown to have structure 45.

45

A number of derivatives of α-lipoic acid and related compounds have been prepared; these are listed in Table 2. α-Lipoic acid shows the reactions expected of a 1, 2-dithiolane, several of them having been already mentioned in the discussion on the proof of structure. A variety of oxidizing agents—di-t-butyl peroxide,[90,415] iodine and air,[415] alkaline permanganate,[444] hydrogen peroxide in acetic acid[444]—oxidize α-lipoic

[For references, see pp. 585-610.]

acid to a sulfoxide, β-lipoic acid. This in turn can be reduced to α-lipoic acid with hydrogen iodide,[440,444] zinc and acetic acid,[415] and sodium borohydride.[415] The last reagent is unusual because, apparently under other conditions, it reduces α-lipoic acid to the dimercaptan.[91,231,559] 1, 2-Dithiolane itself is reported to be stable to this reagent.[36] The disulfide ring can also be opened with sodium in liquid ammonia[86,87] and with zinc plus hydrochloric acid.[231] (+)-α-Lipoic acid yields (−)-6, 8-dithiooctanoic acid.[231]

A number of salts have been used to characterize both (+)- and DL-α-lipoic acid: the S-benzylthiouronium salt,[85,231,414] the benzhydrylammonium salt,[559] and the l-ephedrine salt.[559] Gunsalus, Barton, and Gruber[231] have recommended the acylurea formed from the acid and di-(p-dimethylaminophenyl)carbodiimide, p-$(CH_3)_2NC_6H_4N$=C=NC_6H_4N $(CH_3)_2$-p, for the characterization of α-lipoic acid. The methyl ester has been prepared from the acid and diazomethane.[231] Treatment of sodium α-lipoate with phosgene gave the acid chloride as an unstable oil.[559,561] According to Kishi[300a] a better yield is obtained by reacting the free acid with ethyl chloroformate and triethylamine. Ammonia converted the acid chloride to a crystalline amide, while reduction of the acid chloride gave the alcohol, which could not be purified completely.[559,260,561] Kishi[300a] also prepared the amide, although in less pure form, from 6, 8-dichlorooctamide and sodium disulfide, while Okumura, Yoshikawa, and Inoue[410a] prepared it from 6, 8-bis(benzylthio)octanoic acid.

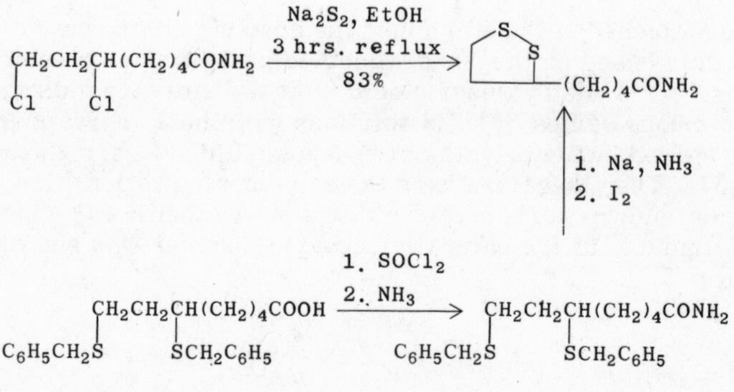

Reed and DeBusk[442,445] coupled α-lipoic acid with thiamin, presumably as shown:

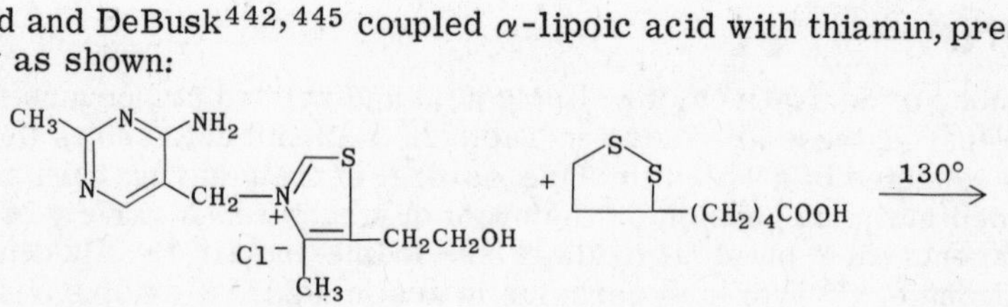

46

They believed **46**, probably as its pyrophosphate, to be the naturally occurring coenzyme for pyruvate oxidation, but this view has been questioned.[325] A number of related compounds were prepared, but no properties were given for any of them. More recently, Nawa, Brady, Koike, and Reed[401,401a] suggested that the α-lipoic acid is bound to the ϵ-amino group of a lysine residue in a protein, and prepared ϵ-N-DL-lipoyl-L-lysine (**48**) by reacting DL-lipoic isobutyl carbonic anhydride (**47**) with the copper chelate of L-lysine.

47

48

Okumura, Yoshikawa, and Inoue[410a] prepared **48** by condensing 6, 8-bis (benzylthio)octanoyl chloride with the copper chelate followed by debenzylation and ring closure in the usual manner.

Wagner, Walton, and co-workers,[559] investigated the stability of α-lipoic acid. It was found to polymerize in solution or in the melt under the influence of light, but to be stable in the dark and in the solid state. Hot aqueous solutions are stable at low pH. At high pH, extensive degradation takes place in the presence of oxygen but not in its absence. The polymerization is reversible; heating the polymer converts it back to α-lipoic acid. This was confirmed by Thomas and Reed,[537] who studied the polymer formed as a by-product in the oxidation of 6, 8-dithiooctanoic acid to α-lipoic acid. The polymer was considered to be a polydisulfide, since its spectrum shows disulfide links and reduction with zinc and hydrochloric acid followed by iodine oxidation gives α-lipoic acid. Under alkaline conditions the polymer is converted rapidly and almost quantitatively to α-lipoic acid at room temperature. The reaction is catalyzed by mercaptide ion, and the authors considered the reaction to involve an anionic displacement of the disulfide link by mercaptide.

[For references, see pp. 585-610.]

TABLE 2. α-Lipoic Acid and Related Compounds

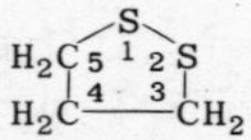

$$H_2C \overset{5}{\underset{4}{}} \overset{S}{\underset{}{}} \overset{1}{\underset{3}{}} \overset{2}{\underset{}{}} \overset{S}{\underset{}{CH_2}}$$

Substituent	Yield (%)	M.p. (°C)	B.p. (°C)	(mm)	Other properties	Ref.
(+)-3-[-(CH₂)₄CO₂H]		47.5-48.5			$[\alpha]_D^{25} + 96.7°$	437, 440, 443
		46-48			$[\alpha]_D^{24.5} + 115.9°$	4
					λ_{max} 333 mμ	108
DL-3-[-(CH₂)₄CO₂H]		61	150	0.1		91, 92
DL-3-[-(CH₂)₄CO₂H] S-Benzylthiuronium salt	54	132-134				85, 231, 414
(+)-3-[-(CH₂)₄CO₂H] Benzhydrylammonium salt		124-126			$[\alpha]_D^{25} + 50.0°$	559
DL-3-[-(CH₂)₄CO₂H] Benzhydrylammonium salt		124.5-125.5				559
DL-3-[-(CH₂)₄CO₂H] l-Ephedrine salt		103-104				559
(+)-3-[-(CH₂)₄CO₂H] (−)-Cinchonidine salt		99.5-156			$[\alpha]_D^{24.1} - 54.6°$	4

Compound	Yield (%)	m.p. (°C)	b.p. (°C)/mm		Ref.
DL-3-[-(CH$_2$)$_4$CO$_2$CH$_3$]	82		129–131 0.7		231
DL-3-[-(CH$_2$)$_4$COCl]	80	124–126			559, 561
DL-3-[-(CH$_2$)$_4$CONH$_2$]	24	129–130			559
	86.7	129–130			300a
		129–130			410a
DL-3-[-(CH$_2$)$_4$CH$_2$OH]	36			n_D^{25} 1.5525 (impure)	559, 260
3-[-(CH$_2$)$_4$CO$_2$H], sulfoxide, S-Benzylthiuronium salt		143–144			90–92
DL-3-$\left[\begin{array}{c}-(CH_2)_4\text{CONCONHC}_6H_4N(CH_3)_2\text{-}p \\ p\text{-}(CH_3)_2NC_6H_4\end{array}\right]$	60	153–154			231
(+)-3-$\left[\begin{array}{c}-(CH_2)_4\text{CONCONHC}_6H_4N(CH_3)_2\text{-}p \\ p\text{-}(CH_3)_2NC_6H_4\end{array}\right]$	61	139–141		$[\alpha]_D^{20}$ + 45.2°	231
DL-3-[-(CH$_2$)$_4$CO$_2$H]-5-CH$_3$-		54–54.5		unstable form m.p. 45–46°	93–96, 98a
DL-3-[-(CH$_2$)$_4$SO$_2$NH$_2$]		68–69			538
DL-3-[-(CH$_2$)$_3$CO$_2$H]		40–41			539
			152–160 0.1	n_D^{20} 1.5355	99

339

TABLE 2. α-Lipoic Acid and Related Compounds (contd)

Substituent	Yield (%)	M.p. (°C)	B.p. (°C)	(mm)	Other properties	Ref.
DL-3-[-(CH$_2$)$_5$CO$_2$H]		31–33				539
DL-3-[-(CH$_2$)$_4$CONH(CH$_2$)$_4$CHCO$_2$H] 　　　　　　　　　　　　NH$_2$		225–229(dec.)				401
		230–235(dec.)				410a

Cavina, Cingolani, and Gaudiano[115] have worked out the conditions for the color reaction with cyanide-nitroprusside for the quantitative determination of α-lipoic acid. Covello and DeVena[137a] reported an analytical procedure for microgram quantities of α-lipoic acid, which involves catalytic reduction and conversion of the liberated hydrogen sulfide to methylene blue; the latter is then determined spectroscopically by its absorption at 665 mμ.

α-Lipoic acid forms an inclusion compound with thiourea.[386a] According to Djerassi, Fredga, and Sjöberg[156b] it shows a strong Cotton effect in optical rotatory dispersion studies.

A number of compounds related to α-lipoic acid have been prepared. Bullock and co-workers[93-96] prepared 5-(5-methyl-1,2-dithiolan-3-yl)pentanoic acid (49, R = CH_3, R' = H) by several routes which parallel the synthesis of α-lipoic acid. The compound contains two asymmetric carbons and the product isolated was believed to be a molecular compound of both pairs of diastereoisomers. One pair appeared to be an antagonist for α-lipoic acid, while the other showed α-lipoic-like activity. Schmidt, Alpes, and Grafen[465e] prepared the corresponding 4-methyl compound (49, R = H, R' = CH_3) by an unstated route and found it to be an antagonist in dehydrogenase activity. The compound was unusual in having its absorption maximum shifted 20 mμ toward the red compared to α-lipoic acid, which they attributed to increased ring strain resulting from a postulated *cis* orientation of the two substituent groups on the 1,2-dithiolane ring. The same authors prepared 4-oxa-5-(1,2-dithiolan-3-yl)pentanoic acid (49a); it possessed α-lipoic acid dehydrogenase activity.

49   **49a**

Thomas and Reed[538] prepared DL-4-(1,2-dithiolan-3-yl) butanesulforn amide (50) from the previously described 6,8-dichlorooctanoic acid.

Chapter 5

1. PhCH$_2$SNa
2. Na, NH$_3$
3. O$_2$, Fe^{3+}

(CH$_2$)$_4$SO$_2$NH$_2$

50

The yellow sulfonamide, showing the expected λ_{max} at 332 mμ was not an antagonist for α-lipoic acid. The same authors[539] prepared DL-6-(1, 2-dithiolan-3-yl)hexanoic acid (**51**) and 4-(1, 2-dithiolan-3-yl)butyric acid (**52**).

ClCH$_2$CH$_2$CH(CH$_2$)$_4$COOC$_2$H$_5$ $\xrightarrow{LiAlH_4}$ ClCH$_2$CH$_2$CH(CH$_2$)$_5$OH $\xrightarrow[2.\ KCN]{1.\ PBr_3}$
       Cl   Cl

ClCH$_2$CH$_2$CH(CH$_2$)$_5$CN $\xrightarrow{EtOH,\ HCl}$ ClCH$_2$CH$_2$CH(CH$_2$)$_5$COOC$_2$H$_5$
     Cl   Cl

PhCH$_2$SNa, etc.

(CH$_2$)$_5$COOH

51

1. PhMgBr
2. Ac$_2$O, AcOH
3. CrO$_3$

ClCH$_2$CH$_2$CH(CH$_2$)$_4$COOC$_2$H$_5$ $\longrightarrow$ ClCH$_2$CH$_2$CH(CH$_2$)$_3$COOH
    Cl   Cl

PhCH$_2$SNa, etc.

(CH$_2$)$_3$COOH

52

Both compounds showed only faint activity, 0.1% and 0.01% of α-lipoic acid, respectively, in the acetate replacing factor assay.

α-Lipoic acid, according to Rausch,[436] is useful for the treatment of hepatic coma and related diseases. Boni, Reduzzi, Bile, and Galloro[76] have recommended its use for other liver disfunctions. There have been two conflicting reports, one[148] that α-lipoic acid shows no effect on mouse cancer and another[322] that it has a definite accelerating effect on the growth of Ascites tumor in mice. α-Lipoic acid has been reported to be useful in cyanide poisoning[140] and in heavy metal poisoning.[213,224,224a,257a,377a] Searle has patented its use as a plant fungicide[492] and as an antioxidant in edible fats and oils.[491] Mochel[390] has claimed that salts of α-lipoic acid increase the light sensitivity of photographic emulsions, while Allen, Illingsworth, and Sagura[10b] claim it to be an antifogging agent. Salzberg[460] has patented the use of α-lipoic acid as a corrosion inhibitor for iron in the presence of acidic materials.

342

c. Spiro Compounds

Spiro-1, 2-dithiolanes have been prepared by the same procedures used for the simple compounds; they are listed in Table 3. Thus, Backer and Evenhuis[21] and Schotte[483] prepared 2, 6, 7-trithiaspiro[3. 4]octane (54) from tetrakis(bromomethyl)methane and sodium disulfide followed by treatment with copper. If the interpretation advanced by Schotte[484] is correct, the reaction is as follows:

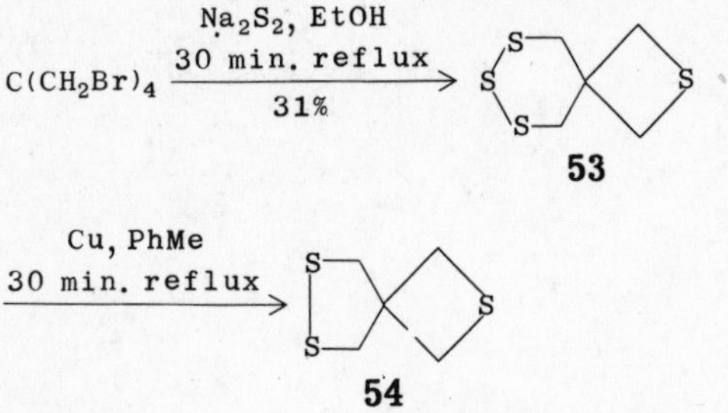

$$C(CH_2Br)_4 \xrightarrow[\text{31\%}]{\substack{Na_2S_2, \text{ EtOH} \\ 30 \text{ min. reflux}}}$$

53

$$\xrightarrow[]{\substack{Cu, PhMe \\ 30 \text{ min. reflux}}}$$

54

Similarly, the bromo compound plus sodium tetrasulfide yielded 2, 3, 4, 8, 9, 10-hexathiaspiro[5. 5]undecane (55). This with copper gave 2, 3, 7, 8-tetrathiaspiro[4. 4]nonane (56), while with potassium sulfide it yielded a mixture of 56 and 2, 3, 7, 8, 9-pentathiaspiro[4. 5]decane (57).

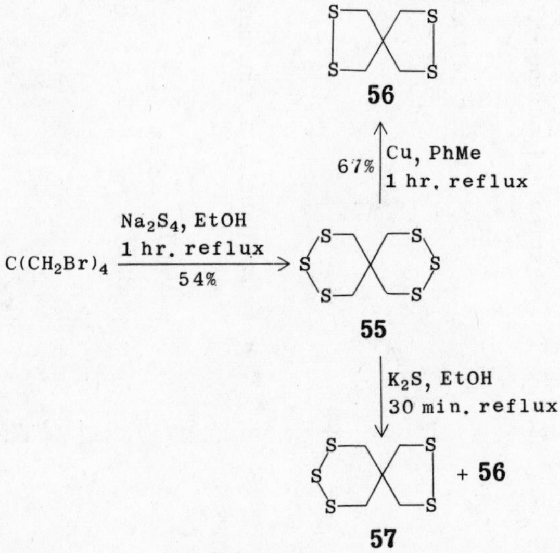

56

$$67\% \uparrow \substack{Cu, PhMe \\ 1 \text{ hr. reflux}}$$

$$C(CH_2Br)_4 \xrightarrow[\text{54\%}]{\substack{Na_2S_4, \text{ EtOH} \\ 1 \text{ hr. reflux}}}$$

55

$$\downarrow \substack{K_2S, \text{ EtOH} \\ 30 \text{ min. reflux}}$$

+ **56**

57

Likewise, 1, 1-bis(bromomethyl)cyclohexane gave 2, 3-dithiaspiro-[4. 5]decane (58), also formed from 1, 1-bis(mercaptomethyl)cyclohexane and iodine.[24]

[For references, see pp. 585-610.]

TABLE 3. Spiro-1,2-dithiolanes

Compound 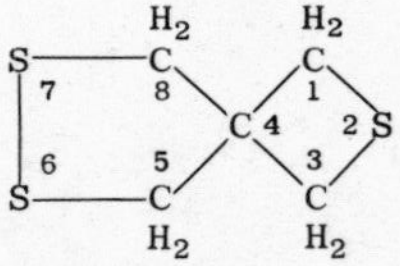	Yield (%)	M.p. (°C)	Ref.
2,6,7-Trithiaspiro[3.4]octane (RRI 781)		55.5-56.5	21
		53-54	483
2,2,6,6-tetroxide 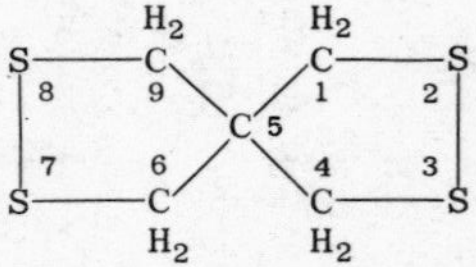	86	~257	21
2,3,7,8-Tetrathiaspiro[4.4]nonane (RRI 966)	36	80-80.5	22
		79-80	483
HgCl$_2$	42	132	22
HgBr$_2$ 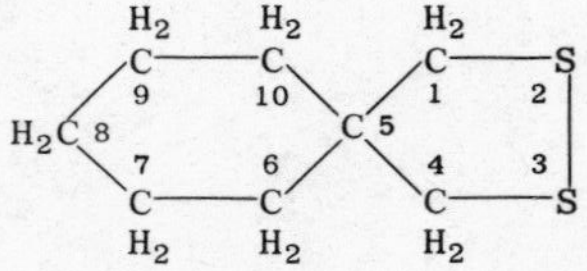	56	127-127.5	22

2,3-Dithiaspiro[4.5]decane (RRI 1247)	52	b.p. 148° (17 mm)	24
HgCl$_2$		b.p. 151° (19 mm)	483
		91	24
2,3,7,8,9-Pentathiaspiro[4.5]decane		117.5-118	22
2,3-Dithia-7,9-dioxaspiro[4.5]decane 8,8-(CH$_3$-)$_2$	7	59-60	188

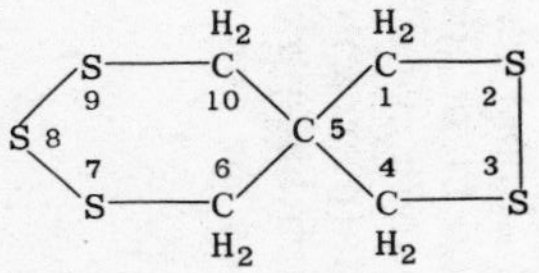

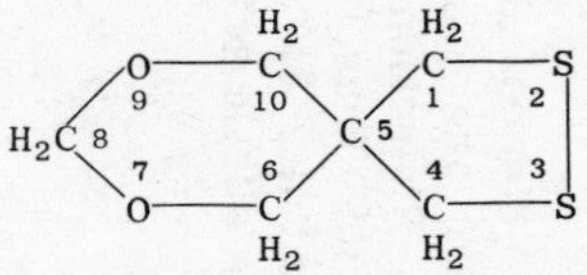

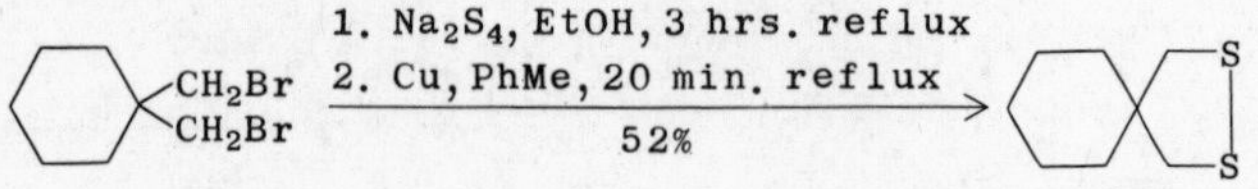

1. Na_2S_4, EtOH, 3 hrs. reflux
2. Cu, PhMe, 20 min. reflux

52%

58

I_2, NaOEt
40%

Na,
liq. NH_3
93%

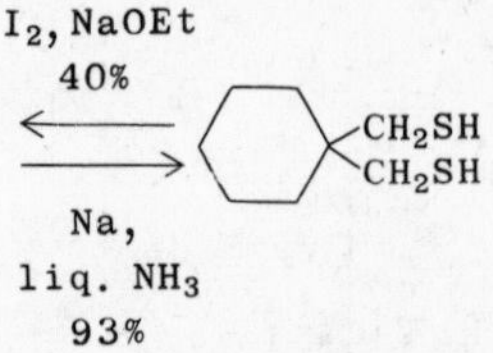

Fitt and Owen[188] investigated the hydrolysis of 2, 2-dimethyl-5, 5-bis (acetylmercaptomethyl)-1, 3-dioxane (59) and found that alkaline hydrolysis yielded 8, 8-dimethyl-2, 3-dithia-7, 9-dioxaspiro[4. 5]decane (60), while acid hydrolysis rearranged the isopropylidene group to 2, 2-dimethyl-5, 5-bis(hydroxymethyl)-*m*-dithiane (61).

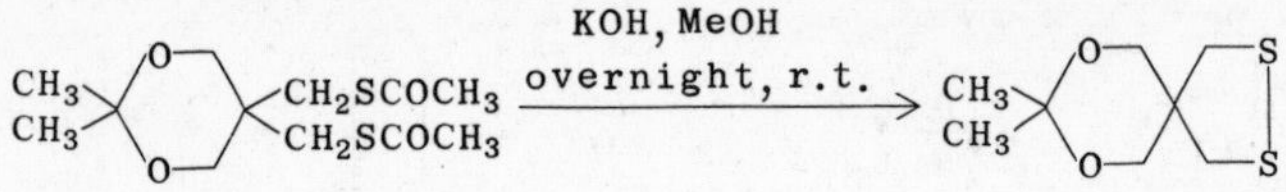

KOH, MeOH
overnight, r.t.

59   **60**

HCl
MeOH, H_2O
2 hrs. reflux

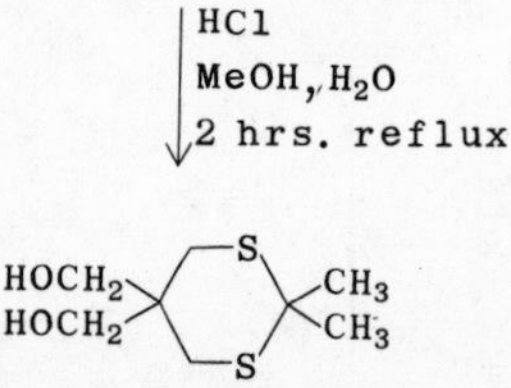

61

The properties of the spiro compounds are almost identical with those of other 1, 2-dithiolanes. They are yellow, and form adducts with mercuric chloride and bromide. Reduction with sodium in liquid ammonia cleaves the sulfur-sulfur bond. Thus, tetrakis(mercaptomethyl)methane is best prepared by reduction of 2, 3, 7, 8-tetrathiaspiro[4. 4]nonane (56).[23] Hydrogen peroxide in acetic acid gives the corresponding sulfonic acid.[22,24]

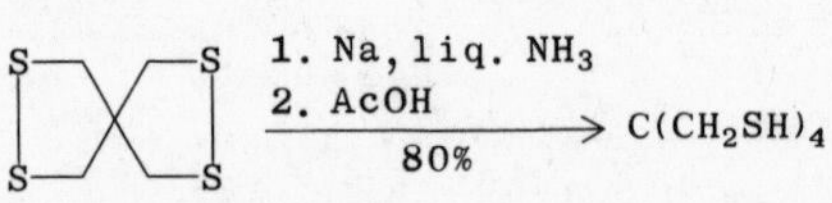

1. Na, liq. NH_3
2. AcOH

$C(CH_2SH)_4$

80%

56

72% H_2O_2, AcOH
8 hrs. 50°

$C(CH_2SO_3H)_4$

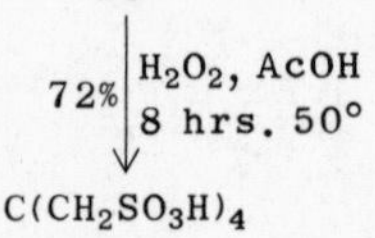

Perbenzoic acid oxidizes 2, 6, 7, 8-tetrathiaspiro[3. 5]nonane (53) to a disulfone assigned the structure 2, 6, 7-trithiaspiro[3. 4]octane 2, 2, 6, 6-tetroxide (62).[21]

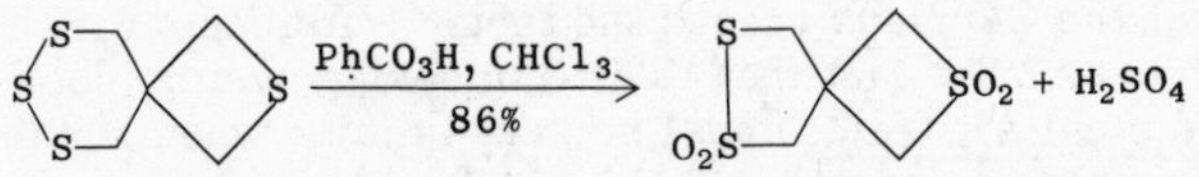

Although 2, 6, 7-trithiaspiro[3. 4]octane (54) is reasonably stable, melting at 54-55°, Campbell[111] was unable to isolate the analogous 2-oxa-6, 7-dithiaspiro[3. 4]octane (64), which was presumably formed, together with 2-oxa-6, 7, 8-trithiaspiro[3. 5]nonane (65), by the acid hydrolysis of the di-Bunte salt (63); it polymerized during attempted distillation at 100° and 2. 5 mm.

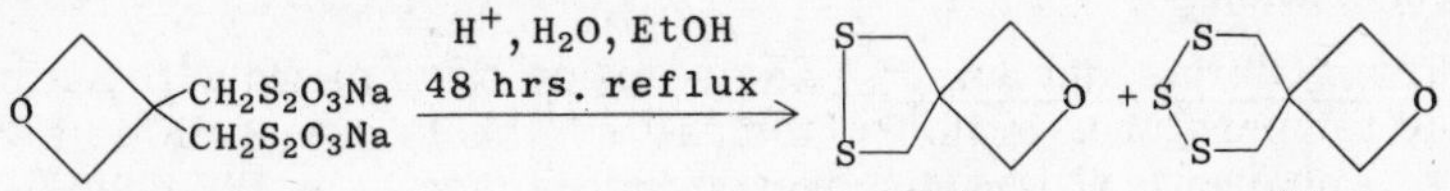

2. 1, 2-Dithiole (2)

a. 1, 2-Dithiole-3-thione and Related Compounds

The parent compound, 1, 2-dithiole, has not been prepared. By far the largest number of compounds of this class are the 1, 2-dithiole-3-thiones, although other 3-substituted derivatives are known. The 1, 2-dithiole-3-thiones reported in the literature are listed in Table 4, while related compounds are listed in Table 5.

The first preparation of a compound of this class was reported in 1884 by Barbaglia,[34,35] who heated isovaleraldehyde with sulfur at 250° and isolated a yellow, crystalline compound, $C_5H_6S_3$, melting at 94. 5°. The compound has since been shown to be 4, 5-dimethyl-1, 2-dithiole-3-thione.

In 1897 Baumann and Fromm[42,43] heated ethyl cinnamate with sulfur and isolated a crystalline compound to which they correctly assigned the structure 5-phenyl-1, 2-dithiol-3-one (66).

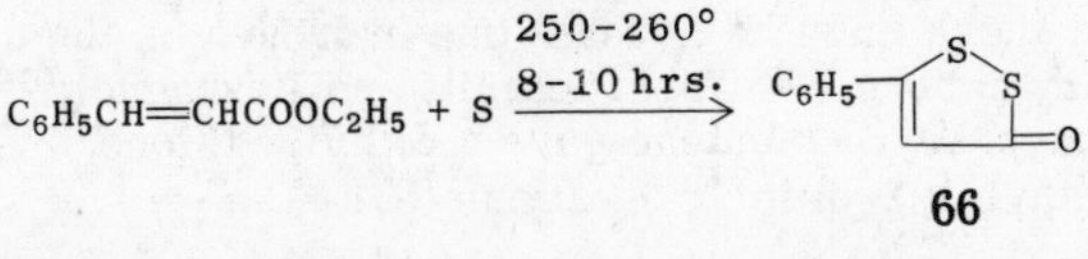

In the intervening years there were numerous reports of ill-defined materials formed by heating various hydrocarbons with sulfur at elevated temperatures. However, in 1942 Böttcher[61] isolated a crystalline compound from the reaction of anethole with sulfur at 190-230°, and in

[For references, see pp. 585-610.]

1947 Böttcher and Lüttringhaus[62,338] correctly formulated this as 5-
p-methoxyphenyl-1, 2-dithiole-3-thione. Since that time there have
been numerous publications on 1, 2-dithiole-3-thiones, chiefly by these
authors and their co-workers and by Lozac'h and his co-workers. As
already mentioned, the Germans coined the term "trithiones" for the
1, 2-dithiole-3-thiones. The fact that their numbering system does not
coincide with <u>Chemical Abstracts</u> must be kept in mind when reading
their papers. The field has been briefly reviewed on several occa-
sions.[40,280b,336,570]

Recently, Jirousek[279] developed a paper chromatographic separation
of 1, 2-dithiole-3-thiones, and he believes that two sulfur-containing
compounds isolated from cabbage by this technique belong to this class
of compounds.[280]

(1) Preparation

(a) <u>From Olefins and Sulfur.</u> The reaction of an olefin with sulfur at
elevated temperatures is the "classical" synthesis of 1, 2-dithiole-3-
thiones. Apparently it was discovered independently by Böttcher,[61] by
Gaudin,[203] and by Voronkov, Braun, and Karpenko.[553] The synthesis is
quite general, as shown by an inspection of Table 4. Böttcher and
Lüttringhaus[62,66] and Gaudin and Lozac'h[204] both showed that anethole
and estragole yield the same compound. The former authors postulated,
therefore, that the generalized synthesis follows the course:

$$RCH_2C(R')=CH_2 \rightleftharpoons RCH=C(R')CH_3 + 5\,S \longrightarrow [\text{dithiole-thione}] + 2\,H_2S$$

According to this equation the olefin must contain a reactive double
bond, a primary carbon atom, and at least four hydrogen atoms. Thus,
5-phenyl-1, 2-dithiole-3-thione (67) is formed from allylbenzene
and 4-phenyl-1, 2-dithiole-3-thione (68) from α-methylstyrene.

$$C_6H_5CH_2CH=CH_2 \xrightarrow{S} [\text{structure}]$$

67

$$C_6H_5C(CH_3)=CH_2 \xrightarrow{S} [\text{structure}]$$

68

It should be noted that there must be at least one hydrogen on the carbon *beta* to the primary carbon.[339] Thus, Schmitt and Lespagnol[468]
found that 2-(p-methoxyphenyl)-2-butene gave a dithiole-thione, 4-(p-
methoxyphenyl)-5-methyl-1, 2-dithiole-3-thione (69),

$$p\text{-}CH_3OC_6H_4\text{---}C(CH_3)=CH\text{---}CH_3 \xrightarrow{S} p\text{-}CH_3OC_6H_4[\text{structure}]$$

69

348

while 3-(*p*-methoxyphenyl)-2-pentene, *p*-CH₃OC₆H₄C(C₂H₅)=CHCH₃, did not. Within these limitations, the reaction is quite general and 1, 2-dithiole-3-thiones have been prepared from olefins in which R and/or R' are hydrogen, phenyl, substituted phenyl, 2-thienyl, and carbethoxy. There are some exceptions however. According to Lozac'h[329] the reaction fails with *o*-allylphenol, the product being 2*H*-1-benzopyran-2-thione or 2-thiocoumarin (70) instead.

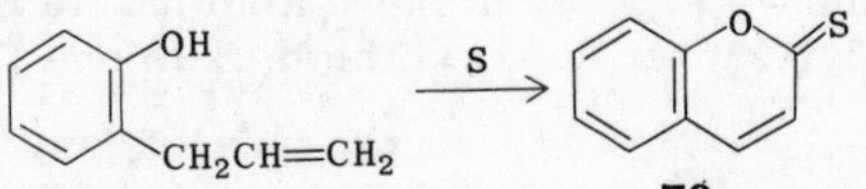

70

On the other hand, Mollier and Lozac'h[393, 395] prepared 5-(2-hydroxy-3-methoxyphenyl)-1, 2-dithiole-3-thione (71, R = H) from 2-allyl-6-methoxyphenol and 4-methyl-5-(2-hydroxy-3-methoxyphenyl)-1, 2-dithiole-3-thione (71, R = CH₃) from 2-methallyl-6-methoxyphenol, although in very low yields. 2*H*-1-Benzothiapyran-2-thiones or dithio-coumarins (72) were formed as by-products.

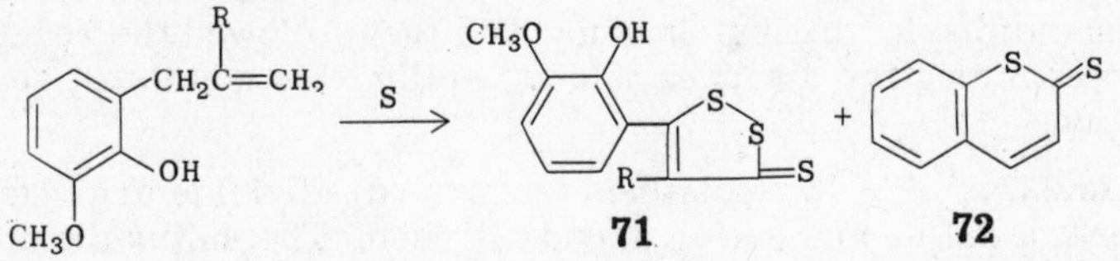

71   **72**

They suggested that the reactions are successful in these cases because the hydroxyl group is hydrogen bonded to the methoxyl group.

Contrary to the usual rule that the position of the double bond is unimportant, Lozac'h and Teste[333] claimed that 5-(2-thienyl)-1, 2-dithiole-3-thione could be obtained from 2-propenylthiophene, but not from 2-allylthiophene.

The case of α-methylcinnamic acid esters is interesting, since two alternative reactions are possible, one leading to a 1, 2-dithiole-3-thione (73) and the other to a 1, 2-dithiol-3-one (74).

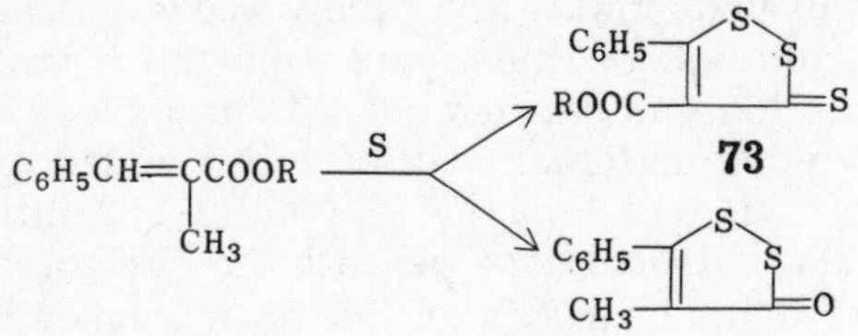

73

74

In several investigations[40,65,209,330] only the 3-thione was isolated. Apparently the thione synthesis takes place under milder conditions

[For references, see pp. 585-610.]

Chapter 5

than that of Baumann and Fromm. [12, 43] However, Raoul and Vialle[435a] have reported that the corresponding ethyl compound reacts differently to form ethyl 2-phenyl-3-thenoate.

$$C_6H_5CH=\underset{CH_3CH_2}{\overset{|}{C}}COOC_2H_5 \xrightarrow{S} \quad \text{(structure)} \quad \begin{matrix} C_6H_5 \\ COOC_2H_5 \end{matrix}$$

According to Teste[535a] 2-benzoyl-1-phenylpropene also reacts like a simple olefin, yielding 4-benzoyl-5-phenyl-1, 2-dithiole-3-thione (74a).

$$C_6H_5CH=\underset{CH_3}{\overset{|}{C}}COC_6H_5 \xrightarrow[45\%]{\underset{3\ \text{hrs.}\ 210-215°}{S,\ PhCOOEt}} \quad \begin{matrix} C_6H_5 \\ C_6H_5CO \end{matrix} \text{(structure)} S$$

74a

The synthesis of 1, 2-dithiole-3-thiones from olefins and sulfur is generally carried out by heating the olefin with 4-5 moles of sulfur at 200-250°. The use of a high-boiling solvent, such as ethyl benzoate, is reported to improve yields.[65,533] Krebs and Weber[311,311a] claimed that the reaction could be carried out in refluxing benzene or toluene in the presence of basic amines. Inasmuch as they followed the reaction only by determining the disappearance of sulfur, this statement requires confirmation.

Stevens and Camp[513] have claimed that improved yields are obtained if a mixture of sulfur and sulfur dioxide is used. The sulfur dioxide presumably converts the hydrogen sulfide formed in the reaction back into sulfur, making the sulfur utilization more efficient and preventing side reactions involving the addition of hydrogen sulfide to the olefin.

$$(CH_3)_2C=CH_2 + 2\ S + SO_2 \xrightarrow[39-42\%]{2\ \text{hrs.}\ 180-195°} CH_3 \text{(structure)} S$$

Frequently the compound is isolated by preparing the mercuric chloride complex and decomposing it with hydrogen sulfide. The yield in many cases leaves much to be desired, since mercaptans, disulfides, thiophenes, and other sulfur-containing compounds are formed as by-products. With aliphatic compounds yields are rarely above 20%. A 38.5% yield of 4-methyl-1, 2-dithiole-3-thione was reported from iso-butylene,[506,511] but this reaction was carried out with an excess of olefin and the yield was calculated from the amount of sulfur added. A 79% yield of a mixture of 4-neopentyl- and 4-methyl-5-t-butyl-1, 2-dithiole-3-thione was claimed by adding diisobutylene beneath the surface of molten sulfur at 210° and removing hydrogen sulfide as it formed, but here too an excess of olefin was used and the yield is based on sulfur.[512] However, Hamilton and Landis[236a] claimed a 90% yield adding only a slight excess of diisobutylene to sulfur at 190-220° drop by drop under reflux, so that hydrogen sulfide escaped from the system. The same

350

authors[236a,312b] reported a 93% yield of 4-neopentyl-5-t-butyl-1,2-dithiole-3-thione (**74b**) using stoichiometric quantities of triisobutylene and sulfur and carrying out the reaction in sulfurized triisobutylene. Triisobutylene must be unusual, however, since even under the usual reaction conditions a 55% yield of **74b** was obtained.

$$(CH_3)_3CCH_2\underset{\underset{CH_3}{|}}{C}{=}CHC(CH_3)_3 \ + \ (CH_3)_3CCH_2\underset{\underset{CH_2}{||}}{C}CH_2C(CH_3)_2$$

$$\xrightarrow[\substack{93\% \text{ crude}}]{\substack{5\ S \\ 16.5\ \text{hrs. } 200-215°}}$$

74b

With monoaryl-substituted olefins the yields are better than with alkyl olefins, being in the range of 25–60%. Substituted α-methylstilbenes, which do not form thiophenes as by-products, give even better yields of 4,5-diaryl-1,2-dithiole-3-thiones.

Apparently alkyl group migration can occasionally take place on heating olefins with sulfur. Thus, Broun, Voronkov, and Katkova[88] reported that 2-pentene yielded 5-ethyl-1,2-dithiole-3-thione. The melting point of 96-96.5° is practically identical with that of the 4,5-dimethyl derivative, which was probably the compound actually formed. The 5-ethyl derivative, prepared by an unequivocal synthesis, melts at 21°.[317] Other examples of isomerization are discussed below.

The detailed mechanism of the synthesis of 1,2-dithiole-3-thiones from an olefin and sulfur is unknown. The reaction is probably free radical, with initial attack of sulfur on the allylic carbon. Lüttringhaus and co-workers[339,342] postulated the following sequence of reactions:

$$\text{Olefin} \xrightarrow[\text{fast}]{S,\,180°} \text{RSH} \xrightarrow[\text{very fast}]{S} R_2S_2 \xrightarrow[\text{very fast}]{S}$$

$$R_2S_3 \xrightarrow[\text{slow}]{>160°} 1,2\text{-dithiole-3-thione}$$

Schmitt and Suquet,[470] on the other hand, felt that the reaction is related to the Willgerodt synthesis, and formulated it in the following manner:

$$C_6H_5CH{=}CHCH_3 \xrightarrow{S} C_6H_5CH{=}CHC\overset{S}{\underset{SH}{\diagdown}}$$

TABLE 4. Substituted 1,2-Dithiole-3-thiones

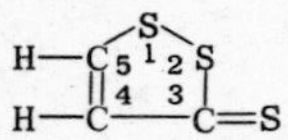

$$\begin{array}{c} H-C_5 \overset{\displaystyle S}{\underset{4}{\big|}} \overset{1}{\underset{3}{\big|}} \overset{2}{} S \\ H-C C=S \end{array}$$

Substituents	Synthesis method	Yield (%)	M.p. (°C)	Other properties	Ref.
None	a	1	82	yellow	69, 124-126, 339
	e	Trace	82	orange	124-126
	f	Trace	78-80		573
	f	10	79-81		374a
	h	<1	72		465b
4-CH₃-	a	39-42	40.5-41.5	orange b.p. 110-112° (1.7 mm) d_4^{20} 1.466	506, 511, 513
	e	2	40		535
	f	12	40		573
	h		40	yellow	314
	g	3.6	38		280a
	f	2.8	33		573
5-CH₃-	e	0.5	32-33		318

352

R	Method	Yield (%)	M.p., °C	Properties / Color	References
	g	Trace			316
	g	1.5	33		280a
	h	30	33	yellow, orange	314, 317, 332, 210, 568
	h	15	33		465b
4-C₂H₅-	j		34	yellow	435
5-C₂H₅-	h		21	red	317
	h		21	yellow	317
4-(CH₃)₃CCH₂-	a	17.2*	86.5-87.3	orange	506, 510
	a	20.6*		b.p. 159° (1.7 mm) d_4^{20} 1.177	506, 510
5-n-C₁₇H₃₅-	f		85-86		312c
	h	42	52-54		465b
4-C₆H₅-	a	30	123, 122	deep orange	62, 209
	a	70*	120-121		175, 178, 179
	a	42	122.8		553
	b	78*	122		175
	h	25	121-122		314, 568
5-C₆H₅-	a	25	126	dark orange-red	62, 69, 209
	a	9	126.2		553

TABLE 4. Substituted 1,2-Dithiole-3-thiones (contd)

Substituents	Synthesis method	Yield (%)	M.p. (°C)	Other properties	Ref.
	e	5			553
	f				339
	f		126.5		67, 339
	g	20			339
	g	4.1	124		280a
	d	2-5	126	red-brown	335
	e				335
	h	45	126		465b
	h	28	125	brown, orange	210, 314, 317, 568
	g	80, 49	126-127	orange	64, 70, 339
	g	92	125-127		301b
	j	83	127	orange	435
	k	78-96	126	orange	541
	e	4	126		321
	a	7	104	yellow-orange	466, 468
4-(p-CH$_3$C$_6$H$_4$-)	b	76*	122.5-123	red	175-177, 179
5-(p-CH$_3$C$_6$H$_4$-)	e	2	119-120	yellow-brown	318, 320
	k	62	119-120		541

Compound	Form	No.	m.p.	Color	Ref.
4-(p-C$_2$H$_5$C$_6$H$_4$-)	j	80	118	yellow	435
4-(p-t-C$_4$H$_9$C$_6$H$_4$-)	b	40*	108		175, 177
4-(p-t-C$_5$H$_{11}$C$_6$H$_4$-)	b	61*	145–146	gold	175–177, 179
5-(p-C$_6$H$_5$-C$_6$H$_4$-)	b	36*	112		175, 177
	k	45	164		541
5-(p-ClC$_6$H$_4$-)	k	78	135		541
	e	2	135–136	red	321
5-(p-BrC$_6$H$_4$-)	j	85	136	red	435
	a	77	119	red–brown	335
	k	1	130–131		541
5-(p-IC$_6$H$_4$-)	e	2	129	red	321
4-(p-CH$_3$OC$_6$H$_4$-)	e	6	198	yellow–brown	321
5-(o-CH$_3$OC$_6$H$_4$-)	a	24	152	red	466, 468
	a		95.5	brown–red	65, 395
5-(p-CH$_3$OC$_6$H$_4$-)			94	red	393
	a	50	111	orange–red	62
			108.5	yellow–orange	203, 69
	a	20–25	111		62
	a		108.5	red–brown	204–206
	d		109	brown	335
	e				335

TABLE 4. Substituted 1,2-Dithiole-3-thiones (contd)

Substituents	Synthesis method	Yield (%)	M.p. (°C)	Other properties	Ref.
5-(p-HOC$_6$H$_4$-)	g	66	108-109		64
			110.5		70, 339, 345
	k	61	109		541
5-(p-CH$_3$CO$_2$C$_6$H$_4$-)		87	190.5	deep red	65
	a	100	189	light maroon	467
5-[p-(CH$_3$)$_2$NC$_6$H$_4$-]			188		335
	a	100	145	red coral	467
			203-204	red-violet	335
5-[2,4-(CH$_3$)$_2$C$_6$H$_3$-]	g	16	201	brick red	65
	h		208		568
5-(2-CH$_3$O-5-CH$_3$C$_6$H$_3$-)	e	1	78		318
5-[2,3-(CH$_3$O)$_2$C$_6$H$_3$-]	a	7	143.5	red	395
5-[2,5-(CH$_3$O)$_2$C$_6$H$_3$-]	a		119	brown-red	393, 395
5-[3,4-(CH$_3$O)$_2$C$_6$H$_3$-]	a		121	orange	395
	e	0.5	124		318
	a		127		329
5-(3-CH$_3$O-4-HOC$_6$H$_3$-)	a		182-183	deep brown	327
5-(2-HO-3-CH$_3$OC$_6$H$_3$-)	a		200	brown	393, 395

5-(3-CH$_3$O-4-CH$_3$O$_2$CCH$_2$OC$_6$H$_3$-)	a		159	brown-red	330
5-[3,4-(HO)$_2$C$_6$H$_3$-]		68	211	brown	72a
5-[3,4-(CH$_3$CO$_2$)$_2$C$_6$H$_3$-]			151	iron buff	72a
5-(3,4-Methylenedioxyphenyl-)	a	36	195		329
5-(3,4,5-I$_3$C$_6$H$_2$-)	h		250–251		465b
4-(1-Naphthyl-)	a	45	198	golden yellow	466, 468
5-(1-Naphthyl-)	a	56	104–105	red-brown	65
4- 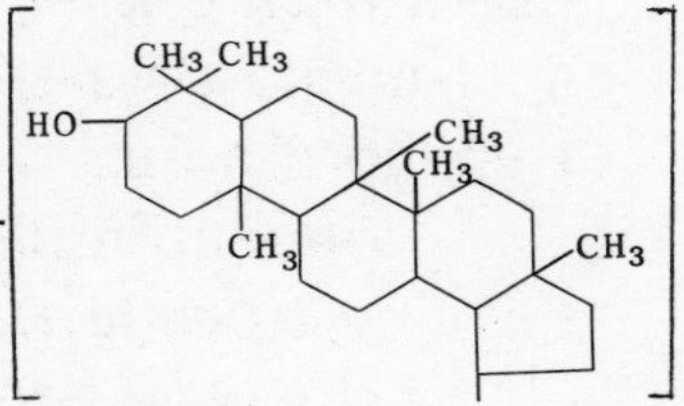 (steroid structure, HO-)	a		262 (dec.)	golden yellow	55
4- 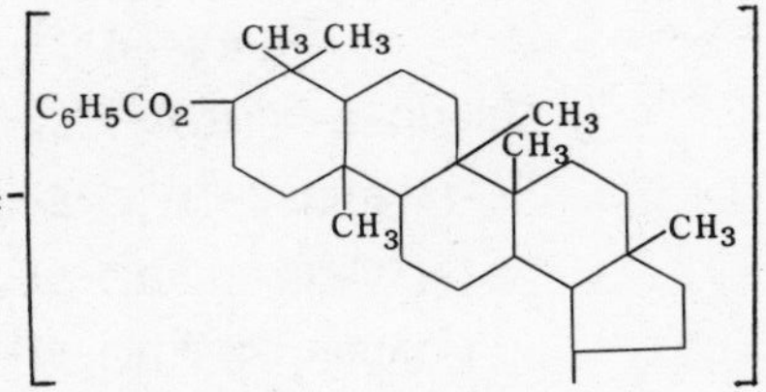 (steroid structure, C$_6$H$_5$CO$_2$-)	a		284	red-yellow	55
5-(2-Furyl-)	g	80	112	yellow	65
4-(2-Thienyl-)	h		100	red	533
5-(2-Thienyl-)	g	90	128	yellow	65
4-(2-Thienyl-)	a		130	brown-red	333, 533
5-(2-Thienyl-)	h		130	brown-red	333, 533

TABLE 4. Substituted 1,2-Dithiole-3-thiones (contd)

Substituents	Synthesis method	Yield (%)	M.p. (°C)	Other properties	Ref.
4-(4-CH₃-2-thienyl-)	d		119.5	red-orange	392, 535
5-(5-CH₃-2-thienyl-)	h		114	orange	534
5-(5-C₂H₅-2-thienyl-)	h	14	68	orange	534
4-[3,4-(CH₃)₂-2-thienyl-]	a		120	red	533
5-(2-Pyridyl-)	h		187	red	317
5-(3-Pyridyl-)	h	7	151	red	317
5-(4-Pyridyl-)	h		217	red	317
5-(C₆H₅CH=CH-)	h	5.5	121.5	brown	425
5-(p-CH₃OC₆H₄CH=CH-)	h		135.5	red-orange	425
5-(2-Furyl-CH=CH-)	h		136	brown	425
5-[p-(CH₃)₂NC₆H₄N=CH-]			215		426a
5-[p-(CH₃)₂NC₆H₄N=CH-]			238		426a
5-C₂H₅OOC-	g		65-66	brick-red	301a
5-HOOC-			136-139(dec.)	purple-brown	301a
4,5-(CH₃-)₂	e		94.5	yellow	35, 494
	c	5	97		62
		9	96		342

Substituent	Method	Yield (%)	M.p. (°C)	Color	Ref.
	j	75	97	orange	435
	e	8	95–96	red	321
	a	4			342
	a	16	95.5		88, 494
	e	13	96		535
	d	3			535
	g		96		316
	h	17	95		320
	h	41	96	yellow	465b
	e	3	95		318
	f	16	96–97		573
	g	17			342
	h		96		568
4-CH_3-5-C_2H_5-	h		29		317
	e	3.5	29	yellow-brown	318
	h	33	29		320
4-C_2H_5-5-CH_3-	h	12	41.5	yellow-brown	317
	d		39		535
4,5-$(C_2H_5\text{-})_2$	h	10	46	golden yellow	317
4-(n-C_3H_7-)-5-CH_3-	h	48	51.5	yellow-orange	568
	h	40	52	yellow	465b
	h	31	48.5	yellow	425

TABLE 4. Substituted 1,2-Dithiole-3-thiones (contd)

Substituents	Synthesis method	Yield (%)	M.p. (°C)	Other properties	Ref.
4-(n-C_4H_9-)-5-CH_3-	h		33	yellow	314
4-CH_3-5-(t-C_4H_9-)	a	10.5	80.5–81.3	orange; b.p. 175° at 5 mm	506, 510
	f		79–80		312c
4-$(CH_3)_3CCH_2$-5-(t-C_4H_9-)	a		93	b.p. 152° at 1 mm; n_D^{20} 1.6478, d_4^{20} 1.18	236a, 312b
	f		25		312c
4-[$(C_2H_5)_2NCH_2CH_2$-]-5-CH_3 · $HClO_4$	h	50	149–151		465b, 568
4-[$(C_2H_5)_2NCH_2CH_2$-]-5-CH_3 · HCl	h		205–207		465b, 568
4-$C_6H_5CH_2$-5-CH_3-	h	60	72		465b, 568
4-CH_3-5-C_6H_5-	a	89	104.6–104.8	orange-red; b.p. 208–209° at 1.5 mm	553
	h		103–104		314, 332
	e	28	104	yellow-orange	318
	e	40	104		321
	g	32	102		280a

Substituent		No.	m.p.	color	ref.
$4\text{-}C_6H_5\text{-}5\text{-}CH_3\text{-}$	a		92		209
	h		92		314
	e	3	92–93		318
$4\text{-}C_2H_5\text{-}5\text{-}C_6H_5\text{-}$	h	22	60	orange	317
$4\text{-}CH_3\text{-}5\text{-}(p\text{-}CH_3C_6H_4\text{-})$	e	33	82	orange	318
$4\text{-}CH_3\text{-}5\text{-}(p\text{-}ClC_6H_4\text{-})$	e	26	156	brick red	321
$4\text{-}CH_3\text{-}5\text{-}(p\text{-}BrC_6H_4\text{-})$	e	25	164–165	red-orange	321
$4\text{-}CH_3\text{-}5\text{-}(p\text{-}IC_6H_4\text{-})$	e	20	155	orange	321
$4\text{-}CH_3\text{-}5\text{-}(o\text{-}CH_3OC_6H_4\text{-})$	e	10	119	red-orange	319
	h	21	119	red-orange	320
$4\text{-}CH_3\text{-}5\text{-}(p\text{-}CH_3OC_6H_4\text{-})$	e	18	75	orange	318
$4\text{-}(p\text{-}CH_3OC_6H_4\text{-})\text{-}5\text{-}CH_3\text{-}$	a		149	red	466, 468
$4\text{-}CH_3\text{-}5\text{-}[2,4\text{-}(CH_3)_2C_6H_3\text{-}]$	e	29	59	yellow	318
	h	18	59		320
$4\text{-}CH_3\text{-}5\text{-}[2,5\text{-}(CH_3)_2C_6H_3\text{-}]$	e	30	73	golden yellow	318
	h	37	73		320
$4\text{-}CH_3\text{-}5\text{-}[3,4\text{-}(CH_3)_2C_6H_3\text{-}]$	e	8	96	yellow-orange	318
$4\text{-}CH_3\text{-}5\text{-}(4\text{-}CH_3O\text{-}3\text{-}CH_3C_6H_3\text{-})$	h	13	120	coral red	320
$4\text{-}CH_3\text{-}5\text{-}(2\text{-}CH_3O\text{-}4\text{-}CH_3C_6H_3\text{-})$	e	11	89	orange	319
	h	14	89		320

TABLE 4. Substituted 1,2-Dithiole-3-thiones (contd)

Substituents	Synthesis method	Yield (%)	M.p. (°C)	Other properties	Ref.
4-CH_3-5-(2-CH_3O-5-$CH_3C_6H_3$-)	e	10	107	red-orange	319
	a		107	red-orange	395
	h		107		320
4-CH_3-5-(2-CH_3S-5-$CH_3C_6H_3$-)	h	32	92	yellow-orange	320
4-CH_3-5-(2-HO-3-$CH_3OC_6H_3$-)	a		128	red	395
4-CH_3-5-[2,4-(CH_3O)$_2C_6H_3$-]	e	2,5	110	yellow-orange	318, 319
	h	8	110		320
4-CH_3-5-[2,5-(CH_3O)$_2C_6H_3$-]	e	5,9	89-90, 93	red, yellow-orange	318, 319
	a		92	red-orange	395
	h	15	93		320
4-CH_3-5-[3,4-(CH_3O)$_2C_6H_3$-]	e	8	114	yellow	318
4-CH_3-5-[2,4,6-(CH_3)$_3C_6H_2$-]	e	34	119	orange	318
4-(1-Naphthyl-)-5-CH_3-	h		137		220
	a		138	orange	471
4-(1-Naphthyl-)-5-C_2H_5-	h		124		221
4-CH_3-5-(2-CH_3O-1-naphthyl-)	e	3	130.5	orange	319
4-CH_3-5-(2-thienyl-)	h	55	90	red	333, 533
	a	18	90	red	533

C_3S_2 Ring Systems

Substituents					
4-(2-Thienyl-)-5-CH_3-	h		76	brown	533
	a			brown	533
4-(5-CH_3-2-thienyl-)-5-CH_3-	a	36	98	red	533
4-CH_3-5-(5-CH_3-2-thienyl-)-	h	38	101	red-brown	534
4-C_2H_5-5-(5-CH_3-2-thienyl-)-	h		96	yellow-brown	534
4-(5-C_2H_5-2-thienyl-)-5-CH_3-	a	28	51	red	534
4-CH_3-5-(5-C_2H_5-2-thienyl-)-	h	32	72.5	red	534
4-C_2H_5-5-(5-C_2H_5-2-thienyl-)-	h		63	yellow	534
4-CH_3-5-[4,5-$(CH_3)_2$-2-thienyl-]	c	2	139	orange	337, 392
	c	10	139	orange	337
4-CH_3-5-(3-pyridyl-)	h		120	red	317
4-C_2H_5-5-(3-pyridyl-)	h	5	95	orange	317
4-n-C_4H_9-5-(3-pyridyl-)	h		62	orange	317
4-CH_3-5-(4-pyridyl-)	h		143		317
4-C_2H_5-5-(4-pyridyl-)	h		105	orange	317
4-C_2H_5-5-(C_6H_5CH=CH-)			97.5	wine red	425
4-CH_3-5-(p-$CH_3OC_6H_4$CH=CH-)			185.5	wine red	425
4-C_2H_5-5-(p-$CH_3OC_6H_4$CH=CH-)			152	garnet	425
4-(n-C_3H_7-)-5-(p-$CH_3OC_6H_4$CH=CH-)			99	garnet	425
4-C_2H_5-5-(2-furyl-CH=CH-)			82	red-brown	425
4-(n-C_3H_7-)-5-(2-furyl-CH=CH-)			73	violet	425

TABLE 4. Substituted 1,2-Dithiole-3-thiones (contd)

Substituents	Synthesis method	Yield (%)	M.p. (°C)	Other properties	Ref.
$4\text{-}C_6H_5\text{-}5\text{-}C_6H_5CH_2\text{-}$	h	13	84	red-brown	465b, 568
$4\text{-}(C_6H_5CO\text{-})\text{-}5\text{-}C_6H_5\text{-}$	a	45	110-111	orange	535a
$4\text{-}(C_6H_5CS\text{-})\text{-}5\text{-}C_6H_5\text{-}$			171-172	red	535a
$4,5\text{-}(C_6H_5\text{-})_2$	a	80	160.4-160.5	red	553
		40	159.5		209, 339
		70	162	red	469
	e	25	161	red	318
	f		161.5		67
	g	48	158		280a
$4\text{-}(p\text{-}CH_3OC_6H_4\text{-})\text{-}5\text{-}C_6H_5\text{-}$	a	20	168	scarlet	466, 468
		60-63	173	scarlet	469
	g	43	155-156		280a
$4\text{-}(p\text{-}HOC_6H_4\text{-})\text{-}5\text{-}C_6H_5\text{-}$		100	233	yellow-orange	467, 469
	a	40	233	brick red	469
$4\text{-}(p\text{-}CH_3CO_2C_6H_4\text{-})\text{-}5\text{-}C_6H_5\text{-}$		100	182		469
	a	49	182	brick red	469
$4\text{-}C_6H_5\text{-}5\text{-}(2\text{-}CH_3O\text{-}5\text{-}CH_3C_6H_3\text{-})$	e	3	115	yellow-orange	319

4,5-(p-CH$_3$OC$_6$H$_4$-)$_2$	a	71	185	red	469
4-[2,4-(CH$_3$O)$_2$C$_6$H$_3$-]-5-C$_6$H$_5$-	e	68	135	coral	469
4-(3-HO$_3$S-4-CH$_3$OC$_6$H$_3$-)-5-C$_6$H$_5$-		72	169	brown	469
4-(3-ClO$_2$S-4-CH$_3$OC$_6$H$_3$-)-5-C$_6$H$_5$-		84	185–186	brick red	469
4-(3-C$_2$H$_5$O$_3$S-4-CH$_3$OC$_6$H$_3$-)-5-C$_6$H$_5$-		100	210 (dec.)	copper	469
4-(3-C$_6$H$_5$NHO$_2$S-4-CH$_3$OC$_6$H$_3$-)-5-C$_6$H$_5$-			278	deep coral	469
4-(3-CH$_3$CO-4-CH$_3$OC$_6$H$_3$-)-5-C$_6$H$_5$-		80	195	permanganate red	469
4-(3-C$_2$H$_5$CO-4-CH$_3$OC$_6$H$_3$-)-5-C$_6$H$_5$-		81	151	brilliant orange	469
4-C$_6$H$_5$-5-(3-pyridyl-)	h	73	162	red	317
4-C$_6$H$_5$-5-(4-pyridyl-)	h		189	red	317
4-C$_6$H$_5$-5-(2-furyl-CH=CH-)			165	brown	425
4-CH$_3$-5-CH$_3$O$_2$C-	g		119	red	40
4-CH$_3$O$_2$C-5-C$_6$H$_5$-	g	7	99		209, 330, 435a
4-C$_2$H$_5$O$_2$C-5-C$_6$H$_5$-	g		oil	red–brown	65
			64	pale red	40
			59		435a
4-C$_6$H$_5$-5-CH$_3$O$_2$C-	g		127–128	dark red	40
4-CH$_3$-5-[p-(CH$_3$)$_2$NC$_6$H$_4$N=CH-]			207–208		426a
4-C$_2$H$_5$-5-[p-(CH$_3$)$_2$NC$_6$H$_4$N=CH-]			173–174		426a
4-(n-C$_3$H$_7$-)-5-[p-(CH$_3$)$_2$NC$_6$H$_4$N=CH-]			122		426a
4-C$_6$H$_5$-5-[p-(CH$_3$)$_2$NC$_6$H$_4$N=CH-]			198–199		426a
4-CH$_3$-5-[p-(CH$_3$)$_2$NC$_6$H$_4$N=CH-]$\overset{O}{}$			212–213		426a

365

TABLE 4. Substituted 1,2-Dithiole-3-thiones (contd)

Substituents	Synthesis method	Yield (%)	M.p. (°C)	Other properties	Ref.
4-C_2H_5-5-[p-$(CH_3)_2NC_6H_4N$=CH-]			200-201		426a
4-(n-C_3H_7-)-5-[p-$CH_3)_2NC_6H_4N$=CH-]			173		426a
4-C_6H_5-5-[p-$(CH_3)_2NC_6H_4N$=CH-]			213		426a
4-HS-5-C_6H_5-	a		124		434a
4-HS-5-(p-$CH_3OC_6H_4$-)	a		115		434a
4-CH_3S-5-C_6H_5-	a		98		434a
	k	45	98	red-orange	434
			98-99	red-orange	259, 434
4-CH_3S-5-(p-$CH_3OC_6H_4$-)	a		91		434a
	k	39	90	orange	434
4-CH_3COS-5-C_6H_5-		111			434a
4-CH_3COS-5-(p-$CH_3OC_6H_4$-)		120			434a
4-C_6H_5COS-5-C_6H_5-			148		434a
4-C_6H_5COS-5-(p-$CH_3OC_6H_4$-)			116		434a
4-CH_3O-5-C_6H_5-	k	50	76	orange	434

* Yield based on sulfur, using excess olefin.

It is quite obvious, however, that the formation of a 1, 2-dithiole-3-thione requires a 1, 3-attack on the allylic system. Undoubtedly the low yields and numerous by-products encountered so frequently result from the ·prevalence of 1, 2-attack. Irrespective of the intimate details of the mechanism, there can be little doubt that the driving force for the reaction is the formation of the pseudo-aromatic 1, 2-dithiole-3-thione (see section I A-2a-(2)).

Two interesting modifications which lead to different types of 1, 2-dithioles were reported recently. Raoul and Vialle[434a] found that heating propenylbenzene with sulfur under an atmosphere of hydrogen sulfide in the presence of benzoyl peroxide yielded 4-mercapto-5-phenyl-1, 2-dithiole-3-thione (74c); p-methoxypropenylbenzene reacted similarly. The structure of 74c was proved by alkylation to the 4-methylthio derivative, which was shown to be identical with an authentic sample prepared by a different procedure (see section I A-2a-(1)(k)).

$$C_6H_5CH\!\!=\!\!CHCH_3 + S + H_2S \xrightarrow[\ 200\text{--}210°\ ]{(PhCOO)_2} $$

74c

In view of its extremely short lifetime at this elevated temperature, it is difficult to see what role benzoyl peroxide plays in this synthesis.

Boberg[56a] found that heating perchloropropene with sulfur led to the elimination of sulfur monochloride and the formation of 3, 3, 4, 5-tetrachloro-1, 2-dithiole (74d). Hydrolysis of 74d yielded 4, 5-dichloro-1, 2-dithiole-3-one (74e), identical with a specimen prepared from trichloroacrylyl chloride and sulfur (see section I A-2a-(1)(g)).

$$Cl_3CC\!\!=\!\!CCl_2 \xrightarrow[65\%]{>160°}$$

74d

$$\downarrow H_2O$$

$$Cl_2C\!\!=\!\!CCOCl \xrightarrow{S, AlCl_3}$$

74e

(b) From Saturated Hydrocarbons and Sulfur. A number of variations of the olefin sulfur synthesis have been reported. Fields[175-179] found that cumene could be substituted for α-methylstyrene in the synthesis of 4-phenyl-1, 2-dithiole-3-thione if a small amount of base, such as di-o-tolyl guanidine, were added. The reaction temperature was lowered, but the rate with olefin was much faster. Yields were slightly improved, but here too the excellent yields reported are based on sulfur. As early as 1941 Friedmann[199] treated paraffins with sulfur at 285° and undoubtedly prepared 1, 2-dithiole-3-thiones, which he formulated as sulfur-substituted thiolanes. Apparently, 2, 2, 4-trimethylpentane gave 4-neopentyl-1, 2-dithiole-3-thione (75),[200] also prepared by Stevens and co-workers[506,510,512] from diisobutylene.

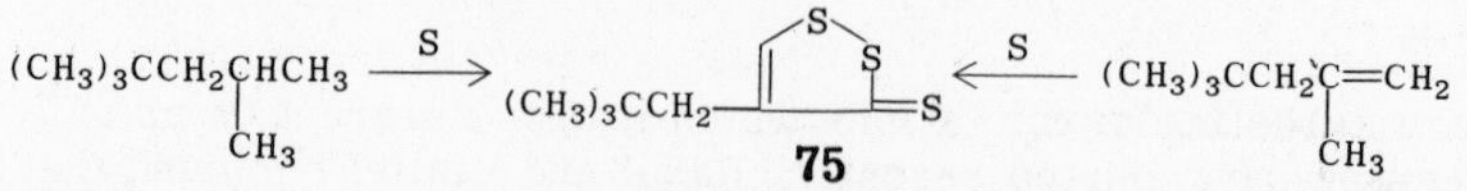

(c) From Dienes or Trienes and Sulfur. Dienes have also been reacted with sulfur to form 1, 2-dithiole-3-thiones. Thus, Böttcher and Lüttringhaus[62,66] reacted isoprene with sulfur and obtained a compound in 5% yield, which Lüttringhaus and Cleve[342] showed to be 4, 5-dimethyl-1, 2-dithiole-3-thione by a number of independent syntheses. Mollier[392] reacted allo-ocimene with sulfur and isolated a compound which he formulated as 4-methyl-5-(4, 5-dimethyl-2-thienyl)-1, 2-dithiole-3-thione (76). Lozac'h and Mollier[337] found that the yield of 76 was improved slightly, from 2 to 10%, by using linalool instead of allo-ocimene. 76 had a spectrum similar to that of other 1, 2-dithiole-3-thiones, lost one sulfur atom on oxidation with permanganate to yield the corresponding ketone (76a), and gave 4, 5-dimethyl-2-thiophenecarboxylic acid on oxidation with alkaline peroxide.

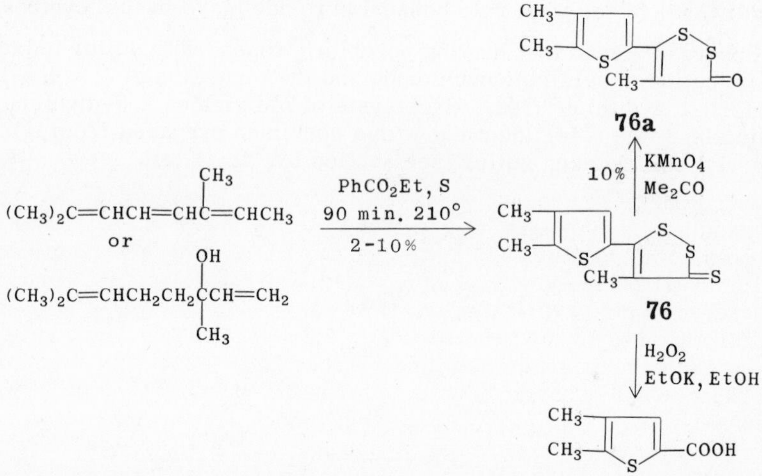

Böttcher and Bauer[64] found that dipentene gave thiocineole and no 1, 2-dithiole-3-thione. Schmitt and Lespagnol[468] claimed, however, that dipentene (and pulegone) gave an orange compound, $C_{10}H_6S_4$, m.p. 209-210°; carvone gave $C_{10}H_6OS_4$, scarlet, m.p. 233°. Lozac'h and Legrand[331] and Fields[176] suggested that these compounds might be thienobenzodithioles.

(d) From Acetylenic Compounds and Sulfur. Lozac'h and co-workers[335] found that acetylenic compounds could be heated with sul-

fur to form 1, 2-dithiole-3-thiones, although yields were lower than with
the corresponding olefins. Thus, p-CH$_3$OC$_6$H$_4$C≡CCH$_3$ gave 5-(p-
methoxyphenyl)-1, 2-dithiole-3-thione. Substituted vinyl bromides reacted similarly, the same compound being formed from p-CH$_3$OC$_6$H$_4$CH=
CBr-CH$_3$, perhaps by intermediate formation of the substituted acetylene. Challenger and co-workers[124-126] isolated a trace of 1, 2-dithiole-
3-thione from the reaction of acetylene and sulfur at 450°. They specu-
lated, probably correctly, that the compound was formed from traces of
acetone in the acetylene. Teste and Lozac'h[535] found that acetylenic alcohols also gave 1, 2-dithiole-3-thiones with sulfur; 3-methyl-3-hydroxy-
1-butyne gave the 4, 5-dimethyl derivative, and 3-methyl-3-hydroxy-1-
pentyne gave the 4-ethyl-5-methyl derivative. 3-Phenyl-3-hydroxy-1-
butyne, however, gave only 3-phenylthiophene. Mollier[392] heated 2, 5-
dimethyl-2, 5-dihydroxy-3-hexyne with sulfur, and isolated a compound
which he formulated as 4-(4-methyl-2-thienyl)-1, 2-dithiole-3-thione
(77).

According to Teste and Lozac'h[535] this acetylenic glycol is unique;
others tested gave only thieno-thiophenes.

(e) From Alcohols, Aldehydes or Ketones with Sulfur or with Sulfur
and Phosphorus Pentasulfide. As already mentioned, the initial synthesis of a 1, 2-dithiole-3-thione was from isovaleraldehyde and sulfur.
Voronkov, Broun, and Karpenko[553] synthesized 5-phenyl-1, 2-dithiole-3-
thione from cinnamyl alcohol and from cinnamaldehyde, although in poor
yields. Teste and Lozac'h[535] prepared several alkyl-substituted 1, 2-
dithiole-3-thiones by heating an alcohol with phosphorus pentasulfide
and sulfur. Inasmuch as the reaction failed in the absence of phosphorus
pentasulfide, they postulated the mercaptan as an intermediate. It is of
interest that phosphorus pentasulfide had no effect on the reaction of
sulfur with the acetylenic alcohols described above. Lozac'h and co-
workers[318,335] prepared 1, 2-dithiole-3-thiones by heating ketones with
sulfur and phosphorus pentasulfide in diphenyl at 210°. The position of
the carbonyl group had no apparent effect on the reaction. Thus, propiophenone and phenylacetone both formed 5-phenyl-1, 2-dithiole-3-
thione.

Yields were 20-35% when R' was aryl and R was methyl or aryl, although with certain aryl substituents the yields were much lower. Yields
were below 5% when R or R' was hydrogen or alkyl.

Legrand and Lozac'h[319] investigated this reaction with a number of
2-methoxyisobutyrophenones; yields were 12% or less, and in certain

instances 2*H*-1-benzothiapyran-2-thiones were formed. Thus, 2-methoxy-5-methylisobutyrophenone yielded 10% 4-methyl-5-(2-methoxy-5-methylphenyl)-1, 2-dithiole-3-thione (78) and 2% 3, 6-dimethyl-2*H*-1-benzothiapyran-2-thione (79). No dithiole-thione was formed when a hydroxyl group was substituted for the methoxyl.

Legrand and Lozac'h[321] also investigated the use of halogenated ketones; they formed the same 1, 2-dithiole-3-thiones as the unhalogenated, but in slightly better yields.

(f) From Sulfur-Containing Compounds. A variety of sulfur-containing compounds have been used as starting materials for the preparation of 1, 2-dithiole-3-thiones. Lüttringhaus, König, and Böttcher[67,339] prepared 5-phenyl-1, 2-dithiole-3-thione by heating cinnamyl mercaptan or disulfide with sulfur; cinnamyl trisulfide required no additional sulfur and hydrogen sulfide was not liberated. Wessely and Siegel[573] prepared a number of ethyl-substituted 1, 2-dithiole-3-thiones by heating alkyl sulfides, disulfides, or polysulfides with sulfur; yields were best with the disulfides, but even so did not surpass 16%. *n*-Amyl and iso-amyl disulfides both yielded 4, 5-dimethyl-1, 2-dithiole-3-thione; this is another example of alkyl group migration.

Landis and Hamilton[312c] reacted two tertiary mercaptans with sulfur, 2, 4, 4-trimethyl-2-mercaptopentane, derived from diisobutylene, and 2, 2, 4, 6, 6-pentamethyl-4-mercaptoheptane, derived from triisobutylene, and isolated the same 1, 2-dithiole-3-thiones as from the corresponding olefins. Yields of 25% were obtained. The authors postulated that the mercaptans were converted to olefins during the reaction, and were able to isolate diisobutylene in one case.

Mayer and Kubasch[374a] prepared 1, 2-dithiole-3-thiones from 1, 3-dimercaptans and sulfur in 7-65% yields; 1, 2-dithiole-3-thione was obtained in 10% yield by this procedure.

(g) From α, β-Unsaturated Carbonyl Compounds. The synthesis of 5-phenyl-1, 2-dithiol-3-one (66) from ethyl cinnamate and sulfur, described originally by Baumann and Fromm,[42,43] constitutes a fairly convenient synthesis of this class of compound, yields of 40-65% having been reported.[198,307,301b]

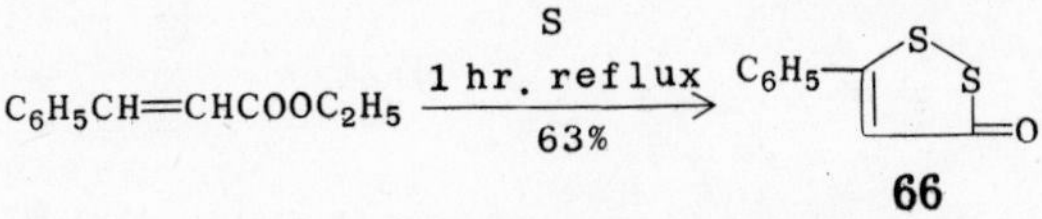

$$C_6H_5CH{=}CHCOOC_2H_5 \xrightarrow[\text{63\%}]{\text{S} \quad \text{1 hr. reflux}} \quad \mathbf{66}$$

A fair number of 5-aryl-1,2-dithiol-3-ones have been prepared by this procedure, as listed in Table 5. The method has its limitations, however. Thus, as already mentioned (see section I A-2a-(1)(a)) α-methylcinnamates yield 4-carbalkoxy-5-phenyl-1,2-dithiole-3-thiones instead, α-ethylcinnamates yield thiophene derivatives, and 2-benzoyl-1-phenyl-propene yields 4-benzoyl-5-phenyl-1,2-dithiole-3-thione. However, according to Raoul and Vialle[435a] α-phenylcinnamates yield 4,5-diphenyl-1,2-dithiol-3-one (**79a**) and benzalmalonic esters yield 4-carbalkoxy-5-phenyl-1,2-dithiol-3-ones (**79b**).

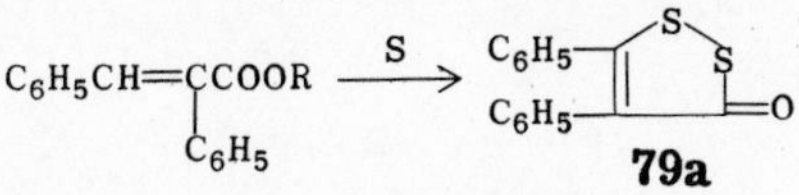

$$C_6H_5CH{=}C(C_6H_5)COOR \xrightarrow{\text{S}} \quad \mathbf{79a}$$

$$C_6H_5CH{=}C(COOR)COOR \xrightarrow{\text{S}} \quad \mathbf{79b}$$

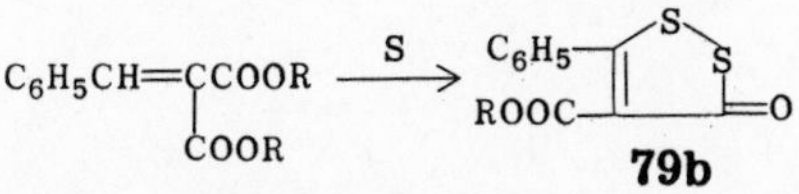

On the other hand, Quiniou[426b] reported that the reaction with cinnam-ylidenemalonates takes a different course and yields (5-aryl-1,2-dithiol-3-ylidene)malonates (**79c**).

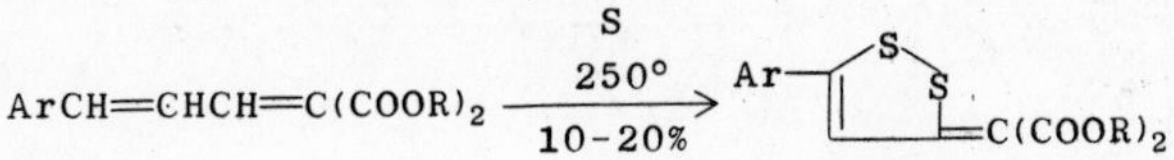

$$ArCH{=}CHCH{=}C(COOR)_2 \xrightarrow[\text{10-20\%}]{\text{S} \quad 250°} \quad \mathbf{79c}$$

Klingsberg[301a] was successful in applying the reaction to diethyl fumar-ate, impure 5-carbethoxy-1,2-dithiol-3-one (**79d**) being obtained in low yield.

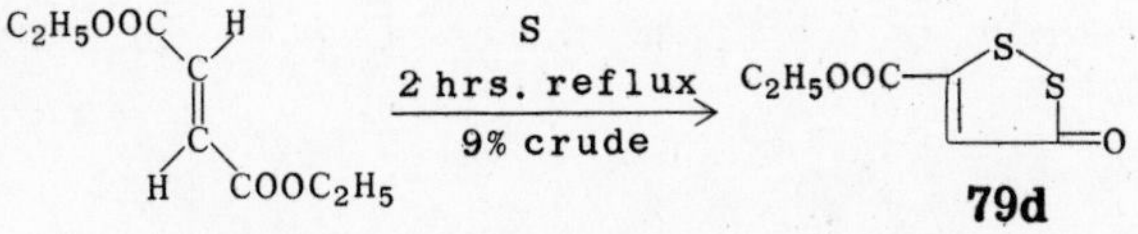

$$\text{(}C_2H_5OOC, H\text{)}C{=}C(H, COOC_2H_5) \xrightarrow[\text{9\% crude}]{\text{S} \quad \text{2 hrs. reflux}} \quad \mathbf{79d}$$

Boberg[56a] carried out a modification of this process to prepare 4,5-dichloro-1,2-dithiol-3-one (**74e**) from trichloroacrylyl chloride, sulfur, and aluminum chloride. **74e** was also obtained by hydrolysis of 3,3,4,5-tetrachloro-1,2-dithiole (see section I A-2a-(1)(a)).

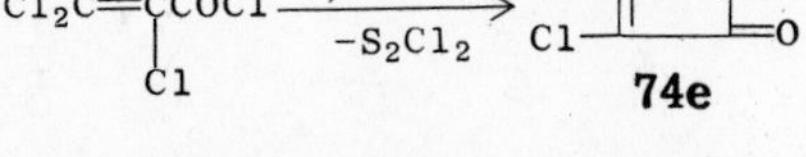

$$Cl_2C{=}C(Cl)COCl \xrightarrow[\text{$-S_2Cl_2$}]{\text{S, AlCl}_3} \quad \mathbf{74e}$$

TABLE 5. 1,2-Dithioles with Various Substituents in 3-Position

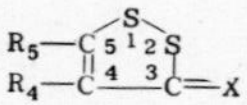

$R_5\!-\!\overset{\displaystyle S}{\underset{\displaystyle 4\ \ 3}{\underset{\displaystyle |}{C}}}\!\!\begin{smallmatrix}S\\5\ 1\ 2\end{smallmatrix}\!\!\underset{\displaystyle }{C}\!-\!X$ (structure: 1,2-dithiole ring, positions 5,1,2 S and 4,3 C—X)

Substituents			Yield (%)	M.p. (°C)	Other properties	Ref.
R_4	R_5	X				
CH_3-	H	$\diagup\!\!\!\diagdown$ Cl, Cl		160.5-161	white	506
H	CH_3-	$=O$	20		yellow b.p. 50-51° at 0.05 mm n_D^{23} 1.633	435
$(CH_3)_3CCH_2-$	H	$\diagup\!\!\!\diagdown$ Cl, Cl		182-183 (dec.)	white	506
$(CH_3)_3CCH_2-$	H	$=O$		54-56	yellow b.p. 137° at 10 mm	506
CH_3-	CH_3-	$=O$	17		yellow b.p. 57-58° at 0.05 mm n_D^{23} 1.617	435
CH_3-	CH_3-	$=NOH$		180	bright yellow	62, 568
CH_3-	$(CH_3)_3C-$	$\diagup\!\!\!\diagdown$ Cl, Cl	68	dec. 223	yellow	506
CH_3-	$(CH_3)_3C-$	$=O$	35-36		b.p. 142-143° at 10 mm	506

			%	m.p.	Color	Ref.
$(CH_3)_3CCH_2-$	$(CH_3)_3C-$	>C(Cl)(Cl)	89	151-152		312b
$(CH_3)_3CCH_2-$	$(CH_3)_3C-$	=O	57		b.p. 132-135° at 0.6-0.8 mm	312b
C_6H_5-	H	=NOH		172.5 (dec.)	yellow	62, 553
				175		568
H	C_6H_5-	=O		117	yellow	42, 339, 345
			40-45			198
			47	116-116.8		307
			63	114-117		301b
				116		542a
			58			307
			87-94	118-119	yellow	63
				116.6-117		553
			80	118	white	435
H	C_6H_5-	=NOH		137-139		553
				137		542a
H	C_6H_5-	$=NC_6H_5$	30			351
H	C_6H_5-	$=NC_6H_3-3-OH-4-CO_2H$	51	217	orange	350, 352
H	C_6H_5-	$=C(CO_2CH_3)_2$		147		426b
H	C_6H_5-	$=C(CO_2C_2H_5)_2$		90		426b
H	C_6H_5-	$=C(CN)(CO_2C_2H_5)$		139		396a
H	C_6H_5-	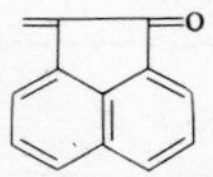 (acenaphthenequinone-type structure)		234		394
			90	240	brown	396b

TABLE 5. 1,2-Dithioles with Various Substituents in 3-Position (contd)

R₄	R₅	X	Yield (%)	M.p. (°C)	Other properties	Ref.
H	C_6H_5-	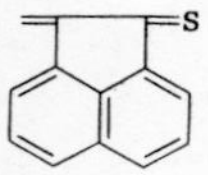 (acenaphthylene-thione structure, =S)		208	red	396b
H	C_6H_5-	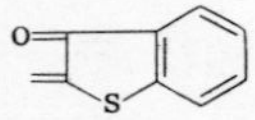 (benzo[b]thiophenone structure, =O)		178		394
H	$p\text{-}CH_3C_6H_4-$	=O	76	105	white	435
H	$p\text{-}ClC_6H_4-$	=O	81	96	white	435
H	$o\text{-}CH_3OC_6H_4-$	$=C(CO_2CH_3)_2$		148		426b
H	$o\text{-}CH_3OC_6H_4-$	$=C(CO_2C_2H_5)_2$		104		426b
H	$p\text{-}CH_3OC_6H_4-$	=O		118.5		339
			100	114–117	yellow-brown	63
				115	red-brown	204, 205, 339, 345
				118		329
H	$p\text{-}CH_3OC_6H_4-$	$=CHCO_2C_2H_5$		113		396a
H	$p\text{-}CH_3OC_6H_4-$	$=C(CO_2CH_3)_2$		136		426b
H	$p\text{-}CH_3OC_6H_4-$	$=C(CO_2C_2H_5)_2$		99		396a, 426b
H	$p\text{-}CH_3OC_6H_4-$	$=C(CN)(CO_2C_2H_5)$		181		396a
H	$p\text{-}CH_3OC_6H_4-$	=NOH		169–170	yellow	62
			85	170		350, 352

			No.	m.p.	Color	References
H	$p\text{-}CH_3OC_6H_4\text{-}$	$=NC_6H_5$	96	144	yellow	350, 352, 465c
H	$p\text{-}CH_3OC_6H_4\text{-}$	$=NC_6H_4CH_3\text{-}m$		146		396
H	$p\text{-}CH_3OC_6H_4\text{-}$	$=NC_6H_4CH_3\text{-}p$		110		396
H	$p\text{-}CH_3OC_6H_4\text{-}$	$=NC_6H_4OH\text{-}p$		135		396
H	$p\text{-}CH_3OC_6H_4\text{-}$	$=NC_6H_4OCH_3\text{-}p$		185		74
H	$p\text{-}CH_3OC_6H_4\text{-}$	$=NC_6H_4N(CH_3)_2\text{-}p$		175		396
H	$p\text{-}CH_3OC_6H_4\text{-}$	$=NC_6H_4N(CH_3)_2\text{-}p$	73	176	orange	350, 352, 465c
H	$p\text{-}CH_3OC_6H_4\text{-}$	$=NC_6H_4CO_2H\text{-}p$	76	257	yellow	350, 352, 465c
H	$p\text{-}CH_3OC_6H_4\text{-}$	$=NC_6H_4SO_2NH_2\text{-}p$		270		396
H	$p\text{-}CH_3OC_6H_4\text{-}$	$=NC_6H_3\text{-}3\text{-}OH\text{-}4\text{-}CO_2H$		212–215		350
H	$p\text{-}CH_3OC_6H_4\text{-}$			183–185		74
H	$p\text{-}CH_3OC_6H_4\text{-}$	$=N\text{-}NHC_6H_5$	67	151	yellow	350, 352, 465c
H	$p\text{-}CH_3OC_6H_4\text{-}$	$=N\text{-}NHCOC_6H_5$	52	164–165	light yellow	350, 352, 465c
H	$p\text{-}CH_3OC_6H_4\text{-}$	$=N\text{-}NHCO$ (4-pyridyl)	46, 35	212	orange	350, 352, 465c
H	$p\text{-}CH_3OC_6H_4\text{-}$	$=N\text{-}N=CHC_6H_5$	64	143, 168	orange (dimorphic)	350, 352, 465c
H	$p\text{-}CH_3OC_6H_4\text{-}$	$=N\text{-}N=C(CO_2H)(CH_3)$	49, 40	159	yellow–green	350, 352, 465c
H	$p\text{-}CH_3OC_6H_4\text{-}$	$=N\text{-}N=C(CH_2CH_2CO_2H)_2$	65	190	pale yellow	465c
H	$p\text{-}CH_3OC_6H_4\text{-}$	$=N\text{-}N=C[(CH_2)_3CO_2H][(CH_2)_2CO_2H]$	54	158	pale yellow	465c
H	$p\text{-}CH_3OC_6H_4\text{-}$	$=N\text{-}N=C[(CH_2)_2CH=CH_2][(CH_2)_2CO_2H]$	37	102	reddish	465c

TABLE 5. 1,2-Dithioles with Various Substituents in 3-Position (contd)

Substituents						
R_4	R_5	X	Yield (%)	M.p. (°C)	Other properties	Ref.
H	$p\text{-}CH_3OC_6H_4\text{-}$	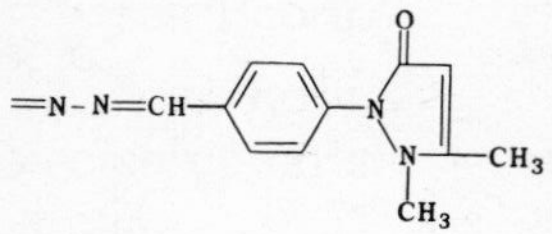	34	252	yellow-red	465c
H	$p\text{-}CH_3OC_6H_4\text{-}$	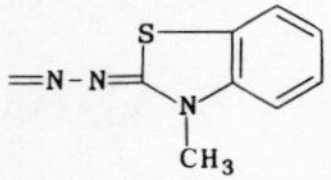	82	177	light orange	350, 352
H	$p\text{-}CH_3OC_6H_4\text{-}$	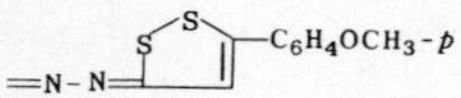	54	254	red	350, 352, 465c
H	$p\text{-}CH_3OC_6H_4\text{-}$	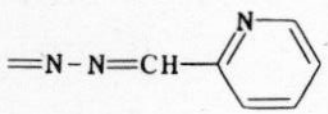	49	156	yellow-red	465c
H	$p\text{-}CH_3OC_6H_4\text{-}$	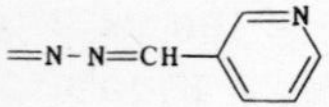	49	175	yellow-red	465c
H	$p\text{-}CH_3OC_6H_4\text{-}$	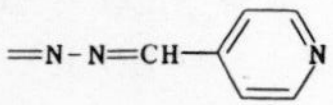	49	174	yellow-red	465c
H	$p\text{-}CH_3OC_6H_4\text{-}$	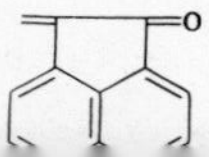		216.5	red	392, 394, 396b

R	Substituent	Structure	Yield (%)	M.p. (°C)	Color	Ref.
H	p-CH₃OC₆H₄-	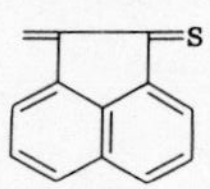 (acenaphthene, =S)		223	red-violet	396b
H	p-CH₃OC₆H₄-	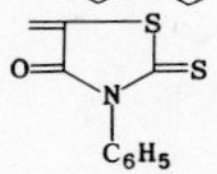 (thiazolidine: S, =S, N-C₆H₅, =O)	29	265	red	465a
H	p-CH₃OC₆H₄-	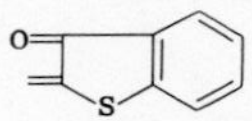 (benzo ring: S, =S, =O)		234.5	red	392, 394
H	p-CH₃OC₆H₄-	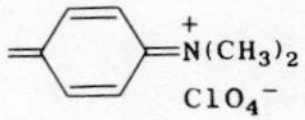 (=N(CH₃)₂⁺ ClO₄⁻, =CH-)	72	252 (dec.)	green	465a
H	p-CH₃OC₆H₄-	(benzothiazole, =CH-)	75	225 (dec.)	yellow-red	465a
H	p-CH₃OC₆H₄-	(benzothiazolium N-CH₃ I⁻, =CH-)	27	251 (dec.)	dark brown	465a
H	p-CH₃OC₆H₄-	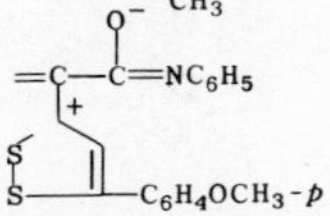 (betaine: O⁻, =N-C₆H₅, S-S, =C₆H₄OCH₃-p)		253	bronze-green	465a
H	p-HOC₆H₄-	=O	100	167	yellow	467
H	p-CH₃CO₂C₆H₄-	=O	100	147	bright yellow	467
H	p-(CH₃)₂NC₆H₄-	=O	5	190 (impure)		65
H	3,4-(CH₃O)₂C₆H₃-	=O		124		329
H	3,4-(CH₃O)₂C₆H₃-	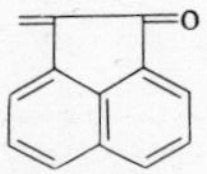 (acenaphthenone, =O)		206	red	396b

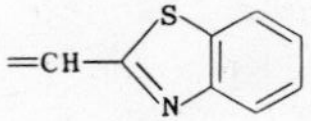

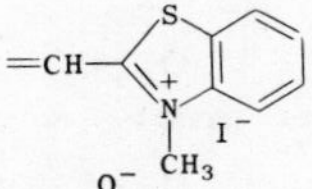

TABLE 5. 1,2-Dithioles with Various Substituents in 3-Position (contd)

R₄	R₅	X	Yield (%)	M.p. (°C)	Other properties	Ref.
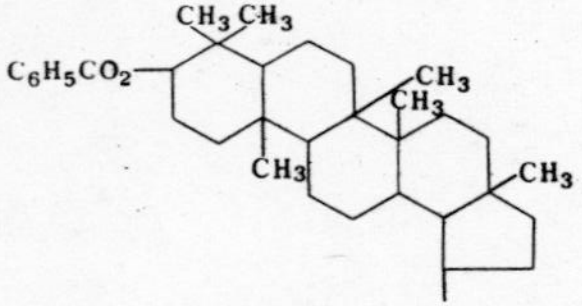 $C_6H_5CO_2$ (steroid)	H	=O		264	pale yellow	55
H	2-Furyl-	=O	15	96-97		65
H	2-Thienyl-	=O	38	92-93 (impure)	grey-brown	65
H	2-Thienyl-	=NOH		182-183	yellow	533
CH_3-	C_6H_5-	=O		56		435a
CH_3-	C_6H_5-	=C(CN)CO₂C₂H₅		170		396a
CH_3-	C_6H_5-	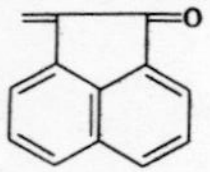 (=O ring)		181	red	394, 396b
CH_3-	C_6H_5-	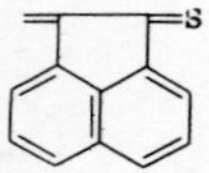 (=S ring)		200	red-violet	396b
CH_3-	p-$CH_3C_6H_4$-	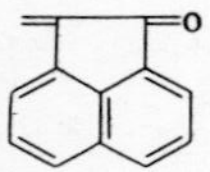 (=O ring)		224	red-orange	396b
CH_3-	p-$CH_3C_6H_4$-	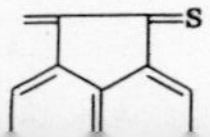 (=S ring)		249	brown-green	396b

378

			Yield			Ref.
CH₃-	2,4-(CH₃O)₂C₆H₃-	$=C(CN)CO_2C_2H_5$		160		396a
C₂H₅-	C₆H₅-	=O		85		435a
CH₃-	2-Thienyl-	=NOH		156	yellow	533
CH₃-	2-Thienyl-	=NOH		184		394
		[fused naphthalene structure with =O]		190	brown-red	396b
CH₃-	5-CH₃-2-thienyl-	=NOH		158	yellow	534
CH₃-	5-C₂H₅-2-thienyl-	=NOH		127	yellow	534
CH₃-	4,5-(CH₃)₂-2-thienyl-	=O	10	95	yellow	337
C₂H₅-	3-Pyridyl-	=NOH		191	orange	317
C₂H₅-	4-Pyridyl-	=NOH		221		315
n-C₄H₉-	3-Pyridyl-	=NOH		165	yellow	317
C₆H₅-	C₆H₅-	=O		117		435a
C₆H₅-	3-Pyridyl-	=NOH		200		315
H	C₂H₅O₂C-	=O	9		b.p. 125-140° at 5 mm	301a
CH₃O₂C-	C₆H₅-	=O		46		435a
C₂H₅O₂C-	C₆H₅-	=O		69		435a
C₆H₅-	Cl	=O	50-57	99-100		148a
Cl	C₆H₅-	=O		62		56b
p-CH₃C₆H₄-	Cl	=O	61	75		148a
Cl	Cl	[Cl—C—Cl structure]	65	dec. 235		56a
Cl	Cl	=O		61		56a
Cl and (C₂H₅)₂N-		=O		65		56a

379

TABLE 5. 1,2-Dithioles with Various Substituents in 3-Position (contd)

R₄	R₅	X	Yield (%)	M.p. (°C)	Other properties	Ref.
Cl	and 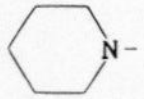 (piperidin-1-yl)	$=O$		82		56a
Cl	and 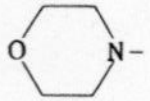 (morpholin-4-yl)	$=O$		128		56a
Cl	and C_6H_5NH-	$=O$		164		56a
Cl	and $C_6H_5N(CH_3)-$	$=O$		72		56a
Cl	and $C_6H_5N(C_2H_5)-$	$=O$		79		56a
Cl	and $o\text{-}CH_3C_6H_4NH-$	$=O$		127		56a
Cl	and $m\text{-}CH_3C_6H_4NH-$	$=O$		152		56a
Cl	and $p\text{-}CH_3C_6H_4NH-$	$=O$		175		56a
Cl	and $o\text{-}CH_3OC_6H_4NH-$	$=O$		120		56a
Cl	and $p\text{-}CH_3OC_6H_4NH-$	$=O$		191		56a
Cl	and $o\text{-}C_2H_5OC_6H_4NH-$	$=O$		106		56a

Lüttringhaus, König, and Böttcher[70,339] found that treatment of 1,2-dithiol-3-ones with phosphorus pentasulfide gives 1,2-dithiole-3-thiones in fairly good yield. The reaction was carried out initially in refluxing xylene, but Böttcher and Bauer[64,65] found the yields to be much better in carbon disulfide. According to Klingsberg[301b] the best yield (92%) is obtained in refluxing pyridine. This two-step process constitutes a fairly convenient sythesis of 1,2-dithiole-3-thiones, and it has been applied to the syntheses of a number of aromatic and heterocyclic-substituted 1,2-dithiole-3-thiones.

Combining these two steps into one, i.e., heating an α,β-unsaturated ester with sulfur and phosphorus pentasulfide, was an obvious extension of this reaction,[339,342] but yields are rather poor.

Thus, angelic or tiglic esters, $CH_3CH{=}C(CH_3)COOR$, gave a 17% yield of 4,5-dimethyl-1,2-dithiole-3-thione. Surprisingly, ethyl α-ethylacrylate gave the same compound, another instance of alkyl migration. Legrand[316] has shown that α,β-unsaturated ketones undergo the same reaction, also in low yield.

Jirousek and Stárka[280a] investigated the synthesis from α,β-unsaturated esters, phosphorus pentasulfide and sulfur, and came to the conclusion that α,β-unsaturated acids give somewhat better yields than the esters. The differences are not large, however, and in fact Lüttringhaus, König, and Böttcher[339] reported a considerably better yield of 5-phenyl-1,2-dithiole-3-thione from ethyl cinnamate than Jirousek and Stárka[280a] obtained from cinnamic acid. The latter authors reported that yields improved when the cinnamic acid contains an α-substituent. They formulated the reaction as follows, since an α-substituted cinnamic acid could not form **79g** and would have to yield **79h**, which they considered to be the 1,2-dithiole-3-thione precursor.

However, only in the cinnamic acids was there a large yield difference between α-substituted and unsubstituted acids, and, as already mentioned, their yield from cinnamic acid itself was unusually low.

(h) From β-Keto Esters and β-Keto Aldehydes. The most versatile synthesis of 1, 2-dithiole-3-thiones was first reported by Lozac'h and Legrand,[332] although it was apparently discovered independently by Lüttringhaus and his co-workers.[465b] This involved the reaction of a β-keto ester with a technical grade of phosphorus pentasulfide in refluxing xylene according to the following scheme:

$$\text{RCOCHCOOR''} + P_4S_{10} \longrightarrow$$

By this procedure Lozac'h and his co-workers have prepared 1, 2-dithiole-3-thiones substituted by alkyl, aryl, thienyl, and pyridyl groups[220,221,314-317,332,333,533,534] and by condensensed rings (see following sections). The reaction has been patented.[210]

Initially the yields were quite poor, but later work,[316,317,533] showed that they could be improved considerably by using refluxing tetralin as a solvent instead of xylene, so as to raise the temperature of the reaction, and by using an excess of phosphorus pentasulfide. In this way ethyl acetoacetate gave a 30% yield of 5-methyl-1, 2-dithiole-3-thione. Yields ranged, however, from 5% in some cases to as high as 73% in one.

Schmidt, Lüttringhaus, and Trefzger[465b] investigated this reaction, and found that yields could be improved by using a mixture of sulfur and phosphorus pentasulfide and by using carbon disulfide as solvent. By this means the temperature could be lowered to 120°, and yields of 40-50% were obtained in many instances. However, it is necessary to use an autoclave because of the low boiling point of the solvent. The synthesis has been patented.[568] According to Klingsberg[301b] the reaction is carried out more conveniently in refluxing pyridine. Schmidt, Lüttringhaus, and Trefzger[465b] postulated that the reaction proceeds as follows:

$$\text{RCOCHCOOC}_2\text{H}_5 \xrightarrow{P_4S_{10}} \text{RC}=\text{CCOOC}_2\text{H}_5 \xrightarrow{S}$$

$$\xrightarrow{P_4S_{10}}$$

As proof of this they reacted ethyl phenylpropiolate with sulfur and phosphorus pentasulfide under hydrogen sulfide pressure in the presence of a catalytic quantity of piperidine and obtained a 10% yield of 5-phenyl-1, 2-dithiole-3-thione. Presumably the first step involves the base-catalyzed addition of hydrogen sulfide to the triple bond to form a β-mercaptoacrylate.

The reaction can also be carried out with β-keto aldehydes, yields of 10-40% being reported with a mixture of phosphorus pentasulfide and sulfur.[316,320,533] Here, too, as with the isobutyrophenones, Legrand[320] found that formylketones with methoxyl groups *ortho* to the carbonyl group yielded 4-thiochromones or 2-thiocoumarins as by-products.

In a somewhat related synthesis Tornetta[542a] reacted benzoylacetaldehyde monoxime with phosphorus pentasulfide. At low temperatures 5-phenylisoxazole was formed, but at 150° both the isoxazole and the oxime yielded 5-phenyl-1, 2-dithiol-3-one in unstated yield.

$C_6H_5COCH_2CH{=}NOH$

P_4S_{10}

P_4S_{10} 150°

C_6H_5

C_6H_5

(i) <u>From Derivatives of Propiolic Acid.</u> Lüttringhaus, Schmidt, and Alpes[351] published an unusual synthesis for 5-phenyl-1, 2-dithiol-3-one (66), involving the acid-catalyzed condensation of phenylpropiolyl chloride with hydrogen disulfide. The N-phenylimide chloride yielded the corresponding anil (80).

H_2S_2, $ZnCl_2$

C_6H_5—C≡C—COCl $\xrightarrow[58\%]{C_6H_6}$ C_6H_5

66

C_6H_5—C≡C—C$\diagdown$ $\xrightarrow[30\%]{H_2S_2,\ C_6H_6}$ C_6H_5

80

This reaction took place spontaneously at room temperature. Since ultraviolet light improved the yield, the reaction is probably free radical in nature, involving the addition of H_2S_2 to the triple bond, followed by elimination of hydrogen chloride. The role of zinc chloride would then be obscure. The reaction failed with aliphatic acetylenic acids.

(j) <u>From β-Thioketo Esters.</u> Raoul and Vialle[435] described a synthesis of 1, 2-dithiol-3-ones and their conversion to 1, 2-dithiole-3-thiones which is of interest because of the stepwise introduction of the sulfur atoms. The synthesis started with the enolic form of β-thioketo esters, prepared from β-keto esters and hydrogen sulfide. The second sulfur atom was introduced by reaction with acetyl chlorosulfide, followed by ring closure with hydrogen chloride in methanol. Treatment of the resulting 1, 2-dithiol-3-one with phosphorus pentasulfide yielded the 1, 2-dithiole-3-thione.

H_2S, HCl EtOH

CH_3COSCl, Et_2O 1 hr., r.t.

MeOH, HCl
reflux → R—S—S / R'—O

P$_4$S$_{10}$, xylene
reflux → R—S—S / R'—S

Yields in the cyclization step were excellent when R was aryl but not when R was alkyl. The method was applied to the preparation of 5-substituted and 4,5-disubstituted derivatives, but not to the preparation of 4-substituted derivatives.

(k) From Ketones and Carbon Disulfide. Recently, Thuillier and Vialle[541] described a synthesis of 5-aryl-1,2-dithiole-3-thiones in excellent yields starting with methyl aryl ketones. Kelber[291] was the first to prepare 3,3-dimercapto-1-aryl-2-propen-1-ones (80a) by the condensation of methyl aryl ketones with carbon disulfide. Thuillier and Vialle improved the yield from the initially reported 20% to 80% in the case of acetophenone by using sodium t-amyloxide instead of potassium hydroxide as the condensing agent. Treatment of 80a with phosphorus pentasulfide gave 5-aryl-1,2-dithiole-3-thiones in yields of 45-78%; the yield of 5-phenyl-1,2-dithiole-3-thione was 66% for the two steps based on acetophenone. Alkylation of the disodium salt of 80a with methyl iodide gave the corresponding bis(methylthio) compound (80b), while ethylene bromide gave a 1,3-dithiolane derivative (80c) (see section II A-1a). Treatment of these compounds with phosphorus pentasulfide gave improved yields of 5-aryl-1,2-dithiole-3-thiones. Thus, whereas 80a (Ar = C$_6$H$_5$) gave a 78% yield of the 5-phenyl derivative, 80b gave an 87% yield and 80c a 96% yield.

$$ArCOCH_3 + CS_2 \xrightarrow{t\text{-}C_5H_{11}ONa} ArCOCH=C\begin{smallmatrix}SNa\\SNa\end{smallmatrix} \xrightarrow{H^+} ArCOCH=C\begin{smallmatrix}SH\\SH\end{smallmatrix}$$

80a

MeI, MeOH

(CH$_2$Br)$_2$
MeOH

P$_4$S$_{10}$, xylene reflux 45 min. reflux

$$ArCOCH=C\begin{smallmatrix}SCH_3\\SCH_3\end{smallmatrix}$$
80b

ArCOCH=C—S—S
80c

P$_4$S$_{10}$

P$_4$S$_{10}$

Ar—S—S / —S

According to Kelber and Schwarz[293] the preparation of compounds of the type of 80a failed with ketones other than methyl aryl ketones, but Thuillier and Vialle[541a] recently reported the successful preparation of 5-methyl-1,2-dithiole-3-thione from acetone by this route.

In 1910 Höhn and Bloch[259] isolated a resin from the reaction of cinnamaldehyde with hydrogen polysulfide in the presence of hydrogen chloride; methylation of the resin yielded an orange or orange-brown crystalline solid melting at 98-99°. Raoul and Vialle[434] have shown this to be

4-methylthio-5-phenyl-1, 2-dithiole-3-thione (**81**) by an independent synthesis based on that of Thuillier and Vialle.

$$C_6H_5COCH_2SCH_3 + CS_2 \xrightarrow[\quad 0° \quad]{t\text{-}C_5H_{11}ONa, \, C_6H_6} \left[C_6H_5CO\underset{\underset{SCH_3}{|}}{C}=C \underset{SNa}{\overset{SNa}{\diagdown}} \right]$$

$$\xrightarrow[\quad 70\% \quad]{\underset{3\,hrs.\,r.\,t.}{Me\,I}} C_6H_5CO\underset{\underset{SCH_3}{|}}{C}=C\underset{SCH_3}{\overset{SCH_3}{\diagdown}} \xrightarrow[\quad 45\% \quad]{P_4S_{10}, \, PhMe \atop 5 \, min. \, reflux} \text{(structure 81)}$$

81

4-Methoxy-5-phenyl-1, 2-dithiole-3-thione was prepared in a similar fashion from ω-methoxyacetophenone.

(2) Structure

Baumann and Fromm's formulation of the reaction product from ethyl cinnamate and sulfur as 5-phenyl-1, 2-dithiol-3-one (**66**)[42] was a brilliant deduction based essentially only on its hydrolysis to acetophenone.

(structure 66) $+ \, 4 \, KOH \longrightarrow C_6H_5COCH_3 + K_2CO_3 + K_2S + S + H_2O$

66

The correct structure of the 1, 2-dithiole-3-thiones was elucidated by Böttcher, Lüttringhaus, and König, [62,63,338,339] and apparently independently by Voronkov, Broun, and Karpenko. [553] The so-called "trithione" from anethole and sulfur was shown to have the formula $C_{10}H_8OS_3$. Chromic acid oxidation or oxidation with nitric acid or hydrogen peroxide[203] yielded anisic acid, showing that a condensed ring had not been formed and that the *p*-methoxyphenyl moiety was still attached to a carbon atom. The lack of active hydrogen in the molecule ruled out the presence of sulfhydryl groups. The stability of the structure was shown by its inertness to hot hydrochloric and hydrobromic acids and to copper powder. Sodium and ethanol removed two sulfur atoms as sodium sulfide, and alkaline peroxide removed them as sulfate ions. Hot alcoholic potassium hydroxide yielded anisic acid, and this was shown to be a hydrolytic reaction and not an oxidation. Treatment with hydroxylamine gave a yellow monoxime with the loss of one sulfur atom, indicating the presence of a thione group. At this point Böttcher and Lüttringhaus[62] were struck by the similarity of the "trithione" and the known compound, 3*H*-1, 2-benzodithiole-3-thione (see section I F); they are both orangered, and they both form yellow oximes, yellow mercuric chloride complexes, and red methiodides. The correctness of this hypothesis was shown by a comparison of the "trithione" with the compound prepared from ethyl *p*-methoxycinnamate according to the procedure of Baumann and Fromm. Both compounds gave the same oxime. Treatment of the "trithione" with potassium permanganate according to the procedure of

Gaudin and Lozac'h[204] or with mercuric acetate according to the procedure of Biedebach[55] gave a compound identical with that prepared from the cinnamate and sulfur, while reaction of the latter with phosphorus pentasulfide gave the "trithione". There remained little doubt, therefore, that "anethole trithione" was 5-(p-methoxyphenyl)-1, 2-dithiole-3-thione.

Gaudin and Lozac'h,[204] who published before the German structure elucidation was available, formulated "anethole trithione" as a persulfide (82) on the basis of negative tests for thiol and thione groups and the removal of one sulfur by permanganate.

82

They agreed with the 1, 2-dithiole-3-thione structure, however, as soon as it was published.[327] Selker and Kemp,[494] on the other hand, believed that the compound formed by the sulfuration of 2-methyl-2-butene, was a substituted thiolane (83) rather than a 1, 2-dithiole-3-thione.

83

There can be little doubt, from the work of Lüttringhaus and Cleve,[342] that the compound is 4, 5-dimethyl-1, 2-dithiole-3-thione. That the compound is not a 4- or 5-ethyl derivative was shown by a number of independent syntheses and by the fact that it gave two molecules of acetic acid in a Kuhn-Roth chromic anhydride oxidation.

An elegant method of determining the position of substituents on the dithiole ring was devised by Spindt, Stevens, and Baldwin,[506] based on the fact that alkaline hydrolysis leads to cleavage of the ring at the double bond.

Thus, sulfuration of isobutylene gives 4-methyl-1, 2-dithiole-3-thione, since hydrolysis yields propionic and formic acids. The reaction of diisobutylene with sulfur gives two products; one is the 4-neopentyl derivative (84), since hydrolysis gives 4, 4-dimethylpentanoic and formic acids, while the other is the 4-methyl-5-t-butyl derivative (85), since the hydrolysis products are propionic and trimethylacetic acids.

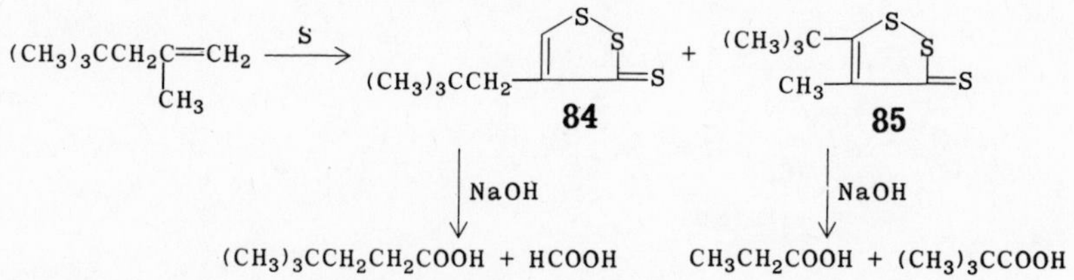

$(CH_3)_3CCH_2C=CH_2$ (with CH_3 below) $\xrightarrow{S}$ **84** + **85**

$\downarrow$ NaOH $\downarrow$ NaOH

$(CH_3)_3CCH_2CH_2COOH + HCOOH$ $CH_3CH_2COOH + (CH_3)_3CCOOH$

Similarly, Landis and Hamilton[312b] showed that triisobutylene yields 4-neopentyl-5-t-butyl-1, 2-dithiole-3-thione (**74b**) by hydrolysis to trimethylacetic and 4, 4-dimethylpentanoic acids.

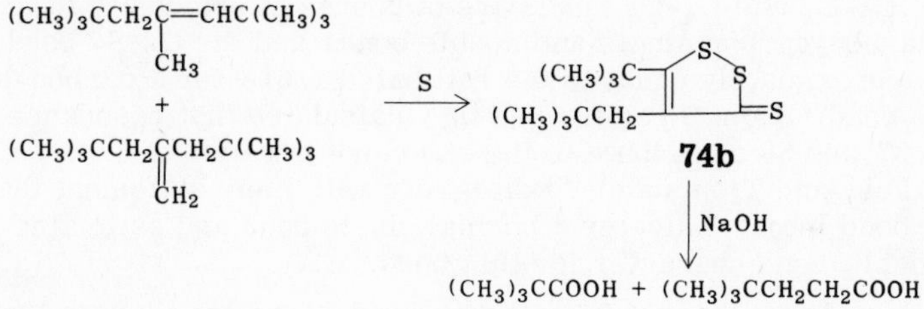

$(CH_3)_3CCH_2C=CHC(CH_3)_3$ (with CH_3 below)

+

$(CH_3)_3CCH_2CCH_2C(CH_3)_3$ (with CH_2 below)

$\xrightarrow{S}$ **74b**

$\downarrow$ NaOH

$(CH_3)_3CCOOH + (CH_3)_3CCH_2CH_2COOH$

The mode of hydrolysis of 1, 2-dithiole-3-thiones is discussed in greater detail below.

The formulation of this class of compounds as 1, 2-dithiole-3-thiones was completely confirmed by an X-ray crystallographic determination of the structure of 4-methyl-5-phenyl-1, 2-dithiole-3-thione by Zaslavskiĭ and Kondrashov.[585,586] The unit cell contains four molecules, and, in order to pack these into the unit cell, it was necessary to assume that the planes of the benzene ring and the heterocyclic ring are perpendicular to each other.

Lüttringhaus[338,340,342] appeared to be the first to realize that 1, 2-dithiole-3-thione has six electrons available for resonance and is therefore a pseudo-aromatic compound, resonance forms **86-88** contributing to its structure.

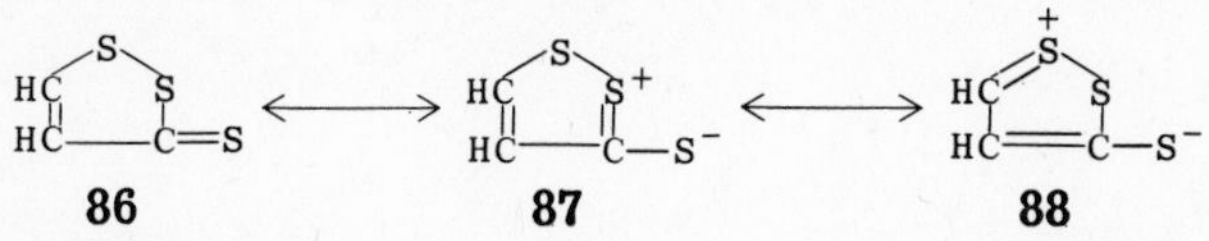

86 ⟷ **87** ⟷ **88**

Lozac'h[329] agreed with this conclusion. This accounts for the remarkable stability of these compounds as compared to the 1, 2-dithiolanes described in section I A-1. That the molecule is stabilized by resonance was shown by Kehl and Jeffrey,[289,290] who carried out a detailed crystallographic determination of the structure of 4-methyl-1. 2-dithiole-3-thione (**89**), subsequently refined by Jeffrey and Shiono.[278a]

[For references, see pp. 585-610.]

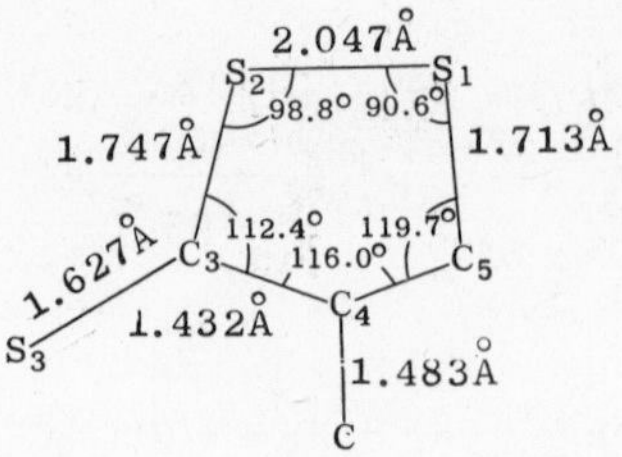

The molecule is planar. The distances indicate 75% double-bond character for the S_1-C_5 bond and 50% double-bond character for the S_2-C_3 bond. The C_3-C_4 and C_4-C_5 bonds are of course intermediate in length between carbon-carbon single and double bonds, and the C_3-S_3 bond length is approximately equal to the estimated 1.61A for a carbon-sulfur double bond. From these figures they calculated that resonance forms **86, 87,** and **88** contribute to the structure in ratios of 5 : 1 : 4. However, Foss and Tjomsland[193] disagreed with their statement that the S_1-S_2 bond length indicates a normal single bond and estimated 20-30% double-bond character for this bond.

According to Schmidt, [465d] Lüttringhaus and Baron have shown that S_2 and the thione S are equivalent in 5-*p*-methoxyphenyl-1, 2-dithiole-3-thione by the following series of reactions using labeled phosphorus pentasulfide.

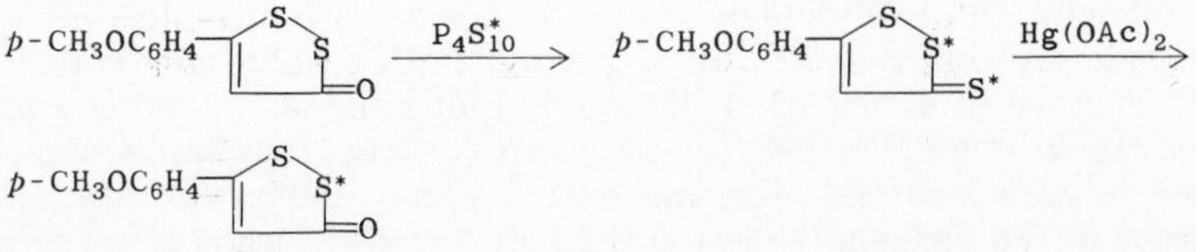

Undoubtedly, ring opening must occur during the reaction of the 1, 2-dithiol-3-one with phosphorus pentasulfide to yield an intermediate in which the two sulfur atoms are equivalent (see section I F-2).

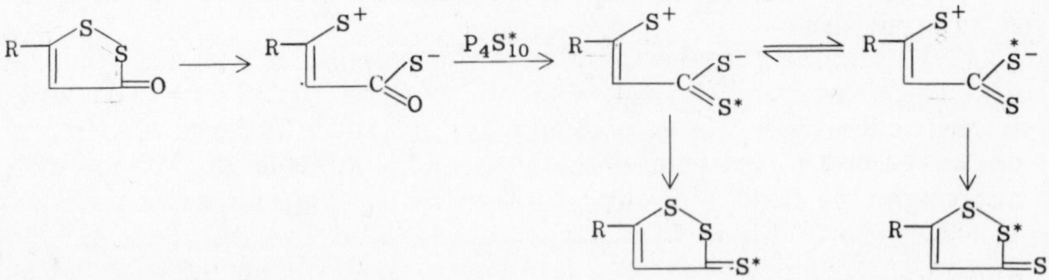

(3) Properties and Reactions

1, 2-Dithiole-3-thiones are generally odorless, although 1, 2-dithiole-3-thione itself and lower alkyl derivatives do have a characteristic odor. They have a pronounced bitter taste. [40] The unusual electronic configuration of 1, 2-dithiole-3-thiones is reflected in a number of their physical

388

properties. Thus, they are all colored, varying generally from yellow to some shade of red. The ultraviolet spectra of several compounds have been reported. Challenger and co-workers[125] gave $\lambda_{max.}$ for 1, 2-dithiole-3-thione in cyclohexane of 230, 254, 336, and 415 mμ. Spindt, Stevens, and Baldwin[506] and Landis and Hamilton[312b] showed that alkyl substituents shift the absorption bands only slightly, while Lüttringhaus and Cleve[342] showed somewhat greater shifts for aryl substituents, al-- though the curves are similar. Mecke, Mecke, and Lüttringhaus[376] determined the infrared spectra of a number of 1, 2-dithiol-3-ones and 3-thiones. The spectrum of the thione apparently showed the aromatic character of the ring.[125] Lüttringhaus and Grohmann[345] determined the dipole moments of several 1, 2-dithiol-3-ones and 3-thiones, the latter having higher moments and being more intensely colored. The proton magnetic resonance spectra of several 1, 2-dithiole-3-thiones have been reported. Thus, Landis and Hamilton[312b] found only two types of hydrogen in 4-neopentyl-5-t-butyl-1, 2-dithiole-3-thione (74b), a doublet for the methyl hydrogens at 129 and 148 c.p.s., referred to water as an external standard, and a singlet for the methylene hydrogens at 66 c.p.s., in the ratio of 8. 4 : 1.

Zahradník and Koutecky[584c] have carried out molecular orbital calculations on 3-substituted-1, 2-dithioles. According to these calculations electrophilic reactions should occur in the 4-position and nucleophilic and free radical reactions in the 5-position of the dithiole ring.

The 1, 2-dithiole-3-thiones have surprisingly high melting points; only one compound has been reported which melts below room temperature. The compounds are soluble to some extent in the usual organic solvents, and are insoluble in water. Surprising, however, is their solubility in concentrated mineral acids[342,506] and their extreme stability under acidic conditions. This solubility is probably a result of salt formation (90), with the resultant positive charge spread over the ring. It is interesting that 1, 2-dithiol-3-ones do not show this stability to acids. [339]

90

1, 2-Dithiole-3-thiones form unstable complexes with halogens, according to Lozac'h and Gaudin,[328,207,208] when mixed with a benzene solution of the halogen; the compounds are listed in Table 6. Challenger and co-workers[125] showed that the halogen does not add to the carbon-carbon double bond, inasmuch as treatment of the bromine adduct of 1, 2-dithiole-3-thione with water regenerated the original compound. Since dialkyl sulfide-halogen complexes are considered to have the structure $(R_2SX)^+X^-$,[59] a reasonable formulation for these compounds might be that of Mollier and Lozac'h,[391] with the added proviso that the positive charge be distributed about the ring (91).

91

[For references, see pp. 585-610.]

Whereas Lozac'h and Gaudin[208,328] reported that 5-(p-methoxyphenyl)-
1,2-dithiole-3-thione gives a complex with iodine, $C_{10}H_8OS_3 . I_2$, Selker
and Kemp[494] claimed that 4,5-dimethyl-1,2-dithiole-3-thione gives a
triiodide, $C_5H_6S_3 . I_3$. The structure of the latter is obscure.

Mollier and Lozac'h[391] reported that certain phenyl-substituted 1,2-
dithiole-3-thiones form unstable 2:1 complexes with thionyl chloride
and with sulfuryl chloride. Their structures (92) are undoubtedly similar to the halogen complexes.

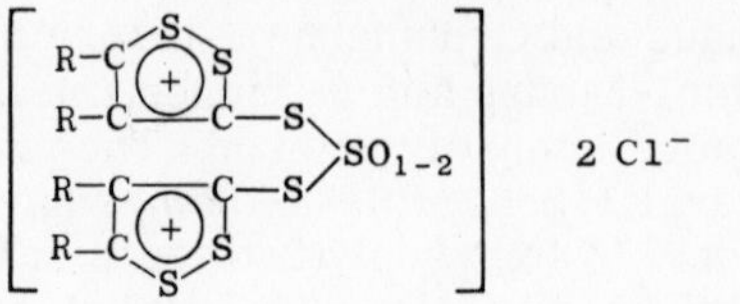

92

In contrast to these results, Spindt, Stevens, and Baldwin[506] found that
several alkyl-substituted 1,2-dithiole-3-thiones react with chlorine in
acetic acid to form dichlorides with elimination of a sulfur atom (see
Table 5). Since hydrolysis of these compounds resulted in replacement
of the halogens by an oxo group, the compounds were formulated as 3,3-
dichlorides (93). Landis and Hamilton[312b] obtained the same results
with chlorine in carbon tetrachloride.

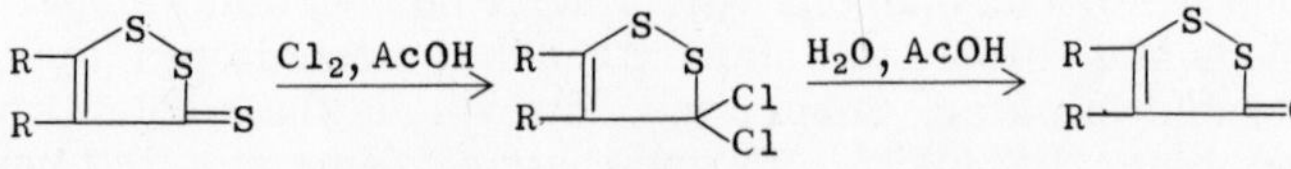

93

Diveley, Lohr, and Brack[148a,77a] found that treatment of 4-aryl-1,2-
dithiole-3-thiones with chlorine results in chlorination in the 5-position
as well as in the 3-position. Although the trichlorides could not be isolated as pure species, hydrolysis yielded crystalline 4-aryl-5-chloro-1,
2-dithiol-3-ones (93a, Ar = C_6H_5 and p-$CH_3C_6H_4$).

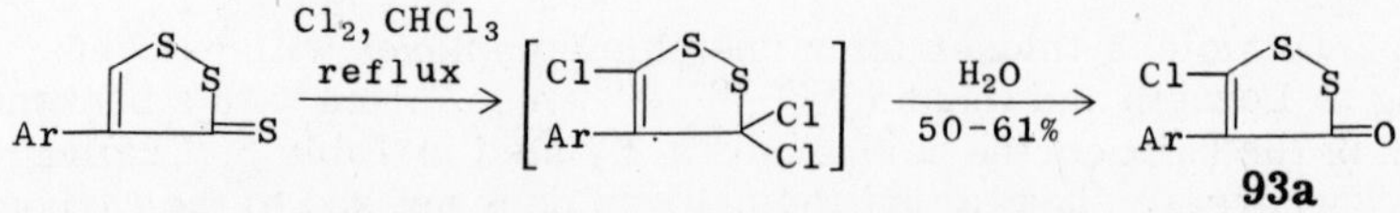

According to Boberg[56b], however, chlorination of 5-phenyl-1,2-dithiol-
3-one with chlorine or with sulfuryl chloride yields 4-chloro-5-phenyl-
1,2-dithiol-3-one (93b). This, on treatment with base in alcohol is converted into 2,5-diphenyl-3,6-dicarbethoxy-p-dithiin (93c) (see Chapter
12, section III A-2a).

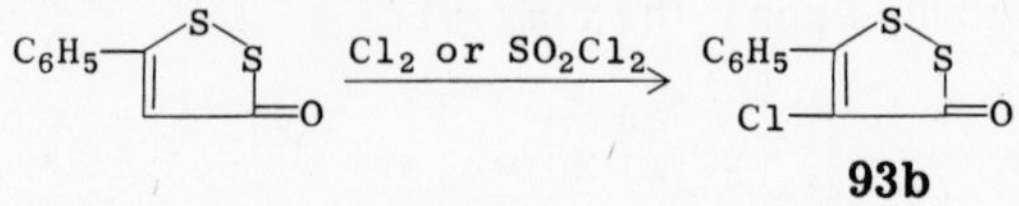

93b

TABLE 6. 1, 2-Dithiole-3-thione Complexes

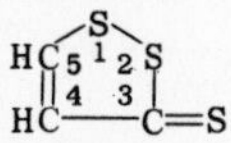

$$\begin{array}{c} HC_{5}^{S}{}_{2}^{1}S \\ HC^{4}{}_{3}{-}C{=}S \end{array}$$

Substituents	Complexing group	M.p. (°C)	Color	Ref.
None	$HgCl_2$	218-219 (dec.)	canary yellow	125, 126
	$AgNO_3$	135 (dec.)		125, 126
4-C_6H_5-	$HgBr_2$	dec. 170		553
5-C_6H_5-	$HgBr_2$	155		553
	$HgCl_2$	220		459b
5-(p-$CH_3OC_6H_4$-)	Cl_2	98	yellow-orange	207, 328
	Br_2	156	yellow-orange	207, 328
	I_2	164	red-brown	208, 328
	$HgCl_2$	220	yellow	328
	$SbCl_3$	132	yellow-orange	328
	$\frac{1}{2}$ $SnCl_4$	185	ochre	328
5-$[3, 4-(CH_3O)_2C_6H_3-]$	$HgCl_2$	225 (dec.)		329
	$SnCl_4$	195 (dec.)		329
5-(3, 4-Methylene-dioxyphenyl-)	$HgCl_2$	240 (dec.)		329
	$\frac{1}{2}$ $SnCl_4$	230 (dec.)		329
4, 5-$(CH_3-)_2$	HgI_2	192. 5	yellow	494
	I_3	135. 2-136		494
4-$(CH_3)_3CCH_2$-5-$(CH_3)_3C$-	$HgCl_2$	218-221 (dec.)		312b
	$\frac{1}{2}$ CdI_2	145-148		312b
	$ZnCl_2$	189-194		312b
	$\frac{1}{2}$ $PtCl_4$	168-171		312b
	$\frac{1}{2}$ $AgNO_3$	145-149		312b
4-CH_3-5-C_6H_5-	$HgBr_2$	215. 2 (dec.)		553

[For references, see pp. 585-610.]

93f $\xrightarrow{\text{EtOH, OH}^-}$

93c

The direct syntheses of 3, 3, 4, 5-tetrachloro-1, 2-dithiole(**74d**) from perchloropropene and sulfur and of 4, 5-dichloro-1, 2-dithiol-3-one (**74e**) from trichloroacrylyl chloride and sulfur or by hydrolysis of **74d** has already been mentioned (see section I A-2a-(1)(a) and (g)). Boberg[56a] found that one of the two chlorines in **74e** is reactive and can be replaced by a variety of alkyl or arylamines to form either 4-amino-5-chloro-(**93d**) or 4-chloro-5-amino-1, 2-dithiol-3-ones (**93e**).

74e   **93d**   **93e**

A characteristic reaction of 1, 2-dithiole-3-thiones is their formation of crystalline complexes with a variety of heavy metal halides, such as mercuric chloride. Those complexes for which physical properties have been reported are listed in Table 6. In addition to these, complexes have been described with $AgNO_3$,[62,553] $SbCl_5$,[328,391] $AuCl_3$,[62,553] $ZnCl_2$,[553] $ZnClI$,[553] $CdCl_2$,[553] $BiCl_3$,[391,553] $PtCl_4$,[553] $PdCl_2$,[553] Cu_2Br_2,[553] and $FeCl_3$.[553] Mollier and Lozac'h[391] have pointed out that in these complexes the metal atoms generally have their expected coordination numbers. Thus, 1 : 1 complexes with $SbCl_3$ and $SbCl_5$ give antimony coordination numbers of four and six, respectively. $SnCl_4$ generally forms a 1 : 2 complex, giving tin a coordination number of six. An exception is the 1 : 1 complex of $SnCl_4$ with 5-(3-methoxy-4-hydroxyphenyl)-1, 2- dithiole-3-thione. Inasmuch as a coordination number of five for tin is unlikely, these authors suggest that the dithiole-thione occupies two positions, presumably because of the free hydroxyl group.

The very ready alkylation of 1, 2-dithiole-3-thiones is one of their most characteristic reactions. According to Fields[175] quantitative yields of methiodides can be obtained by reacting the thiones with excess methyl iodide in refluxing butyl acetate for two hours. Böttcher and Lüttringhaus[62] formulated the methiodides initially as **94**.

94

A number of observations indicated the incorrectness of this structure. 1, 2-Dithiol-3-ones do not form methiodides,[64] and treatment of the methiodides with weak acid readily liberates methyl mercaptan.[340] Lüttringhaus[338, 340] therefore formulated these compounds with the methyl group on the thione sulfur (**95**), drawing an analogy with the alkylation of thiourea:

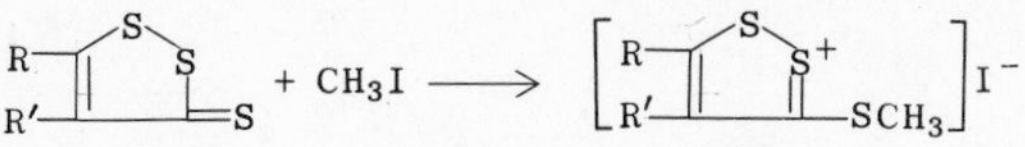

95

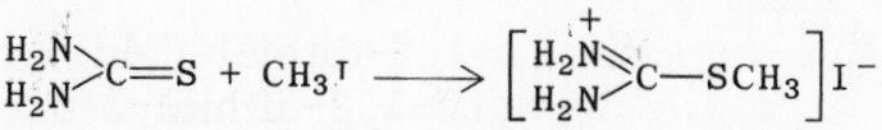

Here again the aromatic character of the 1, 2-dithiole-3-thiones is shown, and the compounds may be formulated with the positive charge spread around the ring (**96**).

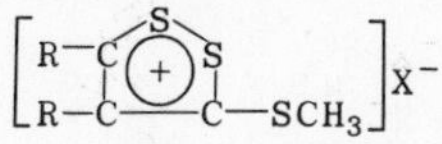

96

A wide variety of sulfonium salts have been prepared; they are listed in Table 7. Lüttringhaus[344] has reviewed the field briefly. The compounds are usually deeply colored. The reaction of course is not limited to methyl iodide; dimethyl sulfate gives methosulfates or in some cases acid sulfates, when apparently hydrolysis occurred during isolation. The halides are only slightly soluble in water, while the methosulfates are quite soluble.[64,344] A number of thionium compounds, prepared by exchanging the methosulfate anion for other anions, have been patented by Böttcher.[68, 71-73] The great tendency for formation of these compounds is illustrated by an attempt to prepare 5-(3, 4-dihydroxyphenyl)-1, 2-dithiole-3-thione by demethylation of the corresponding dimethoxy compound with concentrated hydrobromic acid. The compound actually isolated was the methobromide (**97**).[72a,344] Demethylation to 5-(3, 4-dihydroxyphenyl)-1, 2-dithiole-3-thione (**98**) was successful, however, with pyridine hydrochloride.[72a]

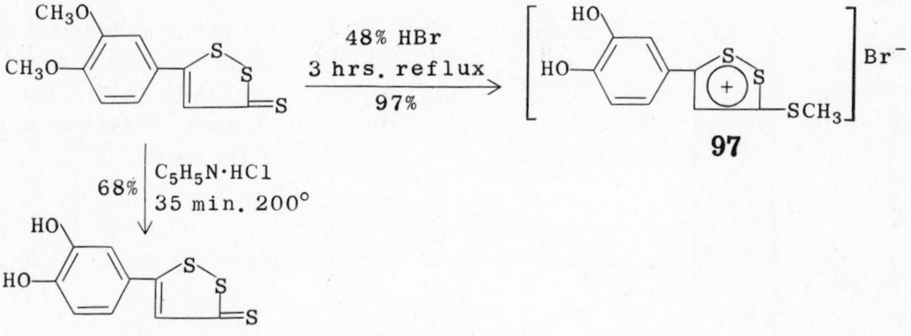

97

98

Voronkov, Broun, and Karpenko[553] claimed that 4-phenyl-, 5-phenyl-, and 4, 5-diphenyl-1, 2-dithiole-3-thione form dimethiodides when treated with an excess of methyl iodide. Inasmuch as no other dimethiodides have been reported, the formulas assigned to these compounds are open to question.

[For references, see pp. 585-610.]

TABLE 7. Thionium Derivatives of 1,2-Dithiole-3-thiones

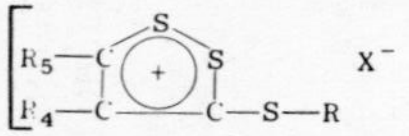

| Substituents | | | | | | | |
R$_1$	R$_5$	R	X	Yield (%)	M.p. (°C)	Color	Ref.
H	H	CH$_3$-	I		175 (dec.)	orange	125, 126
CH$_3$-	H	CH$_3$-	I		175 (dec.)	yellow	506
(CH$_3$)$_3$CCH$_2$-	H	CH$_3$-	I		157-158	yellow	506
CH$_3$-	CH$_3$-	CH$_3$-	I		148.5-149.3	gray-green	342
					150.5-151	brick-red	436, 494
CH$_3$-	CH$_3$-	CH$_3$-	HgI$_3$		131-131.2	yellow	494
CH$_3$-	(CH$_3$)$_3$C-	CH$_3$-	I		148-149	orange	506
(CH$_3$)$_3$CCH$_2$-	(CH$_3$)$_3$C-	CH$_3$-	I		159-161	pale yellow	312b
C$_6$H$_5$-	H	CH$_3$-	I	100	194 (dec.)		175
H	C$_6$H$_5$-	CH$_3$-	3,4-(HO$_2$C)(HO)C$_6$H$_3$SO$_3$-			yellow	68, 73
H	C$_6$H$_5$-		Dimethiodide		155		553
p-CH$_3$C$_6$H$_4$-	H	CH$_3$-	I	100	178.5-179		175, 177
p-C$_2$H$_5$C$_6$H$_4$-	H	CH$_3$-	I	100	163-164		175, 177
(t-C$_4$H$_9$C$_6$H$_4$-)	H	CH$_3$-	I	100	161-161.5		175, 177
(t-C$_5$H$_{11}$C$_6$H$_4$-)	H	CH$_3$-	I	100	155-156 (dec.)		175, 177
p-CH$_3$OC$_6$H$_4$-	H	CH$_3$-	I		189	yellow	62, 64
p-CH$_3$OC$_6$H$_4$-	H	C$_2$H$_5$-	I		149 (dec.)	red-brown	62
p-CH$_3$OC$_6$H$_4$-	H	CH$_3$-	Methosulfate	80	167	yellow	64
p-CH$_3$OC$_6$H$_4$-	H	CH$_3$-	HSO$_4$	56	227		64
p-CH$_3$OC$_6$H$_4$-	H	CH$_3$-	Salicylate		186	yellow	68, 72, 73
p-CH$_3$OC$_6$H$_4$-	H	CH$_3$-	p-Aminosalicylate		137-139	red-yellow	71

R1	R2	R3	X (salt/group)	mp	color	ref
H	p-CH$_3$OC$_6$H$_4$-	CH$_3^-$	Succinate	225–227 (dec.)	yellow	68, 73
H	p-CH$_3$OC$_6$H$_4$-	CH$_3^-$	3,4-(HO$_2$C)(HO)C$_6$H$_3$SO$_3^-$	177–178	brown	68, 73
H	p-CH$_3$OC$_6$H$_4$-	CH$_3^-$	2,4-(H$_2$N)(O=As)C$_6$H$_3$O$^-$			68, 73
H	p-CH$_3$OC$_6$H$_4$-	CH$_3^-$	[NaO–C$_6$H$_3$(NH$_2$)–As=As–C$_6$H$_3$(NH$_2$)–O$^-$ structure]	200 (dec.)		68, 73
H	p-CH$_3$OC$_6$H$_4$-	CH$_3^-$	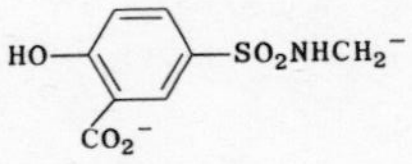 [HO–C$_6$H$_3$(SO$_2$NHCH$_2$)–CO$_2^-$ structure]	219–221 (dec.)	brown	68, 73
H	p-CH$_3$OC$_6$H$_4$-	CH$_3^-$	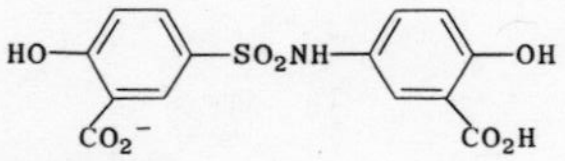 [HO–C$_6$H$_3$(SO$_2$NH)(CO$_2$H)–CO$_2^-$ structure]	>200 (dec.)	brown	68, 73
H	p-CH$_3$OC$_6$H$_4$-	CH$_3^-$	Thiourea	222–226	brown	68, 73
H	p-HOC$_6$H$_4$-	CH$_3^-$	I	235	dark red-brown	65
H	p-HOC$_6$H$_4$-	CH$_3^-$	HSO$_4$	208	green-yellow	65
H	p-(CH$_3$)$_2$NC$_6$H$_4$-	CH$_3^-$	I		deep red	65
H	3,4-(HO)$_2$C$_6$H$_3$-	CH$_3^-$	Br	230–238 (dec.) [97]	yellow-brown	72a, 344
H	2-Furyl-	CH$_3^-$	Methosulfate		green-yellow	65
H	2-Furyl-	CH$_3^-$	3,4-(HO$_2$C)(HO)C$_6$H$_3$SO$_3^-$		yellow	68, 73
2-Thienyl-	H	CH$_3^-$	I	180	orange	533
H	2-Thienyl-	CH$_3^-$	HSO$_4$		pale brown	65
H	5-CH$_3$-2-thienyl-	CH$_3^-$	I	176–177	brown-black	534
H	5-C$_2$H$_5$-2-thienyl-	CH$_3^-$	I	~150	green-brown	534
3,4-(CH$_3$)$_2$-2-thienyl-	H	CH$_3^-$	I	175–180	orange	533
CH$_3^-$	C$_6$H$_5$-	CH$_3^-$	I	136 (dec.)		553
C$_2$H$_5$O$_2$C-	C$_6$H$_5$-	CH$_3^-$	I		red	65
2-Thienyl	CH$_3^-$	CH$_3^-$	I	~170	brown	533

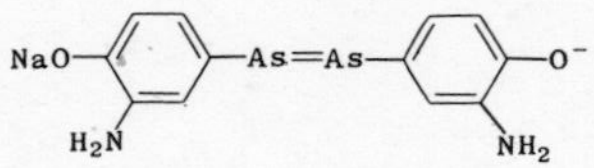

TABLE 7. Thionium Derivatives of 1,2-Dithiole-3-thiones (contd)

Substituents						
R_4	R_5	R	X	Yield (%)	M.p. (°C)	Color	Ref.
CH_3-	2-Thienyl-	CH_3-	I		~160	brick red	533
5-CH_3-2-thienyl-	CH_3-	CH_3-	I		165	brown	533
CH_3-	5-CH_3-2-thienyl-	CH_3-	I		~160	brown-red	534
C_2H_5-	5-CH_3-2-thienyl-	CH_3-	I		140 (dec.)	wine red	534
CH_3-	5-C_2H_5-2-thienyl-	CH_3-	I		150	brown-red	534
C_2H_5-	5-C_2H_5-2-thienyl-	CH_3-	I		120	grenadine red	534
C_6H_5-	C_6H_5-		Dimethiodide		170-171.5		553

Lozac'h[327],[334] found that 5-(3-methoxy-4-hydroxyphenyl)-1,2-dithiole-3-thione (99), prepared by the sulfuration of eugenol, has acid-base properties, the color of an aqueous solution changing from yellow to deep red on addition of sodium hydroxide or amines. He attributed this to quinone formation (100).

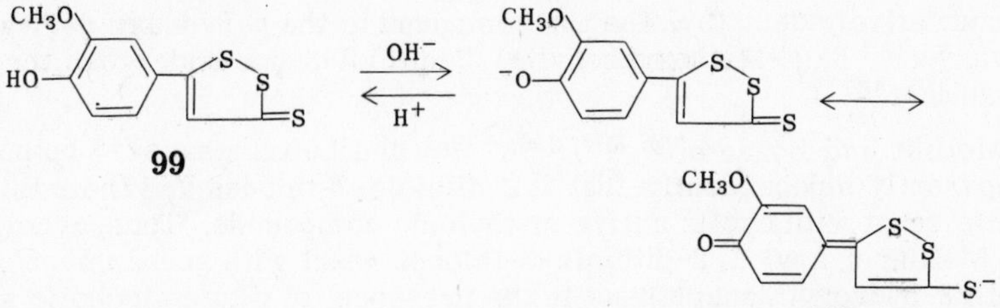

In anhydrous media the thione plus diethylamine gives a brown-black precipitate, presumably the diethylammonium salt of the quinoid form. Lüttringhaus[344],[72a] found the same effect with the methobromide of 5-(3,4-dihydroxyphenyl)-1,2-dithiole-3-thione (97). This orange-yellow compound turns red at pH 6, then violet on raising the pH further. In this case the ion is a *zwitterion* and the quinone a neutral molecule. The colored product could therefore be extracted into chloroform.

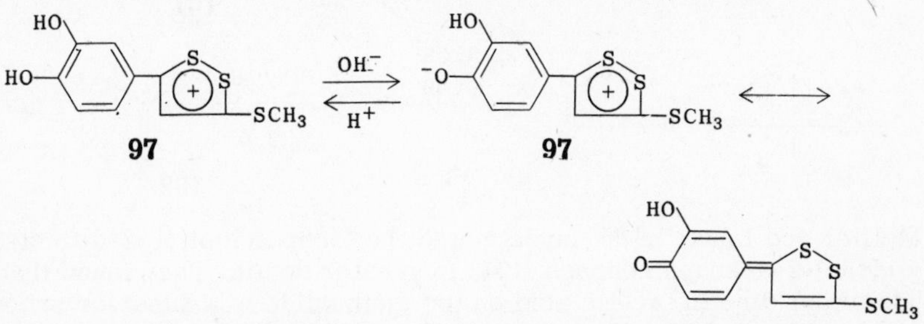

It is interesting that these structures require the two rings to be coplanar.

Several other reactions, which leave the 1,2-dithiole ring intact, have been carried out. The compounds in which the 3-thione group has been converted into another function are listed in Table 5. Thus, as already mentioned, potassium permanganate[204] and mercuric acetate[55],[63] convert the 3-thione group of 1,2-dithiole-3-thiones into an oxo group. Hydroxylamine reacts with either the 3-thione or the 3-oxo compounds to form oximes; according to Lüttringhaus, König, and Böttcher[339] the thione compounds react more readily than the oxo compounds, a surprising conclusion in view of the resonance stabilization of the former. Mollier and Lozac'h[396b] claim that 5-aryl-1,2-dithiole-3-thiones form oximes more readily than compounds without the 5-aryl group.

The extreme stability of the 1,2-dithiole-3-thiones to acidic reagents, a property not shown to as great an extent by the 1,2-dithiol-3-ones, [339]

[For references, see pp. 585-610.]

Chapter 5

makes possible a number of reactions. Schmitt and Suquet[469] sulfonated, chlorosulfonated, and acylated 4-(*p*-methoxyphenyl)-5-phenyl-1, 2-di-thiole-3-thione without affecting the 1, 2-dithiole-3-thione structure. Their assignment of these substituents to a position *ortho* to the *p*-methoxy group appears to be reasonable. Treatment of 5-(*p*-methoxy-phenyl)-1, 2-dithiole-3-thione with pyridine hydrochloride at about 200° quantitatively demethylates the compound to the *p*-hydroxy deriva-tive. [65,467] 5-(*p*-Methoxyphenyl)-1, 2-dithiol-3-one undergoes the same reaction. [467]

Mollier and Lozac'h[392,394, 396a-396c] and Lüttringhaus[344] both found, apparently independently, that 1, 2-dithiole-3-thiones and their thionium salts react with cyclic active methylenic compounds. Thus, according to Mollier 5-aryl-1, 2-dithiole-3-thiones react with acenaphthenone or with 3-hydroxythianaphthene in the presence of dilute alcoholic sodium hydroxide to form **101** and **102**, respectively.

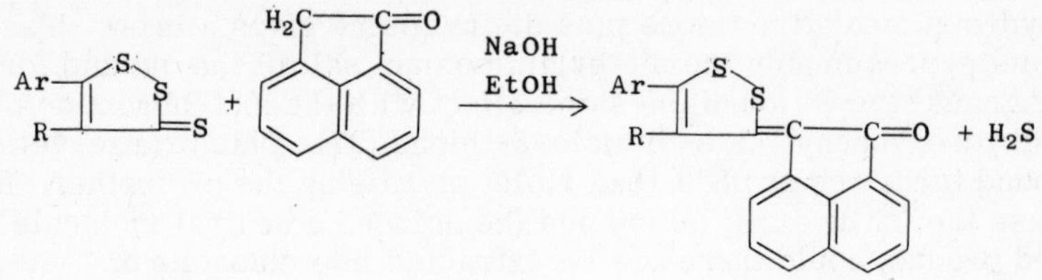

101

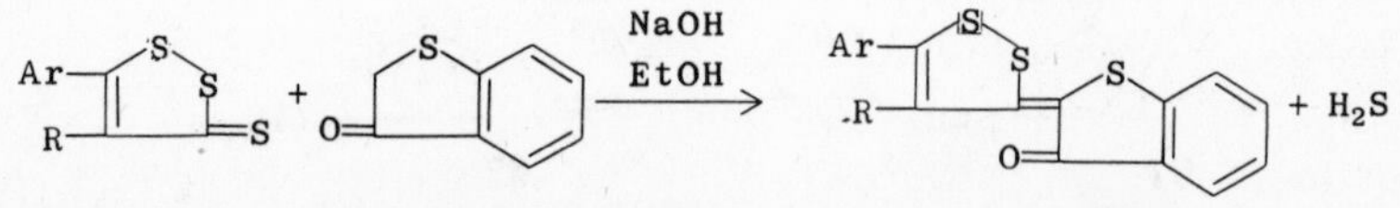

102

Mollier and Lozac'h[396b] investigated the formation of (1, 2-dithiol-3-ylidene)-2-acenaphthenones (**101**) in greater detail. They found that the use of pyridine in acetic acid on the methiodide is a superior procedure, yields of about 90% being obtained. Infrared spectra indicated that the sulfur atoms in **101** are *trans* to the carbonyl group. Treatment of **101** with phosphorus pentasulfide yielded the corresponding acenaphthene-thiones. Most interestingly, in the absence of a 5-aryl group the reac-tion with alcoholic base took a different course, forming acenaphtho-[1, 2-*b*] thiapyran-10-thiones (**103**).

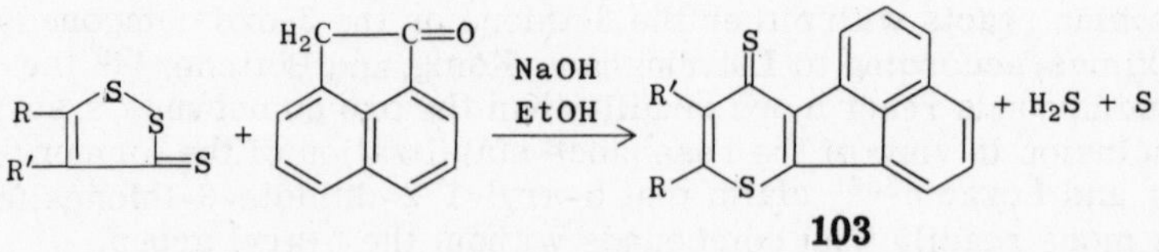

103

The authors attribute this difference to stabilization of the 1, 2-dithiole ring by resonance with a 5-aryl substituent, presumably involving

398

forms such as **103a** and **103b**, which cannot be involved with a 4-aryl substituent.

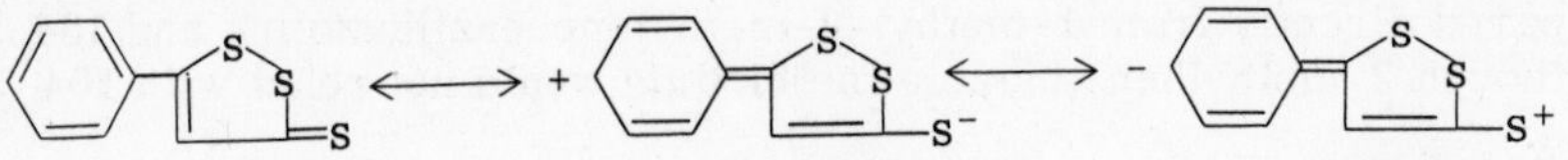

103a   **103b**

Mollier[396a] found that 5-aryl-1, 2-dithiole-3-thiones react with cyanoacetic ester to give good yields of ethyl (5-aryl-1, 2-dithiol-3-ylidene)-cyanoacetates (**103c**). Alcoholysis of the 5-methoxy derivative yielded ethyl [5-(p-methoxypheny)-1, 2-dithiol-3-ylidene]acetate (**103d**, Ar = p-CH₃OC₆H₄-, R = H) plus a trace of the corresponding malonate (**103e**, Ar = p-CH₃OC₆H₄-, R = H). **103e** was identical with the compound prepared by Quiniou[426b] from diethyl p-methoxycinnamylidenemalonate and S (see section I A-2a-(1)(g)).

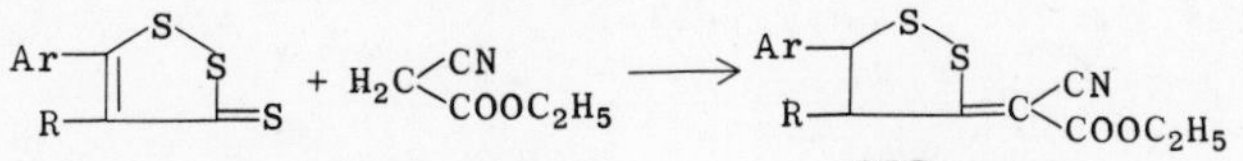

103c

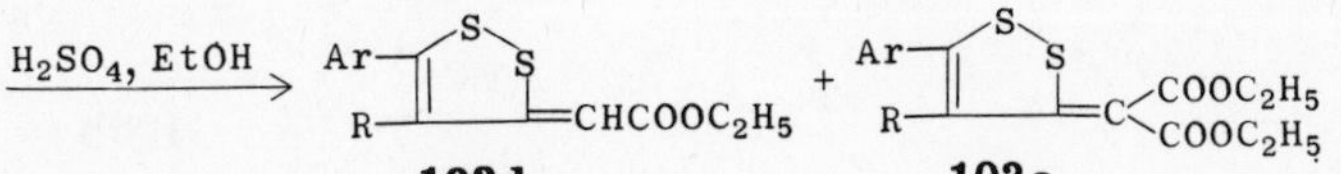

103d   **103e**

Schmidt, Scheuring, and Lüttringhaus[465a] found that 5-p-methoxy-phenyl-1, 2-dithiole-3-methylthionium methosulfate (**104**) reacts with heterocycles containing active hydrogen to form cyanine-type dyes.

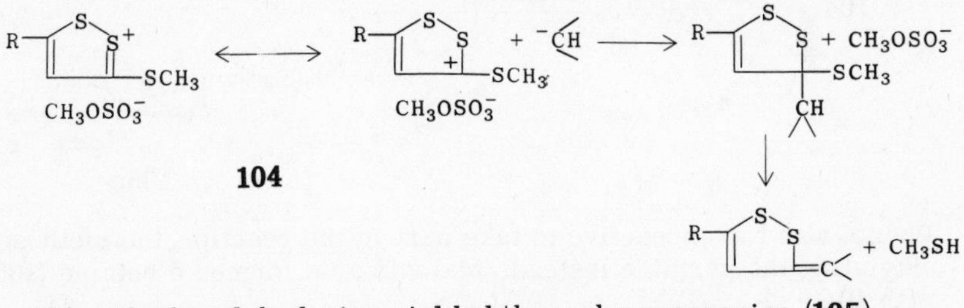

104

Thus, **104** with phenylrhodanine yielded the red merocyanine (**105**).

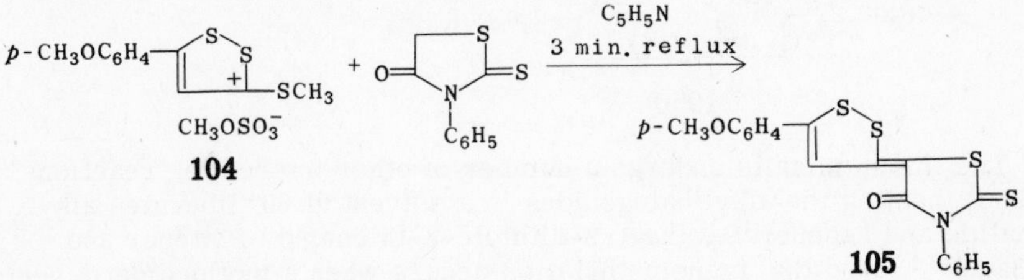

104   **105** C_6H_5

[For references, see pp. 585-610.]

Ethyl 2-benzothiazolylpyruvate reacted with **104** to yield **105a**, which was methylated to the dark brown monomethine (**105b**). The latter was prepared directly from 1-methyl-2-methylenebenzthiazoline and **104**, although 2-methylbenzthiazole methiodide would not react with **104**.

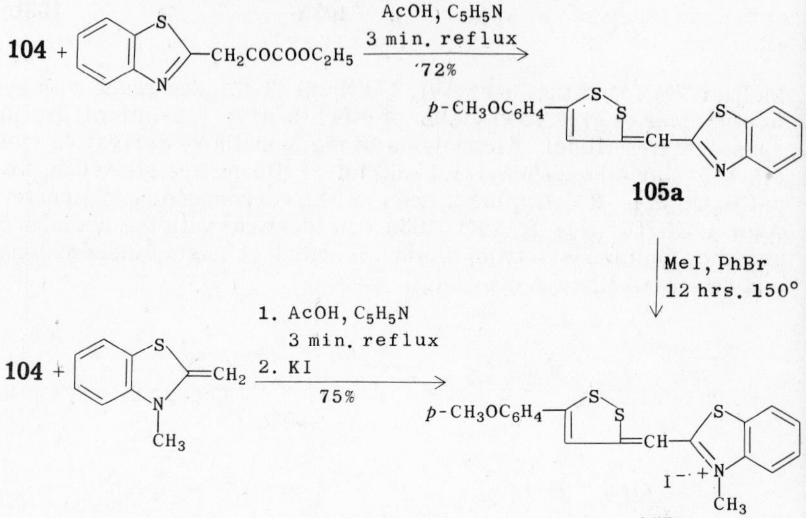

104 + [benzothiazole–CH₂COCOOC₂H₅ structure] $\xrightarrow[\text{72\%}]{\begin{array}{c}\text{AcOH, C}_5\text{H}_5\text{N}\\\text{3 min. reflux}\end{array}}$

[structure p-CH₃OC₆H₄—dithiole=CH—benzothiazole]

105a

$\downarrow \begin{array}{c}\text{MeI, PhBr}\\\text{12 hrs. 150°}\end{array}$

104 + [1-methyl-2-methylenebenzothiazoline =CH₂] $\xrightarrow[\text{75\%}]{\begin{array}{c}\text{1. AcOH, C}_5\text{H}_5\text{N}\\\text{3 min. reflux}\\\text{2. KI}\end{array}}$

[structure p-CH₃OC₆H₄—dithiole=CH—benzothiazolium, I⁻, N⁺–CH₃]

105b

Dimethylaniline, on the other hand, yielded a green quinone dyestuff (**105c**).

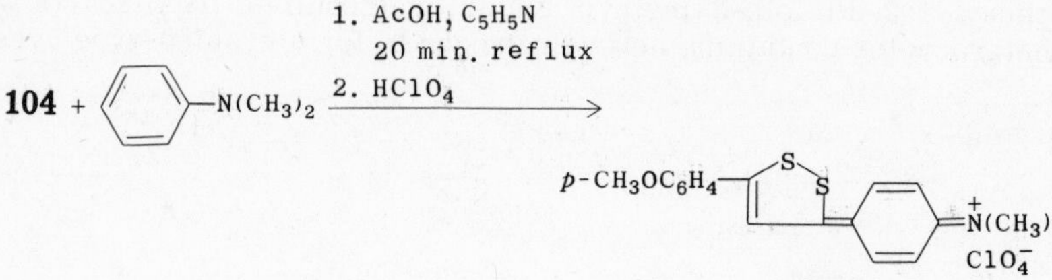

104 + [C₆H₄—N(CH₃)₂] $\xrightarrow{\begin{array}{c}\text{1. AcOH, C}_5\text{H}_5\text{N}\\\text{20 min. reflux}\\\text{2. HClO}_4\end{array}}$

[structure p-CH₃OC₆H₄—dithiole—C₆H₄=N⁺(CH₃)₂, ClO₄⁻]

105c

Phenol was too unreactive to take part in the reaction, the methosulfate alkylating the pyridine instead. Malonic acid formed a betaine (**105d**) with **104**.[344]

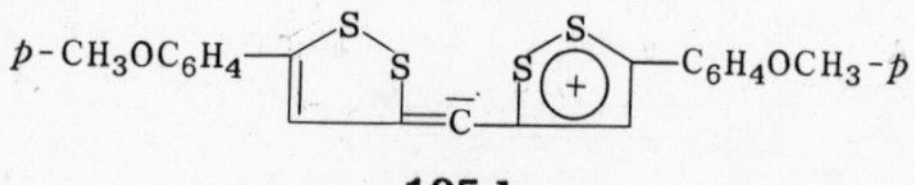

[structure p-CH₃OC₆H₄—dithiole—C⁻—dithiolium⁺—C₆H₄OCH₃-p]

105d

The thionium salts undergo a number of other interesting reactions. Thus, heating the alkyl halogenides in a solvent at 60° liberates alkyl halide and regenerates the 1, 2-dithiole-3-thione.[344] Böttcher and Bauer[64] found that transmethylation occurs when a methiodide is heated

400

in pyridine; the 1, 2-dithiole-3-thione is regenerated and pyridinium methiodide is formed. Lüttringhaus[344] extended this to other tertiary amines, and found that sodioacetoacetic ester is C-methylated. The ready hydrolysis to alkyl mercaptan and 1, 2-dithiol-3-one in weakly acidic media has already been mentioned. Lüttringhaus and Schmidt,[344, 350, 352, 465c] found that this reaction could be generalized to include other active hydrogen compounds, especially those containing nitrogen.

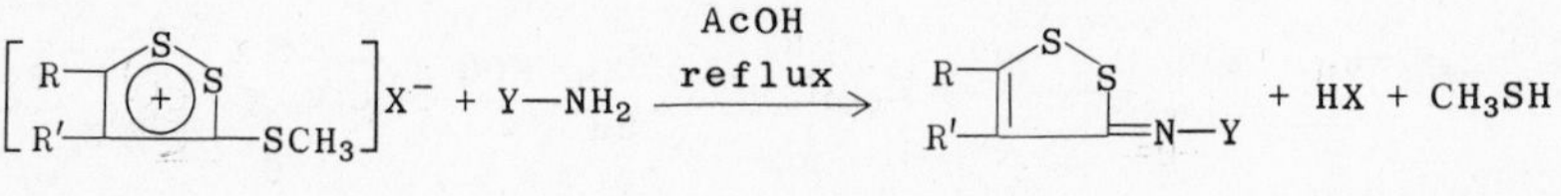

The condensations were carried out in excellent yields to form oximes, anils, phenylhydrazones, azines, mixed azines with aldehydes or ketones, etc. An unusual reaction was reported between the anil and acetic anhydride, a betaine-like compound (106) being formed.[465a]

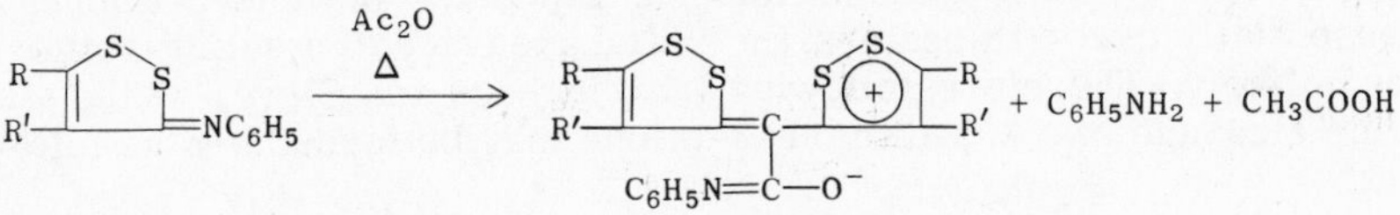

106

The general condensation of the sulfonium compounds with amines has also been patented by Böttcher.[74]

Quiniou and Lozac'h[425] found that the methyl group in 5-methyl-1, 2-dithiole-3-thiones (107) is activated, as would be expected, by the dithiole ring. They thus prepared a number of 5-styryl-1, 2-dithiole-3-thiones (108) by reacting 107 with aromatic aldehydes using an amine catalyst; yields were not reported. Structures were proved in several examples by unequivocal syntheses.

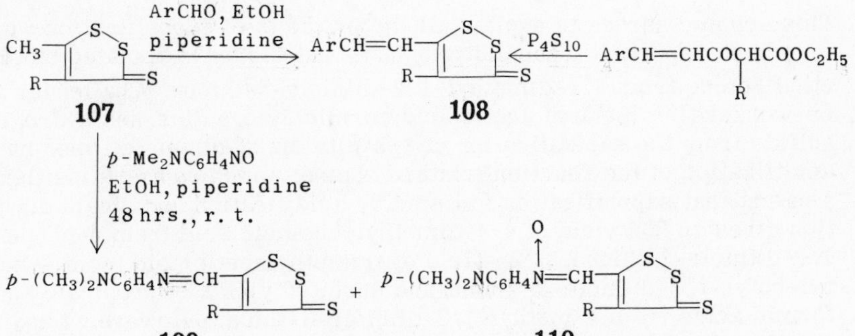

Similarly, Quiniou[426, 426a] reacted p-nitrosodimethylaniline with 107 and obtained a mixture of anil (109) and nitrone (110). The nitrone was favored by excess nitroso compound, but heating converted it into anil.

[For references, see pp. 585-610.]

Several reactions which open the 1, 2-dithiole ring are known. Undoubtedly the most important of these is saponification. The alkaline hydrolysis of 5-phenyl-1, 2-dithiol-3-one to acetophenone and of 5-*p*-methoxyphenyl-1, 2-dithiole-3-thione to anisic acid have already been mentioned. These are end products of the reaction, probably derived from a common type of intermediate, and the reaction itself is quite complex. Voronkov, Braun, and Karpenko[553] formulated the hydrolysis of 5-phenyl-1, 2-dithiole-3-thione thus:

Schmitt and Lespagnol[467] pointed out that the intermediate is probably a β-keto acid, which can undergo ketonic or acid cleavage, thus explaining the two types of products formed. Since 1, 2-dithiole-3-thiones are essentially cyclic thioesters, the initial cleavage of a sulfur-sulfur bond is unlikely. Therefore, following Lüttringhaus and Cleve,[342] the alkaline cleavage of a 1, 2-dithiole-3-thione may be formulated as follows:

This scheme serves to explain all the products of saponification which have been reported. Thus, Lüttringhaus and Cleve[342] isolated methyl ethyl ketone from 4, 5-dimethyl-1, 2-dithiole-3-thione. Challenger and co-workers[125] isolated acetic acid, formic acid, sulfur, and hydrogen sulfide from the saponification of 1, 2-dithiole-3-thione followed by acidification of the reaction mixture. Spindt and Stevens[505] claimed in a patent that saponification followed by acidification and steam distillation gives an 80% yield of 4, 4-dimethylpentanoic acid from 4-neopentyl-1, 2-dithiole-3-thione, a 59% yield of trimethylacetic acid from 4-methyl-5-*t*-butyl-1, 2-dithiole-3-thione, and unstated yields of propionic and formic acids from 4-methyl-1, 2-dithiole-3-thione. However, Landis and Hamilton[312b] reported only 35% and 23% yields of trimethylacetic and 4, 4-dimethylpentanoic acids, respectively, from the saponification of 4-neopentyl-5-*t*-butyl-1, 2-dithiole-3-thione. In a more detailed discussion Spindt, Stevens and Baldwin[506] described several ways of working up the complex solution formed on saponification. Treatment with hydrogen peroxide converted the three sulfur atoms to sulfate and the expected acids could then be isolated. Treatment with dimethyl sulfate gave dimethyl sulfide, dimethyl disulfide, and the expected acids; from the 4-neopentyl derivative was isolated in addition methyl 4, 4-dimethyl-thiopentanoate, $(CH_3)_3CCH_2CH_2COSCH_3$.[507] Finally, steam-distillation of the complex from the 4-methyl-5-t-butyl derivative yielded ethyl t-butyl ketone.

The reaction of the thionium salts with compounds containing amino groups is in sharp contrast to the reaction of 1, 2-dithiol-3-ones and 3-thiones. Baumann and Fromm[42] reported that refluxing 5-phenyl-1, 2-dithiol-3-one with excess phenylhydrazine led to 4, 4'-bis(diphenyl-pyrazolone) (112), presumably by phenylhydrazine oxidation of 1, 3-diphenylpyrazolone (111), which was not isolated.

111   **112**

Böttcher and Bauer[64] ran the reaction under milder conditions in an unsuccessful attempt to isolate intermediates in the reaction. They isolated the same bis(diphenylpyrazolone) (112) and the mother liquors, on long standing in air, deposited two more compounds, 113 and 114, both of which can be considered to be derived from 1, 3-diphenylpyraz-olone (111).

113   **114**

5-p-Methoxyphenyl-1, 2-dithiol-3-one reacted similarly. The corresponding 3-thiones reacted differently, the products being the imides of the pyrazolones (115).

115

Diphenylurea and dibenzylurea were isolated from the reaction of aniline and benzylamine, respectively, with 5-phenyl-1, 2-dithiol-3-one. Here, too, the reaction of the thione took a different course. Aniline yielded two compounds, $C_{27}H_{23}N_3$, m.p. 214-216°, and $C_{21}H_{16}N_2S$, m.p. 144-146°, neither of which have been definitely identified. Benzylamine yielded only one compound, $C_{23}H_{22}N_2S$, m.p. 67-68°, also unidentified. 5-p-Methoxyphenyl-1, 2-dithiole-3-thione reacted with benzylamine to give dibenzylthiourea as the only isolable product.

[For references, see pp. 585-610.]

According to Friedlaender and Kielbasinski[198] the ring of 2-phenyl-1, 2-dithiol-3-one can be opened with sodium sulfide. Treatment with sodium chloroacetate followed by heating with acetic anhydride and sodium acetate led to the formation of 2-phenyl-4-acetoxythiophene (116).

$$C_6H_5 \overset{S}{\underset{\quad}{\bigvee}} \!\!\! {}_{S} {=} {O} \xrightarrow[\substack{1.\ Na_2S,\ 100^b \\ 2.\ ClCH_2COONa \\ 3.\ HCl}]{} C_6H_5\underset{\underset{CHCOSCH_2COOH}{||}}{C}SCH_2COOH \xrightarrow[\Delta]{Ac_2O,\ AcONa}$$

$$CH_3COO \overset{S}{\underset{\quad}{\bigvee}}\!\!\! C_6H_5$$

116

Lüttringhaus and Deckert[348] found that Raney nickel desulfurization of 5-p-methoxyphenyl-1, 2-dithiole-3-thione led to simultaneous reduction and dimerization.

$$p\text{-}CH_3OC_6H_4 \overset{S}{\underset{\quad}{\bigvee}}\!\!\! {}_{S}{=}{S} \xrightarrow[\substack{\text{hot xylene} \\ 39-48\%}]{Ni} p\text{-}CH_3OC_6H_4\text{---}(CH_2)_6\text{---}C_6H_4OCH_3\text{-}p$$

Stárka and Jirousek[509a] have reported that 1, 2-dithiole-3-thiones show two steps in polarographic reduction, the procedure being suitable for analysis.

(4) Uses

A variety of uses have been suggested for these compounds. Voronkov and Tsiper[554] proposed that certain phenyl-substituted 1, 2-dithiole-3-thiones be used as qualitative color reagents for copper, mercury, platinum, and palladium. Airs and David[9] patented aryl-substituted 1, 2-dithiole-3-thiones as ingredients of extreme pressure lubricants, while Fields[176,177] has patented 4-p-alkylphenyl-1, 2-dithiole-3-thiones as corrosion inhibitors in lubricating oils; the ρ-t-butylphenyl derivative was reported to be most active. Stevens and co-workers[510,511] claimed that their alkyl-substituted 1, 2-dithiole-3-thiones, prepared by the sulfurization of isobutylene and of diisobutylene, are useful for improving the cetane number of diesel fuels. Gould, Putnam, and Wright[219] patented the use of 1, 2-dithiole-3-thiones as free-radical polymerization inhibitors. They have also been patented as antioxidants.[249a]

Lüttringhaus and Goetze[341,343] described the use of a number of 1, 2-dithiole-3-thiones as corrosion inhibitors for the acid pickling of iron. They were especially effective with hot aqueous hydrochloric acid. Their activity was explained on the assumption that the $\underset{S \quad S}{\diagdown C \diagup}$ distance is equal to the Fe-Fe distance in α-iron, so that the molecule could attach itself in two places. Activity was reported to be increased by the use of a mixture of 4, 5-disubstituted-1, 2-dithiole-3-thione, a trithiocarbonate, and either dibenzyl sulfoxide or di-o-tolylthiourea.[344b]

A number of pharmaceutical applications of 1, 2-dithiole-3-thiones have been suggested. Kourilsky and Gaudin [308] reported in 1947 that 5-(p-methoxyphenyl)-1, 2-dithiole-3-thione acts as a diuretic and stimulates bile secretion. The compound is nontoxic, and a number of papers related to its choleretic action have been published; [114,235,236,309,312,363d,386] it is known as Sulfarlem in Germany. A number of related compounds have been patented by Gaudin for this use. [206,209] Enders [162-164] found that the mixed azine prepared from 5-(p-methoxyphenyl)-1, 2-dithiole-3-thione and pyruvic acid (**117**) is a much more active chole-retic agent than the parent compound, and Lüttringhaus and Schmidt [350,352] have patented this class of compounds.

$$p-CH_3OC_6H_4 \quad + \quad CH_3COCOOH \quad + \quad N_2H_4 \longrightarrow$$

$$p-CH_3OC_6H_4 \qquad = N—N=CCOOH$$
$$\overset{|}{CH_3}$$

117

According to Schroeder, Menhard, and Perry, [488] 5-(p-methoxyphenyl)-1, 2-dithiole-3-thione lowers blood pressure in hypertensive rats. Böttcher and Bauer [68,71-73] have patented a number of 1, 2-dithiole-3-methylthionium compounds with a variety of anions (**116**) which they claim inhibit the growth of *Staphylococci* and *Streptococci;* some are reported to have tuberculostatic properties.

$$\left[\begin{array}{c} R \\ R' \end{array} \overset{S}{\underset{SCH_3}{\oplus}} S \right] X^-$$

96

Diveley, Lohr, and Brack [148a] have reported that 4-aryl-5-chloro-1, 2-dithiol-3-ones, in which the aryl group is phenyl or p-tolyl, are excellent fungicides with very low mammalian toxicity.

b. 1, 2-Dithiolium Salts

Simple 1, 2-dithiolium salts were prepared, apparently simultaneously and independently, by Leaver and Robertson [313a] and by Klingsberg. [301a] Two different syntheses were used. Klingsberg prepared 1, 2-dithiolium iodide (**118a**) from 5-carbethoxy-1, 2-dithiole-3-thione (**118**).

$$C_2H_5OOC \overset{S}{\underset{S}{\quad}} S \xrightarrow[\text{r. t.}]{Na_2S, H_2O} HOOC \overset{S}{\underset{S}{\quad}} S \xrightarrow[\text{2. KI}]{1. HClO_4, Me_2CO} \left[\overset{S}{\underset{\oplus}{\quad}} S \right] I^-$$

118   **118a**

4-Phenyl- and 3-phenyl-1, 2-dithiolium salts were prepared by pera-cetic acid oxidation of 4-phenyl- and 5-phenyl-1, 2-dithiole-3-thione, respectively. [301b] Leaver and Robertson prepared 3, 5-diphenyl-1, 2-

dithiolium perchlorate (**118b**) from dibenzoylmethane and hydrogen
disulfide in the presence of acid.

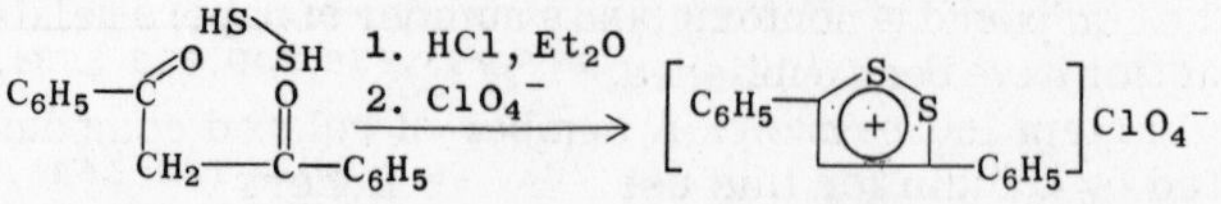

118b

Benzoylacetone yielded 3-methyl-5-phenyl-1, 2-dithiolium perchlorate
(**118c**), but apparently the reaction failed with no aryl substituent in the
β-diketone.

1, 2-Dithiolium salts are stable, crystalline compounds, yellow or
orange, some of which are soluble in water. Klingsberg pointed out
that they are pseudo-aromatic cationoid systems, isosteric with the
tropylium ion. They are presumably resonance hybrids which may be
represented by the following structures:

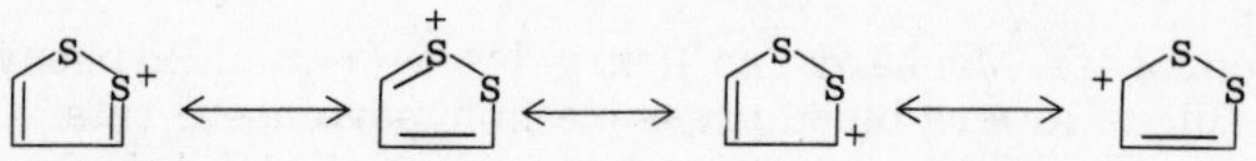

Zahradník and Koutecky[584c] have carried out molecular orbital calculations on the cation. The ultraviolet spectrum depends on the substituents. Thus, the 4-phenyl derivative has absorption maxima at 242
and 345 mμ, while the 3-phenyl derivative absorbs at 287 and 356 mμ.[301]
In view of their cationoid nature, it is not surprising that they are stable
to acid. The 3- and 4-phenyl derivatives nitrate smoothly in the phenyl
ring, the 4-isomer giving exclusively *para* nitration and the 3-isomer
a mixture of *meta* and *para*. Klingsberg[301b] attributed this to deactiva-
tion of the *p*-position in the 3-isomer.

It is also not surprising that the dithiole ring is cleaved by base. Thus,
Klingsberg found that the 4-phenyl derivative yields 4-phenylpyrazole
(**118d**) with hydrazine, the 3-phenyl derivative yielding 3-phenylpyrazole.

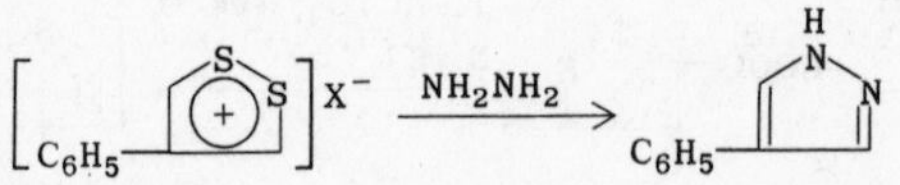

118d

Leaver and Robertson[313a] found that 3, 5-diphenyl-1, 2-dithiolium perchlorate (**118b**) yields 3, 5-diphenylisothiazole (**118e**) with alcoholic
ammonia.

$$\left[C_6H_5\text{—}\underset{\text{—}C_6H_5}{\overset{S}{\underset{+}{\bigcirc}}}S\right]ClO_4^- \xrightarrow[50\%]{NH_3,\ EtOH} C_6H_5\text{—}\overset{S}{\underset{}{\diagdown}}\underset{\text{—}C_6H_5}{N}$$

118b	**118e**

The latter authors found, too, that 3-methyl-5-phenyl-1,2-dithiolium perchlorate (**118c**) reacts with *p*-dimethylaminobenzaldehyde to yield a styryl derivative, presumably **118f**, which would have the positive charge distributed on the benzene ring as well.

$$\left[C_6H_5\text{—}\underset{\text{—}CH_3}{\overset{S}{\underset{+}{\bigcirc}}}S\right]ClO_4^- + p\text{-}(CH_3)_2NC_6H_4CHO \xrightarrow[\quad]{\overset{AcOH}{\Delta}}$$

118c

$$\left[C_6H_5\text{—}\overset{S\text{—}S^+}{\underset{}{\diagdown}}\text{—}CH=CH\text{—}\!\!\!\!-\!\!\!\!-N(CH_3)_2\right] \longleftrightarrow$$

118f

$$C_6H_5\text{—}\overset{S\text{—}S}{\underset{}{\diagdown}}\!\!=\!CH\text{—}CH\!\!=\!\!\!\!-\!\!\!\!=\overset{+}{N}(CH_3)_2\ \Big]ClO_4^-$$

Strictly speaking, 1,2-dithiole-3-thione methiodide and related compounds are 1,2-dithiolium salts and should be included here. However, they have already been treated in section I A-2a-(3).

Recently, Faust and Mayer[173a] showed that the previously reported 3,3-dichloro-1,2-dithioles (see sections I A-2a-(1a), -(1g), and -(3)) are actually 3-chloro-1,2-dithiolium chlorides (**118g**). Thus, they are soluble in water and insoluble in organic solvents, and treatment with sodium perchlorate or with perchloric acid converts them into perchlorates. The chlorine is readily replaced by nucleophiles; hot water gives 1,2-dithiol-3-ones and hydrogen sulfide the corresponding 3-thiones. The chlorides are prepared readily in good yields by treating the 3-ones or 3-thiones with oxalyl chloride.

$$\left[\underset{R'}{\overset{R}{\diagdown}}\overset{S}{\underset{+}{\bigcirc}}S\text{—}Cl\right]ClO_4^-$$

$$\uparrow NaClO_4$$

$$\underset{R'}{\overset{R}{\diagdown}}\overset{S\text{—}S}{\underset{}{\diagup}}\!\!=\!\!O \quad or \quad \underset{R'}{\overset{R}{\diagdown}}\overset{S\text{—}S}{\underset{}{\diagup}}\!\!=\!\!S \xrightarrow{(COCl)_2} \left[\underset{R'}{\overset{R}{\diagdown}}\overset{S}{\underset{+}{\bigcirc}}S\text{—}Cl\right]Cl^-$$

118g

$$\uparrow H_2O \qquad \uparrow H_2S$$

TABLE 8. 1,2-Dithiolium Salts

Substituents	X⁻	Yield (%)	M.p. (°C)	Color	Ref.
None	I		179-181 (dec.)	orange	301a
3-C_6H_5-	HSO_4	90	205-207 (dec.)	yellow	301a, 301b
	ClO_4		180-182.5	buff	301a, 301b
	I		164-167 (dec.)	orange	301a, 301b
4-C_6H_5-	HSO_4	85	236.5-237 (dec.)	yellow	301a, 301b
	ClO_4		210-212 (dec.)	yellow	301a, 301b
	Br		237-240 (dec.)	yellow	301a, 301b
	I		199-201 (dec.)	orange	301a, 301b
	SCN		139-140 (dec.)	yellow-brown	301b
3-(m-$NO_2C_6H_4$-)	HSO_4		187-188.5		301b
3-(p-$NO_2C_6H_4$-)	Br	26	220-222 (dec.)		301b
4-(p-$NO_2C_6H_4$-)	HSO_4	66	220-222 (dec.)	yellow	301b

3-CH$_3$-5-C$_6$H$_5$-	ClO$_4$	92	104-105	313a
3,5-(C$_6$H$_5$-)$_2$	ClO$_4$	39	258-259	313a
3,5-(NH$_2$)$_2$	I	100	180 (dec.)	464
	Picrate		213 (dec.)	464
	Cl	100	220-240 (dec.)	464
3,5-(NH$_2$)$_2$-4-C$_6$H$_5$-	I	100	240 (dec.)	464
	Picrate		188 (dec.)	464
3,5-(NH$_2$)$_2$-4-(NCCH$_2$CH$_2$-)	I	100	236 (dec.)	464
	Picrate		215 (dec.)	464

A still different type of 1, 2-dithiolium salt was prepared by Schmidt,[464] who oxidized dithiomalonamide with iodine and isolated a pale yellow, crystalline compound, which he formulated as 3, 5-diamino-1, 2-dithiolium iodide (119) and which he considered to be a pseudo-aromatic system to explain its properties.

119

119 is soluble in water and in alcohol, indicating its salt-like character. It is stable for weeks in concentrated sulfuric acid, but is decomposed immediately by base. Its instability to base precluded the preparation of the free di-imine and prevented condensation with benzaldehyde. Treatment of the iodide with picric acid gives the corresponding picrate. Oxidation of dithiomalonamide with hydrogen peroxide in hydrochloric acid gives the corresponding chloride quantitatively; dithiomalonamide is regenerated by treatment of the chloride with aqueous hydrogen sulfide and pyridine or with dilute sodium hydroxide at room temperature. Phenyldithiomalonamide and β-cyanoethyldithiomalonamide both react analogously to yield the 4-phenyl and 4-β-cyanoethyl derivatives, respectively. As already mentioned (see section I A-1a-(1)) dithiomalonanilide yields 3, 5-bis(phenylimino)-1, 2-dithiolane (120), the phenyl groups apparently decreasing the basicity sufficiently to prevent salt formation with hydrogen iodide, although a picrate can be isolated.

120

The 1, 2-dithiolium salts, other than the 3-methylthio compounds derived from 1, 2-dithiole-3-thiones, are listed in Table 8.

c. Thiothiophthene. (5-Methyl-1, 2-dithiol-3-ylidene)-2-propanethione

In 1925 Arndt, Nachtwey, and Pusch[16] reacted diacetylacetone with phosphorous pentasulfide and isolated an orange, crystalline compound, $C_7H_8S_3$, to which they tentatively assigned the structure 3, 7-dimethyl-5H-1, 2-dithiepin-5-thione (121); 2, 6-dimethyl-4H-pyran-4-thione (122) and 2, 6-dimethyl-4H-thiapyran-4-thione (123) were also formed.

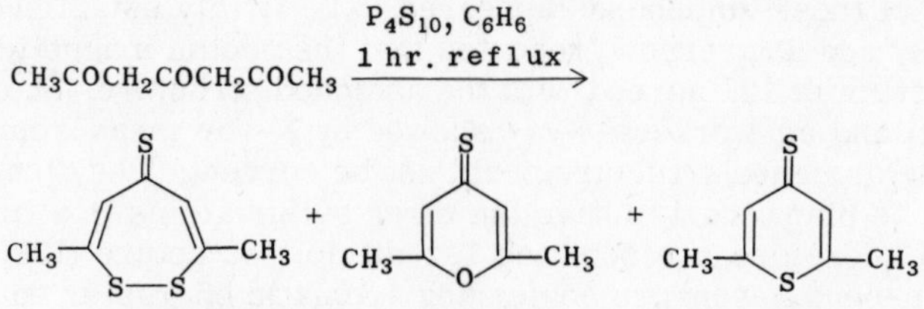

$$CH_3COCH_2COCH_2COCH_3 \xrightarrow[\text{1 hr. reflux}]{P_4S_{10},\ C_6H_6}$$

121 (40%) + **122** + **123**

Further work by Arndt and co-workers[17] appeared to confirm this structure. Thus, one sulfur could be removed by 70% perchloric acid or by concentrated sulfuric acid to give a yellow, crystalline compound formulated as the 5-oxo derivative (**124**), and treatment of this with phosphorus pentasulfide regenerated the thione.

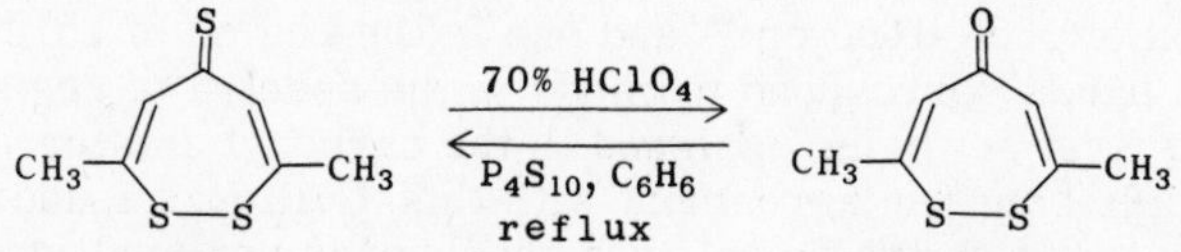

121 $\underset{\substack{P_4S_{10},\ C_6H_6 \\ reflux}}{\overset{70\%\ HClO_4}{\rightleftharpoons}}$ **124**

Traverso[543-547] devised other syntheses for compounds of this type. Treatment of 4*H*-pyran-4-thiones (**125**) with alkali sulfide or hydrosulfide yielded 5*H*-1,2-dithiepin-5-ones (**126**); reaction with phosphorus pentasulfide according to Arndt gave the 5-thione (**127**). If the alkali sulfide treatment was continued, **126** was converted into 4*H*-thiapyran-4-thiones (**128**); the rate of conversion depended on the nature of the substituents. Alkaline hydrolysis of the mercuric chloride complex of **128** converted it into **126**; by this procedure Traverso[547] was able to prepare the unsubstituted compound.

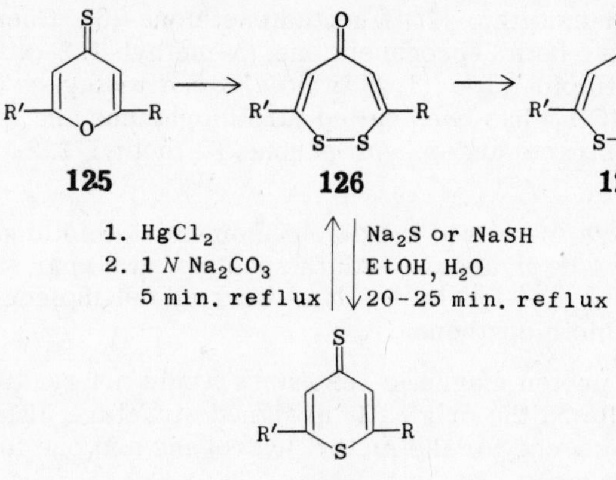

125 $\longrightarrow$ **126** $\longrightarrow$ **127**

1. HgCl$_2$
2. 1 *N* Na$_2$CO$_3$
   5 min. reflux

Na$_2$S or NaSH
EtOH, H$_2$O
20-25 min. reflux

128

[For references, see pp. 585-610.]

The structure of these compounds appeared to be firmly established when Bothner-By and Traverso[77] reported that the proton magnetic resonance spectrum of **121** agreed with the assigned structure. Shortly thereafter Bezzi and co-workers[54,54a] showed by X-ray measurements, however, that the assigned structure could not be correct. They found the molecule to be planar and to have the three sulfur atoms in a line. They postulated, therefore, a resonating 1, 2-dithiole structure (**129**, $R = CH_3$), the no-bond resonance conferring aromatic character on the rings.

129

Guillouzo[226] had independently reached the same conclusion, without, however, explicitly stating the resonance nature, by an analysis of the infrared spectrum of the oxo compound (**124**). The spectrum shows two bands in the region of 1550-1600 cm^{-1} and one in the region of 1510-1540 cm^{-1}. These bands correspond to bands in the spectra of chelates of β-diketones, the first set being assigned to the carbonyl and the second to the olefinic bond. In agreement with this, Guillouzo found that the first set disappeared on treatment with phosphorus pentasulfide.

Behringer, Reimann, and Ruff[44a] finally presented chemical evidence by desulfurizing **130** ($R = CH_3$) with Raney nickel. The isolation of 2-heptanone eliminated any possibility of a thiepin structure (**126**).

130

There appears to be little doubt, therefore, that Arndt's original compound has structure **129** ($R = CH_3$). This has been variously called thiothiophthene and meri-epidithio-(2, 4)-heptadienethione-(6). Chemical Abstracts indexes it under both 2-propanethione, (5-methyl-1, 2-dithiol-3-ylidene)- and [1, 2]dithiolo[1, 5-b][1, 2]dithiole, 2, 5-dimethyl-. The oxygen analog (**130**, $R = CH_3$) has been called furothiophthene and is indexed by Chemical Abstracts under 2-propanone, (5-methyl-1, 2-dithiol-3-ylidene)-.

Sanesi and Traverso[460a] measured the dipole moment of thiothiophthene and considered it to be in accord with the postulated planar structure. Several workers[213a,363a-363c,495b] have carried out molecular orbital calculations on thiothiophthene.

It should be noted that proton magnetic resonance would not readily differentiate between **129** and the originally assigned structure, **121**; both should give two peaks, one for the methyl hydrogens and one for the two equivalent vinyl hydrogens.

Hertz, Traverso, and Walter[250] have presented both physical and chemical evidence that furothiophthene (**130**, R = CH$_3$) is not a resonating structure. Its proton magnetic resonance spectrum contains four lines, one being a doublet. Since thiothiophthene has only two kinds of hydrogen, this is further evidence that these compounds are 1,2-dithioles and not 1,2-dithiepins. Since the spectrum of furothiophthene is similar to that of mesityl oxide, there should be little or no no-bond resonance in it. Similarly, **130** (R = H) contains four doublets, one being characteristic of an aldehyde group, again indicating no no-bond resonance. Chemical evidence confirms these conclusions. Thus, **130** (R = CH$_3$ or H) gives 2,4-dinitrophenylhydrazones, whereas the thiones show no thione reactions. However, more recently Mammi, Bardi, Traverso, and Bezzi[364a] determined the crystal structure of furothiophthene. It too is planar, and the authors considered it to be best represented by **130a**.

130a

It is difficult to understand the earlier statement of Traverso and Sanesi[543] that compounds of the type of **129** (R = C$_6$H$_5$ and H or C$_6$H$_5$ and CH$_3$) react with alcoholic hydroxylamine to liberate hydrogen sulfide and to form **130**.

It should be pointed out that, because of the symmetry of **129** there is no ambiguity in structure when the two R's are not equivalent. This is not the case for the unsymmetrical oxo compounds (**130**), and it should be noted that the positions of the substituents in the unsymmetrical oxo compounds listed in Table 9 are not known, i.e., it is not known whether R or R' is attached to the 1,2-dithiole ring. Thus, Traverso[544] prepared **132** from 2-carbethoxy-6-phenyl-4H-pyran-4-thione (**131**); treatment with phosphorus pentasulfide led to decarboxylation and the formation of **133**.

These structures are preferred to the alternative ones with the phenyl group in the side chain because of the ready decarboxylation of **132** and because the acidity of **132**[196] is very close to that of pyruvic acid. This

evidence is indirect, however, and assignments of structure to the unsymmetrical compounds require further evidence. It is quite surprising
that more than one isomer has never been reported. Thus, Behringer,
Reimann, and Ruff[44a] desulfurized **133a** to 1-phenyl-5-hexanone with no
evidence for the presence of any 1-phenyl-1-hexanone to be expected
from **133b**.

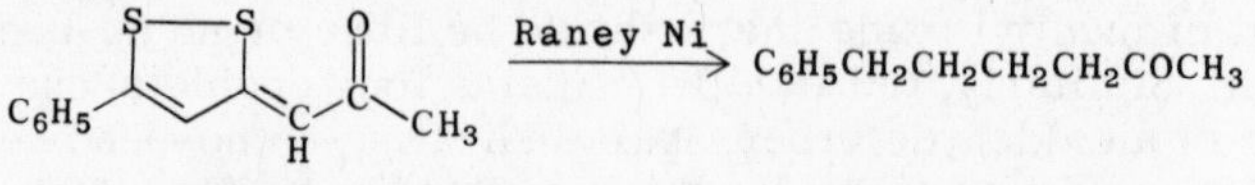

$$C_6H_5 \overset{S-S}{\underset{}{\diagdown}} \;\;\; \xrightarrow{\text{Raney Ni}} \; C_6H_5CH_2CH_2CH_2CH_2COCH_3$$

133a

$$CH_3 \overset{S-S}{\underset{}{\diagdown}} \;\;\; \xrightarrow{\;\; \times \;\;} \; CH_3CH_2CH_2CH_2CH_2COC_6H_5$$

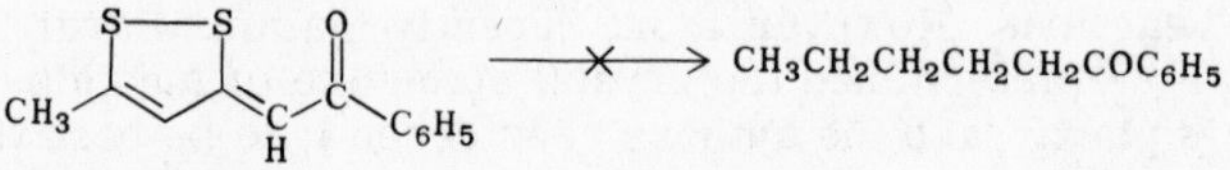

133b

It is an interesting problem to explain these interconversions between
the pyran or thiapyran compounds and these 1,2-dithioles. Hertz,
Traverso, and Walter[250] suggested the following route to explain the
interconversion of a 4H-thiapyran-4-thione (**128**) and a (1,2-dithiol-
3-ylidene)-2-propanone (**130**).

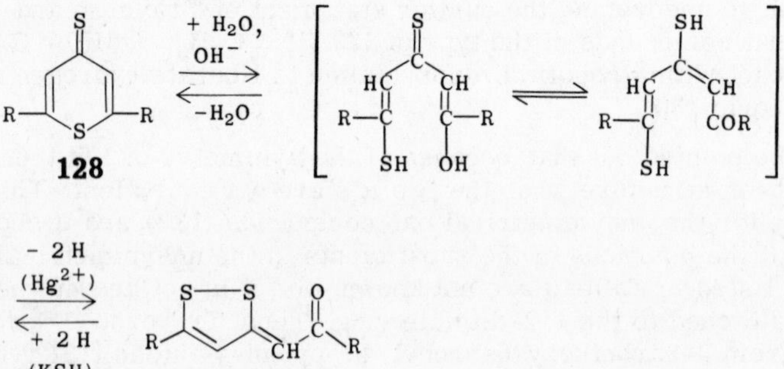

128

130

The conversion of a 4H-pyran-4-thione (**125**) to **130** is more difficult to
explain, inasmuch as the reaction is cleaner than the above and no oxidizing agent is present.

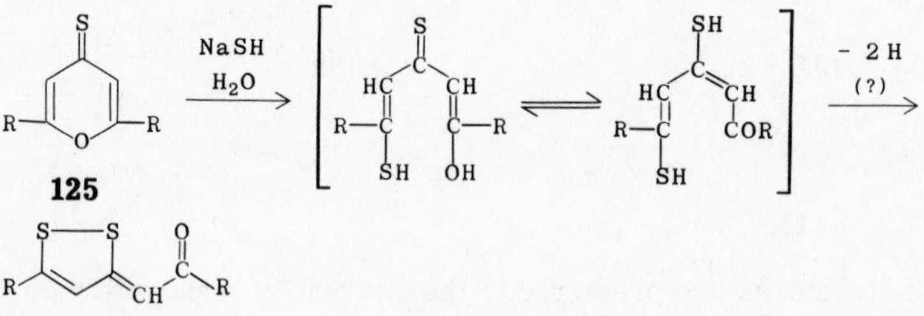

125

130

414

TABLE 9. 1,2-Dithiol-3-alkylidene Derivatives

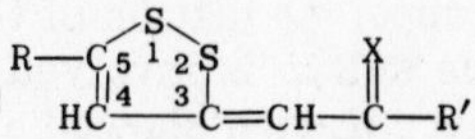

R and R'	X	Yield (%)	M.p. (°C)	Ref.
H and H	=S		114	547
	=O	20-30	9-12	547
		28	29-30	250
	2,4-$(O_2N)_2C_6H_3NHN=$		247-248	250
C_6H_5- and H	=S	84	135-136	543
			133-134	18
	=O	50-57	130	543
CH_3- and CH_3-	=S	40	183-184	16, 17, 546
			182	460a
	=O		104	17
			102.5	460a
		24-33	102	546
	2,4-$(O_2N)_2C_6H_3NHN=$	85	236-238	250
C_2H_5- and C_2H_5-	=S		56	545
		50	57	18
CH_3- and C_6H_5-	=S	78	168-169	543
		80-90	168-169	18
	=O	52	140	543
C_6H_5- and C_6H_5-	=S		162	18
C_6H_5- and HO_2C-	=O		140 (dec.)	544
C_6H_5- and KO_2C-	=O		dec. 280-290	544

One interesting reaction remains to be discussed. Arndt and co-workers[17] found in their early work that thiothiophthene (134) is rearranged by hot methanolic potassium hydroxide into an unstable, crystalline compound which they formulated as a dimercaptothiophene derivative (135) on the basis of its properties. It gave a dibenzyl and a dimethyl compound, showing two mercapto groups. Oxidation of the bis-(sulfides) gave disulfones, indicating that one sulfur is involved in an aromatic system, presumably thiophene. Mercuration showed a free α-position in the thiophene. Refluxing the thiophene derivative in pyridine rearranged it back to thiothiophthene. Arndt and Traverso[18] showed that the rearrangement takes place only if the derivative contains a methylene group, the compound derived from dibenzoylacetone being stable to alkali. Subsequently, Arndt[19] suggested that the rearranged product might be a dimercaptothiepin derivative (136), instead of a thiophene derivative, in an attempt to explain the reversal of the rearrangement with pyridine; a thiophene derivative should be stable. Actually, either structure can be explained from the now accepted 1, 2-dithiole formulation, the product depending upon which sulfur atom is attacked by the initially formed carbanion.

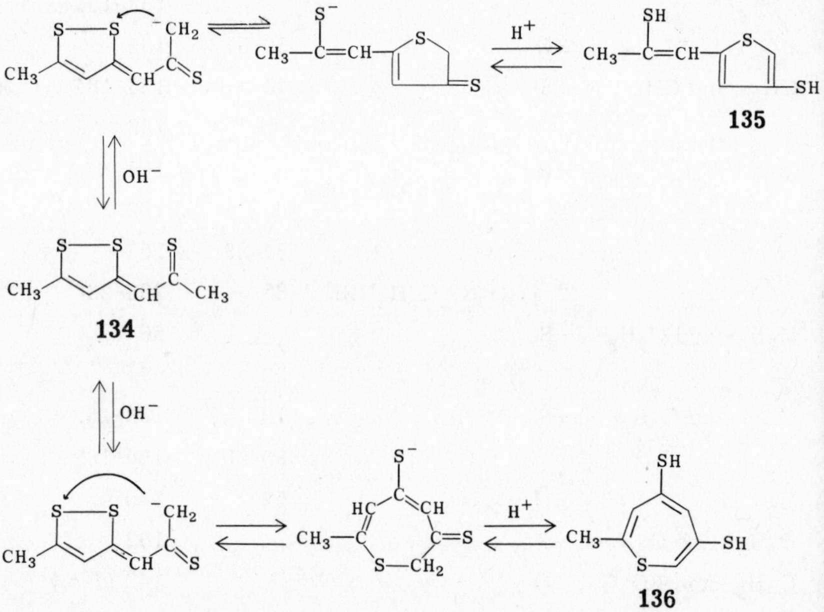

135

134

136

Bothner-By and Traverso[77] investigated the proton magnetic resonance spectrum of the compound and found that it corresponds to the thiepin derivative (136) and not to the thiophene derivative (135). However, Arndt and Walter[19a] have presented chemical evidence in favor of the thiophene structure. Oxidation of the dimethyl ether (135a) yielded a carboxylic acid with an equivalent weight of 200–204; that calculated for 135b is 206.

$$\begin{array}{ccc} \text{135a} & \xrightarrow[\substack{KMnO_4,\ Me_2CO \\ 0°}]{} & \text{135b} \end{array}$$

Additional evidence would be desirable.

B. C_3S_2-C_4N 1,2-DITHIOLO[4,3-b]PYRROLE (137).

ACETOPYRROTHINE

137

(RRI 967)

In 1948 Umezawa, Maeda, and Kosaka[551] isolated a yellow crystalline antibiotic from a strain of *Streptomyces* and named it aureothricin. Maeda[363] assigned to it the formula $C_{13}H_{13}N_3O_3S_3$, m.p. 250° (dec.). In 1950 Tanner, Means, and Davisson[530] described the isolation from a cul-ture of *Streptomyces albus* of thiolutin, a neutral, optically inactive, yellow-orange antibiotic, to which they assigned the formula $C_{13}H_{14}N_3O_3S_3$. Because of the similarity of the two compounds, Celmer, Solomons, and co-workers,[118,119] compared them. Their nonidentity was shown by differences in the infrared spectra of the two compounds and by their separation by paper chromatography.[12] Thiolutin was shown to have the formula $C_8H_8N_2O_2S_2$ and aureothricin the formula $C_9H_{10}N_2O_2S_2$. Both compounds, on desulfurization with Raney nickel, yielded the same base, desthiolutin, $C_8H_{14}N_2O_2$; and careful acidic hy-drolysis yielded the same monoamine, m.p. 191-194° (dec.), which was converted into a crystalline hydrochloride, $C_6H_6N_2OS_2 \cdot HCl \cdot H_2O$. Acetylation of the amine regenerated thiolutin, while propionylation gave aureothricin. Thus, the two antibiotics differ by thiolutin being an acetamide derivative and aureothricin a propionamide derivative of the same nucleus. According to Ito and Amakasu[273b] the two anti-biotics can be determined quantitatively in mixtures by their infrared absorptions at 973 and 943 cm^{-1}.

Celmer and Solomons[120,501] elucidated the structure of the two anti-biotics as the 3-acetamido and 3-propionamido derivatives of 6-amino-4-methyl-1,2-dithiolo[4,3-b]pyrrol-5(4H)-one (**138**), which they called 3-amino-5-methylpyrrolin-4-one[4,3-d]-1,2-dithiole or acetopyrro-thine.

R = CH$_3$CO Thiolutin
R = C$_2$H$_5$CO Aureothricin

138

The infrared spectrum of thiolutin showed the presence of C=O, NH, and C=C bonds. Since it failed to give a test for reactive sulfur groups with nitroprusside, the sulfurs were suspected of being present as a disulfide link attached to unsaturated carbons. To test this hypothesis the compound was compared with 3H-1, 2-benzodithiol-3-one (**139**). Both compounds liberate hydrogen sulfide with strong reducing agents, and both show the unusual property of dissolving in aqueous sodium bisulfide or sodium sulfide and precipitating unchanged on acidification; the latter reaction was formulated thus (see section I F):

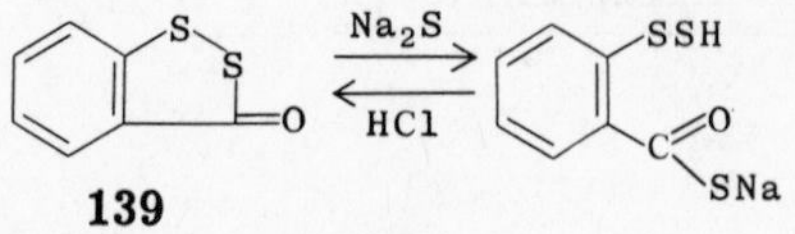

139

Hot aqueous sodium hydroxide liberated methylamine, ammonia, and acetic acid from thiolutin, showing the presence of an N-methyl group. Acid hydrolysis yielded pyrrothine, the monoamide described above; since treatment with acetic and propionic anhydrides regenerated thiolutin and aureothricin, respectively, no rearrangement occurred during hydrolysis. Pyrrothine contains a primary vinyl amine group. Desthiolutin, formed by Raney nickel desulfurization of thiolutin, gave the key to the structure. Analysis indicated that, in addition to the replacement of two sulfur atoms by hydrogen, two olefinic bonds were saturated during the reduction. Mild acid hydrolysis yielded a primary amine, which drastic hydrolysis converted into a diamine acid. Thus a lactam is present in desthiolutin, and its structure was proved to be 3-acetamido-1, 5-dimethyl-2-pyrrolidone (**140**) by an unequivocal synthesis.

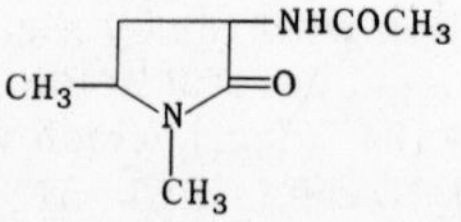

140

The synthetic compound, for which two isomers are possible, was identical in all respects with desthiolutin; the latter must therefore have been racemic. To explain this fact plus the optical inactivity of thiolutin itself, the two double bonds must be arranged as in **141**, and thiolutin must have the structure **138** (R = CH$_3$CO).

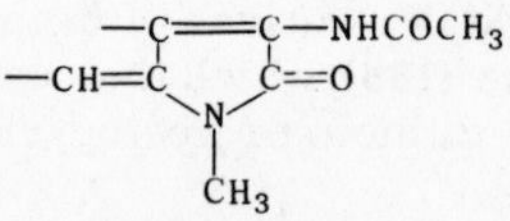

141

More recently, Bhate, Hulyalkar, and Menon[54b] isolated thiolutin, aureothricin, and a third antibiotic from a mixture formed by *Streptomyces pimprina*. The unknown was shown to be isobutyropyrrothine by synthesis from pyrrothine hydrochloride and isobutyryl chloride. Ettlinger, Gäumann, and co-workers,[168a] isolated still another anti-

418

biotic, which they named holomycin, from *Streptomyces griseus*. This was identified as des-N-methylthiolutin (**141a**) by desulfurization to 3-acetamido-5-methyl-2-pyrrolidone (**141b**), which was compared with a synthetic sample.

CH$_3$CONH

$\xrightarrow{\text{Raney Ni}}$

141a   **141b**

Schmidt and Geiger[465g] recently confirmed the structure of thiolutin by its synthesis from N-methylserinaldehyde ester acetal (**141c**).

$(C_2H_5O)_2$CHNHCH$_3$ + CH$_3$OOCCH$_2$COCl $\longrightarrow$ CH$_3$OOC—CH$_2$ COOC$_2$H$_5$

COOC$_2$H$_5$

141c

1. Nitrosation
2. H$_2$ + Ac$_2$O

$\xrightarrow{}$ CH$_3$OOC—CH COOC$_2$H$_5$ $\xrightarrow[\text{condensation}]{\text{ester}}$

CH$_3$CONH—OH 1. PhSO$_2$Cl 2. NaSH, EtOH $\xrightarrow{}$ CH$_3$CONH—SH $\xrightarrow{I_2}$

Holomycin was synthesized similarly from serinaldehyde ester acetal.

Several other derivatives of pyrrothine have been prepared; they are listed in Table 10.

Thiolutin and aureothricin show considerable activity against gram-positive, gram-negative, and acid-fast bacteria, against pathogenic fungi, and against a number of pathogenic protozoa.[134,495,530,531,551] Holomycin[168a] and isobutyropyrrothine[54b] show similar activity. The use of thiolutin as an agricultural chemical has been suggested, since it shows some activity as a soil fungicide,[587] as a control for black rot and fire blight on apples,[217,251,398,421] fungi on orchids,[462] tobacco blue mold,[223] fusarium wilt of tomatoes,[218] and others.[397a,400a,408,562] Combined with penicillin, it gives complete protection against microbiological growth in finished beer.[518] It was ineffective for controlling the bacterial decay of potatoes.[75] In a number of these applications other antibiotics show greater activity, and both stimulation and retardation of plant growth have been reported.[402,403,462]

TABLE 10. Derivatives of 6-Amino-1, 2-Dithiolo[4, 3-*b*]pyrrol-5(4*H*) one

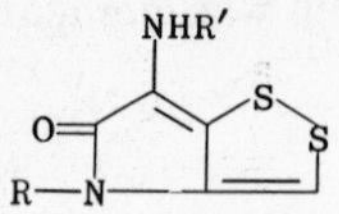

R	R'	M.p. (°C)	λ_{max} (mμ)	Refs.
CH$_3$-	H	191-194 (dec.)		118, 120
CH$_3$-	H · HCl · H$_2$O	Sinters at 200	309, 381	118, 120, 121
CH$_3$-	CH$_3$CO-, Thiolutin	260-270 (dec.) 256-257 (dec.)	250, 311, 388	118, 120, 531 404
CH$_3$-	C$_2$H$_5$CO-, Aureothricin	260-270 (dec.) 250 (dec.) 254 (dec.)	248, 312, 388	118, 120 363 551
CH$_3$-	(CH$_3$)$_2$CHCO-	228-229		54b
CH$_3$-	CH$_3$(CH$_2$)$_{10}$CO-	115. 5-118		419
CH$_3$-	CH$_2$=CH(CH$_2$)$_8$CO-	139-140. 5		419
CH$_3$-	C$_6$H$_5$CO-	197. 5-198. 5		419
CH$_3$-	HO$_2$CCH$_2$CH$_2$CO-	254-255 (dec.)	245, 311, 389	118, 419
CH$_3$-	CH$_3$O$_2$C(CH$_2$)$_5$CO-	163. 5-164	246, 311, 388	118, 120, 419
H-	CH$_3$CO-, Halomycin	264-271 (dec.)	250, 300, 385	168a
H-	C$_2$H$_5$CO-	250-260 (dec.)		168a
H-	*n*-C$_3$H$_7$CO-	215-218		168a

C. C_3S_2-C_5 CYCLOPENTA-1, 2-DITHIOLE (**142**)

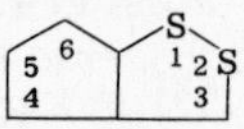

142

(RRI 970)

The only compounds reported with this ring system are 5,6-dihydrocyclo-penta-1, 2-dithiole-3(4*H*)-thione (**143**), and the corresponding 3-one (**143a**). **143** was prepared by Gaudin[210] and by Lozac'h, Legrand, and Mollier[314,332] by treating 2-carbethoxycyclopentanone with phosphorus pentasulfide; Schmidt, Lüttringhaus, and Trefzger[465b,568] used a mixture of phosphorus pentasulfide and sulfur. It was isolated as yellow or brown-violet crystals, m.p. 122-123°. **143a**, m.p. 69°, was prepared by Raoul and Vialle[435] from the corresponding cyclopentanethione.

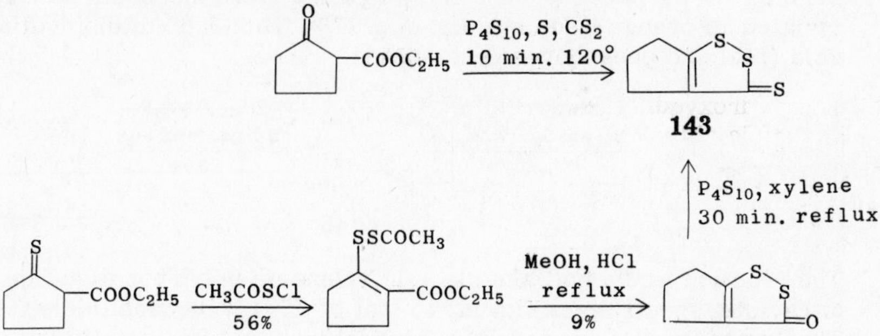

143 has been called 4,5-cyclopentano-1,2-dithiole-3-thione. It could not be obtained from 1-methylcyclopentene and sulfur. Its properties are those expected of a 1,2-dithiole-3-thione.

D. C_3S_2-C_4S_2 1,2-DITHIOLO[4,3-d]-m-DITHIIN (**143b**)

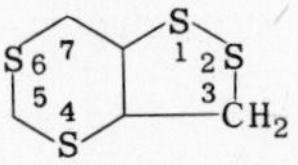

143b

The sole representative of this ring system is 5-methyl-1,2-dithiolo-[4,3-d]-m-dithiin-3(7H)-thione (**143d**), prepared by Lüttringhaus and Prinzbach[353] from ethyl 2-methyl-5-oxo-m-dithiane-4-carboxylate (**143c**) (see Chapter 12, section II A-1a) and phosphorus pentasulfide plus sulfur. The compound was isolated as brown-red crystals melting at 108-109°.

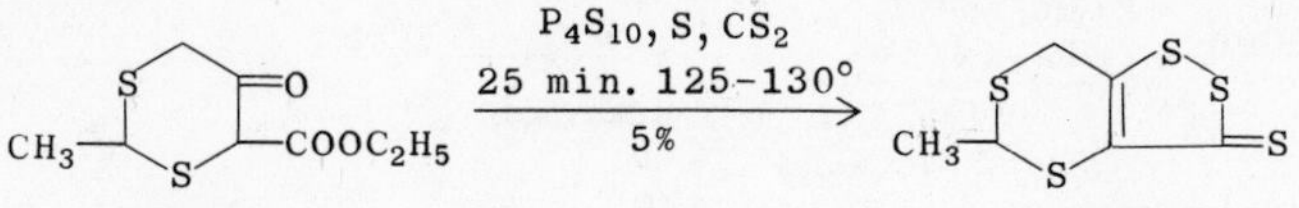

143c   **143d**

E. C_3S_2-C_5N

1. **3H-1,2-Dithiolo[4,3-b]pyridine (144)**

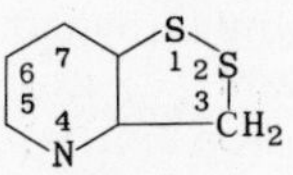

144

(RRI 1241)

[For references, see pp. 585-610.]

This ring system is known only in the form of the 3-thione. It is index-ed in <u>Chemical Abstracts</u> under the above name; an alternative name is 4-aza-3H-1, 2-benzodithiole-3-thione. Lüttringhaus, Cordes, and Schmidt[347] prepared 3H-1, 2-dithiolo[4, 3-b]pyridine-3-thione (**146**), isolated as orange-red crystals, m.p. 178°, from 3, 3′-dithiopicolinic acid (**145**) and phosphorus pentasulfide.

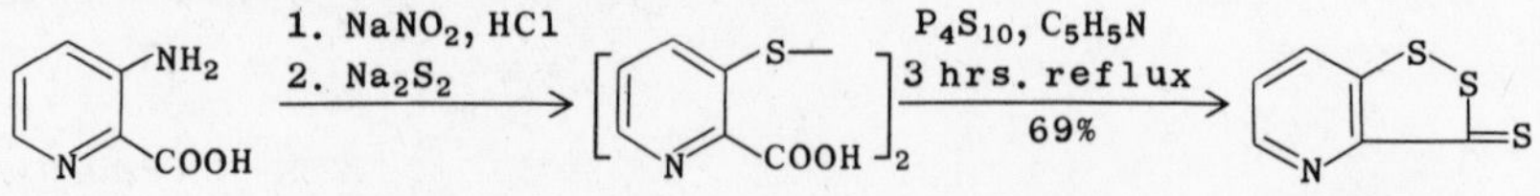

145   **146**

The reaction would not take place in xylene or in carbon disulfide. The ultraviolet spectrum is similar to that of 3H-1, 2-benzodithiole-3-thione. The compound was prepared as a chelating agent for metals, analogous to 8-hydroxyquinoline. It gave 1 : 1 adducts with silver nitrate (red), mercuric chloride (yellow), cadmium chloride (red), lead acetate (brown), and cupric ion (violet-black). No precipitates were formed with chlo-rides of aluminum, zinc, manganese, cobalt, or nickel.

2. 3H-1, 2-Dithiolo[4, 3-c]pyridine (147)

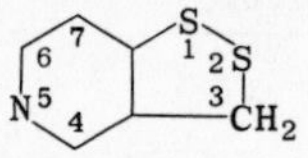

147

(RRI 1242)

This ring system, indexed in <u>Chemical Abstracts</u> under the above name, is also known as 5-aza-3H-1, 2-benzodithiole.

Katz, Schroeder, and Cohen[287,287a] prepared 3H-1, 2-dithiolo[4, 3-c] pyridine-3-thione (**148**) from 4-hydroxynicotinic acid and phosphorus pentasulfide. It was isolated as orange-red crystals, m.p. 206-208°.

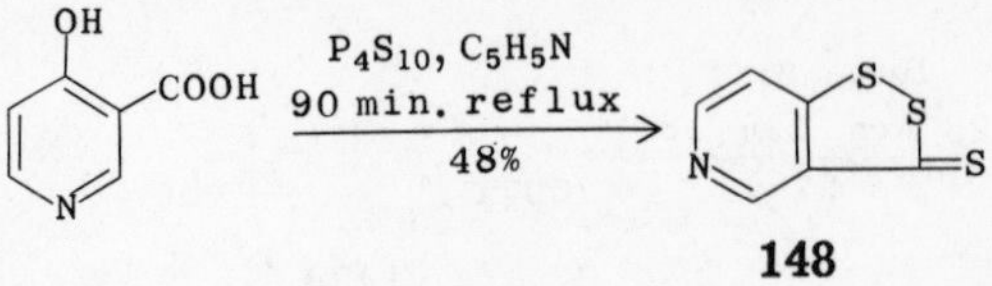

148

The compound is very stable towards hydrolysis; refluxing for sixteen hours with 30% aqueous sodium hydroxide gave a 65% yield of 4-mer-captonicotinic acid.

3. 3H-1, 2-Dithiolo[3, 4-b]pyridine (148a)

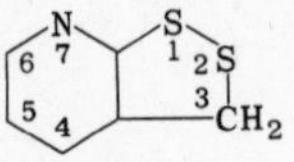

148a

Schmidt and Kubitzek[465f] prepared 4,6-dimethyl-3H-1,2-dithiolo-[3,4-b]pyridine-3-thione (**148b**), red-brown, m.p. 141°, by the following route:

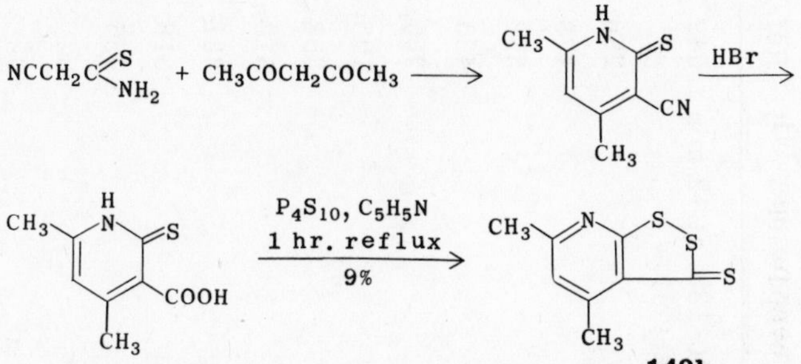

NCCH$_2$C$\langle^S_{NH_2}$ + CH$_3$COCH$_2$COCH$_3$ ⟶

[structure: CH$_3$, H-N, =S, CN, CH$_3$] → HBr →

CH$_3$ [structure H-N, =S, COOH, CH$_3$] → P$_4$S$_{10}$, C$_5$H$_5$N / 1 hr. reflux / 9% → CH$_3$ [structure with N, S-S, =S, CH$_3$]

148b

F. C_3S_2-C_6 3H-1,2-BENZODITHIOLE (149)

[structure 149 with numbering 4,5,6,7,1,2,3 S-S-CH$_2$]

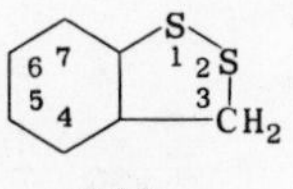

149

(RRI 1243)

A number of compounds containing this ring system are known. At the present time <u>Chemical Abstracts</u> names this class of compounds as shown above. 1,2-Benzodisulfole was used until 1916, and 1,2- or 1,2,3-benzodithiole until 1946. Other names which have been used are 1,2-dithiahydrindane, 2-dithiobenzoyl and benzoylene disulfide for the 3-oxo derivative, and 2,3-dithiosulfindene and 2,3-benzotrithione for the 3-thione derivative. Manessier[365-367] used a different numbering system (**150**).

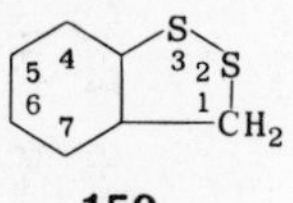

[structure 150 with numbering 4,5,6,7,3,2,1 S-S-CH$_2$]

150

1. Preparation

Table 11 lists the compounds containing this ring system which have been reported in the literature. The parent member of the series, 3H-1,2-benzodithiole (**149**), was prepared by Lüttringhaus and Hägele[349] by oxidizing 2-mercaptomethylthiophenol.

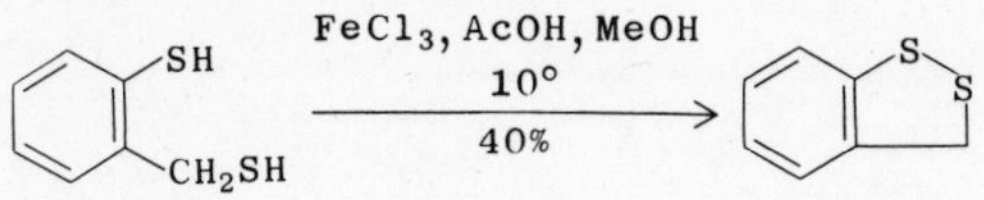

[structure: benzene with SH and CH$_2$SH] → FeCl$_3$, AcOH, MeOH / 10° / 40% → [structure 149]

149

TABLE 11. $3H$-1,2-Benzodithiole Derivatives

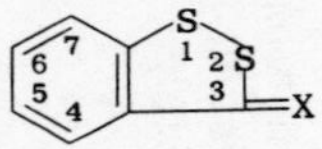

Substitutents	X	Yield (%)	M.p. (°C)	Other properties	Ref.
None	⟨ H / H	40		b.p. 130–133° at 12 mm, orange-yellow	349
	=O		75–76	yellow	256
			77		478
		85	77		358, 362, 497
		95	77	yellow	435
	=S	75	98	red	365, 366
		53	95	orange	195, 314
			94–95	red	358
			93–94		316
			89–90	orange	331
			94	orange	318
		trace	94–95	red	435
	=S · HgCl$_2$	83	225	yellow	62
	=S · CH$_3$I		139–140	wine red	62
	=NCH$_3$		138–139	yellow	358

	Yield	m.p.	Color	Ref.
=NC$_2$H$_5$	98	63–64	colorless	358
=NCH$_2$C$_6$H$_5$		122–123	colorless	358
=NC$_6$H$_5$		77		358
=NOH	84	210 (dec.)	yellow	367
=NOCOC$_6$H$_5$	90	208	yellow	359
		147		367
=NOCH$_3$		55	yellow	359
=NCH$_2$CH$_2$OH	60	107	yellow	359
=NCH$_2$CH$_2$OCOCH$_3$		64.5	yellow	359
=NNH$_2$		125	orange	359
=NNHCO$_2$C$_2$H$_5$		96	orange	359
=NNHCO$_2$-iso-C$_5$H$_{11}$		105	yellow	359
=NNHC$_6$H$_5$		106	brown	359
NHNHCONH$_2$ / SH		205–212		359
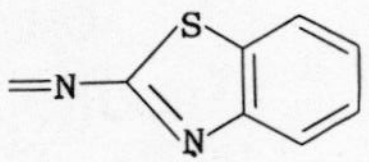 (benzothiazolylidene structure)	61	213	yellow	350, 352
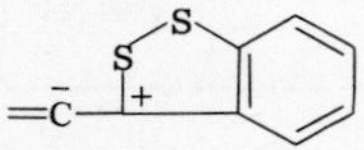 (structure)		228	deep violet	465d

425

TABLE 11. $3H$-1, 2-Benzodithiole Derivatives (contd).

Substituents	X	Yield (%)	M.p. (°C)	Other properties	Ref.
Dioxide	=NOH		177		359
Dioxide	=NOCH$_3$		135	white	359
5-CH$_3$-	=O	88	77	yellow	435
5-CH$_3$-	=S	72	95	orange	435
7-CH$_3$-	=S	44	107	yellow-orange	320
4-CH$_3$-7-(CH$_3$)$_2$CH-	=S	8	74	red-orange	320
5, 7-Cl$_2$	=O	76	114	pale yellow	435
5, 7-Cl$_2$	=S	80	174	red	435
4, 5, 6, 7-H$_4$	=O	30		b.p. 109° at 0.5 mm n_D^{23} 1. 628 yellow	435
4, 5, 6, 7-H$_4$	=S	20	102	orange	314, 465b, 568
			92	orange	21U, 332
			99	yellow	316
		5	102		320
		75	102	yellow-orange	435

3H-1, 2-Benzodithiol-3-one (**151**) was prepared by Smiles and McClelland[497] from 2-thiobenzoic acid or 2, 2$'$-dithiobenzoic acid and a disulfide or mercaptan in concentrated sulfuric acid. By adding a mixture of 2-thiobenzoic acid and thioacetic acid to concentrated sulfuric acid McClelland, Warren, and Jackson[358] obtained the compound in 85% yield.

$$\text{(benzene-SH, COOH)} + CH_3COSH \xrightarrow[85\%]{H_2SO_4} \text{(benzo-S-S ring, =O)}$$

151

The reaction also succeeded with dithioglycollic acid, hydrogen sulfide, phthalyl sulfide,[497] and ethyl mercaptan.[362] Smiles and McClelland[497] formulated the reaction as proceeding *via* the formation of the mixed disulfide (**152**), which they isolated in one case.

$$\left[\text{(benzene-S-, COOH)}\right]_2 + \begin{array}{c} SCH_2COOH \\ | \\ SCH_2COOH \end{array} \xrightarrow[30 \text{ min. } 45°]{H_2SO_4} \text{(benzene-SSCH}_2\text{COOH, COOH)}$$

152

$$\xrightarrow[2 \text{ hrs. } 50-60°]{H_2SO_4} \text{(benzo-S-S ring, =O)}$$

The formation of the mixed disulfide was postulated to take place *via* the intermediate sulfenic acid.

$$RSSR + H_2O \underset{}{\overset{H_2SO_4}{\rightleftharpoons}} RSOH + RSH$$
$$\Big\updownarrow R'SH$$
$$RSSR' + H_2O$$

Prior to this work Hinsberg[256] had heated 2, 2$'$-dithiobenzoic acid and had isolated a compound to which he assigned an unlikely structure (**153**).

$$\left[\text{(benzene-S-, COOH)}\right]_2 \xrightarrow{280°} \text{(structure 153)}$$

153

Schönberg and Mustafa[478] showed that this compound was actually 3H-1, 2-benzodithiol-3-one, identical in all respects with that prepared by Smiles and McClelland.

Raoul and Vialle[435] prepared 3H-1, 2-benzodithiol-3-one by condensing methyl thiosalicylate with acetylsulfenyl chloride followed by ring closure with hydrogen chloride. The synthesis is analogous to that used in the preparation of 1, 2-dithiol-3-ones (see section I A-2a-(1)(j)).

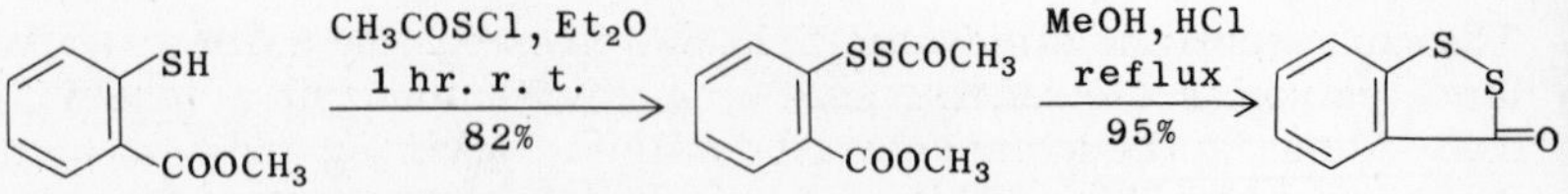

Chapter 5

The synthesis was also applied to the preparation of several substituted compounds by starting with substituted thiosalicylates.

A variety of methods have been used to prepare $3H$-1,2-benzodithiole-3-thiones. The parent compound (154) was first prepared by Mannessier[365,366] from saccharin and phosphorus pentasulfide.

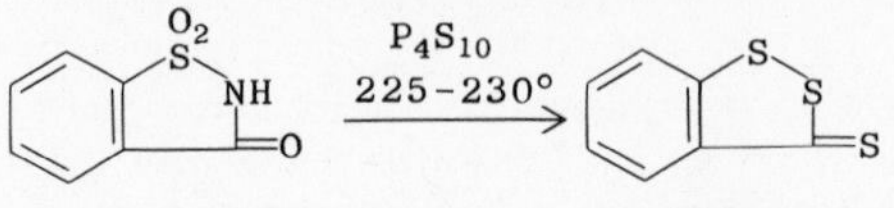

154

The sodium salt of saccharin gave the same reaction, as did thiosaccharin, formed by heating saccharin with phosphorus pentasulfide under milder conditions. As mentioned previously, $3H$-1,2-benzodithiole-3-thione was the first 1,2-dithiole-3-thione reported in the literature, and comparison with it led to the elucidation of the structure of the "trithiones". Mannessier assigned this formula to her compound because it gave an oxime with hydroxylamine, underwent alkaline hydrolysis to 2,2'-dithiobenzoic acid and hydrogen sulfide, and yielded 2,2'-dithiobenzoic acid almost quantitatively on treatment with sodium. $3H$-1,2-Benzodithiole was said to be formed as a by-product of the last reaction, but this claim is doubtful.

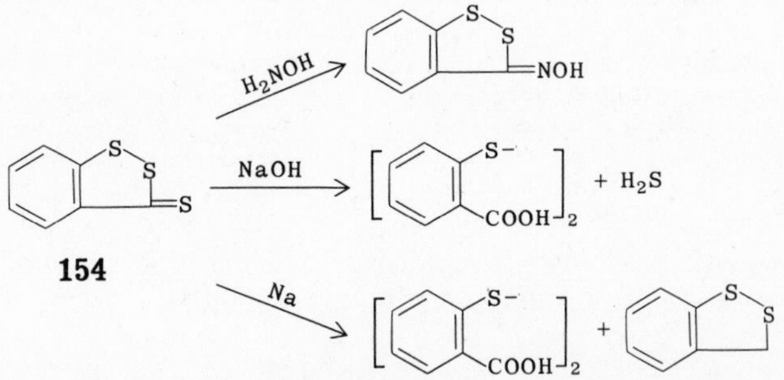

Mannessier made no mention of the yield of $3H$-1,2-benzodithiole-3-thione obtained from saccharin and phosphorus pentasulfide. Legrand, Mollier, and Lozac'h[314] repeated the preparation and reported the yield to be poor. These same authors found that the reaction of sodiosaccharin with phosphorus pentasulfide took place at 140-160° but the yield was not reported. Probably the best synthesis involves the reaction of 2,2'-dithiobenzoic acid with phosphorus pentasulfide.[195,314]

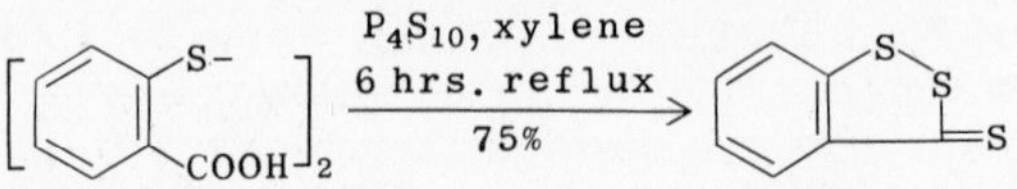

154

428

The corresponding amide and anilide underwent the same reaction in unstated yields.[358] An interesting modification of this synthesis was carried out by the same authors, McClelland, Warren, and Jackson.[358] They found that 2, 2'-dithiobenzonitrile and hydrogen sulfide at 0° gave a 53% yield of 3H-1, 2-benzodithiole-3-thione. These authors also reported that the reaction of 3H-1, 2-benzodithiol-3-one with phosphorus pentasulfide was superior to Mannessier's synthesis of the 3-thione.

Legrand[316] reported that 3H-1, 2-benzodithiole-3-thione (154) could be prepared from ethyl salicylate and phosphorus pentasulfide in refluxing tetralin. If ethyl salicylate is considered to be a β-keto ester in its enolic form, the reaction is reminiscent of the formation of uncondensed 1, 2-dithiole-3-thiones described in section I A-2a-(1)(h). Other syntheses of 1, 2-dithiole-3-thiones have been applied to the preparation of 3H-1, 2-benzodithiole-3-thione (154). Thus, Lozac'h and co-workers[318] isolated it in low yield from the reaction of 2-methylcylohexanone, sulfur, and phosphorus pentasulfide. Similarly, 1-methylcyclohexene plus sulfur yielded the same product.[314,331]

154

Inasmuch as the reaction cannot be carried out with toluene, the tetrahydro compound must have been an intermediate. This compound, 4, 5, 6, 7-tetrahydro-3H-1, 2-benzodithiole-3-thione (155), was prepared by reacting phosphorus pentasulfide with 2-carbethoxycyclohexanone[210,314,332] or with 2-formycyclohexanone.[316] Schmidt, Lüttringhaus, and Trefzger[465b,568] reported a 20% yield from the β-keto ester, phosphorus pentasulfide, and sulfur in carbon disulfide. 155 was also prepared from the thione ester by Raoul and Vialle[435] (see section I A-2a-(1)(j)).

155

Although Legrand[320] found that phosphorus pentasulfide plus sulfur reacted with 2-formylcyclohexanone at 210° in biphenyl to form 155, 2-formyl-6-methylcyclohexanone and formylmenthone reacted under these conditions to give the dehydrogenated products, 7-methyl-3H-1, 2-benzodithiole-3-thione (155a) and 4-methyl-7-isopropyl-3H-1, 2-benzodithiole-3-thione (155b).

155a

[For references, see pp. 585-610.]

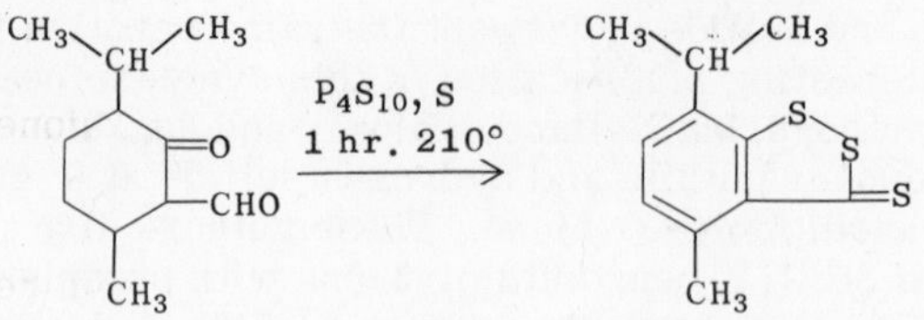

155b

2. Properties and Reactions

In most respects these compounds are very similar to their noncondensed analogs. Thus, the parent compound, 3H-1, 2-benzodithiole (**149**), can be distilled *in vacuo*. It polymerizes readily, however, and is only slightly more stable than 1, 2-dithiolane.[349] The compounds are generally yellow or some shade of red. Lüttringhaus and Cleve[342] found the ultraviolet spectrum of 3H-1, 2-benzodithiole-3-thione (**154**) to be very similar to those of other 1, 2-dithiole-3-thiones. Mecke, Mecke, and Lüttringhaus[376] determined the infrared spectra of 3H-1, 2-benzodithiol-3-one and 3-thione. Lüttringhaus and Grohmann[345] found, in agreement with the results for simple 1, 2-dithiol-3-ones and 3-thiones, that the 3-thione has a higher dipole moment than the 3-one and is more intensely colored. Further similarities of 3H-1, 2-benzodithiole-3-thione are the formation of a yellow oxime,[367] a yellow mercuric chloride adduct,[62] and a red methiodide.[62] The methiodide can be written in a number of resonance forms, similar to those postulated for the 1, 2-dithiole-3-thiones. However, Schmidt[465d] has suggested that an open-chain polar ground state (**156**) must also contribute to the structure, and it is interesting to consider if structures such as **156a** should be considered as well.

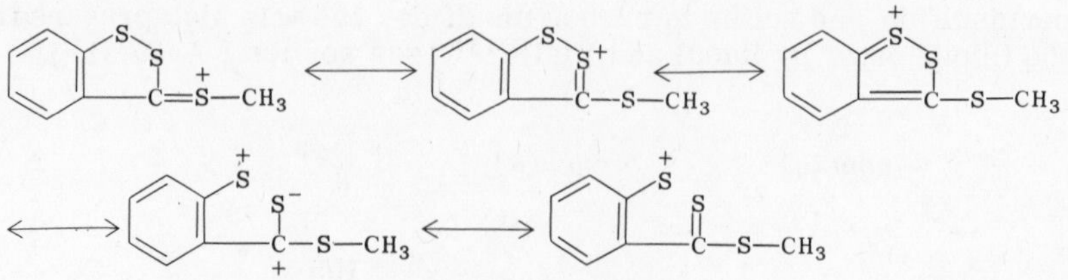

156 **156a**

The 3-thione methosulfate (**157**) was condensed with 2-aminobenzothiazole to yield the corresponding imine, 3-(2-benzothiazolyl)imino-3H-1, 2-benzodithiole (**157a**), reported to have activity as a choleretic and tuberculostatic agent.[350]

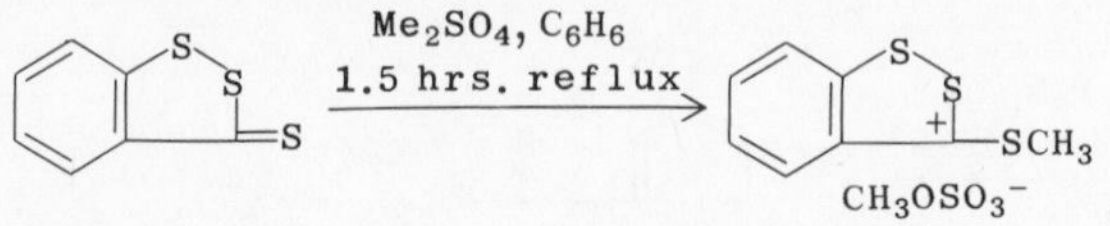

154 **157**

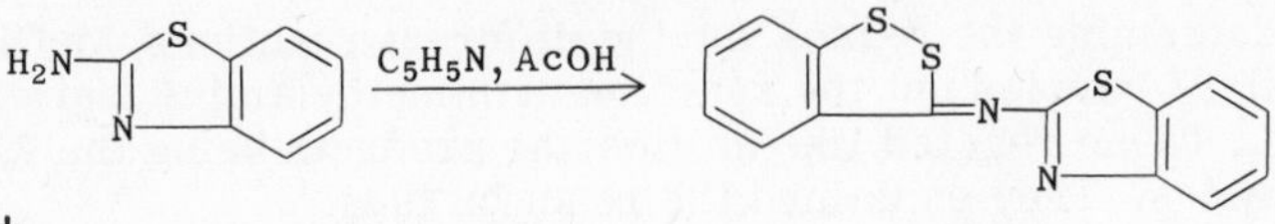

157+　　　　　　　　　　　　　　　　　**157a**

Lüttringhaus and Hägele[349] reduced 3*H*-1, 2-benzodithiole-3-thione · (**154**) to 2-mercaptomethylthiophenol.

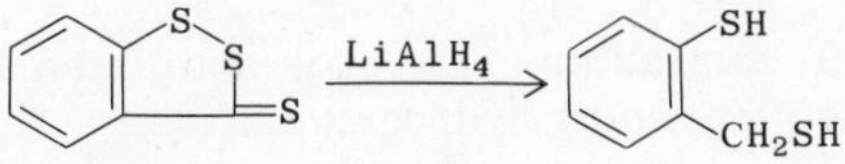

154

The reactions of 3*H*-1, 2-benzodithiol-3-one (**151**) differ considerably from those of the uncondensed compounds. Thus, Smiles and McClelland[497] found that the compound could be cleaved with sodium sulfide, presumably to a disulfido acid, and regenerated with acid. Sodium ethoxide gave 2, 2′-dithiobenzoic acid,[362] zinc and acetic acid gave o-thiobenzoic acid, and aniline gave 2, 2′-dithiobenzanilide.

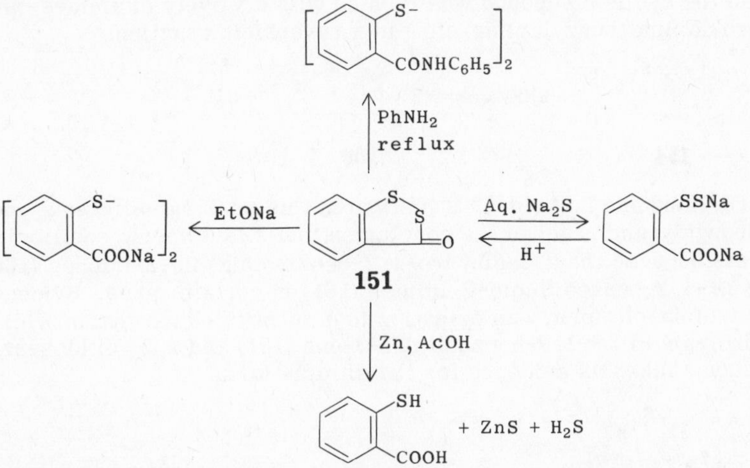

151

McClelland and co-workers investigated these reactions more thoroughly. Thus, McKibben and McClelland[362] found that, in contrast to aniline, *N*-methylaniline, pyridine, and quinoline gave no reaction, whereas ammonia reacted differently, the product being 1, 2-benzoisothiazolone (**158**), identified by oxidation to saccharin.

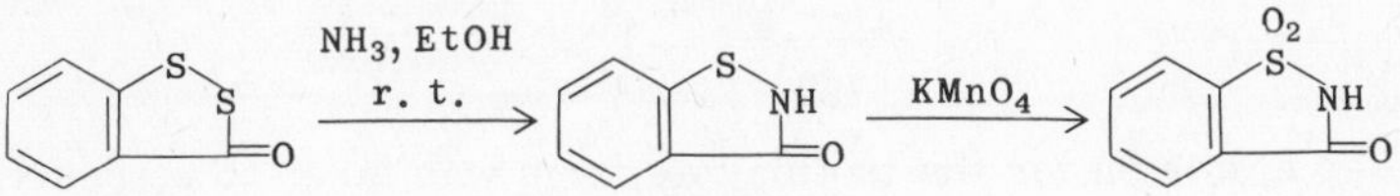

151　　　　　　　　**158**

[For references, see pp. 585-610.]　　　　　　　　　　431

Chapter 5

In order to determine the reason for the different reactions, McClelland and Longwell[357] carried out the reaction with methylamine and with propylamine. These reacted like aniline, the products being the 2, 2'-dithiobenzamides. They explained the reaction thus:

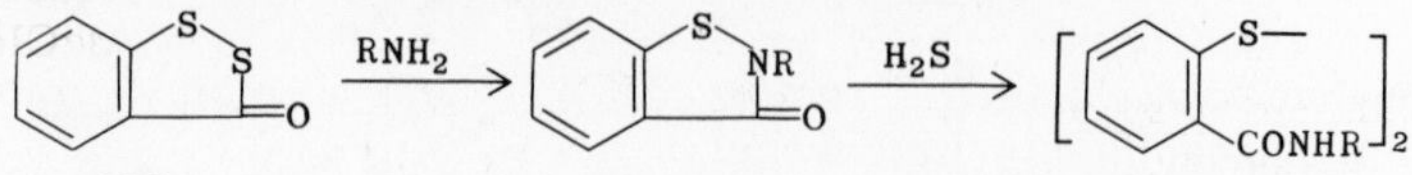

151

Since the ammonia product (**159**) can tautomerize, it is stabilized, and the aromatic ring formed is not cleaved by hydrogen sulfide.

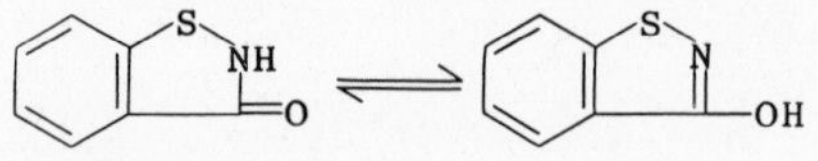

159

This does not explain why the use of aqueous instead of alcoholic ammonia led to the formation of 2, 2'-dithiobenzamide.

3H-1, 2-Benzodithiole-3-thione (**154**) reacted differently.[358] In this case the cyclic compound was formed with a variety of amines—aniline, methylamine, benzylamine, etc.—in a reversible reaction.

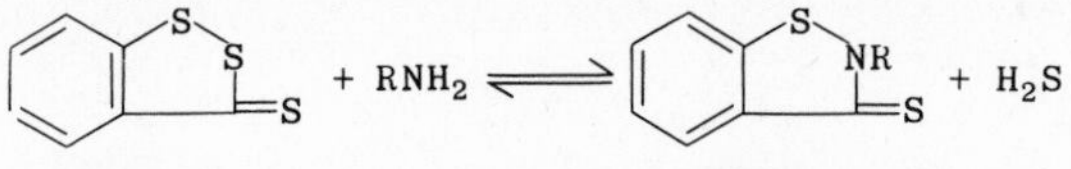

154   **160**

McClelland and Salkeld[359] investigated this puzzling difference more thoroughly, and reached the conclusion that a tautomeric equilibrium exists between the 2, 3-dihydro-1, 2-benzisothiazole-3-thiones (**160**) and the 3H-1, 2-benzodithiole-3-imines (**161**) in certain cases. Evidence for the isothiazole form was oxidation to a substituted saccharin, while hydrolysis to 3H-1, 2-benzodithiol-3-one (**151**) and 2, 2'-dithiobenzoic acid was taken as evidence for the dithiole form.

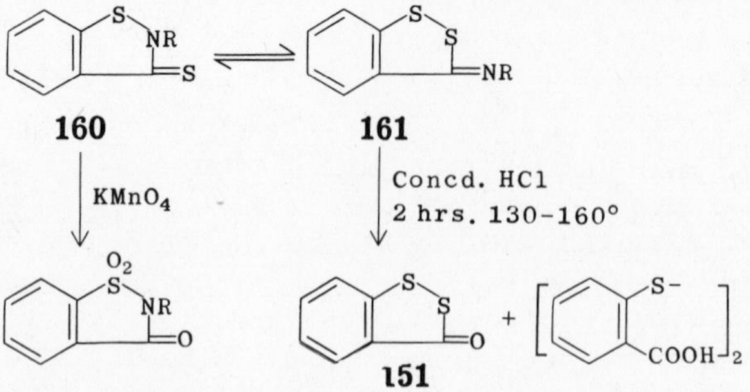

160   **161**

KMnO$_4$

Concd. HCl
2 hrs. 130–160°

O$_2$

151

A further criterion for the isothiazole form was taken to be reaction with hydrogen sulfide to form 3H-1, 2-benzodithiole-3-thione (**154**), but

432

this is a shaky assumption; it appears just as reasonable to assume that the imino form reacts with hydrogen sulfide to displace the amine as to assume a ring opening and closing. McClelland and Salkeld prepared a number of derivatives to test this equilibrium hypothesis; they are shown in the following chart and listed in Table 11.

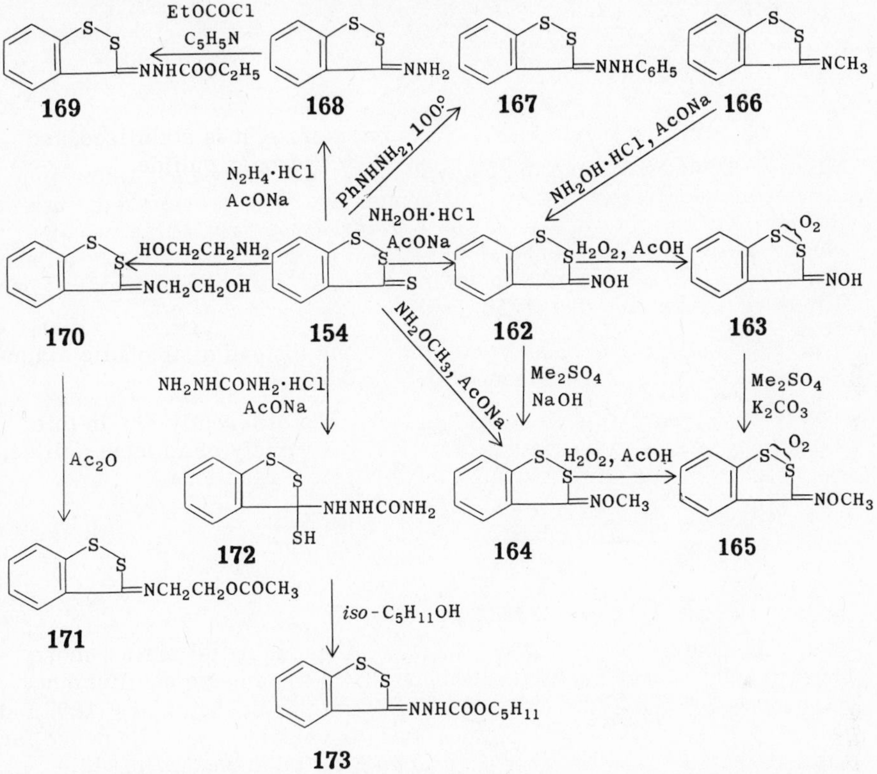

EtOCOCl
C$_5$H$_5$N

169 =NNHCOOC$_2$H$_5$

168 =NNH$_2$

167 =NNHC$_6$H$_5$

166 =NCH$_3$

N$_2$H$_4$·HCl
AcONa

PhNHNH$_2$, 100°

NH$_2$OH·HCl, AcONa

NH$_2$OH·HCl
AcONa

170 HOCH$_2$CH$_2$NH$_2$ =NCH$_2$CH$_2$OH

154 =S

162 =NOH

163 O$_2$ =NOH

H$_2$O$_2$, AcOH

NH$_2$NHCONH$_2$·HCl
AcONa

NH$_2$OCH$_3$, AcONa

Me$_2$SO$_4$
NaOH

Me$_2$SO$_4$
K$_2$CO$_3$

Ac$_2$O

172 SH =NHNHCONH$_2$

164 =NOCH$_3$ H$_2$O$_2$, AcOH

165 O$_2$ =NOCH$_3$

171 =NCH$_2$CH$_2$OCOCH$_3$

iso-C$_5$H$_{11}$OH

173 =NNHCOOC$_5$H$_{11}$

From a preparative point of view it is surprising that a hydrazone and phenylhydrazone could be prepared but not a semicarbazone. The nature of the compounds depended on the group R attached to nitrogen. Only when R was alkyl or aryl (161, R = CH$_3$) was there definite evidence for the existence of two forms; oxidation gave substituted saccharins, hydrolysis gave 3H-1, 2-benzodithiol-3-one and 2, 2'-dithiobenzoic acid (as did all the compounds except 163 and 165, which gave only the acid), and hydrogen sulfide gave the 3-thione (154). The oxime derivatives (162 and 164) showed no evidence for the existence of two forms; oxidation gave a sulfone instead of a saccharin, hydrolysis gave the expected ketone and acid, and the compounds did not react with hydrogen sulfide. The phenylhydrazone (167) and the two related compounds (169 and 173) reacted similarly, except that the sulfone could not be isolated. Surprisingly, the hydrazone (168) and the imine (170) did react with hydrogen sulfide to regenerate 154, and therefore might be considered to be in equilibrium with the isothiazole form.

[For references, see pp. 585-610.]

Schmidt[465d] has suggested a reasonable explanation for these results, based on the assumption that open-chain polar ground states contribute to the structure of 3H-1, 2-benzodithiole-3-thione.

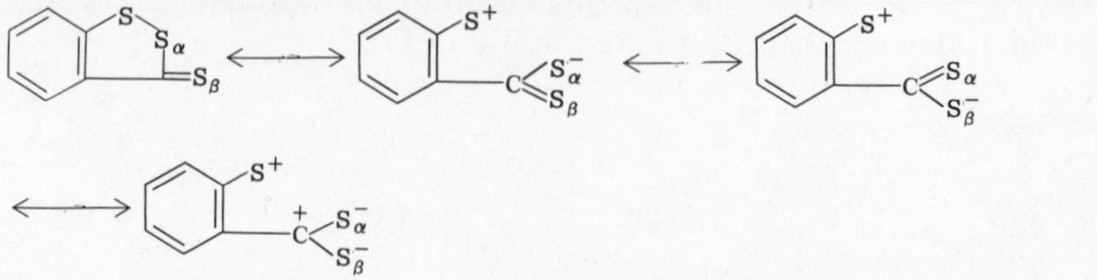

Although S_α and S_β cannot be equivalent in these resonance forms, they can become equivalent if they are formed as actual intermediates in a reaction, and Schmidt has used this explanation to rationalize two unusual reactions of 3H-1, 2-benzodithiole-3-methylthionium methosulfate (157). Thus, 157 reacts with malonic acid in a "normal" manner to form a deep violet methine dye (173b).

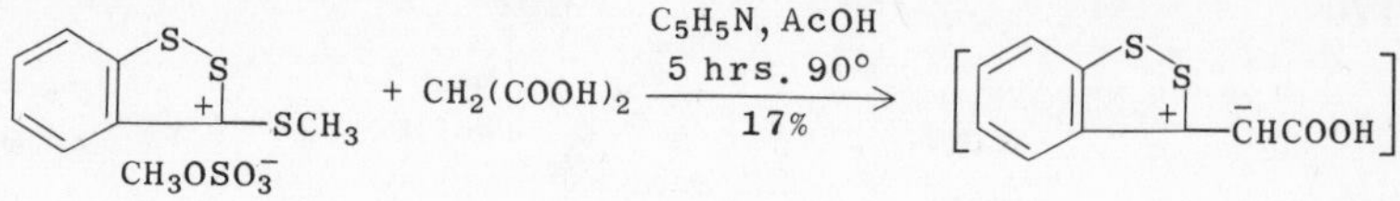

157

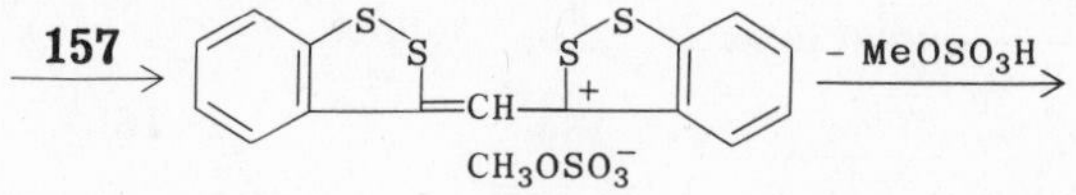

173a

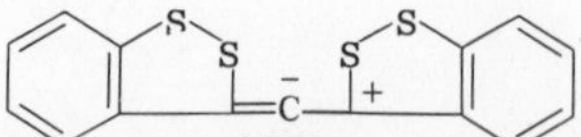

173b

As in similar systems, the red dye-salt (173a) is unstable in neutral media and eliminates acid to give the betaine (173b). Treatment of the betaine with strong acid regenerates the dye-salt. 157 reacts with acetonedicarboxylic acid in an "abnormal" fashion to yield thiapyrano [3, 2-b:5, 6-b']bis(benzothiophene)-6-one (173c).

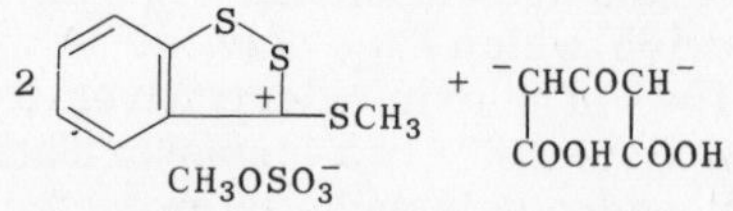

157

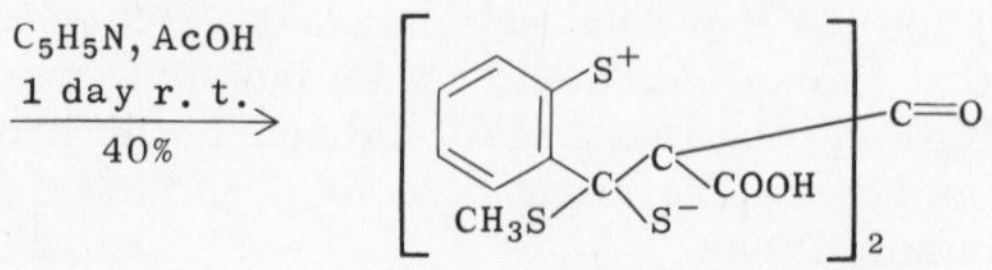

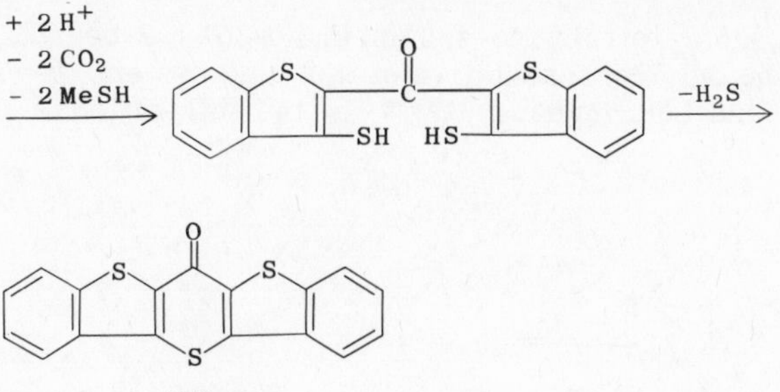

173c

The structure of **173c** was not proved rigorously, but was assigned on the basis of a number of reactions typical of thiapyrones.

Schmidt explained these reactions in the following manner, as illustrated with a carbanion (R = COOH), but the same explanation could be used with amines to explain McClelland's results.

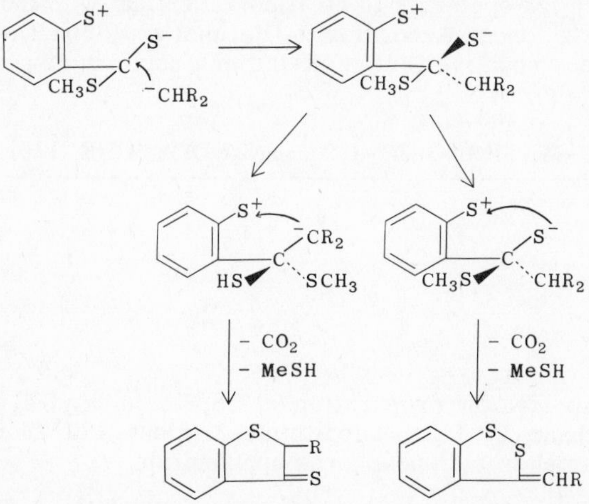

Almost no uses for derivatives of 3H-1, 2-benzodithiole are known. A few derivatives have been reported to have some pharmacological activity,[350] but apparently less than that of 1, 2-dithiole derivatives. 3H-1, 2-Benzodithiole-3-thione has been investigated as a corrosion inhibitor in the acid pickling of iron.[286a]

G. C$_4$-C$_3$S$_2$-C$_6$ 4, 6-METHANO-3H-1, 2-BENZODITHIOLE (**174**)

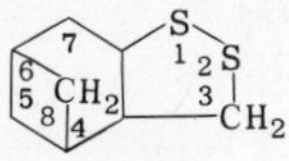

174

(RRI 2158)

[For references, see pp. 585-610.]

8, 8-Dimethyl-4, 5, 6, 7-tetrahydro-4, 6-methano-3H-1, 2-benzodithiole-3-thione (**175**) is the only representative of this ring system. It was prepared by Böttcher and Lüttringhaus[62,66,69] by the sulfuration of α-pinene.

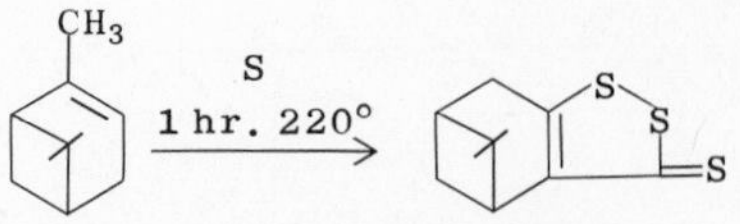

175

The compound, isolated as orange-brown crystals, m.p. 106°, was still optically active, $[\alpha]_D^{25} - 12°$, showing that its asymmetric carbons had not been affected by the reaction. Its reactions were those expected of a 1, 2-dithiole-3-thione; it gave a yellow methiodide, m.p. 141-142° (dec.), and an orange-yellow oxime, m.p. 123°. Lüttringhaus and Cleve [342] found its ultraviolet absorption spectrum to be almost identical with those of other 1, 2-dithiole-3-thiones. According to Djerassi and Lüttringhaus, [156c] it gives four negative Cotton effects in a rotatory dispersion study.

H. C_3S_2-C_5-C_5 4, 7-METHANO-3H-1, 2-BENZODITHIOLE (**176**)

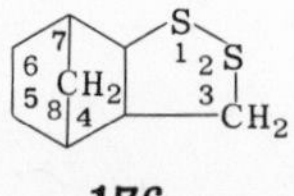

176

Legrand [316,320] reported the preparation of 7, 8, 8-trimethyl-4, 5, 6, 7-tetrahydro-4, 7-methano-3H-1, 2-benzodithiole-3-thione (**177**) from hydroxymethylenecamphor and phosphorus pentasulfide.

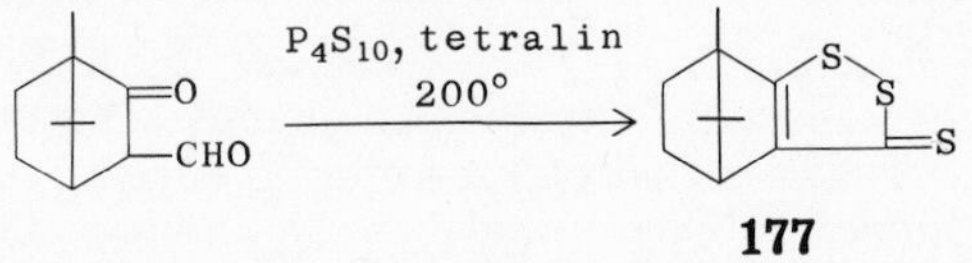

177

The compound from a-camphor melted at 170°, while that from dl-camphor melted at 114°. In a later publication,[320] however, he stated that the product from dl-camphor melts at 170°.

Schmidt, Lüttringhaus, and Trefzger[465b] prepared **177** from camphor-carboxylic ester, phosphorus pentasulfide, and sulfur in carbon disulfide, in 32% yield, and reported a melting point of 173-174. 5°. Djerassi and Lüttringhaus[156c] reported a melting point of 177-178°. In contrast to the α-pinene derivative (see section I G), **177** showed four positive Cotton effects.

I. C$_3$S$_2$-C$_6$-C$_6$

1. 3*H*-Naphtho[2, 3-*c*]-1, 2-dithiole (178)

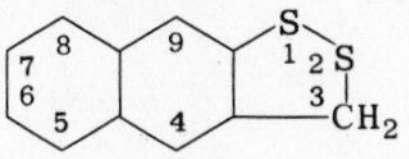

178

(RRI 2833)

Legrand, Mollier, and Lozac'h[314] prepared 3*H*-naphtho[2, 3-*c*]-1, 2-dithiole-3-thione (**179**) by treatment of 3, 3'-dithio-2, 2'-naphthoic acid with phosphorus pentasulfide. The compound formed red crystals, m.p. 144°, and gave a colorless oxime, m.p. 232°.

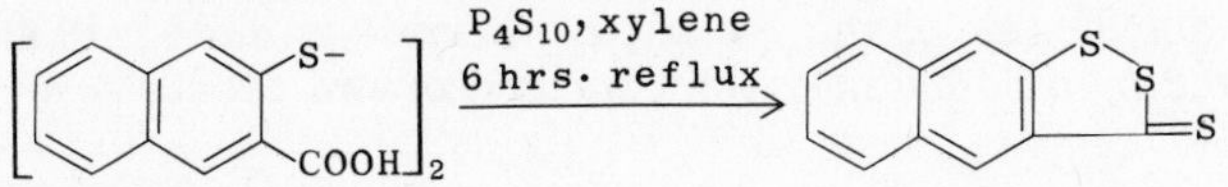

179

2. 3*H*-Naphtho[1, 2-*c*]-1, 2-dithiole (180)

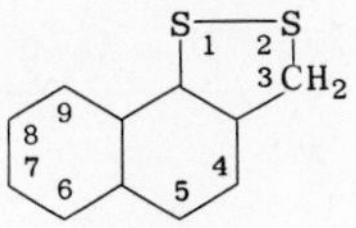

180

(RRI 2835)

Legrand,[320] and Legrand, Mollier, and Lozac'h[314] prepared 3*H*-naphtho[1, 2-*c*]-1, 2-dithiole-3-thione (**181**) by three routes, the reaction of 6, 7-benzosaccharin with phosphorus pentasulfide, the sulfurization of 2-methyl-3, 4-dihydronaphthalene, and the reaction of 2-formyl-1-tetralone with phosphorus pentasulfide and sulfur. It was isolated as yellow-orange crystals, m.p. 170°, and it formed a colorless oxime, m.p. 227-228°.

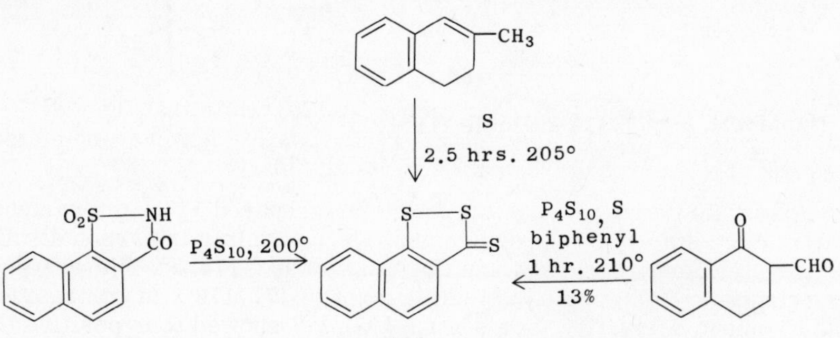

181

[For references, see pp. 585-610.]

Lüttringhaus, Trefzger, and Schmidt[346,465b] prepared a number of 4,5-dihydro derivatives. Thus, 2-carbethoxytetralone with phosphorus pentasulfide and sulfur gave 4,5-dihydro-3H-naphtho[1,2-c]-1,2-dithiole-3-thione (**182**), isolated as red crystals, m.p. 87-88°.

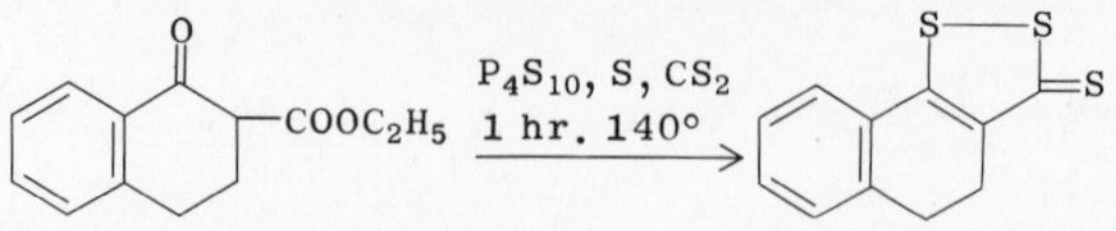

182

Under these milder conditions the ring was not aromatized. Similarly, 2-carbomethoxy-6-methoxytetralone gave the 7-methoxy derivative in 22% yield as an orange-yellow compound, m.p. 151°. Heating this with pyridine hydrochloride gave the 7-hydroxy derivative in 79% yield, which was purified by conversion to the 7-acetoxy derivative (dark red, m.p. 165-166°) followed by acid hydrolysis; it formed brown crystals, m.p. 212-213°.

3. 1H-Naphtho[2,1-c] [1,2]dithiole (183)

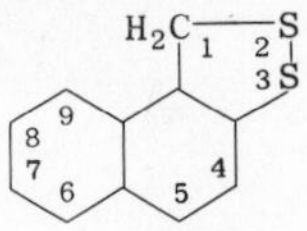

183

(RRI 2836)

Legrand, Mollier, and Lozac'h[314] prepared 1H-naphtho[2,1-c]-[1,2] dithiole-1-thione (**184**) by heating 1-methyl-3,4-dihydronaphthalene with sulfur, while Legrand[320] prepared it by heating 1-formyl-2-tetralone with phosphorus pentasulfide and sulfur. It was isolated as red crystals, m.p. 148-149°, and it formed a yellow oxime, m.p. 161°.

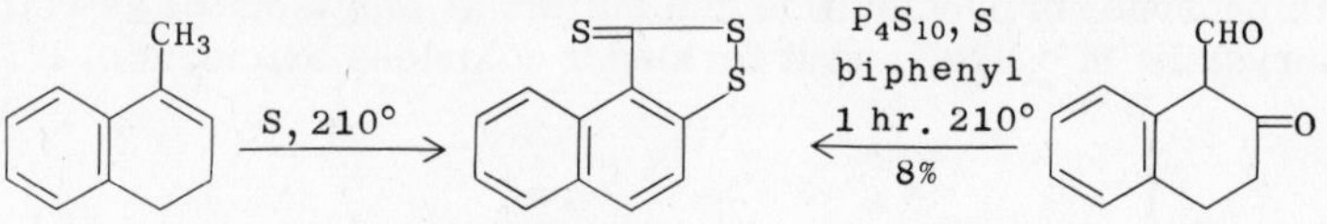

184

4. Naphtho[1,8-cd]-1,2-dithiole (185)

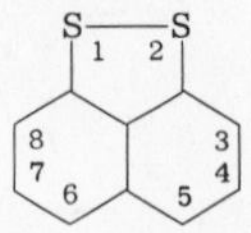

185

(RRI 2837)

Price and Smiles[422] prepared naphtho[1, 8-*cd*]-1, 2-dithiole (**185**) by the oxidation of 1, 8-dimercaptonaphthalene, which they synthesized from 8-aminonaphthalenesulfonic acid. It was obtained as orange crystals, m.p. 116°.

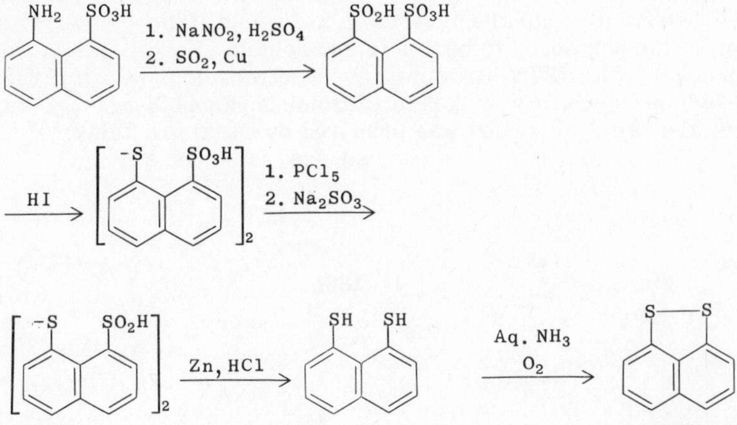

185

The compound has been called *peri*-naphthodithiole and 1, 8-naphthylene disulfide. Treatment with zinc and hydrochloric acid converted it back to 1, 8-dimercaptonaphthalene, while reduction with sodium in liquid ammonia followed by reaction with methyl iodide gave the corresponding dimethyl compound, 1, 8-bis(methylthio)naphthalene.

Actually, naphtho[1, 8-*cd*]-1, 2-dithiole (**185**) had been prepared by Lanfry[312d] in 1911 by passage of naphthalene and sulfur through a red-hot iron tube, although the author assigned an incorrect structure. In 1960 Vorozhtsov and Rodinov[554a] showed it to be identical with the Price and Smiles compound. Both Lanfry and the Russian workers reported a melting point of 118-119°; the yield is very low. Desai and Tilak[147a] reported a black picrate, m.p. 195°.

Marschalk and co-workers[355,412] determined the dipole moment of **185** (1. 49D) and measured its magnetic susceptibility. The low dipole moment was attributed to an atomic moment of hybridization on the sulfur atoms and a large moment of resonance.

Recently Thelin[535b] reported the formation of 3, 4, 5, 6, 7, 8-hexachloronaphtho[1, 8-*cd*]-1, 2-dithiole (**185a**), m.p. 275-277°, from octachloronaphthalene and sodium disulfide.

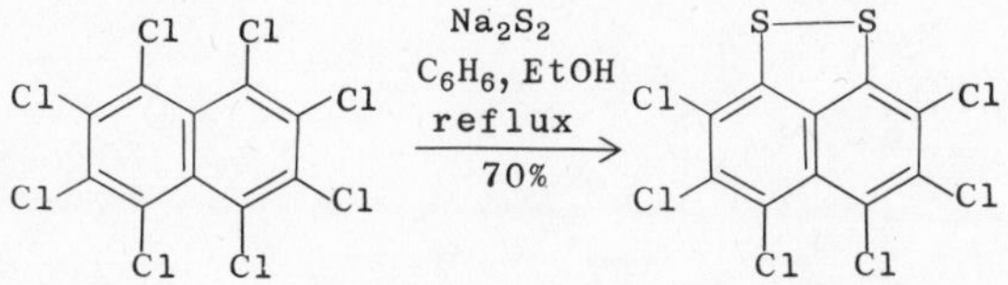

185a

Lanfry[312d] carried out several reactions on naphtho[1, 8-*cd*]-1, 2-
dithiole. Hydrogen peroxide yielded a dioxide, melting at about 130°,
perhaps naphtho[1, 8-*cd*]-1, 2-dithiole 1, 1-dioxide (**185b**). Cold nitric
acid yielded a tetranitro compound, melting above 300°. If the assigned
formula is correct, $C_{10}H_2N_4O_8S_2$, the compound would be expected to be
3, 5, 6, 8-tetranitronaphtho[1, 8-*cd*]-1, 2-dithiole (**185c**). However, Lanfry
reported the compound to be acidic and soluble in alkali, which would not
be in accord with **185c**. Bromine gave a tetrabromide, $C_{10}H_2Br_4S_2$, m.p.
247-248°, presumably 3, 5, 6, 8-tetrabromonapntho[1, 8-*cd*]-1, 2-dithiole
(**185d**); the same compound was prepared by Desai and Tilak.[147a]

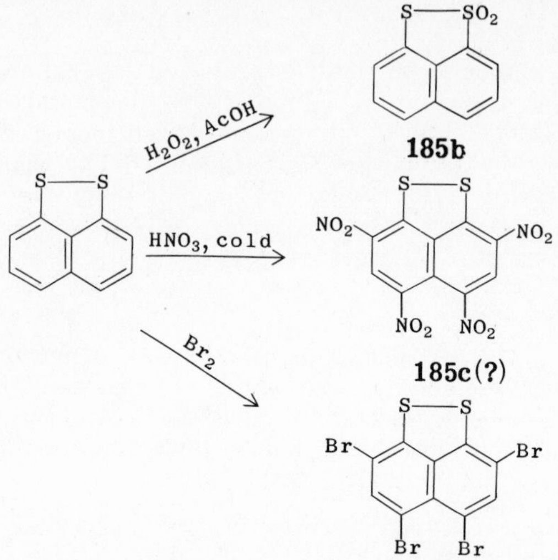

185b

185c(?)

185d

J. C_3S_2-C_5-C_6-C_6 9*H*-ACENAPHTHO[1, 2-*c*][1, 2]DITHIOLE (**186**)

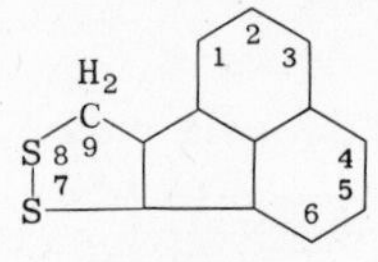

186
(RRI 4220)

Lozac'h and Mollier[330] prepared 9*H*-acenaphtho[1, 2-*c*][1, 2]dithiole-
9-thione (**187**), m.p. 205-206°, by reacting 1-methylacenaphthene with
sulfur.

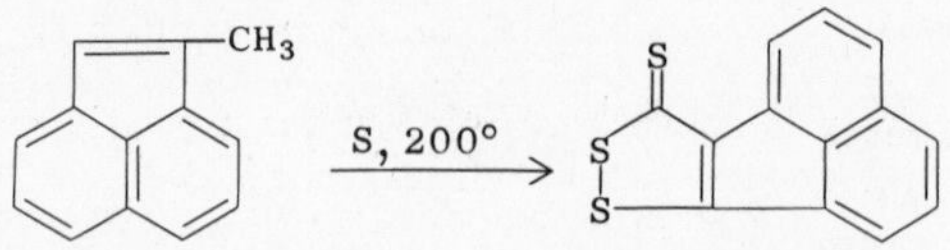

187

Gaudin[209] patented the compound for its choleretic and diuretic action.

K.   C$_3$S$_2$-C$_6$-C$_6$-C$_6$ 1H-PHENANTHRO[1, 2-c][1, 2]DITHIOLE (188)

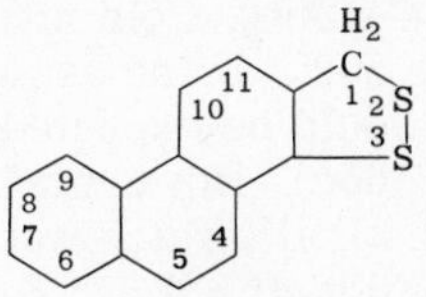

188

(RRI 4480)

Lüttringhaus, Trefzger, and Schmidt[346,465b] prepared several compounds containing this ring system. 10, 11-Dihydro-1H-phenanthro-[1, 2-c][1, 2]-dithiole-1-thione (**190**, R = H) was prepared from 1-oxo-2-carbethoxy-1, 2, 3, 4-tetrahydrophenanthrene (**189**, R = H) by reacting it with phosphorus pentasulfide and sulfur; it was isolated as violet-red crystals, m.p. 185°.

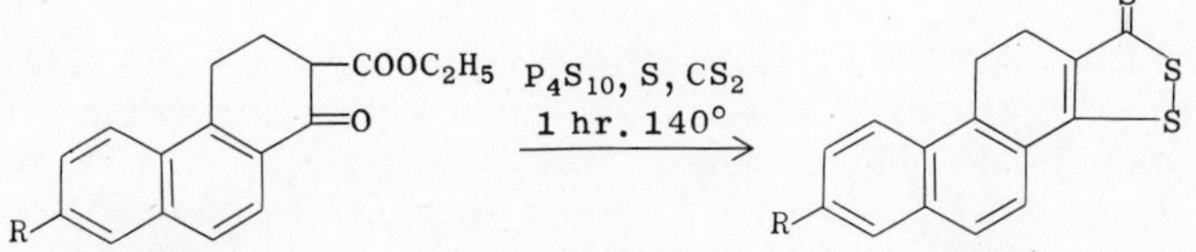

189   **190**

The 7-methoxy derivative (**190**, R = CH$_3$O) was prepared in a similar manner in 53% yield and was isolated as red-brown crystals, m.p. 203°. Demethylation with pyridine hydrochloride gave a 90% yield of the red-brown 7-hydroxy derivative (**190**, R = OH), m.p. 253-255°, which was converted with acetic anhydride to the dark red 7-acetoxy derivative (**190**, R = CH$_3$COO), m.p. 248-259°.

L.   C$_3$S$_2$-C$_3$ON-C$_4$N-C$_4$N$_2$-C$_6$ GLIOTOXIN (191)

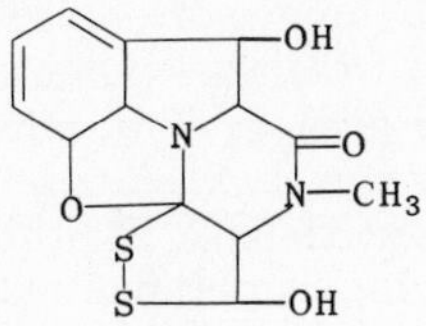

191

Gliotoxin is an antibiotic which has been isolated from a number of molds. Its structure has been studied over a number of years by Johnson and his co-workers at Cornell University,[281] who arrived at **191** as the structure of gliotoxin. More recently, however, Bell, Johnson, Wildi, and Woodward[45] concluded that gliotoxin has structure **192**.

[For references, see pp. 585-610.]

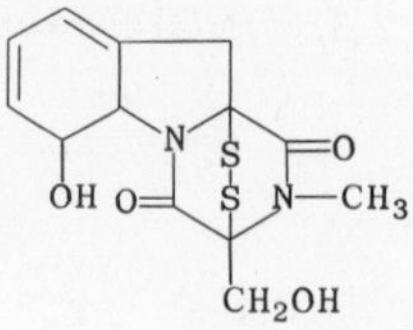

192

M. C_3S_2-C_5-C_6-C_6-C_6 1, 5-EPIDITHIO-5H-CYCLOPENTA[a] PHENANTHRENE (**193**)

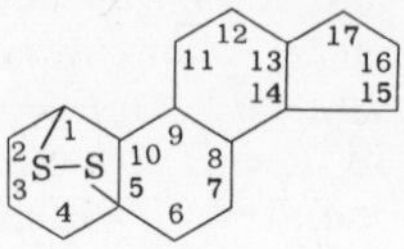

193

Tweit and Dodson,[549,550] while attempting to add hydrogen sulfide to the Δ^2-bond of 1, 4-androstadiene-3, 17-dione (**194**), discovered a new synthesis of 1, 2-dithiolanes. The product, $C_{19}H_{26}O_2S_2$, was formulated as 1α, 5α-epidithioandrostane-3, 17-dione (**195**). Since the yield of **195** was greatly increased by the addition of sulfur to the pyridine used as solvent before the introduction of hydrogen sulfide, the product was considered to result from the addition of hydrogen disulfide.

The structure of **195** was assigned on the basis of its analysis, its spectrum, and its reactions. Failure to react with iodine, as well as the absence of a bond at 4μ, showed the absence of sulfhydryl groups. Raney nickel or methanolic sodium hydroxide regenerated the original unsaturated ketone (**194**), indicating attachment of the two sulfur atoms *beta* to the carbonyl group. Reduction with sodium borohydride yielded a diol-disulfide (**196**) and a diol-dithiol (**197**). Iodine oxidation converted **197** to **196**; Raney nickel desulfurization of the diol-disulfide (**196**) yielded 5-androstene-3α, 17β-diol (**198**), indicating attachment of one sulfur to the 5-position. These reactions are all in accord with the postulated structure. The α-assignment to the bridge was by analogy with other addition reactions, and appears to be confirmed by the formation of the 3α-OH on reduction instead of the usual 3β-configuration.

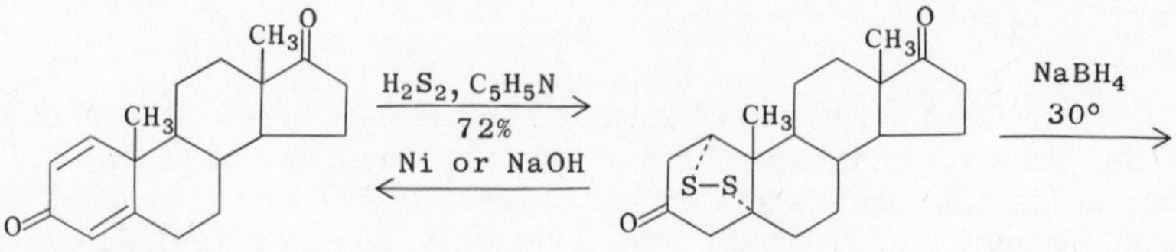

194 H_2S_2, C_5H_5N 72%   Ni or NaOH   **195**   NaBH$_4$ 30°

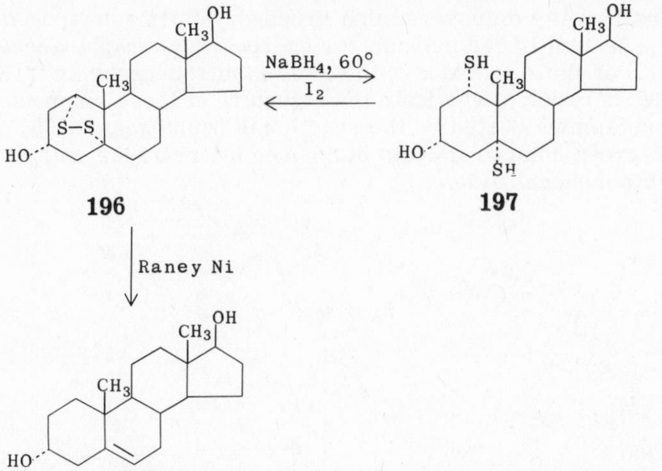

196 197 198

The sodium borohydride reduction, yielding the diol-disulfide (**196**) at 30°, indicates a greater stability for the disulfide ring than in 1, 2-dithiolane itself; the latter is cleaved in α-lipoic acid at 5°.[231]

The ultraviolet spectra of **195** and **196** have been analyzed by Bergson, Sjöberg, Tweit, and Dodson.[53a] **196** has a maximum at 369 mμ, and **195** has two maxima, one at 371 and a very strong one at 268 mμ. Models indicate that the sulfur-sulfur bond distances in these compounds should be greater than in 1, 2-dithiolane, with a dihedral angle of close to 0° This should lead to absorption at longer wave lengths, as found; 1, 2-dithiolane absorbs at 334 mμ.[36] The intense maximum at 268 mμ in the spectrum of **195** was attributed to transannular interaction between the 3-oxo group and the disulfide bridge. These compounds show strong Cotton effects.[156b]

Other steroid disulfides were prepared similarly; the compounds are listed in Table 12. The reaction is not a general one, however; neither benzoquinone, santonin, nor 2, 6-diphenyl-4-pyrone added hydrogen disulfide under the same conditions.

N. C_3S_2-C_3S_2-C_6-C_6-C_6-C_6 NAPHTHACENO[5, 6-*cd*: 11, 12-*c'*, *d'*] BIS [1, 2]-DITHIOLE (**199**)

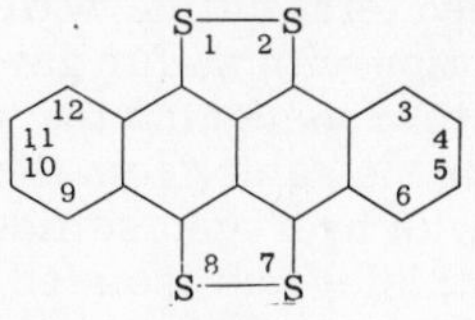

199

(RRI 6624)

[For references, see pp. 585-610.]

In 1939 Marschalk[368] discovered that green, crystalline compounds are formed by heating linear polynuclear hydrocarbons (naphthacene, pentacene, etc.) or their hydrides with sulfur in nitrobenzene or trichlorobenzene. In order to elucidate the structure of these compounds, Marschalk and Stumm[369] studied the reaction of naphthacene (**200**) and found that the green compound could be formed by treatment with either sulfur or sulfur monochloride.

199

That 5, 11-dichloronaphthacene is an intermediate was proved by synthesizing the tetracene tetrasulfide (**199**) from it and sulfur in 87% yield.

Further work by Marschalk[372] made the assigned structure even more probable. 5, 12-Dichloronaphthacene also yielded the tetrasulfide in 87% yield on heating with sulfur. 5, 6, 11-Trichloronaphthacene did not yield the tetrasulfide directly on heating with sulfur, but gave two fractions, one soluble in water and one in dilute acid, which yielded the tetrasulfide on reduction with titanium trichloride or with stannous chloride. 5, 6, 11, 12-Tetrachloronaphthacene and a hexachloronaphthacene did not give the desired compound with sulfur. Heating 5-chloronaphthacene with sulfur in trichlorobenzene at 180° gave some of the green bis(dithiole) and a blue solution; the latter on heating with more sulfur, gave an additional quantity of the tetrasulfide. The two stages of the reaction could be demonstrated more readily with 5-bromonaphthacene. If the heating was interrupted as soon as the evolution of hydrogen bromide had ceased, there was isolated a small amount of naphthacene and a trichlorobenzene-insoluble solid. Reduction of the latter with hydrosulfide gave the green tetrasulfide, while longer heating of the blue trichlorobenzene solution with sulfur gave the same compound. Perhaps the best argument for assigning the sulfur atoms to the 5, 6, 11, 12-positions of naphthacene came from the reaction of 5, 6, 11, 12-tetrachloronaphthacene with hydrogen sulfide in refluxing trichlorobenzene. The green bis(dithiole) was isolated, although in low yield; treatment of the hot blue filtrate with air gave an additional amount, raising the yield to 29%. Neither 5, 11- or 5, 12-dichloronaphthacene gave this reaction.

TABLE 12. 1α,5α-Epidithiosteroids

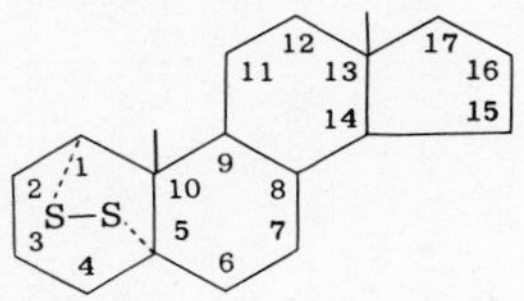

Substituents	Yield (%)	M.p. (dec.) (°C)	$[\alpha]_D$	Ref.
3,17-(O=)$_2$	72	214-218	-21°	549
3α,17β-(OH)$_2$	72	238-239	-56°	549
3-(O=)-17β-OH	10	217-219	-81°	549
3-(O=)-17β-(CH$_3$CO-)		221-222	-4°	549, 550
3-(O=)-17β-(CH$_3$CO$_2$CH$_2$CO-)		188-190	+4°	549, 550
3-(O=)-17α-OH-17β-(CH$_3$CO$_2$CH$_2$CO-)		222-223	-16°	549, 550
3,11-(O=)$_2$17α-OH-17β-(CH$_3$CO$_2$CH$_2$CO-)		235-237	-4°	549, 550
3-(O=)-11β,17α-(OH)$_2$-17β-(CH$_3$CO$_2$CH$_2$CO-)		222-224	+1°	549, 550
3,11-(O=)$_2$-17α-OH-17β-(C$_2$H$_5$CO$_2$CH$_2$CO-)				550
3,11-(O=)$_2$-17β-(CH$_3$CO-)				550
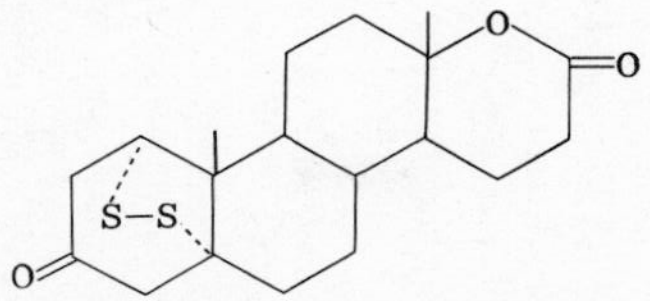	14	232-233	-140°	549

The naphthacenobis(dithiole) (**199**) is quite insoluble and could be recrystallized only from hot trichlorobenzene or nitrobenzene; the crystals are black.[369] It analyzed correctly for $C_{18}H_8S_4$, and a molecular weight determination in naphthalene showed it to be monomeric. It melts with decomposition in the range of 395-400°.[372] The chemical reactions of the compound, as investigated by Marschalk[372] and by Marschalk and Woerth,[370] are in accord with the assigned structure. Heating with zinc dust at 400° in an atmosphere of hydrogen regenerated naphthacene. Reduction with sodium in liquid ammonia followed by treatment with an alkyl halide (methyl iodide, ethyl iodide, benzyl chloride) yielded the expected tetrathioether (**201**). Unfortunately, these compounds could not be made from 5, 6, 11, 12-tetrachloronaphthacene. Alternatively, the tetrachloro compound reacted with p-tolyl mercaptan to give a tetrathioether, but the thioether could not be made from the bis(dithiole). When the sodium reduction was carried out at room temperature and the product was oxidized with chromic anhydride, the known naphthacene-5, 12-dione (**202**) was isolated, indicating that the naphthacene ring is still present in tetracene tetrasulfide.

The tetrasulfide was inert to diazomethane and to maleic anhydride, in accord with its postulated structure.

Although the naphthacenobis(dithiole) is completely stable under alkaline conditions, it is prone to oxidation in the presence of acids.[371,373] Red mono-salts, $(C_{18}H_8S_4)^+X^-$, and yellow di-salts, $(C_{18}H_8S_4)^{2+}X_2^{2-}$, are formed, presumably by the loss of one and two electrons, respectively, from the sulfur atoms. Thus, treatment of the compound with concentrated sulfuric acid gave a yellow compound which analyzed correctly for $(C_{18}H_8S_4)(SO_4H)_2$. Similarly, fuming nitric acid gave a dinitrate, and perchloric acid a diperchlorate. Nonoxidizing acids, such as dilute sulfuric, hydrochloric, and acetic acids, had no effect in the absence of air, but gave the red mono-salts in the presence of air, especially with a trace of sodium nitrite present. More convenient was the use of oxidizing agents — hydrogen peroxide, lead dioxide, manganese dioxide, etc.—

either mono- or di-salts being formed depending on the amount used. Chlorine, sulfur chloride, or sulfuryl chloride could all be used to make the dichloride, and silver sulfate gave a red monosulfate.

Evidence for the oxidative nature of the reaction are numerous. N,N'-Dimethyl-p-phenylenediamine reduced the di-salts to mono-salts, while stronger reducing agents gave tetracene tetrasulfide, although the mono-salts could be isolated as intermediates. Treatment of a di-salt with the unoxidized tetrasulfide gave two molecules of mono-salt. The spectrum of the monochloride has been determined.[578]

Treatment of the salts with alkali under mild conditions gave products resembling pseudo-bases, since treatment with acids under nonoxidizing conditions regenerated the salts. On standing or on heating, however, more deep-seated changes occurred, perhaps the formation of sulfoxides. Marschalk[371] recommended the salts for dyeing cellulose or silk, since reduction or treatment with base converted the soluble salts into insoluble green dyes.

Pecault and Marschalk[412] determined the magnetic susceptibility of tetracene tetrasulfide and found the compound to be diamagnetic, thus ruling out a biradical structure. The monoacetate was too insoluble to be measured accurately, but it was less diamagnetic than the parent compound. From its structure it should, of course, be paramagnetic.

Clar and Marschalk[133] measured the ultraviolet absorption spectrum of tetracene tetrasulfide. They attributed the intense color of the compound to the interpenetration of the electronic orbits of the sulfur atoms, implying a certain amount of conjugation involving the π-electrons. Naerland[398a] reported the infrared spectrum.

II. 1,3-DITHIA COMPOUNDS

A. C_3S_2 1,3-DITHIOLANE (203) AND 1,3-DITHIOLE (204)

203   204

(RRI 138)

1,3-Dithiolanes are represented predominantly by two types of compounds, mercaptals and mercaptoles of 1,2-dimercaptoalkanes and compounds derived from the cyclic ethylene ester of trithiocarbonic acid. Inasmuch as they possess little in common other than the basic ring system, they are discussed separately. Only a few 1,3-dithioles are known. At present Chemical Abstracts indexes these ring systems as 1,3-dithiolane and 1,3-dithiole; the trithiocarbonic acid derivatives, however, are cross-indexed to the acid and the compounds are found under that heading. From 1907-1916 the compounds were indexed under

1, 3-disulfole, and from 1917-1936 under 1, 3-dithiole. Alternative names for 1, 3-dithiolane are 1, 3-dithiacyclopentane, methylene ethylene disulfide, and trimethylene disulfide. Frequently, however, especially in complex compounds, they are named as derivatives of the parent aldehyde or ketone, e.g., 2-methyl-1, 3-dithiolane would be called acetaldehyde cyclic ethylene mercaptal or acetaldehyde ethylenethioacetal. 1, 3-Dithiole is sometimes called 1, 3-dithia-4-cyclopentene.

1. Mercaptals and Mercaptoles of 1, 2-Dimercaptoalkanes

a. Preparation

The parent compound, 1, 3-dithiolane (**203**), was not isolated until 1930, although Baumann and Walter[41] prepared derivatives of it as early as 1893. It was synthesized by Gibson,[214] along with polymer, by adding 1, 2-dimercaptoethane to formalin containing a trace of hydrochloric acid. Challenger and co-workers[125] obtained the compound in 30% yield by this procedure. A better synthesis, which is reported to give the compound in 50-60% yield, involves the reaction of the bis(Bunte salt) (**205**) with formalin and hydrochloric acid, 1, 3-dithiolane being isolated by steam-distillation.[214] Dermer,[147] however, obtained only polymer by this procedure.

$$BrCH_2CH_2Br \xrightarrow{Na_2S_2O_3} NaO_3S_2CH_2CH_2S_2O_3Na \xrightarrow{CH_2O, HCl}$$

205

Tucker and Reid[548] devised a different synthesis; the reaction of 1, 2-dimercaptoethane with methylene chloride in the presence of base gave a 26% yield of 1, 3-dithiolane, a trace of a ten-membered ring, and a large amount of polymer. Heating the polymer with hydrogen chloride gave a 30% yield of 1, 3-dithiolane.

$$HSCH_2CH_2SH \xrightarrow[\substack{CH_2Cl_2 \\ 30\,min.\;reflux}]{EtONa, EtOH}$$

$$+ \quad \begin{array}{c} CH_2-S-CH_2-S-CH_2 \\ | \qquad\qquad\qquad | \\ CH_2-S-CH_2-S-CH_2 \end{array} \quad + \quad [-CH_2SCH_2CH_2S-]_n$$

$$\xrightarrow{HCl, \Delta}$$

Meadow and Reid[375a] found that the polymers would not break down in the absence of halogen. Presumably, 1, 3-dithiolane is formed as a result of reversible sulfonium salt formation. Thus, Meadow and Reid isolated 1, 3-dithiolane and amyl bromide from the reaction of ethylene dibromide with methylenebis(n-amyl sulfide).

$$C_5H_{11}SCH_2SC_5H_{11} + BrCH_2CH_2Br \rightleftharpoons C_5H_{11}SCH_2\overset{+}{S}\overset{C_5H_{11}}{\underset{CH_2CH_2Br}{<}} \rightleftharpoons$$
$$Br^-$$

448

$$C_5H_{11}SCH_2SCH_2CH_2Br \rightleftharpoons C_5H_{11} \overset{+}{\underset{Br^-}{S}} \begin{matrix} CH_2-S \\ | \\ CH_2-CH_2 \end{matrix} \rightleftharpoons \begin{matrix} S \\ \square \\ S \end{matrix} + C_5H_{11}Br$$
$$+ C_5H_{11}Br$$

The same mechanism could be written for polymer with a terminal halogen group.

Chakravarti and Saha[123] claimed that heating 1, 2-dimercaptoethane and dichloroacetic acid in xylene gave 1, 3-dithiolane, presumably by intermediate formation of 1, 3-dithiolane-2-carboxylic acid followed by decarboxylation. However, their product was reported to melt at 192-194° and was undoubtedly a polymer.

Substituted 1, 3-dithiolanes were prepared first by Fasbender[172,173] in 1887. The synthesis consisted of treating the aldehyde or ketone and a 1, 2-dimercaptan with dry hydrogen chloride and allowing the mixture to stand at room temperature. By this procedure he prepared a number of 2-substituted and 2, 2-disubstituted-1, 3-dithiolanes from the corresponding aldehydes and ketones. This procedure, and minor modifications of it, is the preferred method of synthesis and yields are generally good. Inert solvents, such as dioxane, ether, alcohol, or acetic acid, have been used. The use of toluenesulfonic acid as a catalyst and removal of the water by azeotroping with toluene has been recommended,[60,284] as has the use of boron trifluoride etherate in acetic acid;[187] the latter catalyst is much used in the steroid series. Mazover[375] applied Gibson's Bunte salt procedure to the preparation of 2, 2-dimethyl-1, 3-dithiolane (**206**).

$$\begin{matrix} CH_2S_2O_3Na \\ | \\ CH_2S_2O_3Na \end{matrix} + (CH_3)_2C{=}O \xrightarrow[\substack{53\%}]{\substack{EtOH, HCl \\ r.\ t.}} \begin{matrix} S \\ \square \\ S \end{matrix} \overset{CH_3}{\underset{CH_3}{<}}$$

206

It is doubtful that Mazover isolated pure 1, 3-dithiolanes by this procedure, since he claimed that none of his compounds could be distilled, even *in vacuo*, without decomposition. Matter[374] patented the synthesis of 2-methyl-1, 3-dithiolane by heating an ethylene sulfide polymer, (-CH$_2$CH$_2$S-)$_x$, in a stream of hydrogen sulfide. The mechanism of this reaction is obscure, and it is of doubtful utility.

A wide variety of 1, 3-dithiolanes have been prepared by these procedures. Table 13 lists simple derivatives, Table 14 lists 1, 3-dithiolanes derived from sugars, and Table 15 lists compounds with two 1, 3-dithiolane rings. 1, 3-Dithiolanes derived from cyclic ketones are discussed in the section on spiro compounds.

In certain cases, other functional groups in the molecule react at the same time as the dimercaptan. Thus, Roberts and Cheng[452] isolated 2-ethyl-2-methyl-4-chloromethyl-1, 3-dithiolane (**209**) when the condensation of 2, 3-dimercaptopropanol with methyl ethyl ketone was carried out by passing a stream of dry hydrogen chloride through the reactants

[For references, see pp. 585-610.]   449

TABLE 13. 1,3-Dithiolanes

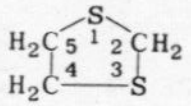

$$\begin{array}{c} \text{S} \\ \text{H}_2\text{C}^{5}\ {}^{1}\ {}^{2}\text{CH}_2 \\ \text{H}_2\text{C}_{4}\ {}_{3}\text{S} \end{array}$$

Substituents	Yield (%)	M.p. (°C)	B.p. (°C)	(mm)	Other properties	Ref.
None	50-60		175	760	n_D^{15} 1.5975	214
	30		61	11	d^{17} 1.259	214
	56		67	14		125
	20	−51	179-180	760	n_D^{25} 1.5983	548
						147
None · HgCl₂		119				214
		126				125
1-Oxide			115-120	1		214
1-Oxide methiodide		96				214
1,3-Dioxide		157-158.5 (dec.)				46
1,1,3-Trioxide		128				46
1,1,3,3-Tetroxide		204-205				41,128,548
		224				214
	80	210-211				81a
2-CH₃-			172-173			173,374
			58	12		125
2-CH₃-1,1,3,3-tetroxide		198				173
2-C₂H₅-			191-192			173
2-C₂H₅-1,1,3,3-tetroxide		124				173
2-[C₂H₅O₂C(CH₂)₄-]	67		126-127	0.55	n_D^{25} 1.5164-8	238
2-[HO₂C(CH₂)₄-]		51-52				238
2-C₆H₅-		29				172,173

Compound	Yield (%)	M.p. (°C)	B.p. (°C)	mm	n_D^{20}, d_{20}	Ref.
2-(p-$CH_3C_6H_4$-)			198	24		284
2-(p-ClC_6H_4-)		62	150–151	0.5		284
2-(p-HOC_6H_4-)		119–120				284
2-(p-$CH_3OC_6H_4$-)		64–65				173
2-(2,4-$Cl_2C_6H_3$-)		38				284
2-(3,4-Methylenedioxyphenyl-)		48–49				284
2-HO_2C-		90				128
2-$C_2H_5O_2C$-1,1,3-tetroxide		90–91				81a
2-(CH_3COCH_2-)	60		143–145	10	n_D^{20} 1.5579, d_{20} 1.2080	302a
2-(CH_3COCH_2-)1,1,3,3-tetroxide	97	124.5–125				302a
2-($C_2H_5COCH_2$-)	51		130–132	8	n_D^{20} 1.5464, d_{20} 1.1693	302a
2-($C_2H_5COCH_2$-)1,1,3,3-tetroxide	92	149.5–150				302a
2-(n-$C_3H_7COCH_2$-)	49		136–138	5	n_D^{20} 1.5381, d_{20} 1.1311	302a
2-(n-$C_3H_7COCH_2$-)1,1,3,3-tetroxide	90	128.5–129				302a
2-($C_6H_5COCH_2$-)		80				294
2-(m-$CH_3C_6H_4COCH_2$-)	50	74.5–75				302a
2-(p-$BrC_6H_5COCH_2$-)	50	66–66.5				302a
2-(2-Thenoylmethyl-)	90	101–102				302a
2-(C_6H_5COCH=)		98–99				294
2-(C_6H_5COCH=)		80				292, 541
2-(p-$CH_3C_6H_4COCH$=)		136				541
2-(p-$CH_3OC_6H_4COCH$=)		90				541
2-(p-ClC_6H_4COCH=)		120				541
2-(p-BrC_6H_4COCH=)		153				541
2-(p-$C_6H_5C_6H_4COCH$=)		186				541
2-$\left(\begin{smallmatrix}C_6H_5CO\\C_6H_5\end{smallmatrix}C{=}\right)$		157.5–158				582

TABLE 13. 1,3-Dithiolanes (contd)

Substituents	Yield (%)	M.p. (°C)	B.p. (°C)	(mm)	Other properties	Ref.
$2\text{-}[(C_2H_5O_2C)_2C=]$			202	2.5		295
$2\text{-}(HO_2CCH=)$		150				295
$2\text{-}(C_6H_4\,\substack{CO\\CO}NCHCH_3)$	25				From DL-isomer	30
	70	96	160–170	0.03	$[\alpha]_D$ +48.7° from L-isomer	30
$2\text{-}(C_6H_4\,\substack{CO\\CO}NCHCH_2CH_2\text{-})\;CH_3$	80		130	0.005	$[\alpha]_D$ +41° from (+)-isomer	32
$2\text{-}(C_6H_4\,\substack{CO\\CO}NCHCH_2\text{-})\;C_2H_5$	60	121–122			$[\alpha]_D^{17}$ +34° from (−)-isomer	32
$2\text{-}(C_6H_4\,\substack{CO\\CO}NCHCH_2\text{-}CH_2CH(CH_3)_2)$		81–82.5			$[\alpha]_D^{19}$ +18.9°	288b
$2\text{-}(C_6H_4\,\substack{CO\\CO}NCHCH_2SCH_2C_6H_5)$	72.3	98–100	230–235	0.04	$[\alpha]_D^{21}$ −60.14° from L-isomer	30
$2\text{-}(C_6H_4\,\substack{CO\\CO}NCHCH_2C_6H_4OCH_3\text{-}p)$	89	103			$[\alpha]_D^{18}$ −105° L-isomer	30
$2\text{-}(CH_3CHNH_2)$	67		145–155	12	$[\alpha]_D^{19}$ +18.5°	30
$2\text{-}(C_6H_5CH_2CH_2SCH_2CHNH_2)$			150–180	0.04	$[\alpha]_D^{26}$ −19.2°	30
$2,2\text{-}(CH_3\text{-})_2$			171		d^{18} 1.12	173
	53					375
	55					147

Compound	Yield (%)	M.p. (°C)	B.p., °C (mm)	n_D, d, $[\alpha]_D$	Ref.
2,2-$(CH_3)_2$ 1,1,3,3-tetroxide		232			173
2-CH_3-3-C_2H_5-	56		55 (3)	d^{18} 1.02	375
2-CH_3-3-C_2H_5-1,1,3,3-tetroxide	43	240–242			375
2-CH_3-3-iso-C_3H_7-	74		61 (3)	n_D^{25} 1.5350, d_4^{25} 1.0680	448
2-CH_3-3-iso-C_3H_7-1,1,3,3-tetroxide	40	124–125			375
2,2-$(n$-C_3H_7-$)_2$	43		86 (2)	n_D^{25} 1.5302, d_4^{25} 1.0511	448
2-C_2H_5-2-n-C_4H_9-	87		102 (5)	n_D^{25} 1.5200, d_4^{25} 1.0158	448
2,2-$(iso$-C_3H_7-$)_2$	66		94 (4)	n_D^{25} 1.5191, d_4^{25} 1.0126	448
2-iso-C_4H_9-4-CH_3-			124.5–124.8 (30)	n_D^{30} 1.5119, d^{30} 1.0045	448
2-iso-C_4H_9-4-CH_3-1,1,3,3-tetroxide		92.5–93.5			452
2-n-C_6H_{13}-4-CH_3-			171–172 (40)	n_D^{30} 1.5030, d^{30} 0.9780	452
2-n-C_6H_{13}-4-CH_3-1,1,3,3-tetroxide		61–62			452
2-CH_3-3-n-C_6H_{11}-			120 (6)	n_D^{25} 1.5110, d_4^{25} 0.9926	452
2,2-$(iso$-C_4H_9-$)_2$			115 (6)	n_D^{25} 1.5115, d_4^{25} 0.9892	448
2,2-$(iso$-C_4H_9-$)_2$ 1,1,3,3-tetroxide		40			448
2-CH_3-3-2-$(C_2H_5O_2CCH_2$-$)$	84		86 (0.1)	n_D^{25} 1.5213	238
2-CH_3-3-2-$(HO_2CCH_2CH_2$-$)$	83	56–56.5			238
2-CH_3-3-2-$[HO_2C(CH_2)_4$-$]$	72	40–40.5			238
2-$[CH_3O_2C(CH_2)_4$-$]$-4-CH_3-	78		122–124 (0.5)	n_D^{27} 1.5340	238
2-$[HO_2C(CH_2)_4$-$]$-4-CH_3-		126–128			238
2-$[CH_3O_2C(CH_2)_4$-$]$-4-$HOCH_2$-			144 (0.07)	n_D^{26} 1.5352	238
2-CH_3-3-$(C_6H_4\langle CO{-}CO\rangle N{-}CH_2CHCH_3)$	100			$[\alpha]_D^{20}$ +14°	33a, 33b
2-CH_3-3-$[C_6H_4\langle CO{-}CO\rangle N{-}CHCH_2CH(CH_3)_2]$	67	115–116		$[\alpha]_D^{22}$ −41°	288b
2-$[CH_3(CH_2)_{14}$-$]$-2-$(C_6H_4\langle CO{-}CO\rangle N{-}CHCH_3)$	75			Oil	424

TABLE 13. 1,3-Dithiolanes (contd)

Substituents	Yield (%)	M.p. (°C)	B.p. (°C)	(mm)	Other properties	Ref.
2-($C_6H_4\langle$CO,CO$\rangle$NCHCH₃)-2-HO₂C-	87	149-150			$[\alpha]_D^{17}$ +25° from L-isomer	33
2-($C_6H_4\langle$CO,CO$\rangle$NCH₂CH₂CH₂-)-2-HO₂C-	66	157-158				361
2-($H_2NCH_2CH_2CH_2$-)-2-HO₂C-	84	262-263				361
2-($H_2NCH_2CH_2CH_2$-)-2-HO₂C- · HCl	90	165-167				361
2-($H_2NCH_2CH_2CH_2$-)-2-HO₂C- · HBr	100	149-150				361
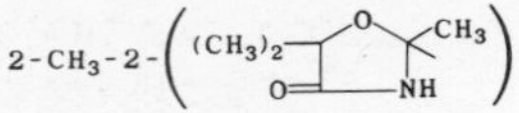 2-CH₃-2-(CH₃)₂ ... (structure)	74	152-153				161
2-CH₃-2-C_6H_5-	78.8		162-163.5	11		243
			131	3	n_D^{25} 1.6162, d_4^{25} 1.1819	448
2-C_2H_5-2-C_6H_5-			135	3	n_D^{25} 1.6050, d_4^{25} 1.1542	448
2-n-C_3H_7-2-C_6H_5-			145	4	n_D^{25} 1.5915, d_4^{25} 1.1287	448
2-n-C_4H_9-2-C_6H_5-			154	4	n_D^{25} 1.5830, d_4^{25} 1.1035	448
2-n-C_5H_{11}-2-C_6H_5-			169	4	n_D^{25} 1.5755, d_4^{25} 1.0838	448
2-CH₃-2-(p-ClC_6H_4-)			145	1		284
	.81		202	30		49
2-C_2H_5-2-(p-ClC_6H_4-)			154	1.5		284
2-CH₃-2-(p-FC_6H_4-)	65		170-172	30	n_D^{22} 1.591, d_4^{22} 1.2523	49
2-n-C_6H_{11}-2-(p-ClC_6H_4-)			172	0.7		284
2-CH₃-2-(2-thienyl-)			123	1.4	n_D^{25} 1.6300, d_4^{25} 1.2756	448
2-CH₃-2-(3-pyridyl-)	90		134-135	2		521
2-CH₃-2-(3-pyridyl-) · picrate		146-148				521

Substituent	Yield, %	M.p., °C		Remarks	Reference
2-CH₃-2- (ring system)	90	80-83			521
2-CH₃-2- · picrate (ring system)		141-143			521
2-(p-ClC₆H₄-)-4-CH₃-		168-170	3.5		284
2-(3,4-Methylenedioxyphenyl)-4-CH₃-		165-169	0.8		284
2-C₆H₅CH₂-4-C₆H₅-1,1,3,-tetroxide	27	206			299
2-C₆H₅-4-(CH₂=)	54	52			381
2-CH₃-4-HOCH₂-	59	57-58	0.8		509b, 515
2-CH₃-4-ClCH₂-	69	94	2		515
2-CH₃-4-BrCH₂-	65	50-55 (bath)	0.01		509b
2-CH₃-4-(CH₃)₂NCH₂-	94	95-100	18		509b
2-CH₃-4-[(CH₃)₃NCH₂-]⁺ I⁻		194-196 (dec.)			509b
2-CH₃-4-HO₂C-		102			173
2-[...(O₂N)...S...CH=C(Br)...]-4-HOCH₂- (ring system)	85		1.5	Oil	112, 112a
2-C₆H₅-4-HOCH₂-	94	207		Mixture of isomers	418, 515
	56	77; 90		}Two isomers	381
2-C₆H₅-4-HOCH₂-1,1,3-tetroxide	43	88.5-89.0; 87.5-88.0		}Two isomers	452
		159-161			452
2-C₆H₅-4-[3,5-(O₂N)₂C₆H₃CO₂CH₂-]	91	112-113; 101-102		}Two isomers	452
2-C₆H₅-4-[3,5-(O₂N)₂C₆H₃CO₂CH₂-]1,1,3,-tetroxide	61-72	178-180			452

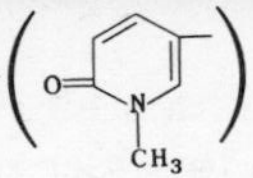

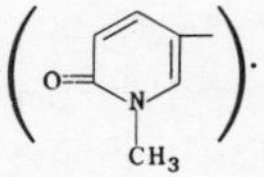

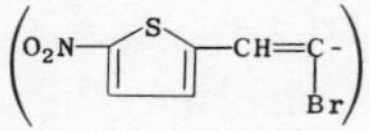

TABLE 13. 1,3-Dithiolanes (contd)

Substituents	Yield (%)	M.p. (°C)	B.p. (°C)	(mm)	Other properties	Ref.
2-(p-ClC$_6$H$_4$-)-4-[3,5-(O$_2$N)$_2$C$_6$H$_3$CO$_2$CH$_2$-]		164-165 135-137			}Two isomers	452
2-(p-ClC$_6$H$_4$-)-4-[3,5-(O$_2$N)$_2$C$_6$H$_3$CO$_2$CH$_2$-]-1,1,3,3-tetroxide	47-64	215-217				452
2-C$_6$H$_5$-4-ClCH$_2$-	84	70-71	150	0.8		381
	61	69-70				515
2-C$_6$H$_5$-4-BrCH$_2$-	85	81				381
2-C$_6$H$_5$-4-CH$_3$OCH$_2$-	42		100 (bath)	10^{-4}	n_D^{20} 1.5990	381
2-C$_6$H$_5$-4-(HO$_3$SCH$_2$-), Na salt	95	dec. 233-235				418a
2-C$_6$H$_5$-4-(HO$_3$SCH$_2$-), S-benzylthiouronium salt		143-144				418a
2-(p-ClC$_6$H$_4$-)-4-HOCH$_2$-		78-78.5			Oil	284
2-C$_6$H$_5$-4-HO$_2$C-		98-100				450
2-(C$_6$H$_5$CH=CH-)-4-HO$_2$C-		69				450
2-C$_6$H$_5$-4-NCCH$_2$-	72	94-95	155-160	1		515
2-C$_6$H$_5$-4-[(C$_2$H$_5$)$_2$NCH$_2$-]	37					233
2-C$_6$H$_5$-4-(p-CH$_3$C$_6$H$_4$OCH$_2$-)	65	162-164				233
2-C$_6$H$_5$-4-(p-HO$_2$CC$_6$H$_4$OCH$_2$-)	33	135-137				233
2-C$_6$H$_5$-4-(p-O$_2$NC$_6$H$_4$OCH$_2$-)	66	150-152				233
2-C$_6$H$_5$-4-(p-CH$_3$CONHC$_6$H$_4$OCH$_2$-)	58	157				233
2-C$_6$H$_5$-4-[(C$_2$H$_5$)$_2$NCH$_2$CH$_2$OCH$_2$-]	63	95-96				233
2-C$_6$H$_5$-4-C$_6$H$_5$CO$_2$CH$_2$-	60	98-99				5b
2-C$_6$H$_5$-4-(p-O$_2$NC$_6$H$_4$CO$_2$CH$_2$-)	89	168-169				233
2-C$_6$H$_5$-4-(3-pyridyl-OCH$_2$-) · picrate	35		140 (bath)	10^{-4}	n_D^{15} 1.6290	233
2-C$_6$H$_5$-4-CH$_3$COSCH$_2$-	90					382

Substituents	Yield (%)	M.p., °C	B.p. (mm)	Other data	Ref.
2-C_6H_5-4-(p-$CH_3C_6H_4SCH_2$-)	60	68–70			5a
2-C_6H_5-4-$HSCH_2$-	84	52			382
2-C_6H_5-4- 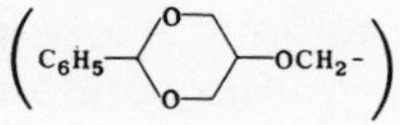 (C_6H_5)—OCH₂— [ring structure]			130–140 (bath) 10^{-4}	n_D^{15} 1.6041, n_D^{20} 1.6020	381
2-C_6H_5-4- 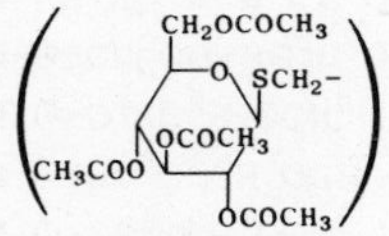 [structure: CH_2OCOCH_3, SCH_2-, CH_3COO, $OCOCH_3$]	81	121–122		$[\alpha]_D^{18}$ −22.0°	382
2-C_6H_5-4- 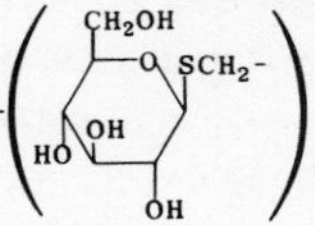 [structure: CH_2OH, SCH_2-, HO, OH]				Glass, $[\alpha]_D^{20}$ −32.6°	382
2-C_6H_5-2-C_6H_5CO-	74	94–95			128
	80	95–96			187
		94–95		λCHl. 5.97, 6.25, 6.31μ	270
2- [structure: CH_3, C_6H_5, OCH_3, OCH_3, $CONH_2$ — 2-($HO_2CCH_2CH_2$-)] 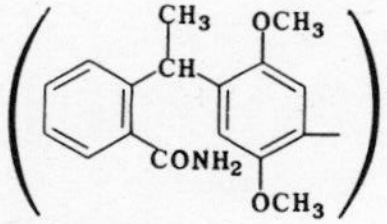	98.5	202.5–203.3			202
2,2-(C_6H_5-)₂		106			173
2-C_6H_5-2-(p-ClC_6H_4-)		44			284
2-C_6H_5-2-(2-thienyl-)		53.5			448
2-CH_3-2-Br-1,1,3-tetroxide		248			215
2,2-F_2	82		51 (11)		237a
2,2-Cl_2-1,1,3-tetroxide		222–223 (dec.)			41
2,2-Br_2-1,1,3-tetroxide		233			215
2,2,4-(CH_3-)₃		271 (dec.)	43–45 (3.8)	n_D^{30} 1.5042 impure	41,128 452

TABLE 13. 1,3-Dithiolanes (contd)

Substituents	Yield (%)	M.p. (°C)	B.p. (°C)	(mm)	Other properties	Ref
2,2,4-(CH$_3$-)$_3$ 1,1,3,3-tetroxide	57	124-124.5				452
2,2-(CH$_3$-)$_2$-4-n-C$_4$H$_9$-	87		110	12	$n_D^{22.5}$ 1.5052	27
2,4-(CH$_3$-)$_2$-2-C$_2$H$_5$-	83		96-98	25	n_D^{30} 1.5151, d^{30} 1.0229	452
2,4-(CH$_3$-)$_2$-2-C$_2$H$_5$-1,1,3,3-tetroxide	13	96-97.5			}Two isomers	452
	31	67-69				452
2,4-(CH$_3$-)$_2$-2-n-C$_3$H$_7$-	91		116-117	30	n_D^{30} 1.5115, d^{30} 1.0028	452
2,4-(CH$_3$-)$_2$-2-n-C$_3$H$_7$-1,1,3,3-tetroxide	15	96-97			}Two isomers	452
	30	65-66				452
2-C$_2$H$_5$-2-n-C$_{11}$H$_{23}$-4-CH$_3$-	70		184-185	3.5	n_D^{30} 1.4920	452
2-C$_2$H$_5$-2-n-C$_{11}$H$_{23}$-4-CH$_3$-1,1,3,3-tetroxide	37	74-75.5			}Two isomers	452
	29	70-71				452
2-CH$_3$-2-C$_2$H$_5$-4-[3,5-(O$_2$N)$_2$C$_6$H$_3$CO$_2$CH$_2$-]		94-95			}Two isomers	452
		81-82				
2,2-(CH$_3$-)$_2$-4-HOCH$_2$-	66	54-55	105	1		515
2,2-(CH$_3$-)$_2$-4-HOCH$_2$-1,1,3,3-tetroxide	79	110-112				60
2,2-(CH$_3$-)$_2$-4-CH$_3$CO$_2$CH$_2$-	100		65	10^{-2}	n_D^{19} 1.5190	381
			60	10^{-3}	n_D^{15} 1.5250	381
2,2-(CH$_3$-)$_2$-4-C$_6$H$_5$CO$_2$CH$_2$-	71	82-83				5b
2-CH$_3$-2-C$_2$H$_5$-4-HOCH$_2$-	75		113-116	4.1	n_D^{30} 1.5328	452
2-CH$_3$-2-C$_2$H$_5$-4-ClCH$_2$-	76		82-84	1.4	n_D^{30} 1.5381	452
2-CH$_3$-2-C$_2$H$_5$-4-ClCH$_2$-1,1,3,3-tetroxide	33	122.5-124.5			}Two isomers	452
	17	104.5-106.5				452
2-CH$_3$-2-C$_2$H$_5$-4-C$_2$H$_5$OCH$_2$-	76		102-104.5	2.8	Impure	452
2-CH$_3$-2-C$_2$H$_5$-4-C$_2$H$_5$OCH$_2$-1,1,3,3-tetroxide	18	173-174			}Two isomers	452
	34	149-150				452

Compound	Yield (%)	m.p. (°C)	b.p. (°C)/mm	Notes	Ref.
2-CH₃-2-C₂H₅-4-[3,5-(O₂N)₂C₆H₃CO₂CH₂-]	45	168.5-170.5		From 95° isomer	452
1,1,3,3-tetroxide	38	110-112		From 82° isomer	267
2,2-(CH₃)₂-4-(p-CH₃OC₆H₄OCH₂-)	56	65-66			267
2,2-(CH₃)₂-4-(p-BrC₆H₄OCH₂-)	56	69-70			60
2-CH₃-2-n-C₅H₁₁-4-HOCH₂-	66		93/1	n_D^{21} 1.5453	515
2,2-(CH₃-)₂-4-ClCH₂-	72		80/0.7		381
2,2-(CH₃)₂-4-HO₂C-	52	51-53	54/0.1		416
2,2-(CH₃)₂-4-CH₃O₂C-	93		121-122/1.5	n_D^{12} 1.5535	416
2,2-(CH₃)₂-4-H₂NOC-	82	89-90	73-74/0.5		416
2,4-(CH₃)₂-2-(HO₂CCH₂CH₂-)	25	43.5-46	142.5/0.65		163a
2,2-(CH₃)₂-4-(C₅H₅N⁺CH₂-) (tosylate⁻)	57	135-136			381
2,2-(CH₃-)₂-4-[(CH₃)₂ ... CH₂OCH₂-]		63, 82		Stereoisomers	170
2,2-(CH₃-)₂-4-[(CH₃)₂ ... CH₂OCH₂-]			98/10	n_D^{23} 1.5265	169
2,2-(CH₃-)₂-4-[(CH₃)₂ ... CH₂SCH₂- S]		132			383
2,2-(CH₃-)₂-4-[(CH₃)₂ ... OCH₂-]		67			169
2,2-(CH₃-)₂-4-[CH₂OCOCH₃, OCH₃, OCOCH₃, CH₃COO, OCOCH₃]	57	122			381

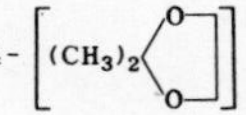

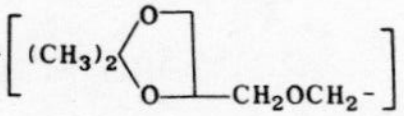

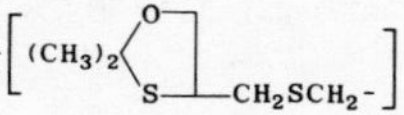

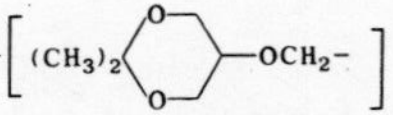

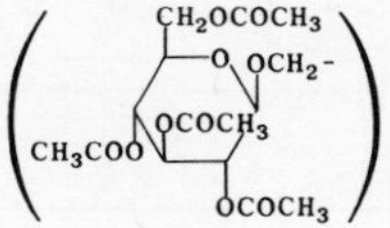

TABLE 13. 1,3-Dithiolanes (contd)

Substituents	Yield (%)	M.p. (°C)	B.p. (°C)	(mm)	Other properties	Ref.
2,2-(CH$_3$-)$_2$-4- 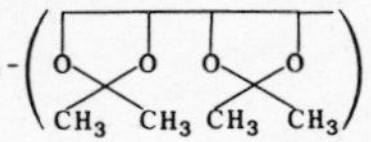 (ring structure)		40-41			L-gulitol derivative	273a
2,4-(CH$_3$-)$_2$-2-C$_6$H$_5$-	24		135-136	4.4	n_D^{30} 1.5935 }Two isomers	452
	26		146-149	4.4	n_D^{30} 1.5924	452
2,4-(CH$_3$-)$_2$-2-C$_6$H$_5$-1,1,3,3-tetroxide	53	132.5-133.7			From 136° isomer	452
	72	134.5-136.2			From 149° isomer	452
2-C$_2$H$_5$-2-C$_6$H$_5$-4-CH$_3$-	19		112-113	2	n_D^{30} 1.5821 }Two isomers	452
	24		122-123	2	n_D^{30} 1.5811	452
2-C$_2$H$_5$-2-C$_6$H$_5$-4-CH$_3$-1,1,3-tetroxide	50	134-135.5			From 113° isomer	452
	42	129-130.5			From 123° isomer	452
2-CH$_3$-2-C$_6$H$_5$-4-(HO$_3$SCH$_2$-), Na salt		142-145				418a
2-CH$_3$-2-C$_6$H$_5$-4-(HO$_3$SCH$_2$-), S-benzylthiouronium salt		170				418a
2-C$_2$H$_5$-2-(p-ClC$_6$H$_4$-)-4-CH$_3$-			158-159	3.5		284
2-n-C$_6$H$_{11}$-2-(p-ClC$_6$H$_4$-)-4-CH$_3$-			159	0.2		284
2,2-(CH$_3$-)$_2$-4-HOCH$_2$-5-HO-	72	112-113				521a
cis-2,2-(CH$_3$-)$_2$-4,5-(HO$_2$C-)$_2$	74	165-166				212b
cis-2,2-(CH$_3$-)$_2$-4,5-(HO$_2$C-)$_2$, anhyd.	89	140-142				212b
cis-2,2-(CH$_3$-)$_2$-4,5-(CH$_3$O$_2$C-)$_2$		35-36, 62-63			Two modifications	212b
trans-2,2-(CH$_3$-)$_2$-4,5-(HO$_2$C-)$_2$	66	156-157				212b
Furostane derivatives (See Table 18)						

dissolved in benzene or chloroform. This ready displacement of hydroxyl was attributed to the stabilization of the intermediate cation as a sulfonium ion (208). The desired 4-hydroxymethyl derivative (207) was obtained by the use of a few drops of hydrochloric acid as the catalyst.

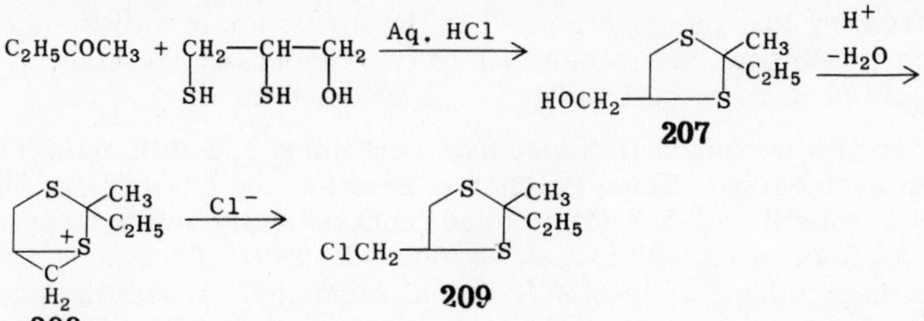

Evans and Owen[169] found that, in the reaction of 2, 3-dihydroxy-2', 3'-dimercaptodipropyl ether (210) with acetone, the glycol portion also reacted to give 4-[(2, 2-dimethyl-1, 3-dioxolan-4-ylmethoxy)methyl]-2, 2-dimethyl-1, 3-dithiolane (211).

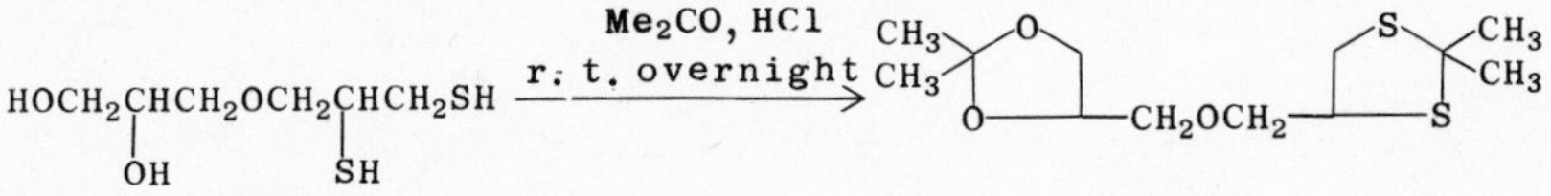

Similarly, 1, 3-dihydroxy-2-propyl 2, 3-dimercaptopropyl ether (212) gave 4-(2, 2-dimethyl-m-dioxan-5-yloxymethyl)-2, 2-dimethyl-1, 3-dithiolane (213).

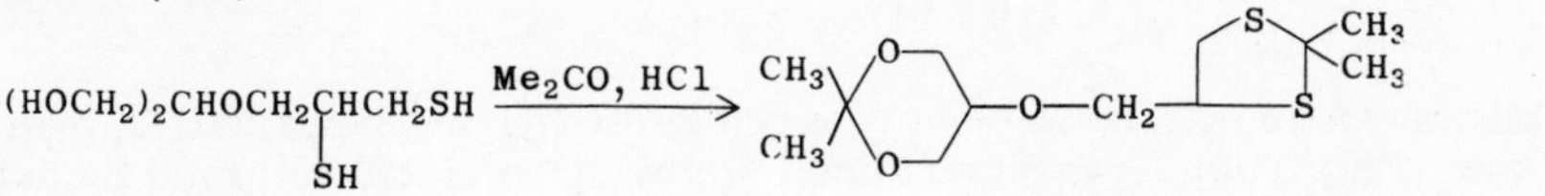

Miles and Owen[381] also prepared the corresponding dibenzylidene compound with benzaldehyde. The same authors[383] made the diisopropylidene derivative of 3-hydroxy-2, 2', 3'-trimercaptodipropyl sulfide (214), 4-[(2, 2-dimethyl-1, 3-oxathiolan-4-ylmethylthio)methyl]-2, 2-dimethyl-1, 3-dithiolane (215).

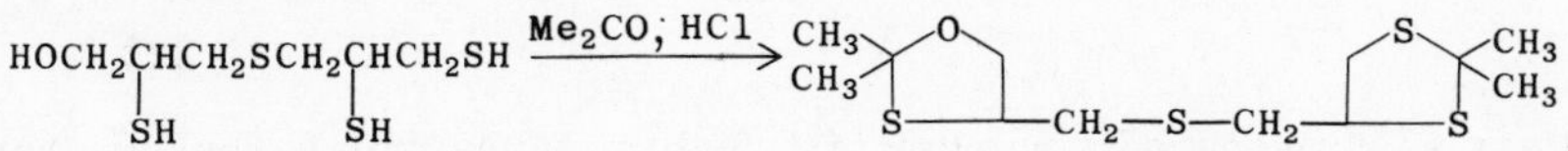

Evans, Fraser, and Owen[170] found that 1, 2-dihydroxy-3, 4-dimercapto-butane exists in two forms, *threo* and *erythro*, but configurations were not assigned; each form gave a different diisopropylidene derivative, 4-(2, 2-dimethyl-1, 3-dioxolan-4-yl)-2, 2-dimethyl-1, 3-dithiolane (216).

[For references, see pp. 585-610.]   461

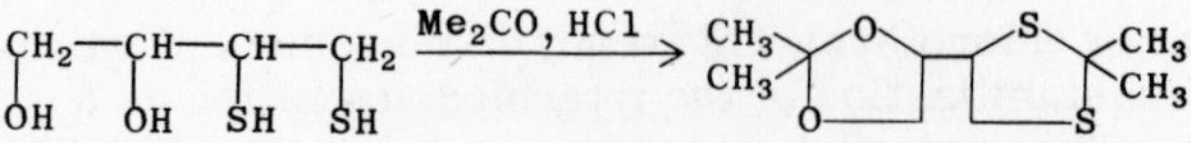

216

It is interesting that the reaction led to the formation of a dioxolane ring and a dithiolane ring rather than to two condensed oxathiane rings, which would have resulted from 1,3-2,4 condensation.

A number of other unusual compounds containing 1,3-dithiolane rings have been synthesized. Thus, Balenović, Bregant, and co-workers,[30] prepared 2-substituted-1,3-dithiolanes from optically active α-aminoaldehydes, as illustrated with L-alanine aldehyde (**217**). Treatment with 1,2-dimercaptoethane yielded 2-(1-phthalimidoethyl)-1,3-dithiolane (**218**), which was converted with hydrazine into optically active 2-(1-aminoethyl)-1,3-dithiolane (**219**).

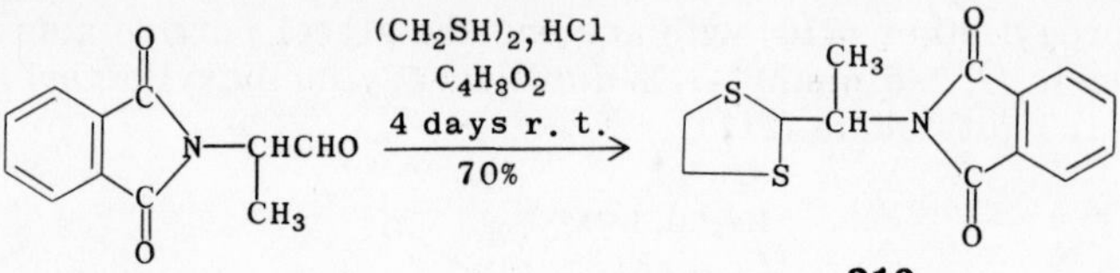

217   **218**

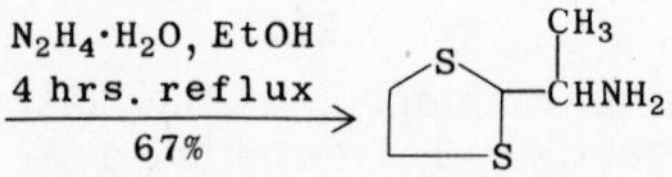

219

Sugasawa and Kirisawa[521] prepared 2-methyl-2-(3-pyridyl)-1,3-dithiolane (**220**) from 3-acetylpyridine. Methylation of **220** followed by oxidation with ferricyanide yielded the corresponding pyridone, 2-(1,6-dihydro-1-methyl-6-oxo-3-pyridyl)-2-methyl-1,3-dithiolane (**221**).

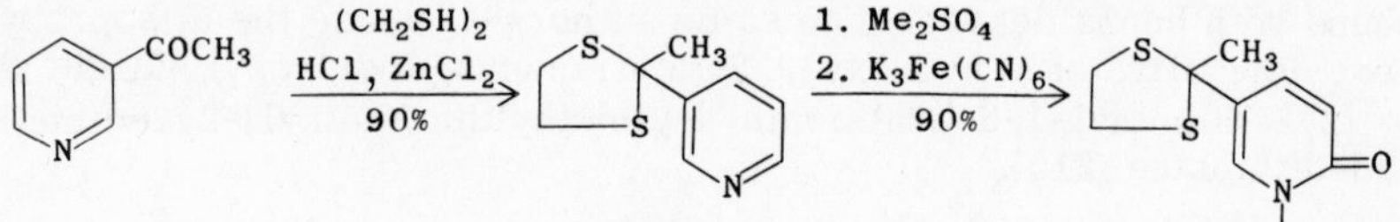

220   **221**

Harris[238] prepared a number of 1,3-dithiolanes with carboxylic acid or ester side chains in the 2-position (**222**).

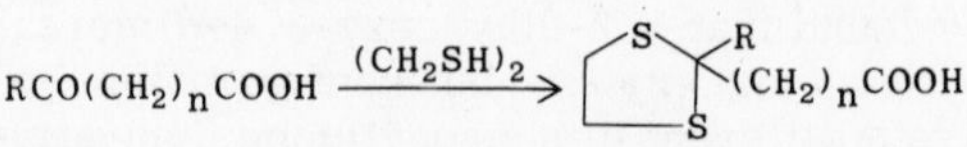

222

Gerecke, Friedheim, and Brossi[212b] used 1, 3-dithiolane formation to determine the structures of the two isomeric 2, 3-dimercaptosuccinic acids. Thus, the higher melting, less soluble isomer was shown to be the *meso* isomer by condensation with acetone to *cis*-2, 2-dimethyl-1, 3-dithiolane-4, 5-dicarboxylic acid (**222a**), the *cis* configuration being demonstrated by ready anhydride formation.

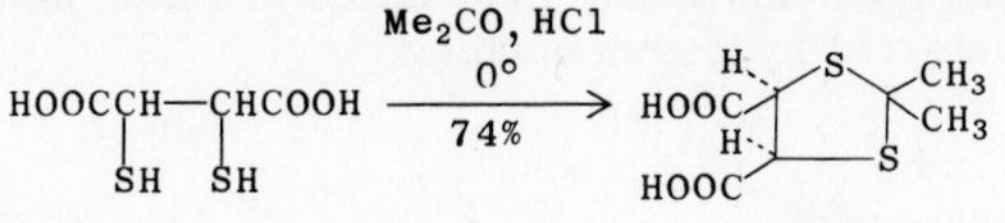

222a

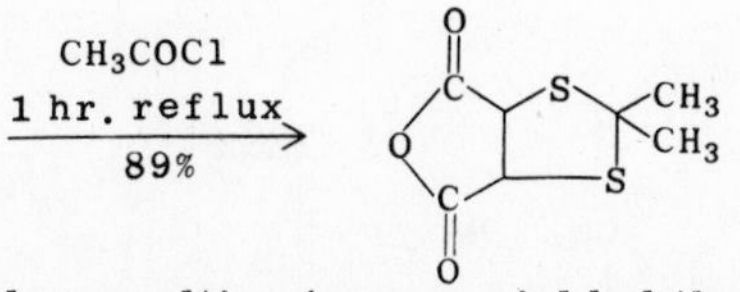

The low-melting isomer yielded the *trans*-dicarboxylic acid, which could not be dehydrated to the cyclic anhydride and was resolved *via* its brucine salt.

Sullivan and Williams[521a] prepared an interesting 1, 3-dithiolane from glycidaldehyde and hydrogen sulfide. In dry acetone the product was predominantly 2-mercapto-3-hydroxypropionaldehyde, isolated as its dimer (**222b**) (see Chapter 12, section III A-1 j); the expected mode of addition would have formed the 3-mercapto derivative instead. In aqueous acetone the major product was 2, 2-dimethyl-4-hydroxymethyl-1, 3-dithiolan-5-ol (**222c**), undoubtedly formed from the mercaptoalde-hyde by further addition of hydrogen sulfide to the carbonyl group, since under the same conditions a better yield was obtained from **222b**.

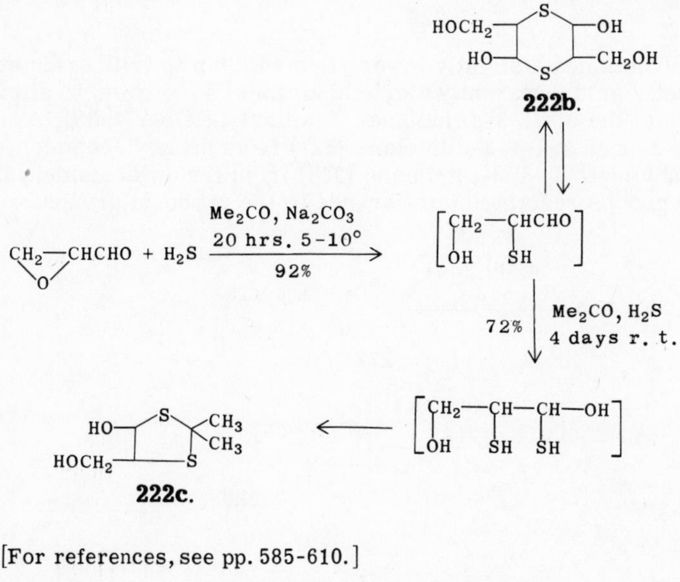

222b.

222c.

[For references, see pp. 585-610.]

Although there are very few reports in the literature of carbonyl groups which fail to react with 1, 2-dimercaptoethane, a few are known. Thus, Gates and Dickinson[202] reported the normal formation of an ethylenethioketal, 2-[4-(o-carbamoyl-α-methylbenzyl)-2, 5-dimethoxyphenyl]-1, 3-dithiolane-2-propionic acid (**223a**), from the hydroquinone dimethyl ether derivative (**223**). Both the demethylated compound (**224**) and 1, 4-dihydroxy-10-methyl-9-anthrone (**225**) failed to react, however, presumably because of internal hydrogen bonding.

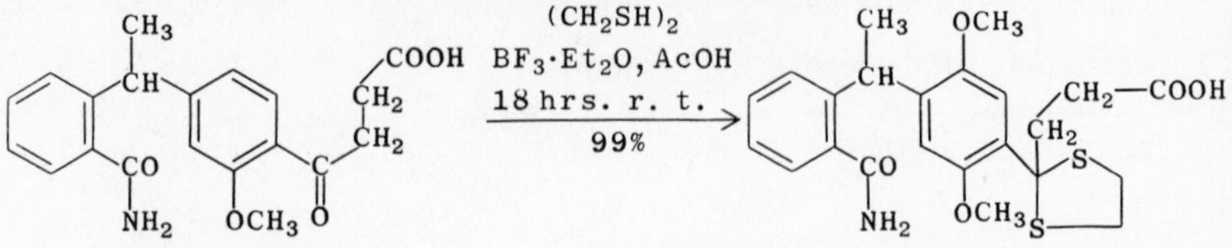

223

223a

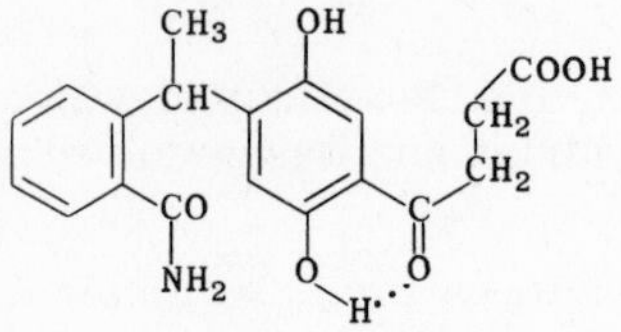

224 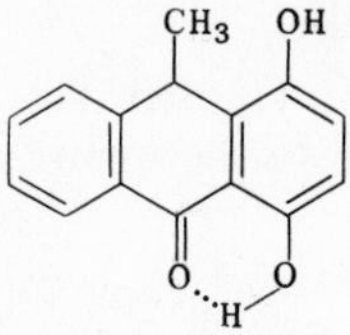   **225**

Hurtley and Smiles[270] prepared the mono(ethylene mercaptole) of benzil, 2-phenyl-2-benzoyl-1, 3-dithiolane (**226**).

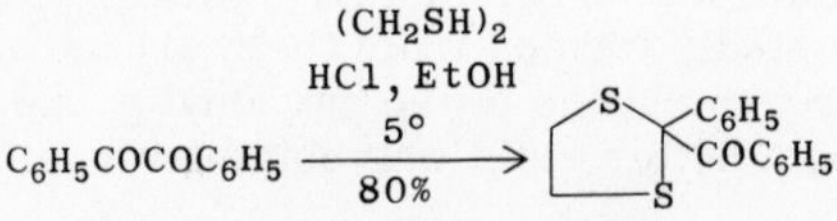

226

Fieser[187] obtained a slightly lower yield with boron trifluoride etherate in acetic acid; apparently steric hindrance is too great to allow the formation of the bis(1, 3-dithiolane). Similarly, Kelber and Schwarz[294] prepared 2-phenacyl-1, 3-dithiolane (**227**) from benzoylacetaldehyde and 2-(2-thenoylmethyl)-1, 3-dithiolane (**228**) from thenoylacetaldehyde, the aldehyde groups reacting in preference to the carbonyl groups.

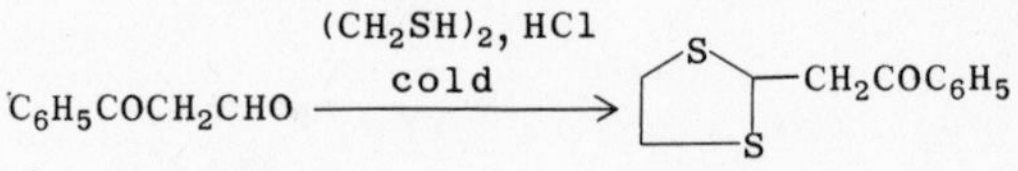

227

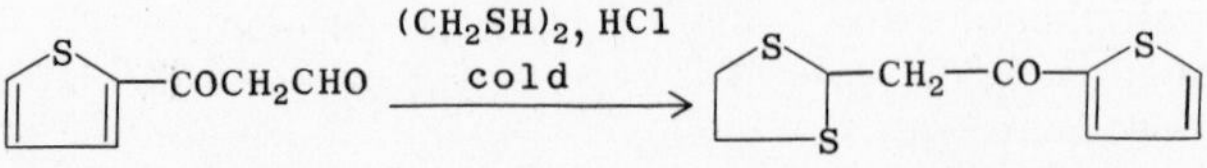

228

Chivers and Smiles[128] prepared 2-phenyl-2-benzoyl-1, 3-dithiolane (**226**) by a different procedure, which involved the reaction of 1, 2-ethane-bis(p-toluenethiolsulfonate) (**229**) with desoxybenzoin.

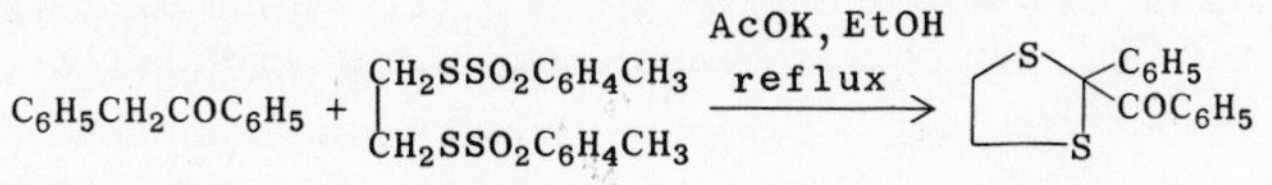

The reaction undoubtedly succeeded because of the active hydrogens in desoxybenzoin, and malonic ester reacted similarly; hydrolysis and decarboxylation yielded 1, 3-dithiolane-2-carboxylic acid (**230**).

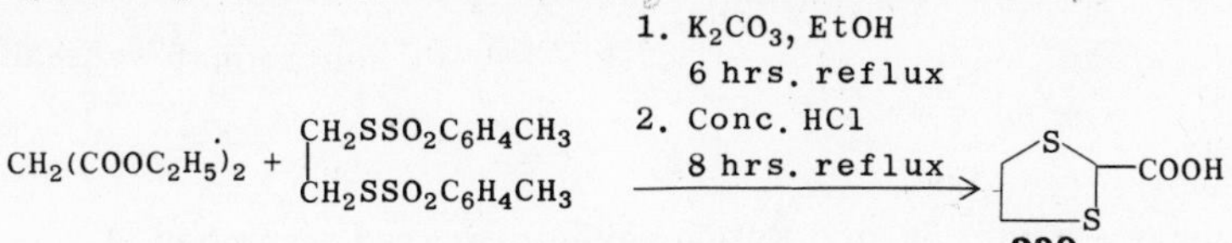

Chakravarti and Saha[123] claimed to have prepared **230** by a different procedure.

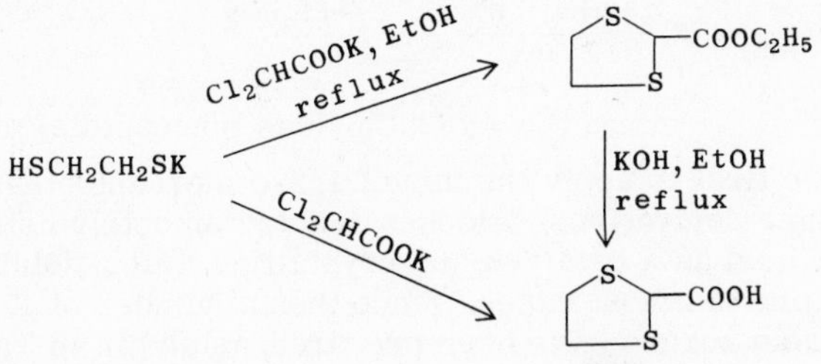

Both the ester and the acid were described as oils. If the reaction followed this course at all, their compounds were undoubtedly impure.

Kelber and Schwarz[292] prepared 2-phenacylidene-1, 3-dithiolane (**232**) by a different synthesis, involving the reaction of a *gem*-dithiol, 3, 3-dimercapto-1-phenyl-2-propen-1-one (**231**), with ethylene bromide.

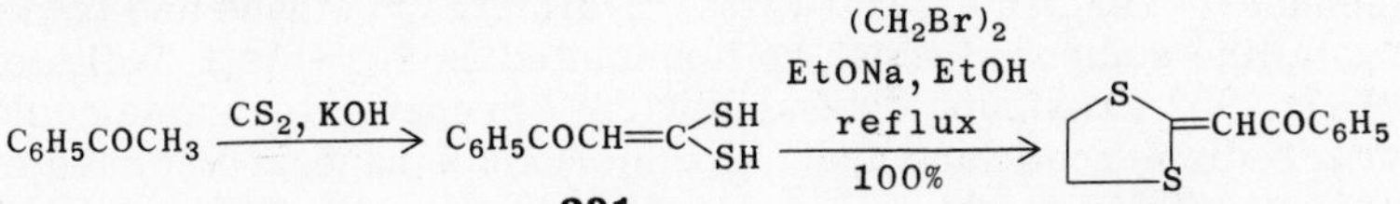

The structure of **232** was assigned on the basis of reduction with zinc and alkali to propiophenone and 1, 2-dimercaptoethane. Thuillier and Vialle[541] improved the synthesis of the *gem*-dithiol by carrying out the condensation with sodium t-amyloxide instead of with potassium hydroxide,[291] **231** being obtained in 80% yield. They also extended the synthesis to include a number of substituted acetophenones. Kendall and Edwards[295] carried out the same reaction on diethyl malonate. Methylation with methyl iodide yielded the corresponding methylmercaptal (233), while reaction with ethylene bromide gave (1, 3-dithiolan-2-ylidene)malonic ester (234), which was hydrolyzed to (1, 3-dithiolan-2-ylidene)acetic acid (235).

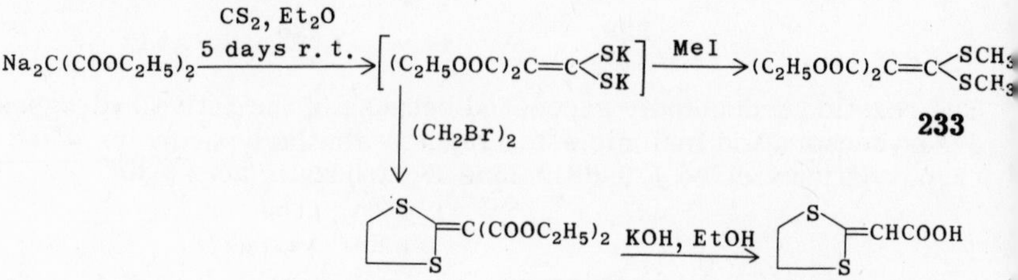

234   235

Kochetkov, Nifant'ev, and Kulakov[302a] prepared a number of 2-(acylmethyl)-1, 3-dithiolanes (235a) by the base-catalyzed condensation of β-chlorovinyl ketones with 1, 2-dimercaptoethane.

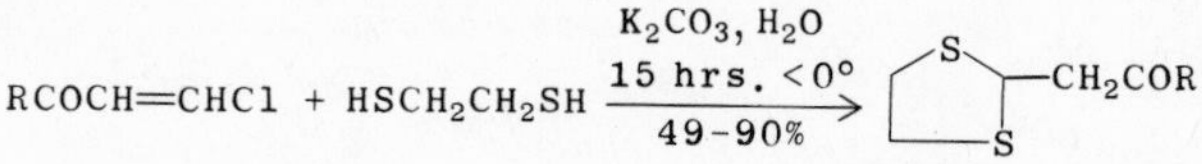

235a

Lawrence[313] was the first to apply tne use of 1, 2-dimercaptoethane to the preparation of sugar derivatives. Aldoses reacted smoothly using aqueous hydrochloric acid as a catalyst, and crystalline water-soluble derivatives were obtained in most cases. Since then a number of 1, 3-dithiolanes derived from sugars have been prepared, as shown in Table 14. Zinner[589] recommended the use of ion-exchange resins to remove the excess hydrochloric acid. According to Lawrence ketoses do not react.

The fact that benzil and benzoylacetaldehyde yield compounds containing only one 1, 3-dithiolane ring has already been mentioned. Table 15 lists those compounds with two carbonyl groups which react to give bis(1, 3-dithiolanes). Only one of these is worthy of comment. In 1888 Fasbender[173] reacted glyoxal with 1, 2-dimercaptoethane and obtained a crystalline compound which he formulated as 2, 2'-bis(1, 3-dithiolane) (236). In 1952 Proštenik and Balenović[423] prepared the same compound from 2, 3-dichlorodioxane and 1, 2-dimercaptoethane, and pointed out that the compound might be 1, 4, 5, 8-tetrathiadecalin (237), which could form just as well from glyoxal.

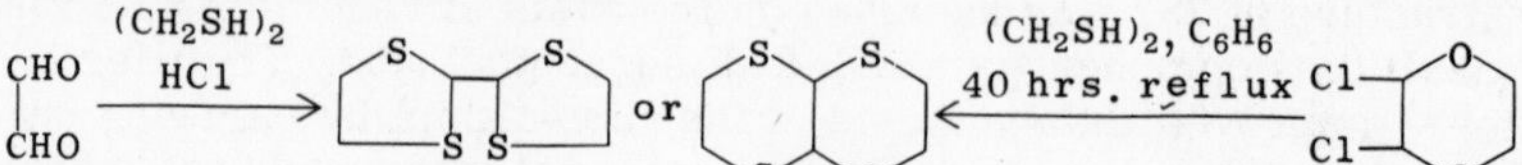

236   237

Brahde[78] determined the crystal structure and proved beyond any doubt that the correct structure is that of the bis(1, 3-dithiolane) (236). It is most interesting that the two five-membered rings form in preference to the condensed six-membered rings. Presumably a trace of water caused hydrolysis of the dichlorodioxane to glyoxal; the latter reacted with the dimercaptan to give the compound plus water, so a trace of water sufficed to convert all the dichlorodioxane to the bis(1, 3-dithiolane).

b. Structure, Properties and Reactions

The structure of the 1, 3-dithiolanes followed readily from their analyses, their method of preparation, and their reactions. The five-membered ring should be almost planar; Brahde[78] determined the crystal structure of 2, 2'-bis(1, 3-dithiolane) and found that the ring was slightly puckered, C_4 and C_5 being above and below the plane defined by S_1-C_2-C_3. In other respects the distances and angles appeared to be normal. No other X-ray or electron diffraction studies have been carried out.

1, 3-Dithiolanes are generally colorless, water-insoluble, organo-soluble solids or high-boiling liquids. According to Bergmann, Zimkin, and Pinchas[48] the liquids show a slight depression of molecular refraction below the calculated values. With few exceptions they are thermally stable to temperatures as high as 200-250°. They are quite resistant to both alkaline and acid hydrolysis, being more stable to acid than non-cyclic mercaptals and mercaptoles. The ring can be cleaved, however, by cadmium carbonate and mercuric chloride, a well-known reagent for hydrolyzing mercaptals, as demonstrated by Hach[233] on 2-phenyl-4-hydroxymethyl-1, 3-dithiolane (238).

Adams, Doyle, and co-workers,[5a] used silver nitrate to convert 2-phenyl-4-p-tolylthiomethyl-1, 3-dithiolane (238a) into 3-p-tolylthio-1, 2-dimercaptopropane.

Macholán[361] used the cadmium-mercury procedure to prepare 2-oxo-5-aminopentanoic acid (240) from the 5-phthalimido derivative (239), since direct hydrolysis of 239 did not yield 240.

[For references, see pp. 585-610.]

TABLE 14. 1,3-Dithiolanes Derived From Sugars

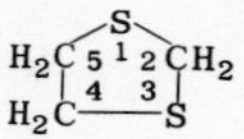

$H_2C \underset{4}{\overset{5}{C}} \overset{S}{\underset{3}{\overset{1}{}}} \overset{2}{C} H_2$ (1,3-dithiolane ring structure)

Substituent	Parent sugar	Yield (%)	M.p. (°C)	$[\alpha]_D^t$	t (°C)	Ref.
2-[(CHOH)$_3$CH$_2$OH]	D-Ribose	75-85	108	-29		237
	D-Lyxose	54	105-105.5	-23.2	24	588, 589
	D-Lyxose	75-85	141	+12.5		237
	L-Arabinose	80	142	+17.5	23	591
			154			313
	D-Arabinose	62	154.5	+11.4	24	591
	DL-Arabinose	96	159-160			354
	D-Xylose	76	76-77	-5.9	19	598
2-[(CHOCOCH$_3$)$_3$CH$_2$OCOCH$_3$]	D-Lyxose		83	+39		237
2-[(CHOCOC$_6$H$_5$)$_3$CH$_2$OCOC$_6$H$_5$]	D-Arabinose	86	100	+35.9	24	591
2-[(CHOCOC$_6$H$_4$NO$_2$-p)$_3$CH$_2$OCOC$_6$H$_4$NO$_2$-p]	D-Arabinose	78	109	+55.0	21	591
	D-Lyxose	83	213	+21.8	22	591
	D-Ribose	35	132-134	-6.3	20	593
2-[(CHOH)$_3$CH$_2$OC(C$_6$H$_5$)$_3$]	D-Ribose	99	Impure	-6.2	22	590
	D-Lyxose	84	139	+11.2	23	591

Compound	Sugar	Yield	M.p.	Rotation		Ref.
$2\text{-}[(CHOCOCH_3)_3CH_2OC(C_6H_5)_3]$	D-Arabinose	84	130	+25.5	23	591
	D-Ribose	66	127-128	-3.7	22	590
	D-Lyxose	76	133.5	+0.8	22	591
$2\text{-}[(CHOCOC_6H_5)_3CH_2OC(C_6H_5)_3]$	D-Arabinose	86	176	+32.3	22	591
	D-Lyxose	84	144	+15.5	23	591
	D-Arabinose	66	169	+42.9	24	591
$2\text{-}[(CHOH)_3CH_2OCOC_6H_5]$	D-Xylose	32	147	+19.6	19	598
	D-Lyxose	50	152	+21.7	19	598
$2\text{-}[(CHOCOCH_3)_3CH_2OCOC_6H_5]$	D-Xylose	86	83-84	+23.6	19	598
$2\text{-}[-CH_2(CHOH)_2CH_2OH]$	D-Ribose	69	97.5	-38.7	21	595
$2\text{-}[-CH_2(CHOH)_2CH_2OCOC_6H_5]$	D-Ribose	38	118	-15.4	18	597
$2\text{-}[-CH_2(CHOCOCH_3)_2CH_2OCOCH_3]$	D-Ribose	80	Oil	-3.9	21	595
$2\text{-}[-CH_2(CHOCOC_6H_5)_2CH_2OCOC_6H_5]$	D-Ribose	84	127	-13.9	18	596
$2\text{-}[\ -CH-CH-(CHOH)CH_2OH\ ](O\text{-}C(CH_3)_2\text{-}O)$ 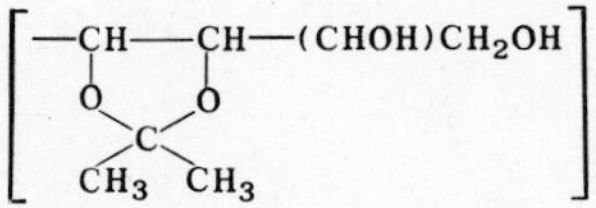	D-Arabinose	45	$(n_D^{20}\ 1.5459)$	+56.7	19	594
$2\text{-}[-(CHOH)_2-CH-CH_2\ ](O\text{-}C(CH_3)_2\text{-}O)$ 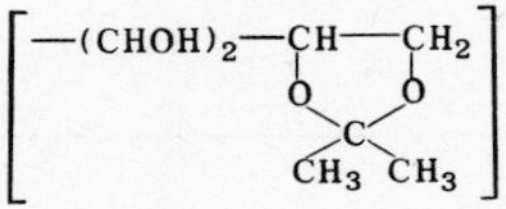	D-Arabinose	61	115-116	-15.5	20	594

TABLE 14. 1,3-Dithiolanes Derived From Sugar (contd)

Substituent	Parent sugar	Yield (%)	M.p. (°C)	$[\alpha]_D^t$	t (°C)	Ref.
2-[-(CHOCOCH₃)₂-CH-CH₂ dithiolane ring, CH₃ CH₃] 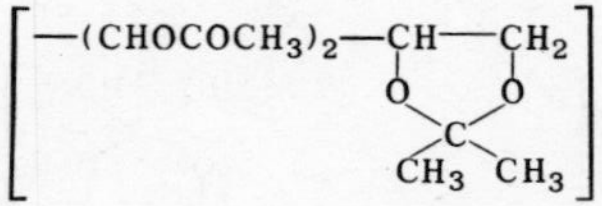	D-Arabinose	80	80-81	+31.3	20	594
2-[bis-dithiolane structure, CH₃ CH₃] 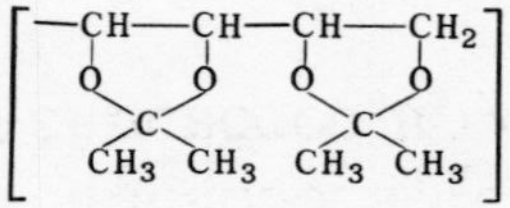	D-Arabinose	75	(n_D^{23} 1.5128)	+47.6	20	594
2-[bis-dithiolane structure with C=O] 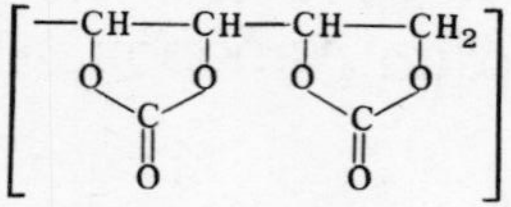	D-Arabinose	57	184	+41.1	18	599
2-[=CH(CHOH)₂CH₂OH] 1,1,3,3-tetroxide	D-Lyxose	95	169	-13.3	20	592
2-[-(CHOH)₄CH₃]	D-Fucose		191-191.5			557
	L-Fucose		191-191.5			557
2-[-(CHOH)₄CH₂OH]	Glucose	100	143	-10.81	20	313
		50-58	143	-10.56	18	211
	D-Mannose		153-154	+12.88	20	313

470

Substituent	Sugar					
2-[-(CHOCOCH₃)₄CH₂OCOCH₃]	D-Mannose	77	130-131	+34	25	232a
2-[-(CHOH)₄CH₂O₃SC₆H₄CH₃-p]	D-Mannose	40	153-154 (dec.)	-3	24	232a
2-[-(CHOCOCH₃)₄CH₂O₃SC₆H₄CH₃-p]	D-Mannose	80	143-144	+32	19	232a
2-[-(CHOCOCH₃)₄CH₂I]	D-Mannose	94	144-145	+37	19	232a
2-[-(CHOH)₄CH₂OH]	Galactose		149			313
2-[-(CHOCOCH₃)₄CH₂OCOCH₃]	Glucose	98	100.9-101.1	+5.03	19	211
2-[-(CHOCOC₆H₅)₄CH₂OCOC₆H₅]	Glucose	56	174.5-175.5	+26.18	15	211
2-[-(CHOH)₄CH₂OH]-4-CH₂OH	Glucose	96	155-156	+13.22	19	211
2-[-(CHOCOCH₃)₄CH₂OCOCH₃]-4-CH₂OCOCH₃	Glucose	49	101.3-101.5	+25.05	19	211
2-[-(CHOCOCH₃)₄CH₂OCOCH₃] 1-monoxide	Glucose	42	150-150.2	+1.59	19	211
	Glucose		152-153	-7		311c
$2-\left[-(CHOH)_3CH \underset{S-CH_2}{\overset{S-CH_2}{\big<}} \right]$	Xylo-pentodialdose	62	148.5-150			360

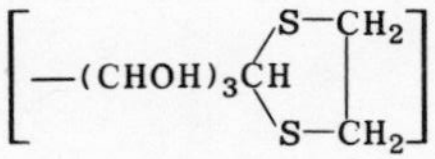

471

TABLE 15. Compounds With Two C_3S_2 Rings

Compound	Yield (%)	M.p. (°C)	Ref.
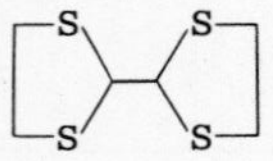 (bis-1,3-dithiolane structure)		133	173
		135.5	78, 423
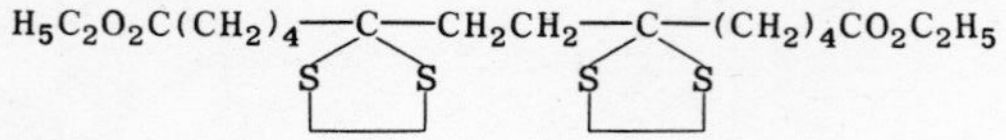 $H_5C_2O_2C(CH_2)_4$—C(dithiolane)—$(CH_2)_4CO_2C_2H_5$	64.6	60–61.5	167
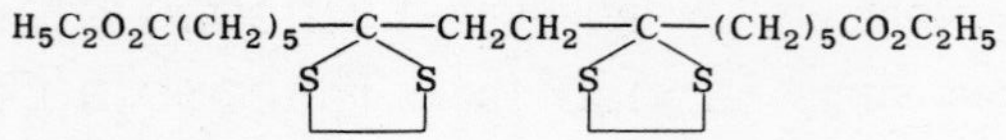 $H_5C_2O_2C(CH_2)_5$—C(dithiolane)—$(CH_2)_5CO_2C_2H_5$		36.5–39	167
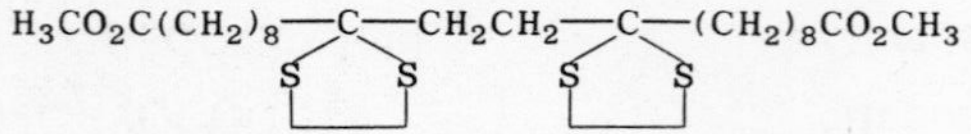 $H_3CO_2C(CH_2)_8$—C(dithiolane)—$(CH_2)_8CO_2CH_3$	97	62–63	258
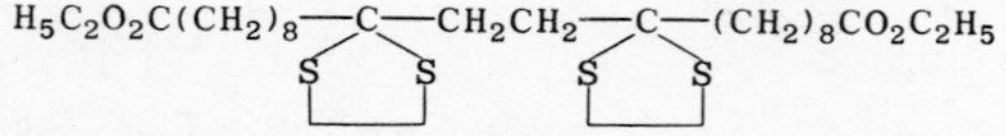 $H_5C_2O_2C(CH_2)_8$—C(dithiolane)—$(CH_2)_8CO_2C_2H_5$		oil	167
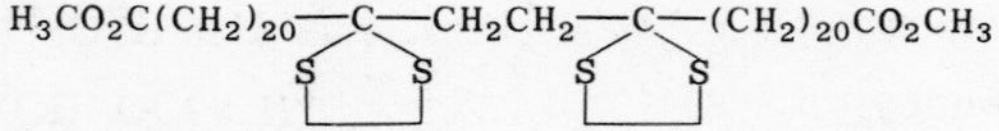 $H_3CO_2C(CH_2)_{20}$—C(dithiolane)—$(CH_2)_{20}CO_2CH_3$		63–77	258

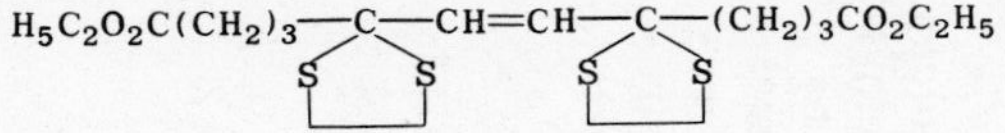

H$_5$C$_2$O$_2$C(CH$_2$)$_3$—C—CH=CH—C—(CH$_2$)$_3$CO$_2$C$_2$H$_5$

100   oil   168

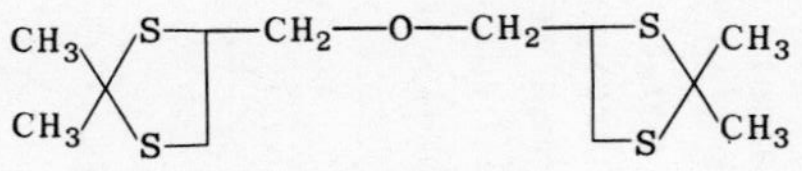

42   79   381

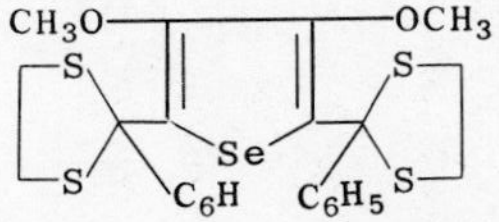

87   172   31

239

1. N$_2$H$_4$, NaHCO$_3$, EtOH
   reflux
2. HCl

$\xrightarrow{90\%}$

$\xrightarrow[51\%]{HgCl_2, CdCO_3}$ H$_2$N(CH$_2$)$_3$COCOOH

240

The stability of the ring to a variety of other chemical reagents is indicated by the reactions described below.

1, 3-Dithiolane has been reported to form a crystalline mercuric chloride adduct.[125,214]

Although suitably substituted 1, 3-dithiolanes should exist in *cis* and *trans* forms, until recently no examples had been reported in which two isomers had been separated from a reaction mixture. Miles and Owen[381] isolated *cis*- and *trans*-2-phenyl-4-hydroxymethyl-1, 3-dithiolane (**238**), but this was done by chemical transformations (*vide infra*). In 1958 Roberts and Cheng[452] condensed 1, 2-dimercaptopropane and 2, 3-dimercapto-1-propanol with a number of aldehydes and unsymmetrical ketones, and succeeded in separating the two isomers in several instances. Thus, 2, 4-dimethyl-2-phenyl-1, 3-dithiolane (**241**, R = CH$_3$) and 2-ethyl-2-phenyl-4-methyl-1, 3-dithiolane (**241**, R = C$_2$H$_5$) were separated by distillation, the two isomers boiling 10-15° apart. Forty-two systematic crystallizations would not separate **238** into its isomers, but the corresponding 3, 5-dinitrobenzoate esters could be separated readily; hydrolysis then gave *cis*- and *trans*-**238**, whose melting points agreed well with those reported by Miles and Owen.[381] The corresponding 2-*p*-chlorophenyl compounds were separated similarly, as were the isomeric 3, 5-dinitrobenzoates of 2-ethyl-2-methyl-4-hydroxymethyl-1, 3-dithiolane (**242**). In no case, however, were structural assignments made.

238 **241** **242**

Adams, Doyle, and co-workers,[5b] prepared 4-benzoyloxymethyl-2-phenyl-1, 3-dithiolane (**238a**) by two routes, esterification of **238** and reaction of 3-benzoyloxy-1, 2-dimercaptopropane with benzaldehyde, proving thereby that these compounds are 1, 3-dithiolanes and not 1, 3-oxathiolanes or 1, 4-oxathianes. Recrystallization of **238a** yielded one of the two possible isomers.

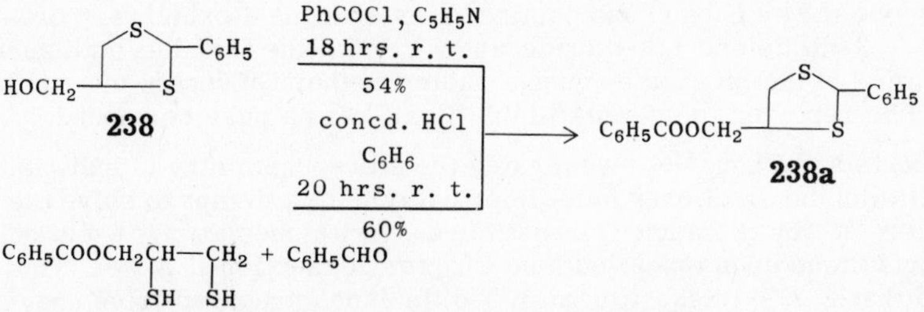

The analogous 2, 2-dimethyl compounds were prepared similarly. Fasbender[173] claimed that the 1, 3-dithiolane ring is less stable to oxidation than noncyclic mercaptals. He was able, however, to prepare disulfones from 2-alkyl-1, 3-dithiolanes by oxidation with potassium permanganate; 2-aryl derivatives decomposed. A number of disulfones have been prepared since then, as shown in Table 13. Gibson[214] oxidized 1, 3-dithiolane with hydrogen peroxide in acetic acid at 50° and isolated an 80% yield of the disulfone, prepared previously by Baumann and Walter[41] with permanganate (Gibson's reported melting point is probably a typographical error). Hydrogen peroxide is probably superior to permanganate, although Mazover[375] reported disulfone yields as high as 74% on oxidizing 2, 2-dialkyl-1, 3-dithiolanes with potassium permanganate in acetic acid. Fasbender[173] found that oxidation of 2-methyl-1, 3-dithiolane-2-carboxylic acid (243) gave 2-methyl-1, 3-dithiolane 1, 1, 3, 3-tetroxide (244); spontaneous decarboxylation took place as expected.

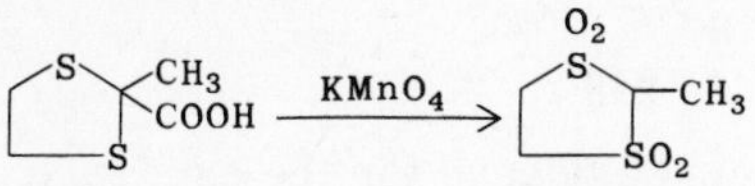

Chivers and Smiles[128] found the same effect on oxidizing 1, 3-dithiolane-2-carboxylic acid.

Breslow and Mohacsi[81a] prepared ethyl 1, 3-dithiolane-2-carboxylate 1, 1, 3, 3-tetroxide (244a) by alkylating 1, 3-dithiolane 1, 1, 3, 3-tetroxide with ethyl chloroformate.

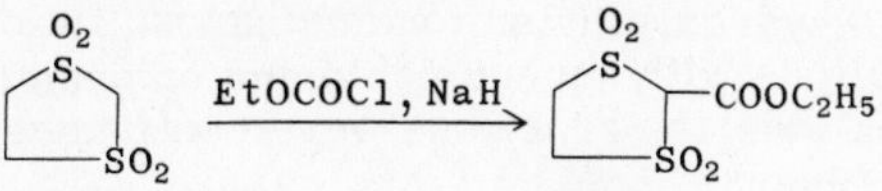

According to Gibson[214] a monoxide is formed when 1, 3-dithiolane is oxidized with hydrogen peroxide in acetic acid at room temperature instead of at 50°. He claimed that it formed a crystalline methiodide, and that it disproportionated on heating with warm hydrochloric acid to 1, 3-dithiolane and a dioxide, which he reported as an amorphous, insoluble solid, m.p. 134°. The dioxide was undoubtedly a polymer, since Bennett and Statham[46] oxidized 1, 3-dithiolane under the same conditions as used by Gibson and obtained a crystalline dioxide, very probably 1, 3-dithiolane 1, 3-dioxide, and a crystalline trioxide, both soluble in water. In fact, it may be questionable whether Gibsons's monoxide, which he reported to be a distillable liquid, was a pure compound.

Roberts and Cheng[452] investigated the stereochemistry of substituted 1, 3-dithiolane disulfones quite intensively in an attempt to solve the problem of why isomeric trisubstituted-s-trithianes always yield only one trisulfone upon oxidation (see Chapter 10, section II A-3e). They found that 2, 2, 4-trisubstituted-1, 3-dithiolanes prepared from unsymmetrical ketones (245) invariably gave two isomeric disulfones upon oxidation. If the two geometrical isomers were oxidized separately, two isomeric disulfones were obtained, whereas when an inseparable mixture of the two isomers was oxidized, the two isomeric disulfones could be separated by crystallization. On the other hand, in no case were they able to isolate two disulfones from the oxidation of 2, 4-disubstituted-1, 3-dithiolanes (247), whether they oxidized the pure isomers or an isomeric mixture.

245   246

247   248

These results appear to offer convincing evidence for the existence of d-orbital resonance in sulfur compounds, the disulfone derived from aldehydes (248) being capable of forming a planar anion whereas that derived from ketones (246) being unable to form an anion and therefore existing in separable stereoisomeric forms.

Fasbender[173] described the disulfones as being stable to concentrated sulfuric and nitric acids and readily decomposed by base. Baumann and Walter[41] hydrolyzed 1, 3-dithiolane 1, 1, 3, 3-tetroxide (249) with barium hydroxide and isolated β-hydroxyethylsulfonemethanesulfinic acid 250. Treatment of the disulfone with aqueous chlorine or bromine gave the corresponding 2, 2-dihalides; the reactions were confirmed by Chivers and Smiles[128] and by Gibson.[215]

249   250

Gibson also described 2-methyl-2-bromo-1, 3-dithiolane 1,1,3,3-tetroxide without any details as to its preparation. According to Kötz[303] the

disulfone (249) reacts with formaldehyde to give a crystalline conden-
sate, m.p. 238° (dec.), consisting of one molecule of disulfone and two of
formaldehyde.

Kochetkov, Nifant'ev, and Kulakov[302a] cleaved 2-acetonyl-1,3-dithio-
lane 1,1,3,3-tetroxide (250a) to acetol and the unsubstituted disulfone.
Thus, under sufficiently mild conditions the disulfone ring is stable to
base.

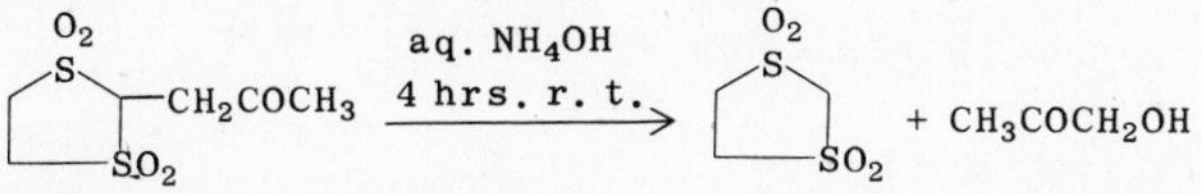

250a

1,3-Dithiolanes can be reduced to regenerate the parent dimercaptan.
Thus, Stoken[515] reduced 2-phenyl-4-hydroxymethyl-1,3-dithiolane (238)
with sodium and ethanol in liquid ammonia to 2,3-dimercapto-1-propan-
ol; the fate of the benzal portion of the molecule was not determined.

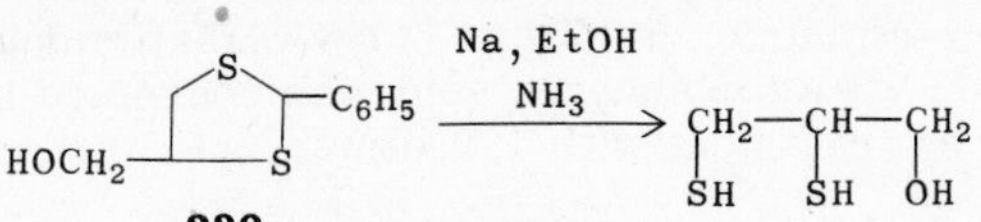

238

This reaction was confirmed by Miles and Owen.[381] Surprisingly, the
corresponding isopropylidene derivative, 2,2-dimethyl-4-hydroxymethyl-
1,3-dithiolane (251), was not reduced to 2,3-dimercapto-1-propanol but
to a compound which is probably 3-mercapto-2-isopropylthio-1-propan-
ol (252).

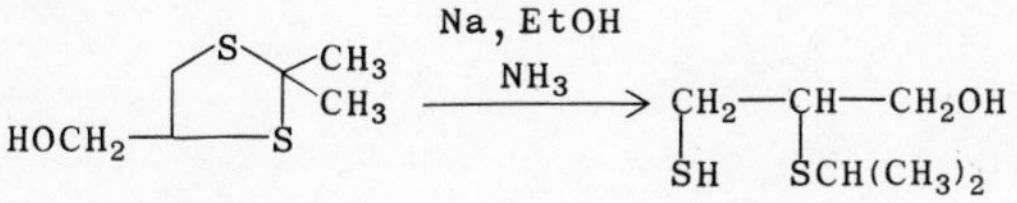

251   **252**

Similarly, Challenger, Mason, and co-workers,[125] reported that the reduction of 1,3-dithiolane with sodium in alcohol yielded 2-methylthio-
ethyl mercaptan instead of 1.2-dimercaptoethane.

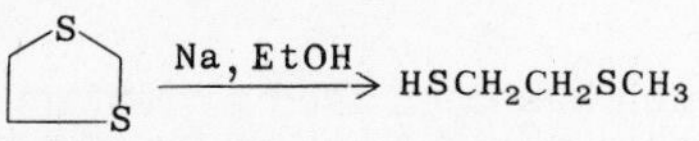

Kelber and Schwarz[292,294] reduced several 2-substituted-1,3-dithio-
lanes with zinc and sodium hydroxide; the sulfur-containing portion of
the molecule was converted to 1,2-dimercaptoethane and the original
carbonyl group was reduced.

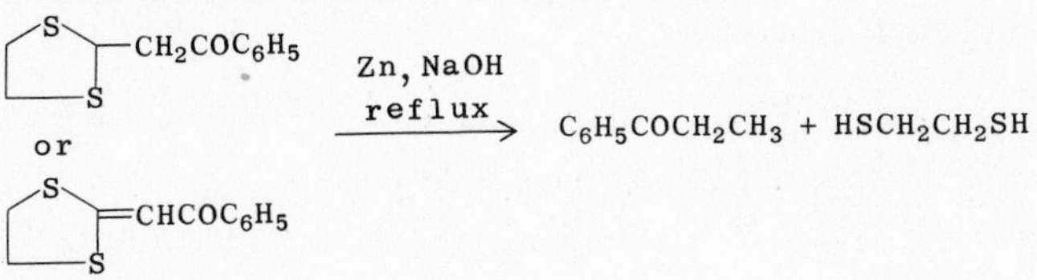

Condensation of a ketone with 1, 2-dimercaptoethane followed by reduction of the 1, 3-dithiolane with Raney nickel has been much used to convert a carbonyl group to a methylene group. Thus, Ernest and co-workers[167,168,258] used this procedure to prepare long-chain α, ω-dicarboxylic acids.

$$C_2H_5OOC(CH_2)_3COCl \xrightarrow{CH_2N_2} C_2H_5OOC(CH_2)_3COCHN_2 \xrightarrow{CuO}$$

$$C_2H_5OOC(CH_2)_3COCH{=}CHCO(CH_2)_3COOC_2H_5 \xrightarrow{(CH_2SH)_2}$$

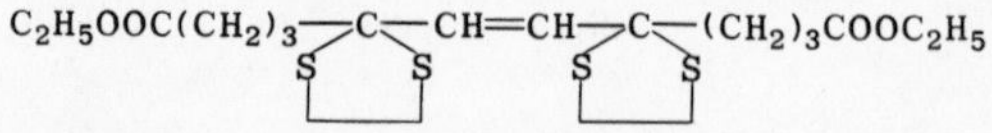

$$C_2H_5OOC(CH_2)_3{-}C{-}CH{=}CH{-}C{-}(CH_2)_3COOC_2H_5$$

$$\xrightarrow[\text{EtOH}]{\text{Raney Ni}} C_2H_5OOC(CH_2)_{10}COOC_2H_5$$

Balenović, Bregant, and Cerar[32] correlated the structure of β-aminobutyric acid with that of α-amino acids. Thus, (+)-β-phthalimidobutyraldehyde prepared from (+)-β-aminobutyric acid, was converted into (+)-2-phthalimidobutane by treatment with 1, 2-dimercaptoethane followed by Raney nickel.

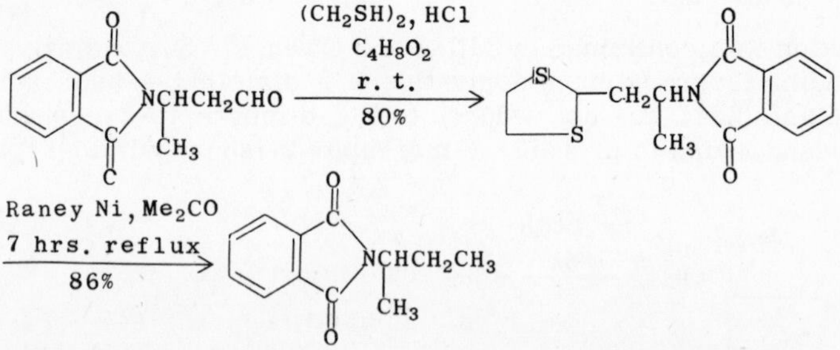

In a similar fashion, (−)-α-phthalimidobutyraldehyde, derived from (−)-α-aminobutyric acid, yielded (−)-2-phthalimidobutane. Thus, (+)-β-aminobutyric acid has the L-configuration. Balenović and Bregant[33a,33b] used the same procedure to correlate (−)-α-methyl-β-alanine with (−)-2-methylbutanol.

This desulfurization procedure, which has been used a great deal in the steroid field, is discussed in greater detail in section II A-4b. The reaction was reviewed recently by Hauptmann and Walter.[246b]

Hauptmann and Wladislaw[243] found that Raney nickel, which had been freed of hydrogen by heating *in vacuo* at 200°, yields an olefin instead of the hydrocarbon. Thus, 2-methyl-2-phenyl-1, 3-dithiolane (**253**) yielded *trans*-2, 3-diphenyl-2-butene.

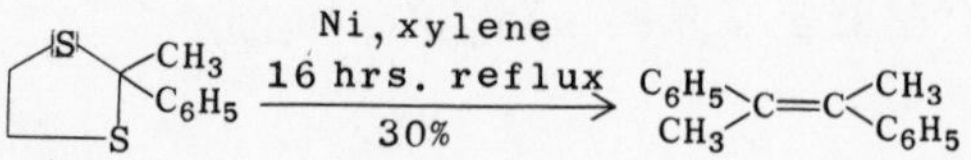

253

Georgian, Harrisson, and Gubisch[212] have recently suggested the use
of hydrazine for the desulfurization of 1, 3-dithiolanes. Thus, heating
the 1, 3-dithiolane with hydrazine hydrate in a glycol solvent up to 190°,
preferably in the presence of potassium hydroxide, gave 60-95% yields
of hydrocarbon.

$$R_2C=O \xrightarrow{(CH_2SH)_2} \text{[dithiolane]} \xrightarrow{N_2H_4, KOH} RCH_2R'$$

In certain cases where desulfurization is slow with Raney nickel, Crossley and Henbest[137c] recommend the use of lithium in ethylamine.
However, hydrogenation may also occur under these conditions.

According to Challenger, Mason, and co-workers,[125] heating 1, 3-
dithiolane with sulfur yields ethylene trithiocarbonate (254).

$$\text{[dithiolane]} \xrightarrow{200-230°} \text{[254]}$$

254

Thuillier and Vialle[541] found that heating 2-phenacylidene-1, 3-dithio-
lane (232) with phosphorus pentasulfide gives an almost quantitative
yield of 5-phenyl-1, 2-dithiole-3-thione (255); other aryl compounds
reacted similarly (see section I A-2a-(1)(k)).

$$\text{232} \xrightarrow[\substack{45 \text{ min. reflux} \\ 96\%}]{P_4S_{10}, \text{ xylene}} \text{255}$$

232　　　　　　　　　**255**

Because of the discovery during World War II that 2, 3-dimercapto-1-
propanol, "British Anti-Lewisite" (BAL), is a potent antidote for heavy
metal poisoning, a number of derivatives of it were prepared. The synthesis frequently involved blocking the mercaptan groups with benzaldehyde to give 2-phenyl-4-hydroxymethyl-1, 3-dithiolane (238), operat-
ing on the hydroxyl function, and then removing the blocking group by
reduction with sodium and alcohol in liquid ammonia as already described. In fact, Doyle and Nayler[159] recommended this as a purification procedure for BAL. The first reported work of this kind was that
of Stocken,[515] who carried out the following sequence:

$$\text{CH}_2\text{-CH-CH}_2 \xrightarrow[94\%]{PhCHO, HCl} \text{238} \xrightarrow[61\%]{SOCl_2}$$

238

$$\text{256} \xrightarrow[72\%]{KCN} \text{NCCH}_2\text{...}$$

256

[For references, see pp. 585-610.]　　　479

The 2-methyl and the 2, 2-dimethyl derivatives were also converted to the corresponding chloromethyl compounds. Stocken reported that his 2-phenyl-4-hydroxymethyl-1, 3-dithiolane melted at 77°. As already mentioned, this compound should exist in *cis* and *trans* forms, and Miles and Owen[381] showed that Stocken's compound was actually a mixture. The following sequence shows the method used to isolate the two isomers:

$$\underset{\underset{\text{OH}}{|}\ \underset{\text{SH}}{|}\ \underset{\text{SH}}{|}}{CH_2-CH-CH_2} \xrightarrow{\text{PhCHO, HCl}} \underset{\text{m. p. 68-71°}}{HOCH_2-\overset{S}{\underset{S}{\diagup}}-C_6H_5} \xrightarrow{\substack{\text{chromatography} \\ \text{recryst.}}}$$

$$\underset{\text{m. p. 88-89°}}{HOCH_2-\overset{S}{\underset{S}{\diagup}}-C_6H_5}$$

$$\xleftarrow[\substack{PBr_3, Et_2O \\ 85\%}]{} \underset{\text{m. p. 65°}}{BrCH_2-\overset{S}{\underset{S}{\diagup}}-C_6H_5} \xrightarrow{\text{recryst.}} \underset{\text{m. p. 81°}}{BrCH_2-\overset{S}{\underset{S}{\diagup}}-C_6H_5} \xrightarrow[59\%]{\substack{\text{aq. NaOH} \\ C_4H_8O_2}}$$

$$\underset{\text{m. p. 90°}}{HOCH_2-\overset{S}{\underset{S}{\diagup}}-C_6H_5}$$

In spite of the similarity in melting points, a mixed melting point determination showed that the two compounds are not identical.

Roberts and Cheng[452] reacted 2-ethyl-2-methyl-4-chloromethyl-1, 3-dithiolane (**209**) with alcoholic base and isolated a mixture of 2-ethyl-2-methyl-4-hydroxymethyl-1, 3-dithiolane (**207**) and 2-ethyl-2-methyl-4-ethoxymethyl-1, 3-dithiolane (**257**, R = C_2H_5), formed, according to the authors, through a sulfonium ion intermediate (**208**).

$$\underset{\textbf{209}}{ClCH_2-\overset{S}{\underset{S}{\diagup}}\diagdown\substack{CH_3 \\ C_2H_5}} \xrightarrow[\substack{C_4H_8O_2, H_2O \\ 12 \text{ hrs. r. t.}}]{\text{NaOH, EtOH}} \left[\overset{S}{\underset{\underset{H_2}{C}}{\diagup}}\overset{+}{\diagdown}\substack{CH_3 \\ C_2H_5} \right]$$

$$\textbf{208}$$

$$\xrightarrow{\hspace{1cm}} \underset{\textbf{207}}{HOCH_2-\overset{S}{\underset{S}{\diagup}}\diagdown\substack{CH_3 \\ C_2H_5}} + \underset{\textbf{257}}{ROCH_2-\overset{S}{\underset{S}{\diagup}}\diagdown\substack{CH_3 \\ C_2H_5}}$$

Presumably, the isomeric mixture of **209** was used, so mixtures of isomers were formed. Similarly, Miles and Owen[381,382] carried out a number of reactions on a mixture of *cis*- and *trans*-4-bromomethyl-2-phenyl-1, 3-dithiolane (**258**). Their results, however, were rather different from those of Roberts and Cheng. Thus, 4-methylene-2-phenyl-

1, 3-dithiolane (**259**) was isolated when an attempt was made to prepare ethers by treatment of the bromide with sodium alkoxides. **259**, which was unstable, was assigned this structure because ozonolysis yielded benzaldehyde, formaldehyde, and hydrogen sulfide.

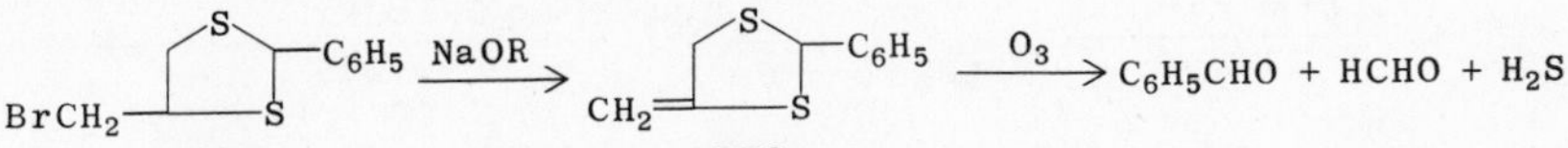

These results are in agreement with the reaction of 2, 2'-dichlorodiethyl sulfide. Helfrich and Reid[247] found that this β-chloro-sulfide reacts with alkoxides to give divinyl sulfide rather than the expected ethers.

$$ClCH_2CH_2SCH_2CH_2Cl \xrightarrow{NaOR} CH_2{=}CH{-}S{-}CH{=}CH_2$$

Similarly, Matlack, Chien, and Breslow[373a] found that most nucleophilic reagents react with 2, 4, 6-tris(chloromethyl)-s-trithiane by elimination rather than by substitution (see Chapter 10, section II A-3g). Ethers were formed, on the other hand, by treatment of the bromide with silver oxide and an alcohol, a reaction which is probably better evidence for an $S_N 1$ reaction involving the sulfonium ion intermediate (**208**) than that cited by Roberts and Cheng. In this way were prepared 4-methoxymethyl-2-phenyl-1, 3-dithiolane (**257**, R = CH_3) from methanol, and 2-phenyl-4-(2-phenyl-4-m-dioxan-5-yloxymethyl)-1, 3-dithiolane (**260**) from 1, 3-benzylideneglycerol; **260** was also prepared from 1, 3-dihydroxy-2-propyl 2, 3-dimercaptopropyl ether (**261**) and benzaldehyde.

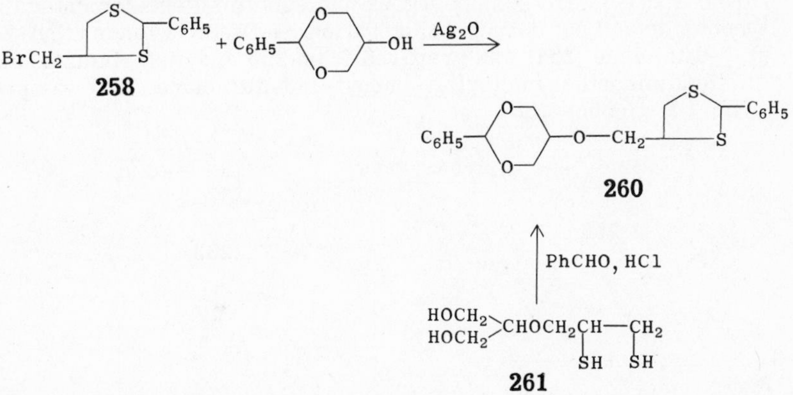

Inasmuch as the O-glucoside of 2, 3-dimercapto-1-propanol was found to be more effective and less toxic than the parent compound,[141] Miles and Owen[382] prepared the corresponding β-thioglucoside (**262**) by the following scheme:

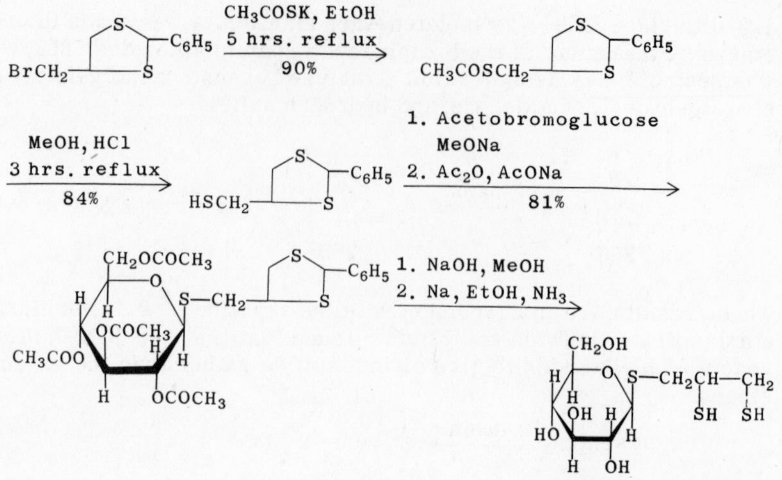

262

It is interesting that, when Miles and Owen[381] treated the isomeric mixture of 2-phenyl-4-hydroxymethyl-1, 3-dithiolane (**238**) with methanesulfonyl chloride in pyridine, they isolated an 84% yield of 2-phenyl-4-chloromethyl-1, 3-dithiolane (**256**) with the same melting point as the compound prepared by Stocken[515] with thionyl chloride. Either the chloride is a mixture of isomers or only one isomer was isolated.

Hach[233] prepared a number of aromatic ethers (**263**) of 2-phenyl-4-hydroxymethyl-1, 3-dithiolane by reacting their sodium salts with the chloromethyl compound (**256**). Thus, if the chloromethyl compound is a mixture of isomers, the derivatives are too. In this respect **256** parallels 2, 2'-dichlorodiethyl sulfide in reactivity, since Helfrich and Reid[247] found that mustard gas undergoes nucleophilic displacement with sodium phenoxide and not dehydrohalogenation. 4-Diethylaminomethyl-2-phenyl-1, 3-dithiolane (**264**) was prepared from **256** and diethylamine, and 4-(2-diethylaminoethoxymethyl)-2-phenyl-1, 3-dithiolane (**265**) was prepared from the alcohol (**238**).

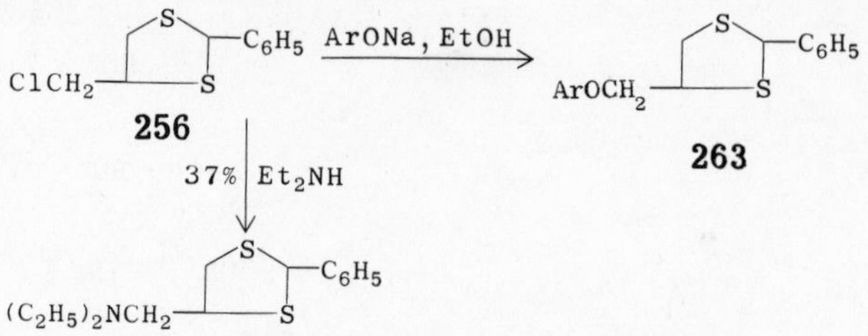

256

263

264

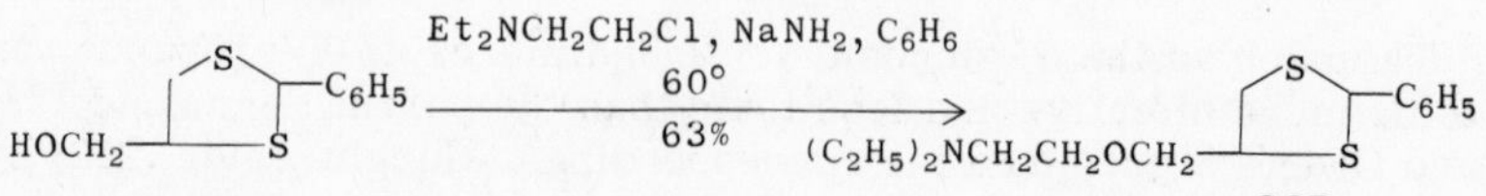

238

265

Several of these compounds were converted into 2, 3-dimercaptopropanol derivatives by cleavage with cadmium carbonate and mercuric chloride.

In a similar series of reactions Štefanac, Bregant, and Balenović[509b] prepared 4-dimethylaminomethyl-2-methyl-1, 3-dithiolane methiodide (265a), which showed some muscarinic activity. Presumably all the compounds were isomeric mixtures.

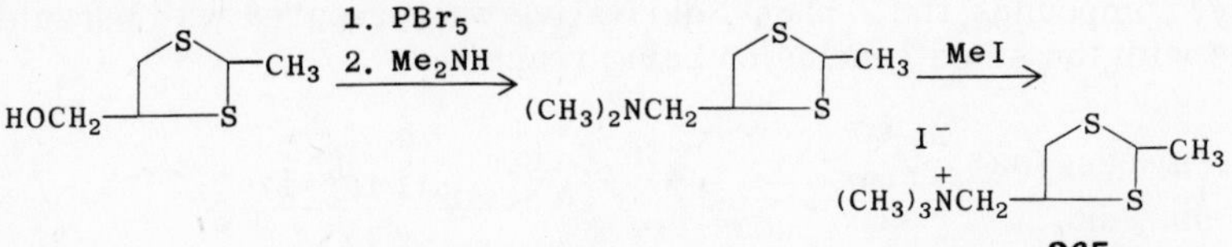

265a

Miles and Owen[381] carried out several reactions with 2, 2-dimethyl-4-hydroxymethyl-1, 3-dithiolane (266), which does not have *cis-trans* isomers. Treatment with α-D-acetobromoglucose in the presence of silver carbonate gave the corresponding β-glucoside (267), but it could not be reduced to the BAL derivative. When the sodium derivative of 266 was reacted with acetobromoglucose, only 4-acetoxymethyl-2, 2-dimethyl-1, 3-dithiolane (268) could be isolated, an interesting example of alcoholysis.

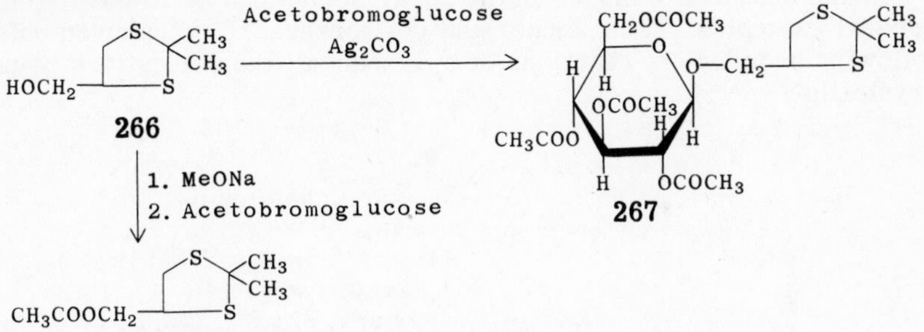

266

267

268

It is also interesting that a tosylate of 266 could not be prepared. With pyridine as solvent, the major product (52%) was the chloride (269), a trace of pyridinium tosylate (270) being isolated, whereas in the presence of caustic only the dimeric ether (271) was obtained.

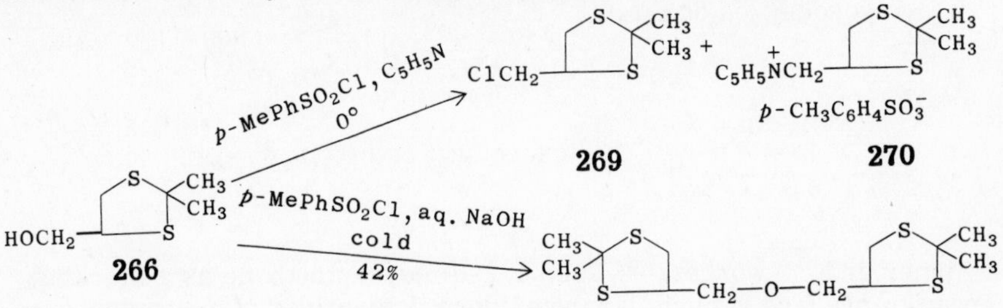

269

270

266

271

[For references, see pp. 585-610.]

Pavlic, Lazier, and Signaigo[416] prepared 2, 2-dimethyl-1, 3-dithiolane-4-carboxylic acid (272) by reacting α,β-dimercaptopropionic acid with acetone. The corresponding methyl ester was prepared from methyl α,β-dimercaptopropionate. Heating the acid with urea or the ester with ammonia gave 2, 2-dimethyl-1, 3-dithiolane-4-carboxamide (273). Ritter and Lover[450] prepared 2-styryl-1,3-dithiolane-4-carboxylic acid (274) from α,β-dimercaptopropionic acid and cinnamaldehyde, and concluded that this type of derivative is not suitable for the identification of carbonyl compounds; the 2-phenyl derivative was prepared with benzaldehyde with the same conclusion being reached.

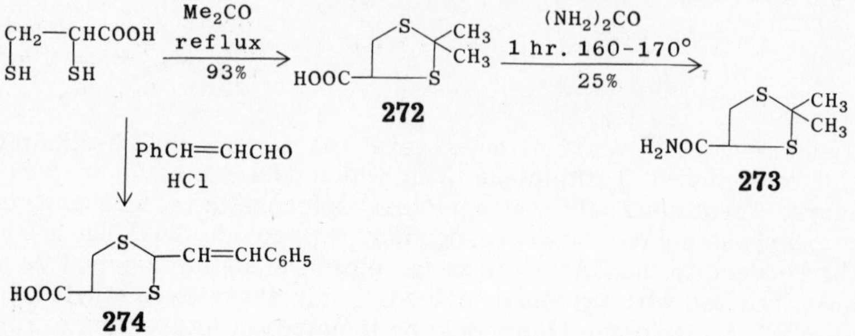

The use of 1, 3-dithiolanes in the sugar series can be illustrated by several examples. Thus, Zinner and co-workers[591,592] carried out the following sequence of reactions on D-lyxose, all the derivatives being crystalline:

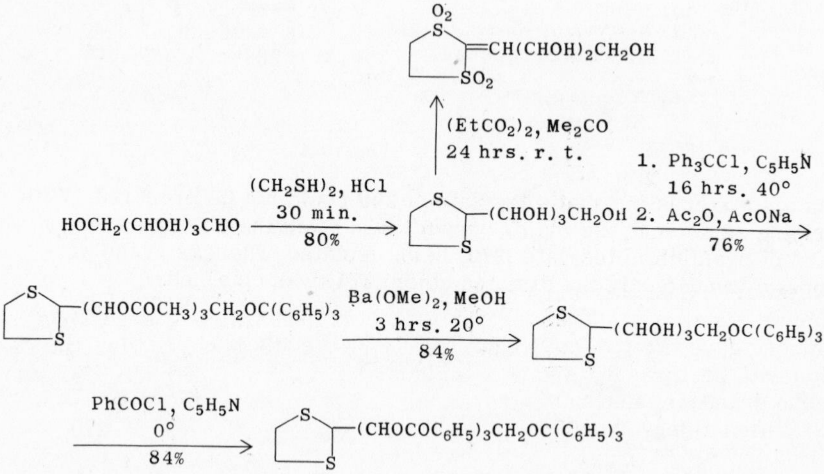

Zinner and co-workers[594] used 1, 2-dimercaptoethane as a blocking group to prepare various isopropylidene derivatives of D-arabinose, as well as the cyclic carbonate.[599]

484

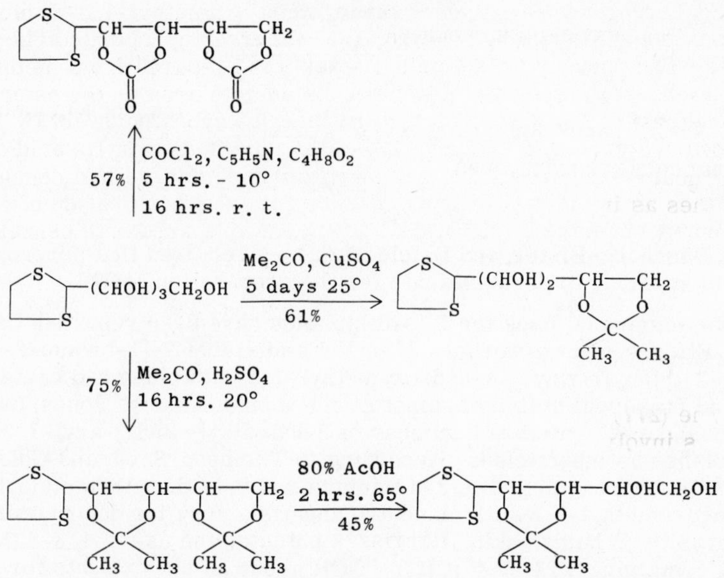

Zinner and co-workers[595-598] also prepared several derivatives of 2-desoxy-D-ribose.

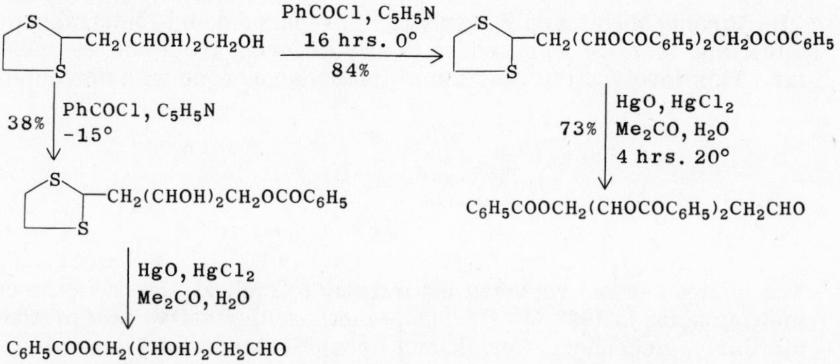

Similarly, Gauthier and Vaniscotte[211] utilized 1, 3-dithiolane formation as a means of preparing derivatives of aldehydo hexoses. Thus, glucose gave the 1, 3-dithiolane (**275**), which could be esterified. Oxidation with permanganate gave what appeared to be a monoxide (**276**), and more drastic oxidation destroyed the molecule, but bromine gave the esterified aldehydo-sugar.

275

[For references, see pp. 585-610.]

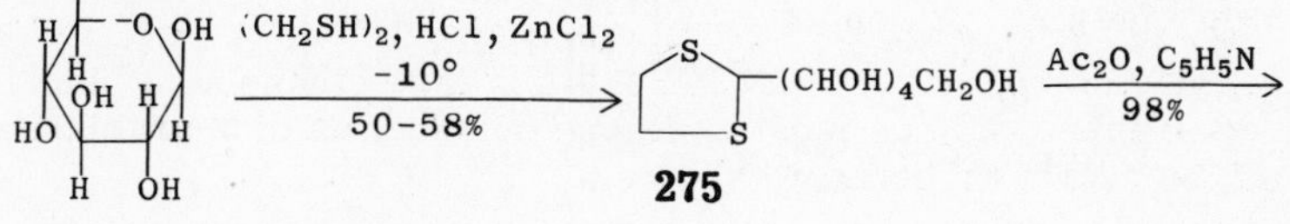

$$\text{S}\!\!-\!\!(CHOCOCH_3)_4CH_2OCOCH_3 \xrightarrow[49\%]{\substack{KMnO_4,\ AcOH \\ 10\ min.\ reflux}} \text{O} \atop \text{S}\!\!-\!\!(CHOCOCH_3)_4CH_2OCOCH_3$$

$$67\% \Big\downarrow \substack{Br_2 \\ AcOH,\ H_2O}$$

$$CH_3COOCH_2(CHOCOCH_3)_4CHO$$

Kuhn, Baschang-Bister, and Dafeldecker[3][11c] reported that perpropionic acid is superior to permanganate for the preparation of **276**.

Few commercial uses for 1, 3-dithiolanes have been reported. Carrara, Ettorre, and co-workers,[112,112a] stated that 2-[1-bromo-2-(5-nitro-2-thienyl)-vinyl]-4-hydroxymethyl-1, 3-dithiolane had bactericidal and fungicidal activity against *E. coli* and *M. aureus*. Jones, Lukes, and Bashour[283] patented a number of 2-haloalkyl- and 2-aryl-1, 3-dithiolanes as insecticides. According to Thomson, Savit, and Goldwasser[540] 4-hydroxymethyl-1, 3-dithiolane and 2-(p-dimethylaminophenyl)-4-hydroxymethyl-1, 3-dithiolane are unsatisfactory for decontamination of Lewisite on human skin. Harris[238] patented the use of 1, 3-dithiolanes containing a 2- or 4-$(CH_2)_n COOH$ group as antioxidants for edible oils and as plant fungicides.

2. 1, 3-Dithiolanes Prepared from Diazo Compounds

Bergmann, Magat, and Wagenberg[47] prepared 4, 4, 5, 5-tetraphenyl-1, 3-dithiolane (**277**) by a procedure totally different from any described thus far. This involved the reaction of thiobenzophenone with diazomethane.

$$(C_6H_5)_2C\!\!=\!\!S \xrightarrow[58\%]{CH_2N_2,\ Et_2O} \substack{C_6H_5 \\ C_6H_5 \\ C_6H_5 \\ C_6H_5}\ \text{ring}$$

277

The compound was reported incorrectly to melt at 166-167°; the correct melting point is 199°.[475,476] The p-methoxy derivative was prepared similarly. Schönberg, Černik, and Urban[475] prepared 2-methyl-4, 4, 5, 5-tetraphenyl-1, 3-dithiolane by an analogous reaction with diazoethane, and the corresponding 2-carbethoxy derivative by reaction with diazoacetic ester; the latter was too unstable to be isolated as a pure compound. In contrast to these, diphenyldiazomethane yielded only tetraphenylethylene sulfide, presumably by decomposition of the corresponding 1, 3-dithiolane.

$$(C_6H_5)_2C\!\!=\!\!S + (C_6H_5)_2CN_2 \longrightarrow \left[\substack{C_6H_5 \\ C_6H_5 \\ C_6H_5 \\ C_6H_5}\ \text{ring}\ \substack{C_6H_5 \\ C_6H_5}\right]$$

$$\longrightarrow (C_6H_5)_2C\!\!=\!\!S + \substack{C_6H_5 \\ C_6H_5}C\!\!-\!\!C\substack{C_6H_5 \\ C_6H_5}$$

486

Other thioketones reacted similarly. Thus, Bergmann, Magat, and Wagenberg[47] found that 10-thioxanthone reacted with diazomethane to form dispiro[xanthene-9, 4'-[1, 3]dithiolane-5', 9"-xanthene] (278).

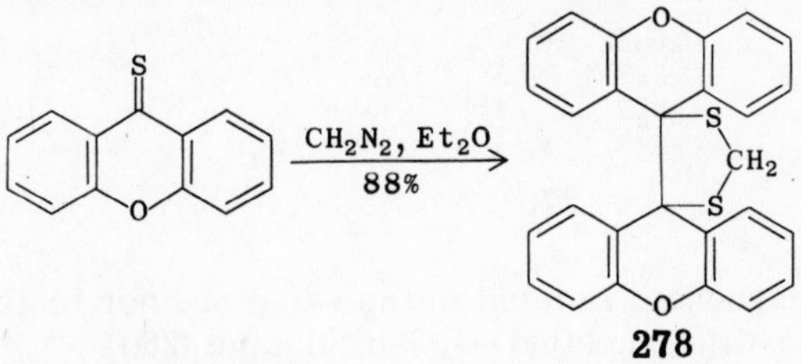

278

2, 6-Diphenyl-4-thiopyrone and related compounds were shown by Schönberg and co-workers[474,477,479] to undergo the same type of reaction (see Table 16).

The compounds reported by Bergmann[47] and Schönberg[475-477] and their co-workers have properties quite different from the 1, 3-dithiolanes described so far. Thus, the product of the reaction between thiobenzophenone and diazomethane was assigned the structure 277 because treatment with zinc and hydrochloric acid gave tetraphenylethylene. [47]

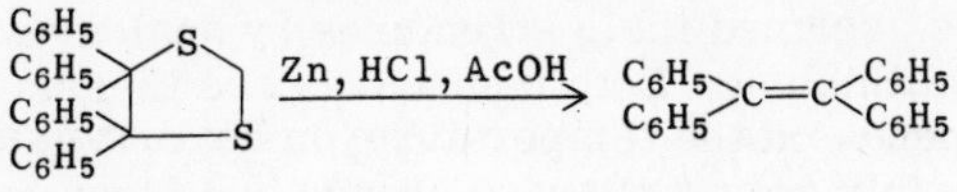

277

Phenyllithium gave tetraphenylethylene and lithium thiophenoxide, a reaction which Schönberg, Kaltschmitt, and Schulten[477] formulated as follows:

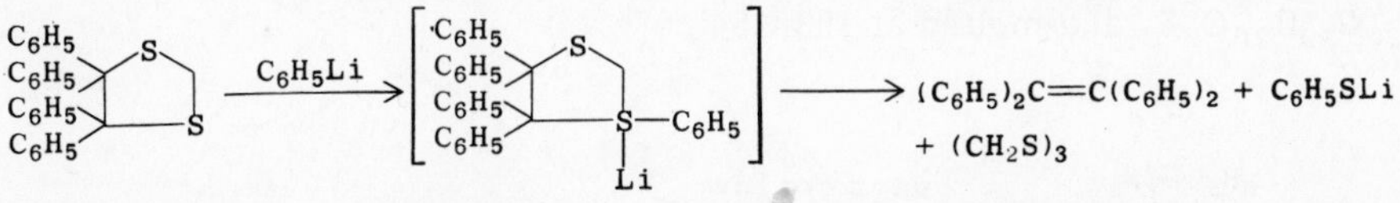

The other product of the reaction, s-trithiane, could not be isolated. The other alternatives for 277, 3, 3, 5, 5-tetraphenyl-1, 2-dithiolane or 3, 3, 4, 4-tetraphenyl-1, 2-dithiolane, would not have given tetraphenylethylene. 277, which is colorless, gives a blue melt, indicating that it reverts to thiobenzophenone on heating. Schönberg, Cernik, and Urban[475] isolated thiobenzophenone and 1, 1-diphenylethylene and postulated decomposition in the following manner:

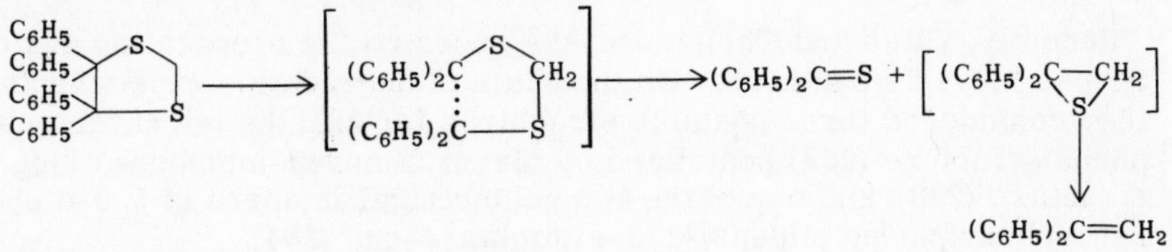

[For references, see pp. 585-610.]

Schönberg, Nickel, and Černik[476] found that diphenyl trithiocarbonate plus diazomethane yielded 4, 4, 5, 5-tetrakis(phenylthio)-1, 3-dithiolane (**279**).

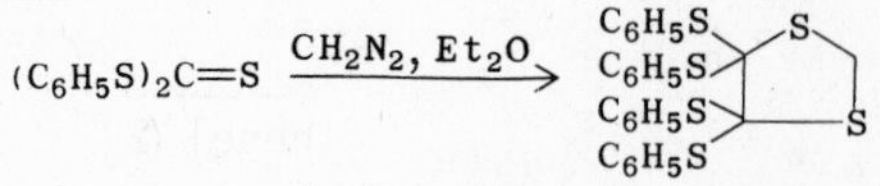

279

Methyl α-naphthylthiocarbonate reacted in the same manner to give 4, 5-bis(methylthio)-4, 5-di(α-naphthyl)-1, 3-dithiolane (**280**).

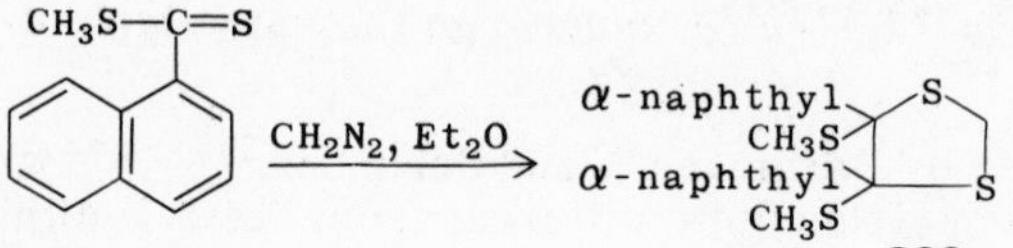

280

No other diazo compound underwent this reaction to give a 1, 3-dithiolane. Both **279** and **280** were assigned their structures by analogy with that of the tetraphenyl-1, 3-dithiolane. Both compounds are thermochromic, i.e. their color depends on the temperature; on heating in ethyl benzoate they change reversibly from yellow to orange and from pale yellow-orange to red-orange, respectively.[476]

There is another type of 1, 3-dithiolane which has been prepared from a diazo compound. In 1925 Meyer[378] reacted benzoylphenyldiazomethane or azobenzil with carbon disulfide and isolated a yellow, crystalline solid (**281**) in excellent yield. The compound analyzed as $C_{29}H_{20}O_2S_2$ and melted at 153-154°.

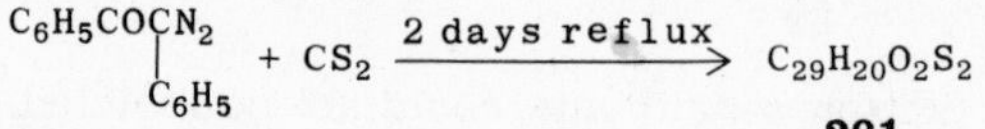

281

Meyer formulated the compound as 3-benzoyl-3, 5, 5-triphenyl-4-oxotetrahydrothiophene-2-thione (**282**) because alcoholic alkali hydrolyzed it to benzoic acid, phenylacetic acid, and an unidentified sulfur-containing acid which he considered to be thiobenzilic acid.

Recently, Yates and Christensen[583] repeated the preparation and confirmed Meyer's synthesis. On the basis of degradation experiments they considered three possible structures for **281**, the tetrahydrothiophene structure (**282**) postulated by Meyer, a seven-membered ring structure (**283**), and one of the two geometrical isomers of 5, 5-diphenyl-2-(α-phenylphenacylidene)-1, 3-dithiolan-4-one (**284**).

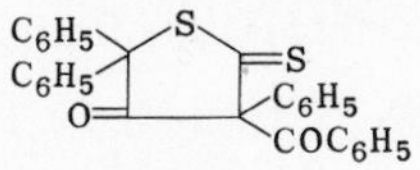

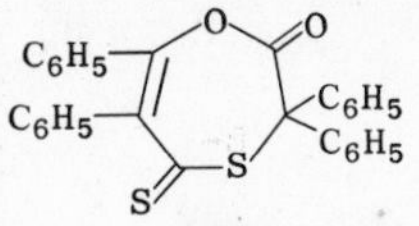

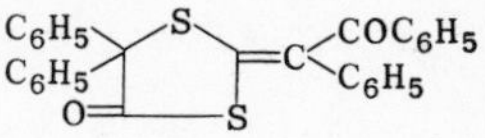

282   **283**   **284**

Alkaline hydrolysis gave benzoic acid, phenylacetic acid, and 2, 2, 5, 5-tetraphenyl-3, 4-dithiaadipic acid (**285**). Acid hydrolysis gave diphenyl-acetic acid, desoxybenzoin, and sulfur, while Raney nickel disulfuriza-tion in ethanol gave 1, 2-diphenyl-1-propanone, ethyl diphenylacetate, and a small amount of diphenylmethane.

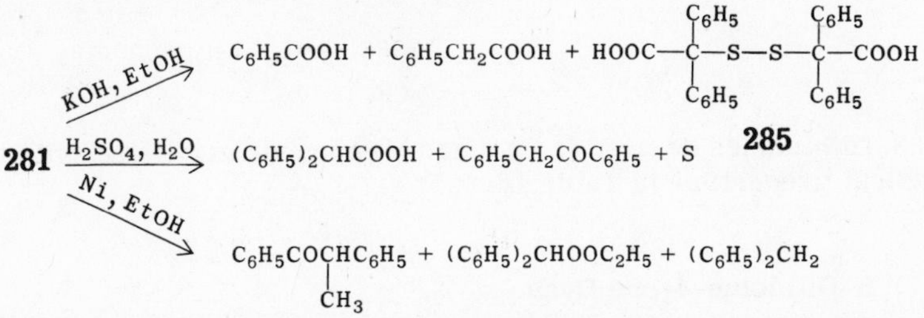

These degradation products could be derived from any one of the three postulated structures. However, ozonolysis yielded benzil, benzoic acid, and a little diphenylacetic acid, which would appear to rule out **282**, since it is difficult to see how this structure could give benzil.

$$281 \xrightarrow{O_3} C_6H_5COCOC_6H_5 + C_6H_5COOH + (C_6H_5)_2CHCOOH$$

Only the 1, 3-dithiolane structure (**284**) is compatible with the infrared and ultraviolet absorption spectra of **281**. **281** shows two bands in the infra-red, one at 5.86μ, attributable to the enol thiollactone structure, and a weak band at 6.17μ, attributable to the highly conjugated α, β-unsatura-ted phenyl ketone group; it absorbs at 254 and 347 mμ in the ultraviolet. Further confirmation comes from the fact that 2-(α-phenylphenacyli-dene)-1, 3-dithiolane (**286**) has an almost identical spectrum, having a weak band at 6.20μ in the infrared and two bands at 257 and 350 mμ in the ultraviolet.[582]

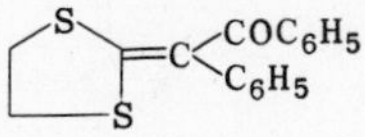

286

The chemistry of **281** is also in accord with the assigned structure. Reduction with zinc and acetic acid yielded a crystalline compound which was formulated as 5, 5-diphenyl-2-(α-phenylphenacyl)-1, 3-dithiolan-4-one (**287**), since hydrolysis yielded desoxybenzoin and di-phenylacetic acid, while Raney nickel desulfurization yielded 1, 2-di-phenyl-1-propanone and ethyl diphenylacetate.

[For references, see pp. 585-610.]   489

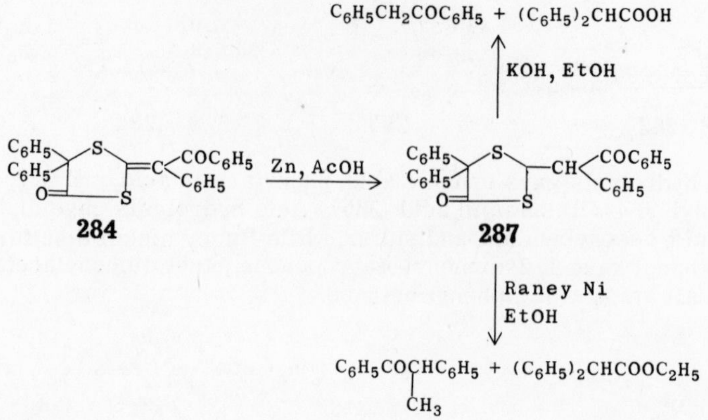

$$C_6H_5CH_2COC_6H_5 + (C_6H_5)_2CHCOOH$$

$$\uparrow \quad KOH, EtOH$$

284     $\xrightarrow{\text{Zn, AcOH}}$ 287

$$\downarrow \quad \begin{array}{l} Raney\ Ni \\ EtOH \end{array}$$

$$C_6H_5COCHC_6H_5 + (C_6H_5)_2CHCOOC_2H_5$$
$$\overset{|}{C}H_3$$

1,3-Dithiolanes derived from diazo compounds are listed, with their physical properties, in Table 16.

3. 1,3-Dithiolan-4-one Dyes

Knott[302] prepared several complex cyanines containing the 1,3-dithiolan-4-one ring system. Thus 3-ethyl-2-methylbenzothiazole tosylate (288) was reacted with carbon disulfide and the product was alkylated with chloroacetic acid and ring-closed with phosphorus trichloride to 2-(3-ethyl-2-benzothiazolemethylene)-1,3-dithiolan-4-one chloride (289), which was not isolated as a pure compound. Condensation of 289 with 2-(2-acetanilidovinyl)benzothiazole ethiodide (290) yielded [3-ethyl-2-benzothiazole][5-(3-ethylbenzothiazolin-2-ylidene-ethylidene)-2-(1,3-dithiolan-4-one)]methincyanine iodide (291) as black crystals melting at 275°.

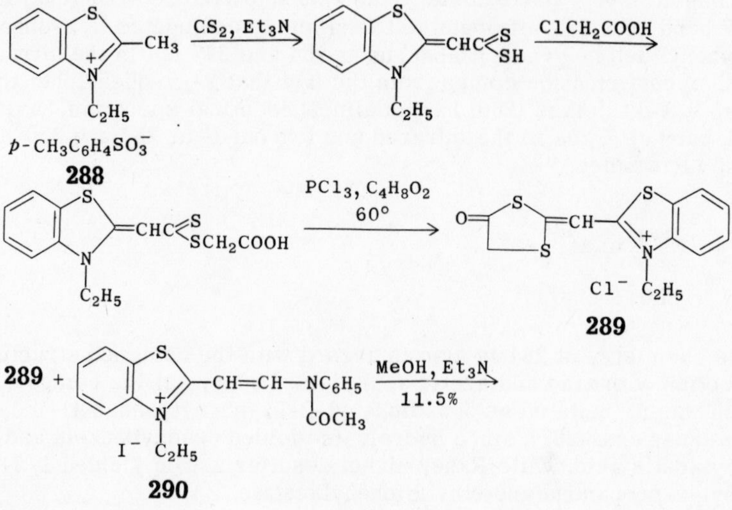

p-CH$_3$C$_6$H$_4$SO$_3^-$

288

289

289 +
$\xrightarrow[11.5\%]{\text{MeOH, Et}_3\text{N}}$

290

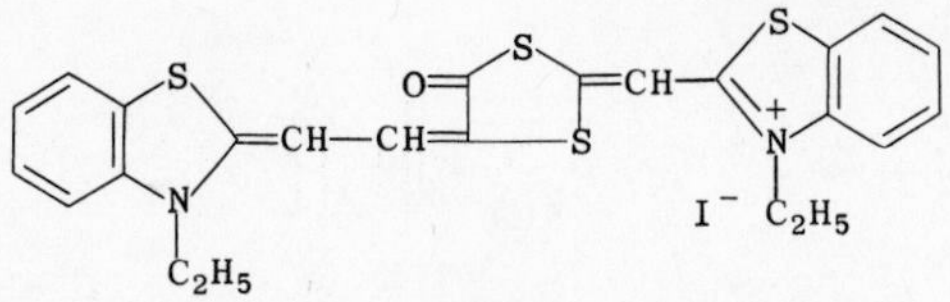

291

Similarly, **289** with 2-(2-acetanilidovinyl)benzoxazole ethiodide (**292**) yielded [3-ethyl-2-benzothiazole][5-(3-ethylbenzoxazolin-2-ylidene-ethylidene)-2-(1, 3-dithiolan-4-one]methincyanine iodide (**293**) as green crystals melting at 262°.

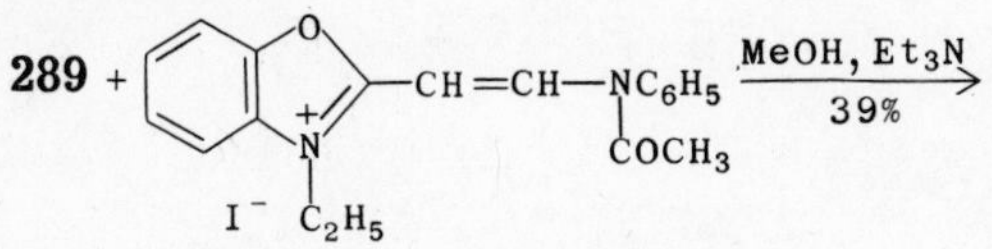

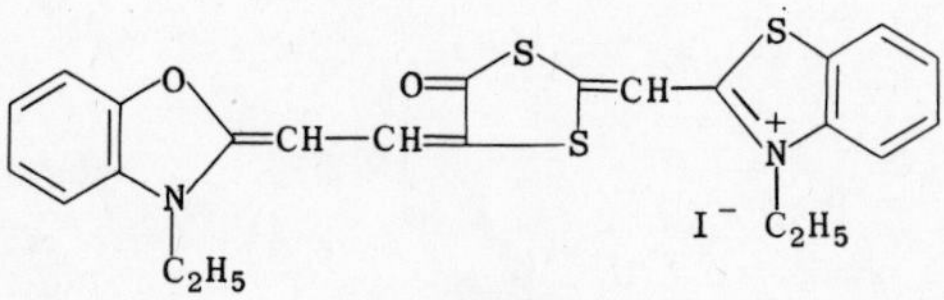

293

2-(3-Methyl-2-thiazolinemethylene)-1, 3-dithiolane (**294**) was prepared in the same manner as **289**. Reaction with **292** yielded [3-methyl-2-thiazolin][5-(3-ethylbenzoxazolin-2-ylidene-ethylidene)-1, 3-dithiolan-4-one]methincyanine iodide (**295**) as magenta crystals melting at 261°.

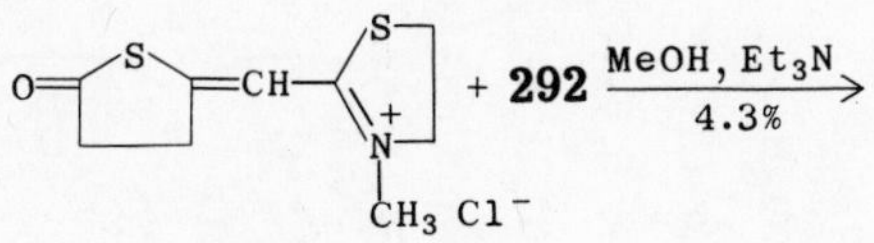

294

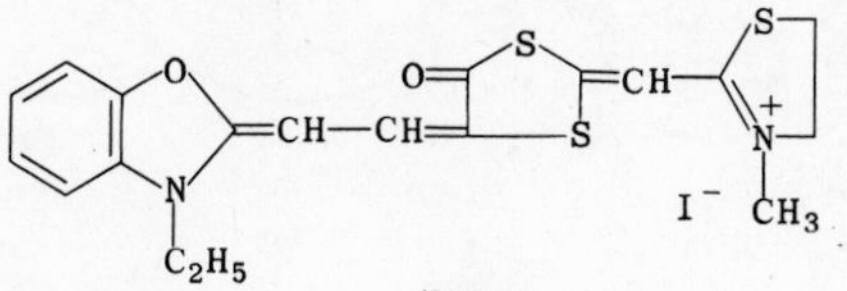

295

The absorption spectra of these compounds indicated that the thiolester bridge ($-\overset{\overset{\text{O}}{\|}}{\text{C}}-\text{S}-$) functions as an efficient transmitter of electrons between the auxochromes of the dyes.

[For references, see pp. 585-610.]

TABLE 16. 1,3-Dithiolanes Derived From Diazo Compounds

Compound	Yield (%)	M.p. (°C)	Ref.
$\underline{C_3S_2}$			
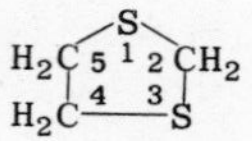			
1,3-Dithiolane			
4,4,5,5-(C₆H₅-)₄	58	199 (dec.)	47, 475
4,4,5,5-(p-CH₃OC₆H₄-)₄	48	161-162	47
2-CH₃-4,4,5,5-(C₆H₅-)₄		170-172 (dec.)	475
4,4,5,5-(C₆H₅S-)₄			476
4,5-(α-Naphthyl-)₂-4,5-(CH₃S-)₂		~140 (dec.)	476
2-$\left(\begin{smallmatrix}C_6H_5CO\\C=\\C_6H_5\end{smallmatrix}\right)$-4-(O=)-5,5-(C₆H₅-)₂	92	154-155	378, 583
2-$\left(\begin{smallmatrix}C_6H_5CO\\CH-\\C_6H_5\end{smallmatrix}\right)$-4-(O=)-5,5-(C₆H₅-)₂		209.5-210.5	583
$\underline{C_3S_2-C_5O-C_5O}$			

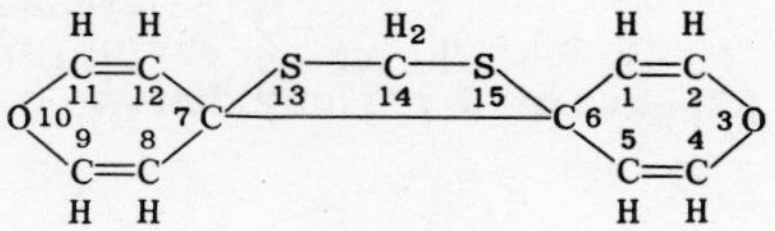

3,10-Dioxa-13,15-dithiadispiro[5.0.5.3]-pentadeca-1,4,9,11-tetraene

2,4,9,11-(C$_6$H$_5$-)$_4$		49	479

C$_3$S$_2$-C$_5$O-C$_5$O-C$_6$-C$_6$

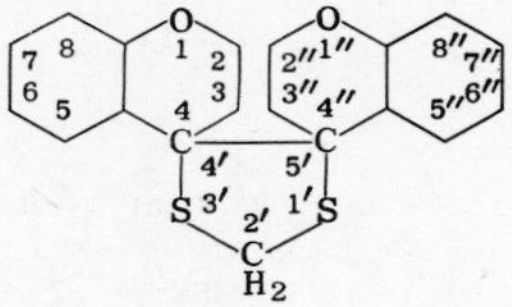

Dispiro[4H-1-benzopyran-4,4'-[1,3]dithiolane-5',4''-[4H-1]benzopyran] (RRI 5857)

2,2''-(C$_6$H$_5$-)$_2$		182-183 (dec.)	474, 477
2,2''-(C$_6$H$_5$CH=CH-)$_2$	80	180 (dec.)	479
2,2''-(p-CH$_3$OC$_6$H$_4$CH=CH-)$_2$	80	176 (dec.)	479

C$_3$S$_2$-C$_5$O-C$_5$O-C$_6$-C$_6$-C$_6$

493

TABLE 16. 1, 3-Dithiolanes Derived From Diazo Compounds (contd)

Compound	Yield (%)	M.p. (°C)	Ref.
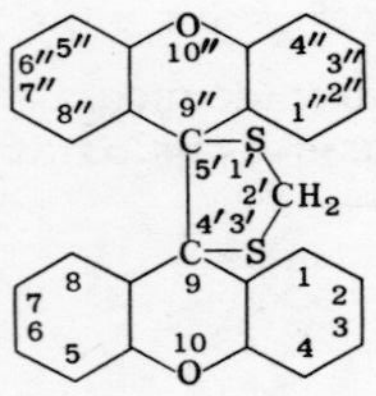 Dispiro[xanthene-9, 4'-[1, 3]dithiolane-5', 9"-xanthene] (RRI 7183)	88	224	47
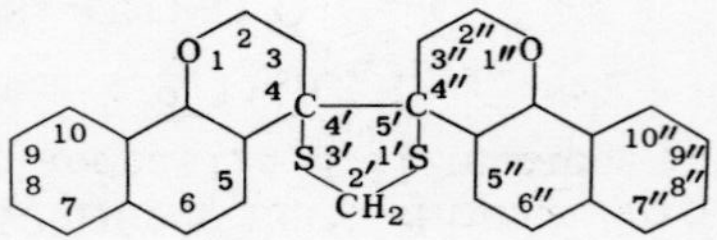 Dispiro[4H-naphtho[1, 2-o]pyran-4, 4'-[1, 3]dithiolane-5', 4"-[4H]naphtho[1, 2-o]pyran] (RRI 7184)			

2,2"-(C$_6$H$_5$-)$_2$		164-165	474, 477
2,2"-(C$_6$H$_5$CH=CH-)$_2$	70	188 (dec.)	479
2,2"-(p-CH$_3$OC$_6$H$_4$CH=CH-)$_2$	70	175 (dec.)	479

C$_3$S$_2$-C$_5$S-C$_5$S-C$_6$-C$_6$-C$_6$-C$_6$

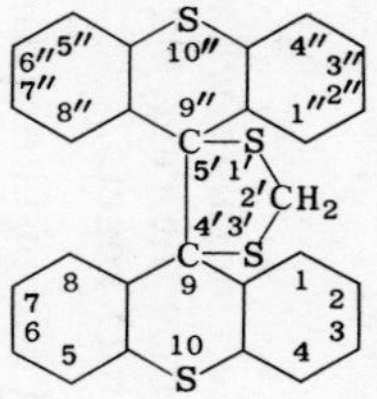

Dispiro[thiaxanthene-9, 4'-[1, 3]-dithiolane-5', 9"-thiaxanthene] (RRI 7185)   168-170 (dec.)   477

4. Spiro Derivatives of 1, 2-Dimercaptoalkanes

The reaction of 1, 2-dimercaptoalkanes with cyclic ketones leads to spiro-1, 3-dithiolanes. These are discussed in two sections, steroids and related compounds and nonsteroids.

a. Nonsteroid Spiro Derivatives

These compounds are listed in Table 17. Their preparations are frequently the same as the corresponding nonspiro compounds, and their chemistry is discussed only when points of interest arise.

Reid and Jelinek[448] prepared 1, 4-dithiaspiro[4. 5]decane (296) from cyclohexanone and 1, 2-dimercaptoethane with hydrogen chloride as a catalyst in a straightforward reaction.

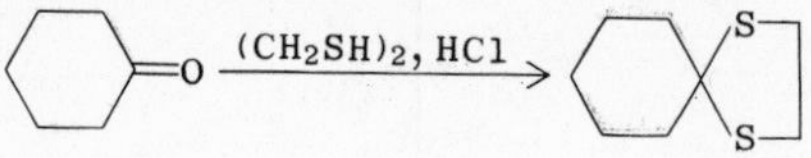

296

Mazover[375] used the bis-Bunte salt, $(CH_2S_2O_3Na)_2$, for the same purpose, and probably did not obtain the pure compound, since he reported it could not be distilled without decomposition; there is no reason, however, to doubt the purity of the disulfone, prepared by permanganate oxidation in acetic acid.

Hauptmann[244] introduced the use of fused zinc chloride, with anhydrous sodium sulfate to take up the water of reaction, for the preparation of 1, 3-dithiolanes. He classified this reagent as being milder than hydrogen chloride. It is interesting that camphor reacts with 1, 2-dimercaptoethane but not with simple mercaptans. Hauptmann proposed the following mechanism for mercaptole formation:

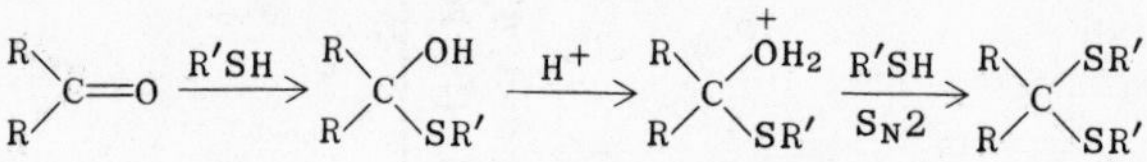

The S_N2 reaction is subject to steric hindrance with the monomercaptan but not with the dimercaptan. Since the cage structure of camphor hinders an S_N2 reaction, only the latter reacts.

Jaeger and Smith[275-277] carried out an interesting series of reactions on 1, 4-dithiaspiro[4. 5]decan-6-one (297), as shown in the following series of reactions:

C₃S₂ Ring Systems

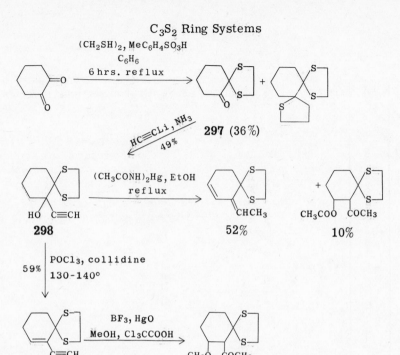

297 (36%)

298

52%

10%

The reaction of interest is the dehydration of 6-ethynyl-1,4-dithia-spiro[4.5]decan-6-ol (**298**) with phosphorus oxychloride and collidine, which takes place normally here but with double bond migration away from conjugation with the ethynyl group in the case of the corresponding oxathiolane (see Chapter 4, section II A-2b-(6)). Jaeger and Smith attribute this to steric strain in the oxathiolane but not in the dithiolane.

MacDonald and Fischer[360] found that *myo*inonose-2 (**299**) reacts normally with 1,2-dimercaptoethane, in contrast to D-fructose which, according to Lawrence,[313] does not react. This is probably another example of the tendency of a cyclohexane carbon to be tetracoordinate,[89] although the steric effect might be a factor.

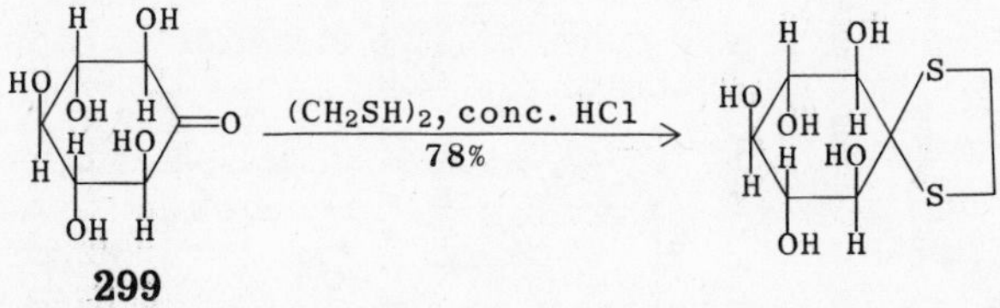

299

Takeda, Kitahanoki, and Igaraschi[528] used 1,3-dithiolane formation to prove that hydroquinone reacts with maleic anhydride to give 2,5-dioxobicyclo[2.2.2]octane-7,8-dicarboxylic anhydride (**300**).

TABLE 17. Spiro Derivatives of 1,2-Dimercaptoalkanes

Compound	Yield (%)	M.p. (°C)	B.p. (°C) (mm)	Other properties	Ref.
$C_3S_2-C_4O$					
7-Oxa-1,4-dithiaspiro[4.4]nonane (RRI 968)	54		98-98.5 3	n_D^{20} 1.5756 d^{20} 1.2629	306
1,1,4,4-tetroxide		154.5-155			306
$C_3S_2-C_4S$					
1,4,7-Trithia[4.4]nonane (RRI 969)	76		128-128.5 4	n_D^{20} 1.6317 d^{20} 1.3040	306
1,1,4,7,7-hexaoxide	95	dec. 210			306
$C_3S_2-C_5$					
1,4-Dithiaspiro[4.4]nonane (RRI 971)			89 5	n_D^{25} 1.5679 d_4^{25} 1.1464	448
6-(O=)-7-$C_2H_5O_2$C-8-CH_3-	63				459d
$C_3S_2-C_4S_2$					

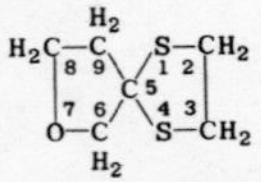

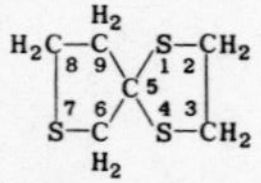

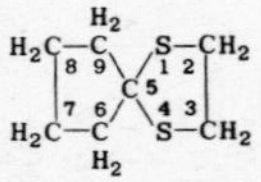

C_3S_2 Ring Systems

1,4,6,9-Tetrathia[4.5]decane (RRI 1240)

Ring system skeleton (spiro, positions numbered 1–10):

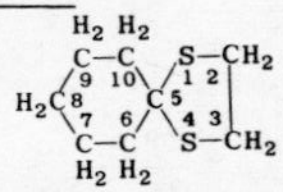

H_2 H_2
C—C S—CH₂
(9) (10) (1) (2)
C₂ (8)(7) (6)(5) (3)(4) C
H_2 H_2 S—CH₂

C_3S_2–C_6

Compound	Yield (%)	m.p. (°C)	b.p. (°C)	mm	n_D / d / notes	Refs.
1,4,6,9-Tetrathia[4.5]decane (RRI 1240)	81	98–99				25
1,4-Dithiaspiro[4.5]decane (RRI 1246)	60		114–115	6	n_D^{25} 1.5650, d_4^{25} 1.1288	244
	77	165–166	107	5	n_D^{25} 1.5478, d_4^{25} 1.0907	375
1,1,4,4-tetroxide	31		126	13		448
8-CH_3-	48		113–115	3.5		375
9-CH_3-6-iso-C_3H_7	69	70	150	0.8		448
2-($HOCH_2$-)	83		190–195	0.1		244
6-($C_2H_5O_2C$-)-6-[$C_2H_5O_2C(CH_2)_3$-]	36	57.5	94	0.2		515
6-(O=)	49	79.5				542
6-HO-6-(HC≡C-)	59	78				275, 276
6-(HC≡C-)-6-ene	52		150–160	15		275, 277
6-(CH_3CH=)-7-ene	10	110				275, 277
6-(CH_3CO-)-7-(CH_3CO_2-)		52.5				277
6-(CH_3CO-)-7-CH_3O-	76	210–211				277
6-(HO_2CCH_2-)-7-(HO_2C)-7-CH_3-	78	263–265 (dec.)			from myoinonose-2	277
6,7,8,9,10-(HO-)₅	94	144.6–145.4				7
8-(4-$trans$-benzoxycyclohexyl-)		~280				360
7-(HO_2C-)-8-CH_3-8-[4-carboxy-1-(1,5-dimethylhexyl)hexahydro-7a-methyl-5-indanyl-]		144–145				576
7-(CH_3O_2C-)-8-CH_3-8-[4-carbomethoxy-1-(1,5-dimethlhexyl)hexahydro-7a-methyl-5-indanyl-]						183
						183

TABLE 17. Spiro Derivatives of 1,2-Dimercaptoalkanes (contd)

Compound	Yield (%)	M.p. (°C)	B.p. (°C)	(mm)	Other properties	Ref.
C_3S_2–C_{10}						
1,4-Dithiaspiro[4.9]tetradecane			128	10		520a
7,13-$(CH_3)_2$-10-$[(CH_3)_2CH-]$						
C_3S_2–C_5–C_5						
Spiro[1,3-dithiolane-2,2'-norbornane] (RRI 2231)		69.4–70.3				36a
3'-CH_3-3'-(p-$CH_3OC_6H_4$-)	45		108–110	5		244
1',7',7'-$(CH_3)_3$			131	4	n_D^{25} 1.5606, d_4^{25} 1.0839	448
C_3S_2–C_3S_2–C_6						
1,4,7,10-Tetrathiadispiro[4.0.4.4]tetradecane (RRI 2433)		156				276
C_3S_2–C_4N–C_6						

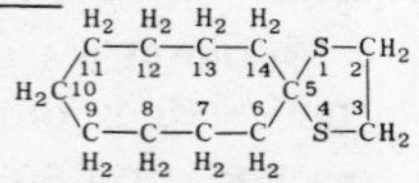

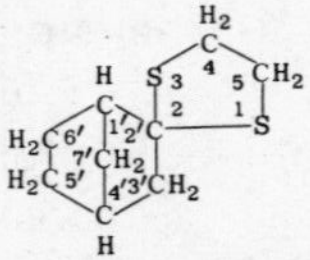

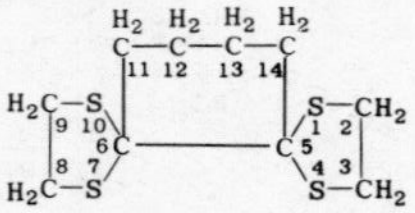

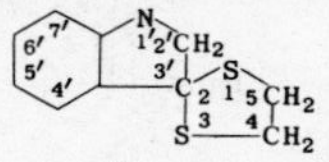

Spiro[1,3-dithiolane-2,3'-indoline]

1,2-H$_2$-2-(O=)   200-201   571

C$_3$S$_2$-C$_5$-C$_6$

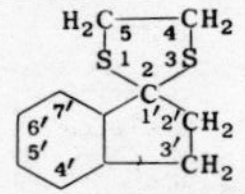

Spiro[1,3-dithiolane-2,1'-indane]

2'-(o-HO$_2$CC$_6$H$_4$CH$_2$CH$_2$-)   77   141.5-142   250a

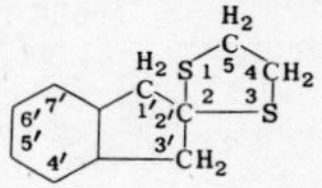

Spiro[1,3-dithiolane-2,2'-indan] (RRI 2434)

$\Delta^{1,7a'}$-1'-CH$_3$-H$_6$ 79   66.0-67.4   239

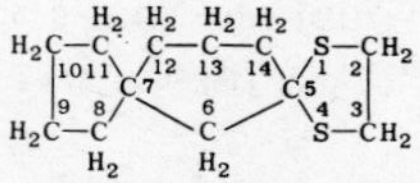

1,4-Dithiadispiro[4.1.4.3]tetradecane

8-(CH$_3$)$_2$CH-11,14-(CH$_3$-)$_2$-9-(O=)   77-78.5 $[\alpha]_D^{20}$ +111.6°   526a

C$_3$S$_2$-C$_5$-C$_7$

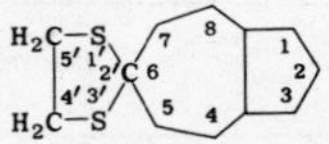

Spiro[azulene-6 (1H),2'-[1,3]dithiolane]   504

TABLE 17. Spiro Derivatives of 1,2-Dimercaptoalkanes (contd)

Compound	Yield (%)	M.p. (°C)	B.p. (°C) (mm)	Other properties	Ref.
H_8	97				504
4-HO-2,3,8-$(CH_3)_3$-5-HO_2CCH_2-H_8,γ-lactone	80	145-146			116,117
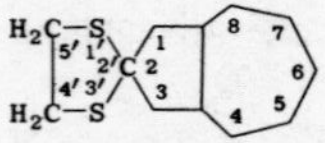 Spiro[azulene-2(1H),2'-[1,3]dithiolane]					
4,6-$(HO)_2$-3,8-$(CH_3)_2$-5-(CH_3CHCO_2H)-H_8,γ-lactone	79	122			250b
C_3S_2-C_3S_2-C_{16}					
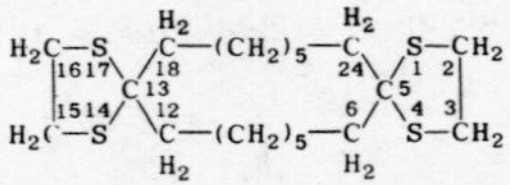 1,4,14,17-Tetrathiadispiro[4.7.4.7]tetracosane (RRI 2594)	24	210.5-212			56
C_3S_2-C_3S_2-C_{18}					
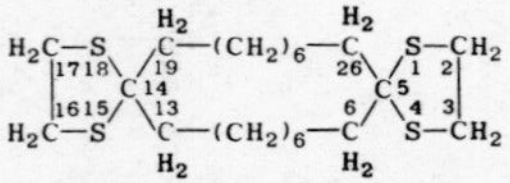 1,4,15,18-Tetrathiadispiro[4.8.4.8]hexacosane (RRI 2595)		191.1-193.5			56
C_3S_2-C_6-C_6					

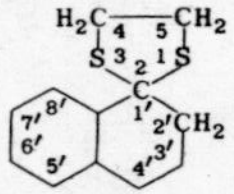

502

Spiro[1,3-dithiolane-2,1'(2'H)-naphthalene] (RRI 2838)

Substituents	Yield	M.p.	$[\alpha]$	Ref.
3',4'-H$_2$-2'-CH$_3$-2'-CH$_3$O$_2$C-	82	109		581
4',5',8',8'a-H$_4$-8'-CH$_3$O$_2$C-	54	118–118.5		581b
4'a,5',6',7',8',8'a-H$_6$-6'-CH$_3$CO$_2$-7'-CH$_3$O-8'-CH$_3$O$_2$C-	47	112–113		581b
H$_8$-7'-HO-4',8'a-(CH$_3$-)$_2$-6'-(CH$_3$CHCO$_2$H), γ-lactone	8	175–176		133a
3',4',6',7',8',8'a-H$_6$-7'-HO-4',8'a-(CH$_3$-)$_2$-6'-(CH$_3$CHCO$_2$H)	71	180–181	$[\alpha]_D^{19} + 83.4°$	133a
6',7',8',8'a-H$_4$-7'-HO-4',8'a-(CH$_3$-)$_2$-6'-(CH$_3$CHCO$_2$H)	63	186–187	$[\alpha]_D^{20} + 173.4°$	133a
6',7',8',8'a-H$_4$-7'-HO-4',8'a-(CH$_3$-)$_2$-6'-(CH$_3$CHCO$_2$H), γ-lactone	21	185–186	$[\alpha]_D^{19} + 85.3°$	133a

Spiro[1,3-dithiolane-2,2'(1'H)-naphthalene] (RRI 2839)

Substituents	Yield	M.p.	$[\alpha]$	Ref.
1'-(O=)-H$_8$	49	96–97		212a
3'α-CH$_3$CO$_2$-3',4',4'a3,5',6',7',8',8'aα-H$_8$	64	96		10a
1',4'a-(CH$_3$-)$_2$-1',5'-(HOCH$_2$-)$_2$-6'-HO$_2$C-H$_8$, γ-lactone	95	185–186.5	$[\alpha]_D + 10°$	155a
1',4'a-(CH$_3$-)$_2$-1',5'-(CH$_3$CO$_2$CH$_2$-)$_2$-6'-HO$_2$C-H$_8$, γ-lactone	61	176–177	$[\alpha]_D + 24°$	155a
1',4'a-(CH$_3$-)$_2$-7'-(CH$_3$CHCO$_2$H)-8'-HO-H$_8$, γ-lactone	99	191	$[\alpha]_D^{15} + 50.8°$	274
1',4'a-(CH$_3$-)$_2$-6',8'-(HO)$_2$-7'-(CH$_3$CHCO$_2$H)-H$_8$, 8'-γ-lactone	81	195–196	$[\alpha]_D^{20} + 44.7°$	310
	94	122–123	$[\alpha]_D^{20} - 11.1°$	310
	62	166–167	$[\alpha]_D^{20} + 37.9°$	310
		292		521b
3'α-CH$_3$CO$_2$-1',4'a-(CH$_3$-)$_2$-8'-HO-7'-(CH$_3$CHCO$_2$H)-H$_8$, γ-lactone	100	219–220	$[\alpha]_D^{26} + 27.9°$	581c

TABLE 17. Spiro Derivatives of 1,2-Dimercaptoalkanes (contd)

Compound	Yield (%)	M.p. (°C)	B.p. (°C)	(mm)	Other properties	Ref.
3'β-CH$_3$CO$_2$-1',4'a-(CH$_3$-)$_2$-8'-HO-7'-(CH$_3$CHCO$_2$H)-H$_8$, γ-lactone	74	163-165.5			$[\alpha]_D^{26}$ − 32.3°	581d
	94	200-203			$[\alpha]_D^{26}$ + 35.6°	581c
	57	176-177.5			$[\alpha]_D^{26}$ − 58.3°	581d
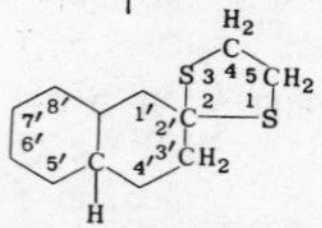 Spiro[1,3-dithiolane-2,2'(3'H)-naphthalene]						
4',4'a,5',6',7',8'-H$_6$-4'a-CH$_3$-	99	58-59				502
4',4'a,5',6',7',8'-H$_6$-4'a,7',7'-(CH$_3$-)$_3$	91	70.5-71				502a
4',4'a,5',6',7',8'-H$_6$-4'a-C$_2$H$_5$O$_2$C-	100		154-156	0.1		457a, 457b
C$_3$S$_2$-C$_3$S$_2$-C$_5$-C$_6$						
1,4,10,13-Tetrathiatrispiro[4.1.1.4.2.3]octadecane		95-57				526a
C$_3$S$_2$-C$_3$S$_2$-C$_6$-C$_6$						
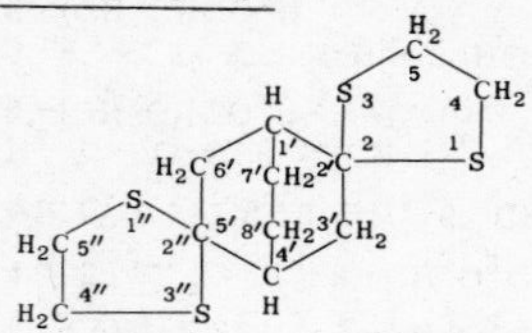 Dispiro[1,3-dithiolane-2,2'-bicyclo[2.2.2]octane-5',2"-[1,3]dithiolane] (RRI 4217)		91.8-92.7				451
1',4'-(C$_2$H$_5$O$_2$C-)$_2$						

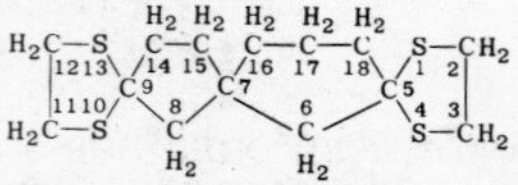

C$_3$S$_2$-C$_5$-C$_5$O-C$_6$

7',8'-(HO$_2$C-)$_2$, anhydride	35	235-237	528
1',4'-(CH$_3$-)$_2$-7',8'-(HO$_2$C-)$_2$, anhydride	86	227-228	529

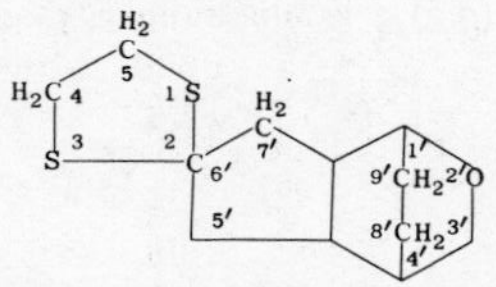

Spiro[1,3-dithiolane-2,6'(7'H)-1,4-ethanocyclopenta[c]pyran] (RRI 4219)

8'-(CH$_3$)$_2$CH-9'-HO-3'-(O=)-H$_6$	95	250	136,137

C$_3$S$_2$-C$_5$-C$_6$-C$_6$

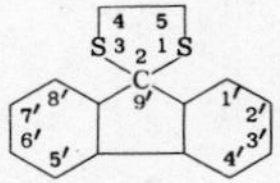

Spiro[1,3-dithiole-2,9'-fluorene] (RRI 4221)

4,5-H$_2$	125	448

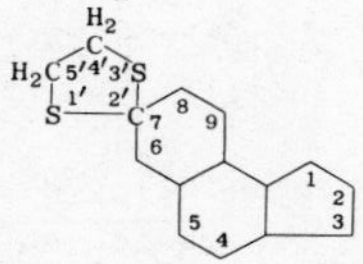

Spiro[7H-benz[e]indene-7,2'-[1,3]dithiolane]

3a,6-(CH$_3$-)$_2$-3-HO-1,2,3,3a,4,5,8,9-H$_8$	99	163-164	460b
3a,6-(CH$_3$-)$_2$-3(3aH)-(O=)-1,2,4,5,8,9-H$_6$	80	192	460b

505

TABLE 17. Spiro Derivatives of 1,2-Dimercaptoalkanes (contd)

Compound	Yield (%)	M.p. (°C)	B.p. (°C)	(mm)	Other properties	Ref.
$C_3S_2-C_6-C_6-C_6$						
Spiro[1,3-dithiolane-2,9'(10'H)-anthracene]						
1',4',4'aα,5',8',8'aα,9'aβ,10'aβ-H$_8$-10-(O=)	92	128.5-131.5				255a
Spiro[1,3-dithiolane-2,2'(1'H)-phenanthrene] (RRI 4481)						
1'α-CH$_3$O$_2$C-4'a-CH$_3$-3',4',4'aα,9',10',10'aβ-H$_6$	80	165-166.5				572
(4'aH)-1'-CH$_3$O$_2$C-4'a-CH$_3$-3',4',9',10'-H$_4$	74	124.5-125.5				572
Spiro[1,3-dithiolane-2,3'(2'H)-phenanthrene] (RRI 4482)						
1',4'b,8',8'-(CH$_3$-)$_4$-2'-(CH$_3$O$_2$CCH$_2$-)-H$_{12}$	74	211-212				298a
4'a-CH$_3$-5',6'-(CH$_3$O)$_2$-1',4',4'a,9',10',10'a-H$_6$	97	87-88				286

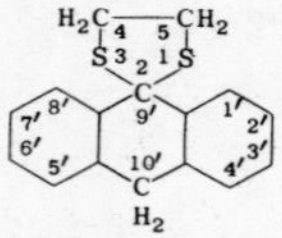

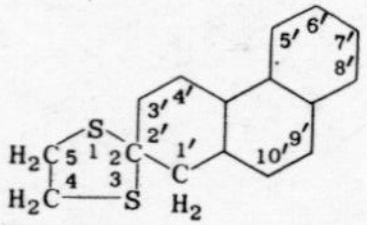

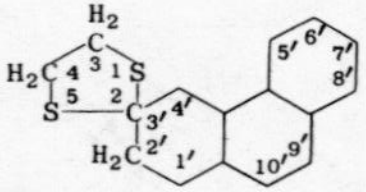

C$_3$S$_2$-C$_6$-C$_6$-C$_7$

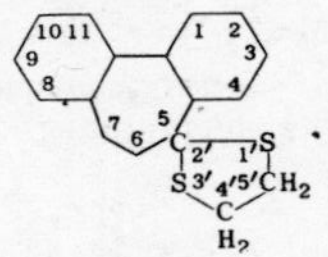

Spiro[5H-Dibenzo[a,c]cycloheptene-5,2'-[1,3]dithiolane]   323a

cis-9,10,11-(CH$_3$O)$_3$-1,2,3,4,4a,6,7,11b-H$_8$ 166   67

C$_3$S$_2$-C$_3$S$_2$-C$_6$-C$_6$-C$_6$

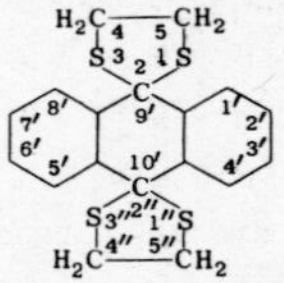

Dispiro[1,3-dithiolane-2,9'(10'H)-anthracene-10',2''-[1,3]dithiolane]

1',4',4'aα,5',8',8'aβ,9'aα,10'aβ-H$_8$ 297-300   255
257-259   255a

1',4',4'aα,5',8',8'aβ,9'aβ,10'aα-H$_8$ 254-255   94   137c
284-285   82   137c

1',2',3',4',4'aα,5',6',7',8',8'aβ,9'aβ,10'aα-H$_{10}$ 263-264   94   137c

507

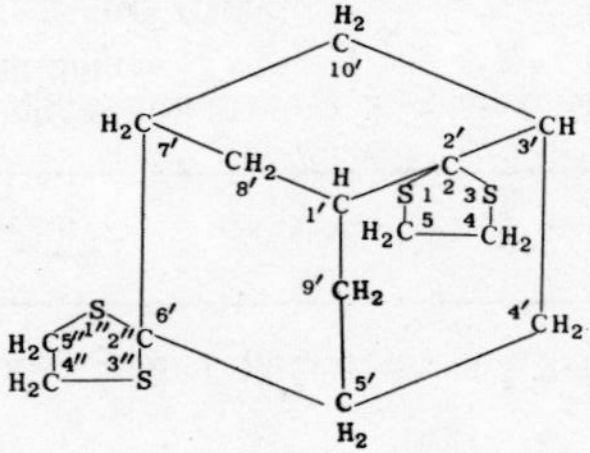

TABLE 17. Spiro Derivatives of 1,2-Dimercaptoalkanes (contd)

Compound	Yield (%)	M.p. (°C)	B.p. (°C)	(mm)	Other properties	Ref.
Dispiro[1,3-dithiolane-2,2'-adamantane-6',2''-[1,3]dithiolane]						
3',7'-(HO₂C-)₂		212–215				312a
$C_3S_2-C_4N-C_6-C_6-C_6$						
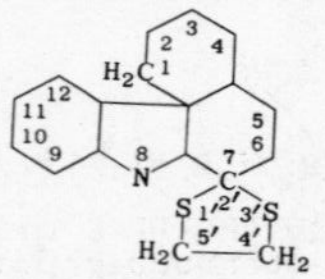						
Spiro[benzo[d]carbazole-7(1H),2'-[1,3]dithiolane]						
2,3,4,4a,5,6-H₆	32	155–155.8				212a
2,3,4,4a,5,6-H₆ picrate		163–164 (dec.)				212a
2,3,4,4a,5,6-H₆-9-CH₃O-		176–177				212a
2,3,4,4a,5,6-H₆-9-CH₃O- picrate		176–177 (dec.)				212a
$C_3S_2-C_5-C_6-C_6-C_6$						
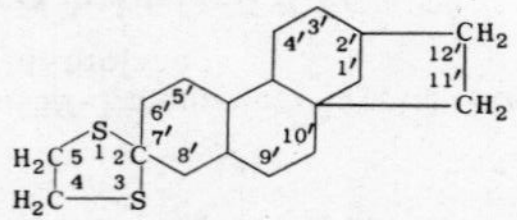						
Spiro[1,3-dithiolane-2,7'-[7H-2,10a]ethanophenanthrene]						
8'-C₂H₅-4'b,12'-(CH₃-)₂-H₁₂	77	130–131			$[\alpha]_D - 67°$	156a
$C_3S_2-C_5-C_6-C_6-C_7$						

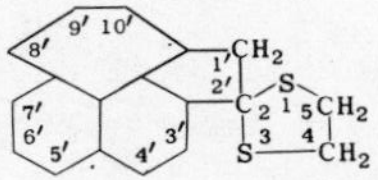

Spiro[1, 3-dithiolane-2, 2'(1'H)-naphth[2, 1, 8-cde]azulene]

8', 9', 10'a-H$_4$

$C_3S_2-C_6-C_6-C_6-C_6$

95   133-135.5   201a

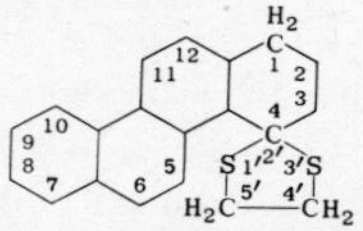

Spiro[chrysene-4(1H), 2'-[1, 3]dithiolane]

1, 8-(CH$_3$CO$_2$-)$_2$-10a-CH$_3$-2, 3, 4a, 4b, 5, 6, 6a, 7, 8, 9, 10, 10a, 12, 12a-H$_{14}$

50   167-168   401b

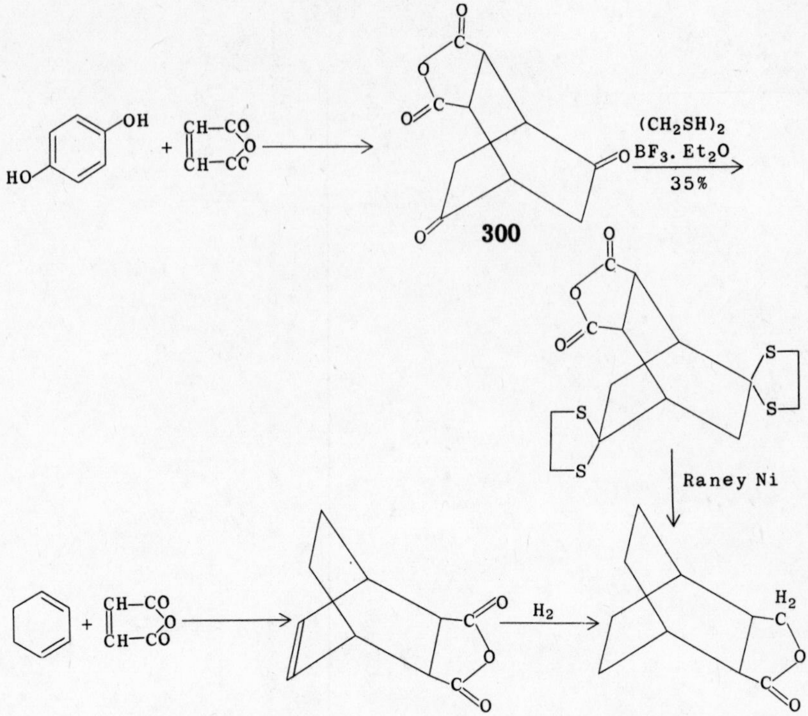

300

Hill, Martin, and Stouch[255,255a] and Crossley and Henbest[137c] used the dithiolane desulfurization procedure to prove the structure of the bisbutadiene-benzoquinone (**300a**) adduct. Since the Diels-Alder reaction gives only *cis* ring junctions, **300a** was assumed to be the *cis-syn-cis*. The actual structure was shown to be *cis-anti-cis* by the following series of transformations:

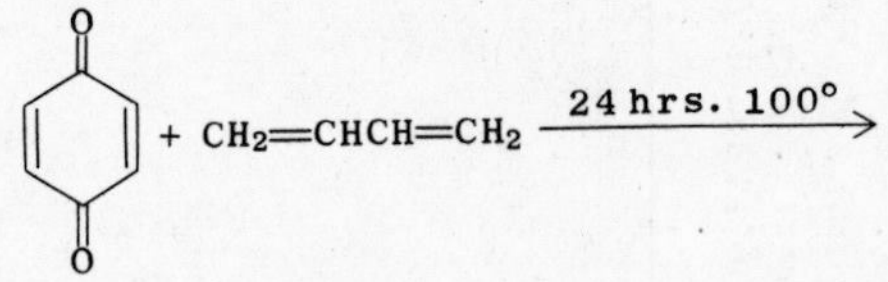

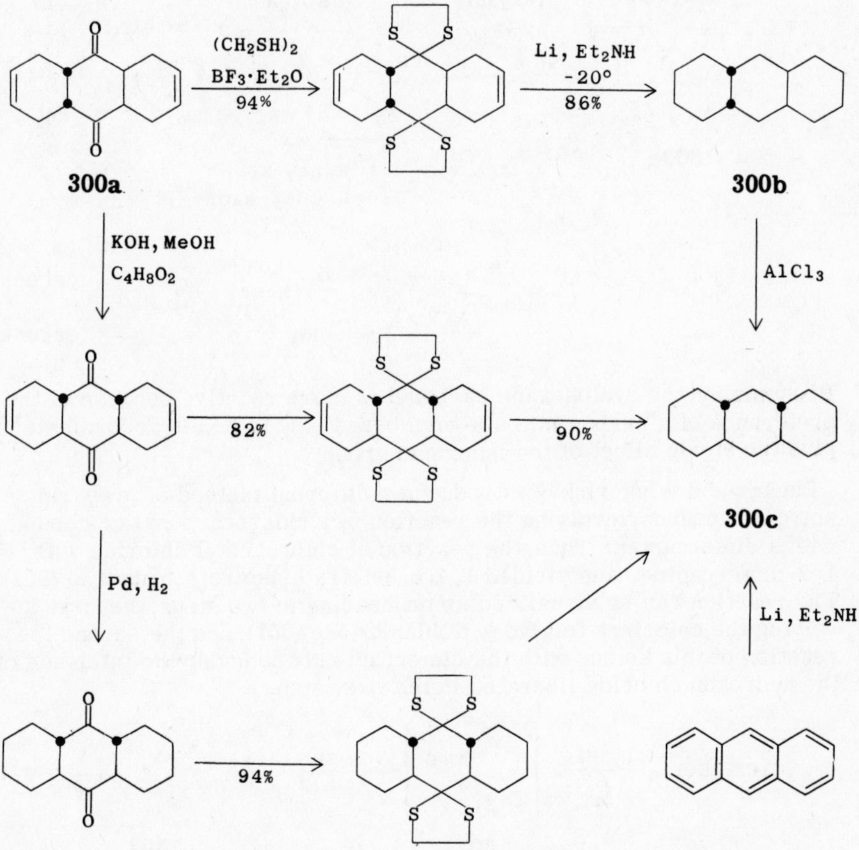

(CH₂SH)₂
BF₃·Et₂O
94%

Li, Et₂NH
-20°
86%

300a

300b

KOH, MeOH
C₄H₈O₂

AlCl₃

82%

90%

300c

Pd, H₂

Li, Et₂NH

94%

300c is obviously the most stable isomer. It has only equatorial carbons on the central ring, whereas **300b** has two axial carbons on the central ring in the chair form. Furthermore, **300b** is different from the known *cis-syn-cis* and *cis-trans* isomers, and in the other alternative, *trans-anti-trans*, the central ring would have to be in the boat form and is therefore less likely.

Sýkora, Herout, Plíva, and Šorm[526a] prepared the mono-and bis-cyclic ethylenethioketals of acorone (**300d**) and proved that the mono-adduct has the ethylenethioketal on the six-membered ring by degradation.

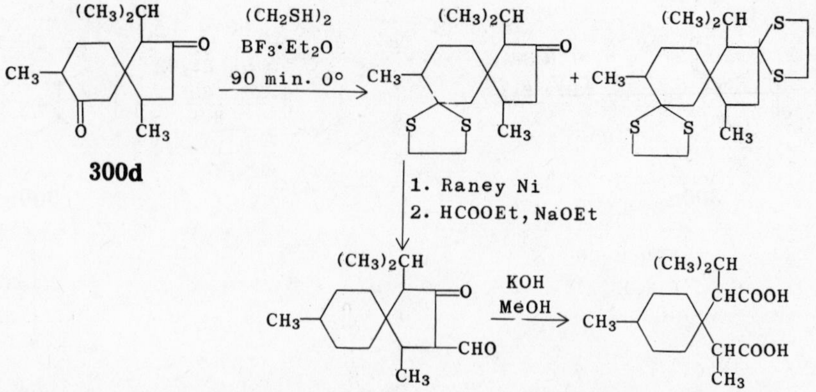

300d

1. Raney Ni
2. HCOOEt, NaOEt

Presumably, the cyclohexane carbonyl is more reactive because of the preference of a carbon in a six-membered ring to be tetracoordinate[89] plus the steric effect of the isopropyl group.

Backer and Wiggerink[25] introduced a different method of preparing spiro compounds, involving the reaction of a chlorocarbonyl compound with a dimercaptan. Thus, the reaction of chloroacetyl chloride with 1, 2-dimercaptoethane yielded 1, 4, 6, 9-tetrathiaspiro[4. 5]decane (**302**). The reaction can be visualized as proceeding in two steps, the first involving the chlorines to give p-dithian-2-one (**301**), and the second the reaction of this ketone with the dimercaptoethane under the influence of the hydrogen chloride liberated in the first step.

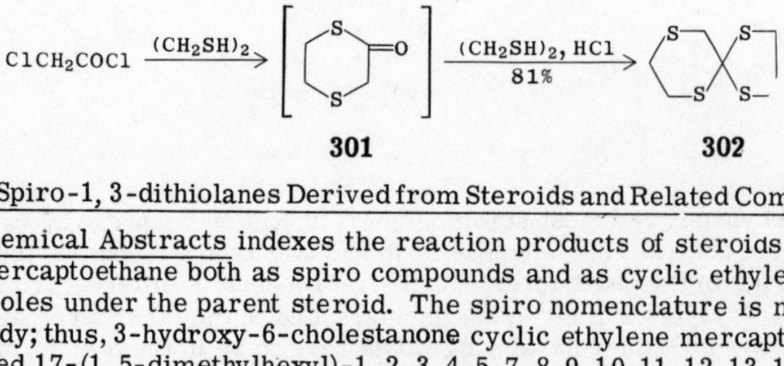

301   **302**

b.   Spiro-1, 3-dithiolanes Derived from Steroids and Related Compounds

Chemical Abstracts indexes the reaction products of steroids and 1, 2-dimercaptoethane both as spiro compounds and as cyclic ethylene mercaptoles under the parent steroid. The spiro nomenclature is most unwieldy; thus, 3-hydroxy-6-cholestanone cyclic ethylene mercaptole is called 17-(1, 5-dimethylhexyl)-1, 2, 3, 4, 5, 7, 8, 9, 10, 11, 12, 13, 14, 15, 16, 17-hexadecahydro-10, 13-dimethyl-spiro[6H-cyclopenta[a]phenanthrene-6, 2'-[1, 3-dithiolane]-3-ol (**303**).

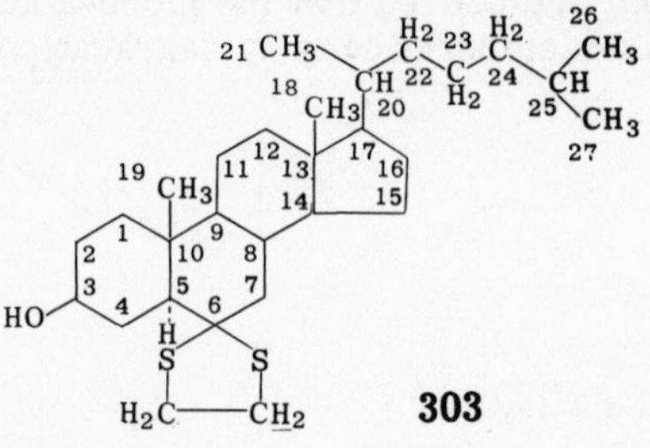

303

Because the spiro system is so cumbersome and does not indicate conformations, the system of naming these compounds as derivatives of the parent steroid will be used. They are frequently called ethylenethioketals in the literature.

Hauptmann[241,242,245,246] was apparently the first to use 1,2-dimercaptoethane as a reagent in steroid chemistry to convert a carbonyl group to a methylene group without affecting the rest of the molecule. Thus, treatment of 4-cholesten-3-one (304) with 1,2-dimercaptoethane in the presence of anhydrous zinc chloride and sodium sulfate gave the corresponding cyclic mercaptole (305). Refluxing of this with Raney nickel in alcohol gave 4-cholestene (306).

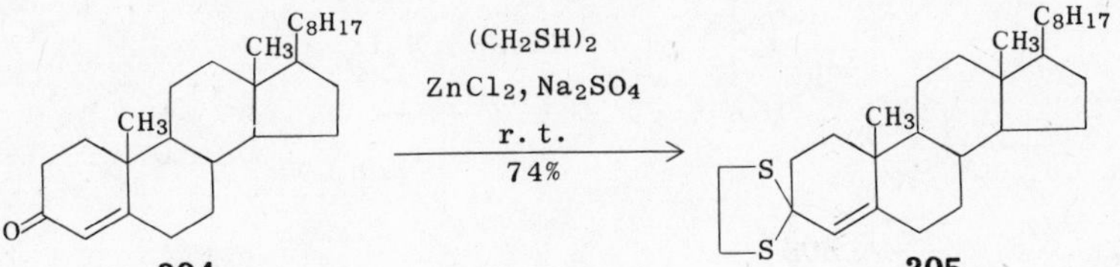

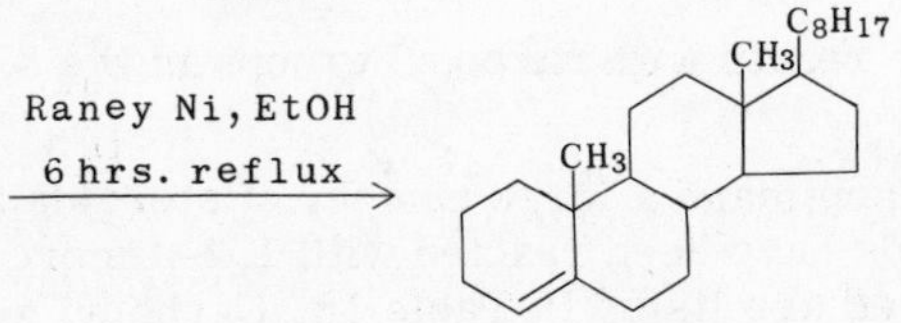

The double bond, it should be noted, did not react with the mercaptan, in spite of its being conjugated with the carbonyl group, and it was neither isomerized during the reaction nor reduced by the Raney nickel. This accounts for the popularity of this sequence for converting a carbonyl group into a methylene group. An excellent review of the desulfurization reaction appeared recently.[246b]

The same result could be arrived at with benzyl mercaptan. However, neither it nor other simple mercaptans could be made to react cleanly with carbonyl groups in other than the 3-position, whereas 1,2-dimercaptoethane reacted smoothly. For example, Hauptmann[242] found that ethyl dehydrocholate (307) reacted with three moles of 1,2-dimercaptoethane in the presence of dry hydrogen chloride; the weaker reagent, zinc chloride plus sodium sulfate did not give complete reaction. Treatment with Raney nickel gave ethyl cholanate (308).

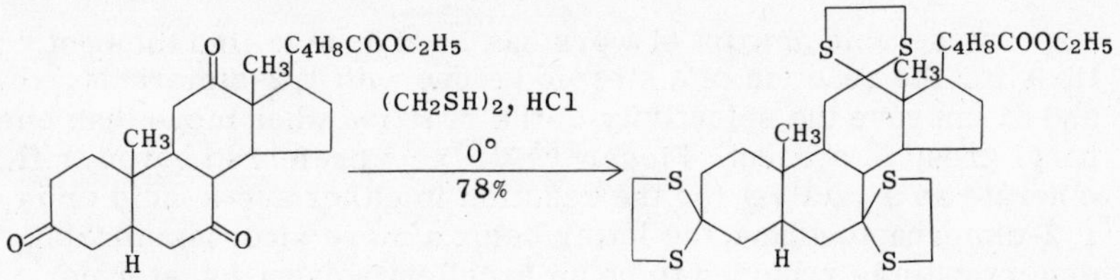

[For references, see pp. 585-610.]

308

Estrone acetate (**309**) reacted similarly.

309

Thus, 1, 2-dimercaptoethane reacts with carbonyl groups in the 3, 7, 12, and 17-positions.

Since the initial work of Hauptmann a large number of steroids and related polycyclic compounds have been reacted with 1, 2-dimercaptoethane; the compounds formed are listed in Table 18. Carbonyl groups in positions 2, 3, 4, 6, 7, 12, 16, and 17 of the steroid nucleus have been reacted. Only 11-oxosteroids have failed to react;[245] Hauptmann and Campos[246] have suggested that the methyl group on C-10 offers too much steric hindrance to allow formation of the intermediate hemimercaptole. Carbonyl groups at C-20[458] and at C-24[326] of the steroid side chain have been reacted, while a carbonyl group at C-22 would not react,[326] presumably also because of steric hindrance.

In order to determine the relative reactivity of the carbonyl groups, Hauptmann and Bobbio[246a] reacted ethyl dehydrocholate (**307**) with 1, 2-dimercaptopropane, 1-phenyl-1, 2-dimercaptoethane, and with 2, 3-dimercaptotetralin (of unspecified configuration). The first reagent, propylene dimercaptan, yielded a tris(mercaptole), although in much lower yield than with ethylene dimercaptan. The second reagent, styrene dimercaptan, yielded a 3, 7-bis(mercaptole); while the third reagent yielded a 3-mercaptole. Thus, the order of reactivity is 3 > 7 > 12.

A considerable amount of work has been done to find the best conditions for the reaction of a steroid ketone with 1, 2-dimercaptoethane and to improve the selectivity of the reaction when more than one carbonyl group is present. Fieser[183-187,514] preferred boron trifluoride etherate as a catalyst for the reaction in either acetic acid or in excess 1, 2-dimercaptoethane, the latter being a more vigorous method. The dimercaptan is reported to be an excellent solvent for steroid ketones.[187] A number of steroid ketones were reacted in this fashion.

Nazer and Issidorides[401c] encountered difficulty in applying these procedures to methyl 3-oxo-4-cholenate. They found that a smooth reaction took place in excellent yield using boron trifluoride etherate in
methanol. 4-Cholesten-3-one and methyl 3-oxocholanate also reacted
well under these conditions. The reaction of only one carbonyl group in
diketones was accomplished, in unstated yields, by limiting the amount
of 1, 2-dimercaptoethane; the carbonyl group in the 3-position is the
most reactive one, as described above. Ralls and Riegel[428,430] claimed
that the 3-oxo group in a number of di- and trioxo steroids could be
reacted selectively by using p-toluenesulfonic acid as a catalyst in
acetic acid at room temperature. Small amounts of bis(mercaptoles)
were generally formed and some unreacted steroids were recovered.
According to Romo, Rosenkranz, and Djerassi,[454] however, the Hauptmann procedure is to be preferred for general use.

Louw, Strating, and Backer[326] worked out conditions for the Raney nickel
desulfurization. According to these workers at least five parts of
Raney nickel are required per part of steroid mercaptole. Refluxing
for five hours in a mixture of dioxane and methanol gave 70-90% yields
of desulfurized compounds in a number of cases. Lithium aluminum
hydride had no effect on the 1, 3-dithiolane ring.

Although, as already mentioned, this sequence owes its popularity to
the unreactivity of double bonds in the steroid nucleus, a few examples
of migration during reduction have been noted. Striebel and Tamm[519]
found that 1-cholesten-3-one 3-(ethylene mercaptole) (310) was reduced
to 2-cholestene (311).

310

311

The authors attributed the difference between their results and pre-
vious reports to the fact that the nonmigrating double bonds are all
secondary-tertiary, whereas here the double bond is secondary-secon-
dary. Similarly, Mijović, Voser, and co-workers,[380] found that the
double bond of the triterpernoid, 2-acetoxy-$\Delta^{4b,8a}$-lanostene-5,9-dione
9-(ethylene mercaptole) (312), migrated to the 8a, 9-position (313) on
reduction with Raney nickel.

[For references, see pp. 585-610.]

TABLE 18. Spiro-1,3-dithiolanes of Steroids and Related Compounds

Ketone	Position of 1,3-dithiolane	Yield (%)	M.p. (°C)	$[\alpha]_D$	t	Ref.
17-Androstanone, 3β,16α-diacetoxy-	17	65	118-119	−79°	20	171
5α-Androstane-7,11-dione, 3β,17β-diacetoxy-	7		203-204	−33°		130
5-Androstene, 3β-acetoxy-16α-acetyl-17-acetamido-	16-acetyl	91	194-195	−78°	20	456
5-Androsten-17-one, 3β-acetoxy-	17	91	191-192	−86.4°		187
	17		188-189			558
5-Androsten-7-one, 3β-acetoxy-17β-benzoxy-	7		216-219	+52.3°	29	201
7,11-Androstanedione, 3β,17β-diacetoxy-	7	99	203-204	−33°	22	253
4-Androstene-3,17-dione	3					379
	3	89	173-174.5			430
	3,17	8.5	174-176			430
4-Androstene-3,11,17-trione	3	31	164-165	+205°		430, 433
4-Androstene-3,17-dione,11β-hydroxy-	3	49	247-249			430, 433
	3,17	3	215-218			430
4-Androstene-17β-carboxylic acid,17-methyl-3-oxo-, methyl ester	3	89.2	118.5-119.55 / 154.5-155.5		23	165
Cholanic acid, 3α-acetoxy-7,11-dioxo-, methyl ester	7 / 7	71	162-163.5 / 165	+27.6°	24	180,181 / 252
Cholanic acid, 3α-hydroxy-7,12-dioxo-	7,12	94	230-231	+69.6°	27	242
Cholanic acid, 3α-hydroxy-7,12-dioxo-, ethyl ester	7,12	77	191-193	+73.5°	22	242
Cholanic acid, 3α-formoxy-11,12-dioxo-, methyl ester	12		128.5-130.5			15
Cholanic acid, 7-oxo-3α,6ξ,12α-triacetoxy-, methyl ester	7		214-215	+66.9°	23	527

Compound			m.p.	$[\alpha]$		Ref.
Cholanic acid, 3α,7α-diacetoxy-12-oxo-, methyl ester	12	95	175-176	+65.8°	20	461
1-Cholenic acid, 3-oxo-, methyl ester	3	84	109-110	+125°		401c
4-Cholenic acid, 3-oxo-, methyl ester	3	92	110-111	+109°		401c
5-Cholenic acid, 3α,12α-diacetoxy-7-oxo-, ethyl ester	7	70	84-86			528a
Allocholanic acid, 3-acetoxy-7,11-dioxo-4,4,14-trimethyl-, methyl ester	7	89	206-208	+22°		129
3-Cholestanone	3	96	144-144.6			558
3-Cholestanone	3	92	146.5-147.5	+32.0°		187
	3		142-143	+20.7°	32	201
4-Cholestanone	4	77	119-120	-5°		514
3-Cholestanone, 2α-hydroxy-	3		193	+59°		184
3-Cholestanone, 4α-hydroxy-	3		166	+28°		184
2-Cholestanone, 3β-acetoxy-	2	78	188-189	+4.6°	26	495a
3-Cholestanone, 4α,5-dihydroxy-	3	87	242-243			160
6-Cholestanone, 3β-acetoxy-	6	80	148-151			245
	6		156-157			187a
4-Cholesten-3-one	3	62	112-114	+104°	27	14
	3	96	118.5-119.5	+111.8°		187
	3	73.5	106-107	+119°	27	241, 242
	3		111-113	+112°		514
5-Cholesten-3-one	3	22	162-163	-14°		160a
1-Cholesten-3-one	3	28	141	+28.1°		420
	3		141-142	+30.3°	21	519
4,7-Cholestadiene-3-one	3	53	95-103	+108°	29	14
4-Cholesten-3-one, 2α-acetoxy-	3	85	148	+42°		184
4-Cholesten-3-one, 2α-hydroxy-	3	73	164	+30°		184
4-Cholesten-3-one, 6α-(2-mercaptoethylthio-)	3	65	131-132	+66°		187a
8-Cholesten-7-one, 3β-benzoxy-	7	87	188-191			182
6-Cholestanol, 7-oxo-	7		198	-3.5°	20	459, 459a

TABLE 18. Spiro-1,3-dithiolanes of Steroids and Related Compounds (contd)

Ketone	Position of 1,3-dithiolane	Yield (%)	M.p. (°C)	$[\alpha]_D$	t	Ref.
5-Cholestene-3β-malonic acid, 7-oxo-, diethyl ester	7	65	169.5-170.5			428, 429
3,6-Cholestanedione	3		131-132	+24.4°		187
	3,6	94	219-220	+30.4°		186, 187, 187a
4-Cholestene-3,6-dione	3		158.5-159.5	+81.2°		187
	3,6		202-203	+86.1°		187, 187a
7,11-Cholestanedione, 3β-acetoxy-	7	60	190-191			253
			198-199	+1.4°		185
Cholesterol, 7-oxo-	7		186-188			201
	7	52	163			459, 459a
Cholesterol acetate, 7-oxo-	7	40	189-190	-81.4°	26	201
	7		188.2-188.8			427
	7	90	182-184	-92°	20	459, 459a
Cholesterol benzoate, 7-oxo-	7	88	241-242.5	-41.2°	28	201
	7		231-232			459, 459a
3-Coprostanone, 4β,5-dihydroxy-	3	93	169-170			160
Coprastane-3,4-dione	3		126-128	+125°		514
β-Noraprostane-3,6-dione	3,6	96	199-200	-30.7°		183
Δ5-Norcholenyl isobutyl ketone, 3α-hydroxy-	24	96	121-121.5			326
Δ5-Norcholenyl isobutyl ketone, 3β-acetoxy-	24	90	131.5-132.5	-38.9°		326
Δ5-Norcholenyl isobutyl ketone, 3β-(3,5-dinitrobenzoxy)-	24	79	191-192.5	-13.7°		326
Δ5-Norcholenyl isamyl ketone, 3β-acetoxy-	24	79	138-140			326
Cortisone	3		210-213			430, 431
Cortisone acetate	3	66	256-258	+210°		430, 431
Cortisone benzoate	3					431
Corticosterone, 17-hydroxy-	3					431

Compound	Position		m.p.	[α]		Ref.
Corticosterone, 17-hydroxy-, acetate	3		214-217			431
Dehydrocholic acid	3,7,12	91	276-278			242
Dehydrocholic acid, ethyl ester	3,7,12	77.5	181-182	+69.9°		242
Dehydrocholic acid, ethyl ester (propylene dimercaptan)	3,7,12	25	197-199			246a
(styrene dimercaptan)	3,7	53	88-90			246a
16-Equilenone, 17β-hydroxy-14,15-dehydro-	16	80	222-223			577
16-Equilenone, 17β-acetoxy-14,15-dehydro-	16	96	189.2-189.9			577
22-Ergostene-7,11-dione, 3β-acetoxy-	7		230-233			127
	7	84	224-225			252,130
8,22-Ergostadiene-7,11-dione, 3β-acetoxy-	7		164.5-165.5			127
4,7,22-Ergostatrien-3-one	3	16	114.5-115.2	+74.9°	28	14
Estrone acetate	17	94	141.5-142	+20.2°	27	242
9(11)-Etiocholene-17β-carboxylic acid, 3α-hydroxy-12-oxo-, methyl ester	12	94	178			113
5α-Furostane	26	54	96.5-98	+8°		156
5α-Furostane	3,26	60	159-160.5	+11°		156
5α-Furostane, 3β-acetoxy-	26	70	123-124.5	-7°		156
5β-Furostane, 3β-acetoxy-	26	69	121-123	+1.8°		156
5α-Furostane, 3β-acetoxy-	12	60	155-157	+30°		156
5α-Furostane, 3β-acetoxy-	12,26	75	165-166.5	+39°		156
5-Furostene, 3β-acetoxy-	26	55	140-142	-31°		156,418b
5-Furostene, 3β-hydroxy-	26	80	148-149	-22°		156
Hecogenin acetate, 9,11-dehydro-	12	83	180-182	-5.8°	23	257
Kryptogenin, 5,6-dihydro-	16	100	195-197	-28°	20	463
Kryptogenin diacetate, 5,6-dihydro-	16	90	193-194	-37°	20	463
12-Oleanen-24-oic acid, 2-oxo-, methyl ester	2	100	232-233			552
4-Oxa-5α-pregnan-20-one	20		202-203			418c
5-Pregnan-7-one, 3β,20β-diacetoxy-	7	85	216-217	-71°	20	454

TABLE 18. Spiro-1,3-dithiolanes of Steroids and Related Compounds (contd)

Ketone	Position of 1,3-dithiolane	Yield (%)	M.p. (°C)	$[\alpha]_D$	t	Ref.
Pregnane-3,11,20-trione	3,20	63	150-151	+43.4°	16	458
5α-Pregnan-21-oic acid, 3β-benzoxy-16-oxo-, ethyl ester	16	90	219-220	-38°	20	122
4-Pregnene-3,20-dione, 21-acetoxy-	3		175-176			432
4-Pregnene-3,20-dione, 17α-hydroxy-21-acetoxy-	3	51	227-229	+154°		430, 432
Allopregnane-7,11-dione, 3β,20β-diacetoxy-	7	73	207-209	-10°	20	453
Allopregnane-7-one, 3β,11α,20β-trihydroxy-	7	78	281-283	+6.2°	20	453
Allopregnane-20-one, 3β-acetoxy-	20	81	206-208, 209-210	+2.1°	16	458
Allopregnane-3,20-dione	3,20	74	180-182, 197-198	+23.1°	19	458
A-Norallopregnan-2(and 3)-oic acid, 20-one, methyl ester	20	85	105.5-107	+1°		413
A-Norallopregnan-20-one, 2-hydroxymethyl-	20	51	150-151	+5.4°		413
A-Norallopregnan-20-one, 3(and 2)-hydroxymethyl-	20	42		-8.3°		413
A-Norallopregnan-20-one, 2-hydroxymethyl-, cathylate	20	72	44-46	+6.3°		413
A-Norallopregnan-20-one, 2-hydroxymethyl-, N-phenylcarbamate	20	77	175-179			413
A-Norallopregnan-20-one, 2-formyl-	20	68	147.5-148.5	+12.4°		413
18-Nor-5,13-isopregnadien-20-one, 3β,16α-diacetoxy-17β-methyl-	20	43	149-151	-108°	20	456
Progesterone	3	12	184-186	+211°		430, 433
5β,22a-Spirostane-7,11-dione, 3α-acetoxy-	7	45	285-287	-23°	20	457
5α,22a-Spirostan-15-one, 2α,3β-dihydroxy-, dicathylate	15	66	244.5-246	-110°		301

22a-Spirostan-7,11-dione, 3α-acetoxy-	7	285-287	-27°		155
22a-Spirost-5-en-7-one, 3β, 11α-diacetoxy-	7	280-283	-133°	20	455
22a, 25a-Spirost-4-en-3-one	3	265-267	+30°	25	151, 153
22-Isoallospirostane-11,12-dione, 3β-hydroxy-	12	289-291 / 295-296			149, 152 / 11
22-Isoallospirostan-7-one, 9α, 11α-epoxy-3β-acetoxy-	7	288-290	-86°	20	150
Testosterone, 17-methyl-	3				379
Tigogenin	3	307-309	-67.7°	16	418b
12-Ursen-3-one	3	248-250	+71°		288
Dumortierigenin acetate	22	333-336	0°		154
Dehydroabietic acid, 2-oxo-	2	183-186			517
12α-Hydroxy-3-oxo-13β-methyl-12-nor-11β,14α-abietane-15-oic lactone	3	289-291			520
Lanostan-9-one, 2, 5-diacetoxy-	9	226-227	+8.5°		380
Lanostene-5, 9-dione, 2-acetoxy-	9	205-206	+94°		380
Lanostane-5, 9-dione, 2-acetoxy-	9	181-182	+29°		555
Trisnorlanostanedionic acid, 2-acetoxy-, methyl ester	9	206-208	+22°		556
3-Epialloyohimbone hydrochloride	71	318-320			26
3-Epialloyohimbone	62	155-158			26
3-Epialloyohimbone, 11-methoxy-, hydrochloride	96	310 (dec.)			268
Steviol		166-168	-35.4°		158
Isosteviol		170-171	-59.3°		158
Δ15(20)-Yohimbene, 18-oxo-	18	129-130 (dec.)			399a
Δ15(20)-Yohimbene, 18-oxo-, hydrochloride	18	299-301 (dec.)			399a

521

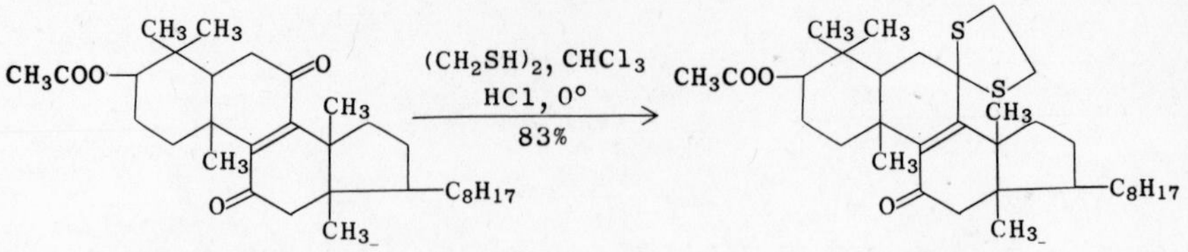

312

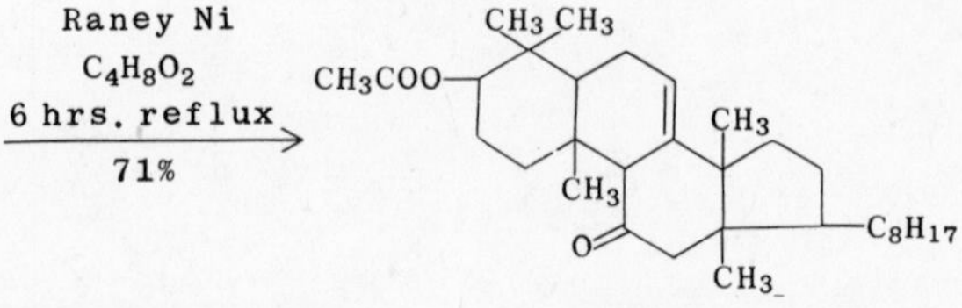

313

Here a tertiary-tertiary double bond moved to a secondary-tertiary position, interestingly enough away from conjugation with the unreacted carbonyl group.

Nazer and Issidorides[401c] investigated Raney nickel desulfurization of methyl 3-oxo-4-cholenate cyclic ethylene mercaptole (**313a**) with Raney nickel. With active W-2 catalyst in methanol, a mixture of methyl cholanate and methyl allocholanate was obtained, whereas the same catalyst in 1 : 1 methanol-acetone gave methyl 4-cholenate in excellent yield.

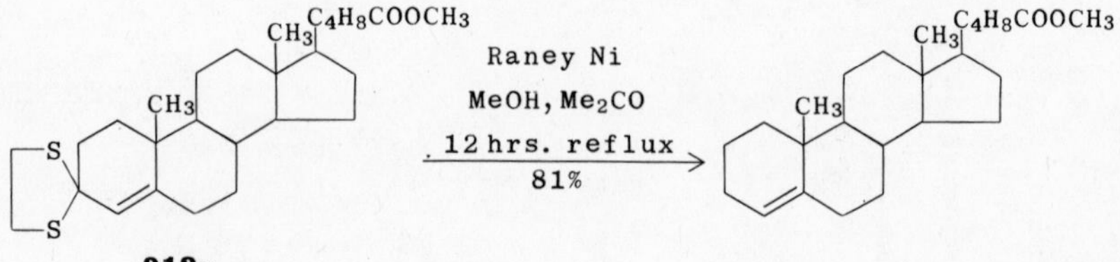

313a

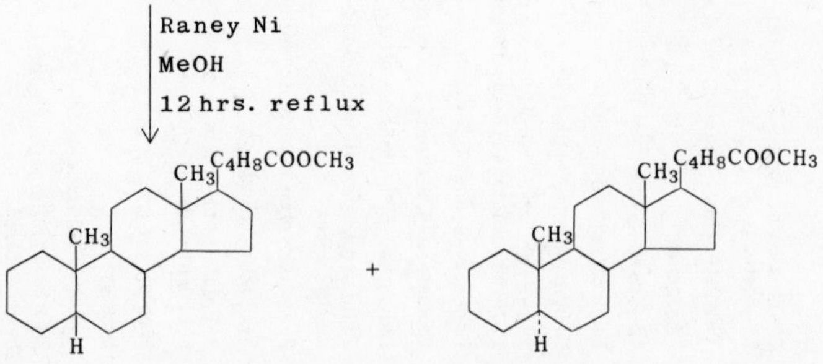

Similarly, methyl 3-oxo-1-cholenate cyclic ethylene mercaptole (**313b**) yielded methyl cholanate with W-2 Raney nickel in methanol, whereas the double bond was not reduced using methanol-acetone. On the basis of molecular rotation the authors tentatively considered the product in

522

the latter case to be methyl 1-cholenate (313c), although it is difficult to see why rearrangement should take place with the 1-cholestene product and not here.

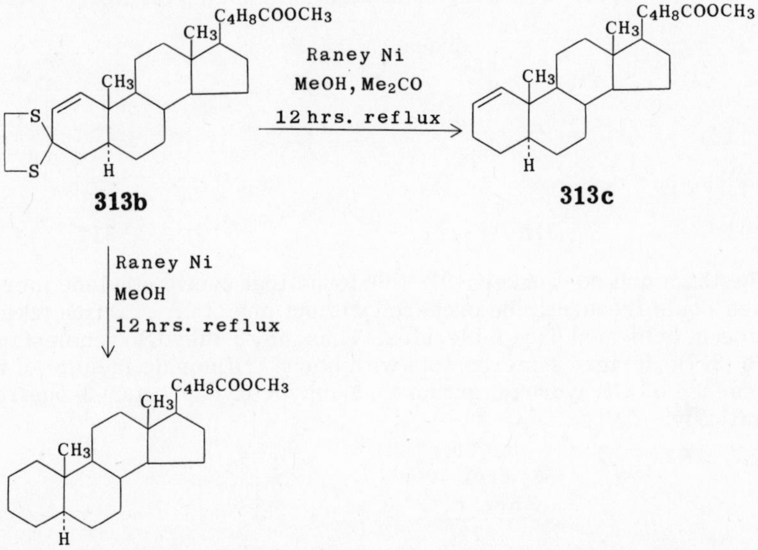

313b   **313c**

In another atypical reaction Fajkoš and Šorm[171] found that 3β,16α-diacetoxyandrostan-17-one cyclic ethylene mercaptole (314), when treated with Raney nickel, yielded 3β-acetoxyandrostane (315), the 16-acetoxy group being lost.

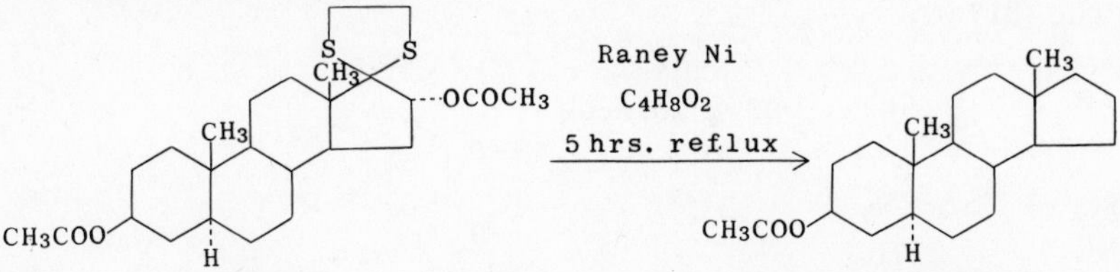

314   **315**

Sheehan and Erman[495 a] obtained the same result on Raney nickel desulfurization of 3β-acetoxycholestan-2-one cyclic ethylene mercaptole, cholestane being formed. Yanagita and Yamakawa[581d] found that both *cis*- and *trans*-2-acetoxy-γ-tetrahydrosantonin cyclic ethylene mercaptole (315a) lost the acetoxy group on treatment with Raney nickel.

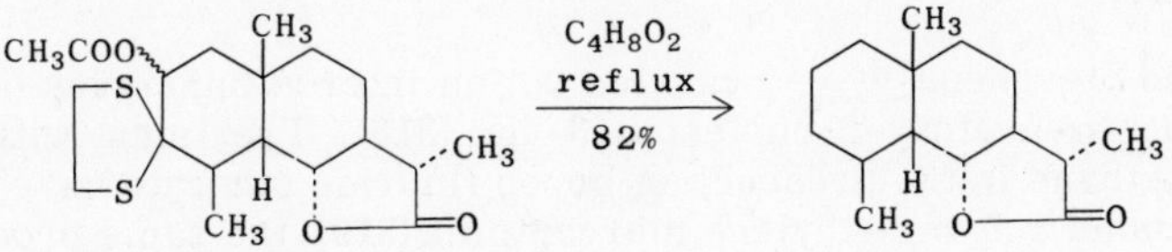

315a

[For references, see pp. 585-610.]

These results are surprising in view of the fact that according to Heusser, Jeger, and Ruzicka,[254] the reaction proceeded normally with 3β,17β-diacetoxy-14-methylandrostan-16-one cyclic ethylene mercaptole (316), 14-methyl-3β,17β-diacetoxyandrostane (317) being formed.

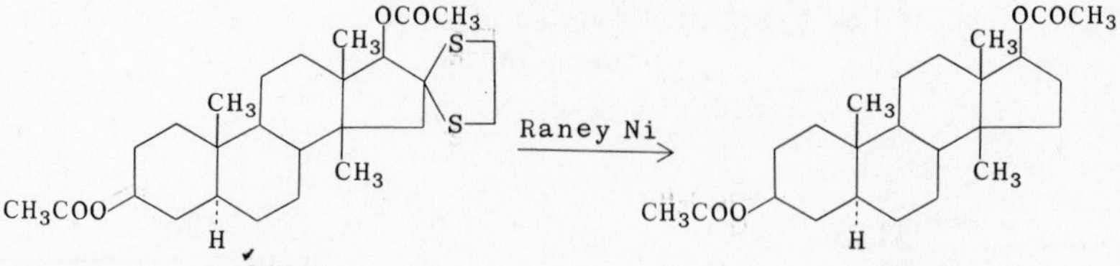

316 → Raney Ni → **317**

Eastham and co-workers[160,160a] found that cyclic ethylene mercaptoles could frequently be prepared without any other reaction taking place in acid-sensitive molecules. Thus, 4α,5-dihydroxycholestan-3-one (317a) formed a mercaptole with boron trifluoride in spite of the presence of a *t*-hydroxyl group; 4β,5-dihydroxycaprostan-3-one reacted similarly.

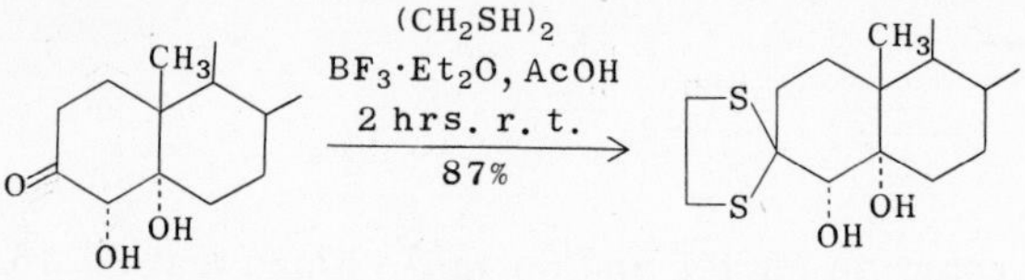

317a

5-Cholesten-3-one (317b) formed the corresponding mercaptole, in spite of the fact that it is readily isomerized by acid to 4-cholesten-3-one (317c).

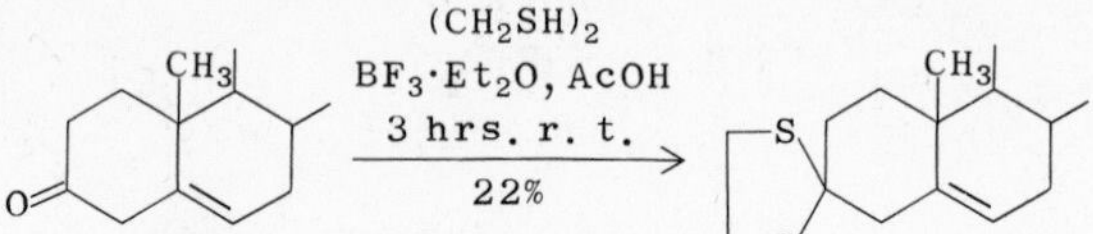

317b

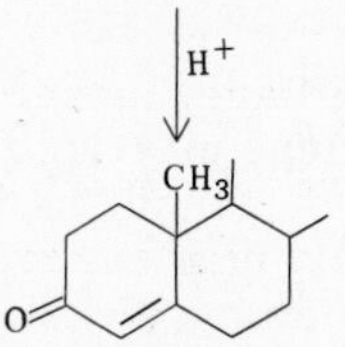

317c

Fieser and Stevenson[186,514] carried out an interesting series of reactions on 4α-acetoxy-5-cholesten-3-one (318). Treatment with 1,2-dimercaptoethane in the presence of boron fluoride etherate gave 3,6-cholestanedione 3,6-bis(ethylene mercaptole) (319); the same product was obtained from 3,6-cholestanedione. Acid or basic hydrolysis of

318 yielded 4-hydroxy-4-cholesten-3-one (**320**), and this gave 3, 4-coprostanedione 3-(ethylene mercaptole) (**321**). Raney nickel desulfurization of **321** gave 4-coprostanone (**322**), which could be isomerized by acid or base to the isomeric 4-cholestanone (**323**). Both 4-coprostanone and 4-cholestanone yielded 4-cholestanone 4-(ethylene mercaptole) (**324**), identified by desulfurization to cholestane (**325**).

318 **319** **325** **320** **324** **321** **322** **323**

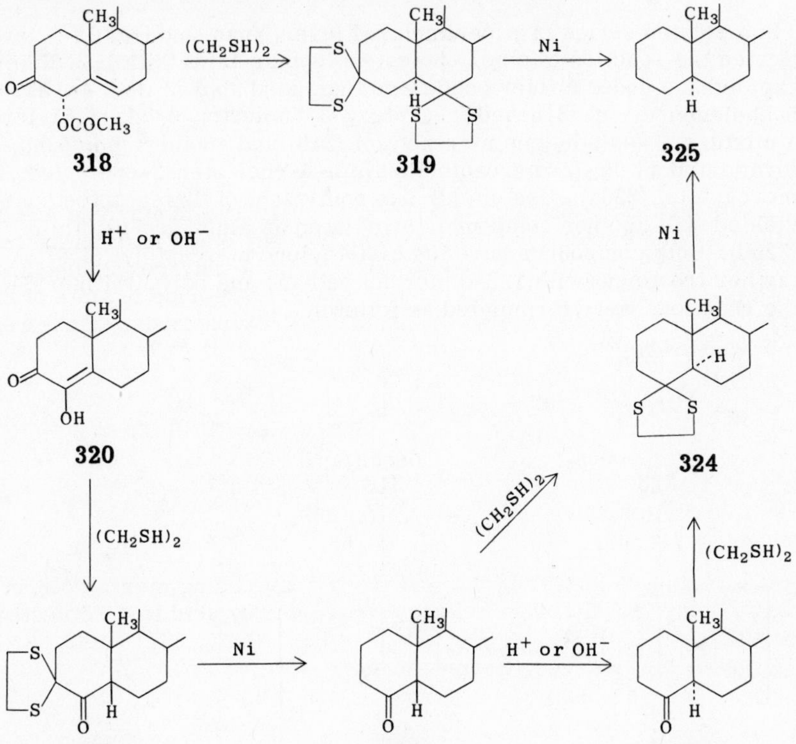

The unusual part of the sequence of reactions arises from the fact that 4-coprostanone (322) was found to be stable to boron trifluoride etherate. The authors explained the isomerization during the reaction with 1, 2-dimercaptoethane by assuming that the large group in the intermediate hemithioketal (**322a**) would be equatorial (β). Since the hydroxyl group and the hydrogen would both be axial, elimination would occur to form an unsaturated sulfide (**322b**) which then would add the second mercapto group to yield the more stable cholestane compound (**324**).

322 **322a**

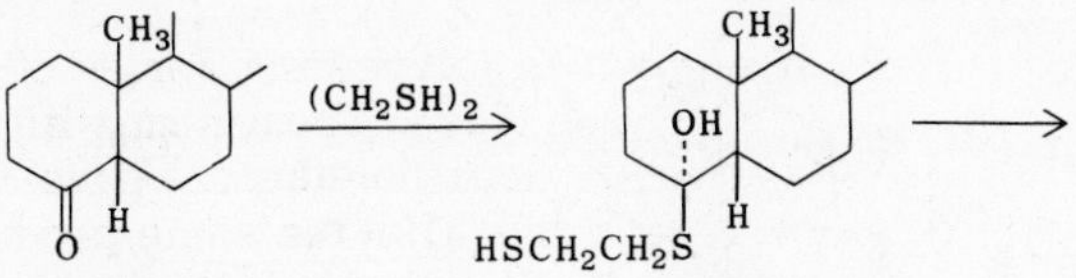

[For references, see pp. 585-610.]

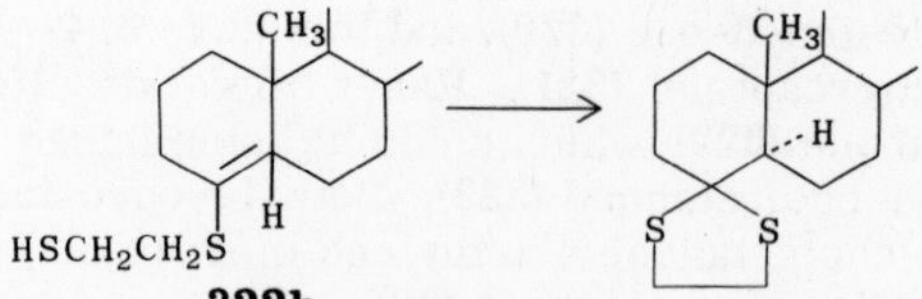

CH3
H
HSCH2CH2S
CH3
H
S
S

322b **324**

In a related series of experiments, Fieser, Yuan, and Goto[187a] investigated the reaction of other cholestenolone acetates with 1, 2-dimercaptoethane under milder conditions than used above. Both 4α-acetoxy-5-cholesten-3-one (**318**) and 6β-acetoxy-4-cholesten-3-one (**326**) yielded a mixture of bis(ethylene mercaptole) (**319**) and another compound, formulated as 6α-(2-mercaptoethylthio)-4-cholesten-3-one 3-(ethylene mercaptole) (**326a**). Use of only one equivalent of dimercaptoethane yielded still another compound, formulated as a dihydro-*p*-dithiin (**326b**). Both compounds gave the bis(ethylene mercaptole) (**319**) on further treatment with 1, 2-dimercaptoethane and boron trifluoride, and the reactions were formulated as follows:

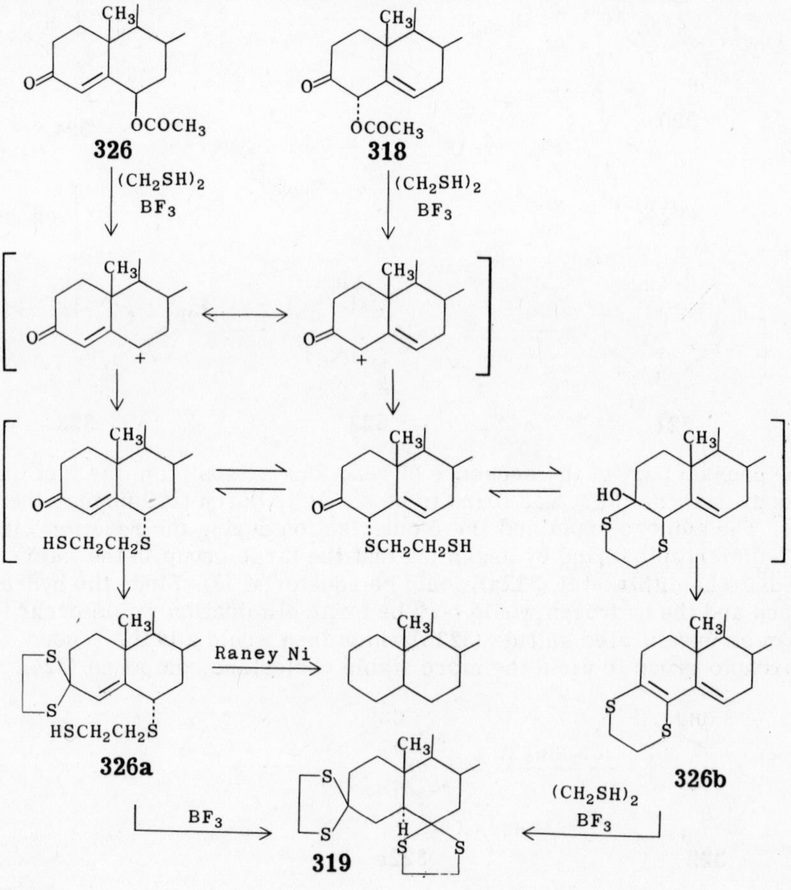

CH3
O
OCOCH3
326
CH3
O
OCOCH3
318
(CH2SH)2
BF3
(CH2SH)2
BF3
HSCH2CH2S
SCH2CH2SH
HO
Raney Ni
HSCH2CH2S
326a
326b
(CH2SH)2
BF3
BF3
319

326a yielded cholestane with Raney nickel, an illustration of double bond saturation with this reagent.

3β-Acetoxy-4-cholesten-6-one (**327**) with excess 1,2-dimercapto-ethane yielded a compound formulated as a *cis-p*-dithiane 6-(ethylene mercaptole) (**327a**). With one equivalent of 1,2-dimercaptoethane a different compound was obtained, formulated as a *trans-p*-dithiane 6-oxo derivative (**327b**). This, on treatment with additional 1,2-dimercaptoethane, yielded a compound isomeric with **327a** and formulated as the corresponding *trans* isomer (**327c**). The reactions were formulated as follows:

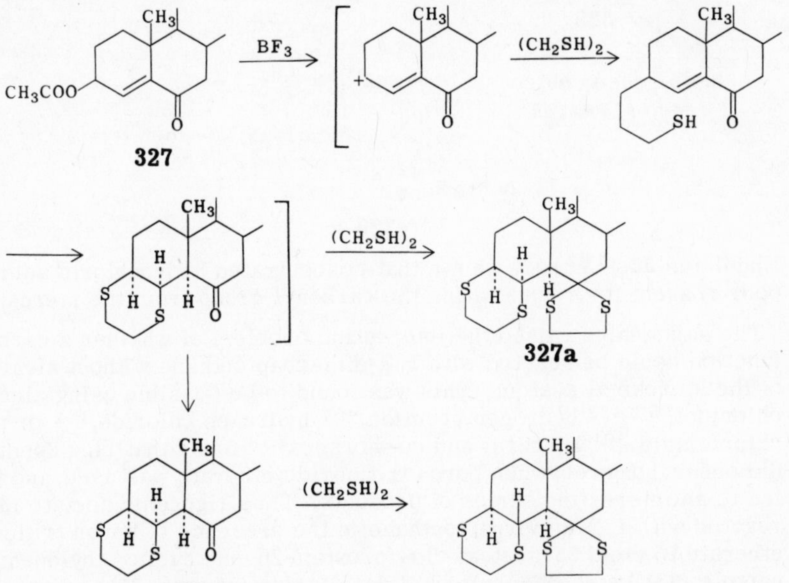

In both of the sequences, structures were assigned on the basis of ultraviolet and proton magnetic resonance spectra. In the course of this work Fieser, Yuan, and Goto[187a] made the surprising observation that 4-cholesten-3,6-dione 3,6-bis(ethylene mercaptole) (**327d**) is reduced to the corresponding cholestane derivative (**327e**) by 1,2-dimercaptoethane and boron trifluoride.

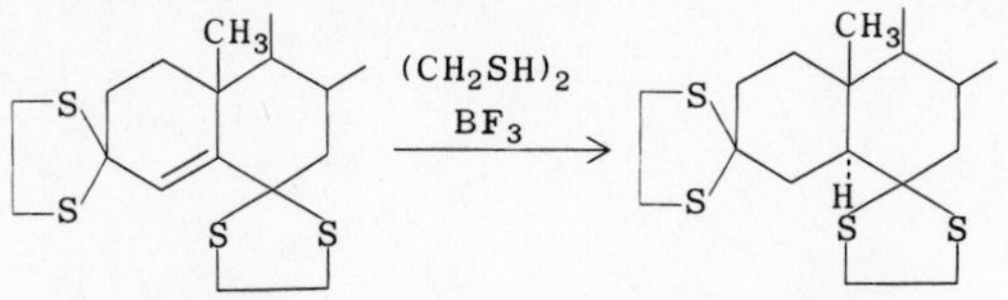

Miescher[379] used 1,2-dimercaptoethane to block the reactive 3-

position in 4-androstene-3,17-dione. Thus, the 3-(ethylene mercaptole) (328) was reacted with methylmagnesium bromide and the mercaptole was cleaved with mercuric chloride and cadmium carbonate to form 17-methyltestosterone.

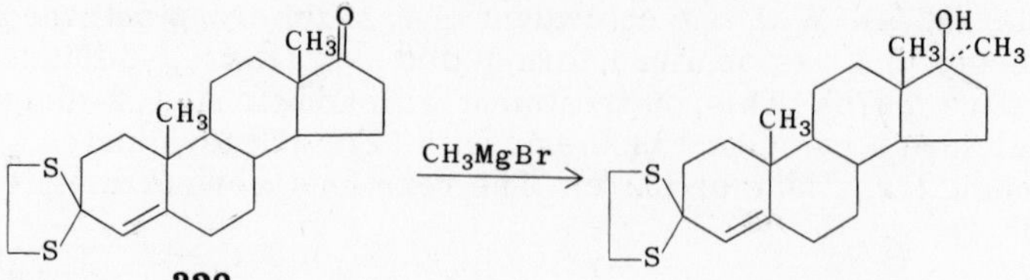

328

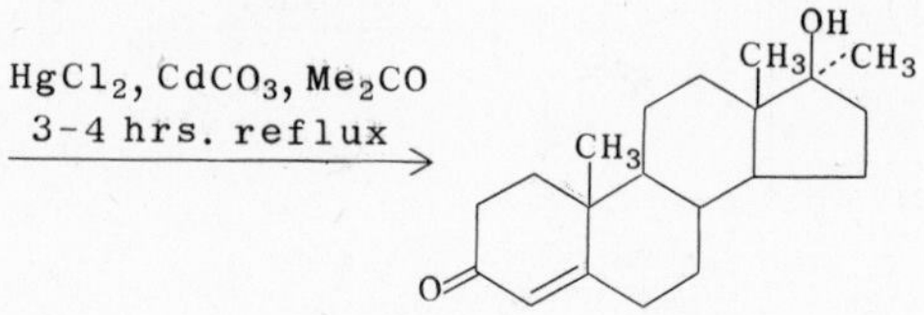

CH$_3$MgBr $\longrightarrow$

HgCl$_2$, CdCO$_3$, Me$_2$CO
3-4 hrs. reflux $\longrightarrow$

329

Engel and Just[165] have shown that concentrated hydrochloric acid is a poor reagent for regenerating the carbonyl group from the mercaptole.

The sapogenins raised the interesting problem of whether a carbonyl function could be reacted with 1,2-dimercaptoethane without cleavage of the spiroketal system. This was found to be possible using zinc chloride,[150,453] hydrogen bromide,[457] hydrogen chloride,[152] or perchloric acid.[301] Djerassi and co-workers[156] found that ring opening did occur, however, when boron trifluoride etherate was used, and this led to an interesting series of products. Thus, tigogenin acetate (330) reacted with 1,2-dimercaptoethane in the presence of boron trifluoride etherate to yield 3β-acetoxy-5α-furostan-26-one cyclic ethylenemercaptole (331), since Raney nickel desulfurization gave 3β-acetoxy-5α-furostane (332), whose structure was proved by various transformations and degradation experiments. Similarly, diosgenin acetate (333) and hecogenin acetate (335) yielded the 26-(ethylene mercaptole) (334) and the 12,26-bis(ethylene mercaptole) (336), respectively, both of which were converted into 332.

Pettit and Bowyer[418b] obtained the same results with diosgenin acetate (333) using an aluminum chloride catalyst, and postulated the following mechanism to explain the formation of the 26-aldehyde (p. 530):

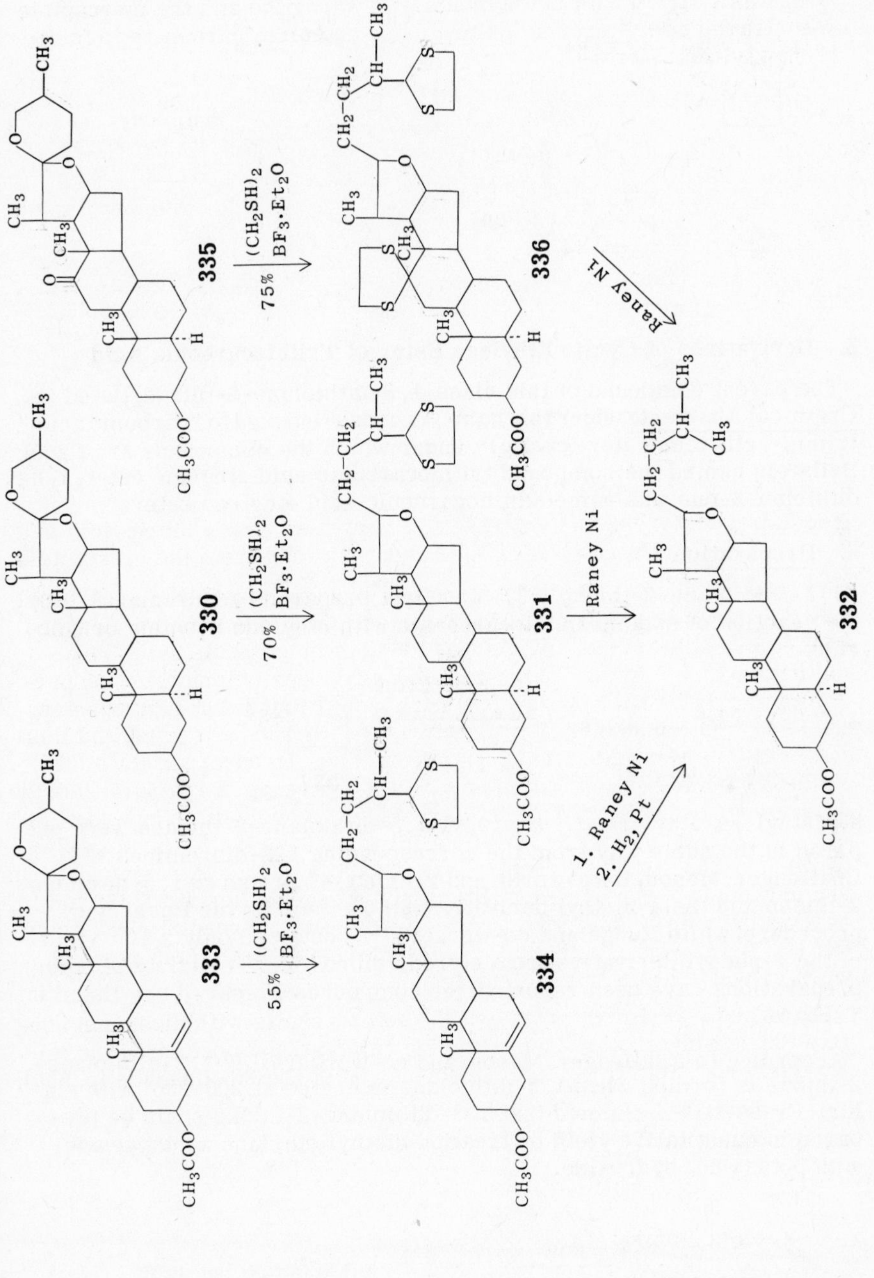

333
(CH2SH)2
BF3·Et2O
55%
334
330
(CH2SH)2
BF3·Et2O
70%
331
335
(CH2SH)2
BF3·Et2O
75%
336
1. Raney Ni
2. H2, Pt
Raney Ni
Raney Ni
332

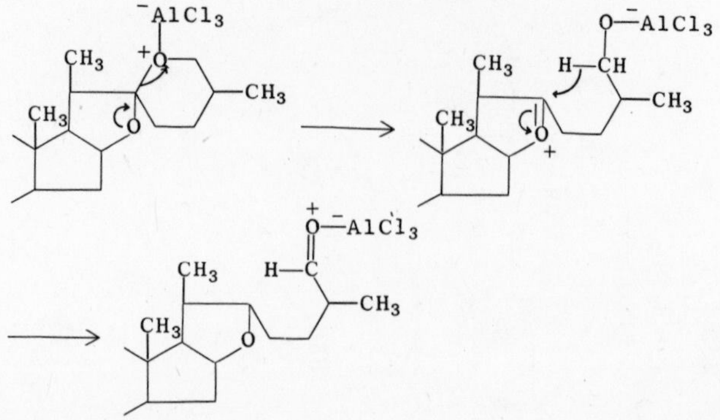

5. Derivatives of Cyclic Ethylene Ester of Trithiocarbonic Acid

The parent compound of this class, 1, 3-dithiolane-2-thione, listed in Chemical Abstracts under this name, is cross-indexed to "carbonic acid, trithio-, ethylene ester (cyclic)", under which the compounds are found. Beilstein named the compound trithiocarbonic acid ethylene ester; 1, 3-dithiolan-2-one was named dithiocarbonic acid ethylene ester.

a. Preparation

1, 3-Dithiolane-2-thione (337) was first prepared by Husemann[272] by the reaction of sodium trithiocarbonate with ethylene bromide or chloride.

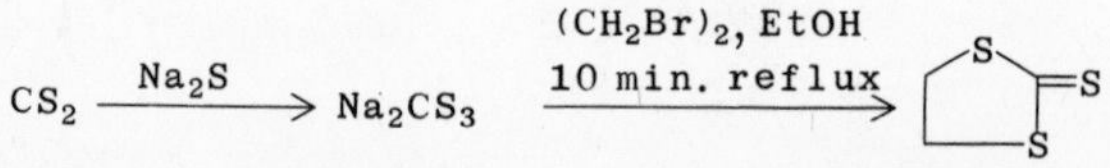

337

4-Methyl-, 4-ethyl-, and 4-n-propyl-1, 3-dithiolane-2-thiones were prepared in the same way from the corresponding 1, 2-dibromides.[273] Challenger, Mason, Holdsworth, and Emmett[125] prepared 1, 3-dithiolane-2-thione and the 4-methyl derivative in 60% yield by the Husemann procedure, while Runge and co-workers[459b] obtained only a 10% yield of the 4-phenyl derivative from styrene dibromide. A variety of other preparations have been reported; the compounds prepared are listed in Table 19.

According to Challenger, Mason, and co-workers,[125] 1, 3-dithiolane-2-thione is formed when 1, 3-dithiolane is heated at 200-230° with sulfur. Frassetti[197] claimed that 1, 3-dithiolane-2-thione could be prepared in quantitative yield by treating diethyl ethylene xanthogenate with potassium hydroxide.

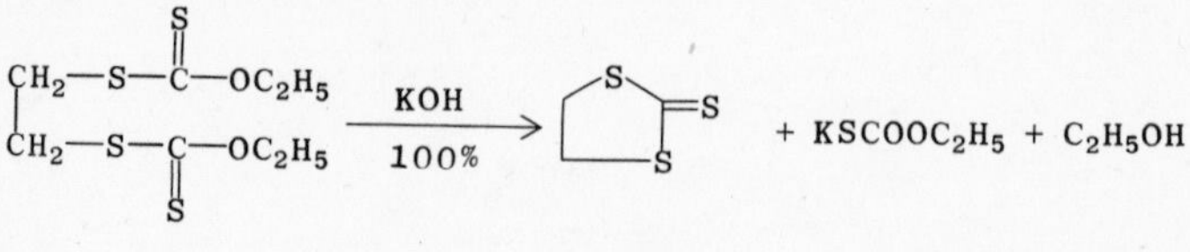

Tarbell and Harnish[532] formulated the reaction as follows:

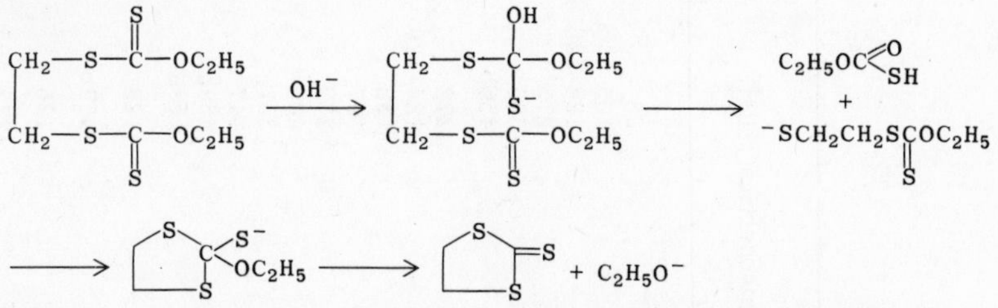

Coltof[135] prepared ethylene trithiocarbonate by treating ethylene dichloride and carbon disulfide with aqueous potassium hydroxide at 50-55°; the reaction is reported to give a 90% yield.[405] The same patent mentions the use of ethylene glycol, ethylene oxide, and ethylene chlorohydrin, but with no details. Culvenor, Davies, and Pausacker[138] investigated these syntheses in greater detail. Probably the best synthesis of 1,3-dithiolane-2-thione, according to these authors, is the reaction of ethylene oxide with carbon disulfide and potassium hydroxide in methanol.

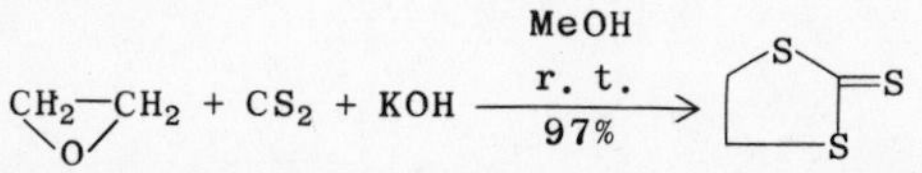

Under the same conditions ethylene chlorohydrin gave a 42% yield and 1,2-dimercaptoethane an 83% yield; the latter reaction had been reported previously by Hurtley and Smiles.[269] The same procedure applied to styrene oxide gave a 77% yield of 4-phenyl-1,3-dithiolane-2-thione, but tetramethylethylene oxide gave only a 5% yield of 4,4,5,5-tetramethyl-1,3-dithiolane-2-thione. Propylene oxide gave a 70% yield of 4-methyl-1,3-dithiolane-2-thione, while isobutylene oxide gave 4,4-dimethyl-1,3-dithiolane-2-thione.[139] 4-(p-Tolysulfonylmethyl)-1,3-dithiolane-2-thione (**338**) was prepared from the chlorohydrin.[139]

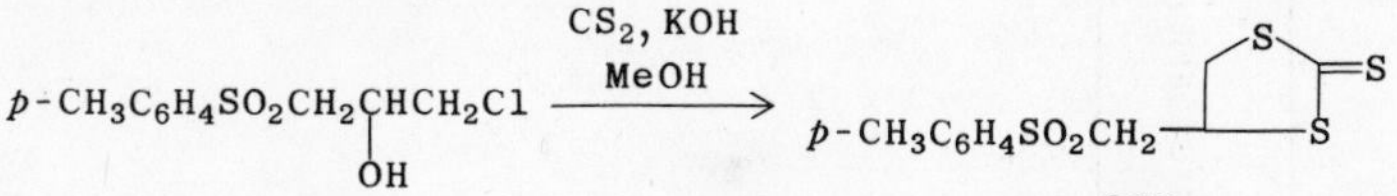

338

Davies and Savige[142] prepared 4-(N-methylanilinomethyl)-1,3-dithiolane-2-thione (**339**) from N-methylanilinomethyloxirane and excess potassium methylxanthate.

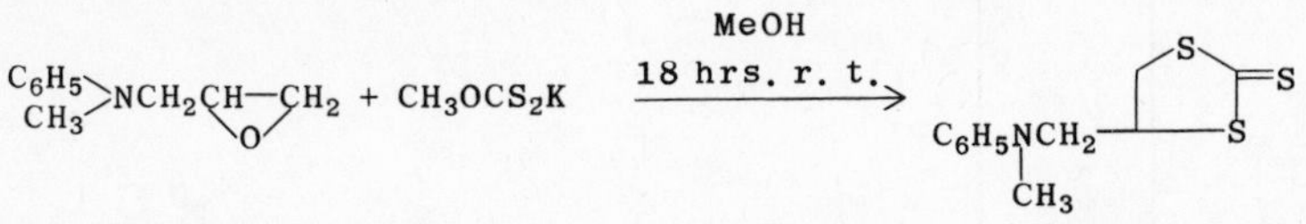

339

Bashour[37] prepared a number of 4-aryloxymethyl-1,3-dithiolane-2-thiones from glycidyl ethers by the same procedure.

[For references, see pp. 585-610.]

TABLE 19. Derivatives of 1,3-Dithiolan-2-one

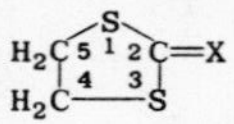

$$\underset{\substack{H_2C\ 4 \\ \ \ \ 3}}{\overset{\substack{S\ 5\ 1 \\ }}{\bigcirc}}\overset{2}{C}{=}X \qquad \substack{S}$$

=X	Other substituents	Yield (%)	M.p. (°C)	B.p. (°C)	(mm)	Other properties	Ref.
=O		83	34-35.5	74-75	3		25
			39				105
		62	35				124-126, 411
			31				273
		73	33-34	249-251			305
			34				459b
=S		60	36.5				272
		97	36				124-126
		100	36-37				138
			39				197
			37.				269
		90	40-41				405
			33-36				387
							147
		26	33-34				459b
		77					159a
=S·HgCl$_2$			166				125
=S·3HgCl$_2$							459b
=S·Br$_2$			120				125
=S	4-CH$_3$-	60		157	10		273, 405
		70		136	0.2		125
		36		126	3		139
							159a

	Substituent	Yield (%)	M.p.	Notes	Ref.
=S	4-C$_2$H$_5$-				273
=S	4-n-C$_3$H$_7$-				273
=S	4-(CH$_3$)$_2$CHOCH$_2$-	74			37
=S	4-C$_6$H$_5$OCH$_2$-	31.6			37
=S	4-(p-ClC$_6$H$_4$OCH$_2$-)	40.5			37
=S	4-(p-O$_2$NC$_6$H$_4$OCH$_2$-)	13.2	121-123		37
=S	4-(p-CH$_3$OC$_6$H$_4$OCH$_2$-)	9.4	69		37
=S	4-(p-CH$_3$C$_6$H$_4$SO$_2$CH$_2$-)		128		139
=S	4-[C$_6$H$_5$N(CH$_3$)CH$_2$-], picrate		124-125		142
=S	4-C$_6$H$_5$-	77	87-88		138
		22	83-85		159a
		77	86-88		246a
		10	86.5		459b
=S · 3HgCl$_2$	4-C$_6$H$_5$-		179.5-180.5		459b
=S	4- (structure, OH / CH$_3$ / CH$_3$)	95	179-180	L-Idose deriv.	362a
					137b
=S	4- (structure, CH$_3$ / CH$_3$ / CH$_3$)	93	183-183.5	L-Iditol deriv.	362a
		26	182-183	D-Glucitol deriv.	137b
			100-110 (bath)	0.005	137b
=S	4- (structure, CH$_3$ CH$_3$ / CH$_3$ CH$_3$)	94	95-96	L-Gulitol deriv.	362a
			95-96		137b

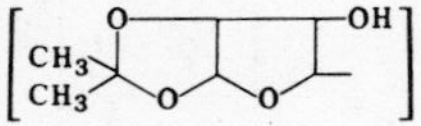

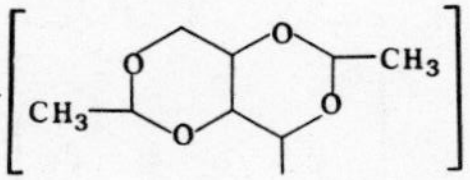

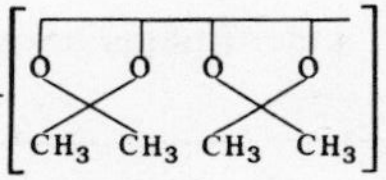

TABLE 19. Derivatives of 1,3-Dithiolan-2-one (contd)

=X	Other substituents	Yield (%)	M.p. (°C)	B.p. (°C)	(mm)	Other properties	Ref.
=S	[structure] 4- 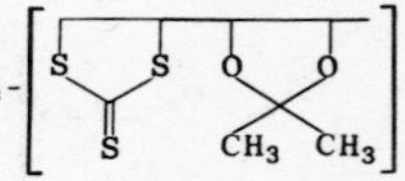	25	108–110			L-Iditol deriv.	273a
=S	4,4-(CH₃-)₂	27	40–41	162–170	24		139
=S	trans-4,5-(CH₃-)₂	27	108–110				273a
=S	[structure] 4,5-						273a
=S	4,4,5,5-(CH₃-)₄	5	156				138
=NH · HCl			202				387
			212 (dec.)				574
			207–209				496
			220–221 (dec.)				561a
=NH · HSCN			109 (dec.)				561a
=NH · HSCN	4-CH₃-	2	86				561a
=NOH			126–128				125, 387
=NCH₃ · HI			182–184 (dec.)				387
=NC₆H₄CH₃-p · HCl			168				387
=NC₆H₄OH-p			204–205				387
=NCOCH₃			69				387
=NCOC₆H₅		43	141–143				387
		43	80–81				574

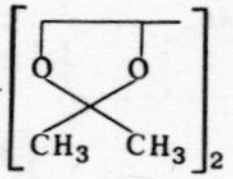

534

Substituent		M.p. (°C)	References
$=NNHC_6H_5$		88	387
		94	102, 105
		92	106
		91	459b
$=NNHC_6H_5 \cdot HCl$		188 (dec.)	102
$=NNHC_6H_4CH_3\text{-}p$		124	103
$=NNHC_6H_4Br\text{-}p$		141	105
$=NNHC_6H_4OCH_3\text{-}o$		85–86	104
$=NNHC_6H_4OCH_3\text{-}o \cdot HCl$		163–164	104
$=NNC_6H_4OCH_3\text{-}o$ ($\vert$ $COCH_3$)		150	104
$=NNH(\alpha\text{-naphthyl})$		148	104
$=NNH(\alpha\text{-naphthyl}) \cdot HCl$		182–183	104
$=NNH(\beta\text{-naphthyl}) \cdot HCl$		200–201	104
$=N(C_2H_5)_2^{+} (C_6H_5)_4B^{-}$	4-CH_3-	42, 208	296
$=NH \cdot HCl$	4-$HOCH_2$-	172–175	387
$=NH \cdot HCl$	4-CH_3-		166
$=NCOCH_3$	4-C_6H_5-	59.5	387
$=NCOC_6H_5$	4-C_6H_5-	135	574
$=NNHC_6H_5$	4-C_6H_5-	134	459b

A reasonable mechanism for this synthesis involves the reaction of the epoxide or chlorohydrin with xanthate to form the thiirane, followed by reaction of the thiirane with more xanthate.[137b,138]

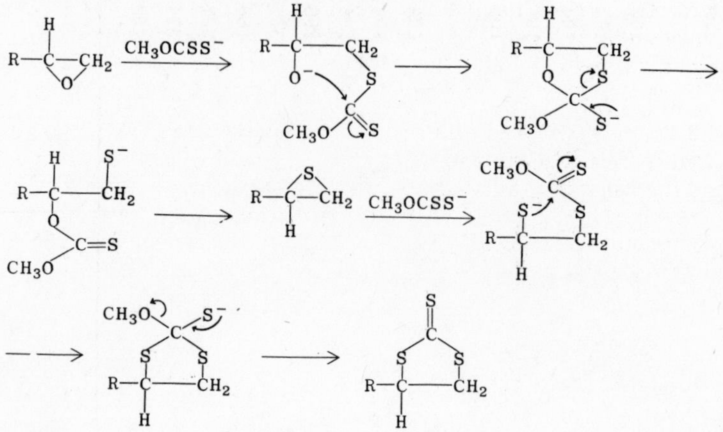

The stereochemical implication is, of course, that the thiirane is formed with inversion and opened by attack on the terminal carbon, resulting overall in inversion at the nonterminal carbon atom.

Several authors have used this procedure to prepare 1,3-dithiolane-2-thiones in the sugar series. For example, McSweeney and Wiggins[362a] reacted 1,3:2,4-di-O-ethylidene-5,6-anhydrosorbitol (**339a**) with carbon disulfide and caustic in methanol and isolated a trithiocarbonate which they formulated as being formed without rearrangement. Creighton and Owen[137b] showed that this compound is actually the rearranged product, 5,6-dideoxy-1,3:2,4-di-O-ethylidene-5,6-(thiocarbonyldithio)-L-iditol (**339b**), by the following transformations:

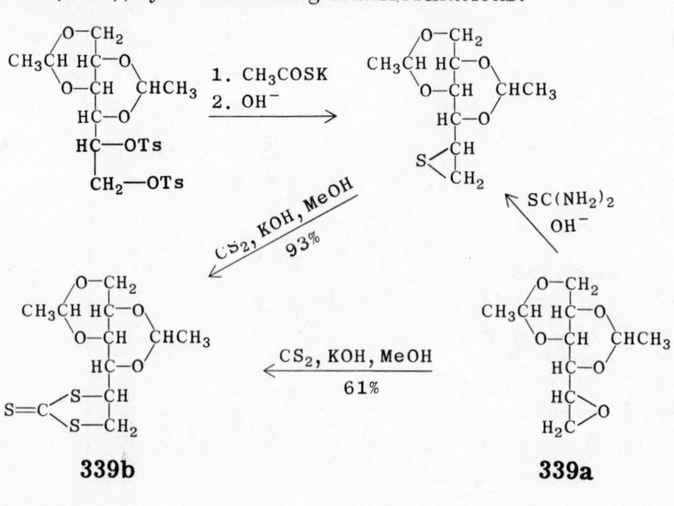

339b   **339a**

There can be little doubt that the thiirane is formed from the tosylate and the oxirane with inversion. It is quite reasonable to assume, therefore, in accord with the above mechanism, that the trithiocarbonate is formed from oxirane with inversion and from thiirane with retention. A number of other sugar derivatives reacted similarly.[137b,273a,362a] McSweeney and Wiggins[362a] used this procedure to prepare 5, 6-dideoxy derivatives by Raney nickel desulfurization, while Iqbal and· Owen[273a] reduced the derivatives to di- and tetramercaptans.

Iqbal and Owen [273a] used this procedure to prepare *trans*-4, 5-dimethyl-1, 3-dithiolane-2-thione (**339c**) from *cis*-2, 3-dimethyloxirane. In this case the formation of thiirane would involve inversion on both carbon atoms, and ring opening with inversion would give the *trans* isomer. This assignment has recently been confirmed by Overberger and Drucker[411a] by the use of NMR.

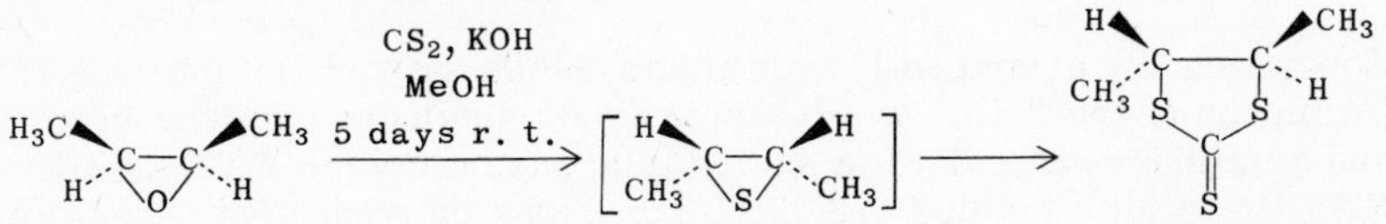

339c

Durden, Stansbury, and Catlette[159a] prepared 1, 3-dithiolane-2-thione by reacting ethylene oxide with carbon disulfide under pressure using a catalytic quantity of tertiary amine.

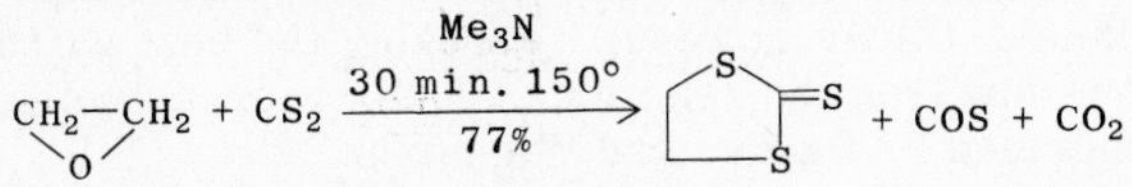

With other epoxides, however, the yields were inferior to those obtained by the xanthate procedure. The reaction was presumed to take the following course:

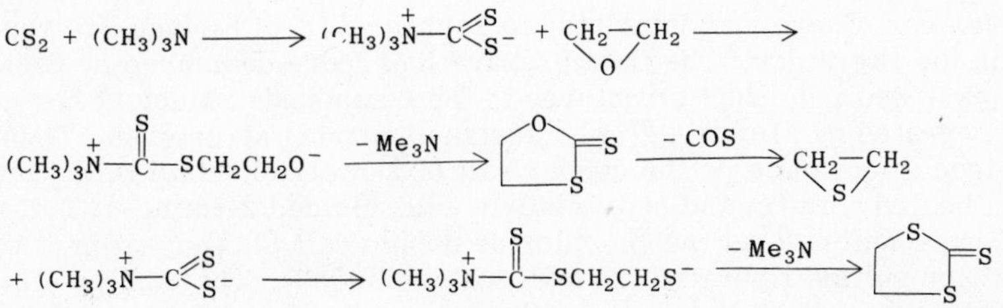

Runge and co-workers[459b] described the synthesis of 1, 3-dithiolane-2-thione from 1, 3-dithiolan-2-one (**340**) and phosphorus pentasulfide.

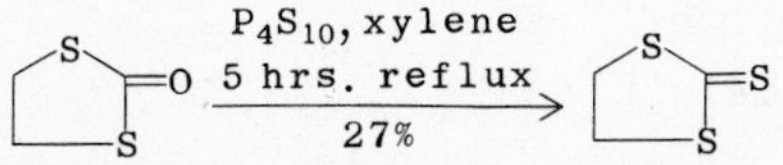

1, 3-Dithiolan-2-one (**340**) was first prepared by Husemann[273] by treating 1, 3-dithiolane-2-thione with dilute nitric acid.

[For references, see pp. 585-610.]

340

Runge and co-workers[459b] reported a 73% yield using permanganate in acetone. According to Challenger and co-workers[125] a 62% yield of 1,3-dithiolan-2-one can be obtained with mercuric acetate in acetic acid; this has been confirmed by Overberger and Bonsignore.[411]

Runge and co-workers[459b] prepared 1,3-dithiolan-2-one by acid hydrolysis of ethylene bis(thiocyanate).

$$\text{NCSCH}_2\text{CH}_2\text{SCN} \xrightarrow[\substack{15\ \text{hrs. reflux}\\26\%}]{\substack{25\%\ \text{aq. H}_2\text{SO}_4}}$$

Konowalow[305] prepared 1,3-dithiolan-2-one without the intermediate formation of the 3-thione. Heating carbon disulfide, ethylene bromide, and aluminum bromide in a sealed tube gave a complex, $\text{CS}_2 \cdot \text{AlBr}_3 \cdot \text{C}_2\text{H}_4\text{Br}_2$, which yielded 1,3-dithiolan-2-one on treatment with water. According to the patent literature[405] 1,3-dithiolan-2-one is a by-product in the preparation of 1,3-dithiolane-2-thione from ethylene chloride, carbon disulfide, and potassium hydroxide. Husemann[273] found that heating p-dithiane with thiocarbonyl bromide, S=CBr_2, and water gave the same compound; a better yield was obtained by nitric acid oxidation of 1,3-dithiolane-2-thione, however. Probably the best synthesis of 1,3-dithiolan-2-one involves the reaction of 1,3-dimercaptoethane with phosgene as described by Backer and Wiggerink.[25]

$$\text{HSCH}_2\text{CH}_2\text{SH} \xrightarrow[\substack{r.\ t.\\83\%}]{\substack{\text{COCl}_2,\ \text{Et}_2\text{O}}}$$

A number of compounds related to 2-imino-1,3-dithiolane are reported in the literature. The first preparations were described by Glutz,[216] who assigned incorrect structures to the compounds. Much of his work was repeated by Miolati,[387] who assigned correct structures. Thus, ethylene thiocyanate or the copper salt of 2-mercaptoethyl thiocyanate, when heated with tin and hydrochloric acid, yielded 2-imino-1,3-dithiolane hydrochloride as the tin chloride double salt (**341**); treatment with hydrogen sulfide liberated the hydrochloride (**342**). The ethylene thiocyanate preparation has been confirmed by Siegel and Rosenblatt.[496]

341

342

The hydrochloride could be formed directly by omitting the tin but the yield was lower.[304,387] Treatment of ethylene thiocyanate with phosphorus triodide gave 2-imino-1,3-dithiolane hydroiodide. Miolati prepared 4-methyl-2-imino-1,3-dithiolane hydrochloride from propylene thiocyanate, and Engle[166] prepared 2-imino-4-hydroxymethyl-1,3-dithiolane hydrochloride (343) from 2,3-bis(thiocyano)-1-propanol.

$$HOCH_2CHCH_2SCN \quad \xrightarrow{\text{Sn, HCl}} \quad$$

with SCN below the middle carbon, giving product **343**:

$$HOCH_2 - \text{(1,3-dithiolane ring)} = NH \cdot HCl$$

343

Aldridge[10] postulated the formation of **343** as an intermediate in his test for BAL, 2,3-dimercapto-1-propanol, which involved the reaction of BAL with cyanogen chloride and base. This hypothesis has been discussed by Siegel and Rosenblatt,[496] and led Addor[6a] to investigate the preparation of 2-imino hydrochlorides from *vic*-dimercaptans and cyanogen chloride. Excellent yields are obtained when the reaction is catalyzed by hydrogen chloride and ethanol, and this constitutes the best synthesis for this class of compound.

Wheeler and Merriam[574] prepared **342** by reacting 2-chloroethyl thiocyanate with thiobenzoic acid.

$$ClCH_2CH_2SCN + C_6H_5COSH \quad \xrightarrow[\text{reflux}]{C_6H_6} \quad \text{(1,3-dithiolane ring)} = NH \cdot HCl$$

342

The same reagent applied to ethylene thiocyanate gave a compound to which they assigned the structure 2-benzoylimino-1,3-dithiolane (344), since the tin chloride salt (341) prepared by Glutz[216] and by Miolati[387] yielded the same compound when treated with benzoyl chloride in a Schotten-Baumann reaction. Their compound melted at 80-81°. Miolati claimed to have prepared the same compound, m.p. 141-143°, by treatment of 2-acetylimino-1,3-dithiolane (345) with benzoyl chloride.

$$\begin{array}{c} CH_2SCN \\ CH_2SCN \end{array} \quad \xrightarrow[\text{6-8 hrs. reflux}]{PhCOSH, C_6H_6} \quad \text{(ring)} = NCOC_6H_5 \quad \xleftarrow[\text{NaOH}]{PhCOCl} \quad \left[\text{(ring)} = NH_2^+ \right]_2 SnCl_4^{2-}$$

344   **341**

↑ PhCOCl

$$\text{(1,3-dithiolane ring)} = NCOCH_3$$

345

Although Wheeler and Merriam's evidence appears to be more convincing, the structure of **344** remains in doubt, as does that of 4-phenyl-2-

benzoylimino-1,3-dithiolane prepared from 1-phenyl-1,3-bis(thio-cyano)ethane and thiobenzoic acid.

Wagner-Jauregg and Häring[561a] prepared 2-imino-1,3-dithiolane hydrothiocyanate (**341a**) from ethylene sulfide and thiocyanic acid; silver chloride converted it into the hydrochloride (**342**). Propylene reacted similarly; apparently the yields are very low.

341a   **342**

Busch[102] prepared 1,3-dithiolane-2-phenylhydrazone (**347**) by an unusual sequence of reactions. Phenylhydrazine reacted with carbon disulfide and potassium hydroxide to form the potassium salt of phenyl-hydrazinedithiocarbonic acid (**346**); this, on treatment with ethylene bromide in ethanol, gave the phenylhydrazone.

$$C_6H_5NHNH_2 + CS_2 \xrightarrow{\text{KOH, EtOH}} C_6H_5NHNHC{\lesssim}^S_{SK} \text{ or } C_6H_5NHN{=}C{\lesssim}^{SK}_{SK}$$

346

$$\downarrow \begin{array}{c}(CH_2Br)_2 \\ EtOH\end{array}$$

347

Initially the wrong structure was assigned to **347**; it was corrected when it was found that the compound could be hydrolyzed to 1,3-dithio-lan-2-one, and that it was identical with the phenylhydrazone prepared by Mioloti[387] from the imine hydrochloride (**342**) and phenylhydra-zine.[105,106] Busch and co-workers[103-106] prepared analogous compounds from a number of arylhydrazines.

Kennard and VanAllan[296] found that 2-hydroxyethyl N,N-diethyldithio-carbamate (**348**) could be cyclized to 1,3-dithiolan-2-diethylimmonium tetraphenylboron (**349**) by treatment with tosyl chloride and precipita-tion with sodium tetraphenylboron. The reaction is discussed in greater detail in Chapter 12, section II A-1a.

$$(C_2H_5)_2N{-}C{\lesssim}^S_{SCH_2CH_2OH} \xrightarrow[\text{3 hrs. r. t.}]{p\text{-}C_6H_4PhSO_2Cl, C_6H_6, Et_3N}$$

348

$$(C_2H_5)_2N{-}C{\lesssim}^S_{SCH_2CH_2O_3SC_6H_4CH_3\text{-}p} \xrightarrow[\text{2. NaB}(C_6H_5)_4]{\text{1. 90 min. reflux}}$$

$$\left[\begin{array}{c} S \\ \\ S \end{array} {=}N(C_2H_5)_2 \right]^+ \quad (C_6H_5)_4B^-$$

349

b. Structure and Reactions

1, 3-Dithiolane-2-thiones are generally oils or low-melting crystalline solids, soluble in the usual organic solvents and insoluble in water.
They are invariably yellow, whereas the corresponding 2-ones are
colorless. Challenger and co-workers[125] and Haszeldine and Kidd[240]
determined the ultraviolet absorption spectrum of 1, 3-dithiolane-3-
thione. They found λ_{max} at 460, 311 and 292 mu. Haszeldine and Kidd
assigned the 9. 27 u band in the infrared spectrum to the C=S stretching vibration; Jones, Kynaston, and Hales[282] agreed with this assignment, as did Iqbal and Owen[273a] and Bellamy and Rogasch.[45a] Mecke,
Mecke, and Lüttringhaus[376],[377] found a band at 9. 45μ for 1, 3-dithio-
lane-2-thione and at 6. 10μ for 1, 3-dithiolan-2-one; they also determined
the Raman spectra. For both ketones and thioketones the position of the
C=X stretching vibration varied widely with the structure. Lüttringhaus
and Grohmann[345] measured the dipole moments of the two compounds,
that for the 2-thione (4. 86 D) being higher than that for the 2-one
(4. 46 D). They interpreted this as indicating a greater polarity for the
$\diagdown$C=S group, in agreement with the yellow color of the 2-thione.

Husemann[272],[273] assigned the correct structure to 1, 3-dithiolane-2-
thione by virtue of its method of synthesis and its cleavage reactions.
Thus, ammonia gave 1, 2-dimercaptoethane and ammonium thiocyanate,
potassium hydrogen sulfide gave the dimercaptan and potassium trithiocarbonate, and fuming nitric acid gave 1, 2-ethanedisulfonic acid.

$$\begin{array}{c} S \\ \\ S \end{array}{=}S \quad \begin{array}{l} \xrightarrow{NH_3, 150^\circ} HSCH_2CH_2SH + NH_4SCN \\ \xrightarrow{KSH} HSCH_2CH_2SH + K_2CS_3 \\ \xrightarrow{HNO_3} HO_3SCH_2CH_2SO_3H \end{array}$$

Alcoholic potassium hydroxide, according to Frassetti,[197] gave a 70%
yield of 1, 2-dimercaptoethane, but Culvenor and Davies[139] reported
generally unsatisfactory yields by this procedure. Delaby and co-
workers[145],[146],[569],[459c] investigated the reaction of 1, 3-dithiolane-2-
thione with secondary amines at 40°. According to these workers, the
major product was the 2-mercaptoethyl dithiocarbamate (**350**), obtained
in 95% yield with dimethylamine, piperidine, or morpholine, but in only
30% yield with diethylamine. A by-product with piperidine, especially
in the presence of excess amine, was the ethylenebis(dithiocarbamate)
(**351**), whose yield could be increased by carrying out the reaction in the
presence of alcoholic potassium hydroxide; it is probably a secondary
product of the reaction.

[For references, see pp. 585-610.]

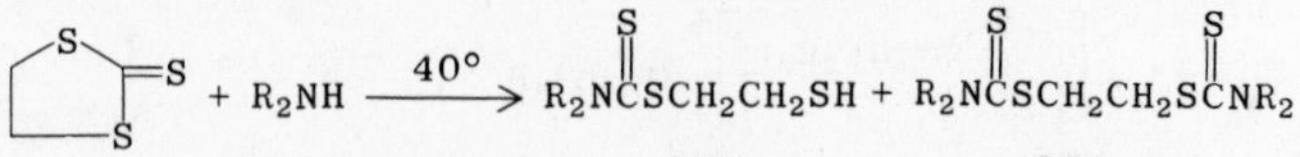

$$\text{(1,3-dithiolane-2-thione)} + R_2NH \xrightarrow{40°} R_2N\overset{S}{\overset{\|}{C}}SCH_2CH_2SH + R_2N\overset{S}{\overset{\|}{C}}SCH_2CH_2S\overset{S}{\overset{\|}{C}}NR_2$$

350   **351**

Challenger and co-workers[124-126] confirmed Delaby's results with piperidine and found in addition that at 100° the sole product was the piperidine salt of piperidinodithiocarbamic acid (**352**). The 2-mercaptoethyl dithiocarbamate (**350**) was unaffected by piperidine at 100°, so it could not be an intermediate for this reaction.

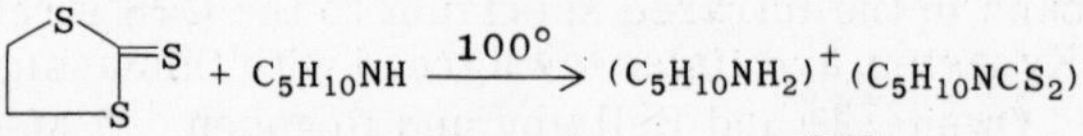

$$\text{(1,3-dithiolane-2-thione)} + C_5H_{10}NH \xrightarrow{100°} (C_5H_{10}NH_2)^+(C_5H_{10}NCS_2)^-$$

352

According to Durden, Stansbury, and Catlette,[159a] however, the product of the Delaby reaction is the disulfide (**352a**) and not the mercaptan, as evidenced by molecular weight determinations and by the absence of a sulfhydryl band in the infrared. These authors found that primary amines yield N,N'-dialkylthioureas.

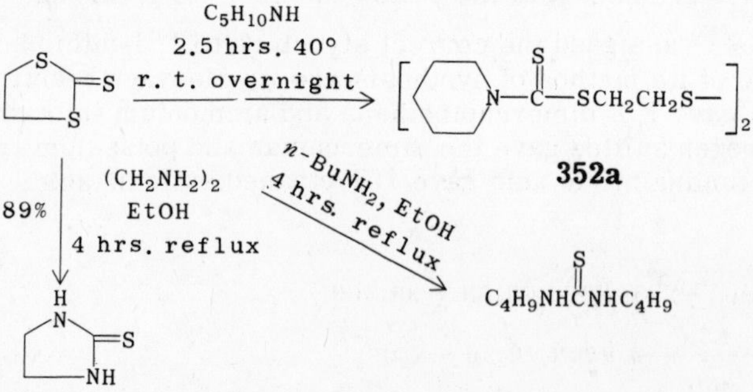

Challenger and co-workers[124-126] investigated several other reactions of 1, 3-dithiolane-2-thione. Reduction with sodium in alcohol yielded 1, 2-dimercaptoethane and hydrogen sulfide. Surprisingly, no methyl mercaptan was isolated; the reaction does not proceed *via* intermediate formation of 1, 3-dithiolane, since it was shown that the latter compound is reduced to 2-methylthioethyl mercaptan (see section II A-1b).

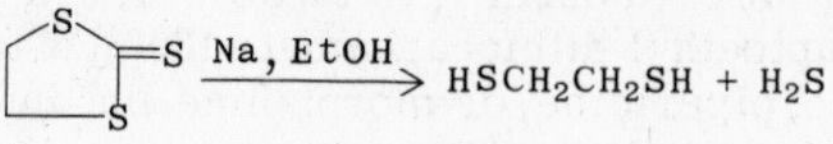

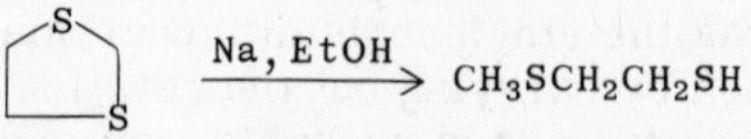

$$\text{(1,3-dithiolane-2-thione)} \xrightarrow{\text{Na, EtOH}} HSCH_2CH_2SH + H_2S$$

$$\text{(1,3-dithiolane)} \xrightarrow{\text{Na, EtOH}} CH_3SCH_2CH_2SH$$

According to Iqbal and Owen[273a] and Hauptmann and Bobbis[246a] good to excellent yields of dimercaptans are obtained by lithium aluminum hydride reduction; the fate of the cleaved $>C=S$ group was not determined. As expected, Raney nickel desulfurization yields the hydrocarbon.[362a]

Although Challenger and co-workers[125] reported a crystalline 1 : 1 adduct of 1, 3-dithiolane-2-thione with mercuric chloride, Runge and co-workers[459b] claimed that compounds of this type form amorphous 1 : 3 adducts, and that this can be used to differentiate between dithiolanes and dithioles, the latter forming 1 : 1 complexes.

According to Challenger and co-workers[125] 1, 3-dithiolane-2-thione forms an addition compound with bromine, probably on the thione sulfur, since water regenerates the parent compound.

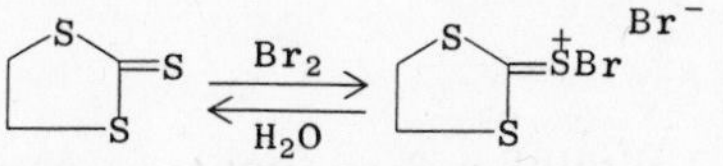

Bashour[38] reported that chlorination of 1, 3-dithiolane-2-thione in carbon tetrachloride gives a material with the average composition $C_3H_3S_2Cl_3$. This was investigated in greater detail by Runge and his co-workers. The first product formed was an insoluble 1 : 1 adduct, presumably analogous to the dibromide reported by Challenger. Additional chlorine then yielded an unstable resin, which liberated hydrogen chloride on standing.

Harder and Smith[237a] prepared 2, 2-difluoro-1, 3-dithiolane (**352b**) from 1, 3-dithiolane-2-thione and sulfur tetrafluoride. Hydrolysis of the difluoride yielded 1, 3-dithiolane-2-one.

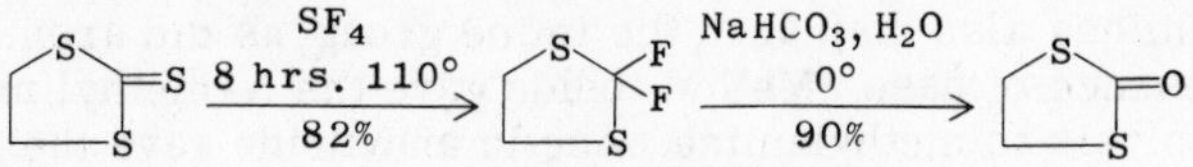

352b

1, 3-Dithiolane-2-thione could be converted to p-dithiane and thiocarbonyl bromide, according to Husemann,[273] by heating it with ethylene bromide.

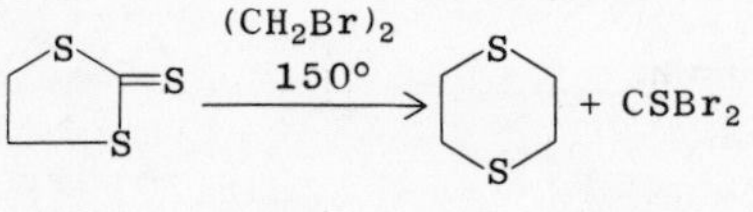

Davies and Savige[142] reported that 4-(N-methylanilinomethyl)-1, 3-dithiolane-2-thione (**339**) yields dimethylaniline on heating.

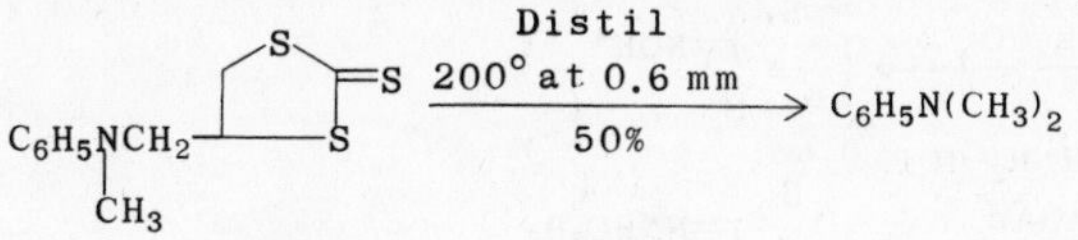

339

[For references, see pp. 585-610.]

This unusual reaction is not completely without precedent; dimethyl-aniline is formed when epichlorohydrin is heated with methylaniline.

The synthesis of 1,3-dithiolan-2-one from 1,3-dithiolane-2-thione and dilute nitric acid, potassium permanganate, or mercuric acetate in acetic acid has already been mentioned. It is conceivable that rearrangement could have occurred in the reaction to form the isomeric 1,3-oxothiolane-2-thione; that this did not take place was shown by oxidation with fuming nitric acid to 1,2-ethanedisulfonic acid,[273,387] and by cleavage with alcoholic ammonia to 1,2-dimercaptoethane and urea.[305]

$$\text{(ring, S, =O)} \xrightarrow{\text{Fuming HNO}_3} HO_3SCH_2CH_2SO_3H$$

$$\downarrow \text{NH}_3, \text{EtOH } 100°$$

$$HSCH_2CH_2SH + (NH_2)_2CO$$

Both 1,3-dithiolane-2-thione and 1,3-dithiolan-2-one form an oxime with hydroxylamine,[124-126] while the former is also reported to form a phenylhydrazone.[459b] Overberger and Bonsignore[411] were unable to dehydrogenate 1,3-dithiolan-2-one to 1,3-dithiol-2-one.

The structure of 2-imino-1,3-dithiolane hydrochloride (342) was also proved by its reactions.[387] Concentrated nitric acid yielded 1,2-ethane-disulfonic acid. The free imine could be isolated by treatment of the hydrochloride with dilute base, but it was highly unstable. 1,3-Dithiolan-2-one could not be isolated after hydrolysis of the hydrochloride, but treatment of the hydrochloride with potassium sulfide in alcohol yielded 1,3-dithiolane-2-thione, identical with the compound prepared by Husemann.[272] The imine hydrochloride formed an oxime and a phenylhydrazone. Aliphatic amines also displaced the imine group, as did aromatic amines in the presence of base. Methyl iodide gave the N-methylimine, as shown by hydrolysis to methylamine. Acetic anhydride gave the N-acetyl derivative (345) which, upon treatment with benzoyl chloride gave the N-benzoyl derivative (344); the structure of 344, as already mentioned, is in doubt.

342 $\xrightarrow{\text{Conc. HNO}_3}$ $HO_3SCH_2CH_2SO_3H$

$\xrightarrow{\text{K}_2\text{CO}_3, \text{H}_2\text{O}}$ =NH

$\xrightarrow{\text{K}_2\text{S, EtOH}}$ =S

$\xrightarrow[\text{Na}_2\text{CO}_3]{\text{NH}_2\text{OH·HCl}}$ =NOH

$\xrightarrow[\text{NaOAc}]{\text{PhNHNH}_2\text{·HCl}}$ =NNHC$_6$H$_5$

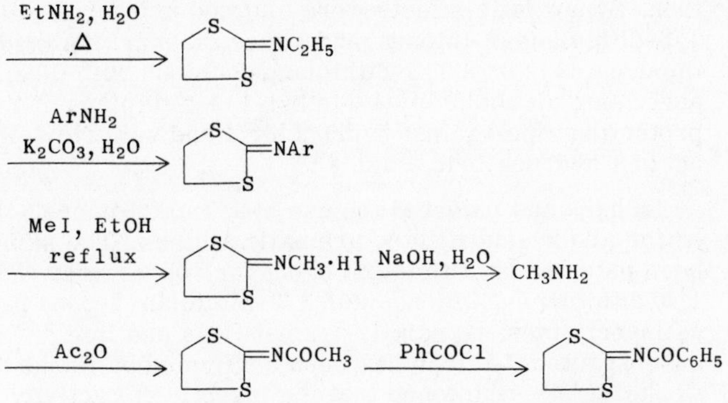

345　　　　　　　　　**346**

According to Miolati[387] hydrolysis of **342** yields ethylene tetrasulfide. This was disproved by Siegel and Rosenblatt,[496] who showed that hydrolysis yields thiocyanate ion and either ethylene sulfide or its polymer, presumably *via* intermediate formation of **353**. A neighboring group effect explains the unusual hydrolysis of an organic thiocyanate to thiocyanate ion.

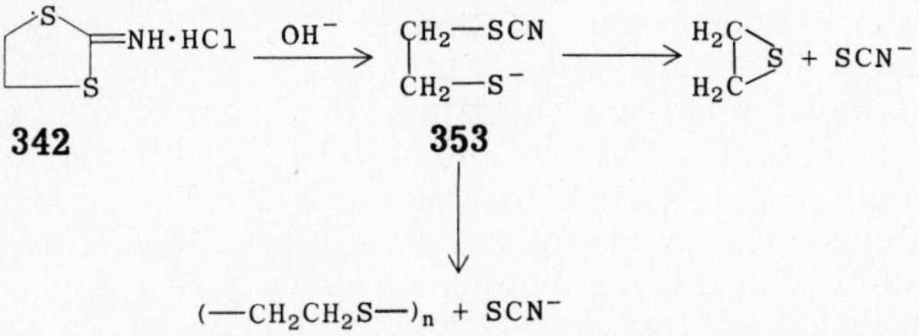

342　　　　　　　　**353**

$$(—CH_2CH_2S—)_n + SCN^-$$

It is interesting that, although Miolati[387] was unable to hydrolyze 2-imino-1,3-dithiolane to 1,3-dithiolan-2-one, Busch and Lingenbrink[105] succeeded in hydrolyzing the phenylhydrazone. Several hydrazones were also acetylated to give compounds of the type of **354**.[102,104]

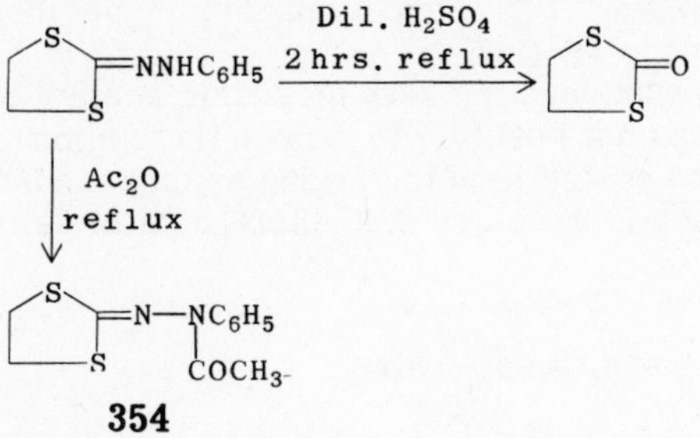

354

c. Uses

Lüttringhaus and Goetze[343] described the use of 1,3-dithiolane-2-thione and its 4-methyl derivative as inhibitors for the acid pickling of iron. Synergistic effects were claimed using 1, 2-dithiole-3-thiones, 1, 3-dithiolane-2-thiones, and either dibenzyl sulfoxide or di-*o*-tolyl-thiourea,[344b] or a 1, 3-dithiolane-2-thione with dibenzyl sulfoxide or an acetylenic alcohol.[344a] 4-Methyl-1, 3-dithiolane-2-thione was active in protecting zinc against hydrochloric and sulfuric acids, and aluminum against hydrochloric acid.[343]

Linch[323] has patented the use of 1, 3-dithiolane-2-thione as a stabilizer for alkoxy-substituted aromatic amines. The same compound has been patented as a flotation agent for copper ores.[405,406] A number of 1, 3-dithiolane-2-thiones and 1, 3-dithiolan-2-ones have been patented as insecticides, especially against fleas and lice.[249] The activity of the unsubstituted 3-thione has been confirmed by Runge and co-workers,[459b] who found that the insecticidal activity decreased with increasing ring size. Although Bashour[38] claimed that chlorinated 1, 3-dithiolane-2-thione is useful as an agricultural fungicide, Runge and co-workers reported it to be too unstable for this purpose. Gerner and Konz[212c] patented the use of 1, 3-dithiolane-2-*p*-tolylhydrazone as a pesticide.

6. 1, 3-Dithiole

The first compound containing this ring system was prepared in 1952 by Challenger, Mason, Holdsworth, and Emmott,[124-126] who reacted sulfur with acetylene at 450°. In addition to thiophene and condensed thiophenes there was isolated in trace quantities (25 g from 25 kg of sulfur) a mixture of two compounds. One was shown to be 1, 2-dithiole-3-·thione (see section I A-2a-(1)); the other was proved to be the isomeric 1, 3-dithiole-2-thione (**355**) by the following reactions. Reduction with sodium in alcohol or with lithium aluminum hydride gave 1, 2-dimercaptoethane; in addition, the former reagent gave methyl mercaptan, in contrast to 1, 3-dithiolane-2-thione. It reacted with piperidine at 100° to give piperidinium piperidinodithiocarbamate (**352**), just as did the saturated analog. Hydroxylamine gave glyoxime, and alcoholic sodium hydroxide gave sodium trithiocarbonate. Therefore, the compound must

contain a two-carbon chain and a $\overset{\text{S}}{\underset{\text{-S-C-S-}}{\|}}$ grouping. Further evidence for the thiocarbonyl function was reaction with mercuric acetate to form 1, 3-dithiol-2-one (**356**). It was not possible to reduce the compound to 1, 3-dithiolane-2-thione; zinc and acetic acid yielded a compound, m.p. 150-151°, which was assigned the structure 2, 2'-bis(1, 3-dithiole) (**357**).

$$\xrightarrow{\text{Na, EtOH}} HSCH_2CH_2SH + CH_3SH$$

355

$$\xrightarrow[\text{100°}]{C_5H_{10}NH} (C_5H_{10}NH_2)^+ (C_5H_{10}NCS_2)^-$$

352

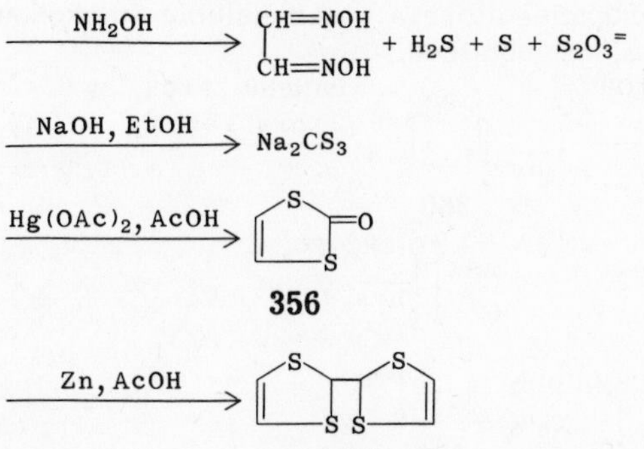

$$\xrightarrow{NH_2OH} \quad \begin{array}{l} CH{=}NOH \\ | \\ CH{=}NOH \end{array} + H_2S + S + S_2O_3^=$$

$$\xrightarrow{NaOH,\,EtOH} \quad Na_2CS_3$$

$$\xrightarrow{Hg(OAc)_2,\,AcOH}$$

356

$$\xrightarrow{Zn,\,AcOH}$$

357

The ultraviolet spectrum of **355** resembles that of 1, 3-dithiolane-2-thione, the shift to longer wave lengths indicating that the double bond is conjugated with the trithiocarbonate group. Actually, the similarity of the spectrum to that of 1, 3-dithiolane-2-thione is surprising, inasmuch as the same resonance forms written for 1, 2-dithiole-3-thione (see section I A-2a-(2)) are possible here and the compound should show aromatic character.

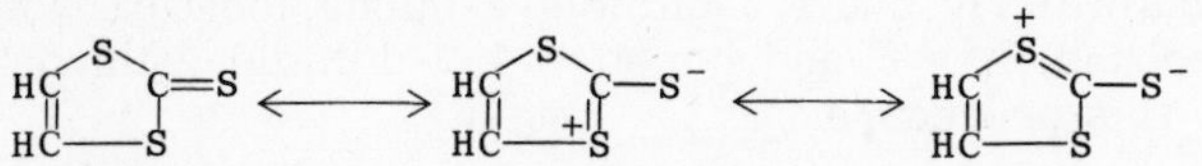

355

Inasmuch as the compound appears to be less stable than its saturated counterpart, these resonance forms apparently contribute little to its structure. Mecke, Mecke, and Lüttringhaus[376,377] have determined the infrared and Raman spectra of the compound.

An x-ray examination confirmed the assigned structure,[125] but details of this work have not been published.

1, 3-Dithiole-2-thione forms a methiodide (**358**), which is dealkylated by pyridine, indicating that it is an alkylating agent just like the 1, 2-dithiole-3-thionium salts (see section I A-2a-(3)). It forms a mono- and a di-mercuric chloride adduct, as well as a crystalline adduct with silver nitrate. Bromine gives a crystalline dibromide (**359**), which reverts to the parent compound on treatment with water.

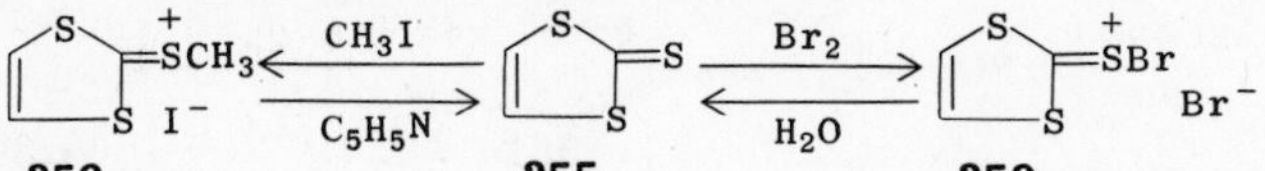

358   **355**   **359**

More recently, Runge and co-workers[459b] prepared 4-phenyl-1, 3-dithiole-2-thione (**360**) from 1-phenyl-1, 2-dibromoethylene. **360** formed a crystalline 1 : 1 adduct with mercuric chloride and yielded a phenylhydrazone. A certain amount of aromatic character was indicated by

[For references, see pp. 585-610.]

heating **360** with propanesultone; a water-soluble amorphous product, formulated as **360a**, was obtained.

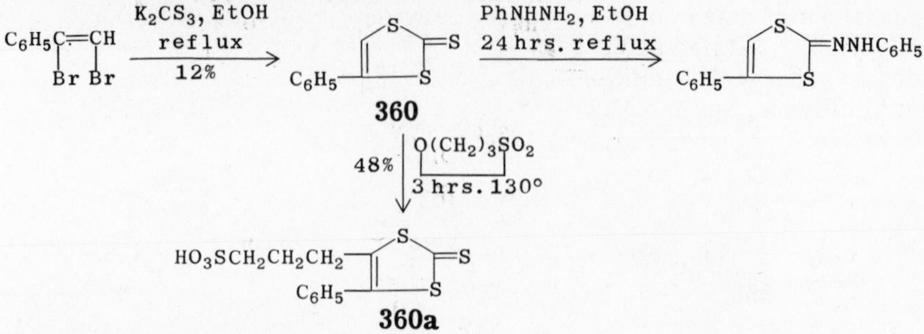

360

360a

Leaver and Robertson[313a] reported still another synthesis of 1,3-dithiole-2-thiones. Heating methyl phenacyl trithiocarbonate with phosphorus pentasulfide yielded 4-phenyl-1,3-dithiole-2-thione (**360**) in rather low yield.

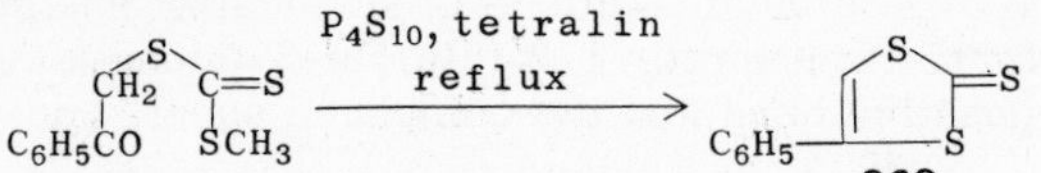

360

Xanthates reacted similarly, and 1,3-dithiole-2-thione, identical with Challenger's compound,[124-126] and 4-methyl-1,3-dithiole-2-thione were prepared by this procedure.

The intriguing discovery of Bähr and his co-workers (see Chapter 12, section III A-2a) that the disodium salt of dimercaptomaleonitrile (**361**, M = Na) can be prepared from sodium cyanide and carbon disulfide led to a different type of substituted 1,3-dithiole. Thus, these workers[28,29] reported that the silver salt of **361** reacts with methylene iodide to give 4,5-dicyano-1,3-dithiole (**362**), isolated as brown-yellow needles, while Wolf, Degener, and Petersen[171a,581a] reported that 4,5-dicyano-1,3-dithiole-2-thione (**362a**), prepared from **361** (M = Na) and thiophosgene, and the corresponding 2-one (**362b**), prepared from **361** (M = Na) and phosgene, show cytostatic and fungistatic activity.

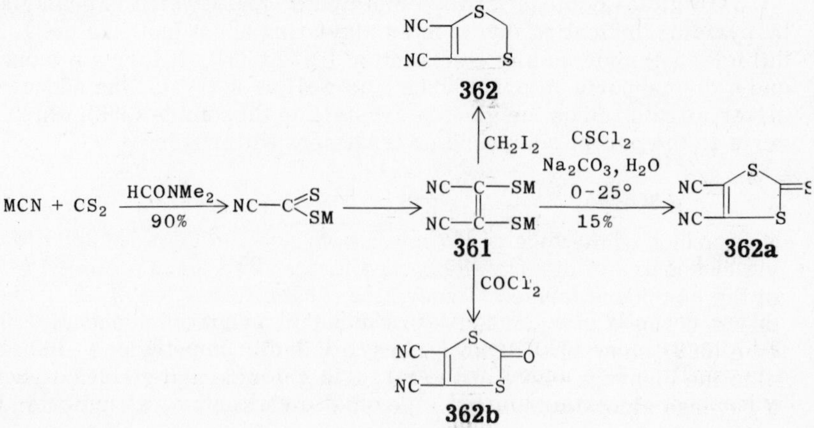

362

361

362a

362b

Kirmse and Horner[299,300] prepared a third type of 1,3-dithiole derivative. In the course of their investigations into the photochemical reactions of diazo compounds, they carried out the photolysis of 4-phenyl-1,2,3-thiadiazole (**363**). Nitrogen was evolved and 2-benzylidene-4-phenyl-1,3-dithiole (**364**), which they called 2,ω-diphenyl-1,4-dithiafulvene, was isolated in good yield in the form of lemon-yellow crystals.

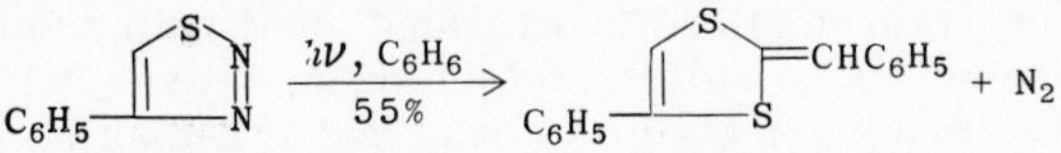

Three structures for the product were considered. 2,5-Diphenyl-p-dithiin (**366**) would be formed by dimerization of the intermediate diradical (**365**).

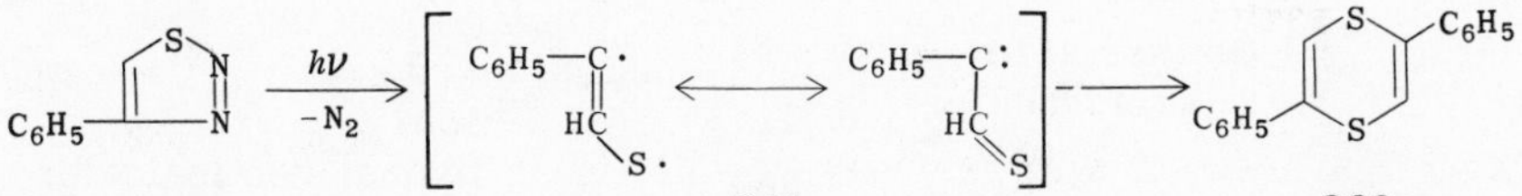

This compound is known, however, and it differs from the compound isolated. A second possibility (**367**) would involve rearrangement of **365** and dimerization of the resulting thioketene.

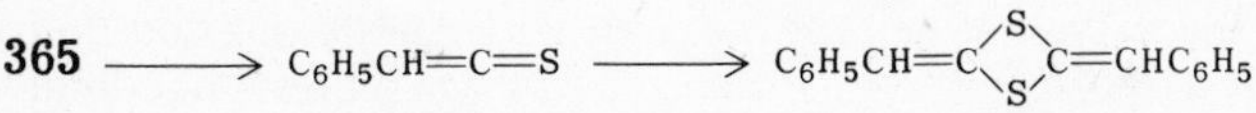

The third possibility would involve condensation of **365** with the thioketene to yield **364**, which Huisgen and Weberndörfer[268a] suggested as another example of the now well-known 1,3-dipolar cycloaddition reaction.

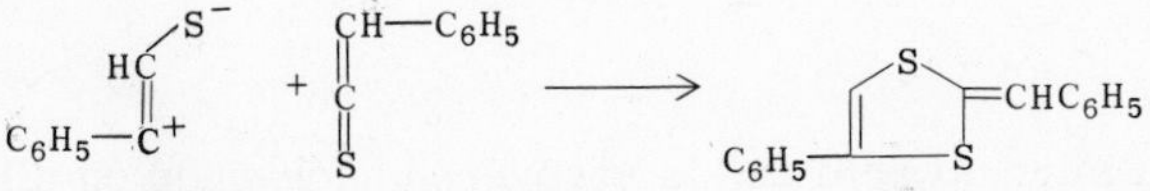

Compounds of the type of **367** are known, and the infrared and ultraviolet spectra of diphenylthioketene dimer are indeed similar to those of the compound formed. Raney nickel desulfurization of **364** gave ethylbenzene plus a trace of 1,4-diphenylbutane. Oxidation yielded a disulfone (**368**), showing that both sulfur atoms are present as sulfides, and alkaline cleavage of the disulfone yielded benzaldehyde, presumably by a reverse aldol condensation. These reactions show the presence of the group $C_6H_5CH=C-SO_2-$, and do not serve to differentiate between **364** and **367**. Other reactions showed quite definitely, however, that the compound is the 1,3-dithiole derivative (**364**). Thus, careful reduction yielded a dihydro derivative, indicating that the two double bonds are different; the dihydro product, formulated as 2-benzyl-4-phenyl-1,3-dithiole (**369**), could be oxidized to a disulfone (**370**). More drastic reduction yielded 2-benzyl-4-phenyl-1,3-dithiolane, isolated as its disulfone (**371**); compounds of this type are known to exist in only one form.[452] Furthermore, treatment of the disulfone (**368**) with sodium methoxide split off one sulfur as sulfite and introduced three methoxyl groups. Since 1,1-disulfones are stable to base and 1,2-disulfones are not, this reaction favors **364** as the correct structure. The reactions were formulated as follows:

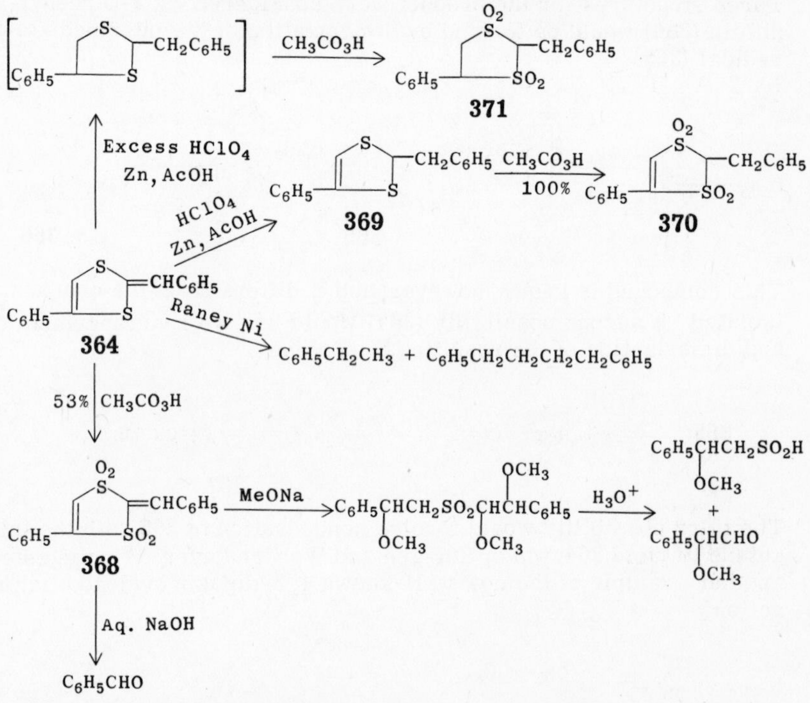

364 dissolves in mineral acid and is recovered unchanged on dilution. The salt (**372**) is undoubtedly a pseudo-aromatic system stabilized by resonance, akin to the analogous 1,3-benzodithiole compounds (section II D), although Kirmse and Horner pointed out that the ease of proton removal indicates the resonance energy is not very large.

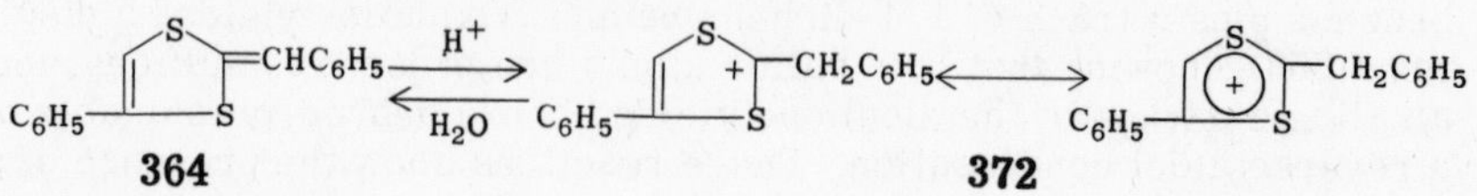

364 is oxidized to a red-violet dye, which can be isolated as a black picrate; the structure of the oxidation product is unknown.

Other 4-aryl-1,2,3-thiadiazoles gave the same type of photochemical reaction. 4,5-Diphenyl-1,2,3-thiadiazole (**373**) reacted differently, however, yielding two compounds, one identified as tetraphenyl-p-dithiin (**374**) (see Chapter 12, section III A-2a) and the other as 2-diphenylmethylidene-4,5-diphenyl-1,3-dithiole (**375**). **375** differed from the known diphenylthioketene dimer, and showed the expected reactions.

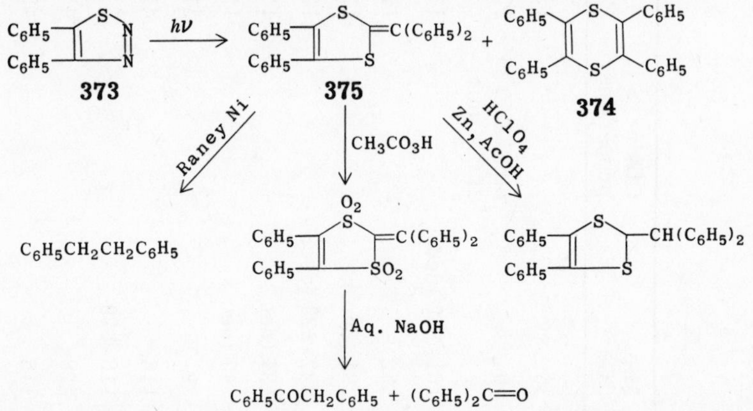

Methyl 5-phenyl-1,2,3-thiadiazole-4-carboxylate (**376**) reacted somewhat differently, yielding only a small amount of dimethyl 2-benzylidene-5-phenyl-1,3-dithiole-4,α-dicarboxylate (**377**), the major product being dimethyl 2,5-diphenylthiophene-3,4-dicarboxylate (**378**). The structure of **377** was proved by hydrolysis to 2-benzylidene-4-phenyl-1,3-dithiole (**364**).

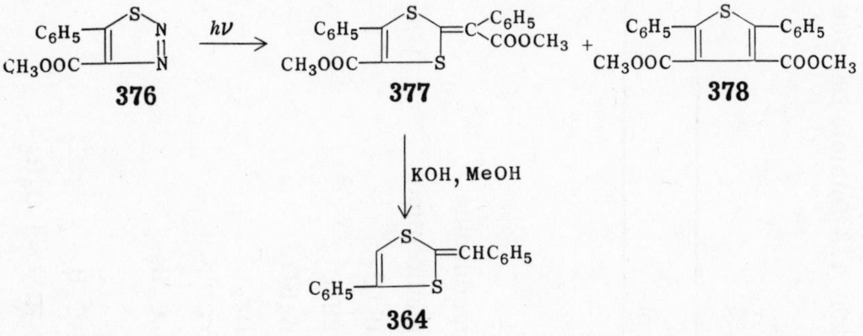

The 1,3-dithioles which have been reported are listed in Table 20.

7. 1,3-Dithiolium Salts

The only known 1,3-dithiolium salts, other than the 2-benzyl-4-phenyl derivative reported by Kirmse and Horner[299],[300] (see section II A-6),

TABLE 20. 1,3-Dithiole Derivatives

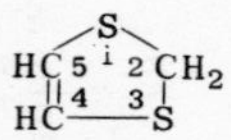

$$HC\underset{4\ \rule{0pt}{0pt}}{\overset{5\ \overset{S}{\diagup}\ 1\ \diagdown\ 2}{\diagup}}CH_2$$
$$HC\underset{3}{\overline{\hspace{1.2em}}}S$$

Substituents	Yield (%)	M.p. (°C)	Other properties	Ref.
2-(O=)		35		124-126
2-(S=)		50	b.p. 122-123° at 0.8 mm	124-126, 313a
2-(S=) · methiodide		131-132 (dec.)		125
2-(S=) · methosulfate		132		125
2-(S=) · HgCl$_2$		191 (dec.)		125
2-(S=) · 2HgCl$_2$		222-223 (dec.)		125
2-(S=) · AgNO$_3$		124 (dec.)		125
2-(S=) · Br$_2$	90	147 (dec.)		125
2-(S=)-4-CH$_3$-		29-30		313a
2-(S=)-4-C$_6$H$_5$-	12	116		459b
		118-119		313a
2-(S=)-4-C$_6$H$_5$- · HgCl$_2$		228		459b
2-(C$_6$H$_5$NHN=)-4-C$_6$H$_5$-		113		459b
4,5-(CN)$_2$		94.5		28, 29

2-($C_6H_5CH_2$-)-4-C_6H_5-		58-59	299
2-($C_6H_5CH_2$-)-4-C_6H_5-1,1,3,3-tetroxide	100	161	299
2-(C_6H_5CH=)-4-C_6H_5-	55	207	299
2-(C_6H_5CH=)-4-C_6H_5- · $HClO_4$	100	113	299
2-(C_6H_5CH=)-4-C_6H_5-1,1,3,3-tetroxide	53	240 (dec.)	299
2-(p-$C_6H_5C_6H_4CH$=)-4-(p-$C_6H_5C_6H_4$-)	28	305 (dec.)	299
2-(α-Naphthyl-CH=)-4-(α-naphthyl-)	24	168	299
2-(β-Naphthyl-CH=)-4-(β-naphthyl-)	25	258-260	299
2-[(C_6H_5)$_2$C=]-4,5-(C_6H_5-)$_2$	19	234	299
2-[(C_6H_5)$_2$C=]-4,5-(C_6H_5-)$_2$ 1,1,3,3-tetroxide		dec. 330-335	299
2-[(C_6H_5)$_2$CH-]-4,5-(C_6H_5-)$_2$		184-185	299
2-($C_6H_5CCO_2CH_3$)-4-(CH_3O_2C-)-5-C_6H_5-	1-2	198 (dec.)	299
2- 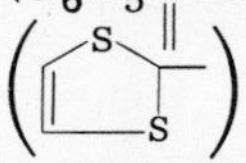		150-151	125
2-(S=)-4,5-(CN)$_2$	15	123-124	171a
2-(O=)-4,5-(CN)$_2$		123-124	171a

were prepared by Leaver and Robertson[313a] by cyclization of phenacyl or acetonyl carbodithioates (378a).

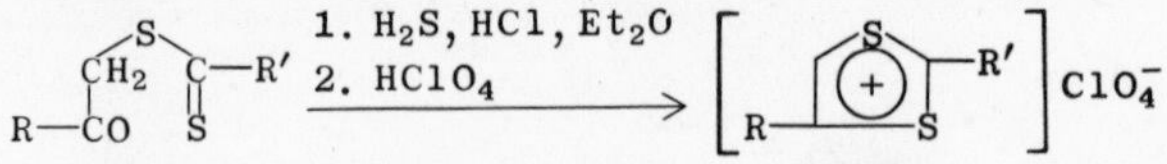

378a   1. H_2S, HCl, Et_2O 2. $HClO_4$ → **378b**

By this procedure they prepared 2,4-diphenyl-1,3-dithiolium perchlorate (**378b**, R = R′ = C_6H_5), m.p. 209-209.5°, in 98% yield; 4-methyl-2-phenyl-1,3-dithiolium perchlorate (**378b**, R = CH_3, R′ = C_6H_5), m.p. 148-149° (dec.), in 79% yield; and 2-methyl-4-phenyl-1,3-dithiolium perchlorate (**378b**, R = C_6H_5, R′ = CH_3), m.p. 102-103°, in 13% yield. The reaction failed when R or R′ was not phenyl.

The 1,3-dithiolium ion is isosteric with the tropylium ion and is therefore a pseudo-aromatic system represented by the following resonance forms:

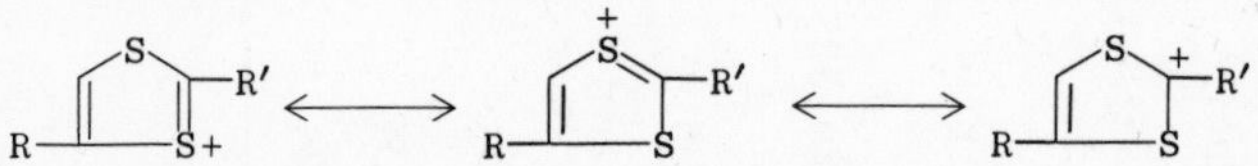

A molecular orbital calculation for the ion was carried out by Koutecký.[309a,584c] Leaver and Robertson found that 4-methyl-2-phenyl-1,3-dithiolium perchlorate reacts with p-dimethylaminobenzaldehyde to give 4-p-dimethylaminostyryl-2-phenyl-1,3-dithiolium perchlorate (**378c**), although the corresponding 2-methyl-4-phenyl derivative would not react under these conditions.

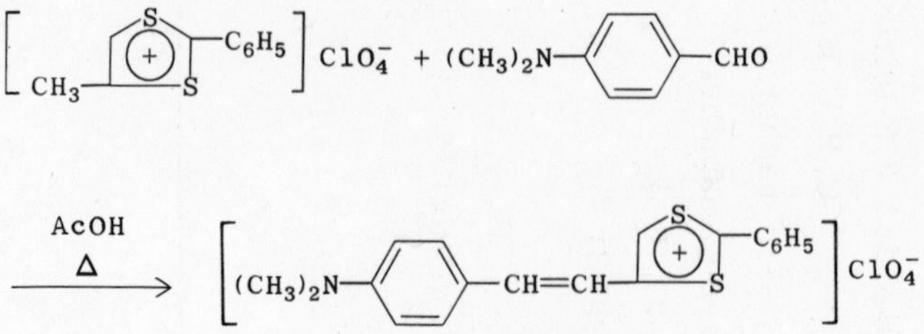

378c

B. C_3S_2-C_3S_2

1.   2,5,7-Trithiabicyclo[2.2.1]heptane (379)

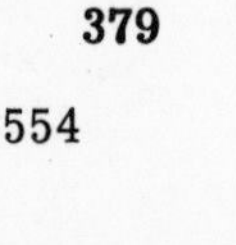

379

In 1942 Böhme, Pfeifer, and Schneider[57] reacted chloroacetone with
hydrogen sulfide and hydrogen chloride and isolated a compound,
C$_6$H$_{10}$S$_3$, b.p. 116-118° at 14 mm, m.p. 50-51°. It formed a mercuric
chloride adduct which decomposed at about 110°. The compound did
not react with hydroxylamine or phenylhydrazine, showing the absence
of a thiocarbonyl group. Its nonreactivity with diazomethane and with
Grignard reagents showed it was not a mercaptan, and the lack of reduction with sodium showed the absence of disulfide links. Oxidation
with permanganate gave a trisulfone, C$_6$H$_{10}$O$_6$S$_3$, which sublimed at
210-220° and decomposed above 255°. On the basis of these results,
Böhme and co-workers[57,58] formulated the compound as 1, 5-dimethyl-
3, 6, 7-trithiabicyclo[3. 1. 1]heptane (**380**).

$$\text{ClCH}_2\text{COCH}_3 \xrightarrow[\substack{5 \text{ hrs. } 0° \\ 52\%}]{\text{H}_2\text{S, HCl, EtOH}}$$

380

Brintzinger and Ziegler[82] repeated the preparation and isolated a
compound with the same formula, b.p. 100-102° at 23 mm, d^{20} 1. 203,
which they formulated as bis(thioacetonyl) sulfide (**381**), with no experimental evidence. Apparently they subsequently agreed with the formula
proposed by Böhme.

$$\text{CH}_3\overset{\parallel}{\underset{\text{S}}{\text{C}}}\text{CH}_2\text{—S—CH}_2\overset{\parallel}{\underset{\text{S}}{\text{C}}}\text{CH}_3$$

381

Hromatka and Engel[265] isolated the same compound from the reaction
of the acetonyl Bunte salt (**382**) with hydrochloric acid; they reported a
melting point of 45. 5-46°, but proved its identity with the previously
reported compound by a mixed melting point. These authors[266] suggested, however, that the compound is actually 1, 4-dimethyl-2, 5, 7-trithia-
bicyclo[2. 2. 1]heptane (**383**), by virtue of the fact that diacetonyl sulfide
gave none of the compound, whereas if Böhme were correct, it should
form more readily than from chloroacetone.

$$\xrightarrow[\text{——✗——}]{\text{H}_2\text{S, HCl}}$$

There is actually little doubt that Hromatka and Engel are correct. The
compound is probably a derivative of mercaptoacetone, formed as
follows:

$$\text{CH}_3\text{COCH}_2\text{Cl} \xrightarrow{\text{Na}_2\text{S}_2\text{O}_3} \text{CH}_3\text{COCH}_2\text{S}_2\text{O}_3\text{Na} \xrightarrow{\text{HCl}} \text{CH}_3\text{COCH}_2\text{SH}$$

382

[For references, see pp. 585-610.]

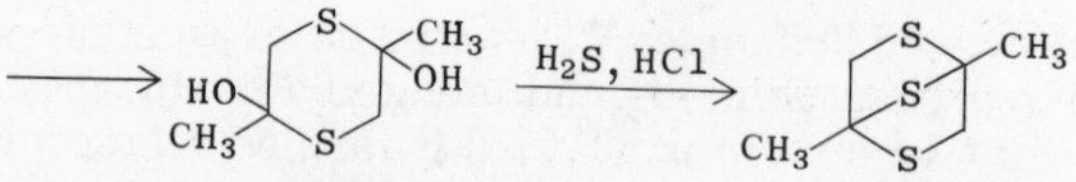

384

383

Inasmuch as the mercaptoacetone dimer (**384**) dehydrates to 1,4-dimethyl-7-oxa-2,5-dithiabicyclo [2.2.1]heptane (see Chapter 4, section II B-1) and reacts with amines to form 1,4-dimethyl-7-aza-2,5-dithia bicyclo[2.2.1]heptanes (see Chapter 12, section III. A-1j), there is little doubt that it should react with hydrogen sulfide to give the same type of symmetrical structure, **383**.

2. 2,6,7-Trithiabicyclo[2.2.1]heptane (385)

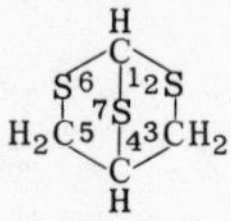

385
(RRI 965)

Doering and Levy[157] prepared **385** from ethyl orthoformate and 1,2,3-trimercaptopropane; the latter was prepared from the tribromide and sodium tetrasulfide followed by reduction according to the procedure of Backer and co-workers.[22,24]

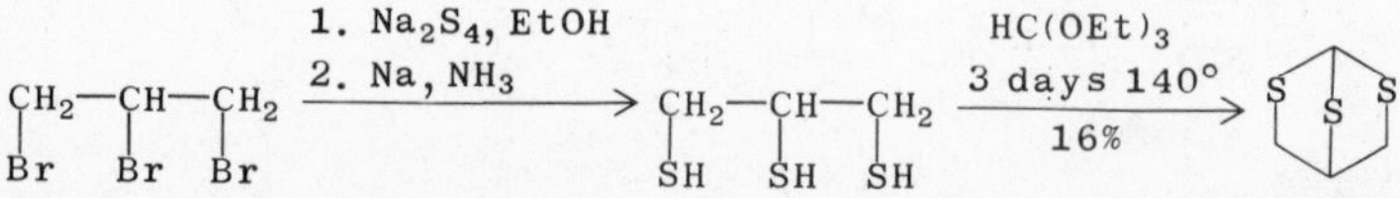

385

The compound, which could be sublimed *in vacuo* at 130°, polymerized on attempted recrystallization, indicating a considerable amount of strain in this ring system. An analytical sample sintered at 145° and finally melted at 198°. An attempt to oxidize the compound to the corresponding trisulfone was unsuccessful; a tetroxide of unknown structure was formed instead.

C. C_3S_2-C_5 CYCLOPENTA-1,3-DITHIOLE (386)

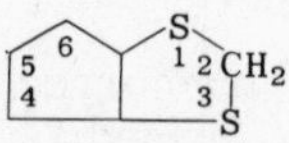

386

Iqbal and Owen[273a] prepared *trans*-tetrahydrocyclopenta-1,3-dithiole-2-thione (**387**), m.p. 147°, from cyclopentene sulfide and potassium methyl xanthate.

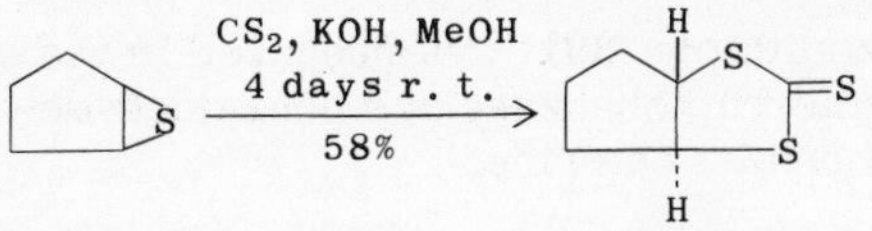

$$\text{(cyclopentene oxide)} \xrightarrow[58\%]{\substack{CS_2, KOH, MeOH \\ 4 \text{ days r.t.}}} \textbf{387}$$

The reaction was formulated as follows, ring opening taking place with inversion:

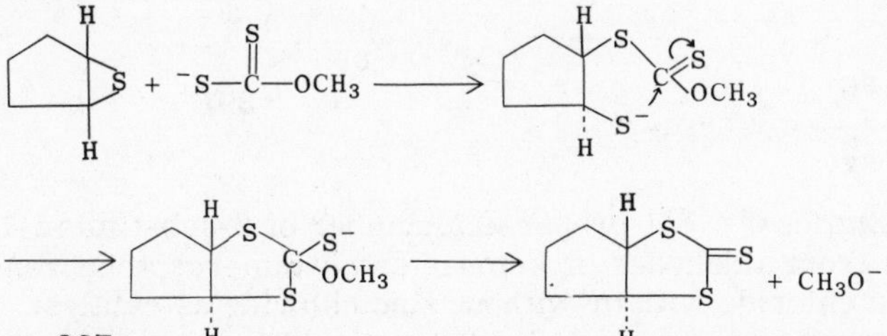

387a

It is interesting that the reaction failed with cyclopentene oxide, although it gives excellent yields with cyclohexene oxide (section II D-1). Iqbal and Owen attributed this to the difficulty of *trans*-fusion of two five-membered rings in the cyclopenta-1,3-oxathiolane analogous to **387a**, the resistance to ring closure being overcome in **387a** by the greater nucleophilicity of sulfur as compared to oxygen.

D. C_3S_2-C_6 1,3-BENZODITHIOLE (388) AND 1,3-BENZODITHIOL-1-IUM SALTS (389)

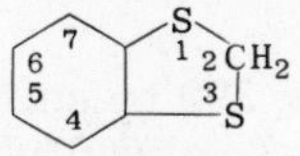

388

(RRI 1244)

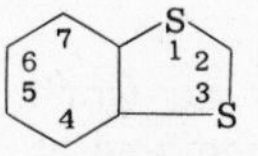

389

(RRI 1245)

1,3-Benzodithiole is indexed in Chemical Abstracts as such, but the salt is indexed as 1,3-benzodithiylium. The 1,3-benzodithiolium nomenclature recommended by the Revised Ring Index seems more logical and is used here.

1. 1,3-Benzodithiole Derivatives

The simplest members of this class of compounds are reaction products of *o*-dimercaptobenzene (dithiocatechol) with aldehydes or ketones. Thus, Guha and Chakladar[225] prepared 2-(*o*-nitrophenyl)-1,3-benzodithiole (**390**) from dithiocatechol and *o*-nitrobenzaldehyde.

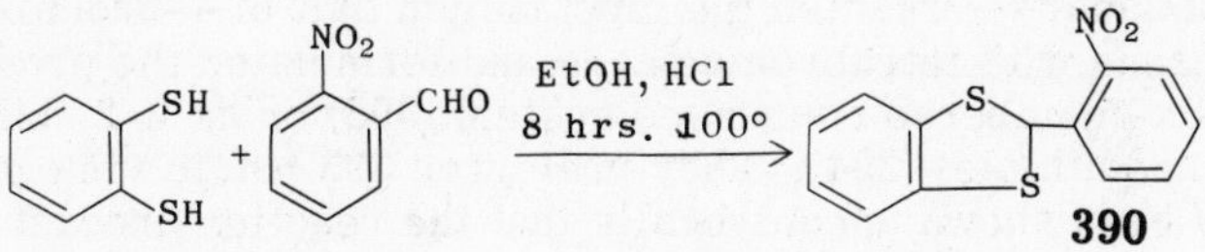

390

[For references, see pp. 585-610.]

2-Phenyl-5-bromo-1,3-benzodithiole (**391**) was prepared in the same manner from 4-bromo-1,2-dimercaptobenzene and benzaldehyde or from the dipotassium salt and benzal chloride.

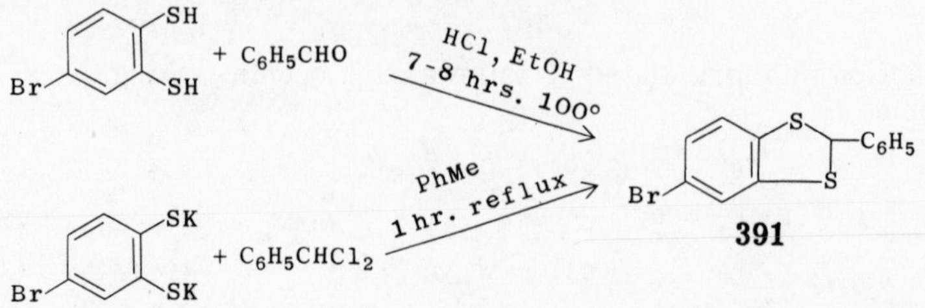

Hurtley and Smiles[269-271] prepared a number of 2-substituted-1,3-benzodithioles from aldehydes or ketones and o-dimercaptobenzene, using hydrogen chloride with or without zinc chloride as catalyst. Only one carbonyl group in 1,2- and 1,3-diketones reacted, just as with 1,2-dimercaptoethane.

Culvenor and Davies[139] reacted what was probably *trans*-1,2-dimercaptocyclohexane[356] with benzaldehyde to form *trans*-hexahydro-2-phenyl-1,3-benzodithiole (**392**); piperonal reacted similarly. Iqbal and Owen[273a] prepared the corresponding 2,2-dimethyl derivative.

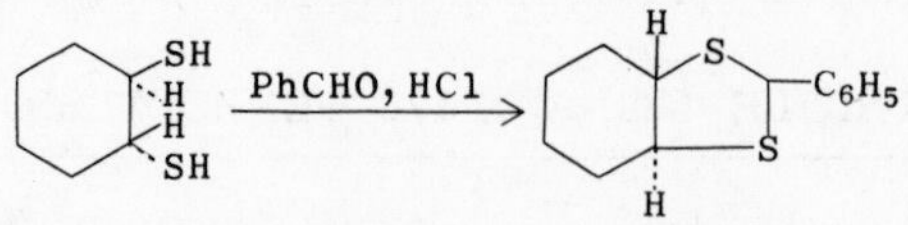

Bateman and co-workers[39] prepared the *cis* isomer of **392** by sulfuration of cyclohexene at 140°, reduction of the cyclohexene polysulfide with lithium aluminum hydride to *cis*-1,2-dimercaptocyclohexane, which was then reacted with benzaldehyde. The product was different from that reported by Culvenor and Davies and was therefore assigned the *cis* configuration.

Breslow and Mohacsi[81a] prepared ethyl 5-methyl-1,3-benzodithiole-2-carboxylate 1,1,3,3-tetroxide (**392a**) by alkylation of the disulfone with ethyl chloroformate.

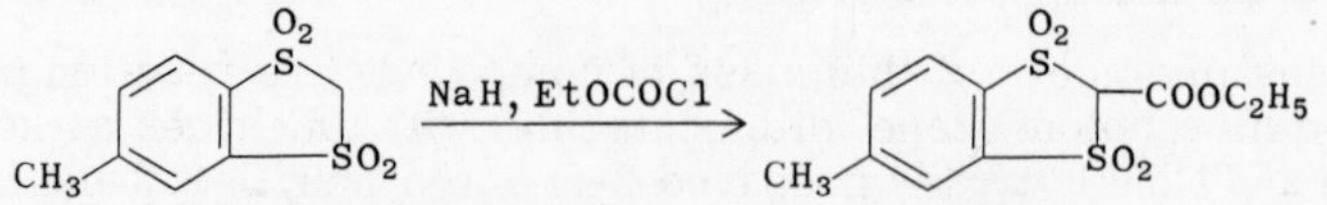

Guha and Chakladar[225] reacted the dipotassium salt of 4-bromo-1,2-dimercaptobenzene with tetrabromoethane and formulated the product as either the six-membered condensed system (**393**) or as 2,2'-bis(5-bromo-1,3-benzodithiole) (**394**). They preferred **393** but, in view of the fact that it has been shown unequivocally that the reaction product of

558

glyoxal and 1, 2-dimercaptoethane is 2, 2′-bis(1, 3-dithiolane) (section II A-la), **394** would appear to be a more reasonable structure for this compound.

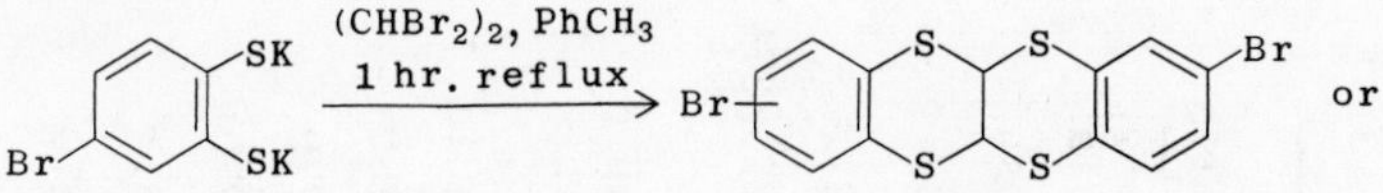

393

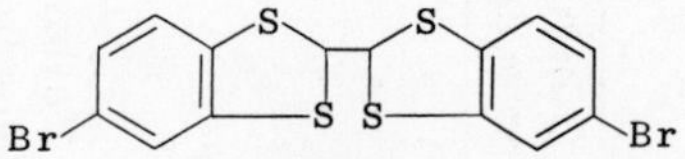

or

394

Hurtley and Smiles[270] found that o-dimercaptobenzene underwent an unusual series of reactions with oxalyl chloride. With excess oxalyl chloride the product was 1, 4-benzodithiane-2, 3-dione (see Chapter 12, section III E-1). With excess o-dimercaptobenzene, however, the product was a colorless compound, too unstable to be isolated pure, which the authors formulated as 2, 2′-dihydroxy-2, 2′-bis(1, 3-benzodithiole) (**395**) on the basis of its conversion to 2, 2′-bis(1, 3-benzodithiolene) (**396**) and other reactions; the mechanism of formation of **396** from **395** is obscure.

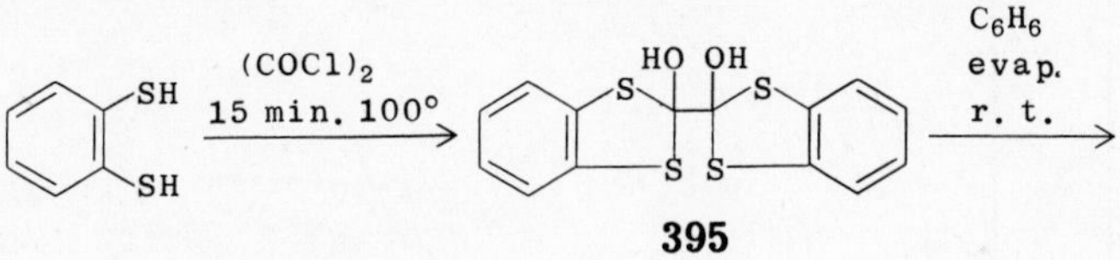

395

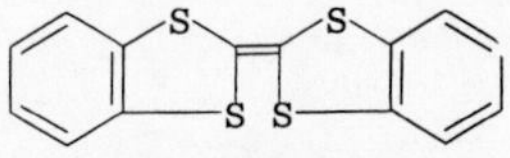

396

Hurtley and Smiles prepared a number of other unusual 1, 3-benzodithiole compounds. These are discussed under the 1, 3-benzodithiolium salts (section II D-2).

1, 3-Benzodithioles which have been reported are listed in Table 21.

The second class of compounds in this series are the condensed analogs of ethylene trithiocarbonate; these too, are listed in Table 21. Hurtley and Smiles[269] prepared 1, 3-benzodithiol-2-one (**397**) from o-dimercaptobenzene and phosgene in the presence of base.

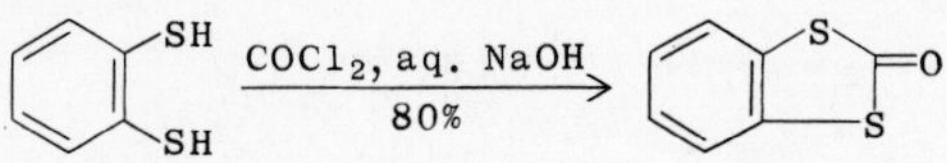

397

TABLE 21. 1,3-Benzodithiole Derivatives

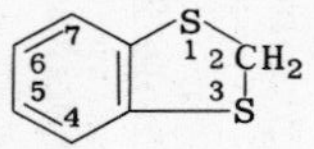

Substituents	Yield (%)	M.p. (°C)	Other properties	Ref.
$5\text{-}CH_3\text{-}1,1,3,3\text{-tetroxide}$		166-167		81a
$2\text{-}C_6H_5\text{-}$		72		269
$2\text{-}(p\text{-}CH_3OC_6H_4\text{-})$	100	72		271
$2\text{-}(p\text{-}HOC_6H_4\text{-})$		118		271
$2\text{-}(o\text{-}O_2NC_6H_4\text{-})$		106	Yellow needles	225, 271
$2\text{-}[p\text{-}(CH_3)_2NC_6H_4\text{-}]$		116		401d
$2\text{-}(C_2H_5CH{=}CH\text{-})$		80		271
$2\text{-}[p\text{-}(CH_3)_2NC_6H_4CH{=}CH\text{-}]$		132-134		401d
$2\text{-}CH_3\text{-}2\text{-}C_6H_5\text{-}$		83		269
$2\text{-}CH_3\text{-}2\text{-}CH_3CO\text{-}$	80-85	156		270
$2\text{-}CH_3\text{-}2\text{-}(CH_3COCH_2\text{-})$	60-65	119		270
$5\text{-}CH_3\text{-}2\text{-}C_2H_5O_2C\text{-}1,1,3,3\text{-tetroxide}$		153-154		81a
$2\text{-}C_6H_5\text{-}2\text{-}C_6H_5CO\text{-}$	90-95	175	Pale yellow	270
$2\text{-}C_6H_5\text{-}5\text{-}Br$		170		225

Structure	Yield	M.p.	Description	Ref.
2- 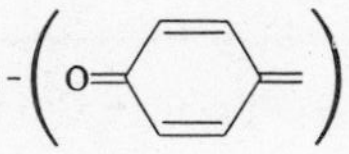		212–213	Scarlet leaflets	271
2- 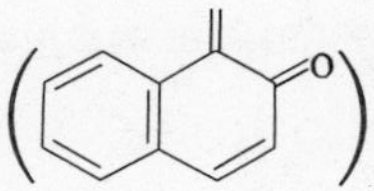	70	165	Red needles	271
2-(=O)	80	78–79		269
2-(=O)-x-NO$_2$	56	78–78.5		25
2-(=S)		151		269
2-(=S)-5-CH$_3$-	100	165		269
2-(=S)-5-Br		84		499
2-(=NOH)		140	Yellow needles	225
2-		129–130		269
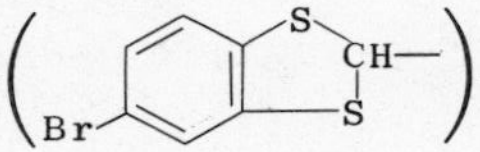 2-		236–238		225
2- 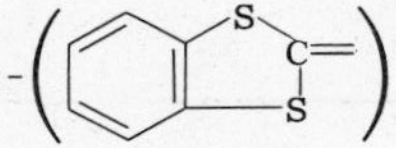		234	Golden needles	270
2- 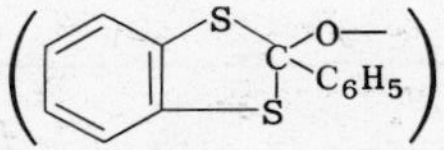		134		269

TABLE 21. 1,3-Benzodithiole Derivatives (contd.)

Substituents	Yield (%)	M.p. (°C)	Other properties	Ref.
2-(structure: C$_6$H$_4$OCH$_3$-p) 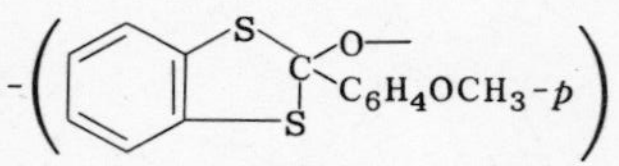		158		271
trans-Hexahydro-2-C$_6$H$_5$-		115.5		139
cis-Hexahydro-2-C$_6$H$_5$-		133-134		39
trans-Hexahydro-2-(3,4-methylenedioxyphenyl-)		125		139
trans-Hexahydro-2,2-(CH$_3$-)$_2$	73	37-38		273a
trans-Hexahydro-2-(=S)	87	169	Yellow crystals	138
	11	165-166		384
	3.5	165-166		159a
cis-Hexahydro-2-(=S)		99-99.5		39
trans-Hexahydro-2-(=NNHC$_6$H$_5$)	87	181.5-182		384
trans-Hexahydro-2-(=NNH-pyridine structure) 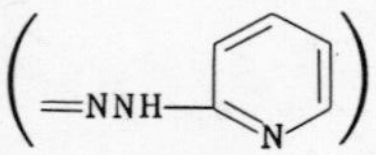		167-168.5	Yellow	384
trans-Hexahydro-5-CN-2-(=S)	19	183-185		159a

Backer and Wiggerink[25] obtained a somewhat lower yield by carrying out the reaction thermally in dioxane at 160°. The heterocyclic ring is so stable that the benzene ring could be nitrated without affecting the rest of the molecule; the position of the nitro group was not determined.[269]

Guha and Chakladar[225] reacted the dipotassium salt of 4-bromo-1,2-dimercaptobenzene with thiophosgene and isolated 5-bromo-1,3-benzodithiole-2-thione (398).

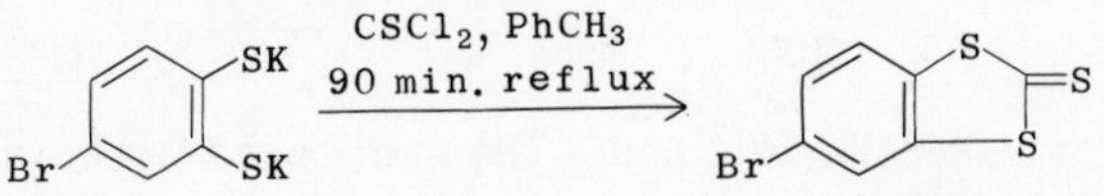

398

Hurtley and Smiles[269] prepared the unbrominated compound (399) from the dimercaptan and carbon disulfide in quantitative yield.

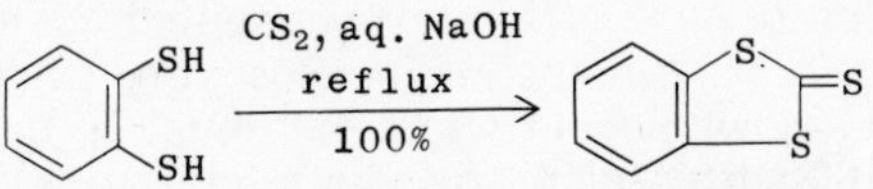

399

Treatment with hydroxylamine hydrochloride and sodium acetate in the usual fashion gave the corresponding oxime. Huisgen and Weberndörfer[268a] prepared 399 by heating 1,2,3-benzothiadiazole with carbon disulfide. Similarly, reaction with phenyl isothiocyanate yielded 2-phenylimino-1,3-benzodithiole (399a). The reactions are considered to be examples of 1,3-dipolar cycloadditions.

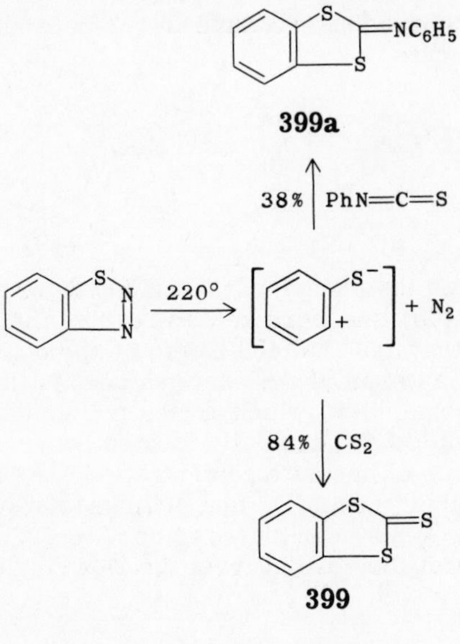

399a

399

Mills and Schindler[384] prepared *trans*-hexahydro-1,3-benzodithiole-2-thione (**400**) from 2-iodocyclohexanol and potassium trithiocarbonate in low yield. Culvenor, Davies, and Pausacker[138] prepared the same compound in much better yield from cyclohexene oxide and carbon disulfide.

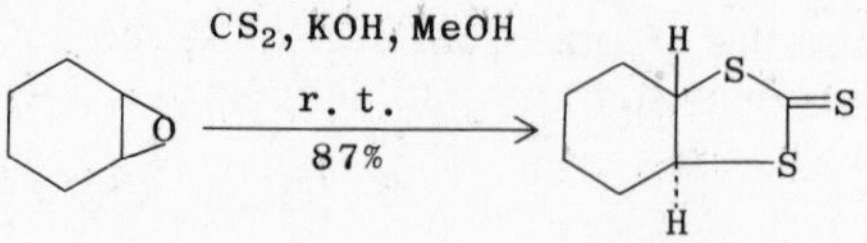

400

Cyclohexene sulfide gave a 95% yield under the same conditions, while the yield from 2-chlorocyclohexanol was only 43%. Durden, Stansbury, and Catlette[159a] obtained **400** and the corresponding 5-cyano derivative in low yields from the cyclohexene oxide and carbon disulfide in the presence of a catalytic amount of trimethylamine. The mechanism was discussed in connection with the synthesis of 1,3-dithiolane-2-thione from ethylene oxide (see section II A-5a). No stereochemical assignment of the ring fusion was made when these compounds were first reported. Lyle and Lyle[356] have shown recently that **400** must be the *trans* isomer. Hydrolysis of **400** with alcoholic sodium hydroxide[139] yielded the same 1,2-dimercaptocyclohexane as obtained by reaction of cyclohexene sulfide with hydrosulfide ion. As ring opening of the latter undoubtedly gives the *trans* isomer, and hydrolysis of **400** should not affect the stereochemistry, **400** must also be the *trans* isomer. The more recent work of Iqbal and Owen[273a] agrees with this conclusion. These authors found that lithium aluminum hydride reduction of **400** is superior to alkaline hydrolysis for the preparation of *trans*-1,2-dimercaptocyclohexane; a 90% yield was obtained.

Bateman and co-workers[39] prepared *cis*-hexahydro-1,3-benzodithiole-3-thione (**401**) by the following route:

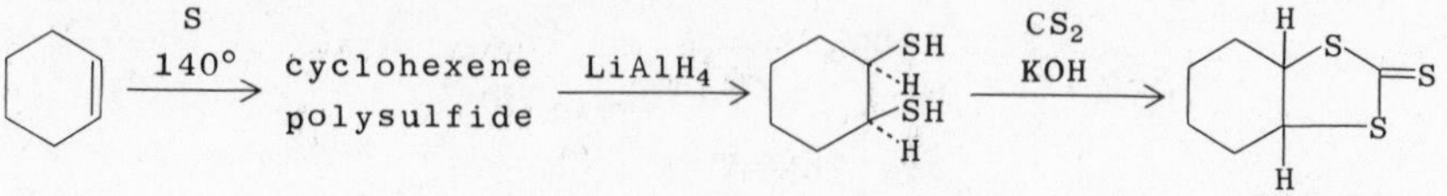

401

Mills and Schindler[384] prepared the phenylhydrazone and 2-pyridylhydrazone of the *trans* isomer (**400**), and were able to resolve the 2-pyridylhydrazone. At the time, they felt that **400** had to be the *cis* isomer and that the resolution was an example of what has been called "geometrical enantiomorphic isomerism", which arises from having an unsymmetrically substituted double bond centrally located between two similar asymmetric carbon atoms of opposite configuration.[356] Mills and Saunders[385] recognized shortly thereafter that **400** need not be *cis* and, as already mentioned, it has since been shown to be *trans*. There is nothing unusual, therefore, about the resolution of the 2-pyridylhydrazone of **400**.

400 has been patented as a stabilizer for alkoxy-substituted aromatic amines.[323]

2. 1,3-Benzodithiol-1-ium Salts

Hurtley and Smiles[269] prepared the first 1,3-benzodithiolium salts by the oxidation of 2-phenyl-1,3-benzodithiole (**402**). Thus, treatment of **402** with nitric acid at 40° gave the yellow 2-phenyl-1,3-benzodithiolium nitrate (**403**). For convenience, only one of the possible resonance forms will be written. Treatment of **403** with water gave an oxide (**404**);

402

the intermediate hydroxide could not be isolated. Mineral acids reacted with the oxide to give a series of orange or yellow 2-phenyl-1,3-benzo-dithiolium salts (**405**).

403   **404**

405

Thus, concentrated hydrochloric acid, when added to an acetone solution of the oxide, gave greenish-yellow needles of a salt, which analyzed as $(C_{13}H_9S_2Cl)_2 \cdot HCl$; storage over base removed the excess acid to give the orange chloride (**405**, X = Cl). Chloroplatinic acid on the oxide gave the chloroplatinate (**405**, X = $\frac{1}{2}$ $PtCl_6$), and bromine gave a perbromide (**405**, X = Br_3).

A more detailed investigation by Hurtley and Smiles[271] showed that electron-attracting groups, such as in 2-(p-nitrophenyl)-1,3-benzodi-thiole, prevent oxidation, while electron-donating groups, such as in 2-(p-methoxyphenyl)-1,3-benzodithiole, facilate oxidation and make the salts more stable. This is in accord with theory, since electron-dona-ting groups should stabilize a positive charge on the ion. 2-(p-Meth-oxyphenyl)-1,3-benzodithiole gave a red nitrate, analyzing as $(C_{14}H_{11}OS_2NO_3) \cdot 2HNO_3$. Dilute base gave the oxide corresponding to **404** which, on treatment with concentrated hydrochloric acid, yielded the yellow chloride, $(C_{14}H_{11}OS_2Cl)_3 \cdot 2HCl$. 2-($p$-Hydroxyphenyl)-1,3-

benzodithiole (**406**) oxidized even more readily; however, if these compounds are formulated correctly, the nitrate could not have been pure, since it had the formula $(C_{13}H_9OS_2)_2 \cdot HNO_3$. Treatment with aqueous potassium carbonate yielded the quinone (**407**) as scarlet leaflets, formed presumably by spontaneous elimination of water from the intermediate hydroxide. The quinone reacted with hydrogen chloride to give the orange chloride (**408**).

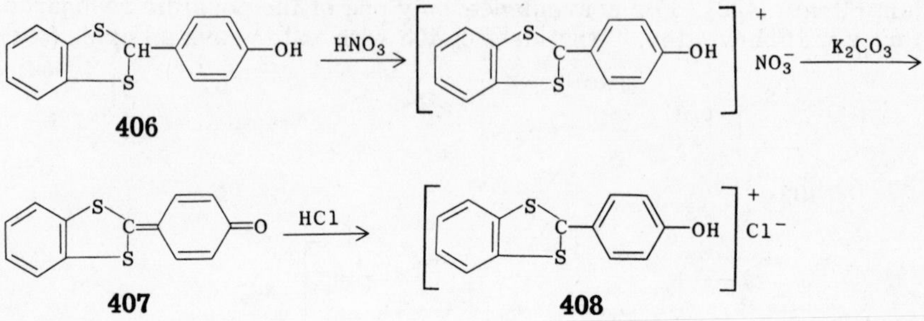

406　**407**　**408**

2-(2-Hydroxy-1-naphthyl)-1,3-benzodithiole (**409**) oxidized so rapidly that it could not be isolated; treatment of 2-hydroxy-1-naphthaldehyde with o-dimercaptobenzene and hydrogen chloride in ether, followed by aqueous sodium hydroxide, gave the red quinone (**410**). This with hydrochloric acid yielded the red chloride (**411**).

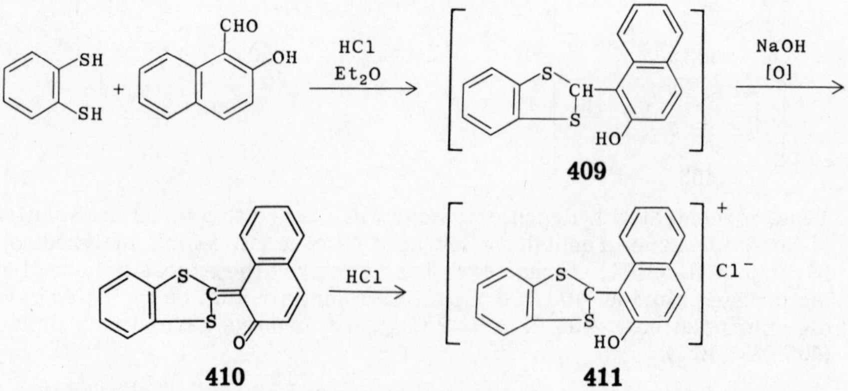

409　**410**　**411**

Cinnamaldehyde reacted normally to give 2-styryl-1,3-benzodithiole. This with nitric acid gave a complex nitrate, from which a pure oxide could not be isolated.

Hurtley and Smiles[270] also succeeded in preparing unsubstituted 1,3-benzodithiolium salts, and these underwent an unusual series of reactions. Treatment of ethyl orthoformate and o-dimercaptobenzene with hydrogen chloride gave the chloride (**412**), isolated as the tetrachlorozincate (**413**) and as the chloroplatinate (**414**).

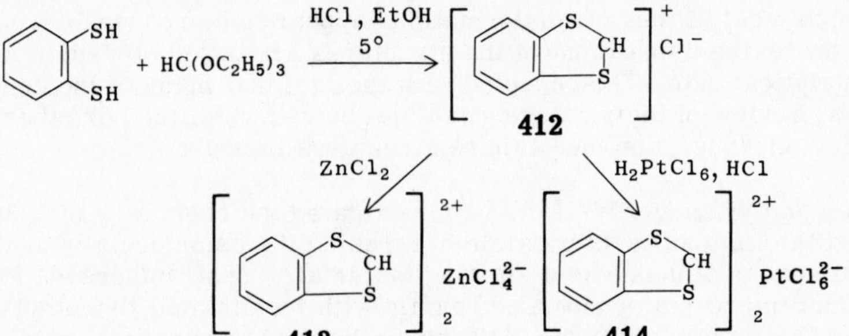

As in the case of the 2-phenyl derivative, the salts hydrolyzed readily. Treatment of the zinc chloride double salt (**413**) with hot acetic anhydride yielded 2, 2'-bis(1, 3-benzodithiolene) (**396**), presumably *via* the intermediate acetate (**415**); the same compound was formed from the disodium salt of *o*-dimercaptobenzene and tetrachloroethylene.

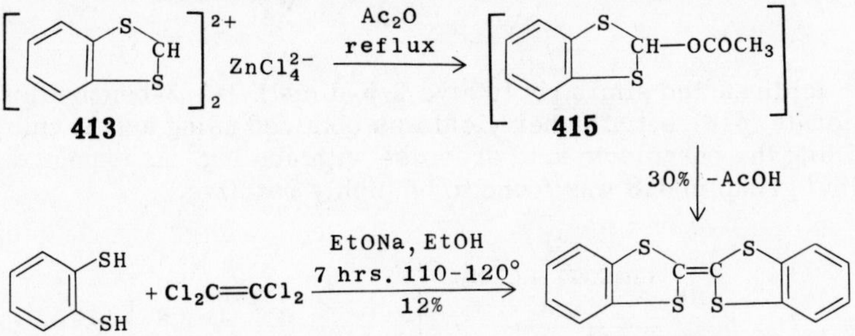

As already mentioned, *o*-dimercaptobenzene reacts with oxalyl chloride to give a compound which Hurtley and Smiles formulated as 2, 2'-dihydroxy-2, 2'-bis(1, 3-benzodithiole) (**395**) (section II D-1). Reaction of it with acetic anhydride and sulfuric acid gave a purple compound, m.p. 268-270° (dec.), with the unlikely formula $(C_{14}H_8S_4 \cdot SO_4)_2 \cdot H_2SO_4 \cdot 2H_2O$, which Hurtley and Smiles formulated as 2, 2'-bis(1, 3-benzodithiolium sulfate), and which presumably should be the bisulfate (**416**), which actually fits the analysis better. Reduction with zinc and acid or treatment with hot ammonium hydroxide converted the salt into 2, 2'-bis (1, 3-benzodithiolene) (**396**).

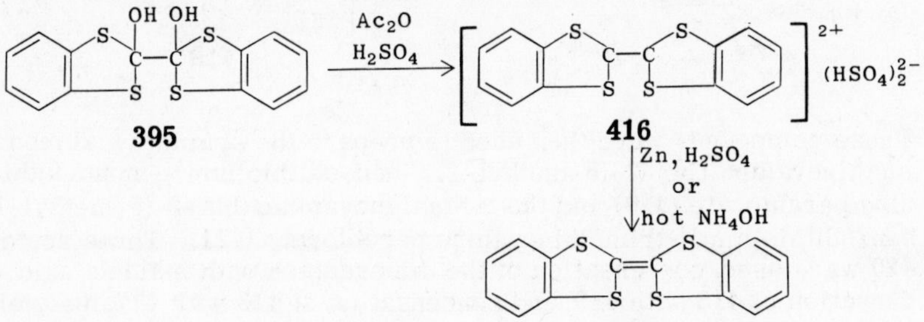

[For references, see pp. 585-610.]

567

Although most of these transformations appear to be reasonable, it must be realized that most of the structures are based on rather limited analytical data. This, coupled with the fact that many of the compounds, in view of their nature, could not be recrystallized or otherwise purified, must leave some of these structures in doubt.

Soder and Witzinger[499,500,579] investigated the chemistry of 1,3-benzodithiolium salts as possible dyes, using the commercially available 3,4-dimercaptotoluene as a starting material. These authors[499] found that the dimercaptan condensed readily with formic acid, 5-methyl-1,3-benzodithiolium perchlorate (**417**) being isolated in excellent yield.

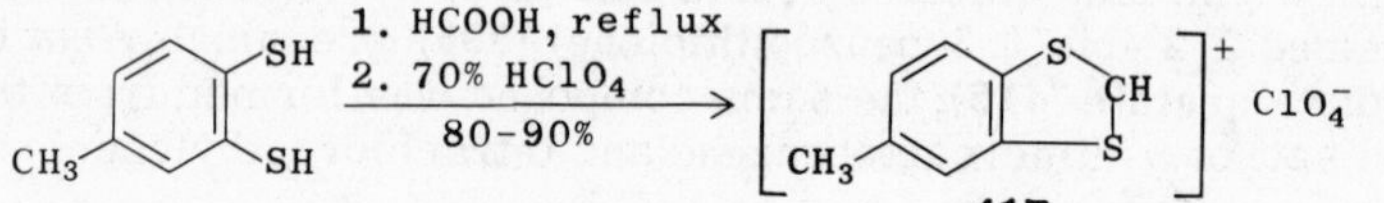

1. HCOOH, reflux
2. 70% HClO4
80-90%
SH
SH
CH3
S
CH
S
CH3
+
ClO4-

417

Acetic acid reacted similarly to give 2,5-dimethyl-1,3-benzodithiolium perchlorate (**418**), but a higher yield was obtained using acetyl chloride and adding the perchloric acid dropwise with cooling. As expected, the 2-methyl group in **418** was found to be highly reactive.

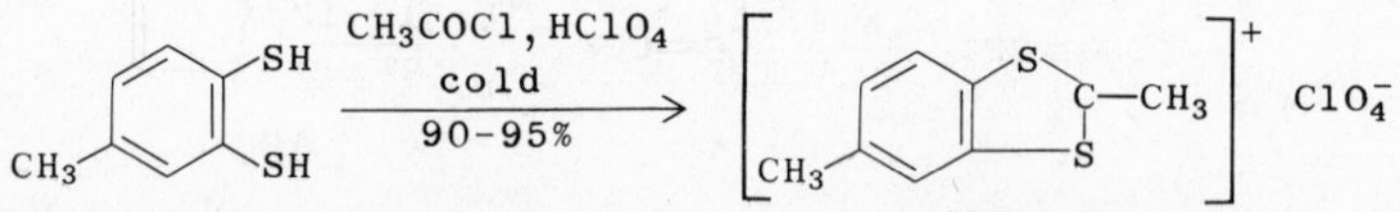

CH3COCl, HClO4
cold
90-95%
SH
SH
CH3
S
C—CH3
S
CH3
+
ClO4-

418

Both compounds are colorless but turn red on exposure to light. A different synthesis was used to prepare 2-methylthio-5-methyl-1,3-benzodithiolium perchlorate (**419**).

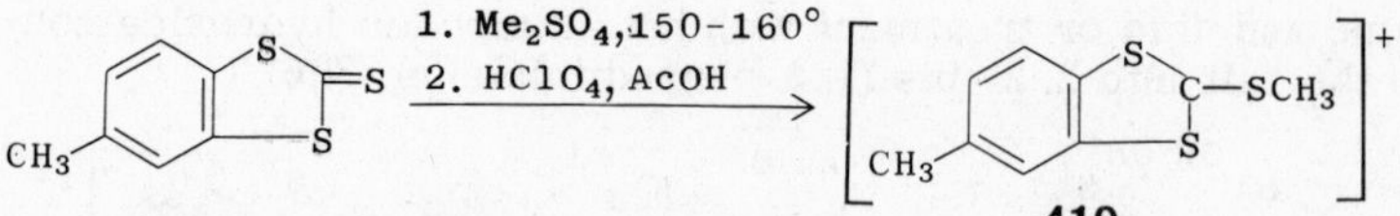

1. Me2SO4,150-160°
2. HClO4, AcOH
S
=S
S
CH3
S
C—SCH3
S
CH3
+
ClO4-

419

These compounds were then used to prepare the symmetrical monomethincyanine, [bis-2-(5-methyl-1,3-bensodithiolium)]-monomethincyanine perchlorate (**420**) and the trimethincyanine, [bis-2-(5-methyl-1,3-benzodithiolium)]-trimethincyanine perchlorate (**421**). Three routes to **420** were used: condensation of the dimercaptan with malonic acid, condensation of **418** with **419**, and condensation of **418** with **417**; the yield in the last synthesis was inferior to those in the first two.

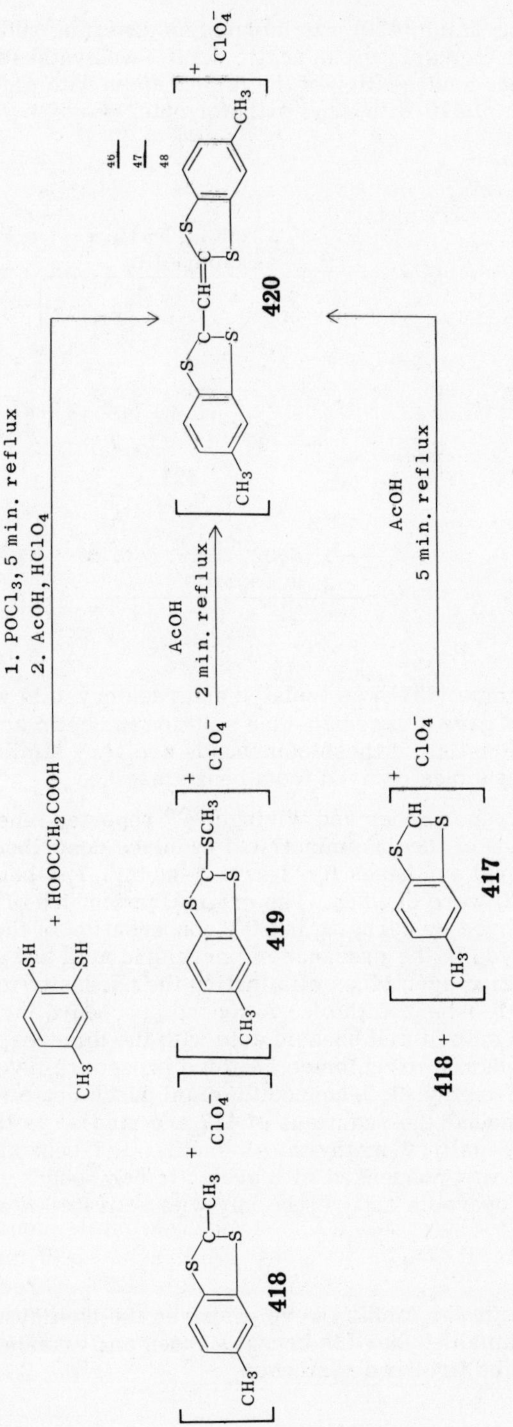
1. POCl3, 5 min. reflux
2. AcOH, HClO4
+ HOOCCH2COOH
AcOH
2 min. reflux
AcOH
5 min. reflux
418
419
420
417
418 +
46
47
48

The monomethincyanine (**420**) was isolated as gleaming red needles, and gave a bluish-red solution in acetic acid. Two syntheses were developed for **421**: condensation of the dimercaptan with glutaconic acid and condensation of **418** with ethyl orthoformate.

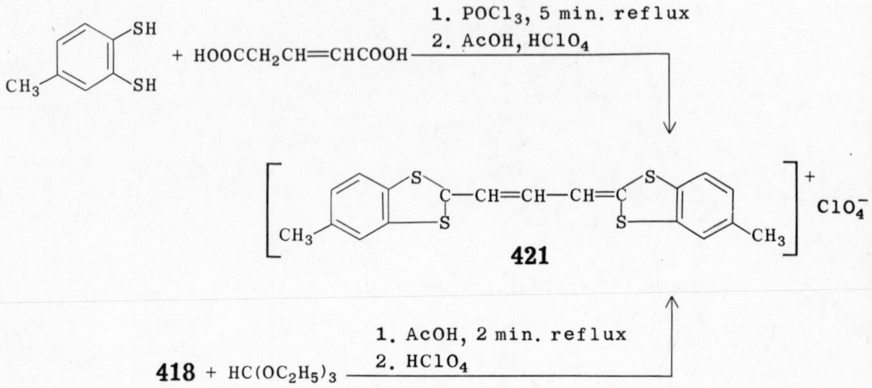

421

The trimethincyanine (**421**) was isolated as green crystals with a metallic lustre; it gave a greenish-blue solution in acetic acid. The spectral characteristics of these compounds are very similar to those of the classical cyanines derived from benzothiazole.

In their second paper Soder and Wizinger[500] reported other methods for the preparation of the unsymmetrical cyanines described by Hurtley and Smiles. Several syntheses for 2-aryl-5-methyl-1,3-benzodithiolium perchlorates (**422**) were devised. The original procedure of Hurtley and Smiles was improved by carrying out the condensation of the dimercaptan and the aldehyde in the presence of perchloric acid and either air or some other oxidizing agent, thus eliminating the necessity for isolating the intermediate 1,3-benzodithiole. A second procedure involved the condensation of a substituted benzoic acid with the dimercaptan in the presence of phosphorus oxychloride. A third procedure involved the condensation of 5-methyl-1,3-benzodithiolium perchlorate (**417**) with an aromatic compound; the reactions of **417** are similar to those of flavylium salts. Finally, 2-methylthio-5-methyl-1,3-benzodithiolium perchlorate (**419**) was condensed with aromatic compounds. The last two methods are operable apparently only with activated aromatic rings.

In a somewhat similar fashion were prepared the hemicyanines (**423**), substituting cinnamaldehydes for benzaldehydes and cinnamic acids for benzoic acids in the first two syntheses.

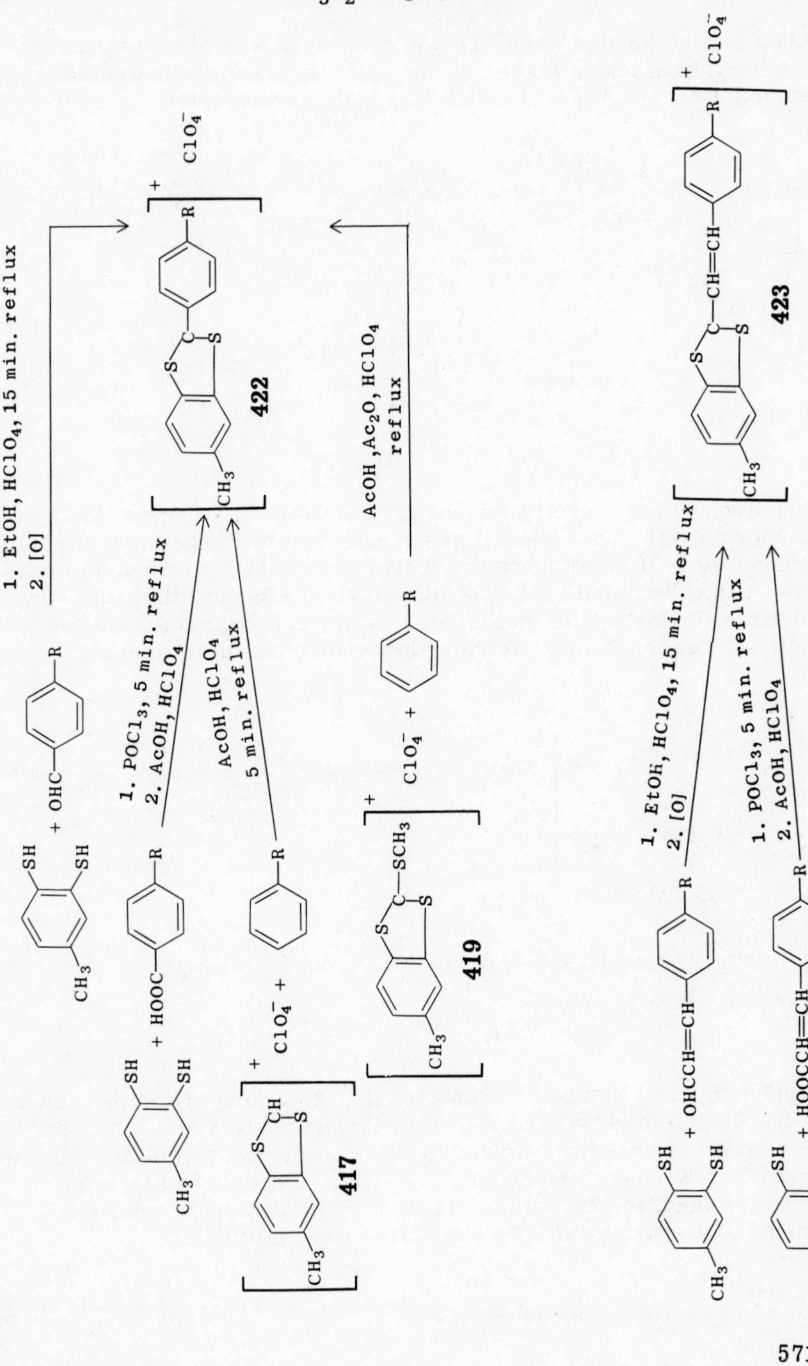
1. EtOH, HClO4, 15 min. reflux
2. [O]
1. POCl3, 5 min. reflux
2. AcOH, HClO4
AcOH, HClO4
5 min. reflux
AcOH, Ac2O, HClO4
reflux
417
419
422
423

423 was also formed when **417** was condensed with cinnamic acids, decarboxylation taking place. In this synthesis quantitative yields were obtained if excess **417** was added as a hydrogen acceptor.

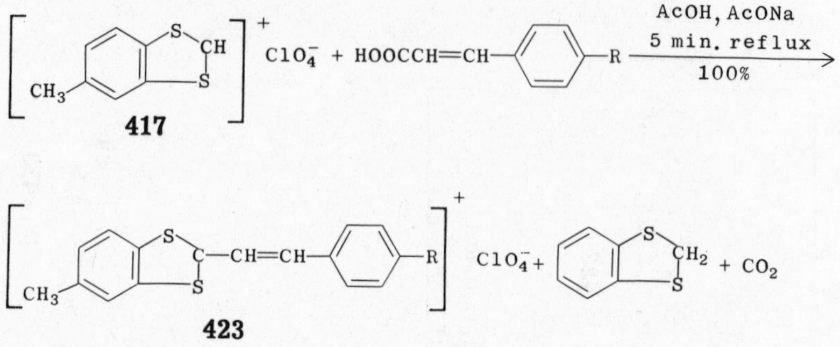

It has already been mentioned that 2,5-dimethyl-1,3-benzodithiolium perchlorate (**418**) has a methyl group activated by the positive charge on the compound. It is not unexpected, therefore, that it was found to condense with substituted benzaldehydes to yield **423** and with *p*-dimethylaminocinnamaldehyde to yield [2-(5-methyl-1,3-benzodithiolium)]-[1-(4-dimethylaminophenyl)]-tetramethincyanine perchlorate (**424**).

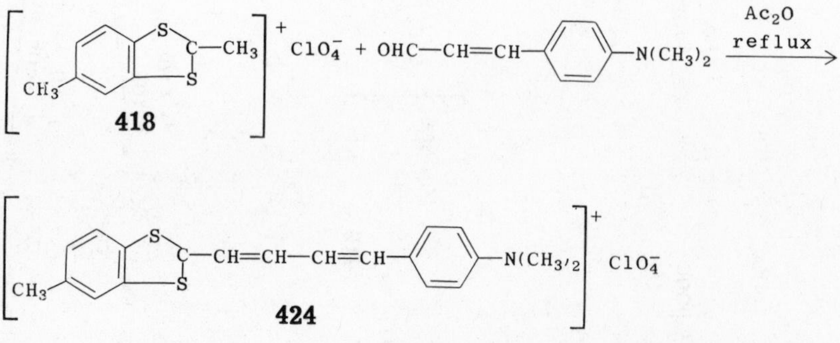

Neunhoeffer and Nowak[401d] reported that 2-(*p*-dimethylaminophenyl)-1,3-benzodithiole (**424a**) and 2-(*p*-dimethylaminostyryl)-1,3-benzodithiole (**424b**) are readily oxidized by air to compounds similar to those prepared by Wizinger and Soder. 2,2′-(Chloromethylene)bis-1,3-benzodithiole (**424c**), as well as the corresponding bromo compound, oxidized to a red dye salt. No structures were postulated.

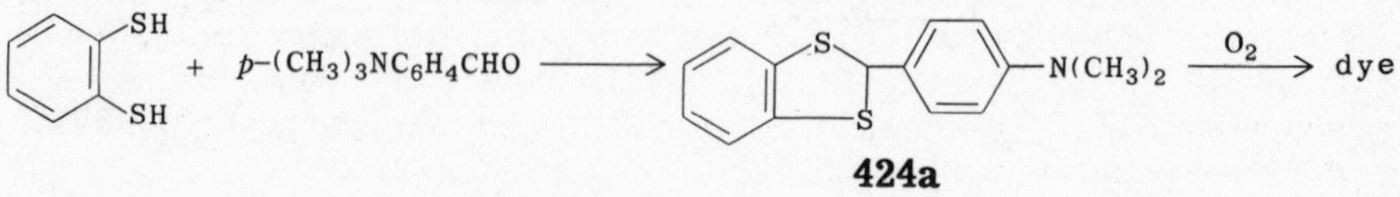

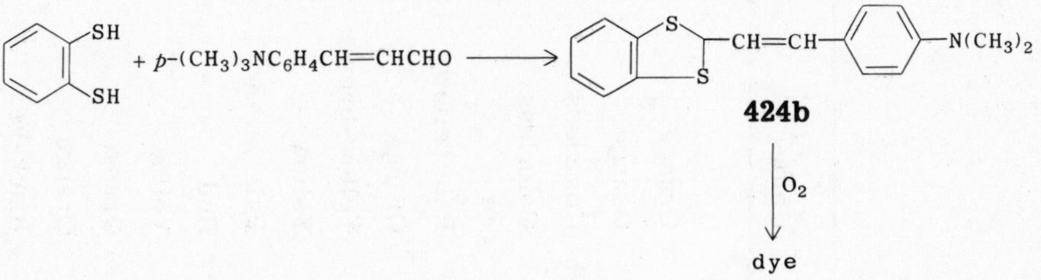

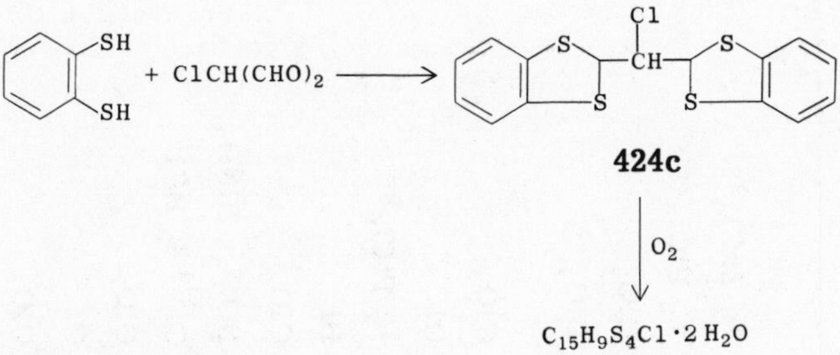

424b

O_2

dye

424c

O_2

$C_{15}H_9S_4Cl \cdot 2\,H_2O$

The 1,3-benzodithiolium salts which have been reported are listed in Table 22.

Koutecký and co-workers[309b,309c,584c] carried out molecular orbital calculations on 1,3-benzodithiolium cation, radical, and anion, using benzotropylium as a model. In agreement with experiment on the cation, the 2-position was calculated to be the most reactive.

3. Spiro Derivatives of 1,3-Benzodithiole

The spiro derivatives of 1,3-benzodithiole which have been reported are listed in Table 23 (p. 578). Huisgen and Weberndörfer[268a] reacted 1,2,3-benzothiadiazole with 1,3-benzodithiole-2-thione and formulated the product, presumably formed by a 1,3-dipolar cycloaddition reaction, as spirobis[1,3-benzodithiole](**424d**). Backer and Wiggerink [25] prepared spiro[1,4-benzodithiin-2(3*H*),2'-[1,3]benzodithiole](**425**) from *o*-dimercaptobenzene and chloroacetyl chloride.

TABLE 22. 1,3-Benzodithiolium Salts

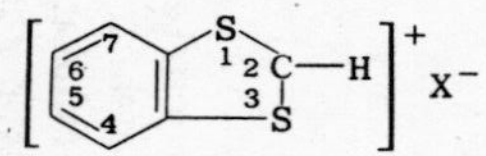

Substituents	X	Yield (%)	M.p. (°C)	Color	Ref.
None	½ $ZnCl_4^{2-}$			Orange	270
	½ $PtCl_6^{2-}$			Orange	270
5-CH_3-	ClO_4^-		80–90 dec. 165	Colorless	499
2,5-(CH_3-)$_2$	ClO_4^-		90–95 dec. 170–172	Colorless	499
2-(CH_3S-)-5-CH_3-	ClO_4^-		dec. 140–142	Pale yellow	499
2-C_6H_5-	Cl^-		~100	Orange	269
	½ $PtCl_6^{2-}$		dec. 240	Yellow-brown	269
	Br_3^-		212	Yellow	269
2-C_6H_5-5-CH_3-	ClO_4^-		dec. 150	Pale yellow	500
2-(p-$CH_3OC_6H_4$-)	NO_3^- · $2HNO_3$			Red	271
	Cl^- · ⅔ HCl			Yellow	271
2-(p-$CH_3OC_6H_4$-)-5-CH_3-	ClO_4^-		dec. 224–227	Orange	500
2-(p-HOC_6H_4-)	Cl^-			Orange	271
2-[p-(CH_3)$_2NC_6H_4$-]-5-CH_3-	ClO_4^-		dec. > 245	Black-red	500

Compound	Anion			Color	Ref.
2-(2-Hydroxy-1-naphthyl-) (structure, 5-CH₃-)	Cl⁻			Red	271
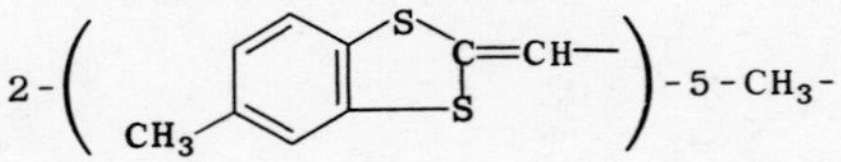 (structure with —CH=CH—, 5-CH₃-)	ClO₄⁻		dec. ca. 270	Red	499
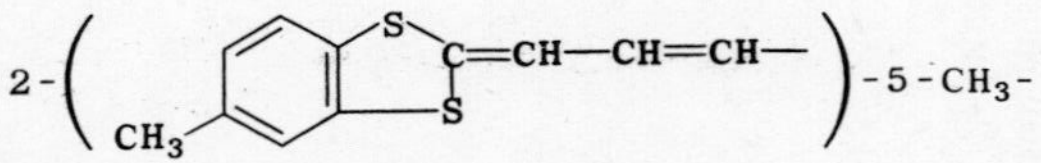 (structure with —CH=CH—CH=CH—, 5-CH₃-)	ClO₄⁻		dec. ca. 265	Green	499
2-(C_6H_5CH=CH-)-5-CH_3-	ClO₄⁻	50	ca. 185	Orange-yellow	500
2-(p-$CH_3OC_6H_4$CH=CH-)-5-CH_3-	ClO₄⁻		dec. 195	Violet-brown	500
2-[p-$(CH_3)_2NC_6H_4$CH=CH-]-5-CH_3-	ClO₄⁻	100	dec. 205	Green	500
2-[p-$(CH_3)_2NC_6H_4$CH=CHCH=CH-]-5-CH_3-	ClO₄⁻		dec. >190	Green	500

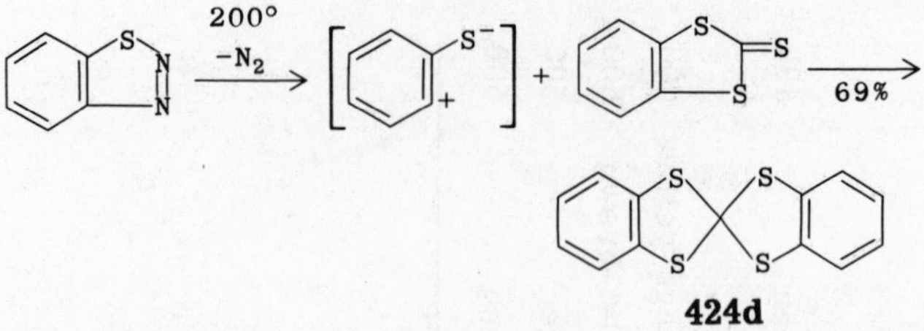

424d

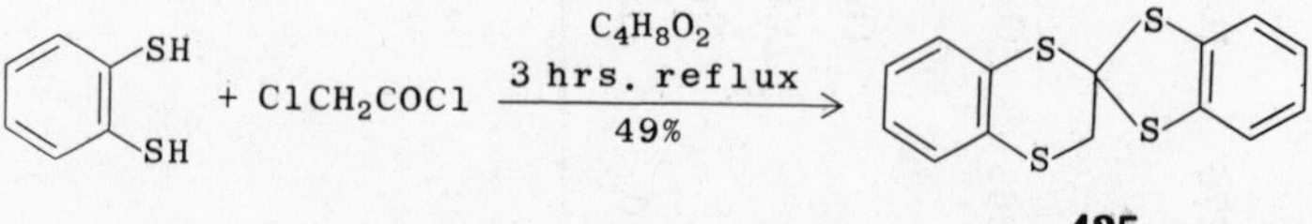

425

Guha and Chaklader[225] prepared spiro[acenaphthene-1, 2'-[1, 3]benzo-
dithiole]-2-one (**426**) from o-dimercaptobenzene and acenaphthoquinone.

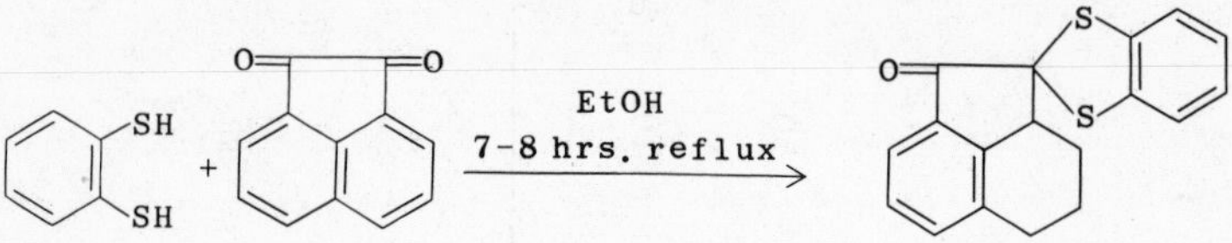

426

4-Bromo-1, 2-dimercaptobenzene and phenanthrenequinone, in the absence of any catalyst, yielded the monomercaptoie, 5-bromospiro[1, 3-
benzodithiole-2, 9'(10'H)-phenanthrene]-10'-one (**427**), while in the presence of hydrogen chloride the dimercaptole, 5, 5''-dibromodispiro[1, 3-
benzodithiole-2, 9'(10'H)-phenanthrene-10', 2''-[1, 3]benzodithiole]
(**428**), was formed. The latter, with the exception of glyoxal, is the only
reported example of a dimercaptole from a 1, 2-dioxo compound.

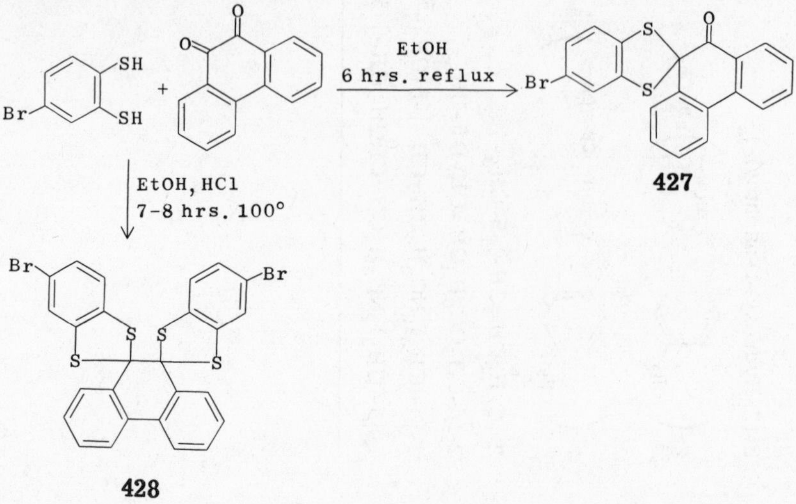

427

428

Hurtley and Smiles[270] reported that their diol (**395**), on treatment with acetic acid, yielded spiro[1,4-benzodithiane-2(3H), 2′-[1,3]benzodithiole]-3-one (**429**), presumably by a pinacol-type rearrangement. The structure was indicated by its formation from 1,4-benzodithiane-2,3-dione (**430**) and o-dimercaptobenzene.

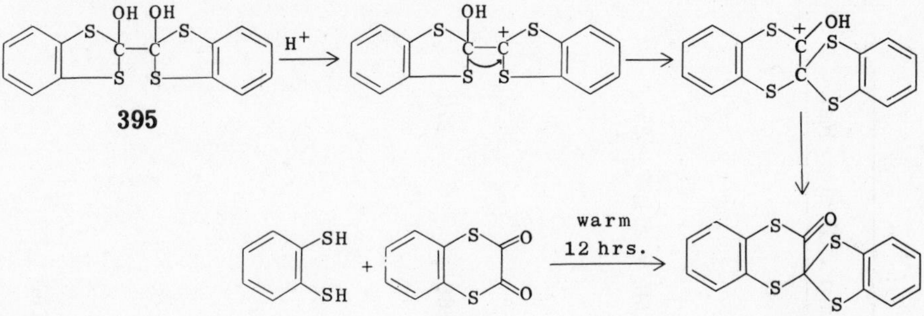

395

430   warm 12 hrs.   **429**

429 could also be prepared from excess o-dimercaptobenzene and oxalyl chloride by lengthening the heating time. It rearranged on heating to 2,2′-bis(1,3-benzodithiolene) (**396**) and 1,3-benzodithiol-2-one (**397**).

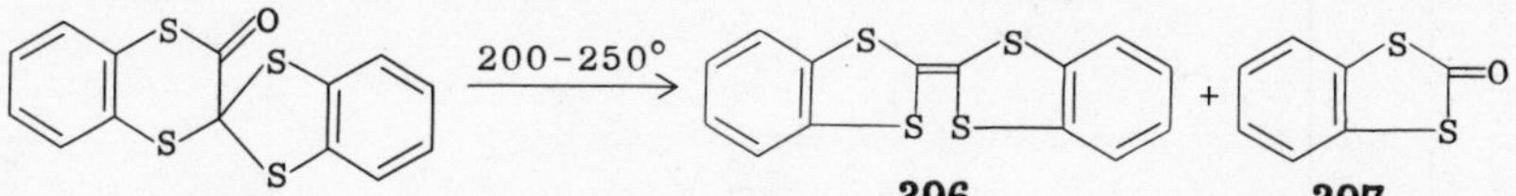

429   200–250°   **396**   **397**

E. C$_3$S$_2$-C$_4$N$_2$-C$_6$ 1,3-DITHIOLO[4,5-b]QUINOXALINE (**430a**)

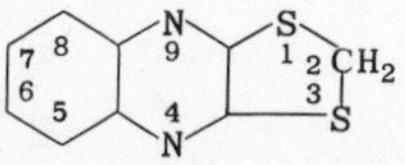

430a

Sasse, Wegler, Unterstenhöfer, and Grewe[460c] prepared a large number of 1,3-dithiolo[4,5-b]quinoxalines. Thus, reaction of the disodium salt of 2,3-dimercaptoquinoxaline with *gem*-dihalides gave a variety of 2,2-disubstituted derivatives (**430b**); these are listed in Table 24.

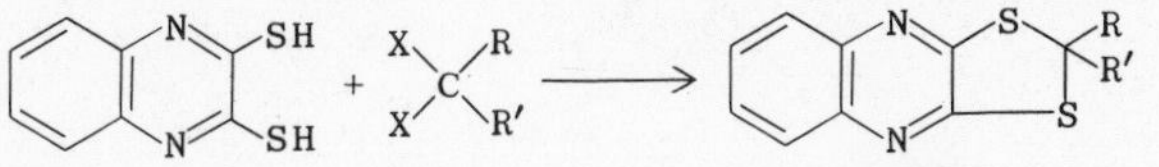

430b

Reaction of the dimercaptan with phosgene yielded the corresponding 2-one (**430c**) and with thiophosgene the corresponding 2-thione (**430d**); these are listed in Table 25.

[For references, see pp. 585-610.]

TABLE 23. Spiro-1,3-benzodithiole Compounds

Compound	Yield (%)	M.p. (°C)	Ref.
$C_3S_2-C_4S_2-C_6-C_6$ Spiro[1,4-benzodithiin-2(3H),2'-[1,3]benzodithiole] (RRI 4479) 3-(=O)	49	250.5-251.5	25
$C_3S_2-C_5-C_6-C_6-C_6$ Spiro[acenaphthene-1,2'-[1,3]benzodithiole] (RRI 5605) 2-(=O)	57	168 190	270 225

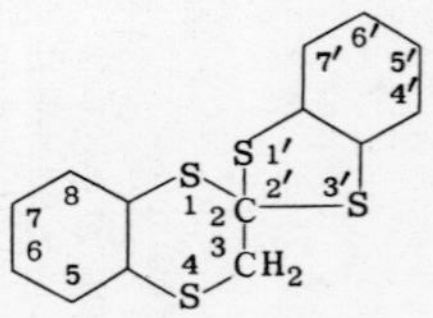

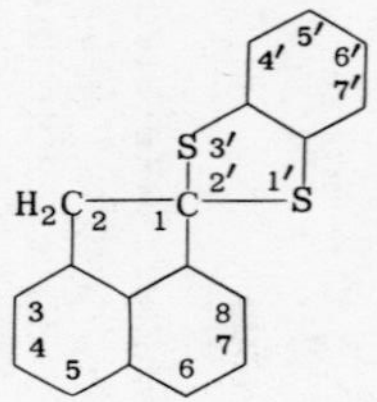

$C_3S_2-C_6-C_6-C_6-C_6$

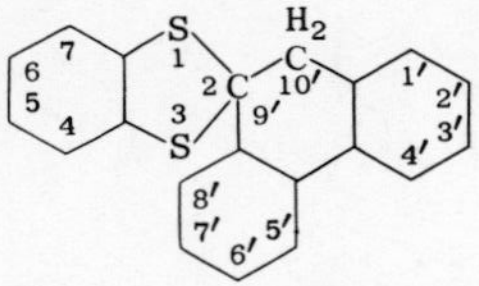

Spiro[1,3-benzodithiole-2,9'(10'H)-phenanthrene] (RRI 5858)

5-Br-10'-(=O)   195   225

$C_2S_2-C_3S_2-C_6-C_6-C_6-C_6-C_6-C_6$

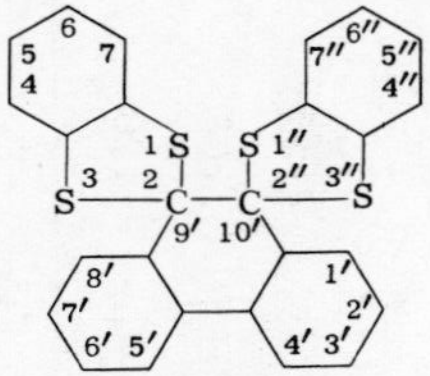

Dispiro[1,3-benzodithiole-2,9'(10'H)-phenanthrene-10',2''-[1,3]benzodithiole] (RRI 7132)

5,5''-Br$_2$ 115   225

TABLE 24. 1, 3-Dithiolo[4, 5-b]quinoxalines

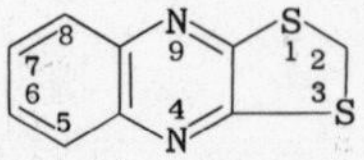

Substituents	M.p. (°C)	Ref.
None	163	460c
5-CH$_3$-	139	460c
6-CH$_3$-	123	460c
6-F$_3$C-	117	460c
5, 7-(CH$_3$-)$_2$	145	460c
2-HO$_2$C-	192	460c
2-C$_2$H$_5$O$_2$C-	115	460c
2-C$_6$H$_5$-	220	460c
2-C$_6$H$_5$CO-	165	460c
2-CH$_3$CO-2-C$_2$H$_5$O$_2$C-	105	460c
2-(C$_2$H$_5$O$_2$C-)$_2$	132	460c
2- 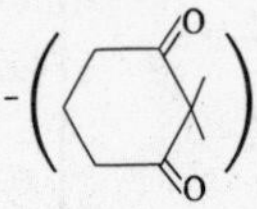	200 (dec.)	460c
2-(CH$_3$CO-)$_2$	142	460c
2-(CH$_3$CO-)$_2$-6-CH$_3$-	106	460c
2-(CH$_3$CO-)$_2$-6-F$_3$C-	120	460c

TABLE 25. 1,3-Dithiolo[4,5-*b*]quinoxalin-2-ones and 2-thiones

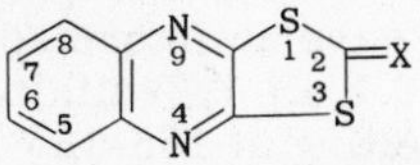

Substituents	M.p. (°C)		Ref.
	X = O	X = S	
None	183	180	460c
5-CH_3-	135	140	460c
6-CH_3-	172	152	460c
6-Cl	209	172	460c
6-F_3C-	135	83	460c
6-CH_3O-	166	159	460c
6-NO_2		143	460c
5,7-$(CH_3-)_2$	180	167	460c
6,7-$(CH_3-)_2$	208	211	460c
6,7-Cl_2	120	125	460c

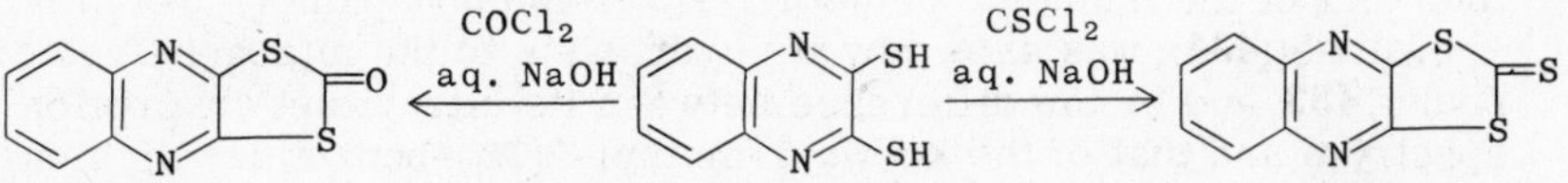

430c   **430d**

All three types of derivatives were found to be active acaricides and fungicides, harmless to warm-blooded animals. **430b** showed weak insecticidal activity as well. Activity seemed to reside in the 2,3-dimercaptoquinoxaline moiety. Changing this to even closely related ring systems destroyed activity (see section II G), whereas a variety of rings could be formed involving the two sulfur atoms without losing activity. 1,3-Dithiolo[4,5-*b*]quinoxaline-2-thione (**430d**), named Eradex by Bayer, and the 6-methyl derivative of **430c**, named Morestan, appeared to have the best balance of properties; the latter is being offered commercially.

F. C_3S_2-C_6-C_6 NAPHTHO[2,3-*d*]-1,3-DITHIOLE (**431**)

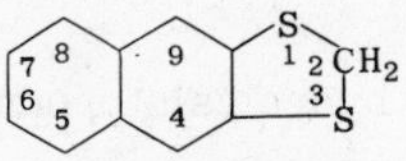

431

(RRI 2834)

Sundholm and Smith[522] investigated the reaction of 2, 3-dichloro-1, 4-naphthoquinone with salts of alkyl-substituted dithiocarbamic acids. Thus, methylammonium N-methyldithiocarbamate gave an intermediate, not isolated, which yielded 2-methyliminonaphtho[2, 3-d]-1, 3-dithiole-4, 9-dione (**432**), isolated as red-violet crystals melting at 185-186°, on recrystallization from alcohol. Acid hydrolysis gave a compound which analyzed as naphtho[2, 3-d]-1, 3-dithiole-2, 4, 9-trione (**433**), m.p. 169-169. 5°.

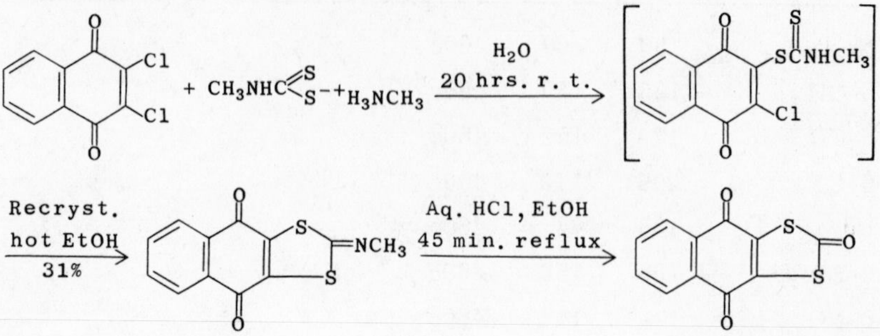

432 **433**

Ethylammonium N-ethyldithiocarbamate yielded the ethyl analog of **432**, 2-ethyliminonaphtho[2, 3-a]-1, 3-dithiole-4, 9-dione, as dark red crystals, m.p. 192-193°.

That the methyl compound has the structure indicated (**432**), rather than that of the isomeric 3-methyl-2(3H)-thiononaphtho[2, 3-d]thiazole-4, 9-dione (**434**), was shown by its hydrolysis to the nitrogen-free compound, **433**, and by the difference between its ultraviolet absorption spectrum and that of the known 3-methyl-2(3H)-benzothiazolethione.[397] Thus, there is apparently no equilibrium between the two forms of the type postulated by McClelland and Salkeld[359] for 3H-1, 2-benzodithiole-3-imines (**161**) and 2-alkyl-3(2H)-benzisothiazolethiones (**160**) (see section I F-2).

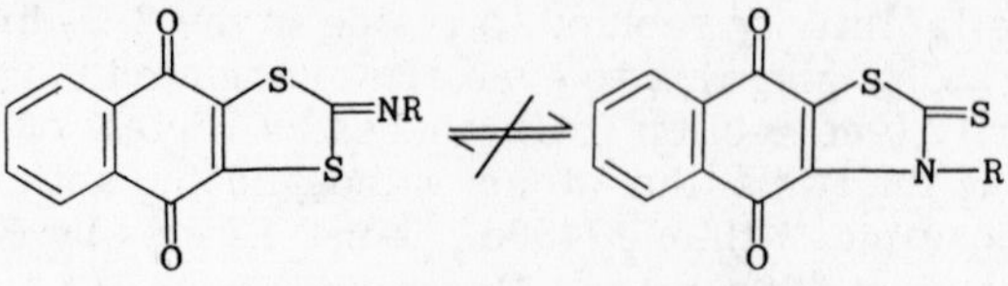

434

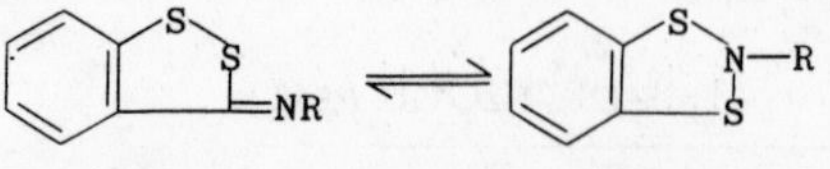

161 **160**

It must be admitted, however, that the low yield of hydrolysis product casts some suspicion on this conclusion.

Dimethylammonium N, N-dimethyldithiocarbamate apparently underwent the same type of reaction to form 4, 9-dioxonaphtho[2, 3-a]-1, 3-

dithiole-2-dimethylimmonium chloride hydrate (**435**), isolated as golden-yellow crystals melting at 226-228° with decomposition. That the compound is a quaternary salt was shown by its solubility in water and its possession of an ionic chlorine. Its structure was indicated by its hydrolysis to naphtho[2, 3-d]-1, 3-dithiole-2, 4, 9-trione (**433**) and its pyrolysis to 2-methyliminonaphtho[2, 3-d]-1, 3-dithiole-4, 9-dione (**432**).

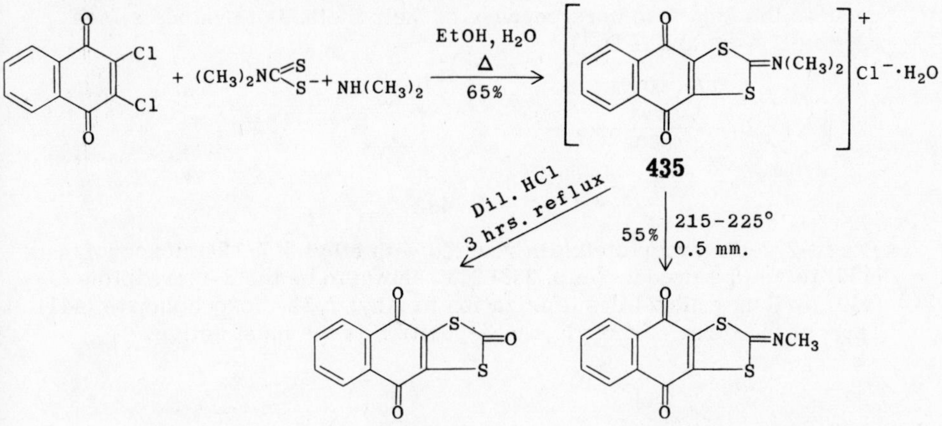

Alkaline hydrolysis of **435** yielded dibenzo[b, i]thianthrene-5, 7, 12, 14-tetrone (**436**), identical with the compound prepared by Brass and Köhler[79] by an independent synthesis (see Chapter 12, section III R-2).

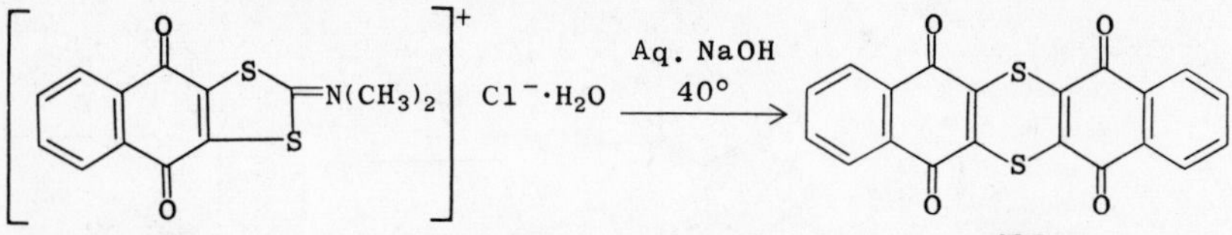

It was not possible to obtain **435** in an anhydrous form. Perhaps it exists as 2-dimethylamino-2-hydroxynaphtho[2, 3-d]-1, 3-dithiole-4, 9-dione (**437**); evidence for this form is given by the fact that aqueous solutions of the salt are acidic.

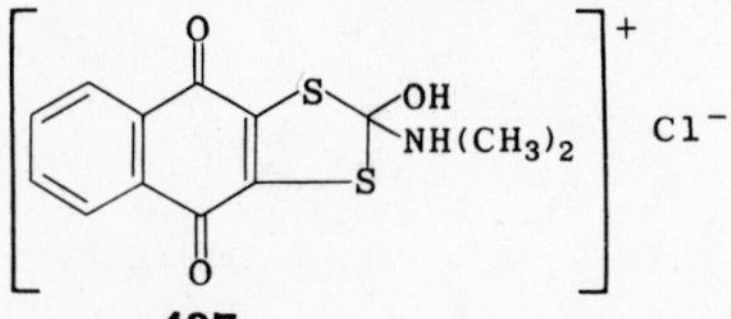

Ammonium dithiocarbamate reacted with 2, 3-dichloro-1, 4-naphthoquinone to give the thianthrene derivative (**436**) rather than the expected

2-iminonaphtho[2, 3-*d*]-1, 3-dithiole-4, 9-dione. The naphthodithioles described here have been patented as fungicides,[523],[524] although their fungicidal activity is weak.[522]

Hauptmann and Bobbio[246a] prepared 3a, 4, 9, 9a-tetrahydronaphtho-[2, 3-*d*]-1, 3-dithiole-2-thione (**438**), m.p. 192-194. 5°, from 2, 3-epoxy-tetralin and potassium methyl xanthate. Lithium aluminum hydride reduction yielded 2, 3-dimercaptotetralin. Both **438** and the dimercaptan must be the *trans* isomers because of their method of synthesis (see section II A-5a and II D-1).

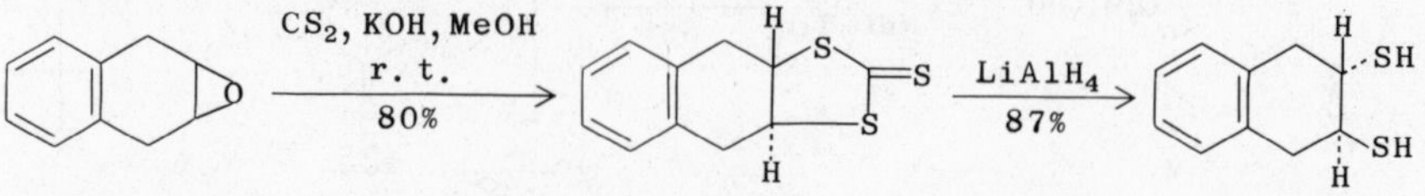

438

Trans-2, 3-dimercaptotetralin reacted with ethyl 3, 7, 12-trioxocholanate (**439**) to yield a product, m.p. 238-243°, shown to be the 3-mercaptole (**440**) by Raney nickel desulfurization to ethyl 7, 12-dioxocholanate (**441**). Thus, of the three carbonyls, the 3-position is the most active.

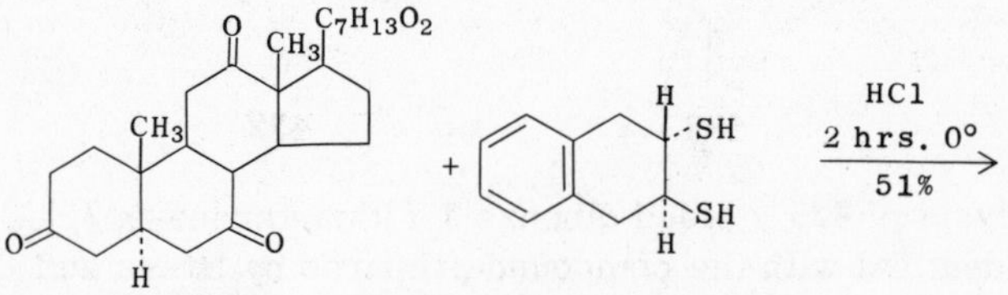

439

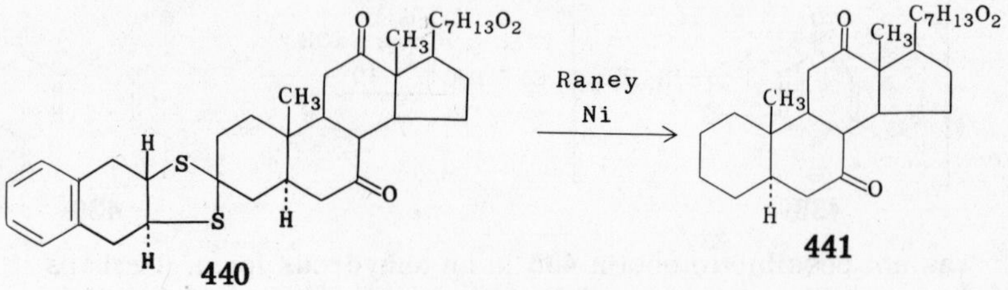

440   **441**

REFERENCES

1. Acker, D. S. (to duPont), U.S. Patent 2,752,373 (1956).

2. Acker, D. S., and C. W. Todd (to duPont), U.S. Patent 2,752,374 (1956).

3. Acker, D. S. (to duPont), U.S. Patent 2,752,375 (1956).

4. Acker, D. S., and W. J. Wayne, J. Am. Chem. Soc., **79**, 6483 (1957).

5. Acker, D. S. (to duPont), U.S. Patent 2,792,406 (1957).

5a. Adams, E. P., F. P. Doyle, D. L. Hatt, D. O. Holland, W. H. Hunter, K. R. L. Mansford, J. H. C. Nayler, and A. Queen, J. Chem. Soc., **1960**, 2649.

5b. Adams, E. P., F. P. Doyle, W. H. Hunter, and J. H. C. Nayler, J. Chem. Soc., **1960**, 2674.

6. Adams, P. T., J. Am. Chem. Soc., **77**, 5357 (1955).

6a. Addor, R. W., J. Org. Chem., **29**, 738 (1964).

7. Adlerová, E., L. Novák, and M. Protirva, Chem. Listy, **51**, 553 (1957); Chem. Abstracts, **51**, 10394 (1957).

8. Affleck, J. G., and G. Dougherty, J. Org. Chem., **15**, 865 (1950).

9. Airs, R. S., and V. W. David (to Shell Development), U.S. Patent 2,653,910 (1953).

10. Aldridge, W. N., Biochem. J., **42**, 52 (1948).

10a. Ali, M. E., and L. N. Owen, J. Chem. Soc., **1958**, 2111.

10b. Allen, C. F. H., B. D. Illingsworth, and J. J. Sagura (to Eastman Kodak Co.), U.S. Patent 2,948,614 (1960).

11. American Syntex Inc., Brit. Patent 736,970 (1955); Chem. Abstracts, **50**, 7887 (1956).

12. Ammann, A., and D. Gottlieb, Appl. Microbiol., **3**, 181 (1955); Chem. Abstracts, **49**, 11061 (1955).

13. Andersen, A. A., D. H. Michener, and H. S. Olcott, Antibiotics & Chemotherapy, **3**, 521 (1953); Chem. Abstracts, **47**, 11324 (1953).

14. Antonucci, R., S. Bernstein, R. Littell, K. J. Sax, and J. H. Williams, J. Org. Chem., **17**, 1341 (1952).

15. Archer, S., T. R. Lewis, C. M. Martini, and M. Jackman, J. Am. Chem. Soc., **76**, 4915 (1954).

16. Arndt, F., P. Nachtwey, and J. Pusch, Ber., **58B**, 1633 (1925).

17. Arndt, F., R. Schwarz, C. Martius, and E. Aron, Rev. faculté sci. univ. Istanbul, **A13**, 57 (1958); Chem. Abstracts, **42**, 4176 (1948).

18. Arndt, F., and G. Traverso, Chem. Ber., **89**, 124 (1956).

19. Arndt, F., Chem. Ber., **89**, 730 (1956).

19a. Arndt, F., and W. Walter, Chem. Ber., **94**, 1757 (1961).

19b. Asahi, Y., Yakugaku Zasshi, **80**, 684 (1960); Chem. Abstracts, **54**, 18886 (1960).

20. Autenrieth, W., and K. Wolff, Ber., **32**, 1368 (1899).

21. Backer, H. J., and N. Evenhuis, Rec. trav. chim., **56**, 129 (1937).

Chapter 5

22. Backer, H. J., and N. Evenhuis, Rec. trav. chim., **56**, 174 (1937).

23. Backer, H. J., and N. Evenhuis, Rec. trav. chim., **56**, 681 (1937).

24. Backer, H. J., and A. F. Tamsma, Rec. trav. chim., **57**, 1183 (1938).

25. Backer, H. J., and G. L. Wiggerink, Rec. trav. chim., **60**, 453 (1941).

26. Bader, F. E., D. F. Dickel, C. F. Huebner, R. A. Lucas, and E. Schlittler, J. Am. Chem. Soc., **77**, 3547 (1955).

27. Bader, H., L. C. Cross, I. Heilbron, and E. R. H. Jones, J. Chem. Soc., **1949**, 619.

28. Bähr, G., G. Schleitzer, and H. Beiling, Chem. Tech. (Berlin), **8**, 597 (1956); Chem. Abstracts, **51**, 9587 (1957).

29. Bähr, G., Angew. Chem., **70**, 606 (1958).

30. Balenović, K., N. Bregant, D. Cerar, D. Fleš, and I. Jambrešić, J. Org. Chem., **18**, 297 (1953).

31. Balenović, K., D. Cerar, and L. Filipović, J. Org. Chem., **19**, 1556 (1954).

32. Balenović, K., N. Bregant, and D. Cerar, J. Chem. Soc., **1956**, 3982.

33. Balenović, K., D. Cerar, and N. Bregant, Croat. Chem. Acta, **28**, 279 (1956); Chem. Abstracts, **51**, 12001 (1957).

33a. Balenović, K., and N. Bregant, Chem. & Ind. (London), **1957**, 1273.

33b. Balenović, K., and N. Bregant, Tetrahedron, **5**, 44 (1959).

34. Barbaglia, G. A., Ber., **13**, 1574 (1880).

35. Barbaglia, G. A., Ber., **17**, 2654 (1884).

36. Barltrop, J. A., P. M. Hayes, and M. Calvin, J. Am. Chem. Soc., **76**, 4348 (1954).

36a. Bartlett, P. D., E. R. Webster, C. E. Dills, and H. G. Richey, Jr., Ann., **623**, 217 (1959).

37. Bashour, J. T. (to Stauffer Chemical Co.), U.S. Patent 2,647,129 (1953).

38. Bashour, J. T. (to Stauffer Chemical Co.), U.S. Patent 2,662,899 (1953).

39. Bateman, L., R. W. Glazebrook, C. G. Moore, M. Porter, G. W. Ross, and R. W. Saville, J. Chem. Soc., **1958**, 2838.

40. Bauer, F., Chem.-Ztg., **75**, 623, 647 (1951).

41. Baumann, E., and G. Walter, Ber., **26**, 1124 (1893).

42. Baumann, E., and E. Fromm, Ber., **30**, 110 (1897).

43. Bayer and Co., Ger. Patent 87,931 (1895).

44. Beesley, R. M., C. K. Ingold, and J. F. Thorpe, J. Chem. Soc., **107**, 1080 (1915).

44a. Behringer, H., R. Reimann, and M. Ruff, Angew. Chem., **72**, 415 (1960).

45. Bell, M. R., J. R. Johnson, B. S. Wildi, and R. B. Woodward, J. Am. Chem. Soc., **80**, 1001 (1958).

45a. Bellamy, L. J., and P. E. Rogasch, J. Chem. Soc., **1960**, 2218.

46. Bennett, G. M., and F. S. Statham, J. Chem. Soc., **1931**, 1684.

47. Bergmann, E., M. Magat, and D. Wagenberg, Ber., **63B**, 2576 (1930).

48. Bergmann, E. D., E. Zimkin, and S. Pinchas, Rec. trav. chim., **71**, 168 (1952).

49. Bergmann, E. D., S. Berkovic, and R. Ikan, J. Am. Chem. Soc., **78**, 6037 (1956).

50. Bergson, G., and G. Claeson, Acta Chem. Scand., **11**, 911 (1957).

51. Bergson, G., Arkiv Kemi, **12**, 233 (1958).

52. Bergson, G., and L. Schotte, Acta Chem. Scand., **12**, 367 (1958).

53. Bergson, G., and L. Schotte, Arkiv Kemi, **13**, 43 (1958).

53a. Bergson, G., B. Sjöberg, R. C. Tweit, and R. M. Dodson, Acta Chem. Scand., **14**, 222 (1960).

54. Bezzi, S., M. Mammi, and C. Garbuglio, Nature, **182**, 247 (1958).

54a. Bezzi, S., C. Garbuglio, M. Mammi, and G. Traverso, Gazz. chim. ital., **88**, 1226 (1958); Chem. Abstracts, **53**, 22007 (1959).

54b. Bhate, D. S., R. K. Hulyalkar, and S. K. Menon, Experientia, **16**, 504 (1960).

55. Biedebach, F., Arch. Pharm., **280**, 304 (1942); Chem. Abstracts, **37**, 6257 (1943).

56. Blomquist, A. T., J. Prager, and J. Wolinsky, J. Am. Chem. Soc., **77**, 1804 (1955).

56a. Boberg, F., Angew. Chem., **72**, 629 (1960).

56b. Boberg, F., Angew. Chem., **73**, 579 (1961).

57. Böhme, H., H. Pfeifer, and E. Schneider, Ber., **75B**, 900 (1942).

58. Böhme, H., and E. Schneider, Chem. Ber., **82**, 208 (1949).

59. Böhme, H., and E. Boll, Z. anorg. u. allgem. Chem., **290**, 17, (1957).

60. Boekelheide, V., L. Liberman, J. Figueras, C. Krespan, F. C. Pennington, and D. S. Tarbell, J. Am. Chem. Soc., **71**, 3303 (1949).

61. Böttcher, B., Fr. Patent 871, 802 (1942); Chem. Zentr., **1942, II**, 2205.

62. Böttcher, B., and A. Lüttringhaus, Ann., **557**, 89 (1945).

63. Böttcher, B., Chem. Ber., **81**, 376 (1948).

64. Böttcher, B., and F. Bauer, Ann., **568**, 227 (1950).

65. Böttcher, B., and F. Bauer, Chem. Ber., **84**, 458 (1951).

66. Böttcher, B., Ger. Patent 855, 865 (1952); Chem. Abstracts, **52**, 10204 (1958).

67. Böttcher, B., Ger. Patent 861, 846 (1953); Chem. Abstracts, **53**, 408 (1959).

68. Böttcher, B., and F. Bauer, Ger. Patent 865, 903 (1953); Chem. Zentr., **1954**, 9096.

69. Böttcher, B., Ger. Patent 869, 799 (1953); Chem. Abstracts, **52**, 16370 (1958).

70. Böttcher, B., Ger. Patent 874, 447 (1953); Chem. Abstracts, **52**, 12925 (1958).

71. Böttcher, B., Ger. Patent 900, 937 (1954); Chem. Abstracts, **49**, 7603 (1955).

72. Böttcher, B., Ger. Patent 906, 329 (1954); Chem. Abstracts, **49**, 7603 (1955).

72a. Böttcher, B., and A. Lüttringhaus (to Schering A.-G.), Ger. Patent 933, 272 (1955); Chem. Abstracts, **53**, 292 (1959).

73. Böttcher, B., and F. L. Bauer, U.S. Patent 2, 729, 649 (1956). Brit. Patent 729, 464 (1955); Chem. Abstracts, **50**, 7142 (1956).

74. Böttcher, B. (to Vereinigte Flussspatsgruben), Ger. Patent 941, 669 (1956); Chem. Abstracts, **53**, 409 (1959).

75.   Bonde, R., Am. Potato J., **30**, 143 (1953); Chem. Abstracts, **48**, 10281 (1954).

76.   Boni, P., F. Reduzzi, G. Bile, and V. Galloro, Clin. terap., **9**, 129 (1955); Chem. Abstracts, **51**, 3045 (1957).

77.   Bothner-By, A. A., and G. Traverso, Chem. Ber., **90**, 453 (1957).

77a. Brack, K. (to Hercules), U.S. Patent 3, 031, 372 (1962).

78.   Brahde, L. B., Acta Chem. Scand., **8**, 1145 (1954).

79.   Brass, K., and L. Köhler, Ber., **55B**, 2543 (1922).

80.   Braude, E. A., R. P. Linstead, and K. R. H. Wooldridge, Chem. & Ind. (London), **1955**, 508.

81.   Braude, E. A., R. P. Linstead, and K. R. H Wooldridge, J. Chem. Soc., **1965**, 3074.

81a. Breslow, R., and E. Mohacsi, J. Am. Chem. Soc., **83**, 4100 (1961).

82.   Brintzinger, H., and H. W. Ziegler, Chem. Ber., **81**, 380 (1948).

83.   Brintzinger, H., M. Langheck, and H. Ellwanger, Chem. Ber., **87**, 320 (1954).

84.   Brockman, Jr., J. A., E. L. R. Stokstad, E. L. Patterson, J. V. Pierce, M. Macchi, and F. P. Day, J. Am. Chem. Soc., **74**, 1868 (1952).

85.   Brockman, Jr., J. A., E. L. R. Stokstad, E. L. Patterson, J. V. Pierce, and M. E. Macchi, J. Am. Chem. Soc., **76**, 1827 (1954).

86.   Brockman, Jr., J. A., and P. F. Fabio (to American Cyanamid), U.S. Patent 2, 767, 195 (1956).

87.   Brockman, Jr., J. A., and P. F. Fabio (to American Cyanamid), U.S. Patent 2, 789, 991 (1957).

88.   Broun, A. S., M. G. Voronkov, and K. P. Katkova, Zhur. Obshcheĭ Khim. (J. Gen. Chem.), **20**, 726 (1950); Chem. Abstracts, **44**, 7755 (1950).

89.   Brown, H. C., J. H. Brewster, and H. Shechter, J. Am. Chem. Soc., **76**, 467 (1954).

90.   Bullock, M. W., J. A. Brockman, Jr., E. L. Patterson, J. V. Pierce, and E. L. R. Stokstad, J. Am. Chem. Soc., **74**, 1868 (1952).

91.   Bullock, M. W., J. A. Brockman, Jr., E. L. Patterson, J. V. Pierce, and E. L. R. Stokstad, J. Am. Chem. Soc., **74**, 3455 (1952).

92.   Bullock, M. W., J. A. Brockman, Jr., E. L. Patterson, J. V. Pierce, M. H. von Saltza, F. Sanders, and E. L. R. Stokstad, J. Am. Chem. Soc., **76**, 1828 (1954).

93.   Bullock, M. W., J. J. Hand, and E. L. R. Stokstad, J. Am. Chem. Soc., **79**, 1975 (1957).

94.   Bullock, M. W., J. J. Hand, and E. L. R. Stokstad, J. Am. Chem. Soc., **79**, 1978 (1957).

95.   Bullock, M. W. (to American Cyanamid), U.S. Patent 2, 776, 298 (1957).

96.   Bullock, M. W. (to American Cyanamid), U.S. Patent 2, 788, 355 (1957).

97.   Bullock, M. W., and J. J. Hand (to American Cyanamid), U.S. Patent 2, 789, 990 (1957).

98.   Bullock, M. W. (to American Cyanamid), U.S. Patent 2, 806, 047 (1957).

98a. Bullock, M. W. (to American Cyanamid), Brit. Patent 796, 894 (1958); Chem. Abstracts, **53**, 227 (1959).

99. Bullock, M. W. (to American Cyanamid), Ger. Patent 1,029,007 (1958).

100. Bullock, M. W. (to American Cyanamid), U.S. Patent 2,872,455 (1959). Brit. Patent 762,575 (1956); Chem. Abstracts, **52**, 456 (1958).

101. Bullock, M. W. (to American Cyanamid), U.S. Patent 2,894,965 (1959).

102. Busch, M., Ber., **27**, 2507 (1894).

103. Busch, M., J. prakt. Chem., [2]**60**, 220 (1899).

104. Busch, M., and F. Best, J. prakt. Chem., [2]**60**, 225 (1899).

105. Busch, M., and E. Lingenbrink, J. prakt. Chem., [2]**61**, 336 (1900).

106. Busch, M., and E. Lingenbrink, J. prakt. Chem., [2]**65**, 473 (1902).

107. Calvin, M., and P. Massini, Experientia, **8**, 445 (1952).

108. Calvin, M., and J. A. Barltrop, J. Am. Chem. Soc., **74**, 6153 (1952).

109. Calvin, M., J. Chem. Soc., **1956**, 1895.

110. Calvin, M., Angew. Chem., **68**, 253 (1956).

111. Campbell, T. W., J. Org. Chem., **22**, 1029 (1957).

112. Carrara, G., R. Ettorre, F. Fava, G. Rolland, E. Testa, and A. Vecchi, J. Am. Chem. Soc., **76**, 4391 (1954).

112a. Carrara, G., and E. Testa (to Lepetit S.p.A.), Brit. Patent 759,378 (1956); Chem. Abstracts, **52**, 1283 (1958).

113. Casanova, R., C. W. Shoppee, and G. H. R. Summers, J. Chem. Soc., **1953**, 2983.

114. Cattan, R. O. Gaudin, and J. Bataille, Presse méd., **61**, 521 (1953); Chem. Abstracts, **48**, 4098 (1954).

115. Cavina, G., E. Cingolani, and A. Gaudiano, Boll. soc. ital. biol. sper., **32**, 1180 (1956); Chem. Abstracts, **51**, 9774 (1957).

116. Čekan, Z., V. Herout, and F. Šorm, Chem. & Ind. (London), **1956**, 1234.

117. Čekan, Z., V. Herout, and F. Šorm, Chem. Listy, **51**, 756 (1957); Chem. Abstracts, **51**, 11313 (1957).

118. Celmer, W. D., F. W. Tanner, Jr., M. Harfenist, T. M. Lees, and I. A. Solomons, J. Am. Chem. Soc., **74**, 6304 (1952).

119. Celmer, W. D., and I. A. Solomons, Antibiotics Ann., 1953-54, Proc. Symposium Antibiotics (Wash., D.C.), **1953**, 622; Chem. Abstracts, **48**, 7851 (1954).

120. Celmer, W. D., and I. A. Solomons, J. Am. Chem. Soc., **77**, 2861 (1955).

121. Celmer, W. D. (to Chas. Pfizer and Co.), U.S. Patent 2,752,359 (1956). Brit. Patent 753,331 (1956); Chem. Abstracts, **51**, 5854 (1957).

122. Černý, V., and F. Šorm, Collection Czechoslov. Chem. Communs., **22**, 85 (1957).

123. Chakravarti, G. C., and J. M. Saha, J. Indian Chem. Soc., **5**, 453 (1928); Chem. Abstracts, **23**, 97 (1929).

124. Challenger, F., E. A. Mason, E. C. Holdsworth, and R. Emmott, Chem. & Ind. (London), **1952**, 714.

125. Challenger, F., E. A. Mason, E. C. Holdsworth, and R. Emmott, J. Chem. Soc., **1953**, 292.

126. Challenger, F., Science Progr., **41**, 593 (1953).

127. Chamberlin, E. M., W. V. Ruyle, A. E. Erickson, J. M. Chemerda, L. M. Aliminosa, R. L. Ericksen, G. E. Sita, and M. Tischler, J. Am. Chem. Soc., **75**, 3477 (1953).

128. Chivers, J. C. A., and S. Smiles, J. Chem. Soc., **1928**, 697.

129. CIBA Ltd., Swiss Patent 297, 010 (1954); Chem. Abstracts, **50**, 5045 (1956).

130. CIBA Ltd., Brit. Patent 764, 320 (1956); Chem. Abstracts, **51**, 16579 (1957).

131. Claeson, G., Acta Chem. Scand., **9**, 178 (1955).

132. Claeson, G., Acta Chem. Scand., **13**, 1709 (1959).

133. Clar, E., and C. Marschalk, Bull. soc. chim. France, **1950**, 433.

133a. Cocker, W., T. B. H. McMurry, and L. O. Hopkins, J. Chem. Soc., **1959**, 1998.

134. Cohen, R., Arch. Pediat., **68**, 259 (1951); Chem. Abstracts, **45**, 8590 (1951).

135. Coltof, W. (to Shell Development), U.S. Patent 2, 193, 415 (1940); Chem. Abstracts, **34**, 4744 (1940).

136. Conroy, H., J. Am. Chem. Soc., **73**, 1889 (1951).

137. Conroy, H., J. Am. Chem. Soc., **74**, 491 (1952).

137a. Covello, M., and C. DeVena, Ricerca sci., **29**, 2552 (1959); Chem. Abstracts, **54**, 12901 (1960).

137b. Creighton, A. M., and L. N. Owen, J. Chem. Soc., **1960**, 1024.

137c. Crossley, N. S., and H. B. Henbest, J. Chem. Soc., **1960**, 4413.

138. Culvenor, C. C. J., W. Davies, and K. H. Pausacker, J. Chem. Soc., **1946**, 1050.

139. Culvenor, C. C. J., and W. Davies, Australian J. Sci. Research, Ser. A, **1**, 236 (1948); Chem. Abstracts, **43**, 7419 (1949).

140. Cutolo, E., and F. Reduzzi, Experientia, **12**, 214 (1956).

141. Danielli, J. F., M. Danielli, J. B. Fraser, P. D. Mitchell, L. N. Owen, and G. Shaw, Biochem. J., **41**, 325 (1947).

142. Davies, W., and W. E. Savige, J. Chem. Soc., **1950**, 890.

143. Davis, F. O. (to Thiokol Chemical Corp.), U.S. Patent 2, 657, 198 (1953).

144. Davis, F. O. (to Thiokol Chemical Corp.), U.S. Patent 2, 715, 635 (1955).

144a. Deguchi, Y., Yakugaku Zasshi, **80**, 924 (1960); Chem. Abstracts, **54**, 24383 (1960).

144b. Deguchi, Y., Yakugaku Zasshi, **80**, 928 (1960); Chem. Abstracts, **54**, 24383 (1960).

144c. Deguchi, Y., Yakugaku Zasshi, **80**, 933 (1960); Chem. Abstracts, **54**, 24384 (1960).

144d. Deguchi, Y., Yakugaku Zasshi, **80**, 937 (1960); Chem. Abstracts, **54**, 24384 (1960).

145. Delaby, R., P. Piganiol, and C. Warolin, Compt. rend., **230**, 1671 (1950).

146. Delaby, R., C. Warolin, P. Chabrier, and P. Piganiol, Compt. rend., **232**, 1676 (1951).

147. Dermer, O. C., WADC Tech. Rept. 55-447 (PB 121796).

147a. Desai, H. S., and B. D. Tilak, J. Sci. Ind. Research (India), **19B**, 390 (1960); Chem. Abstracts, **55**, 11387 (1961).

148. DiCarlo, V., G. Maimone, and G. Giordano, Naturwissenschaften, **45**, 45 (1958).

148a. Diveley, W. R., A. D. Lohr, and K. Brack, Abstracts 139th Meeting American Chemical Society, St. Louis, March 21-30, 1961, p. 24-A.

149. Djerassi, C., H. J. Ringold, and G. Rosenkranz, J. Am. Chem. Soc., **73**, 5513, (1951).

150. Djerassi, C., E. Batres, M. Velasco, and G. Rosenkranz, J. Am. Chem. Soc., **74**, 1712 (1952).

151. Djerassi, C., J. Fishman, and J. A. Moore, Chem. & Ind. (London), **1954**, 1320.

152. Djerassi, C., H. J. Ringold, and G. Rosenkranz, J. Am. Chem. Soc., **76**, 5533 (1954).

153. Djerassi, C., and J. Fishman, J. Am. Chem. Soc., **77**, 4291 (1955).

154. Djerassi, C., C. H. Robinson, and D. B. Thomas, J. Am. Chem. Soc., **78**, 5685 (1956).

155. Djerassi, C., F. Sondheimer, and G. Rosenkranz (to Syntex S. A.), U.S. Patent 2, 790, 799 (1957).

155a. Djerassi, C., F. W. Donovan, S. Burstein, and R. Mauli, J. Am. Chem. Soc., **80**, 1972 (1958).

156. Djerassi, C., O. Halpern, G. R. Pettit, and G. H. Thomas, J. Org. Chem., **24**, 1 (1959).

156a. Djerassi, C., M. Cais, and L. A. Mitscher, J. Am. Cnem. Soc., **81**, 2386 (1959).

156b. Djerassi, C., A. Fredga, and B. Sjöberg, Acta Chem. Scand., **15**, 417 (1961).

156c. Djerassi, C., and A. Lüttringhaus, Chem. Ber., **94**, 2305 (1961).

157. Doering, W. von E., and L. K. Levy, J. Am. Chem. Soc., **77**, 509 (1955).

158. Dolder, F., H. Lichti, E. Mosettig, and P. Quitt, J. Am. Chem. Soc., **82**, 246 (1960).

159. Doyle, F. P., and J. H. C. Nayler, Chem. & Ind. (London), **1955**, 714.

159a. Durden, Jr., J. A., H. A. Stansbury, Jr., and W. H. Catlette, J. Am. Chem. Soc., **82**, 3082 (1960).

160. Eastham, J. F., G. B. Miles, and C. A. Krauth, J. Am. Chem. Soc., **81**, 3114 (1959).

160a. Eatham, J. F., and G. B. Miles, J. Org. Chem., **25**, 826 (1960).

161. Eichenberger, K., E. Ganz, and J. Druey, Helv. Chim. Acta, **38**, 284 (1955).

162. Engers, A., and R. Deckert, Naunyn-Schmiedebergs Arch. exptl. Pathol. Pharmakol., **220**, 418 (1953); Chem. Abstracts, **48**, 3563 (1954).

163. Enders, A., Arzneimittel-Forsch., **3**, 557 (1953); Chem. Abstracts, **48**, 4703 (1954).

164. Enders, A., Naunyn-Schmiedebergs Arch. exptl. Pathol. Pharmakol., **222**, 249 (1954); Chem. Abstracts, **48**, 7788 (1954).

165. Engel, C. R., and G. Just, J. Am. Chem. Soc., **76**, 4909 (1954).

166. Engle, W. D., J. Am. Chem. Soc., **20**, 668 (1898).

167. Ernest, I., Collection Czechoslóv. Chem. Communs., **19**, 1179 (1954).

168. Ernest, I., Chem. Listy, **50**, 581 (1956); Chem. Abstracts, **50**, 13749 (1956).

168a. Ettlinger, L., E. Gäumann, R. Hütter, W. Keller-Schierlein, F. Kradolfer, L. Neipp, V. Prelog, and H. Zähner, Helv. Chim. Acta, **42**, 563 (1959).

169. Evans, R. M., and L. N. Owen, J. Chem. Soc., **1949**, 244.

170. Evans, R. M., J. B. Fraser, and L. N. Owen, J. Chem. Soc., **1949**, 248.

171. Fajkoš, J. and F. Šorm, Collection Czechoslov. Chem. Communs., **20**, 1464 (1955).

171a. Farbenfabriken Bayer A.-G., Brit. Patent 829, 529 (1960); Chem. Abstracts, **54**, 19498 (1960).

172. Fasbender, H., Ber., **20**, 460 (1887).

173. Fasbender, H., Ber., **21**, 1473 (1888).

173a. Faust, J., and R. Mayer, Angew. Chem., **75**, 573 (1963).

174. Fava, A., A. Iliceto, and E. Camera, J. Am. Chem. Soc., **79**, 833 (1957).

175. Fields, E. K., J. Am. Chem. Soc., **77**, 4255 (1955).

176. Fields, E. K. (to Standard Oil of Indiana), U.S. Patent 2, 816, 075 (1957).

177. Fields, E. K. (to Standard Oil of Indiana), U.S. Patent 2, 816, 116 (1957). Brit. Patent 808, 064 (1959); Chem. Abstracts, **54**, 595 (1960).

178. Fields, E. K. (to Standard Oil of Indiana), U.S. Patent 2, 857, 399 (1958).

179. Fields, E. K. (to Standard Oil of Indiana), U.S. Patent 2, 905, 696 (1959).

180. Fieser, L. F., J. C. Babcock, J. E. Herz, W. Y. Huang, and W. P. Schneider, J. Am. Chem. Soc., **73**, 4053 (1951).

181. Fieser, L. F., W. Y. Huang, and J. C. Babcock, J. Am. Chem. Soc., **75**, 116 (1953).

182. Fieser, L. F., and J. E. Herz, J. Am. Chem. Soc., **75**, 121 (1953).

183. Fieser, L. F., J. Am. Chem. Soc., **75**, 4386 (1953).

184. Fieser, L. F., and M. A. Romero, J. Am. Chem. Soc., **75**, 4716 (1953).

185. Fieser, L. F., and W. Y. Huang, J. Am. Chem. Soc., **75**, 5356 (1953).

186. Fieser, L. F., and R. Stevenson, J. Am. Chem. Soc., **76**, 1728 (1954).

187. Fieser, L. F., J. Am. Chem. Soc., **76**, 1945 (1954).

187a. Fieser, L. F., C. Yuan, and T. Goto, J. Am. Chem. Soc., **82**, 1996 (1960).

188. Fitt, P. S., and L. N. Owen, J. Chem. Soc., **1957**, 2240.

189. Foldi, Z., Acta Chim. Acad. Sci. Hung., **3**, 371 (1953); Chem. Abstracts, **49**, 1008 (1955).

190. Foldi, Z., Acta Chim. Acad. Sci. Hung., **3**, 501 (1953); Chem. Abstracts, **49**, 2320 (1955).

191. Foss, O., and L. Schotte, Acta Chem. Scand., **11**, 1424 (1957).

192. Foss, O., and O. Tjomsland, Acta Chem. Scand., **11**, 1426 (1957).

193. Foss, O., and O. Tjomsland, Acta Chem. Scand., **12**, 1799 (1958).

194. Foss, O., and O. Tjomsland, Acta Chem. Scand., **12**, 1810 (1958).

195. Fowkes, F. S., and E. W. McClelland, J. Chem. Soc., **1941**, 187.

196. Franzosini, P., and G. Traverso, Ann. chim. (Rome), **45**, 675 (1955); Chem. Abstracts, **51**, 1733 (1957).

197. Frassetti, P., Ber., **38**, 488 (1905).

197a. Fredga, A., Tetrahedron, **8**, 126 (1960).

198. Friedlaender, P., and S. Kielbasinski, Ber., **45**, 3389 (1912).

199. Friedmann, W., Refiner Natural Gasoline Mfr., **20**, 395 (1941); Chem. Abstracts, **36**, 885 (1942).

200. Friedmann, W., J. Inst. Petroleum, **37**, 40 (1951); Chem. Abstracts, **45**, 6182 (1951).

201. Fukushima, D. K., S. Lieberman, and B. Praetz, J. Am. Chem. Soc., **72**, 5205 (1950).

201a. Gardner, P. D., C. E. Wulfman, and C. L. Osborn, J. Am. Chem. Soc., **80**, 143 (1958).

202. Gates, M., and C. L. Dickinson, Jr., J. Org. Chem., **22**, 1398 (1957).

203. Gaudin, O., and R. Pottier, Compt. rend., **224**, 479 (1947).

204. Gaudin, O., and N. Lozac'h, Compt. rend., **224**, 577 (1947).

205. Gaudin, O., Fr. Patent 941, 543 (1949); Chem. Abstracts, **44**, 9479 (1950).

206. Gaudin, O., U.S. Patent 2, 556, 963 (1951); Chem. Abstracts, **46**, 3079 (1952).

207. Gaudin, O., Fr. Patent 56, 639 (1952); Chem. Abstracts, **52**, 11125 (1958).

208. Gaudin, O., U.S. Patent 2, 657, 216 (1953).

209. Gaudin, O., U.S. Patent 2, 688, 620 (1954).

210. Gaudin, O., Fr. Patent 1, 052, 014 (1954); Chem. Abstracts, **53**, 14123 (1959).

211. Gauthier, B., and C. Vaniscotte, Bull. soc. chim. France, **1956**, 30.

212. Georgian, V., R. Harrisson, and N. Gubisch, J. Am. Chem. Soc., **81**, 5834 (1959).

212a. Georgian, V., U. S. Patent 2, 858, 314 (1958).

212b. Gerecke, M., E. A. H. Friedheim, and A. Brossi, Helv. Chim. Acta, **44**, 955 (1961).

212c. Gerner, F., and W. Konz (to C. H. Boehringer Sohn), Ger. Patent 876, 332 (1953); Chem. Abstracts, **52**, 7608 (1958).

213. Ghiringhelli, L., Atti soc. lombarda sci. med. e biol., **12**, 24 (1957); Chem. Abstracts, **51**, 16931 (1957).

213a. Giacometti, G., and G. Rigatti, J. Chem. Phys., **30**, 1633 (1959).

214. Gibson, D. T., J. Chem. Soc., **1930**, 12.

215. Gibson, D. T., J. Chem. Soc., **1931**, 2637.

216. Glutz, L., Ann., **153**, 310 (1870).

217. Goodman, R. N., Proc. Am. Soc. Hort. Sci., **64**, 186 (1954); Chem. Abstracts, **49**, 9858 (1955).

218. Gopalkrishnan, K. S., and J. A. Jump, Phytopathology, **42**, 338 (1952); Chem. Abstracts, **46**, 8707 (1952).

219. Gould, C. W., S. T. Putnam, and J. C. Wright (to Hercules), U.S. Patent 2, 817, 648 (1957).

220. Graff, Y., Bull. soc. chim. France, **1952**, 926.

221. Graff, Y., Bull. soc. chim. France, **1953**, 561.

222. Grisebach, H., Angew. Chem., **68**, 554 (1956).

223. Grosso, J. J., Plant Disease Reptr., **38**, 333 (1954).

224. Grunert, R. R., C. S. Marvel, and I. F. Walker (to duPont), U.S. Patent 2, 840, 505 (1958).

224a. Grunert, R. R., Arch. Biochem. Biophys., **86**, 190 (1960); Chem. Abstracts, **54**, 15680 (1960).

225. Guha, P. C., and M. N. Chakladar, Quart. J. Indian Chem. Soc., 2, 318 (1925); Chem. Abstracts, **20**, 1797 (1926)

226. Guillouzo, G., Bull. soc. chim. France, **1958**, 1316.

227. Guirard, B. M., E. E. Snell, and R. J. Williams, Arch Biochem., **9**, 361 (1946); Chem. Abstracts, **40**, 4762 (1946).

228. Guirard, B. M., E. E. Snell, and R. J. Williams, Arch Biochem., **9**, 381 (1946); Chem. Abstracts, **40**, 4762 (1946).

229. Gunsalus, I. C., M. I. Dolan, and L. Struglia, J. Biol. Chem., **194**, 849 (1952).

230. Gunsalus, I. C., L. Struglia, and D. J. O'Kane, J. Biol. Chem., **194**, 859 (1952).

231. Gunsalus, I. C., L. S. Barton, and W. Gruber, J. Am. Chem. Soc., **78**, 1763 (1956).

232. Gunsalus, I. C., in W. D. McElroy and B. Glass, "The Mechanism of Enzyme Action", The Johns Hopkins Press, Baltimore, Md., 1954, p. 545 ff.

232a. Gusman de Fernandez-Bolaños, Anales real soc. españo. fis. y quim. (Madrid), **55B**, 693 (1959); Chem. Abstracts, **54**, 19498 (1960).

233. Hach, V., Chem. Listy, **47**, 227 (1953); Chem. Abstracts, **49**, 172 (1955).

234. Hagelberg, L., Ber., **23**, 1083 (1890).

235. Halpern, B. N., and O. Gaudin, Compt. rend. soc. biol., **142**, 779 (1948); Chem. Abstracts, **43**, 2318 (1949).

236. Halpern, B. N., and O. Gaudin, Arch. intern. pharmacodynamie, **83**, 49 (1950); Chem. Abstracts, **44**, 10139 (1950).

236a. Hamilton, L. A., and P. S. Landis (to Socony Mobil Oil Co.), U.S. Patent 2, 995, 569 (1961).

237. Hardegger, E., E. Schreier, and Z. E. Heweihi, Helv. Chim. Acta, **33**, 1159 (1950).

237a. Harder, R. J., and W. C. Smith, J. Am. Chem. Soc., **83**, 3422 (1961).

238. Harris, Jr., J. F., (to duPont), U.S. Patent 2, 839, 445 (1958).

239. Hartman, J. A., J. Org. Chem., **22**, 466 (1957).

240. Haszeldine, R. N., and J. M. Kidd, J. Chem. Soc., **1955**, 3871.

241. Hauptmann, H., Anais. assoc. quím. Brasil, **3**, 231 (1944); Chem. Abstracts, **40**, 569 (1946).

242. Hauptmann, H., J. Am. Chem. Soc., **69**, 562 (1947).

243. Hauptmann, H., and B. Wladislaw, J. Am. Chem. Soc., **72**, 707 (1950).

244. Hauptmann, H., and M. M. Campos, J. Am. Chem. Soc., **72**, 1405 (1950).

245. Hauptmann, H., and M. M. Campos, J. Am. Chem. Soc., **74**, 3179 (1952).

246. Hauptmann, H., and M. M. Campos, Anais. acad. brazil cienc., **25**, 201 (1953); Chem. Abstracts, **49**, 1757 (1955).

246a. Hauptmann, H., and F. O. Bobbio, Chem. Ber., **93**, 2187 (1960).

246b. Hauptmann, H., and W. F. Walter, Chem. Reviews, **62**, 347 (1962).

247. Helfrich, O. B., and E. E. Reid, J. Am. Chem. Soc., **42**, 1208 (1920).

248. Hellstrom, N., Kgl. Lantbruks-Högskol Ann., **22**, 1 (1956); Chem Abstracts, **51**, 5756 (1957).

249. Hentrich, W., and C. Grundmann (to Deutsche Hydrierwerke), Ger. Patent 876,018 (1953); Chem. Abstracts, **48**, 2314 (1954).

249a. Herold, H., and R. Kaufhold, Ger. (East) Patent 11,644 (1956); Chem. Abstracts, **53**, 5664 (1959).

250. Hertz, H. G., G. Traverso, and W. Walter, Ann., **625**, 43 (1959).

250a. Herz, W., J. Am. Chem. Soc., **79**, 5011 (1957).

250b. Herz, W., and R. B. Mitra, J. Am. Chem. Soc., **80**, 4876 (1958).

251. Heuberger, J. W., and P. L. Poulos, Plant Disease Reptr., **37**, 81 (1953); Chem. Abstracts, **47**, 5609 (1953).

252. Heusser, H., K. Eichenberger, P. Kurath, H. R. Dällenbach, and O. Jeger, Helv. Chim. Acta, **34**, 2106 (1951).

253. Heusser, H., K. Heusler, K. Eichenberger, C. G. Honegger, and O. Jeger, Helv. Chim. Acta, **35**, 295 (1952).

254. Heusser, H., O. Jeger, and L. Ruzicka (to CIBA), U.S. Patent 2,782,212 (1957).

255. Hill, R. K., and J. G. Martin, Proc. Chem. Soc., **1959**, 390.

255a. Hill, R. K., J. G. Martin, and W. H. Stouch, J. Am. Chem. Soc., **83**, 4006 (1961).

256. Hinsberg, O., Ber., **43**, 1874 (1910).

257. Hirschmann, R., C. S. Snoddy, Jr., and N. L. Wendler, J. Am. Chem. Soc., **75**, 3252 (1953).

257a. Hitomi, M., H. Fuke, N. Watanabe, F. Honda, and S. Kumada, Yakugaku Kenkyu, **30**, 626 (1958); Chem. Abstracts, **53**, 22491 (1959).

258. Hněvsová, V., V. Smělý, and I. Ernest, Collection Czechoslov. Chem. Communs., **21**, 1459 (1956).

259. Höhn, F., and I. Bloch, J. prakt. Chem., [2]**82**, 486 (1910).

260. Holly, F. W., and E. Walton (to Merck), U.S. Patent 2,811,531 (1957).

261. Hornberger, Jr., C. S., R. F. Heitmiller, I. C. Gunsalus, G. H. F. Schnakenberg, and L. J. Reed, J. Am. Chem. Soc., **74**, 2382 (1952).

262. Hornberger, Jr., C. S., R. F. Heitmiller, I. C. Gunsalus, G. H. F. Schnakenberg, and L. J. Reed, J. Am. Chem. Soc., **75**, 1273 (1953).

263. Hornberger, Jr., C. S., (to duPont), U.S. Patent 2,801,261 (1957).

264. Hornberger, Jr., C. S., (to du Pont), U.S. Patent 2,877,235 (1959).

265. Hromatka, O., and E. Engel, Monatsh., **78**, 29 (1948).

266. Hromatka, O., and E. Engel, Monatsh., **78**, 38 (1948).

Chapter 5

267. Hsieh, Y., Y. Chue, G. Huang, I. Yang, C. Chow, and Z. Kyi, Hua Hsüeh Hsüeh Pao, **23**, 447 (1957); Chem. Abstracts, **52**, 15510 (1958).

268. Huebner, C. F., A. F. St. André, E. Schlittler, and A. Uffer, J. Am. Chem. Soc., **77**, 5725 (1955).

268a. Huisgen, R., and V. Weberndörfer, Experientia, **17**, 566 (1961).

269. Hurtley, W. R. H., and S. Smiles, J. Chem. Soc., **1926**, 1821.

270. Hurtley, W. R. H., and S. Smiles, J. Chem. Soc., **1926**, 2263.

271. Hurtley, W. R. H., and S. Smiles, J. Chem. Soc., **1927**, 534.

272. Husemann, A., Ann., **123**, 83 (1862).

273. Husemann, A., Ann., **126**, 269 (1863).

273a. Iqbal, S. M., and L. N. Owen, J. Chem. Soc., **1960**, 1030.

273b. Ito, A., and O. Amakasu, Yakugaku Zasshi, **79**, 223 (1959); Chem. Abstracts, **53**, 12390 (1959).

274. Iwai, I., E. Ohki, and K. Kanzaki, J. Pharm. Soc. Japan, **76**, 1381 (1956); Chem. Abstracts, **51**, 6559 (1957).

275. Jaeger, R. H., and H. Smith, Chem. & Ind. (London), **1954**, 1106.

276. Jaeger, R. H., and H. Smith, J. Chem. Soc., **1955**, 160.

277. Jaeger, R. H., and H. Smith, J. Chem. Soc., **1955**, 646.

278. Jansen, E. F., J. Biol. Chem., **176**, 657 (1948).

278a. Jeffrey, G. A., and R. Shiono, Acta Cryst., **12**, 447 (1959).

279. Jirousek, L., Naturwissenschaften, **45**, 211 (1958).

280. Jirousek, L., and L. Stárka, Naturwissenschaften, **45**, 386 (1958).

280a. Jirousek, L., and L. Stárka, Collection Czechoslov. Chem. Communs., **24**, 1982 (1959).

280b. Jirousek, L., Chem. Listy, **53**, 501 (1959); Chem. Abstracts, **54**, 2310 (1960).

281. Johnson, J. R., "Roger Adams Symposium", John Wiley and Sons, New York, N.Y., 1955, pp. 60-90.

282. Jones, J. I., W. Kynaston, and J. L. Hales, J. Chem. Soc., **1957**, 614.

283. Jones, R. H., G. E. Lukes, and J. T. Bashour (to Stauffer Chem. Co.), U.S. Patent 2,690,988 (1954).

284. Jones, R. H., G. E. Lukes, and J. T. Bashour (to Stauffer Chem. Co.), U.S. Patent 2,701,253 (1955).

285. Jones, W. H. (to Merck and Co.), U.S. Patent 2,806,048 (1957).

286. Kalvoda, J., P. Buchschacher, and O. Jeger, Helv. Chim. Acta, **38**, 1847 (1955).

286a. Karagounis, G., and H. Rels, Z. Elektrochem., **62**, 865 (1958); Chem. Abstracts, **53**, 1069 (1959).

287. Katz, L., W. Schroeder, and M. Cohen, J. Org. Chem., **19**, 711 (1954).

287a. Katz, L., M. S. Cohen, and W. Schroeder (to Schenley Industries), U.S. Patent 2,824,876 (1958).

288. Kaye, I. A., M. Fieser, and L. F. Fieser, J. Am. Chem. Soc., **77**, 5936 (1955).

288a. Ke, B., Biochim. et Biophys. Acta, **25**, 650 (1957); Chem. Abstracts, **52**, 2614 (1958).

288b. Keglević-Brovet, D., Croat. Chem. Acta, **30**, 63 (1958); Chem. Abstracts, **54**, 2184 (1960).

289. Kehl, W. L., and G. A. Jeffrey, Acta Cryst., **10**, 807 (1957).

290. Kehl, W. L., and G. A. Jeffrey, Acta Cryst., **11**, 813 (1958).

291. Kelber, C., Ber., **43**, 1252 (1910).

292. Kelber, C., and A. Schwarz, Ber., **44**, 1693 (1911).

293. Kelber, C., and A. Schwarz, Ber., **45**, 137 (1912).

294. Kelber, C., and A. Schwarz, Ber., **45**, 2484 (1912).

295. Kendall, J. D., and H. D. Edwards (to Ilford Ltd.), U.S. Patent 2,493,071 (1950); Chem. Abstracts, **44**, 7346 (1950).

296. Kennard, K. C., and J. A. VanAllan, J. Org. Chem., **24**, 470 (1959).

297. Kidder, G. W., and V. C. Dewey, Arch. Biochem., **8**, 293 (1945); Chem. Abstracts, **40**, 3833 (1946).

298. Kidder, G. W., Chairman. American Society of Biological Chemists 1954 Symposium on Metabolic Role of Lipoic (Thioctic) Acid, Federation Proc., **13**, 695 (1954); Chem. Abstracts, **49**, 393 (1955).

298a. King, F. E., T. J. King, and J. M. Uprichard, J. Chem. Soc., **1958**, 3428.

299. Kirmse, W., and L. Horner, Ann., **614**, 4 (1958).

300. Kirmse, W., Angew. Chem., **71**, 537 (1959).

300a. Kishi, T., Yakugaku Zasshi, **81**, 787 (1961); Chem. Abstracts, **55**, 24718 (1961).

301. Klass, D. L., M. Fieser, and L. F. Fieser, J. Am. Chem. Soc., **77**, 3829 (1955).

301a. Klingsberg, E., Chem. & Ind. (London), **1960**, 1568.

301b. Klingsberg, E., J. Am. Chem. Soc., **83**, 2934 (1961).

302. Knott, E. B., J. Chem. Soc., **1955**, 949.

302a. Kochetkov, N. K., E. E. Nifant'ev, and V. N. Kulakov, Doklady Akad. Nauk S.S.S.R., **125**, 327 (1959); Chem. Abstracts, **53**, 19873 (1959).

303. Kötz, A., Ber., **33**, 1120 (1900).

304. Kohler, E. P., Am. Chem. J., **22**, 67 (1899).

305. Konowalow, M. J., Russ. Phys.-Chem. Gesellschaft, **30**, 12 (1897); Chem. Zentr., **1898,II**, 362.

306. Korobitsyna, I. K., Yu. K. Yur'ev, and Yu. M. Polikarpov, J. Gen. Chem. U.S.S.R., **25**, 1531 (1955).

307. Kosak, A. I., R. J. F. Palchak, W. A. Steele, and C. M. Selwitz, J. Am. Chem. Soc., **76**, 4450 (1954).

308. Kourilský, R., and O. Gaudin, Bull. acad. nationale méd., **131**, 267 (1947); Chem. Abstracts, **42**, 2354 (1948).

309. Kourilský, R., B. N. Halpern, and J. Martin, Presse méd., **56**, 457 (1948); Chem. Abstracts, **43**, 1489 (1949).

309a. Koutecký, J., Collection Czechoslov. Chem. Communs., **24**, 1608 (1959).

309b. Koutecký, J., J. Paldus, and R. Zahradník, Collection Czechoslov. Chem. Communs., **25**, 617 (1960).

Chapter 5

309c. Koutecký, J., Trans. Faraday Soc., 55, 505 (1959).

310. Kovács, O., V. Herout, M. Horák, and F. Šorm, Collection Czechoslov. Chem. Communs., 21, 225 (1956).

311. Krebs, H., and E. F. Weber, Z. anorg. u. allgem. Chem., 272, 288 (1953).

311a. Krebs, H., Silicium, Schwefel, Phosphate, Colloq. Sek. anorg. Chem. Intern. Union reine u. angew. Chem., Münster, 1954, 107 (Pub. 1955); Chem. Abstracts, 52, 5015 (1958).

311b. Kuboyama, A., Bull. Chem. Soc. Japan, 30, 678 (1957).

311c. Kuhn, R., W. Baschang-Bister, and W. Dafeldecker, Ann., 641, 160 (1961).

312. Kühn, H. A., and E. Gischler, Arzneimittel-Forsch., 5, 533 (1955); Chem. Abstracts, 50, 7324 (1956).

312a. Landa, S., and Z. Kamýček, Chem. Listy, 52, 1150 (1958); Chem. Abstracts, 52, 17134 (1958).

312b. Landis, P. S., and L. A. Hamilton, J. Org. Chem., 25, 1742 (1960).

312c. Landis, P. S., and L. A. Hamilton, J. Org. Chem., 26, 274 (1961).

312d. Lanfry, M., Compt. rend., 152, 92 (1911).

313. Lawrence, W. T., Ber., 29, 547 (1896).

313a. Leaver, D., and W. A. H. Robertson, Proc. Chem. Soc., 1960, 252.

314. Legrand, L., Y. Mollier, and N. Lozac'h, Bull. soc. chim. France, 1953, 327.

315. Legrand, L., Bull. soc. chim. France, 1953, 561.

316. Legrand, L., Bull. soc. chim. France, 1954, 1029.

317. Legrand, L., and N. Lozac'h, Bull. soc. chim. France, 1955, 79.

318. Legrand, L., and N. Lozac'h, Bull. soc. chim. France, 1956, 1130.

319. Legrand, L., and N. Lozac'h, Bull. soc. chim. France, 1958, 953.

320. Legrand, L., Bull. soc. chim. France, 1959, 1599.

321. Legrand, L., and N. Lozac'h, Bull. soc. chim. France, 1959, 1686.

322. Lettré, H., Naturwissenschaften, 45, 218 (1958).

323. Linch, A. L. (to duPont), U.S. Patent 2,691,681 (1954).

323a. Loewenthal, H. J. E., J. Chem. Soc., 1958, 1367.

324. Long, C., Sci. Progr., 41, 659 (1953).

325. Long, C., Sci. Progr., 43, 672 (1955).

326. Louw, D. F., J. Strating, and H. J. Backer, Rec. trav. chim., 73, 655 (1954).

327. Lozac'h, N., Compt. rend., 225, 686 (1947).

328. Lozac'h, N., and O. Gaudin, Compt. rend., 225, 1162 (1947).

329. Lozac'h, N., Bull. soc. chim. France, 1949, 840.

330. Lozac'h, N., and Y. Mollier, Bull. soc. chim. France, 1950, 1243.

331. Lozac'h, N., and L. Legrand, Compt. rend., 232, 2330 (1951).

332. Lozac'h, N., and L. Legrand, Compt. rend., 234, 1291 (1952).

333. Lozac'h, N., and J. Teste, Compt. rend., 234, 1891 (1952).

334. Lozac'h, N., Bull. soc. chim. France, 1953, 561.

335. Lozac'h, N., M. Denis, Y. Mollier, and J. Teste, Bull. soc. chim. France, **1953**, 1016.

336. Lozac'h, N., Record Chem. Progr. (Kresge-Hooker Sci. Lib.), **20**, 23 (1959).

337. Lozac'h, N., and Y. Mollier, Bull. soc. chim. France, **1959**, 1389.

338. Lüttringhaus, A., Angew. Chem., **59**, 244 (1947).

339. Lüttringhaus, A., H. B. König, and B. Böttcher, Ann., **560**, 201 (1948).

340. Lüttringhaus, A., Angew. Chem., **60**, 71 (1948).

341. Lüttringhaus, A., Angew. Chem., **62**, 450 (1950).

342. Lüttringhaus, A., and W. Cleve, Ann., **575**, 112 (1952).

343. Lüttringhaus, A., and H. Goetze, Angew. Chem., **64**, 661 (1952).

344. Lüttringhaus, A., and U. Schmidt, Chem.-Ztg., **77**, 135 (1953).

344a. Lüttringhaus, A., and H. Goetze, Ger. Patent 912,885 (1954); Chem. Abstracts, **52**, 8929 (1958).

344b. Lüttringhaus, A., and H. Goetze, Ger. Patent 914,698 (1954); Chem. Abstracts, **52**, 8929 (1958).

345. Lüttringhaus, A:, and J. Grohmann, Z. Naturforsch., **10b**, 365 (1955).

346. Lüttringhaus, A., H. Trefzger, and U. Schmidt, Angew. Chem., **67**, 274 (1955).

347. Lüttringhaus, A., R. Cordes, and U. Schmidt, Angew. Chem., **67**, 275 (1955).

348. Lüttringhaus, A., and R. Deckert, Angew. Chem., **67**, 275 (1955).

349. Lüttringhaus, A., and K. Hägele, Angew. Chem., **67**, 304 (1955).

350. Luettringhaus, A., and U. Schmidt, Brit. Patent 730,058 (1955); Chem. Abstracts, **50**, 6515 (1956).

351. Lüttringhaus, A., U. Schmidt, and H. Alpes, Angew. Chem., **69**, 138 (1957).

352. Luettringhaus, A., and U. Schmidt, U.S. Patent 2,846,444 (1958).

353. Lüttringhaus, A., and H. Prinzbach, Ann., **624**, 79 (1959).

354. Lukeš, R., and J. Jarý, Chem. Listy, **49**, 1808 (1955); Chem. Abstracts, **50**, 9293 (1956).

354a. Lukeš, R., and J. Langthaler, Collection Czechoslov. Chem. Communs., **24**, 2109 (1959).

355. Lumbroso, H., and C. Marschalk, J. chim. phys., **48**, 123 (1951); Chem. Abstracts, **46**, 8074 (1952).

356. Lyle, R. E., and G. L. Lyle, J. Org. Chem., **24**, 1679 (1959).

357. McClelland, E. W., and J. Longwell, J. Chem. Soc., **123**, 3310 (1923).

358. McClelland, E. W., L. A. Warren, and J. H. Jackson, J. Chem. Soc., **1929**, 1582.

359. McClelland, E. W., and C. E. Salkeld, J. Chem. Soc., **1936**, 1143.

360. MacDonald, D. L., and H. O. L. Fischer, J. Am. Chem. Soc., **77**, 4348 (1955).

361. Macholán, L., Collection Czechoslov. Chem. Communs., **22**, 479 (1957).

362. McKibben, M., and E. W. McClelland, J. Chem. Soc., **123**, 170 (1923).

362a. McSweeney, G. P., and L. F. Wiggins, Nature, **168**, 874 (1951).

363. Maeda, K., Japan. Med. J., **2**, 85 (1949); Chem. Abstracts, **46**, 7166 (1952).

363a. Maeda, K., Bull. Chem. Soc. Japan, **33**, 1466 (1960).

363b. Maeda, K., Bull. Chem. Soc. Japan, **34**, 785 (1961).

363c. Maeda, K., Bull. Chem. Soc. Japan, **34**, 1166 (1961).

363d. Mahnert, E., Wien-med. Wochschr., **107**, 1055 (1957); Chem. Abstracts, **52**, 5636 (1958).

364. Makino, K., and M. Koike, Enzymologia, **16**, 215 (1953); Chem. Abstracts, **49**, 7571 (1955).

364a. Mammi, M., R. Bardi, G. Traverso, and S. Bezzi, Nature, **192**, 1282 (1961).

365. Mannessier, A., Gazz. chim. ital., **45, I**, 540 (1915); Chem. Abstracts, **10**, 1174 (1916).

366. Mannessier, A., Gazz. chim. ital., **46, I**, 231 (1916); Chem. Abstracts, **10**, 2892 (1916).

367. Mannessier-Mameli, A., Gazz. chim. ital., **62**, 1067 (1932); Chem. Abstracts, **27**, 2682 (1933).

368. Marschalk, C., Bull. soc. chim., [5]**6**, 1122 (1939).

369. Marschalk, C., and C. Stumm, Bull. soc. chim. France, **1948**, 418.

370. Marschalk, C., and L. Woerth, Bull. soc. chim. France, **1950**, 452.

371. Marschalk, C., Chim. & Ind. (Paris), **63**, No. 3 bis, 457 (1950).

372. Marschalk, C., Bull. soc. chim. France, **1952**, 147.

373. Marschalk, C., and J. P. Niederhauser, Bull. soc. chim. France, **1952**, 151.

373a. Matlack, A. S., J. C. W. Chien, and D. S. Breslow, J. Org. Chem., **26**, 1455 (1961).

374. Matter, O., Ger. Patent 313, 650 (1919); Chem. Zentr., **1919, IV**, 617.

374a. Mayer, R., and U. Kubasch, Angew. Chem., **73**, 220 (1961).

375. Mazover, Ya. G., J. Gen. Chem. U.S.S.R., **19**, 829 (1949).

375a. Meadow, J. R., and E. E. Reid, J. Am. Chem. Soc., **56**, 2177 (1934).

376. Mecke, R., R. Mecke, and A. Lüttringhaus, Z. Naturforsch., **10b**, 367 (1955).

377. Mecke, R., R. Mecke, and A. Lüttringhaus, Chem. Ber., **90**, 975 (1957).

377a. Mentesana, G., Folia Med. (Naples). **42**, 399 (1959); Chem. Abstracts, **53**, 15360 (1959).

378. Meyer, J., Helv. Chim. Acta, **8**, 38 (1925).

379. Miescher, K. (to Ciba Pharmaceutical Products), U.S. Patent 2, 435, 013 (1948); Chem. Abstracts, **42**, 2996 (1948).

380. Mijović, M. V., W. Voser, H. Heusser, and O. Jeger, Helv. Chim. Acta, **35**, 964 (1952).

381. Miles, L. W. C., and L. N. Owen, J. Chem. Soc., **1950**, 2938.

382. Miles, L. W. C., and L. N. Owen, J. Chem. Soc., **1950**, 2943.

383. Miles, L. W. C., and L. N. Owen, J. Chem. Soc., **1952**, 817.

384. Mills, W. H., and H. Schindler, J. Chem. Soc., **123**, 312 (1923).

385. Mills, W. H., and B. C. Saunders, J. Chem. Soc., **1931**, 537.

386. Miltein, G., Semana méd. (Buenos Aires), **1955, II**, 443; Chem. Abstracts, **50**, 2063 (1956).

386a. Mima, H., Y. Asahi, H. Okuto, and T. Kanzawa, Chem. & Pharm. Bull. (Tokyo), **7**, 750 (1959); Chem. Abstracts, **54**, 25593 (1960).

387. Miolati, A., Ann., **262**, 61 (1891).

388. Mislow, K., and W. C. Meluch, J. Am. Chem. Soc., **78**, 2341 (1956).

389. Mislow, K., and W. C. Meluch, J. Am. Chem. Soc., **78**, 5920 (1956).

390. Mochel, W. E. (to duPont), U.S. Patent 2,728,668 (1955).

391. Mollier, Y., and N. Lozac'h, Bull. soc. chim. France, **1952**, 1076.

392. Mollier, Y., Bull. soc. chim. France,

393. Mollier, Y., Bull. Soc. chim. France, **1954**, 1029.

394. Mollier, Y., Bull. soc. chim. France, **1954**, 1197.

395. Mollier, Y., and N. Lozac'h, Bull. soc. chim. France, **1958**, 651.

396. Mollier, Y., Bull. soc. chim. France, **1958**, 1315.

396a. Mollier, Y., Bull. soc. chim. France, **1960**, 213.

396b. Mollier, Y., and N. Lozac'h, Bull. soc. chim. France, **1960**, 700.

396c. Mollier, Y., and N. Lozac'h, Bull. soc. chim. France, **1961**, 614.

397. Morton, R. A., and A. L. Stubbs, J. Chem. Soc., **1939**, 1321.

397a. Muller, W. H., Am. J. Botany, **45**, 183 (1958); Chem. Abstracts, **52**, 12299 (1958).

398. Murneek, A. E., Phytopathology, **42**, 57 (1952); Chem. Abstracts, **46**, 4160 (1952).

398a. Naerland, A., Acta Chem. Scand., **12**, 224 (1958).

399. Niak, K. G., J. Chem. Soc., **119**, 1231 (1921).

399a. Naito, K., and O. Nagase, Yakugaku Zasshi, **80**, 629 (1960); Chem. Abstracts, **54**, 22700 (1960).

400. Nakano, I., and M. Sano, J. Pharm. Soc. Japan, **75**, 1296 (1955); Chem. Abstracts, **50**, 8601 (1956).

400a. Natti, J. J., Plant Disease Reptr., **41**, 780 (1957); Chem. Abstracts, **52**, 638 (1958).

401. Nawa, H., W. T. Brady, M. Koike, and L. J. Reed, J. Am. Chem. Soc., **81**, 2908 (1959).

401a. Nawa, H., W. T. Brady, M. Koike, and L. J. Reed, J. Am. Chem. Soc., **82**, 896 (1960).

401b. Nazarov, I. N., and I. A. Gurvich, Bull. Acad. Sci. U.S.S.R., Div. Chem. Sci., **1959**, 269.

401c. Nazer, M. Z., and C. H. Issidorides, J. Org. Chem., **26**, 839 (1961).

401d. Neunhoeffer, O., and A. Nowak, Naturwissenschaften, **45**, 491 (1958).

402. Nickell, L. G., Proc. Soc. Exptl. Biol. Med., **80**, 615 (1952); Chem. Abstracts, **46**, 11547 (1952).

403. Nickell, L. G., Antibiotics & Chemotherapy, **3**, 449 (1953); Chem. Abstracts, **47**, 10633 (1953).

404. Nishimura, H., and T. Kimura, Japan. Patent 5400 (1954); Chem. Abstracts, **49**, 14277 (1955).

405. N. V. de Bataafsche Petroleum Maatschappij, Brit. Patent 496, 290 (1938). Fr. Patent 838, 171 (1939); Chem. Abstracts, **33**, 2912, 7318 (1939).

406. N. V. de Bataafsche Petroleum Maatschappij, Brit. Patent 679, 909 (1952); Chem. Abstracts, **47**, 5341 (1953).

407. Nygård, B., and L. Schotte, Acta Chem. Scand., **10**, 469 (1956).

408. Okabayashi, T., J. Fermentation Technol. (Japan), **31**, 292 (1953); Chem. Abstracts, **48**, 5276 (1954).

409. O'Kane, D. J., and I. C. Gunsalus, J. Bact., **54**, 20 (1947).

410. O'Kane, D. J., and I. C. Gunsalus, J. Bact., **56**, 499 (1948).

410a. Okumura, K , H. Yoshikawa, and I. Inoue, Yakugaku Kenkyu, **33**, 424 (1961); Chem. Abstracts, **55**, 27271 (1961).

411. Overberger, C. G., and P. V. Bonsignore, J. Am. Chem. Soc., **80**, 5427 (1958).

411a. Overberger, C. G., and A. Drucker, J. Org. Chem., **29**, 360 (1964).

412. Pacault, A., and C. Marschalk, Bull. soc. chim. France, **1952**, 141.

413. Pappas, N., and H. R. Nace, J. Am. Chem. Soc., **81**, 4556 (1959).

414. Patterson, E. L., J. A. Brockman, Jr., F. P. Day, J. V. Pierce, M. E. Macchi, C. E. Hoffman, C. T. O. Fong, E. L. R. Stokstad, and T. H. Jukes, J. Am. Chem. Soc., **73**, 5919 (1951).

415. Patterson, E. L., J. V. Pierce, E. L. R. Stokstad, C. E. Hoffmann, J. A. Brockman, Jr., F. P. Day, M. E. Macchi, and T. H. Jukes, J. Am. Chem. Soc., **76**, 1823 (1954).

416. Pavlic, A. A., W. A. Lazier, and F. K. Signaigo, J. Org. Chem., **14**, 59 (1949).

417. Peppel, W. J., and F. K. Signaigo (to duPont), U.S. Patent 2, 402, 665 (1946).

418. Peters, R. A., L. A. Stockton, R. H. S. Thompson, F. N. Woodward, A. F. Millidge, and E. J. Gasson (to Minister of Supply of the United Kingdom), U.S. Patent 2, 432, 797 (1947); Chem. Abstracts, **42**, 2623 (1948).

418a. Petrun'kin, V. E., and N. M. Lysenko, J. Gen. Chem. U.S.S.R., **29**, 313 (1959).

418b. Pettit, G. R., and W. J. Bowyer, J. Org. Chem., **25**, 84 (1960).

418c. Pettit, G. R., and T. R. Kasturi, J. Org. Chem., **26**, 986 (1961).

419. Pfizer, C., and Co., Brit. Patent 755, 968 (1956); Chem. Abstracts, **51**, 9701 (1957). Ger. Patent 956, 226 (1957); Chem. Abstracts, **54**, 17421 (1960).

420. Plattner, P. A., A. Fürst, and H. Els, Helv. Chim. Acta, **37**, 1399 (1954).

421. Poulos, P. L., and J. W. Heuberger, Plant Disease Reptr., **36**, 410 (1952); Chem. Abstracts, **47**, 2921 (1953).

422. Price, W. B., and S. Smiles, J. Chem. Soc., **1928**, 2372.

423. Proštenik, M., and K. Balenović, J. Org. Chem., **17**, 379 (1952).

424. Proštenik, M., M. Munk-Weinert, and D. E. Sunko, J. Org. Chem., **21**, 406 (1956).

425. Quiniou, H., and N. Lozac'h, Bull. soc. chim. France, **1958**, 517.

426. Quiniou, H., Bull. soc. chim. France, **1959**, 1102.

426a. Quiniou, H., Bull. soc. chim. France, **1960**, 47.

426b. Quiniou, H., Bull. soc. chim. France, **1960**, 213.

427. Ralls, J. W., R. M. Dodson, and B. Riegel, J. Am. Chem. Soc., **71**, 3320 (1949).

428. Ralls, J. W., J. Am. Chem. Soc., **75**, 2123 (1953).

429. Ralls, J. W. (to G. D. Searle and Co.), U.S. Patent 2,686,789 (1954).

430. Ralls, J. W., and B. Riegel, J. Am. Chem. Soc., **76**, 4479 (1954).

431. Ralls, J. W. (to G. D. Searle and Co.), U.S. Patent 2,744,108 (1956).

432. Ralls, J. W. (to G. D. Searle and Co.), U.S. Patent 2,744,109 (1956).

433. Ralls, J. W. (to G. D. Searle and Co.), U.S. Patent 2,744,110 (1956).

434. Raoul, J., and J. Vialle, Bull. soc. chim. France, **1960**, 108.

434a. Raoul, J., and J. Vialle, Bull. soc. chim. France, **1960**, 1033.

435. Raoul, P., and J. Vialle, Bull. soc. chim. France, **1959**, 1670.

435a. Raoul, P., and J. Vialle, Bull. soc. chim. France, **1960**, 212.

436. Rausch, F., Arzneimittelforsch., **5**, 32 (1955); Angew. Chem., **67**, 214 (1955).

437. Reed, L. J., B. G. DeBusk, I. C. Gunsalus, and C. S. Hornberger, Jr., Science, **114**, 93 (1951).

438. Reed. L. J., B. G. DeBusk, P. M. Johnston, and M. E. Getzendaner, J. Biol. Chem., **192**, 851 (1951).

439. Reed, L. J., M. E. Getzendaner, B. G. DeBusk, and P. M. Johnston, J. Biol. Chem., **192**, 859 (1951).

440. Reed. L. J., B. G. DeBusk, I. C. Gunsalus, and G. H. F. Schnakenberg, J. Am. Chem. Soc., **73**, 5920 (1951).

441. Reed, L. J., Q. F. Soper, G. H. F. Schnakenberg, S. F. Kern, H. Boaz, and I. C. Gunsalus, J. Am. Chem. Soc., **74**, 2383 (1952).

442. Reed, L. J., and B. G. DeBusk, J. Am. Chem. Soc., **74**, 3457 (1952).

443. Reed, L. J., I. C. Gunsalus, G. H. F. Schnakenberg, Q. F. Soper, H. E. Boaz, S. F. Kern, and T. V. Parke, J. Am. Chem. Soc., **75**, 1267 (1953).

444. Reed. L. J., B. G. DeBusk, C. S. Hornberger, Jr., and I. C. Gunsalus, J. Am. Chem. Soc., **75**, 1271 (1953).

445. Reed, L. J. (to Research Corp.), U.S. Patent 2,694,066 (1954).

446. Reed, L. J., and C. Niu, J. Am. Chem. Soc., **77**, 416 (1955).

447. Reed, L. J., Advances in Enzymology, **18**, 319 (1957).

447a. Reed, L. J., Enzymes, Academic Press, **3**, 2nd Ed., 195 (1960).

448. Reid, E. E., and A. Jelinek, J. Org. Chem., **15**, 448 (1950).

449. Reissert, A., and A. Moré, Ber., **39**, 3298 (1906).

450. Ritter, J. J., and M. J. Lover, J. Am. Chem. Soc., **74**, 5576 (1952).

451. Roberts, J. D., W. T. Moreland, Jr., and W. Frazer, J. Am. Chem. Soc., **75**, 637 (1953).

452. Roberts, R. M., and C. C. Cheng, J. Org. Chem., **23**, 983 (1958).

453. Romo, J., G. Stork, G. Rosenkranz, and C. Djerassi, J. Am. Chem. Soc., **74**, 2918 (1952).

454. Romo, J., G. Rosenkranz, and C. Djerassi, J. Org. Chem., **17**, 1413 (1952).

455. Romo, J., Bol. inst. quím. univ. nacl. autón. Méx., **7**, 53 (1955); Chem. Abstracts, **50**, 12088 (1956).

456. Romo, J., and A. Romo de Vivar, J. Am. Chem. Soc., **81**, 3446 (1959).

457. Rosenkranz, G., M. Velasco, C. Djerassi, and F. Sondheimer, J. Am. Chem. Soc., **75**, 4430 (1953).

457a. Rowe, J. W., A. Melera, D. Arigoni, O. Jeger, and L. Ruzicka, Helv. Chim. Acta, **40**, 1 (1957).

457b. Rowe, J. W., A. Melera, D. Arigoni, O. Jeger, and L. Ruzicka, Festschr. Arthur Stoll, **1957**, 886; Chem. Abstracts, **53**, 8193 (1959).

458. Ruff, A., and T. Reichstein, Helv. Chim. Acta, **34**, 70 (1951).

459. Ruiz, H. I., and F. M. Panizo, Anales real soc. españ. fís. y quím. (Madrid). **52B**, 579 (1956); Chem. Abstracts, **51**, 6670 (1957).

459a. Ruiz, H. I., Anales inst. farmacol. españ., **5**, 323 (1956); Chem. Abstracts, **52**, 10126 (1958).

459b. Runge, F., Z. El-Hewehi, H. J. Renner, and E. Taeger, J. prakt. Chem., [4]**11**, 284 (1960).

459c. Saint-Gobain, Fr. Patent 1,016,882 (1952); Chem. Abstracts, **52**, 1288 (1958).

459d. Sakan, T., A. Fujino, F. Murai, A. Suzui, Y. Butsugan, and Y. Terashima, Bull. Chem. Soc. Japan, **33**, 712 (1960).

460. Salzberg, P. L. (to duPont), U.S. Patent 2,912,386 (1959).

460a. Sanesi, M., and G. Traverso, Chem. Ber., **93**, 1566 (1960).

460b. Sannié, C., C. Neuville, and J. J. Panouse, Bull. soc. chim. France, **1958**, 635.

460c. Sasse, K., R. Wegler, G. Unterstenhöfer, and F. Grewe, Angew. Chem., **72**, 973 (1960).

461. Sato, Y., and N. Ikekawa, J. Org. Chem., **24**, 1367 (1959).

462. Schaffner, C. P., Am. Orchid Soc. Bull., **23**, 798 (1954); Chem. Abstracts, **49**, 4090 (1955).

463. Scheer, I., M. J. Thompson, and E. Mosettig, J. Am. Chem. Soc., **79**, 3218 (1957).

464. Schmidt, U., Chem. Ber., **92**, 1171 (1959).

465. Schmidt. U., and P. Grafen, Chem. Ber., **92**, 1177 (1959).

465a. Schmidt. U., R. Scheuring, and A. Lüttringhaus, Ann., **630**, 116 (1960).

465b. Schmidt, U., A. Lüttringhaus, and H. Trefzger, Ann., **631**, 129 (1960).

465c. Schmidt. U., A. Lüttringhaus, and F. Hübinger, Ann., **631**, 138 (1960).

465d. Schmidt, U., Ann., **635**, 109 (1960).

465e. Schmidt, U., H. Alpes, and P. Grafen, Angew. Chem., **72**, 579 (1960).

465f. Schmidt, U., and H. Kubitzek, Chem. Ber., **93**, 1559 (1960).

465g. Schmidt, U., and F. Geiger, Angew. Chem., **74**, 328 (1962).

466. Schmitt, J., and A. Lespagnol, Compt. rend., **230**, 551 (1950).

467. Schmitt, J., and A. Lespagnol, Compt. rend., **230**, 1774 (1950)

468. Schmitt, J., and A. Lespagnol, Bull. soc. chim. France, **1950**, 459.

469. Schmitt, J., and M. Suquet, Bull. soc. chim. France, **1955**, 84.

470. Schmitt, J., and M. Suquet, Bull. Soc. chim. France, **1956**, 755.

471. Schmitt, J., R. Fallard, and M. Suquet, Bull. soc. chim. France, **1956**, 1147.

472. Schöberl, A., and H. Gräfje, Ann., **614**, 66 (1958).

473. Schöberl, A., and H. Gräfje, Ann., **617**, 71 (1958).

474. Schönberg, A., and S. Nickel, Ber., **64B**, 2323 (1931).

475. Schönberg, A., D. Černik, and W. Urban, Ber., **64B**, 2577 (1931).

476. Schönberg, A., S. Nickel, and D. Černik, Ber., **65B**, 289 (1932).

477. Schönberg, A., H. Kaltschmitt, and H. Schulten, Ber., **66B**, 245 (1933).

478. Schönberg, A., and A. Mostafa, J. Chem. Soc., **1941**, 793.

479. Schönberg, A., M. Elkaschef, M. Nosseir, and M. M. Sidky, J. Am. Chem. Soc., **80**, 6312 (1958).

480. Schotte, L., Arkiv Kemi, **5**, 533 (1953).

481. Schotte, L., Acta Chem. Scand., **8**, 130 (1954).

482. Schotte, L., Arkiv Kemi, **8**, 579 (1955).

483. Schotte, L., Arkiv Kemi, **9**, 309 (1956).

484. Schotte, L., Arkiv Kemi, **9**, 361 (1956).

485. Schotte, L., Arkiv Kemi, **9**, 429 (1956).

486. Schotte, L., Arkiv Kemi, **9**, 441 (1956).

487. Schotte, L., and H. Ström, Acta Chem. Scand., **10**, 687 (1956).

488. Schroeder, H. A., E. M. Menhard, and H. M. Perry, Jr., J. Lab. Clin. Med., **45**, 431 (1955); Chem. Abstracts, **49**, 10516 (1955).

489. Scott, D. W., H. L. Finke, M. E. Gross, G. B. Guthrie, and H. M. Huffman, J. Am. Chem. Soc., **72**, 2424 (1950).

490. Scott, D. W., H. L. Finke, J. P. McCullough, M. E. Gross, R. E. Pennington, and G. Waddington, J. Am. Chem. Soc., **74**, 2478 (1952).

491. Searle, N. E. (to duPont), U.S. Patent 2, 706, 158 (1955).

492. Searle, N. E., and D. E. Wolf (to duPont), U.S. Patent 2, 871, 154 (1959).

493. Segre, A., R. Viterbo, and G. Parisi, J. Am. Chem. Soc., **79**, 3503 (1957).

494. Selker, M. L., and A. R. Kemp, Ind. Eng. Chem., **39**, 895 (1947).

495. Seneca, H., J. H. Kane, and J. Rockenbach, Antibiotics & Chemotherapy, **2**, 357 (1952); Chem. Abstracts, **47**, 3920 (1953).

495a. Sheehan, J. C., and W. F. Erman, J. Am. Chem. Soc., **79**, 6050 (1957).

495b. Shustorovich, E. M., J. Gen. Chem. U.S.S.R., **29**, 2424 (1959).

496. Siegel, J. R., and D. H. Rosenblatt, J. Am. Chem. Soc., **80**, 1753 (1958).

497. Smiles, S., and E. W. McClelland, J. Chem. Soc., **121**, 86 (1922).

498. Snell, E. E., and H. P. Brohquist, Arch. Biochem., **23**, 326 (1949); Chem. Abstracts, **43**, 9144 (1949).

499. Soder, L., and R. Wizinger, Helv. Chim. Acta, **42**, 1733 (1959).

500. Soder, L., and R. Wizinger, Helv. Chim. Acta, **42**, 1779 (1959).

501. Solomons, I. A., Angew. Chem., **66**, 745 (1954).

Chapter 5

502. Sondheimer, F., and D. Rosenthal, J. Am. Chem. Soc., **80**, 3995 (1958).

502a. Sondheimer, F., and S. Wolfe, Can. J. Chem., **37**, 1870 (1959).

503. Soper, Q. F., W. E. Buting, J. E. Cochran, Jr., and A. Pohland, J. Am. Chem. Soc., **76**, 4109 (1954).

504. Šorm, F., and M. Romaňuk, Chem. Listy, **50**, 1277 (1956); Chem. Abstracts, **51**, 296 (1957).

505. Spindt, R. S., and D. R. Stevens (to Gulf Research and Development), U.S. Patent 2,470,876 (1949).

506. Spindt, R. S., D. R. Stevens, and W. E. Baldwin, J. Am. Chem. Soc., **73**, 3693 (1951).

507. Spindt, R. S., and D. R. Stevens (to Gulf Research and Development), U.S. Patent 2,611,783 (1952).

508. Šponar, J., and M. Jirsa, Biochim. et Biophys. Acta, **29**, 434 (1958); Chem. Abstracts, **52**, 19608 (1958).

509. Starker, L. N., and D. B. Cosulich (to American Cyanamid), U.S. Patent 2,759,005 (1956).

509a. Starka, L., and L. Jirousek, Pharmazie, **14**, 473 (1959); Chem. Abstracts, **54**, 8370 (1960).

509b. Štefanac, Z., N. Bregant, and K. Balenović, Croat. Chem. Acta, **32**, 49 (1960); Chem. Abstracts, **54**, 22572 (1960).

510. Stevens, D. R., and W. C. Starnes (to Gulf Research and Development), U.S. Patent 2,535,705 (1950).

511. Stevens, D. R., and A. C. Whitaker (to Gulf Research and Development), U.S. Patent 2,535,706 (1950).

512. Stevens, D. R., and S. C. Camp (to Gulf Research and Development), U.S. Patent 2,658,900 (1953).

513. Stevens, D. R., and S. C. Camp (to Gulf Research and Development), U.S. Patent 2,786,829 (1957).

514. Stevenson, R., and L. F. Fieser, J. Am. Chem. Soc., **78**, 1409 (1956).

515. Stocken, L. A., J. Chem. Soc., **1947**, 592.

516. Stokstad, E. L. R., C. E. Hoffmann, M. A. Regan, D. Fordham, and T. H. Jukes, Arch. Biochem., **20**, 75 (1949); Chem. Abstracts, **43** 6274 (1949).

517. Stork, G., and J. W. Schulenberg, J. Am. Chem. Soc., **78**, 250 (1956).

518. Strandskov, F. B., and J. B. Bockelmann, J. Agr. Food Chem., **1**, 1219 (1953); Chem. Abstracts, **48**, 2318 (1954).

519. Striebel, P., and C. Tamm, Helv. Chim. Acta, **37**, 1094 (1954).

520. Subluskey, L. A., and T. F. Sanderson, J. Am. Chem. Soc., **76**, 3512 (1954).

520a. Suchý, M., and F. Šorm, Chem. Listy, **52**, 1180 (1958); Chem. Abstracts, **52**, 17318 (1958).

521. Sugasawa, S., and M. Kirisawa, Pharm. Bull. (Japan), **3**, 190 (1955); Chem. Abstracts, **50**, 9416 (1956).

521a. Sullivan, W. J., and P. H. Williams, J. Org. Chem., **25**, 2128 (1960).

521b. Sumi, J., J. Am. Chem. Soc., **80**, 4869 (1958).

522. Sundholm, N. K., and A. E. Smith, J. Am. Chem. Soc., **73**, 3459 (1951).

523. Sundholm, N. K. (to United States Rubber Co.), U.S. Patent 2, 547, 723 (1951); Chem. Abstracts, **45**, 8560 (1951).

524. Sundholm, N. K. (to United States Rubber Co.), U.S. Patent 2, 547, 724 (1951); Chem. Abstracts, **45**, 8560 (1951).

525. Sunner, S., Nature, **176**, 217 (1955).

526. Sunner, S., Svensk Kem. Tidskr., **67**, 513 (1955).

526a. Sýkora, V., V. Herout, J. Plíva, and F. Šorm, Chem. Listy, **51**, 1704 (1957); Chem. Abstracts, **52**, 4560 (1958).

527. Takeda, K., and K. Kitahonoki, J. Pharm. Soc. Japan, **76**, 867 (1956); Chem. Abstracts, **51**, 1221 (1957).

528. Takeda, K., K. Kitahonoki, and K. Igarashi, Pharm. Bull. (Japan), **4**, 12 (1956); Chem. Abstracts, **51**, 3475 (1957).

528a. Takeda, K., and T. Yoneno, Japan Patent 9575 (1956); Chem. Abstracts, **52**, 14721 (1958).

529. Takeda, K., and K. Kitahonoki, Ann., **606**, 153 (1957).

530. Tanner, Jr., F. W., J. A. Means, and J. W. Davisson, Abstracts 118th Meeting, American Chemical Society, September 3-8, 1950, p. 18A.

531. Tanner, Jr., F. W., J.W. Davisson, A.C. Finlay, and J.H. Kane (to Chas. Pfizer and Co.), U.S. Patent 2, 689, 854 (1954). Brit. Patent 692, 066 (1953); Chem. Abstracts, **47**, 12771 (1953).

532. Tarbell, D. S., and D. P. Harnish, Chem. Reviews, **49**, 59 (1951).

533. Teste J., and N. Lozac'h, Bull. soc. chim. France, **1954**, 492.

534. Teste, J., and N. Lozac'h, Bull. soc. chim. France, **1955**, 437.

535. Teste, J., and N. Lozac'h, Bull. soc. chim. France, **1955**, 442.

535a. Teste, J., Compt. rend., **252**, 3601 (1961).

535b. Thelin, J. H. (to American Cyanamid), U.S. Patent 2, 905, 695 (1959).

536. Thomas, R. C., and L. J. Reed, J. Am. Chem. Soc., **77**, 5446 (1955).

537. Thomas, R. C., and L. J. Reed, J. Am. Chem. Soc., **78**, 6148 (1956).

538. Thomas, R. C., and L. J. Reed, J. Am. Chem. Soc., **78**, 6150 (1956).

539. Thomas, R. C., and L. J. Reed, J. Am. Chem. Soc., **78**, 6151 (1956).

540. Thomson, J. F., J. Savit, and E. Goldwasser, J. Pharmacol., **89**, 1 (1947); Chem. Abstracts, **41**, 3208 (1947).

541. Thuillier, A., and J. Vialle, Bull. soc. chim. France, **1959**, 1398.

541a. Thuillier, A., and J. Vialle, Bull. soc. chim. France, **1960**, 1033.

542. Tinker, J. F., J. Org. Chem., **16**, 1417 (1951).

542a. Tornetta, B., Ann. chim. (Rome), **48**, 577 (1958); Chem. Abstracts, **53**, 6208 (1959).

543. Traverso, G., and M. Sanesi, Ann. chim. (Rome), **43**, 795 (1953); Chem. Abstracts, **49**, 13981 (1955).

544. Traverso, G., Ann. chim. (Rome), **44**, 1018 (1954); Chem. Abstracts, **50**, 366 (1956).

545. Traverso, G., Ann. chim. (Rome), **45**, 687 (1955); Chem. Abstracts, **51**, 5761 (1957).

Chapter 5

546. Traverso, G., Ann. chim. (Rome), **46**, 821 (1956); Chem. Abstracts, **51**, 6622 (1957).

547. Traverso, G., Chem. Ber., **91**, 1224 (1958).

548. Tucker, N. B., and E. E. Reid, J. Am. Chem. Soc., **55**, 775 (1933).

549. Tweit, R. C., and R. M. Dodson, J. Am. Chem. Soc., **81**, 4409 (1959).

550. Tweit, R. C. (to G. D. Searle), U.S. Patent 2,897,196 (1959).

551. Umezawa, H., K. Maeda, and H. Kosaka, Japan. Med. J., **1**, 512 (1948); Chem. Abstracts, **46**, 568 (1952).

552. Vogel, A., O. Jeger, and L. Ruzicka, Helv. Chim. Acta, **34**, 2321 (1951).

553. Voronkov, M. G., A. S. Broun, and G. B. Karpenko, J. Gen. Chem. U.S.S.R., **19**, a395 (1949).

554. Voronkov, M. G., and F. P. Tsiper, Zhur. Anal. Khim., **6**, 331 (1951); Chem. Abstracts, **46**, 2953 (1952).

554a. Vorozhtsov, Jr., N. N., and V. Ya. Rodinov, Proc. Acad. Sci. USSR, Chem. Sect., **134**, 1127 (1960).

555. Voser, W., M. Montavon, H. H. Günthard, O. Jeger, and L. Ruzicka, Helv. Chim. Acta, **33**, 1893 (1950).

556. Voser, W., O. Jeger, and L. Ruzicka, Helv. Chim. Acta, **35**, 503 (1952).

557. Votoček, E., and V. Veselý, Ber., **47**, 1515 (1914).

558. de Vries, H., and H. J. Backer, Rec. trav. chim., **71**, 719 (1952).

559. Wagner, A. F., E. Walton, G. E. Boxer, M. P. Pruss, F. W. Holly, and K. Folkers, J. Am. Chem. Soc., **78**, 5079 (1956).

560. Wagner, A. F. (to Merck and Co.), U.S. Patent 2,772,300 (1956).

561. Wagner, A. F. (to Merck and Co.), U.S. Patent 2,820,799 (1958). Brit. Patent 796,564 (1958); Chem. Abstracts, **53**, 13176 (1959). Brit. Patent 796,563 (1958); Chem. Abstracts, **53**, 20091 (1959).

561a. Wagner-Jauregg, T., and M. Häring, Helv. Chim. Acta, **41**, 377 (1958).

562. Wallen, V. R., and A. J. Skolko, Plant Disease Reptr., **37**, 421 (1953); Chem. Abstracts, **47**, 11633 (1953).

563. Walton, E., A. F. Wagner, L. H. Peterson, F. W. Holly, and K. Folkers, J. Am. Chem. Soc., **76**, 4748 (1954).

564. Walton, E., A. F. Wagner, F. W. Bachelor, L. H. Peterson, F. W. Holly, and K. Folkers, J. Am. Chem. Soc., **77**, 5144 (1955).

565. Walton, E., and A. F. Wagner (to Merck and Co.), U.S. Patent 2,792,413 (1957).

566. Walton, E. (to Merck and Co.), U.S. Patent 2,792,414 (1957).

567. Walton, E. (to Merck and Co.), U.S. Patent 2,842,574 (1958).

568. Wander, Dr. A., A.-G., Ger. Patent 909,097 (1954); Chem. Abstracts, **52**, 10205 (1958).

569. Warolin, C., and R. Delaby, Compt. rend., **240**, 204 (1955).

570. Wegler, R., E. Kühle, and W. Schäfer, Angew. Chem., **70**, 351 (1958).

571. Wenkert, E., and N. V. Bringi, J. Am. Chem. Soc., **80**, 5575 (1958).

572. Wenkert, E., and B. G. Jackson, J. Am. Chem. Soc., **81**, 5601 (1959).

573. Wessely, F., and A. Siegel, Monatsh. **82**, 607 (1951).

574. Wheeler, H. L., and H. F. Merriam, J. Am. Chem. Soc., **24**, 439 (1902).

575. Whitney, R. B., and M. Calvin, J. Chem. Phys., **23**, 1750 (1955).

576. Wilds, A. L., T. H. Pearson, and C. H. Hoffman, J. Am. Chem. Soc., **76**, 1737 (1954).

577. Wilds, A. L., R. H. Zeitschel, R. E. Sutton, and J. A. Johnson, Jr., J. Org. Chem., **19**, 255 (1954).

578. Wizinger-Aust, R., Angew. Chem., **68**, 528 (1956).

579. Wizinger, R., and L. Soder, Chimia (Switz.), **12**, 79 (1958).

580. Wladislaw, B., Chem. & Ind. (London), **1957**, 263.

581. Wolf, G., and A. M. Seligman, J. Am. Chem. Soc., **73**, 2082 (1951).

581a. Wolf, W., E. Degener, and S. Petersen, Angew. Chem., **72**, 963 (1960).

581b. Woodward, R. B., F. E. Bader, H. Bickel, A. J. Frey, and R. W. Kierstead, Tetrahedron, **2**, 1 (1958).

581c. Yamakawa, K., J. Org. Chem., **24**, 897 (1959).

581d. Yanagita, M., and K. Yamakawa, J. Org. Chem., **24**, 903 (1959).

582. Yates, P., and D. R. Moore, J. Am. Chem. Soc., **80**, 5577 (1958).

583. Yates, P., and B. G. Christensen, Chem. & Ind. (London), **1958**, 1441.

584. Yur'ev, Yu. K., and I. S. Levi, Doklady Akad. Nauk S.S.S.R., **73**, 953 (1950); Chem. Abstracts, **45**, 2934 (1951).

584a. Yurugi, S., T. Fushimi, and M. Murata, Yakugaku Zasshi, **80**, 1165 (1960); Chem. Abstracts, **55**, 4503 (1961).

584b. Yurugi, S., M. Numata, and T. Fushimi, Yakugaku Zasshi, **80**, 1170 (1960); Chem. Abstracts, **55**, 4505 (1961).

584c. Zahradník, R., and J. Koutecký, Tetrahedron Letters, **18**, 632 (1961).

585. Zaslavskiĭ, A. I., and Yu. D. Kondrashov, Doklady Akad. Nauk S.S.S.R., **59**, 1441 (1948); Chem. Abstracts, **42**, 7127 (1948).

586. Zaslavskiĭ, A. I., and Yu. D. Kondrashov, J. Gen. Chem. U.S.S.R., **19**, 1137 (1949).

587. Zentmyer, G. A., Phytopathology, **45**, 398 (1955); Chem. Abstracts, **49**, 13573 (1955).

588. Zinner, H., Chem. Ber., **83**, 275 (1950).

589. Zinner, H., Chem. Ber., **86**, 495 (1953).

590. Zinner, H., Chem. Ber., **86**, 496 (1953).

591. Zinner, H., H. Brandner, and G. Rembarz, Chem. Ber., **89**, 800 (1956).

592. Zinner, H., and K. H. Falk, Chem. Ber., **89**, 2451 (1956).

593. Zinner, H., K. Wessely, W. Bock, K. Rieckhoff, F. Strandt, and W. Nimmich, Chem. Ber., **90**, 500 (1957).

594. Zinner, H., G. Rembarz, and H. P. Klöcking, Chem. Ber., **90**, 2688 (1957).

595. Zinner, H., H. Nimz, and H. Venner, Chem. Ber., **90**, 2696 (1957).

596. Zinner, H., H. Nimz, and H. Venner, <u>Chem. Ber.</u>, **91**, 148 (1958).

597. Zinner, H., and H. Nimz, <u>Chem. Ber.</u>, **91**, 1657 (1958).

598. Zinner, H., W. Bock, and H. P. Klöcking, <u>Chem. Ber.</u>, **92**, 1307 (1959).

599. Zinner, H., G. Sych, and F. Schneider, <u>Chem. Ber.</u>, **93**, 468 (1960).